Goo
Guio

C000195718

THE
Good Food Guide 1997

Edited by Jim Ainsworth

Consumers' Association

Which? Books are commissioned and researched by
Consumers' Association and published by
Which? Ltd, 2 Marylebone Road,
London NW1 4DF

Distributed by The Penguin Group:
Penguin Books Ltd, 27 Wrights Lane,
London W8 5TZ

Base mapping © Map Marketing Ltd/
European Map Graphics 1996
Map information © Which? Ltd 1996

British Library Cataloguing in Publication Data
A catalogue record for this book is
available from the British Library

ISBN 0 85202 621 8

For a full list of Which? books, please write to:
Which? Books, Castlemead, Gascoyne Way,
Hertford X, SG14 1LH

Photoset by Tradespools Ltd, Frome, Somerset
Printed in England by Clays Ltd, St Ives plc

Cover photograph by Steve Baxter Photography
Cover design by Paul Saunders
Typographic design by Tim Higgins

Contents

To all readers

The Good Food Guide is your guide. It is independent, takes no free meals, inducements or advertising, and reflects the experience of thousands of consumers in restaurants throughout the land. It is not a self-appointed arbiter of hide-bound gastronomic taste. It reports on real experiences by real people in search of nourishment, pleasure or celebration.

As a purchaser of this *Guide*, you are part of a huge network of correspondents, and you are a member of the Good Food Club. Please help other readers by recounting your own experiences to us.

There is a form at the back of this book (just before the maps); you can ask for more report forms from the *Guide* office; the address is FREEPOST, so you do not have to use a stamp. Or if you are on the Internet, send your report to: *guidereports@which.co.uk*. Every letter or e-mail received is one more brick in the edifice of next year's *Guide*.

Good Food Guide stickers

Owing to a change of policy at Consumers' Association, restaurants that feature in the 1997 edition of the *Guide* as main entries have been provided with free stickers which they may use for display purposes. The stickers are valid until October 1997. For the first time, too, restaurants will be allowed to state the fact that they are in the current *Guide* in their advertising and promotional material. By issuing our own official stickers, we shall be bringing the achievement of the selected establishments to the notice of a wider audience and, it is hoped, discouraging the trade in bogus 'Good Food Guide' plaques and certificates which we have sought to combat in recent years. If, however, you find a restaurant advertising that it is in the *Guide* when it is not, we would be grateful to hear from you; such claims are in breach of our trade mark and will be referred, as in the past, to our Legal Department.

A service to keep readers up to date

Readers with a touch-tone telephone can use a 24-hour information service giving details of restaurant sales, closures, chef changes and so on, since this edition of *The Good Food Guide* was published. This service for the 1997 edition will be available from 1 December 1996 to 1 May 1997. Telephone (0171) 830 7575 to hear the latest information, or to leave a message.

How to use this *Guide*

All the entries in this year's *Guide* have been rewritten between April and July 1996. The information on which they are based is from reports sent in by readers over the past year and confirmed where necessary by anonymous inspection. No entry is based on a single nomination. In every case, readers and inspectors have been prepared to endorse the quality of the cooking, the dining-room and the value for money.

The rating system grades restaurants, on the basis of their cooking, from 1 to 5. Grading is not based on elegance, ambience, service and value but on food and cooking. The marks reflect the perception of the *Guide* and its reporters, and signify the following:

1 **Competent cooking** Restaurants that achieve a satisfactory stand-ard, endorsed by readers as worthy of the *Guide*.

2 **Good cooking** Restaurants that produce good food in most depart-ments, though some inconsistencies may have been noted. They please most readers much of the time.

3 **Very good cooking** The kitchen achieves consistent quality, rarely disappointing in any department. Seldom faulted by *Guide* reporters.

4 **Excellent cooking** Restaurants with a high level of ambition and achievement. Generally, they delight.

5 **The best** These may excite debate, not as to whether the cooking is good, but whether it is better than their peers'.

* An asterisk next to a mark signifies that the *Guide* and its readers are of the opinion that the restaurant is a particularly fine example within its numeric classification.

The *Guide* office is reliant on proprietors for price information. Each year owners are asked to mark on a questionnaire the cost, for autumn of that year, of any set meals, and also the lowest and highest à la carte prices for each course. We then calculate the lowest and highest prices for a three-course meal per person, including the cost of coffee, service and half a bottle of house wine (or corkage in the case of unlicensed establishments where you can 'bring your own'). The lowest price forms the first figure that you see in the cost line above an entry. In practice, some people may have drinks before the meal and drink a more expensive wine; also, prices are likely to rise during the currency of the *Guide*. To reflect this, the second price in the cost line is the highest price we have calculated for a three-course meal (sometimes four or five courses if it is a set meal) inflated by 20 per cent to bring some realism to bear on the likely upper limit. In essence, the cost line shows the least and the most you are likely to pay, with most meals falling somewhere in-between.

How to read a *Guide* entry

CANTERBURY Kent ¹   map 3 ²

▲ *Mary's Kitchen* ³ ♟ ▮ ⁴ ⁵ ✸ ⁶ £ ⁷   │ NEW ENTRY │ ⁸

16 Elwood Avenue, Canterbury CT41 4RX ⁹
TEL: (01227) 770666 FAX: (01227) 770555 ¹⁰   COOKING 2* ¹²
on B2068, 2m S of Canterbury ¹¹   COST £19–£24 ¹³

(main text) ¹⁴   CELLARMAN'S CHOICE ¹⁵

CHEF: Mary Smith PROPRIETORS: Mary and David Smith ¹⁶   OPEN: Mon to Sat L12 to 2, Tue to Sun D 7 to 9 ¹⁷ CLOSED: Aug ¹⁸ MEALS: alc (main courses £6 to £12). Set L £12, Set D £15 (2 courses) to £25. Cover £1. Minimum £5 L ¹⁹ BYO £2 ²⁰ SERVICE: net prices, card slips closed ²¹ CARDS: Access, Amex, Delta, Diners, Switch, Visa ²² DETAILS: 72 seats. 4 tables outside. Private parties: 26 main room, 10 private room. ²³ Car park. ²⁴ Vegetarian meals. ²⁵ Children's helpings. No children under 10. ²⁶ Jacket and tie. ²⁷ No smoking in dining-room. ²⁸ Wheelchair access (also WC). ²⁹ No music. ³⁰ Air-conditioned ACCOMMODATION: 14 rooms, all with bath/shower. TV. Phone. Air-conditioned. B&B £20 to £40. ³¹ Deposit: £50. ³² Rooms for disabled. ³³ Children welcome. ³⁴ Baby facilities. ³⁵ Dogs welcome. ³⁶ Afternoon teas. ³⁷ Garden. Swimming-pool. ³⁸ (*The Which? Hotel Guide*) ³⁹

1 The town and county. The *Guide*'s main entries are divided into eight sections: London, England, Scotland, Wales, Isle of Man, Channel Islands, Northern Ireland and Republic of Ireland. In the London section, restaurants are listed alphabetically by name; in all other sections, they are listed under town. The maps (at the back of the book) can be used as a starting point to locate areas of interest; then look up the entries under the town name. The London maps locate restaurants by name.

2 The map number. The maps are at the end of the *Guide*.

3 The name of the restaurant. ▲ in front of the name denotes that it offers accommodation too.

4 ♟ denotes a wine list that is good, well above the ordinary. The symbol ▮ indicates a truly outstanding wine list.

5   indicates that the chef has changed since last year's entry. It does not apply to every minor change or promotion, and is used with discretion – i.e. only in cases where the change of chef seems to have made a significant

difference, and where we have either inspected the new regime or have received enough reports to award a cooking score.

6 **✻** indicates that smoking (cigarettes, pipes and cigars) is either banned altogether or that one dining-room is maintained for non-smokers. The symbol does not appear if a restaurant simply has a no-smoking area, or bans smoking at one mealtime only, although these features will be mentioned in the details at the end of an entry. Establishments that do not allow smoking in a dining-room may allow it elsewhere on the premises, such as in the bar or lounge. If you are a smoker, it is always worth checking beforehand.

7 **£** indicates that it is possible to have a three-course meal, including coffee, a half-bottle of house wine and service, at *any* time the restaurant is open (i.e. at dinner as well as at lunch, unless a place is only open for dinner), for £20 or less per person. Meals may often cost much more than this, but, by choosing carefully, you should find £20 achievable.

8 If a restaurant is new to the *Guide* this year (it did not appear as a main entry in the last edition), NEW ENTRY appears opposite its name.

9 The restaurant's address and post code.

10 The restaurant's telephone number and, if it has one, fax number, including STD codes.

11 Any special directions in case the restaurant is difficult to find.

12 The *Guide*'s mark, out of five, for cooking quality, ranging from 1 for competent cooking to 5 for the best. See page 7 or the inside front cover for a full explanation. NEW CHEF is indicated instead of a cooking mark for restaurants which had a change of chef as we went to press. These are not the only places (listed) that have new chefs, but are those where the change was too late for our inspection. (See also point 5.)

13 This is the price range for three-course meals (lunch and/or dinner) for one person, including coffee, wine (or corkage in the case of 'bring-your-own') and service, according to minimum and maximum prices provided by the proprietor for set meals and à la carte dishes. The first figure shows what is probably the least you would have to pay for a three-course meal (often at lunch only), while the second figure indicates a likely maximum amount (sometimes for a set meal of more than three courses). The second figure has been inflated by 20 per cent to reflect (i) that some readers will order extra drinks and some top-range dishes, and (ii) likely price rises that will come into play during the life of the *Guide*.

14 The text is based on reports sent in by readers during the last *Guide* year, confirmed where necessary by commissioned, anonymous inspections.

15 Some entries conclude with a CELLARMAN'S CHOICE. These are wines, usually more expensive than the house wine, that the restaurant assures us will be in stock during 1996, and recommends as suitable for the kind of food served. CELLARMAN'S CHOICE is usually given only for restaurants that have been awarded glass or bottle symbols for above-average or outstanding wine lists.

16 The names of the chef(s) and owner(s).

17 The days of the week the restaurant is open, and the times of first and last orders for meals. It is always advisable to book before going to a restaurant. If you book and then cannot go, please remember to telephone the restaurant to cancel.

18 Annual closures.

19 The types of meals that are available, with any variations for lunch (L) or dinner (D). The letters alc denote an à la carte menu. This is followed by a range of main course prices (rounded up to the nearest 50p). Set L and/or Set D denote set lunches and set dinners, and include the basic charge for those meals. Set meals consist usually of three courses, but can cover anything from one to seven courses. If a set meal has fewer than three courses, this is stated. Coffee is often included in set meals, wine very occasionally. The meal information will be followed by details of any cover charge and minimum charge. (Note that set meals or special menus may not be available at all times – it is always best to check.)

20 BYO means that customers may bring their own alcoholic drinks on to the premises. Any corkage charge is indicated.

21 The restaurant's policy on service charges. Net prices indicates that prices of dishes and wine include service, and this fact is clearly stated on menu and bill; not inc, that service is not included and is left up to the discretion of the customer; 10%, that there is a fixed service charge of 10 per cent automatically added to the bill; 10% (optional), that 10 per cent is automatically added to the bill along with the word 'optional'; and none, that no service charge is made or expected and that money offered is refused. Card slips closed indicates that the total on the slips of credit cards is closed when handed over for signature.

22 The credit cards accepted by the restaurant. If no cards are accepted we state none.

23 Not all restaurants will take private parties. The maximum number of people in a party is given for both main and private rooms.

24 The restaurant has its own car park.

25 Vegetarian meals means that the establishment always lists on the menu at least one vegetarian dish as a first course and one as a main course. Many restaurants which do not have non-meat or non-fish options on their menus may be able to provide a vegetarian meal with prior notice: best to phone ahead and check.

26 Some restaurants, pubs and hotels are not keen on children in the dining-room. Where it says children welcome, this indicates that they don't mind, although children must be well behaved. Any limitations on age are specified. Children's helpings means that smaller portions at a reduced price are available for children.

27 Jackets and ties are compulsory in very few restaurants and this is specified; otherwise, it is indicated if smart dress is preferred.

28 Any no-smoking arrangements as given to us by the restaurants. See also point 6.

29 Wheelchair access means that the proprietor has confirmed that the entrance is at least 80cm wide and passages at least 120cm across – the Royal Association for Disability and Rehabilitation (RADAR) recommendations. This does not guarantee access to all areas of an establishment. If it says 'also WC', then the owner has told us that the toilet facilities are suitable for disabled people. The *Guide* relies on proprietors giving accurate information on wheelchair access. If you find the details in the *Guide* are inaccurate, please tell us. It is always important to ring first and inform the restaurant of any special requirements.

30 Dining-rooms where live or recorded music is never played. Where a restaurant has told us that music may be played, we indicate this.

31 Room details and the price for rooms and breakfast as given to us by hotels. The first price is for one person in a single room or single occupancy of a double, the second is the upper price for two people in a double room or suite. When a price is for dinner, bed and breakfast, it is indicated as D,B&B.

32 The deposit required to secure accommodation. It may sometimes be expressed as a percentage.

33 The establishment has informed us it has bedrooms suitable for wheelchair users.

34 Children are welcome in the accommodation. Any age limitations are specified.

35 At least some facilities, such as cots and high chairs, are available for those guests with babies. It is important to inform the proprietors of any special requirements.

36 Dogs are welcome in the hotel, although they may be restricted to certain rooms.

37 Teas are served to non-residents.

38 Other general details about the establishment.

39 (*The Which? Hotel Guide*) denotes that this establishment is also listed in the 1997 edition of our sister guide to over 1,000 hotels in Britain.

The top-rated restaurants

Mark 5 for cooking

London
Chez Nico at
  Ninety Park Lane, W1
Hyde Park Hotel,
  The Restaurant, SW1
La Tante Claire, SW3

England
Le Manoir aux Quat'Saisons,
  Great Milton

Scotland
Altnaharrie Inn, Ullapool

Mark 4* for cooking

England
Croque-en-Bouche,
  Malvern Wells
Gidleigh Park, Chagford
Lettonie, Bristol

L'Ortolan, Shinfield
Waterside Inn, Bray
Winteringham Fields,
  Winteringham

Mark 4 for cooking

London
Aubergine, SW10
The Capital, SW3
Le Gavroche, W1
Interlude de Chavot, W1
Les Saveurs, W1
Turner's, SW3

England
Adlard's, Norwich
Box Tree, Ilkley
Carved Angel, Dartmouth
Castle Hotel, Taunton
Chester Grosvenor Hotel,
  Arkle, Chester
Cliveden, Waldo's, Taplow
Fischer's Baslow Hall, Baslow
Gordleton Mill Hotel, Provence,
  Lymington

Hambleton Hall, Hambleton
Mr Underhill's, Stonham
Paul Heathcote's, Longridge
Le Poussin, Brockenhurst
Seafood Restaurant, Padstow

Scotland
Airds Hotel, Port Appin
Braeval, Aberfoyle
Peat Inn, Peat Inn
La Potinière, Gullane

Wales
Plas Bodegroes, Pwllheli
Walnut Tree Inn, Llandewi
  Skirrid

Northern Ireland
Roscoff, Belfast

Restaurants with outstanding wine cellars
marked in the text with a ▐

London
Au Jardin des Gourmets, W1
Bibendum, SW3
Clarke's, W8
Fifth Floor, SW1
Leith's, W11
Odette's, NW1
Le Pont de la Tour, SE1
RSJ, SE1

England
Adlard's, Norwich
Angel Inn, Hetton
Bowlish House, Shepton Mallet
Buckland Manor, Buckland
La Cachette, Elland
Carved Angel, Dartmouth
Cherwell Boathouse, Oxford
Chewton Glen, Marryat Restaurant,
    New Milton
Cobwebs, Leck
Corse Lawn House, Corse Lawn
Croque-en-Bouche, Malvern Wells
The Crown, Southwold
Epworth Tap, Epworth
Fox and Goose, Fressingfield
French Partridge, Horton
George of Stamford, Stamford
Gidleigh Park, Chagford
Gravetye Manor, East Grinstead
Hambleton Hall, Hambleton
Harveys, Bristol
Hotel du Vin & Bistro, Winchester
Le Manoir aux Quat'Saisons, Great
    Milton
Markwicks, Bristol
Michael's Nook, Grasmere
Normandie, Birtle
Old Beams, Waterhouses
Old Manor House, Romsey
Old Vicarage, Ridgeway
Old Vicarage, Witherslack
Pheasant Inn, Keyston

Pheasants, Ross-on-Wye
Porthole Eating House, Bowness-on-
    Windemere
Priory Hotel, Wareham
Read's, Faversham
Röser's, Hastings
Seafood Restaurant, Padstow
Sir Charles Napier Inn, Chinnor
Sous le Nez en Ville, Leeds
Summer Lodge, Evershot
Le Talbooth, Dedham
Three Horseshoes, Madingley
Village Restaurant, Ramsbottom
White Hart, Great Yeldham
White Horse Inn, Chilgrove
White House, Williton
White Moss House, Grasmere

Scotland
Airds Hotel, Port Appin
Altnaharrie Inn, Ullapool
Braeval, Aberfoyle
Cellar, Anstruther
Champany Inn, Linlithgow
Clifton House, Nairn
The Cross, Kingussie
Inverlochy Castle, Fort William
Kinnaird, Dunkeld
Knipoch Hotel, Oban
Peat Inn, Peat Inn
La Potinière, Gullane
Summer Isles, Achiltibuie
Ubiquitous Chip, Glasgow
Valvona & Crolla Caffè Bar, Edinburgh

Wales
Fairyhill, Reynoldston
Old Rectory, Llansanffraid Glan
    Conwy
Penhelig Arms Hotel, Aberdovey
Plas Bodegroes, Pwllheli
Walnut Tree Inn, Llandewi Skirrid

Restaurants of the year

This award does not necessarily go to the restaurants with the highest mark for cooking, but rather to ones which have shown particular merit or achievement during the year, whether as all-rounders or in some particular field. It may go to an old favourite or to a new entry, but in either case the places listed below are worth visiting in their own right, and have enhanced the eating-out experience in some way.

London
The Capital SW3
Criterion Brasserie W1
Gay Hussar W1
Odette's NW1

England
Altrincham Juniper
Bolton Abbey Devonshire Arms, Burlington Restaurant
Bray Fat Duck
Bristol Lettonie
Calstock Danescombe Valley
Drewsteignton Hunts Tor
Durham Bistro 21
East Boldon Forsters
Huddersfield Café Pacific
Hythe Boathouse Brasserie
Kington Penrhos Court
Leck Cobwebs
Leeds Rascasse
Lymington Gordleton Mill Hotel, Provence
Minster Lovell Lovells at Windrush Farm
Moulton Black Bull
Nailsworth William's Bistro
Nayland Martha's Vineyard
Oxford Le Petit Blanc
Ramsbottom Village Restaurant
Rye Landgate Bistro

Sandgate Sandgate Hotel, La Terrasse
Southall Brilliant
Stuckton Three Lions
Swaffham Strattons
Tunbridge Wells Thackeray's House
Virginstow Percy's at Coombeshead
Waterhouses Old Beams
Winchcombe Wesley House
York Melton's

Scotland
Edinburgh Valvona & Crolla Caffè Bar
Fort William Inverlochy Castle
Nairn Clifton House
Perth Let's Eat
Port Appin Pierhouse
St Margaret's Hope The Creel

Wales
Abersoch Porth Tocyn Hotel
Clytha Clytha Arms
Llanddeiniolen Ty'n Rhos
Llandrillo Tyddyn Llan
Reynoldston Fairyhill

Ireland
Ballina Mount Falcon Castle
Dublin Thornton's

The *Guide*'s longest-serving restaurants

The *Guide* has seen many restaurants come and go. Some, however, have stayed the course with tenacity. (Qualification for this list is that the restaurant has been in each edition of the *Guide* subsequent to its first entry.)

Connaught, W1	44 years
Gay Hussar, W1	40 years
Porth Tocyn Hotel, Abersoch	40 years
Gravetye Manor, East Grinstead	36 years
Sharrow Bay, Ullswater	36 years
Dundas Arms, Kintbury	34 years
French Partridge, Horton	32 years
Walnut Tree Inn, Llandewi Skirrid	32 years
Black Bull Inn, Moulton	30 years
Chez Moi, W11	28 years
Rothay Manor, Ambleside	28 years
Sundial, Herstmonceux	28 years
Le Gavroche, W1	27 years
Summer Isles Hotel, Achiltibuie	27 years
The Capital, SW3	26 years
Miller Howe, Windermere	26 years
Cringletie House, Peebles	25 years
Old Fire Engine House, Ely	25 years
Ubiquitous Chip, Glasgow	25 years
Peat Inn, Peat Inn	24 years
Plumber Manor, Sturminster Newton	24 years
Druidstone, Broad Haven	24 years
Waterside Inn, Bray	24 years
White Moss House, Grasmere	24 years
Carved Angel, Dartmouth	23 years
Isle of Eriska, Eriska	22 years
Old Woolhouse, Northleach	22 years
Airds, Port Appin	21 years
La Potinière, Gullane	21 years
Stane Street Hollow, Pulborough	21 years

Introduction

'I really wonder if this restaurant is worth its place in the *Guide*,' wrote one of our reporters. Others agreed, we checked it out, and it is no longer included.

'I think you are being a bit mean with the score here,' suggested one correspondent of a different restaurant. The rest of the postbag shared his view, we sent along an inspector, and the cooking mark was raised.

'I think you should have a look at this new interesting place,' one reporter enthused. We did, and it is now a new entry in the *Guide*.

These examples, multiplied across thousands of reports, demonstrate one thing: that without you the reader, the reporter, we would not be able to keep the *Guide* up to date. We need you, we rely on you, and your reports make a difference.

If you don't write in, our information will not be so accurate, and we cannot be as helpful to other users of the *Guide* as we would like. It may seem as if we are asking for public-spiritedness above and beyond the call of duty, but the idea of helping fellow readers, fellow customers, is a benign one.

First of all, it paints a clear picture. If everybody who writes in about a particular restaurant complains about the puddings, then we are pretty confident with an entry that says 'puddings could be improved'. If only two people complain while the other ten find them 'utterly scrummy', then we must go with the majority. But we need to know what the majority feels, in order to go with it. The pay-off is that restaurants respond positively to praise, and do mend their ways in the face of criticism. If they don't, at least you know to avoid the puddings.

Secondly, your reports ensure that the *Guide* remains strongly reader-oriented. We get letters from restaurateurs – about their new chef, or their refurbished dining-room or whatever, all of which we appreciate – but the assessment of a restaurant is based on what the people who eat there have to say. Inspectors help, and we would be lost without their experience and judgement: many travel widely and are able to compare cooking styles and scores right across the country. But if enough readers agree on a view, then that is the one that prevails. The editor has even over-ruled himself on occasion, because this is a democratic book, not the reflection of one person's, nor one small group's, preferences and prejudices.

Even though inspectors are not paid, only reimbursed for the meals we ask them to eat, many people ask, 'How can I become an inspector?' The answer is: it's easy. There is no exam, no interview, no job specification. Just send us lots and lots of reports about every meal you eat. We look for an appropriate amount of detail, breadth of experience, and reliability of judgement. And if you have a special area of expertise, then that's a bonus. Many regular reporters have traded up to become inspectors over the years, and there is always room for more.

It is worth saying that inspecting restaurants is not all fun, because not all restaurants selected for inspection come up to scratch. One suggested new entry this year, for example, merely led us to 'simple ineptitude in cooking, straightforward incompetence, and poor raw materials', egged along by dishes that were variously 'lumpen, ill-conceived, and apallingly foul'. Needless to say, the restaurant does not appear in the *Guide*, though the inspector is happily still with us.

What this pool of talent puts at our – and your – disposal is a wealth of varied experiences accumulated both in Britain and abroad. Some inspectors have lived in Hong Kong or Tokyo, for example, which is invaluable when it comes to checking out Chinese and Japanese restaurants throughout the UK. One recently spent three weeks eating in all the best restaurants in France. You should see the size of him! But he knows his *oignons*.

What inspectors are able to do is to analyse carefully the whole experience. Some reporters, quite naturally, can be so put off by being kept waiting an hour for an aperitif, being brought the wrong dish, and having the bill totted up incorrectly, that they fail to register details of the food. Inspectors have to put up with all this too, but usually remain calm enough to assess the quality of the meat, the freshness of the fish, how the sauces were made, and whether a particular combination of ingredients really did play off well against each other. They report it all as dispassionately as possible, but are by no means immune from a rush of adrenalin at a great new discovery, nor a paragraph of withering criticism when faced with incompetence or pretension.

Eating in a smart British restaurant one day, a neighbourhood Indian or Greek the next, and a country pub at the weekend, is all part of the variety that the *Guide* celebrates. And just as there is no ideal reporter, and no ideal inspector, so there is no ideal restaurant.

When big means beautiful

Some restaurants, however, get more publicity than others. This seems to have been the Year of the Big Restaurant, in London at least. Reporters have been amazed that one place can feed up to 14,000 people a week; they marvel not that the food is good, but that it gets to the table at all.

Such Olympic-sized restaurants create their own problems, and have their own solutions. As far as supplies are concerned, there may be no role for the little bag of chanterelles that a friend of the chef collected at the weekend, but on the other hand, anybody who requires 5,000 portions of lamb shank a week will soon have suppliers queuing up to call them 'Sir'. As for cooking, it may be that at peak times some dishes have to line up on the counter waiting for customers, rather than being pan-fried, roasted or chargrilled to order. And yet the food seems to be perfectly satisfactory, sometimes impressively good.

As far as kitchen staff are concerned, peeling a wagon-load of spuds every week cannot be what they joined up for, but at least they have a job which otherwise they might not have done. Indeed these kitchens and dining-rooms have swallowed up so many staff that rapid training is now required to service them, and Butlers Wharf Chef School is one response. Officially an educational charity jointly founded by the Docklands Development Corporation, Conran restaurants, Southwark Council, and the Hotel Catering and Training Board, it provides training in an apprentice restaurant, and bags of job opportunity afterwards.

An equally important question is 'Where are all the customers coming from?' One view is that smaller restaurants are suffering and losing trade; another is that, as with cars, the more roads you build, the more traffic you create. If these restaurants are indeed helping to generate more custom, then the whole industry must benefit in the longer term, including many of the smaller, more personal restaurants which may have felt rather left out of the limelight recently.

The only problem that huge restaurants don't seem to have addressed successfully is how to book a table, and the frustration felt by all sides is evident. From the restaurant's point of view, it would appear damned if it allows customers a table all night, thus producing an even longer waiting list, and damned if it tries to pack in two or more sittings, because nobody likes to have their meal interrupted half-way through. In the *Guide*'s view, a more sympathetic understanding of how the customer feels might be a good place to start a rapprochement, and any restaurant in doubt about that perspective should take a look at Tim Atkin's well-deserved swipe at the booking chaos on page 23.

Thorns in the flesh

Another source of frustration and division, one that applies to any size of restaurant, is smoking. Non-smokers, I am sure you will have observed, are a dreadful nuisance. They are forever claiming their evening has been ruined by people who chain-smoked French cigarettes or lit up fat cigars before they reached the main course. They always want to be moved, they mutter about pollution, in fact they spoil everybody's enjoyment including their own. On the other hand, smokers are so much more tolerant, don't you find? Never once have they been known to complain about non-smokers. I think they are an example to us all . . . .

Whatever else, eating in a restaurant should not be a hazardous experience. But events during the past year have brought everybody up sharp on that score. There is little to add here to the debate about links between BSE, scrapie and CJD, but at least it has concentrated minds and made more restaurateurs think seriously about their supplies. Many restaurants in the *Guide* use free-range, organic foods, and some go to considerable lengths to procure fresh and healthy materials. In most cases, especially outside cities, local foods are best: they travel shorter distances, and can be eaten within hours of harvesting, or monitored for provenance and hanging time.

Some foods look just as innocent as grazing sheep and cows, and yet can have an immediate and devastating effect. Nuts, for example, can cause rashes, swelling, asthma, eczema and, in severe cases, potentially fatal anaphylactic shock to those who are allergic. In the most acute cases even a tiny trace of peanut oil can kill. Dairy products, gluten, eggs and shellfish can also cause serious problems to some people. Most adults who are susceptible to any of these will probably already know about it. What they may not know is which items they are about to eat in a restaurant secretly contain the substances that provoke an intolerance or allergic reaction. So they ask the waiter, and if the waiter does not know that the ice-cream or bread contains nuts, then he or she could easily give the wrong advice.

One sufferer wrote to us during the year with a two-fold plea: 'one, that no one become ill or die from an allergy as a result of eating food in a restaurant, and two, that no restaurant should be (successfully) sued for supplying food which caused someone injury or death from an allergy.' He added that it is 'vital that waiters should know the ingredients in the food they serve ... or at least that they are able quickly and surely to ascertain them. The latter is not the case at the moment.' We pass on his concern in the hope that it may help to save not only distress, but possibly lives too.

Hard-to-swallow wine prices

Wine can also be quite dangerous in restaurants. Several reporters claim to have nearly suffered heart attacks when seeing some of the prices asked. Whenever the *Guide* complains about the cost of wine, restaurateurs often trot out the old chestnut about having to increase food prices to compensate if wine prices were any lower. As usual we blow a fairly big raspberry at this piece of nonsense.

In the first place quite a few restaurants manage to employ a modest and sensible mark-up, and still survive. To take just one example, the Village Restaurant in Ramsbottom – in existence for over decade – simply adds £5, £7 or £9 to the wine's retail price, thus producing some wonderful bargains. One comment from a reporter this year is particularly revealing. 'Fairly priced wines generally lead us (and, I suspect, other wine lovers) to spend more.' I wish all restaurateurs would cut out that sentence and paste it on the front page of their wine list, or on their forehead so that they see it in the mirror first thing every morning. Its significance cannot be over-estimated.

Sadly, high prices only engender a feeling of resentment among the vast majority of customers who pay with their own money. Imposing a 100 per cent mark-up (or worse) means that people who enjoy good wine are made to suffer unduly. If a standard mark-up were added to all bottles, then the customer would have greater freedom of choice. We would be at liberty to spend as little or as much as we liked in pursuit of our enjoyment, and the positive feeling towards the restaurant would very likely result in higher spending: we are far more likely to buy an extra bottle or two.

Many restaurants also fail to realise that a customer who buys a house wine today, and enjoys it, is more likely to return in the future and buy something more expensive. The world is not simply divided into buyers of either 'cheap' or 'expensive' wine, the former to be dismissed, the latter to be fawned over. Customers are in a position to choose, depending on circumstances, whether to spend a lot or a little on wine. Would the guilty restaurants please allow us, the customers, to exercise our choice in the most effective way possible? Give us lower mark-ups, and we will buy more bottles. You will be surprised at how much more good wine you sell if it is reasonably priced. You will be surprised at how much more money you make. And you will be surprised how much happier your customers are to pay you that extra money. The beauty of a standard mark-up is that nobody loses, everybody gains.

And another thing, guv ...

If I'm beginning to sound like a taxi driver, I crave your indulgence. A restaurant that charges the earth for its wines, and then allows customers at neighbouring tables to smoke, is reducing the value of those wines considerably. The *Guide* is not a supporter of expensive wine lists at the best of times, nor of smoking, but when the two combine, the result is an expensive fiasco. Would 'smoking' restaurants be prepared to sell any wine on their list to non-smokers for £5, which is about what a top Burgundy or first-growth claret is worth when wreathed in smoke? I doubt it. As things stand, such restaurants merely invite ridicule.

Others invite it for a different reason. 'I can understand dress codes prohibiting scruffy clothes, shorts and the like, but not codes which make a totally senseless requirement that men (and it is only men) tie a bit of coloured fabric around their neck as if that suddenly makes them presentable.' The evidence is that if you have a well-known name or face, then the rule doesn't apply, which makes it even more of a silly practice. Hypocrisy is alive and well in some of our top restaurants. What is more, as one reporter pointed out, it was perfectly permissible to eat without a tie at Joel Robuchon's restaurant in Paris (until it closed when he retired in mid-1996), and there are few kitchens that could hold a candle to his. So what is the big deal about ties?

Nobody does it better

Lest this seem like a chip-on-shoulder gripe, it is worth recording that there is much to celebrate. Restaurants in Britain are doing nothing short of a grand job. 'I wish,' confessed one former *Guide* editor over lunch, 'I had had restaurants like you've got.' It is the exuberance, the joy, the fun in both kitchen and dining-room that strikes home. Native talent is doing wonders all around the country. Brasseries, bistros and cafés continue to open. Reverence takes a back seat as sheer pleasure comes to the fore. At long last this country really gets a buzz from eating out, and at long last we have restaurants to cherish and be proud of on a scale never before experienced.

London continues to be a 'destination city' for food. Not every part of it is well served, but the centre has great vitality, and the more peripheral, less ambitious, pub and shop conversions continue, albeit at a gentle pace. Around the country, some city centres are also jumping: look at Leeds, look at Edinburgh. Some of the best chefs around the regions are setting up a café here, a bistro there, and installing trusted sous-chefs to look after them. Sous-chefs gain because they have a degree of independence, without having to stump up tens of thousands of pounds to buy a place of their own. The entrepreneurial chef gains because the protegé that might have been a competitor is now working for him. And the customer gains because the food in most of these places turns out to be exciting and high-quality. Terence Laybourne's Café 21 in Ponteland and Bistro 21 in Durham spring to mind, as do Marco Pierre White's Criterion Brasserie and Les Saveurs in London.

In truth, there has never been a more exciting time to eat out: partly because of the generally high standard, at least in restaurants that appear in the *Guide*, and partly because of the wonderful mix of cooking styles. Some represent a strict national or regional culinary heritage, others borrow ideas and ingredients from wherever the chef fancies, but together they provide unprecedented variety: of food, of price, ambience, location and lots more. It is all simply too good to miss. And while you're enjoying it, please remember to drop us a line.

Hurry up please it's time

Tim Atkin, author and *Observer* wine writer, finds it takes the patience of Job to book a table at some trendy London places – and something of a race to finish once you're in

Ever attempted to book a table in a fashionable London restaurant? I've been trying for the last hour. So far I've been rejected by a push-button answer phone at Pesto, fobbed off by the front desk at Eggplant, snubbed by the assistant doorman at Quango's and laughed at by staff at Bibulous.

My options are dwindling like a gunslinger down to his last silver bullet. Everywhere is full, chocka, *complet*: 'Maybe better come back maybe next week,' as Rolling Stone and celebrated epicurean Mick Jagger once put it. Or next year, perhaps.

But let's keep trying, shall we? It's not as if it's Valentine's Day. Someone must have a table. How about that place whose offal reminded a Saturday newspaper columnist of a Francis Bacon painting? Sounds all right. I dial the number, but someone else has the same idea, repeatedly. I get through 30 minutes later. Time for a 21-gun salute?

'Tripe.'

'Hi, have you got a table for this evening, please?'

'What time?'

'Around eight, eight-thirty.'

'Squeeze you in at six or eleven in smoking.'

'You must have something better than that. There are only two of us.'

'We've been very busy since the write-up.'

'OK. Six it is.'

'Fine. We don't take credit cards. And we want the table back by seven.'

The line goes dead and I'm still in a state of first-degree shock. Have I got this right? I'm preparing to hand over £80 to sit in a half-empty basement when most people are digesting lunch or watching Martyn Lewis on the news. Perhaps they're bluffing? Surely they won't dare throw us out once we've ordered a bottle of wine and just started our main courses?

But they will. Past experience has taught me that if they say seven o'clock, they mean seven o'clock. At Littoral, a car showroom-cum-restaurant, three friends and I were asked in no uncertain terms to vacate our table and finish our meal at the bar. Frites, a Belgian beer-joint, swept away a plate of mussels after three minutes in its haste to encourage me out of the door.

When did this offensive practice begin? I first noticed it in the late 1980s, when the West End's trendier eateries introduced the two-sitting rule. Since then, it has spread to other parts of the capital, though not (yet) to other parts of the country. It happened to me in Putney, of all places, last week when a posse of waiters stood malevolently over the table as I finished my meal.

One restaurant group in particular appears to have adopted the time-is-money approach in all its establishments. It is no coincidence, in my view, that these are often places where the service is cursory, the booking system off-hand to the point of rudeness and the food as patchy as a pair of old jeans.

Why do they do it? The only possible answer is greed. I know busy city-centre restaurants need to turn over their tables at least twice during the evening. But in most places this tends to happen naturally. Few of us wish to spend the night under the table.

What's wrong with allowing people to stay until they've finished their meal? After all, they've paid to be there. You can end up spending £160 or more for four people and feel as if you've eaten in a fast-food joint. This is a flagrant rip-off. Can you imagine someone barging his way down the aisle in the last act of a play and asking you to collect your coat? More to the point, can you conceive of someone trying this on in France, Spain or Italy? He'd get thrown through the nearest monogrammed partition.

If restaurants are busy – as the ingredient-of-the-month places tend to be – I can understand the temptation to pack in as many punters as possible. Sting them, as it were, before they move on to the next fashionable address. But by doing so they risk alienating the ordinary diner: someone who eats out a couple of times a month and doesn't like being treated like a prison visitor.

The other noteworthy thing about this two-sitting business is that your tenancy of a table depends on who you are – or who the restaurant thinks you are. The composer Andrew Lloyd Webber tells a story about visiting the Café de Paris in Monte Carlo. He booked the table in his own name and, as soon as he'd stepped through the door, was surrounded by fawning wine waiters and flunkeys. They thought he was Lord Webber. Imagine how they'd have behaved if they'd known he was Sir Andrew.

London is no different. They don't throw minor celebs out of the Creeper. And if you're important enough, restaurants will always make space for you. You can always tell them you're a friend of Michael Winner. Or impersonate a Windsor. The latter strategy should certainly get you a table. A well-known food writer once interviewed a glamour chef to the sound of his maître d' informing caller after caller that 'we 'ave no tables for this ivenin'. Suddenly his tone changed. 'Princess Margaret? Of course. At what time?'

I also get the feeling that some restaurants deliberately set out to convey an image of bustle and popularity. 'It must be good,' they imagine awed diners telling one another, 'because it took me half an hour to get through on the phone.' Frustrated by a telephone refusal from a very large restaurant, I went to one of these places in person. Did they have any free tables? Of course they did. Was anyone sitting at either of the tables flanking mine? What do you think?

It all reminds me of something I once witnessed in California. Driving past a newly opened restaurant, I saw a queue of people waiting to get into a packed dining-room. 'Pretty busy,' I commented to a friend of mine who works in the catering business. 'Yeah,' he smiled. 'They're all shills.' 'Shills?' I asked. 'Yeah. Actors, freeloaders, hangers-on. They're either paid to be there or they're eating for nothing.' Only an American restaurant would go to so much trouble just to look full. In London they'd just take the phone off the hook. Or tell you they were fully booked.

With a little help from our trends

Emily Green, late of the *Independent*, looks beyond the copycat cooks and finds that cuisine in Britain continues to flower

Sitting beside me as I write is a bulging hamper. It contains menus collected during the last nine years from restaurants throughout England, Wales, Scotland and Ireland. At a rough guess, there are 900 of them, maybe a few more. And what stories they tell: they are samplings of what may have been the greatest flowering of the British and Irish tables.

At their best these menus capture heroic moments. There is Simon Hopkinson defiantly serving fish and chips in great luxury at Bibendum. There is Ian McAndrew showing a prowess of technique previously almost unknown in an English chef, to be equalled only later by Marco Pierre White. There is Franco Taruschio introducing bresaola, first to Gwent, then to Britain. There is Terence Laybourne partnering pease pudding with foie gras in Newcastle. There is Alastair Little going mad with quiveringly fresh sea urchins. There is Stephen Bull doing a quite delicious quiche from Julia Child. Ah, bliss, there is David Wilson's superb smoked haddock pie in Fife. Oooh, there are those perfect pike quenelles from that hippy chef at the Ivory Tower in Cork. Reading these menus does two things: it makes me ravenously hungry, and want to let rip with a cheer.

Copycats

Yet, as I rifle through these menus, another sensation sets in, and it is one of déjà-vu. Yes, there is sea bass served with saffron-flavoured potatoes in Newcastle. There it is again in Dublin. There it is again in West London, and the harshness of the saffron did not suit the fish in any of these places. There is seared tuna cropping up in bastardised versions of salade niçoise all over London. Latterly, Caesar salads have been ubiquitous, but made oddly with fresh anchovy and shaved Parmesan. Here in my wonderful, historic hamper is all-too-vivid evidence of virulent copycat cooking.

What else do we have here? There was a short but furious run on baby vegetables in the late '80s when everyone wanted to be Raymond Blanc. Thai spicing is so common, Schwartz starts bottling it. By the '90s tiramisù is appearing from Land's End to John O'Groats. No corner of the country, no season is free of sweated red peppers. The national loaf becomes ciabatta, the condiment olive oil, the herb basil. Rocket is preferred, even at the height of the English watercress season. There is an unfathomable craze for carpaccio of salmon (an English dish), artichokes are served year-round, and who could have avoided risotto (or, more commonly, a short-cut approximation)? By the mid-'90s coffee bars are the rage, and cappuccino reigns supreme.

The pundit, the cook and the critic

Any idea that these rippling trends are somehow a case of some sort of cosmic coincidence disappears with a visit to the catering industry's annual trade fair, the Restaurant Show. Here rent-a-pundits have the gall to stage seminars telling cooks who have congregated from all over Britain what they should serve if they want to succeed (this is a powerful lure in a business characterised as much by failure as by success). Three or four years ago I was one of the pundits rented for just such an occasion. Members of the audience seemed to think that there was some sort of food particularly attractive to restaurant critics, and knowing what it was would be the key to a good review.

Alas, anticipating the taste of critics is rather like trying to please all the people all the time. Michael Winner likes to be recognised and fawned over. Jonathan Meades of *The Times* made it something of a cause to keep offal on restaurant menus and, at least until BSE came along, was succeeding admirably. Fay Maschler of the London *Evening Standard* is a tireless champion of the ethnic diversity of the London restaurant scene. The food I, personally, have loved best has been bourgeois cooking: carne all'albese with lemon juice and pepper, brandade, roast mackerel with rosemary, rib of beef with yorks and horseradish cream, punchy salads, well-fermented breads. Where I have been harshest is in commenting on some of the wilder slights of ingenuity – say, restaurants serving roast garlic snails with a potato galette on top. In answer to the audience of chefs who wanted to know what critics look for, my contribution was terse: serve what you like to eat.

In principle, I stand by that advice, but today I blush at the glibness of it. I am not, unlike many restaurateurs, up to my eyeballs in debt and beholden to the whims of suppliers. Worse, my counsel presumed that young chefs can afford to eat around enough to decide what they like and formulate a personal style. Throughout our restaurant boom, trainee chefs have been commonly expected to live on as little as £100 take-home pay after a 60- or even 80-hour week. Staff meals tend not to consist of the expensive monkfish sold to the customers. They are more likely to be watery chicken curries served with a fizzy soft drink. Ask the average commis chef what he likes to eat, and the honest one will reply, Mars Bars. So it is natural that when they finally become head chefs they cook what their previous employers used to serve, or look for new ideas in newspaper columns and food guides. Once they spot the flavour of the moment, it is not unreasonable that they should then attempt to cash in on it.

Away from novelty?

So where does this leave us as we head for the millennium? Stuck with a national cuisine so nervous about the market, so style-conscious, so frivolously malleable it has all the backbone of an issue of *Vogue*? I hope not. It seems to me that our brightest stars, their dullest imitators and the wildest of kooky cooks all deserve chestfuls of medals. They have got British kitchens going and have drawn us into a debate about what constitutes good food. It is now up to us all to raise the tone of conversation. I should like to see it turn away from novelty and towards the social responsibility of restaurants: to proper wages for catering workers, to the use of seasonal and local produce, to the promoting of craft food producers, to environmental awareness generally. This may happen. Then again, we may decide we want dancing girls and all go bananas over kumquats.

From the cradle to the gravy

Sarah Fergusson, former member of the *Good Food Guide* editorial staff, asks five personalities to assess a lifetime's love of restaurants

Don't imagine for an instant that all self-confessed foodies have blossomed from idyllically epicurean childhoods, where Mother was a cordon bleu queen of the Aga who consigned 'ketchup' to a list of banned dirty words. Love of restaurants, it would appear, can spring up from all sorts of backgrounds. Here, five famous eaters-out share their past and present preoccupations with restaurants. Ultimately there are no conclusions: just as many different routes to enjoyment, and as many different tastes, as there are recipes for Christmas cake.

Rabbi Julia Neuberger, chairman of Camden & Islington Community Health Services NHS Trust, eats out three to four times a week, often *en famille*. **Jane Asher**, actress, author, cake designer and owner of Jane Asher's Party Cakes Shop and Tea-room in Chelsea, manages to fit in regular flits to restaurants. **Michael Caine**, actor, spends a considerable amount of time abroad, but also is the proprietor of the Canteen, Langan's Brasserie, Shepherd's and Odin's, all in London.

The Earl of Bradford, who owns Porters restaurant in Covent Garden, leads a dual life, partly in London, and partly in Shropshire. His Private Member's Bill in 1996 attempted to abolish service and cover charges, and the practice of leaving credit-card slips open. Restaurants are both his business and his pleasure: he regularly reviews them for two major regional newspapers. **Paul Heathcote**, chef and proprietor of his eponymous restaurant in Longridge, Lancashire, and owner of Heathcote's Brasserie in Preston, takes an active interest in the restaurant scene at home and abroad.

Remembrance of meals past

Memories of meals long past drew mixed reactions from today's most adventurous palates. Lord Bradford comments: 'I hated junket and semolina. I was convinced as a child that they were dishes that had been invented purely for the purpose of torturing children because I never saw grown-ups eat them.' This view wins sympathy from Paul Heathcote, who recollects being cooked for by his father when his mother was out. He describes it as being 'so bad that I was prompted into cooking meals for us. I remember on one occasion my father brought home some tripe. I remember the smell – the memory still lingers. The dog had to eat the lot, it was so awful. The one thing I won't cook today is tripe.' This incident spurred on Paul's decision to go to catering college. Michael Caine's mother was a cook in a Lyons Corner House, which meant a childhood of 'chips with everything – very enjoyable for a 6-year-old'.

Although all the panel were in agreement with Jane Asher that 'in those days, one didn't go out nearly as much as people do now, regardless of money', their early restaurant visits have left lasting impressions, good and bad. Lord Bradford was taken to the Lansdowne Club by his father on occasion, which puzzled him: 'I used to wonder why he had taken me there as the food was usually better at home.' Michael Caine recollects the British Restaurants set up by the government during the Second World War in churches, museums and elsewhere to provide square meals to civilians when food was rationed. By 1945 there were around 2,000 of these 'national' restaurants providing half a million meals a day, and Caine recalls them as serving 'the worst food anywhere in history'. For Julia Neuberger it is the glamour and novelty of eating out that she remembers most vividly. At the Trocadero the great treat was knickerbocker glories: 'those enormous glasses – yet the thought of eating them now makes me feel very peculiar!'

Likewise, Jane Asher can recall a Spanish restaurant which fascinated her, as she watched the waiters pouring wine from carafes with 'the long pointy spouts'. She is convinced that these are the things that you remember as a child, 'rather than the wonderful *boeuf en croûte*', before pausing to wonder if her own children will feel the same, or whether for them it will be simply 'a blur of endless outside meals'.

The explosion of the British restaurant scene that began in the mid-'60s and continued into the '70s seemed to coincide happily for our panel with growing up and having their own disposable income. After his wartime experiences, Michael Caine found that 'I had nowhere to go but up, which I have done.' For many, eating out became a more regular occurrence. London's bistro revolution saw the opening of a number of Italian places, most famously Alvaro's, and a whole new attitude. Jane Asher remembers the pink tablecloths, which until then had been 'just *unheard* of' in English establishments. Lord Bradford recognises that in many of these new haunts 'the food wasn't that wonderful, but compared with anything else that had been around up till then was quite decent', and was similarly impressed by the way these places took the formality out of eating out in Britain.

Italian food actually ingested in Italy has also proved inspirational. Paul Heathcote can recall the first time he ate spaghetti bolognese, during one of the earliest-ever package tours to Elba. Several thousand pasta dishes down the line, he still has an enthusiasm for tucking into fresh spaghetti with pesto when away from the stove. As a student, Julia Neuberger spent some time in Florence in 1969, and acknowledges how much living in Italy affected her tastes. Eating out was *de rigueur* as she was lodging in a *pensione*, and although simple pasta was standard fare in the student union building, feast days would warrant a bus trip out of the city to a Tuscan village to sample country food. In Florence the 'fourteen hundred place', so named because it charged 1,400 lire for a set meal, was a regular haunt. Northern Italian peasant dishes such as the hearty soup *ribollita* and the bread salad *panzanella* have remained firm favourites.

Backing Britain

There was general enthusiasm among the panel for the current UK restaurant scene compared with that of other countries. Paul Heathcote flies out on a regular basis to Paris and New York to try out the competition, but maintains that Britain's eating places are 'as good as anywhere else'. Lord Bradford goes as far as to say that people might now look to London and Sydney as being culinary capitals, 'whereas who would have considered them [as such] 20 years ago?' He applauds the way that the British have borrowed to their advantage from 'the best and the most interesting in the world'. Julia Neuberger asserts that one of the greatest things about being in London is that 'you can eat virtually every "nationality" and mostly very well'. She cites Italian, Indian and Chinese restaurants as frequent ports of call for the whole family as, in her opinion, these are the places that most welcome children. But she would like to see greater provision for family dining, believing that 'good food should be multi-generational'. Otherwise, she asks, 'How can you ever really encourage your children to learn to eat out and be adventurous?'

Jane Asher's day-to-day business is that of specialist cake designing, with her own shop the 'couture' side of all her cake activities. Like cooking, the process is labour-intensive. At the end of her working day, she prefers salads and grilled fish with fresh herbs to anything complicated, or sweet. Restaurants she returns to time after time include the Caprice and the Ivy.

How to end it all

How would the panel have their last meal on earth? Jane Asher's 'last supper' would arrive via room service ('I just love hotels, with the trouser press and the kettle. [I'd take] the Ritz if I was given the choice'). Julia Neuberger's last meal would be eaten at home. An Italian chef would be called in to prepare roasted peppers 'in some shape or form' to start. A Chinatown chef would cook Chinese-style sea bass with ginger, spring onions and soy, and then Irish and British cheeses would be served instead of pudding. A bottle of 1993 Rolly-Gassman Gewurztraminer would 'take care of the fish'.

Michael Caine, though no stranger to the kitchen himself, would fly in Fredy Girardet from his restaurant, Girardet, in Crissier, Switzerland or, alternatively, Gordon Ramsay of Aubergine, London to cook a last supper that would be eaten 'with my family at my home in the country'. His all-time favourite dish is 'roast leg of lamb, simply done'.

Lord Bradford would choose a favourite Paris restaurant, L'Entrecôte at Porte Maillot, but he would be anxious about the precise time of his demise as 'you have to get there for 12 o'clock for lunch'. His meal would be entrecôte steak with a tossed green salad and French bread 'so light it sails up to the ceiling', washed down with claret.

Location is important to Paul Heathcote too, who would eat his last supper at the restaurant where he learnt his trade, Sharrow Bay in the Lake District. His table would have a lake view of Ullswater, and the meal would consist of a large platter of langoustines and mussels, followed by braised oxtail and mashed potato, rounded off with bread-and-butter pudding. To drink? 'Champagne – unquestionably!'

Educating the younger palate

Brian Turner, chef/proprietor of Turner's in London and chairman of the Culinary Academy of Great Britain, contemplates where the next generation of restaurant-goers is coming from

We all talk a lot about the revolution in food and cooking which has been taking place in Britain over the past 15 years. Yet the tremendous improvements have for the most part affected only the top of the eating-out pyramid – the best hotels and restaurants – and the 'trickle-down' effect of these changes through the whole hierarchy of restaurants, pubs and cafés has been a painfully slow one to watch. There is a long way to go yet before the British food revolution becomes an integral part of our culture.

The erosion of food skills

No one will argue that technology hasn't made life easier for cooks, both at home and in the restaurant and catering industries. But the speed at which we now can prepare food – or buy it in ready-prepared – has had the effect of wreaking havoc with our eating habits. As a boy, I used to encounter the wonderful aroma of baking breads and home-cooking when walking down the street. In those days children learnt about food from their mothers, aunts and grannies. We used to hover around the kitchen in anticipation of the sweet and savoury smells of the stove. Mother always encouraged us by letting us stir the pudding or cream the cake mixture and then indulge in what is now an almost extinct delight: licking the spoon.

Such events just don't happen any more in the vast majority of families. We seem to have produced a generation of bland young people who have little or no interest in food. School meals are no longer a compulsory, cooked, sit-down affair, but often a packed lunch or a packet of crisps and a soft drink wolfed down on the trot. Fast-food manufacturers have taken advantage of the cutbacks in education and are encouraging schools to install dispensing machines, with the result that unhealthy and unchallenging foods and drinks are permanently 'on tap'.

Even more discouraging is the fact that domestic science is no longer part of the curriculum: it has been replaced by something called 'food technology'. A student nowadays may be asked to design a colourful pizza or sandwich rather than create a cake from scratch. Domestic science has fallen victim to cost-cutting considerations: it costs a good deal to build and run a proper kitchen with appropriate equipment, whereas food technology can be studied without any cooking taking place, and thus by comparison it costs very little to set up and run. Many teachers, understandably, are exasperated.

Reversing the trend

The fact that children are now growing up with so little knowledge about food or its preparation has also set off alarm bells in the catering industry, which finds that it is attracting fewer newcomers, and that many of those who do come in have never even eaten in a proper restaurant. The Culinary Academy of Great Britain (the British branch of the Académie Culinaire de France), which is an association of more than 150 chefs and restaurant managers in Britain, is attempting to do something about this growing skills shortage. In 1993 it launched a project in partnership with the Scottish food producers Baxters of Speyside called 'Adopt a School', aimed directly at the palates of children between the ages of seven and eleven (although no age group is excluded). The project teaches children how to enjoy eating: the first step to understanding food and the process of cookery.

Although this venture began as a careers exercise, it now extends to three sessions over a school year, each run by the chef/teacher who has 'adopted' that particular school. The sessions cover what it's like to be a chef, why food is important for both sustenance and enjoyment, and how the tongue experiences the various sensations of taste. In many cases, children are invited to tour the restaurant of 'their' chef.

Each year the chef takes on a new class of students from the same school, and so far more than 50 members of the Academy have 'adopted' schools from as far afield as the north of Scotland and the south of England. Even though the majority of these children will not become chefs, the Academy feels that the project has been a success in turning them into better-informed eaters and thus potentially more discerning restaurant-goers.

Education is not enough

Understanding and appreciating food is well and good, but there is much that restaurants in Britain have to do to accommodate children as customers. In Europe the attitude towards children is completely different: all over the Continent children are welcomed in restaurants and indeed are expected to eat out as part of the family. In North America, too, it is widely accepted by restaurateurs that if children can become interested in eating out, that will bring in the families regularly, and so children are very much encouraged. Here in Britain, by contrast, many establishments feel that children should still, to a certain extent, be seen and not heard. For the consumer eating out *en famille* the experience can be an uncomfortable one. (Of course, it is also the responsibility of parents to ensure that children *behave* appropriately in a restaurant, so that their presence never becomes disruptive for other diners, or for the restaurant itself.)

It is not enough merely to offer children's menus; restaurants should also learn how to treat youngsters as young adults and above all as customers. Chefs and restaurateurs in Britain must make more of an effort to adapt their attitudes and make sure this change continues. While I am not suggesting that we look to the ubiquitous children-oriented fast-food outlets as temples of gastronomy whose examples we should slavishly follow, we could take note of their basic philosophy. After all, children are the next generation of customers on whom the success of British restaurants – and the preservation of food knowledge and appreciation – depends. I don't believe anyone would rejoice if those fictional prophecies of 20 years ago came true and we all ended up living on pre-packed pills or at best eating out of plastic bags. Families, educators and the restaurant industry together *can* change attitudes; the knowledge of how to do so is there, and all that is needed is the will to carry it through.

If we had grasped this philosophy years ago, the 'junk' man or woman of today would be eating out at places such as Criterion Brassierie, 21 Queen Street, Pool Court, Heathcote's, the Walnut Tree Inn – or even (if I may say so) Turner's. What is even more important, he or she would be eating out with the family, and thus re-inventing the experience of dining together at a table.

London

Abingdon

NEW ENTRY map 13

54 Abingdon Road, W8 6AP
TEL: (0171) 937 3339   FAX: (0171) 795 6388

COOKING 2
COST £22–£44

If you are going to have a converted pub on the corner of your street, this is definitely the kind to have. Rather than coming up through the ranks, Brian Baker has come down from the top, having cooked in highfalutin style at Hambleton Hall (see entry, Hambleton), then at the Criterion in Piccadilly (see entry) when it was part of Bob Peyton's My Kinda Town plc. That same company is behind this conversion: part of the 1990s tendency to economise on peripherals, with the laudable aim of serving good food at realistic prices.

Baker succeeds admirably. At the end of a leafy road off Kensington High Street, the Abingdon consists of a casual bar and two long, thin dining-rooms: artfully designed, but pleasingly idiosyncratic. Menu choice is generous, its French Mediterranean outlook showing to excellent effect in a terrine of red mullet and scallops served with concentrated kitchen-dried tomatoes. Fish and vegetable dishes (tartlet of artichoke hearts with sauté leeks and basil, for example) figure prominently, alongside grills of lemon chicken or pork chop. Baker's background means he gets the details right – proper sweet shortcrust pastry and crème pâtissière in a prune and orange tart, for instance – which makes the food stand out. The set-price lunch is a bargain, and a dozen or so red and white wines stay mostly under £20. House wine is £9.25.

CHEF: Brian Baker   PROPRIETOR: My Kinda Town plc   OPEN: all week 12 to 2.30 (3 Sun), 6.30 to 11 (10.30 Sun)   MEALS: alc (main courses £8.50 to £13.50). Set L Sun £13.50, Set L Mon to Sat £9.95 (2 courses)   SERVICE: 12.5% (optional), card slips closed   CARDS: Access, Amex, Delta, Switch, Visa   DETAILS: 52 seats. 12 seats outside. Private parties: 18 main room. Vegetarian meals. Children welcome exc in bar area. No cigars/pipes in dining-room. Music

Adams Café £

map 12

77 Askew Road, W12 9AH
TEL/FAX: (0181) 743 0572

COOKING 1*
COST £18–£29

Famed as a stronghold of couscous in all its forms, Frances and Abdel Boukraa's seminal café has recently diversified. The menu now offers harira (Moroccan vegetable and chickpea soup), ojja (spicy 'ratatouille' cooked with an egg in an earthenware dish), a Tunisian mixed grill, and five versions of tajine (stews cooked in cone-lidded pots), not to mention a bigger selection of seafood. You could choose grilled whole red mullet, marinated tuna steak or 'la marmite du pêcheur'. Desserts bring into play such Gallic confections as tarte au citron and cassis sorbet, as well as baklava pastries. To drink there is a choice of mint tea with pine-nuts, and Arabic coffee, plus potent Tunisian digestifs such as Thibarine, made from dates. House French wine is £7.50.

CHEF: Abdel Boukraa PROPRIETORS: Abdel and Frances Boukraa OPEN: all week D only 7 to 11 CLOSED: 25 and 26 Dec, 1 Jan MEALS: alc (main courses £7 to £10). BYO 95p per person SERVICE: not inc CARDS: none DETAILS: 60 seats. Private parties: 36 main room, 24 private room. Vegetarian meals. Children welcome. Wheelchair access (no WC). Music

Ajimura ✸

map 15

51–53 Shelton Street, WC2H 9HE
TEL: (0171) 240 0178 FAX: (0171) 497 2240

COOKING 1
COST £14–£63

In 1997 Ajimura celebrates its 25th anniversary, making it, as the menu is keen to point out, 'the longest-established Japanese restaurant in Britain'. A lot has happened in that time, and there are now almost 100 Japanese restaurants in London alone, some of them trendy, many of them smart and expensive. While it can do you a set dinner at £35, Ajimura appeals for its less formal and more accessible approach, perfectly suited to the casual needs of those who pass through Covent Garden. It offers a fairly wide range of sushi and sashimi, backed up by teriyaki and toban-yaki, tempura, and udon and soba noodle dishes. Good-value lunch and pre-theatre set meals include the 'trimmings' of hors d'oeuvre, miso soup, rice, pickles, salad and fruit. Drink saké, plum wine, green tea or one of the nine Western wines.

CHEF: Tasuo Tanizawa PROPRIETOR: Peachboy Ltd OPEN: Mon to Fri L 12 to 3, Mon to Sat D 6 to 11 MEALS: alc (main courses £7 to £22). Set L £8 to £8.90, Set D Mon to Fri 6 to 7.30 £13 to £14.50, Set D Mon to Sat £19.50 to £35 SERVICE: not inc CARDS: Access, Amex, Diners, Visa DETAILS: 58 seats. Private parties: 25 main room, 18 private room. Vegetarian meals. Children welcome. No smoking in 1 dining-room. Music. Air-conditioned

Alastair Little 🍴

map 15

49 Frith Street, W1V 5TE
TEL: (0171) 734 5183

COOKING 3
COST £39–£46

'If you took away the knives and forks and put chopsticks on the tables instead, it would look like a Japanese restaurant,' thought one reporter. The minimal style of cream walls and black furniture, although much copied, is still dramatic, and the food, also much copied, has reached a new equilibrium under Juliet Peston. Menus are now fixed price only (and good value), and the cooking has an individual stamp on it that is quite different from Alastair Little's. It can be as straightforward as Caesar salad, ham and melon, or six Pacific oysters: food that is hardly intended to set the world on fire, more the stuff of everyday eating, but the plain style works to good effect across the board.

Cep pizza has been a great success: a light base with wafer-thin cep slices pasted on top. 'Intriguing and unusual, yet very simple and enjoyable,' judged an inspector. Some dishes may sound classical but often turn out to be subtly different from their templates. Risi e bisi at one meal was not a strict soupy version, more of a pea risotto, but it was appropriately seasonal and cooked 'just right', while chicken harira was a 'stupendously tasty' version of a Moroccan dish, incorporating lentils, chickpeas and coriander. On top was a piece of thin, flat bread, dramatically gashed with holes, just one example of the excellent and varied bread and pastry-work.

Another example was the pastry of a cherry and almond tart, 'looking like an individual clafoutis, but tasting more like a Bakewell tart', which was served with Black Forest ice-cream (another variation on a theme) containing chewy cherries and crunchy chocolate chips. The food is not gimmicky or wildly exploratory, just gently inventive, and seems to achieve exactly what it sets out to do with quiet confidence. A modern collection of varied wines adds to the enjoyment, and begins at £12.

CHEF: Juliet Peston   PROPRIETORS: Alastair Little, Kirsten Pedersen and Mercedes André-Vega   OPEN: Mon to Fri L 12 to 3, Mon to Sat D 6 to 11.30   CLOSED: bank hols   MEALS: Set L £15 (2 courses) to £27.50, Set D £27.50   SERVICE: not inc   CARDS: Access, Amex, Delta, Switch, Visa   DETAILS: 35 seats. Private parties: 8 main room, 16 private room. Vegetarian meals. Children's helpings. Wheelchair access (no WC). No music. Air-conditioned

Alastair Little Lancaster Road   **NEW ENTRY** map 12

136A Lancaster Road, W11 1QU   COOKING 2
TEL: (0171) 243 2220   COST £30–£36

Since Alastair Little opened his original Soho restaurant in 1985 his activities have broadened: he now writes, runs a cookery school in Italy, and has opened this offshoot, in a pale pink shop conversion just around the corner from Ladbroke Grove tube station. Tables are close together, and meals can get very neighbourly, but then the food is informal too. The idea is to serve simple dishes – that change with the daily ebb and flow of materials – at relatively affordable prices.

It got off to a good start, when he was there in person. A report for 'the most exciting food for these prices I've had for some time' was occasioned by deep-fried spicy baby squid, and bollito misto, while others have enjoyed clam risotto, and grilled calf's liver 'as near perfect as can be'. An inspector later in the year was less impressed, and some of the food, especially first courses, struck one reporter as more the sort of thing 'one would knock up at home for a quick snack'. Herb omelette, or a frisée salad with poached egg and bacon bits might fall into this category, though main courses can be as substantial as calves' kidneys. Service is casual and personable, and wines are well spread and varied within a small compass. Prices start at £11.

CHEF: Toby Gush   PROPRIETORS: Alastair Little, Kirsten Pedersen and Mercedes André-Vega   OPEN: Mon to Sat 12.30 to 2.30 (3 Sat), 7 to 11   CLOSED: bank hols   MEALS: Set L £15 (2 courses), Set D £20   SERVICE: not inc   CARDS: Access, Amex, Delta, Switch, Visa   DETAILS: 50 seats. 15 seats outside. Children's helpings. Wheelchair access (no WC). No music

'One waitress stands permanently on guard, but did not appear to observe anything worth observing. She brought me the sweet menu after I had eaten my starter.'
(On eating in Devon)

Alba

map 13

107 Whitecross Street, EC1Y 8JD
TEL: (0171) 588 1798

COOKING 2
COST £22–£41

The room is pink and restful and, as the name implies, the cooking is Piedmontese, a style that comes into its own during autumn when porcini and white truffles are about. The latter are best shaved over simple dishes of risotto, eggs or pasta, and this is as good a place as any in which to sample them. The rest of the year is taken up with other northern Italian dishes of gnocchi with fontina cheese sauce, bagna cauda, bollito misto, and bunet amaretti, and Alba deserves credit for making a sincere attempt to introduce the food of this relatively neglected Italian region.

Such a mission might occasionally give it the feeling of 'correctness rather than sparkle', but reporters have enjoyed the simple, uncluttered style of food, and appreciate that it can be found within a few minutes' walk of the Barbican. Despite its emphasis on rich northern food, the restaurant is not doctrinaire, and generally includes a good range of pasta (with lobster or wild boar, for example), fish such as sea bream or red snapper, and puddings from tiramisù to pears poached in red wine. Service strikes the right note of informality without being too casual, although the 12.5 per cent service charge evokes a 'small moan'. The succinct wine list is entirely Italian and, as one might expect, majors on Piedmontese wines, Barolo in particular. House white is £9.90.

CHEF: Andrea Marino   PROPRIETOR: Rudi Venerandi   OPEN: Mon to Fri 12 to 3, 6 to 11   CLOSED: 25 Dec to 3 Jan, bank hols   MEALS: alc (main courses £9 to £14). Set D £9.90 (2 courses) to £16.90   SERVICE: 12.5%, card slips closed   CARDS: Access, Amex, Delta, Diners, Switch, Visa   DETAILS: 60 seats. Private parties: 40 main room, 40 private room. Vegetarian meals. Children's helpings. Wheelchair access (no WC). Music. Air-conditioned

Al Bustan

map 14

27 Motcomb Street, SW1X 8JU
TEL: (0171) 235 8277 and 1668
FAX: (0171) 235 1668

COOKING 1*
COST £30–£50

This well-established restaurant continues to provide large portions of authentic Lebanese food. The cover charge pays for a bowl of salad, olives, pitta bread and potent chilli dip; it's worth asking about halibi bread (rather like a thin rectangular nan), which isn't on the menu. An extensive range of hot and cold meze includes excellent sawdat djaj (fried chicken livers with a rich sauce of pomegranate molasses), as well as moutabal (smoky aubergine paste), tabbouleh, and makanek (Lebanese sausages). Main courses are mostly chargrills and kebabs, including baby chicken served in a thin bread parcel. Pastries are 'pleasant'; Turkish coffee hits the spot. A handful of Lebanese wines adds variety to the short, otherwise French list. House wine is £12.

CHEF: Inam Atalla   PROPRIETORS: Mr and Mrs R. Atalla   OPEN: all week noon to 11 (10.30 Sun)   CLOSED: 25 and 26 Dec, 1 Jan   MEALS: alc (main courses £8 to £10.50). Cover £2   SERVICE: not inc   CARDS: Access, Amex, Diners, Visa   DETAILS: 70 seats. 20 seats outside. Private parties: 30 main room, 8 to 15 private rooms. Vegetarian meals. Children welcome. Smart dress preferred. Wheelchair access (no WC). Music. Air-conditioned

Alexandra

507 Kingston Road, SW20 8SF
TEL: (0181) 542 4838   FAX: (0181) 947 3805

map 12

COOKING 1
COST £18–£40

The location seems improbable for a French restaurant – opposite some advertising hoardings half a mile from Raynes Park Station – but there is no mistaking the focus once inside. 'A piece of rural Normandy in south-west London' is how it struck one reporter. Décor is 'spartan', the service friendly and accommodating. 'All our produce comes from Calais,' says Eric Lecras, from fish and cheese to bread and wine, and prices, especially at lunch-time, are a big draw. First courses revolve around fish – soup, perhaps, or salmon terrine – while 'les main courses' feature fowl such as quail or breast of pigeon. Timing is a bit hit and miss, flavours could be bolder, but saucing is good, from a cream and calvados one for pork, to a smooth-textured cinnamon-flavoured accompaniment to guinea-fowl. Desserts are French, along the lines of tarte Tatin or crème brûlée, as are the reasonably priced wines. House French is £8.90.

CHEFS: Eric Lecras and Daniel Touraucheau   PROPRIETOR: Eric Lecras   OPEN: Sun to Fri L 12 to 1.30, Mon to Sat D 7 to 9.30   CLOSED: bank hols   MEALS: Set L Mon to Fri £6.95 (2 courses) to £9.95, Set L Sun £9.95, Set D Mon to Thur £9.95 to £16.95, Set D Fri and Sat £17.95   SERVICE: 12.5% (optional)   CARDS: Access, Visa   DETAILS: 58 seats. 14 seats outside. Private parties: 28 main room, 28 private room. Children's helpings. No children under 12 D. Smart dress preferred. No cigars/pipes in dining-room. Music

Alfred

245 Shaftesbury Avenue, WC2H 8EH
TEL: (0171) 240 2566   FAX: (0171) 497 0672

map 15

COOKING 1*
COST £24–£47

Robert Gutteridge has left, and his sous-chef Alison Connell now runs the kitchen, continuing the commitment to a certain kind of British food – comforting, more grandmotherly than modern – that takes in toad-in-the-hole, knuckle of bacon with pease pudding, or rabbit casseroled in beer. Occupying a table-strewn island at the northern end of Shaftesbury Avenue, Alfred adopts a casual matter-of-fact approach to life, with easy-to-wipe table-tops and staff in functional white jackets.

There is no ceremony to stand on, but ingredients are fresh – helping to make a success of baked cod on a generous bed of cabbage, bacon and peas – and a rustic simplicity informs the cooking. There is a white-bean soup, for instance, without even a hint of fashionable froth or truffle oil, just a gritty, rustic texture with homely pieces of smoked bacon. Vegetables are charged extra, but may not be necessary. Puddings salute the flag with Bakewell tart and the precisely named Trinity College Burnt Cream. Drink English wine or regional beers for preference.

CHEF: Alison Connell   PROPRIETOR: Fred Taylor   OPEN: Mon to Fri L 12 to 3.30, Mon to Sat D 6 to 11.30   CLOSED: 24 Dec to 2 Jan   MEALS: alc (main courses £9 to £15). Set L £11.95 (2 courses) to £15.90, Set D 6 to 7.30 and 10.30 to 11.30 £11.95 to £15.90   SERVICE: not inc   CARDS: Access, Amex, Delta, Diners, Switch, Visa   DETAILS: 60 seats. 38 seats outside. Private parties: 8 main room, 20 private room. Vegetarian meals. Children's helpings. No cigars/pipes in dining-room. Wheelchair access (no WC). No music. Air-conditioned

Al Hamra

map 15

31–33 Shepherd Market, W1Y 7RJ
TEL: (0171) 493 1954 and 6356

COOKING 2
COST £32–£53

Shepherd Market is pedestrianised, and tables are put outside on 'balmy summer nights', when the 'town crier' might amble around uttering loud sound bites for the benefit of tourists. Perhaps it is, one reporter mused, 'the Shepherd Market location that leads the kitchen to offer so many surprising organs of the sheep'. Tongue, liver, kidney and testicles are all here, but vegetarians also do well, from the 'traditional bucket of salad' for which the cover charge pays, to ful medames (brown beans) with a garlicky lemony tang, to hot triangles of spinach in pastry, or grilled halloumi cheese.

'It is a refreshing change to leisurely trawl through 20 dishes at a snail's pace,' remarked one who found the kitchen 'as consistent as ever'. Given the generous variety of meze – nearly 60 of them, averaging around £5 each – it is not difficult to clock up the minimum charge of £20 per head on those alone. Pitta bread is 'lighter and of far higher quality than normally encountered'. Service was 'engagingly old-fashioned' for one reporter, and too hasty by half for another. Sundays, when whole families come out to eat, are particularly relaxing. The value is good, although incidentals bump up the bill. House wine is £11.

CHEFS: Mahir Abboud and A. Rafiey Batah   PROPRIETORS: Riad Nabulsi and Hassan Fansa
OPEN: all week 12 to 10.45   CLOSED: 25 Dec, 1 Jan   MEALS: alc (main courses £9 to £12.50).
Cover £2.50. Minimum £20   SERVICE: not inc   CARDS: Access, Amex, Diners, Visa   DETAILS:
75 seats. 25 seats outside. Private parties: 80 main room. Vegetarian meals. Children's helpings. Smart dress preferred. Wheelchair access (no WC). Music. Air-conditioned

All Saints

map 13

12 All Saints Road, W11 1HH
TEL: (0171) 243 2808

NEW CHEF
COST £24–£43

Colour photographs cover some of the walls, floors are bare, and loud music thumps from speakers hanging from the ceiling. The mood is friendly and cheerful. The New Zealand cooks have gone, and Rosie Bowdrey arrived to give the cooking a noticeable lift, but as we went to press she moved to Tabac (see entry, London), retaining only a supervisory role here, thus making it difficult for us to award a cooking mark. Lively, spicy Eurasion food has been the trade mark, making much of chillies and salsas. Wines by the glass are served in large tumblers, and the short list includes some decent drinking. House wine is £9.50.

PROPRIETOR: Rupert Smith   OPEN: Tue to Sun L 10.30 to 3.30, Mon to Sat D 7.30 to 10.45
MEALS: alc (main courses £8.50 to £12). Set D £15 (2 courses) to £18.50   SERVICE: 12.5%
(optional), card slips closed   CARDS: Access, Visa   DETAILS: 50 seats. Private parties: 18 main room. Vegetarian meals. Children welcome. Wheelchair access (no WC). Music

Card slips closed *in the details at the end of an entry indicates that the total on the slips of credit cards is closed when handed over for signature.*

Al San Vincenzo

map 13

30 Connaught Street, W2 2AF
TEL: (0171) 262 9623

COOKING 2*
COST £34–£52

'Eating here is like being in a family home off a lazy quiet street in Milan.' This residential quarter off the Edgware Road is an amalgam of two cultures: the very English one of Regency terraces overlooking Hyde Park, and the Middle Eastern one of roadside al fresco eating. In between the two stands this tiny oasis, domestic in scale, with a welcome from Elaine Borgonzolo and an atmosphere that is 'wonderfully casual and not a bit stuck up'.

Vincenzo Borgonzolo's cooking is refreshingly untouched by fashion, a world away from state-of-the-art gloss and glamour, yet anything but standard Italian fare. Although it revolves around earthy and rich renderings of peasant-style food such as pig's trotter with cotechino sausage and lentils, the surprise is that 'the food is not heavy'. Thick-cut and 'top-notch' tagliatelle has impressed for its 'intensely rich and eggy' taste and buttery, creamy, saffron-infused sauce, while chunky pieces of 'soft yet firm' new season's lamb have come with peas and shaved Parmesan. Puddings might vary from a panettone version of bread-and-butter to a canny combination of mango and dolcelatte cheese. The short and serviceable wine list is fairly priced, starting at £11.

CHEF: Vincenzo Borgonzolo PROPRIETORS: Elaine and Vincenzo Borgonzolo OPEN: Mon to Fri L 12.30 to 1.45, Mon to Sat D 7 to 9.45 CLOSED: 25 to 27 Dec, 1 Jan MEALS: alc (main courses £12 to £17.50) SERVICE: not inc; 12.5% for parties of 5 or more CARDS: Access, Delta, Visa DETAILS: 22 seats. No children under 10. Smart dress preferred. No cigars/pipes in dining-room. Wheelchair access (no WC). Music

L'Altro

map 13

210 Kensington Park Road, W11 1NR
TEL: (0171) 792 1066 FAX: (0171) 792 1077

COOKING 1
COST £15–£54

The clever design of L'Altro is evocative of a narrow Tuscan alleyway, with street-lamps and weathered iron bars on the distressed stone walls carrying trompe-l'oeil to new levels. The cooking is a mixture of today's Italian favourites, with a fair few vegetarian dishes on the fixed-price menu, and one or two additionals, such as fish-cakes perfumed with ginger, lemon-grass and lime and served with an avocado butter sauce. Regulars pack the place, to enjoy sauté scallops with roasted sweet tomatoes, whole garlic cloves and thyme; fish and shellfish stew in which every item seems correctly timed; and, to finish, tiramisù 'soused with coffee and topped with luscious mascarpone'. The short Italian wine list kicks of with house Isole del Sole at £8.90.

CHEF: Giuseppe Vella PROPRIETOR: L'Altro Restaurants Ltd OPEN: all week L 12 to 3, Mon to Sat D 7 to 11 CLOSED: Christmas, bank hols MEALS: alc (main courses £10.50 to £18.50). Set L £9.95 (2 courses) to £12.95, Set D 7 to 8.30 £9.95 (2 courses) to £12.95 SERVICE: not inc; 12.5% for parties of 5 or more CARDS: Access, Amex, Delta, Diners, Switch, Visa DETAILS: 45 seats. 10 seats outside. Private parties: 45 main room. Vegetarian meals. Children welcome. Wheelchair access. Music. Air-conditioned

Andrew Edmunds £   NEW ENTRY   map 15

46 Lexington Street, W1R 3LH   COOKING 1*
TEL: (0171) 437 5708   COST £19–£31

Andrew Edmunds is an art gallery with a restaurant attached. Crammed-in wooden tables on two floors give the place an enjoyable café ambience, and the short à la carte menus keep things reassuringly simple. Beetroot salad works as a good foil to the smoothness of a chicken liver parfait, and an 'utterly delicious' extra-virgin dressing unifies a starter plate of Parma ham, roasted leeks, asparagus and Parmesan. 'Good racy flavours' mark out a main course of merguez sausages with spicy tomato sauce and bulgar, while duck confit is properly crisped and 'deeply rich', some garlicky chickpeas proving an inspired addition.

Puddings are lifted in full view straight out of the boxes they come in from a superior traiteur, and include chocolate mousse gâteau, prune and armagnac tart and tiramisù. It all represents exemplary value and is served with willingness and cheer. Wines are largely French with a few interlopers. House vin de pays is £8.95.

CHEF: Paul Croal   PROPRIETOR: Andrew Edmunds   OPEN: all week 12.30 (1 Sat) to 3, 6 to 10.45 (10.30 Sun)   CLOSED: 24 to 31 Dec, 4 days Easter   MEALS: alc (main courses £6 to £8.50)   SERVICE: not inc   CARDS: Access, Amex, Delta, Switch, Visa   DETAILS: 56 seats. 4 seats outside. Private parties: 28 main room. Vegetarian meals. No music. Air-conditioned

Anglesea Arms £   NEW ENTRY   map 12

35 Wingate Road, W6 0UR   COOKING 1*
TEL: (0181) 749 1291   FAX: (0181) 749 1291   COST £18–£37

One of the latest arrivals in the burgeoning ranks of aspirational pubs, the Anglesea Arms really packs them in. 'I thought we should go on a Sunday evening...expecting it to be quiet. Wrong!' exclaimed a reporter who had to wait 40 minutes for a table, but enjoyed the fun and was delighted by the food when it arrived. Dan Evans (ex-Odette's and the Fire Station, see entries) and his team work like demons to deliver the goods in a functional room that is 'seriously smoky and very noisy'.

The blackboard menu leapfrogs from tataki of raw tuna with hot mustard and spinach 'oshi-tashi' to chargrilled chicken breast with provençale vegetables. Along the way it also takes in warm pigeon salad with sherry vinegar and a 'mountain' of cockles marinière with thyme and chips. To finish there is 'intensively rich' malted chocolate ice-cream or first-rate Ticklemore cheese with warm goats'-curd tart and a perfectly ripe Cox's apple. Real ales supplement the short but carefully chosen wine list. House Italian is £8.50.

CHEFS: Dan Evans and Jane Lawrence   PROPRIETORS: Dan and Fiona Evans   OPEN: Mon to Sat L 12.30 to 3, Sun L 1 to 4, all week D 7.30 to 11 (Sun 10)   CLOSED: Christmas   MEALS: alc (main courses £6 to £9.50)   SERVICE: not inc, card slips closed   CARDS: Amex, Delta, Switch, Visa   DETAILS: 60 seats. 24 seats outside. Private parties: 20 main room. Children's helpings

Anna's Place ▲

map 13

90 Mildmay Park, N1 4PR
TEL: (0171) 249 9379

COOKING 2
COST £24–£40

This Scandinavian haven in an Islington town house may have become less formal with the years, and the cooking may have opened itself up to one or two influences from the wider world, but the backbone is still the traditional food of Sweden, executed with generosity and aplomb.

Tre kronor is the way to acquaint yourself with it, a starter selection of mustardy cured beef, egg mayonnaise with fish roes and pickle, herring and beetroot in soured cream, and of course gravad lax. Fish is as well handled as one would expect, the cooking of a piece of plaice left on the bone and topped with braised fennel an object-lesson in timing. Meat portions are on the galumphing side, as was discovered by a pair who shared a pungently flavoured and interestingly spiced hunk of pork knuckle. Choklad tårta is 'a densely textured hybrid of brownie and marquise', while blueberry waffles with whipped cream are of unimpeachable ethnic pedigree. Anna herself presides, a cheerfully reassuring presence, still having fun after all these years. The short wine list keeps its prices on an equally short leash. House French is £8.75.

CHEF: Patrick Schyum   PROPRIETOR: Anna Hegarty   OPEN: Tue to Sat 12.15 to 2.15, 7.15 to 10.45 (7 to 11 Fri and Sat)   CLOSED: 2 weeks Christmas, 2 weeks Easter, Aug   MEALS: alc (main courses £8 to £13.50)   SERVICE: 10%   CARDS: none   DETAILS: 42 seats. 25 seats outside. Private parties: 12 main room. Vegetarian meals. Children's helpings. No cigars/pipes in dining-room. Wheelchair access (no WC). Music

Arisugawa

map 14

27 Percy Street, W1P 9FF
TEL: 0171-636 8913   FAX: 0171-323 4236

COOKING 2*
COST £27–£66

Arisugawa is all about the rituals, traditions and ceremony of Japanese food, and is designed to cater for both public and private eating. The entrance lobby leads directly into a teppan room, but the most fascinating dining area is downstairs, where there is a sushi bar as well as a number of private rooms. In the centre, suspended above a communal table, is an antique artefact incorporating a lantern and a cooking pot; at the other side of the room is a raised platform with sliding partitions so that tables can be combined or separated.

Lunch is a relatively simple and affordable affair: the serious business, gastronomically speaking, occurs in the evening. Ingredients – and that includes everything from fish to beautifully crisp vegetables – are strikingly fresh; flavours are delicate rather than assertive. A number of set meals are constructed around sashimi, sushi, tempura and teriyaki, and there is a special version that displays a wide range of classical cooking techniques. Added to this are a *carte* with higher aspirations and a separate list of specialities written on a fan in untranslated Japanese. The charm and skill of the management enhance enjoyment of this high-quality food. Drink tea, saké or Japanese beer. House wine is £10.60.

CHEF: Akira Takeuchi   PROPRIETOR: K. Ohashi   OPEN: Mon to Fri L 12.30 to 2.30, Mon to Sat D 6 to 10   CLOSED: Bank hols   MEALS: alc (main courses £7 to £16). Set L £5 to £12, Set D £25 to £40. Cover £1   SERVICE: not inc L, 15% D, card slips closed   CARDS: Access, Amex, Diners, Switch, Visa   DETAILS: 100 seats. Private parties: 100 main room. Vegetarian meals. Children welcome. No music. Air-conditioned

Les Associés

map 12

172 Park Road, N8 8JY
TEL: (0181) 348 8944

COOKING 1
COST £33–£42

Facing the Crouch End swimming-baths on a busy main road, Les Associés provides an oasis of French civility. The premises are cramped or cosy, depending on your ideal of comfort, and the mood is set by murmuring music and the dignified *bon ton* of the waiters. Menus are now bilingual, in poetical French – '*barbue fantaisie*' – with an English version that actually tells you what you'll get (brill in a curry sauce with ginger and coriander, in this instance). The style is good home cooking, so you might expect skate salad with sauce ravigote, beef fillet wrapped in bacon with mushrooms and red wine, bitter chocolate mousse, or nougat glacé. Occasional complaints are made about the slow pace of service and long waits between courses when the restaurant is full. The short wine list is entirely French, starting with house wine at £9.80.

CHEF: Marc Spindler   PROPRIETORS: Dominique Chéhere and Didier Bertran   OPEN: Wed to Fri L 12.30 to 2, Tue to Sat D 7.30 to 10   CLOSED: 1 week Christmas, 1 week Easter, August MEALS: alc (main courses £10.50 to £15). Set L £15.95, Set D £25   SERVICE: net prices, card slips closed   CARDS: Access, Switch, Visa   DETAILS: 36 seats. No children under 6. Wheelchair access (no WC). Music

Atelier

map 15

41 Beak Street, W1R 3LE
TEL: (0171) 287 2057   FAX: (0171) 287 1767

COOKING 2*
COST £28–£50

A blue plaque outside announces that Canaletto once lived here, and blank canvases stretched down one side of the narrow room continue the artistic theme. But this is no Bohemian haunt of penniless students, rather an artfully contrived dining-room with an attractively rolling repertoire in modern European style. There may be a tendency for Stephen Bulmer to put 'one too many flavours in a dish', but an inspector concluded that if the tastes of sauces and garnishes were as good as the cooking of fine ingredients and the attractive appearance of every dish, 'this would be a very superior place'.

Accurate timing has produced deep-fried chicken livers that are 'crisp outside and meltingly soft inside', as well as 'precisely cooked' Aberdeen Angus beef, and 'succulent pieces of well-flavoured quail breast' with tagliatelle. Reporters have also been impressed by a 'supreme concoction' involving 'luscious, fatty' duck confit with wafer-thin circles of potato galette and roasted shallots, and by a mousse-like sausage of quail in a subtly flavoured marjoram *jus*. Accomplished desserts have included warm bitter chocolate torte, and well-risen pistachio soufflé with chocolate sauce. 'I continue to think the price–quality trade-off 'admirable,' writes a regular visitor who had already factored in the short, reasonably priced wine list. House French is £10.50.

CHEF: Stephen Bulmer   PROPRIETOR: JSB Restaurants Ltd   OPEN: Mon to Fri L 12 to 2.30, Mon to Sat D 6 to 10.45   CLOSED: 2 weeks Christmas, 2 weeks Aug, bank hols   MEALS: alc (main courses £12.50 to £16.50). Set L and D £15.50 (2 courses) to £18, Set D 6 to 8 £10 (2 courses) to £13.50   SERVICE: 10% (optional)   CARDS: Access, Amex, Delta, Diners, Switch, Visa   DETAILS: 45 seats. Private parties: 60 main room, 16 private room. Vegetarian meals. Children's helpings. Wheelchair access (no WC). No music

Atlantic Bar and Grill ♥ ⌣

map 15

20 Glasshouse Street, W1R 5RQ
TEL: (0171) 734 4888   FAX: (0171) 734 3609

COOKING 1*
COST £31–£62

The location is just about as central as central gets in the capital, a short totter from Piccadilly Circus, and thus bound to be a magnet for tourists as well as the West End smarts. Sanjay Dwidedi took over in spring 1996, but the song remains the same: carefully crafted renditions of contemporary brasserie food, though the Californian accent has been slightly muted of late. Good pasta cookery was evident at inspection in an opening dish of penne generously filled with the house tomato sauce; it shared a plate with some peppered carpaccio and a blob of basil pesto. A willingness to cover as many bases as possible is evident from roasted tiger prawns with cauliflower curry, 'smashed' garlic and a coriander nan, and Maine lobster with fish-cakes and coconut rice, while a vegetarian was impressed by a 'huge plateful' of deeply flavoured linguine with a fricassee of wild mushrooms and truffle oil. Coconut parfait topped with a 'flat circular slice' of mango sorbet was an architectonic wonder, and tasted pretty good too. Music is loud but the ceiling is high. The place peaks quite late in the evening, whereupon all is 'crush and scramble'.

There's plenty of interest on the wine list, which – just like that at sister restaurant Coast (see entry, London) – features excellent New World producers among a wide range. Prices are on the steep side here and there, but the French regional wines are a reliable lot and well-priced at around £14. House wines start at £11.50. CELLARMAN'S CHOICE: Mâcon-Clessé 1992, Jean Thévenet, £29.50; Devil's Lair Cabernet Sauvignon 1992, Margaret River, W. Australia, £26.50.

CHEF: Sanjay Dwidedi   PROPRIETOR: Oliver Peyton   OPEN: Mon to Fri L 12 to 3, all week D 6 to 12 (10.30 Sun)   CLOSED: Easter, Christmas, bank hols   MEALS: alc (main courses £8.50 to £19). Set L £14.90 (2 courses). Cover £1   SERVICE: not inc, 12.5% for parties of 8 or more   CARDS: Access, Amex, Delta, Switch, Visa   DETAILS: 180 seats. Private parties: 250 main room, 70 private room. Vegetarian meals. Children welcome. Wheelchair access (via lift; also WC). Music. Air-conditioned

Aubergine

map 14

11 Park Walk, SW10 0AJ
TEL: (0171) 352 3449   FAX: (0171) 351 1770

COOKING 4
COST £33–£79

Reporters continue to be astonished by the 'exciting, intense and long-lasting' flavours that Gordon Ramsay conjures up just off Fulham Road. The light and apparently sun-filled rooms are relaxing, with a carefully engineered sense of space. Linger on a settee by the window, or go straight to a table in the bright yellow dining-room with its simple decorative pictures, and be waited on by seriously attentive staff.

Fish and shellfish figure prominently to start, with a little foie gras perhaps, although luxuries are not overdone. A cappuccino of pure white bean soup has 'a lovely creamy consistency', a dribble of truffle oil adding an exotic note to the girolles and beans that lurk under the frothy topping. Fish and lighter Mediterranean-style dishes have worked particularly well. Jellied layers of pink salmon and red and yellow peppers, surrounded by a slick of gazpacho and 'divinely olivey' oil, was considered 'a triumph' at inspection. A hunk of roasted sea bass, 'delightfully fresh, flaky and moist' and sitting on a small mound of crushed potato and vegetables, was testament to the excellence of materials and the wisdom of simple presentation.

Some dishes can be rich, but what stands out across the board is the combination of lightness and intensity of flavour. Ramsay manages to achieve subtlety and delicacy without sacrificing character. The dessert team seems to thrive in top gear on a diet of Valrhona chocolate – the 'hot and gooey' chocolate fondant with pistachio ice-cream is first-rate – together with excellent ice-creams that feature alongside tarte Tatin of pears, or a sablé of roasted fig.

Some of the peripherals get up reporters' noses, from the unpriced menus for ladies to the price of mineral water, which, at £3.50 a bottle, costs the same as coffee and a plate of intricate and splendid petits fours: one of them a chocolate truffle filled with ice-cream. Then there is the booking problem, a consequence of popularity; a six-week delay for dinner is not uncommon. 'Stacks and stacks of very French service' are on hand to smooth napkins, brush away crumbs, refill and replace glasses, and deliver the right dish to the right person. 'It is obviously a badge of pride for them to speak either fluent French or poor English.' The lengthy wine list features plenty of quality producers, but mark-ups are steep and there is little to choose from under £20. House wines are £15.

CHEF/PROPRIETOR: Gordon Ramsay OPEN: Mon to Fri L 12.15 to 2.30, Mon to Sat D 7 to 11 CLOSED: first 2 weeks Aug, 10 days Christmas MEALS: Set L £22 to £38, Set D £38 to £48. BYO £15 SERVICE: not inc CARDS: Access, Amex, Diners, Switch, Visa DETAILS: 45 seats. Children welcome. Smart dress preferred. No cigars/pipes in dining room. No music. Air-conditioned

Au Jardin des Gourmets 🍾

map 15

5 Greek Street, W1V 6NA
TEL: (0171) 437 1816 FAX: (0171) 437 0043

COOKING 2*
COST £36–£66

At the beginning of 1996 the Jardin's proprietor decided to prune things back a little, with the result that the lower level is no longer part of the restaurant. Now confined to the elegant first-floor dining-room, with one window giving on to a floodlit balcony festooned with ivy, and another keeping an eye on Soho goings-on below, it is a pleasant place at which to eat.

Vincent Hiss's style is modern French: how about a crêpe filled with a mousse of smoked sturgeon in caviare sauce to start? Sweet-and-sour beetroot lends tang to venison medallions, while lentil cream and salsify are partners for duck magret. At inspection, nearly every dish solidly impressed, from the calves' sweetbreads with braised endive and a lime sauce to the plate of mixed desserts that included superb sorbets, bitter chocolate terrine and fine tarte Tatin. Service cracks along at a fair pace. The French wines on the huge list are a noble collection, including reams of fine claret dating back to 1945 and an impressive Burgundy section. Outside France the sections are shorter but standards remains high. Five house wines start at £9.90.

CHEF: Vincent Hiss PROPRIETOR: Novoport Group Ltd OPEN: Mon to Fri L 12.15 to 2.30, Mon to Sat D 6.15 to 11.15 CLOSED: bank hols MEALS: alc (main courses £15 to £17.50). Set L and D £19.50 (2 courses). Cover £2 D SERVICE: 15%, card slips closed CARDS: Access, Amex, Diners, Switch, Visa DETAILS: 50 seats. Private parties: 50 main room, 12 and 24 private rooms. Children's helpings. Smart dress preferred. No-smoking area. No music. Air-conditioned

Avenue ▼   NEW ENTRY   map 15

7–9 St James's Street, SW1A 1EE   COOKING 3
TEL: (0171) 321 2111 FAX: (0171) 321 2500   COST £27–£58

Here is another giant eatery with the declared aim of bringing American, specifically New York, dining style to Central London, this time in staid old St James's. Rick Mather, who designed the Zen restaurants, was retained to do his stuff here, too, and the result is a long bar area lit in lemon with spindly black stools for perching, a bank of TV screens that transmit specially commissioned video-bites shot in NYC, and the requisite huge picture window that offers a gawper's-eye view of all the human traffic outside. Wake up and smell the money.

Enda Flanagan cooks. 'Quags meets nouvelle cuisine' was one thumbnail sketch, and certainly there is a distinct impression that every one of today's gastronomic reference-points has been assiduously hauled in. This is more than mere bandwagon-jumping, though. John Dory with wild mushrooms and rolled pasta verde in an intense cream sauce demonstrates a firm grasp of the essentials of fish cookery. Among the tried and tested items such as highly accomplished classic fish soup with rouille, and calf's liver with polenta and Parma ham, are some bolder ideas that work well too. Duck breast, served 'beautifully pink and succulent', rests on a sweet apple tart with 'excellent flaky pastry' in a green peppercorn sauce. Side-orders must be bought separately, but execution doesn't flag there either: chips are 'light and crisp without a trace of oil'.

A slate of cheese dishes and savouries precedes puddings of fig tart glazed with port, and caramelised banana parfait with walnuts. The highlight of one evening was a wedge of chocolate fondant cake oozing forth a warm liquid chocolate filling, sharpened up with kumquats in syrup: a sensual triumph. High-octane cafetière coffee comes with chocolate coffee-beans to get you well revved up for the rest of the evening. Service is far more conscientious than in many other such places. The Avenue is going to be hard to ignore. The wine list is carefully constructed, with a thoughtful balance between old and new, some enterprising runs from individual Burgundy growers Roty, Arnoux and Lignier, and plenty of choice by the glass. House wines are £12.50.

'Dinner is an occasion for which guests are still expected to dress (even Michael Winner).' (Dorset hotelkeeper)

CHEF: Enda Flanagan   PROPRIETOR: Moving Image Restaurants plc   OPEN: Mon to Sat 12 to 3, 6 to 12, Sun 12 to 4, 7 to 10   CLOSED: 25 and 26 Dec, 1 Jan   MEALS: alc D (main courses £11.50 to £16.50). Set L £16.50 (2 courses) to £19.50, Set D 6 to 7 Mon to Sat £13.50 (2 courses) to £15.50. BYO £4. Bar food available   SERVICE: 12.5% (optional), card slips closed   CARDS: Access, Amex, Delta, Diners, Switch, Visa   DETAILS: 180 seats. Private parties: 200 main room. Vegetarian meals. Children welcome. Music. Air-conditioned

Bahn Thai

map 15

21A Frith Street, W1V 5TS
TEL: (0171) 437 8504   FAX: (0171) 439 0340

COOKING 2
COST £28–£66

Since 1982 Bahn Thai has played a defining role in the progress of Thai cuisine in London. At lunch-time, the ground floor makes an animated setting for bistro-style meals, while upstairs provides a shade more formality. The cooking generally holds its course, although one knowledgeable reporter detected 'a distinct sense of drift' in a spring meal that veered from good soup, carefully handled prawns and accurately spiced red chicken curry to 'overcooked' pork and 'ordinary' noodles. The menu is one of the most wide-ranging of its kind, although dishes may disappear quickly during the course of an evening. Feel lucky and you might have the opportunity to sample poo jaa (crab-cakes with plum sauce), neua khem (fried salt beef), nok tord krob (crisp-fried baby quail with garlic and pepper), and pad pak boong (stir-fried water lily stems with yellow beans). Singha Thai beer is supplemented by a new brew known as Amarit N.B.; otherwise there are excellent teas for refreshment. The wine list makes a convincing case for the fruit of the vine and its affinity to Thai cuisine. House wine is £7.95.

CHEF: Penn Squires   PROPRIETOR: Philip Harris   OPEN: Mon to Sat L 12 to 2.45, Sun L 12.30 to 2.30, Mon to Sat D 6 to 11.15, Sun D 6.30 to 10.30   CLOSED: Christmas, Easter, bank hols   MEALS: alc (main courses £7.50 to £20)   SERVICE: 12.5% (optional), card slips closed   CARDS: Access, Amex, Delta, Diners, Switch, Visa   DETAILS: 120 seats. 8 seats outside. Private parties: 50 main room, 20 to 50 private rooms. Vegetarian meals. Children welcome. No cigars/pipes in dining-room. Wheelchair access (also men's WC). Music. Air-conditioned

Belgo Noord

map 13

72 Chalk Farm Road, NW1 8AN
TEL: (0171) 267 0718   FAX: (0171) 267 7508

COOKING 1*
COST £23–£49

'Excellent mussels, great frites, good beer' is Belgo's winning formula. The design of the place is bizarrely monastic, with wooden tables and chairs, and curious configurations of axe handles; staff move around in monkish garb ('an inspired touch in a Godless age'). Noise echoes around the room, and smoke levels can be irritatingly high, but there's no denying the sheer gusto of the cooking. Great pots of mussels are served 16 ways (the provençale version has been 'brilliant'), the seafood platter groans with piscine delights, and the menu emphasises its Belgian loyalties with wild boar sausages, salmon in Hoegaarden beer with pistachios, 'waterzooi' stews, and wild mushrooms with Trappist cheese and puff pastry. Set lunches and 'beat-the-clock' deals between 6 and 8 on selected dishes (arrive at 6.20, for instance, and you pay £6.20) remain excellent value, although prices elsewhere have crept up. The wine list has been bolstered by some useful whites, but it is hard to resist the 65 Belgian beers and schnapps galore. House wine is £8.95. For details of Belgo Centraal, see entry, London Round-ups.

CHEFS: Philippe Blaise and Muir Picken PROPRIETORS: Denis Blais and André Plisnier OPEN: Mon to Fri 12 to 3, 6 to 11.30, Sat and Sun 12 to 11.30 CLOSED: 25 Dec MEALS: alc (main courses £7 to £18). Set L £5.95 (1 course) to £12 (2 courses), Set D £12 (2 courses), all inc beer SERVICE: 15% (optional), card slips closed CARDS: Access, Amex, Delta, Diners, Switch, Visa DETAILS: 140 seats. Private parties: 24 main room. Vegetarian meals. Children's helpings. Smart dress preferred. Wheelchair access (also WC). Music. Air-conditioned

Bertorelli's ♟ 🍞

map 15

44A Floral Street, WC2E 9DA
TEL: (0171) 836 3969   FAX: (0171) 836 1868

COOKING 1
COST £23–£49

Edward Bleackley stepped into Maddalena Bonino's shoes in 1995 without trepidation and has succeeded in sustaining Bertorelli's venerable reputation. The discreet exterior opposite the Royal Opera House opens into a smart dining-room, and there's a café and bar in the basement; the buzz is audible, and service has heaps of panache. Reporters describe the food as stylish without being prissy, and the menu plunders the Italian regional larder voraciously: buffalo mozzarella, marinated squid, Pecorino shavings, wilted radicchio, and Sardinian gnocchi all find their way on to the plate. The bread basket is bountiful, bruschetta is done to perfection, pasta comes with an array of rich sauces. Recent successes have included wild mushroom risotto, brochette of lamb on a bed of beans, and pan-fried venison with Amarena cherry sauce. Bertorelli's ice-creams top the desserts, and tiramisù is a 'classic'. It is a nice touch to serve 'perfect' cheeses with accompaniments such as pickled walnuts.

Wines are from an impressive line-up of Italian growers, the vast majority under £20, and it is good to see so many exciting wines offered by the glass. CELLARMAN'S CHOICE: Chianti Classico, Felsina Berardenga 1991, £20.50; Soave Classico, Vigneto Calvarino 1994, Pieropan, £19.50.

CHEF: Edward Bleackley PROPRIETOR: Groupe Chez Gérard Restaurants Ltd OPEN: Mon to Sat 12 to 3, 5.30 to 11.30 MEALS: alc (main courses £7 to £16). Cover £1.50. Bistro menu SERVICE: 12.5% (optional), card slips closed CARDS: Access, Amex, Delta, Diners, Switch, Visa DETAILS: 85 seats. Private parties: 36 main room. Car park D only. Vegetarian meals. Children's helpings. Wheelchair access (no WC). No music. Air-conditioned

Bibendum ▮

map 14

Michelin House, 81 Fulham Road, SW3 6RD
TEL: (0171) 581 5817   FAX: (0171) 823 7925

COOKING 3*
COST £39–£86

The oyster bar downstairs acts as a visual appetiser to the inimitable Michelin building. The dining-room's stained glass, light décor, pneumatically curved vases and carafes, and its air of grace and charm are capable of making any occasion feel special. Yet there is not even a hint of standing on ceremony. Service combines professionalism and courtesy in a way that puts customers at ease: 'not casual, or familiar or sloppy,' as one put it; 'just dedicated and lacking in pretence'. However antagonistic reporters feel towards the supposedly 'optional' service charge, these waiters do as much as any to earn it, combining the minimum of interference with the best in timing and delivery.

The menu is a delight, and generous in scope. Despite lemon sole with (much improved) chips and tartare sauce, the thrust is Franco-Italian: snails, salade de museau, haricot beans with lyonnaise sausage, bollito misto with salsa verde. Luxuries show up, but are treated simply and sensibly, as in a first course of warm potato purée with black truffle, or a ballottine of foie gras with a small pile of sweet Madeira-infused gelée, or a lobster and saffron tart. Indeed, it is the simplicity that strikes home: in a dish of sliced calves' kidneys with mustard sauce, or a plate of fat scallops with ceps, garlic and parsley.

Chocolate desserts have impressed as much as any, including the pithiviers which combines excellent pastry with high-quality chocolate. Incidentals include 'wonderful' herby olives, a big basket of sawn-off French bread, and good coffee. Vegetables are charged extra. Wine prices can seem daunting, but there are outstanding wines at every turn of the page, long runs of brilliant Burgundies, Bordeaux and Rhônes, an encyclopedia of different wine styles and mature wines galore. Those with little time to spare might make for the list of eight mixed, high-quality house wines, whose prices start at £9.50. CELLARMAN'S CHOICE: Bernardus Winery, Chardonnay 1992, Monterey, California, £29.50; St-Nicolas-de-Bourgueil, Cuvée Prestige 1993, J.-P. Mabileau, £23.50.

CHEFS: Matthew Harris, Athene O'Neill and Jamie Younger PROPRIETORS: Sir Terence Conran, Paul Hamlyn, Simon Hopkinson and Graham Williams OPEN: all week 12.30 to 2.30 (3 Sat and Sun), 7 to 11.30 (10.30 Sun) CLOSED: 24 to 26 Dec MEALS: alc D (main courses £13.50 to £22.50). Set L £27 SERVICE: 12.5% (optional), card slips closed CARDS: Access, Amex, Delta, Switch, Visa DETAILS: 72 seats. Children's helpings. Wheelchair access (no WC). No music. Air-conditioned

Billboard Café £

map 13

280 West End Lane, NW6 1LJ
TEL: (0171) 431 4188

COOKING 1
COST £19–£38

Billboard Café moved from Kilburn High Road in the spring of 1996 to these rather less dramatic premises where, on sunny days, the clean, triangular space opens up to the pavement. Paper tablecloths set the informal tone, and a changing show of paintings which are for sale. The food still deals in simple Italian dishes of pesto toast, salad, minestrone, and home-made pasta with a variety of sauces from arrabiata to dolcelatte with sun-dried tomatoes. Main courses generally take in chargrilled chicken or steak, and puddings might include dark rum chocolate mousse. 'There's nothing here that couldn't be done by a competent amateur' felt one visitor, but 'you can't help liking the place'. Prices are modest, and a caring attitude pervades both food and service. A short list of mostly Italian wines includes half a dozen by the glass. House wines are £7.95.

CHEF/PROPRIETOR: M.T. Nateghi OPEN: Sat and Sun L 12 to 3, Mon to Sat D 6.30 to 12 MEALS: alc (main courses £5 to £12.50). Set L £6.50 (2 courses), Set D £11 SERVICE: 10%, card slips closed CARDS: Access, Amex, Delta, Switch, Visa DETAILS: 38 seats. 8 seats outside. Private parties: 50 main room. Vegetarian meals. Children's helpings. Smart dress preferred. Wheelchair access (no WC). Music

▲ *Blakes*

map 14

33 Roland Gardens, SW7 3PF
TEL: (0171) 370 6701   FAX: (0171) 373 0442

COOKING 2*
COST £47-116

Blakes lives in a world of its own, where the focus is on style. It is mostly black, inside and out, with white ceiling and floor tiles. 'Random bits of clothing from north Thailand' decorate the walls. If you are going to faint at the prices, may we suggest you do so now. A soufflé Suissesse costs £18.26, crispy chicken with a ginger sauce weighs in at £23.75, and Blakes blini is £44. No luxury item is left unused, and no cuisine is left untouched, judging by inkfish risotto, foie gras with truffles, chicken tikka, Szechuan duck, and beef teriyaki. Rice appears in many guises from wild to flavoured basmatis – lime and mint, or ginger and coriander – and flights of fancy are indulged. How about chicken and crab Fabergé: the two items moulded into the shape of a large egg, tied with a ribbon of nori seaweed, and served with a lime ginger sauce? If you don't expect cheap wines, you won't be disappointed. House wine is £4.50 a glass.

CHEF: Neville Campbell   PROPRIETOR: Anouska Hempel (Lady Weinberg)   OPEN: all week 12.30 to 3, 7.30 to 12   MEALS: alc (main courses £15 to £26.50). Set Post-theatre D £32.50 SERVICE: 15%, card slips closed   CARDS: Access, Amex, Diners, Switch, Visa   DETAILS: 40 seats. Private parties: 60 main room, 15 and 22 private rooms. Children welcome. Smart dress preferred. Music. Air-conditioned   ACCOMMODATION: 52 rooms, all with bath/shower. TV. Phone. Room only £135 to £730. Children welcome. Baby facilities. Afternoon teas. Garden (*The Which? Hotel Guide*)

Blenheim

NEW ENTRY   map 13

21 Loudoun Road, NW8 0NB
TEL: (0171) 625 1222   FAX: (0171) 328 1593

COOKING 1*
COST £18–£37

In the search for informality that ushered in the '90s, pub conversions were a natural way to serve honest, often gutsy, food at attractively low prices. As the decade rolls on, if the Blenheim is anything to go by, the trend is undergoing refinement. This place has lost its pubbiness, been 'tastefully and simply re-decorated', but retains informality and good value. Light wood and colourful paintings brighten the smart L-shaped room, and a flexible *carte* mixes sunny Mediterranean pastas, vegetables and fish with heartier honey roast ham hock with a cassoulet of butter-beans. Sound ingredients provide a firm foundation, and slow cooking and last-minute grilling or pan-frying work equally well. Some flavours aim to be forceful, with aïoli and salsas accompanying fish from mackerel to halibut, though other combinations may be gentler. Portions are generous. Young, sharp service helps to keep it informal. Around 70 up-to-date wines, half of them under £20, are arranged by style, and include 16 by the glass. House Vin de Pays d'Oc is £9.50. A new branch, Blenheim Bis, has opened at 37 Kensington Park Road, W11, (0171) 243 0666.

CHEF: Harry Greenhalgh   PROPRIETOR: Woodstock Group plc   OPEN: Tue to Sat L 12 to 3 and Sun brunch 11 to 4, all week D 6 to 11.30 (10.30 Sun and Mon to Sat 7 to 11 winter)   CLOSED: 25, 26 and 31 Dec, 1 Jan, Sun D in winter   MEALS: alc (main courses £9 to £10.50). Set L £8 (2 courses) to £10. Minimum £8 L   SERVICE: not inc   CARDS: Access, Amex, Delta, Switch, Visa DETAILS: 70 seats. 85 seats outside. Private parties: 70 main room, 20 and 35 private rooms. Car park. Vegetarian meals. Children welcome. No-smoking area. Music

Blue Elephant

map 12

4–6 Fulham Broadway, SW6 1AA
TEL: (0171) 385 6595   FAX: (0171) 386 7665

COOKING 1
COST £32–£57

First-timers may imagine they have died and gone to nirvana on entering this landmark Thai restaurant across from Fulham Broadway tube station. A bridge over a lake, in which fish swim contentedly, connects the dining-areas; ornate brass table adornments and traditionally attired serving staff add more than a touch of class. The kitchen operates at the more festive end of Thai gastronomy with 'pleasingly complex' tom yum soup, chicken-stuffed prawns in rice-paper with plum dipping sauce, and grilled beef with mint and coriander in lime and chilli dressing. Carved vegetable garnishes appear quite often. Dishes advertised as hot may be gentle to real aficionados, but the balance of spicing is carefully built up none the less, and there is no stinting on the coriander. Desserts are humdrum. The fixed-price menu spans the repertoire but doesn't come cheap. 'Female diners get an orchid when they leave, but for this sort of money I would have expected a small shrubbery and someone to water it.' The wine list is decent, 'but with fairly stiff mark-ups'. House Bordeaux is £10.50.

CHEF: Rungsan Mulijan   PROPRIETOR: Blue Elephant International plc   OPEN: Sun to Fri L 12 to 2.30, all week D 7 to 12.30   MEALS: alc (main courses £7.50 to £16). Set L and D £29 to £34. Cover £1.50   SERVICE: not inc   CARDS: Access, Amex, Delta, Diners, Visa   DETAILS: 240 seats. Private parties: 50 main room. Vegetarian meals. Children welcome. Smart dress preferred. Wheelchair access (also WC). Music. Air-conditioned

Blue Print Café

map 13

First Floor, Design Museum, 22 Shad Thames, Butlers Wharf, SE1 2YD
TEL: (0171) 378 7031   FAX: (0171) 378 6540

COOKING 2
COST £31–£53

The location above the Design Museum comes into its own on balmy evenings, when a window table offers riverside views of Tower Bridge, the blinking light on top of Canary Wharf and the regular passage of party-boats plying up and down the Thames. The culinary style remains constant under new chef Jeremy Lee, but there has been a distinct sense this year of a kitchen shaking itself and putting on a spurt. Tomato soup is not just a sweet red broth, but contains counterpoint notes of bacon and chilli, with an 'unsieved mush of tomato pulp' adding textural interest. Morcilla (Spanish black pudding) with a salad of sauté potatoes is another thought-provoking starter, while the Hispanic note resounds again in a zarzuela of hake with mussels and clams that offers plenty to chew over. Meat options might take in peppered chicken with couscous or a slow-cooked rabbit leg with girolles and garlic. Puddings include highly boozed praline and armagnac parfait, pear feuilleté with crème pâtissière, and a fair bit of chocolate. House wines are from £10.95.

CHEF: Jeremy Lee   PROPRIETORS: Sir Terence Conran and Joel Kissin   OPEN: all week L 12 to 3 (3.30 Sun), Mon to Sat D 6.30 to 11   CLOSED: 3 days Christmas, 1 Jan   MEALS: alc (main courses £10 to £15). Minimum £10   SERVICE: 12.5% (optional), card slips closed   CARDS: Access, Amex, Diners, Switch, Visa   DETAILS: 85 seats. 64 seats outside. Private parties: 90 main room. Car park. Vegetarian meals. Children welcome. Smart dress preferred. Wheelchair access (also WC). No music

Bombay Brasserie

map 14

Courtfield Close, Courtfield Road, SW7 4UH
TEL: (0171) 370 4040 and 373 0971
FAX: (0171) 835 1669

COOKING 1
COST £37–£51

Echoes of the colonial Raj in all its resplendent but faded glory set the tone in this de luxe Indian brasserie. The menu is a gastronomic tour around the Sub-continent, and it promises a great deal: from the roadsides and beaches of Bombay come snacks such as aloo tuk (deep-fried jacket potatoes with an 'excellent' tamarind and yoghurt sauce), while the Parsee tradition brings papri ma gosht (meltingly tender lamb with a complex sauce containing mange-tout). Elsewhere you might find Goan fish curries, tandooris from the north-west, and a contingent of red-hot specialities from the south. Prices are steep, the food yo-yos between first-rate pomfret wrapped in banana leaves with mint and coconut paste to vegetables in sauces that are 'not at all distinctive'. Basmati rice is generally spot on. At lunch-time there is a popular ten-dish buffet. Service is 'efficient'. Kingfisher beer suits the food, and there is a modest international wine list. House wine is £10.50.

CHEF: Udit Sarkhel   PROPRIETOR: Taj International   OPEN: all week 12.30 to 3, 7.30 to 12 (11.30 Sun)   CLOSED: 25 and 26 Dec   MEALS: alc D (main courses £12.50 to £15). Buffet L £14.95. Minimum £25 D   SERVICE: not inc   CARDS: Access, Diners, Switch, Visa   DETAILS: 175 seats. Private parties: 90 main room. Vegetarian meals. No children under 10 D. Smart dress preferred. No music. Air-conditioned

Boyd's ♥

map 13

135 Kensington Church Street, W8 7LP
TEL: (0171) 727 5452   FAX: (0171) 221 0615

COOKING 2*
COST £24–£55

Boyd Gilmour considers his 40-seater restaurant something of an antidote to the rash of big London dining-rooms seating hundreds. The narrow, quiet, plant-strewn, glass-roofed room feels half-way to a conservatory, a pleasant refuge from the bustle of nearby Notting Hill Gate. The food, too, is less frenzied than some, taking a gentle line with fish-cakes, or black pudding with cider and apples to begin, followed by roast best end of lamb, or honey-roast quail with braised cabbage.

At the same time, the kitchen moves with the times, turning to Italy for risotto (of scallops, perhaps) or tortellini of goats' cheese, and takes to roasting and chargrilling as its principal ways of dealing with meat (such as saddle of venison) or the day's fish. White chocolate mousse or tropical fruit brûlée might be among the puddings. The set-price lunch now looks an even better bargain than before. The wine list has recently been overhauled and lengthened. Two hundred and fifty wines cover most tastes and pockets, from the French regions to major New World countries. Half-bottles get a good look in, and it is encouraging to see 11 house wines offered by the glass as well as the bottle, starting at £10. CELLARMAN'S CHOICE: Jeffrey Grosset Piccadilly Chardonnay 1994, Piccadilly Hills, S. Australia, £23.50; Cabernet Sauvignon Reservas 1992, Cousiño Macul, Chile, £14.75.

CHEF/PROPRIETOR: Boyd Gilmour OPEN: Mon to Sat 12.30 to 2.30, 7 to 11 CLOSED: 2 weeks Christmas, 4 days Easter MEALS: alc (main courses £12 to £17). Set L £9.95 (2 courses) to £13.95 SERVICE: not inc CARDS: Access, Amex, Diners, Visa DETAILS: 40 seats. Private parties: 40 main room. Vegetarian meals. Children welcome. Wheelchair access (no WC). Music. Air-conditioned

Brackenbury

map 12

129–131 Brackenbury Road, W6 0BQ
TEL: (0181) 748 0107 FAX: (0181) 741 0905

COOKING 2*
COST £18–£36

'This establishment gives value for money that I have not found in 30 years in the Midlands and 15 years in the South-west; and yet there was no obvious cost-cutting.' So writes a reporter who has been using the *Guide* since its first edition. Décor is not the Brackenbury's strongest point – the restaurant is a converted wine bar, with bare wooden tables and matching chairs – and the food does not go in for refinement either. Adam Robinson is adept at making a dish out of next to nothing, such as purple-sprouting broccoli with warm anchovy dressing, a potato, onion and truffle oil tart, or Poor Knights of Windsor with ginger ice-cream and rhubarb. Such parsimony has a great attraction for both kitchen and customer alike: it helps to keep costs and prices down, and bubbles with interest and variety.

A strong sense of Mediterranean peasant food pervades, in Andalucian tripe and bean broth, or deep-fried salt-cod cakes with aïoli, for example. Warm salads are a feature – lambs' sweetbreads with mushrooms and bacon, for instance – and unusual cuts of meat crop up, including veal onglet, served with lentils and roast garlic. Pâtés and terrines are 'very gamey', soft crumbly bread is home-made, and much of the cooking is good, but the aim is rustic simplicity, so if that means approximate seasoning or timing now and then, well that is just how things are. Service for one reporter was 'super, though they did bring each dish as it was ready, causing us to eat at different speeds'. The wine list manages to appear both fashionable and user-friendly, with most bottles under £20 and the vast majority available by the glass. House wines are French and £8.75.

CHEF: Adam Robinson PROPRIETORS: Adam and Katie Robinson OPEN: Tue to Fri and Sun L 12.30 to 2.45, Mon to Sat D 7 to 10.45 CLOSED: 25 Dec, bank hols MEALS: alc (main courses £4.50 to £10). BYO by arrangement £5 SERVICE: not inc CARDS: Access, Amex, Delta, Diners, Switch, Visa DETAILS: 55 seats. 20 seats outside. Private parties: 8 main room. Vegetarian meals. Children's helpings. No cigars/pipes in dining-room. Wheelchair access (no WC). No music

Bradleys

NEW ENTRY map 13

25 Winchester Road, NW3 3NR
TEL: (0171) 722 3457

COOKING 2*
COST £24–£46

Bradleys is described as 'unashamedly American' and as a 'serene, cool oasis' – quite a feat in the hurly-burly of Swiss Cottage. A recent refurbishment has brought a maroon and yellow colour scheme to the dining-area, which is dominated by a vast abstract oil, looking as if it lost its way *en route* to the Royal Academy Summer Exhibition. The menu deals in modern brasserie cooking with more than a hint of California cool in mille-feuille of monkfish and sweet potato with mango and basil sauce, or veal rump with bok choy and shiitake ginger gravy. The compass needle points further south for blackened snapper with 'dirty rice', the fish dusted with Cajun spices and partnered with chilli lime chutney 'bursting with fresh citrus flavour'.

Desserts receive rave notices for originality, a peach sorbet acquiring extra intensity through the roasting of the fruit and the incorporation of strawberry slivers. White chocolate cheesecake with wild cherry sauce is an 'absolutely faultless' amalgam of assertive but beautifully balanced flavours. Good, powerful espresso plays its part, too, in what is clearly a hugely confident operation. Wines drawn entirely from the US and the southern hemisphere add up to a bold and imaginative selection, and – what's more – nearly everything comes in at under £20. House wines are £9.50 (from Chile) or £10.50 (South Africa).

CHEF: Amandar Keller   PROPRIETOR: Simon Bradley   OPEN: Mon to Fri and Sun L 12 to 3, all week D 6 to 11   CLOSED: 1 week Christmas   MEALS: alc D (main courses £9.50 to £13.50). Set L £12 (2 courses) to £15   SERVICE: not inc   CARDS: Access, Amex, Delta, Switch, Visa   DETAILS: 62 seats. Private parties: 62 main room. Vegetarian meals. Children's helpings. Smart dress preferred. Wheelchair access (no WC). Music. Air-conditioned

Brady's £

map 12

513 Old York Road, SW18 1AR
TEL: (0181) 877 9599

COOKING 1
COST £15–£21

'This is a chippy, albeit an excellent example of the genre,' writes a connoisseur from Surrey. The fish is as fresh as can be, the batter is light and grease-free, the chips are excellent. True to form, the place also does take-aways. Staples of cod, haddock and plaice are hard to fault, while more luxurious items such as full-flavoured lemon sole and 'meaty slabs' of grilled tuna are equally good. Deep-fried calamares make a pleasant starter. Chilean house wine is £6.95. A 'somewhat quieter' branch operates at 696 Fulham Road, SW6 5SA, (0171) 736 3938.

CHEF: Luke Brady   PROPRIETORS: Luke and Amelia Brady   OPEN: Mon to Sat D only 7 to 10.45   MEALS: alc (main courses £3.50 to £6)   SERVICE: 10% (optional)   CARDS: none DETAILS: 38 seats. Children welcome. Music

Brasserie St Quentin

map 14

243 Brompton Road, SW3 2EP
TEL: (0171) 581 5131 and 589 8005
FAX: (0171) 584 6064

COOKING 2
COST £27–£50

Like its relative, Grill St Quentin in Yeoman's Row (see entry, London), the brasserie is a bastion of bourgeois French cooking. The standard *carte* offers such old favourites as duck liver terrine, cold wild salmon with asparagus salad, and grilled veal chop with rosemary alongside more contemporary ideas from further afield. French beans are served as a starter with oyster cream and hazelnuts, red mullet comes with spiced aubergine, and shoulder of lamb is cooked with chickpeas. In the evening, variety is provided by several *plats du jour* which are based on seasonal produce. St Quentin's bitter chocolate and orange dessert is a fixture; otherwise the pudding list extends to prune and armagnac mousse, crème brûlée, and tarte Tatin. The wine list never strays over the French border, but, like the menu, offers good value across the range, and half-bottles show up well. House wine is £9.20.

CHEF: Nigel Davis   PROPRIETOR: Savoy Group plc   OPEN: Mon to Sat 12 to 3, 7 to 11.30, Sun 12 to 3.30, 6.30 to 11   MEALS: alc (main courses £10 to £16). Set L £10 (2 courses), Set D 7 to 7.30 £10 (2 courses)   SERVICE: 12.5% (optional), card slips closed   CARDS: Access, Amex, Delta, Diners, Switch, Visa   DETAILS: 80 seats. Private parties: 8 main room, 25 private room. Vegetarian meals. Children welcome. Smart dress preferred. No music. Air-conditioned

B Square

NEW ENTRY | map 12

8 Battersea Square, SW11 3RA
TEL: (0171) 924 2288   FAX: (0171) 924 6450

COOKING 1*
COST £27–£32

'A much-needed watering-hole south of the river' was one reporter's welcome to Sebastian Snow's smart new venture. There is a bar for casual eating and drinking – Caesar salad, or french fries with chilli mayonnaise – while the dining-room's offerings are 'modern enough to be interesting', with half a dozen choices per course. Presentation is straightforward, making use of grilled bread, risotto and pasta in association with pot-roasts of guinea-fowl or chicken, baked cod, and chargrills and roasts of meat. 'Chargrilled focaccia, parasol mushrooms, bone marrow' reads one item; 'olive oil and Sauternes cake, clotted cream ice-cream' reads another, leaving customers to ponder whether these are materials from which they have to construct their own dish, Masterchef-style. Baked custard tart with Agen prunes, and pear and apple crumble have been successful. Not all reporters have found the service to their liking, but those who have reckon it to be attentive yet relaxed and not intrusive. Good producers characterise the wine list, and there is fair choice under £20 with over a dozen by the glass.

CHEFS: Sebastian Snow and Matthew Read   PROPRIETORS: Ian McKerracher and Sebastian Snow   OPEN: all week noon to 11pm (10.30 Sun)   CLOSED: 25 and 26 Dec, Easter   MEALS: Set L and D £9.50 (1 course) to £17.50. Bar food available   SERVICE: 12.5% (optional), card slips closed   CARDS: Access, Amex, Delta, Diners, Switch, Visa   DETAILS: 120 seats. 40 seats outside. Private parties: 100 main room, 40 private room. Vegetarian meals. Children's helpings. Children under 5 free. Wheelchair access (also WC). Music. Air-conditioned

Bu-San

map 13

43 Holloway Road, N7 8JP
TEL: (0171) 607 8264

COOKING 1
COST £21–£70

Set in a bustling but hardly glamorous corner of North London, Bu-San continues to feed a crowd of city dwellers with authentic Korean food. Co-owner Mr Lee cooks and provides his customers with a mixture of authentic specialities and original recipes, and a smattering of Japanese ideas for good measure. The 75-dish menu contains most of the Korean staples, from ferocious kim-chee pickle to bulgogi (marinated beef or chicken) and jap chae (fried vegetables with beef and vermicelli noodles). Mr Lee is also proud of his ornately sculpted vegetables, which are carved into the shapes of birds and flowers. One-dish lunches are a bargain. To drink there is green or Korean ginseng tea, and you can finish off with a shot of ginseng brandy. House wine is £8.50.

CHEF: Young Hyung Lee   PROPRIETORS: Young Hyung Lee and Mrs T.S. Lee   OPEN: Mon to Fri L 12 to 2.30, all week D 6 to 11   MEALS: alc (main courses £4 to £27). Set L £4.20 to £6.60 (1 course), Set D £14.80 to £19   SERVICE: 10%, card slips closed   CARDS: Access, Switch, Visa DETAILS: 47 seats. Private parties: 50 main room. Vegetarian meals. Children's helpings. Smart dress preferred. Wheelchair access (also women's WC). Music. Air-conditioned

Butlers Wharf Chop House ♥

map 13

36E Shad Thames, Butlers Wharf, SE1 2YE
TEL: (0171) 403 3403   FAX: (0171) 403 3414

COOKING 1*
COST £30–£64

Among the eateries of Conranville on the waterfront at Shad Thames, the Chop House is nearest to Tower Bridge. The theme is reconstructed British, executed by new chef Henrik Iversen. When the cooking succeeds, the results are strikingly impressive. A dish of smoked haddock baked under a gratinated breadcrumb top with cheese and tomato makes a substantial and comforting starter, while veal chop with mild anchovy butter is a triumph of timing, the blush-pink meat retaining uncommon depth of flavour. Potato pancake topped with sweet-cooked onions, and lightly cooked but dryish duck livers were less successful at inspection. Hugely popular steak and kidney pudding packs an offal punch that carries across adjacent tables when the knife is inserted. Cambridge burnt cream, gooseberry sponge, and a good lemon meringue pie with cold custard are among the homespun puddings. The attention span of service has proved rather short on occasion.

Moneyed customers are well looked after, with fine claret, Sauternes and Burgundy, although quality is high at all price levels. Italy and the New World add interest, as do four English wines. Choice by the (large) glass is generous, starting with Dom. Virginie Merlot at £2.85. CELLARMAN'S CHOICE: Shaw & Smith Sauvignon 1994, Adelaide Hills, S. Australia, £21.50; Simonsig Cabernet 1992, Stellenbosch, South Africa, £19.75.

CHEF: Henrik Iversen   PROPRIETORS: Sir Terence Conran and Joel Kissin   OPEN: Mon to Fri and Sun L 12 to 3, Mon to Sat D 6 to 11   CLOSED: first week Jan   MEALS: alc (main courses £9.50 to £20). Set L £18.75 (2 courses) to £22.75. Bar meals available   SERVICE: 12.5% (optional), card slips closed   CARDS: Access, Amex, Diners, Switch, Visa   DETAILS: 115 seats. 44 seats outside. Private parties: 30 main room. Vegetarian meals. Children welcome. Wheelchair access (also WC). No music

Le Cadre

map 12

10 Priory Road, N8 7RD
TEL: (0181) 348 0606   FAX: (0181) 340 3890

COOKING 1*
COST £23–£42

Over the last decade David Misselbrook has turned this into one of the most pleasing provincial bistros in North London. The restaurant consists of a narrow room decorated with intriguing pictures ('my husband was facing a few of nude ladies') and the mood is jolly. Chef Yannick Chuat hails from Normandy, and his cooking is staunchly Gallic. The word 'warm' looms large among the starters: artichoke hearts served warm with scallops on a bed of tomato fondue, fresh asparagus with a warm vinaigrette of sweet peppers and basil, for example. Elsewhere, there have been votes for body-warming wild boar sausages, fillet of beef topped with foie gras served with an intense Madeira sauce, and 'very good' tarte Tatin. Service is friendly and unfussy. The all-French wine list covers the regions, and prices are seldom frightening. House wine is £9.

CHEF: Yannick Chuat PROPRIETORS: David Misselbrook and Marie Fedyk OPEN: Mon to Fri L 12 to 2.15, Mon to Sat D 7 to 11 CLOSED: 25 to 30 Dec, bank hols MEALS: alc (main courses £11 to £14). Set L £7.50 (2 courses) to £14.50, Set D Mon to Thur £14.50, Set D Fri and Sat £16.50 SERVICE: 10%, card slips closed CARDS: Access, Amex, Delta, Diners, Switch, Visa DETAILS: 50 seats. 16 seats outside. Private parties: 50 main room. Vegetarian meals. Children welcome. Music

Café dell'Ugo

map 13

56–58 Tooley Street, SE1 2SZ
TEL: (0171) 407 6001   FAX: (0171) 357 8806

COOKING 1*
COST £21–£45

'London's most stylish railway arch' is how manager Sean Gavin describes this outpost of the Antony Worrall-Thompson empire. The arch belongs to London Bridge Station, and the café keeps company with the London Dungeon. On the ground floor is a reverberating bar where legions of young bloods drink and eat tapas; above is the restaurant 'with immense headroom' and views of the action. New chef David Massey is keeping the kitchen in line, and the food is currently some of the best that the AW-T circus has to offer. The approach is familiar enough – almost any ingredient and cooking style under the sun is called into play, provided it sounds good and looks colourful – and in this case the results are consistent. Recent highlights have included rabbit terrine with kumquat marmalade, air-dried duck breast with sharp pickled cherries, sizzling spatchcocked chicken, and a piscine mixed grill with fennel, peppery mash and steamed Chinese greens. Italian cheeses are kept in good order and are 'remarkable value'. The wine list offers plenty of pickings from around the world. House Italian is £8.95.

CHEFS: Antony Worrall-Thompson and David Massey PROPRIETORS: Simpsons of Cornhill plc OPEN: Mon to Fri L 12 to 3, Mon to Sat D 6 to 11 CLOSED: bank hols MEALS: alc (main courses £9 to £13.50). Set D £10 (2 courses) to £12.95 SERVICE: not inc CARDS: Access, Amex, Delta, Diners, Switch, Visa DETAILS: 85 seats. Private parties: 110 main room. Vegetarian meals. Children welcome. Smart dress preferred. Music

Le Café du Jardin

map 15

28 Wellington Street, WC2E 7BD
TEL: (0171) 836 8769   FAX: (0171) 836 4123

COOKING 1
COST £21–£49

The café fits the Covent Garden bill: sharp black and white décor, a trendy menu, multi-cultural staff and customers, and a timetable that takes account of theatreland. It tries to do an awful lot, and the simple treatment of good ingredients for which Andrew Barber was noted at Simply Nico doesn't seem to have made the trip across town with him. Maybe the press of customers blunts the finesse, but there is no doubting the enthusiasm of a menu that takes in boudin blanc made with goose liver, warm blue cheese tart, and tiger prawns in a Thai-spiced broth of coconut milk and tomato. Pear sorbet with a substantial deep slice of chocolate tart pleased one reporter, although an attempt to represent a tropical paradise through the medium of sorbet, cinnamon stick and assorted fruits elicited only laughter from one reporter. The optional service charge can drive up the bill, although the set-price menu available at lunch and either side of the theatre should help to keep things reasonable. Wines cover a multitude of styles at a range of prices, and some good producers are included. House French is £9.50.

CHEFS: Andrew Barber and Tony Howorth PROPRIETORS: Robert Seigler and Tony Howorth
OPEN: Mon to Sat 12 to 3 (4.30 Sat), 5.30 to 12, Sun noon to 11 CLOSED: 25 Dec MEALS: alc
(main courses £8 to £13). Set L and D (7.30 to 10) £9.95 (2 courses) to £13.50 SERVICE: 15%
(optional), card slips closed CARDS: Access, Amex, Delta, Diners, Switch, Visa DETAILS: 105
seats. 20 seats outside. Private parties: 60 main room. Vegetarian meals. Children's helpings.
Smart dress preferred. Wheelchair access (no WC). Music. Air-conditioned

Café Fish

map 15

39 Panton Street, SW1Y 4EA
TEL: (0171) 930 3999 FAX: (0171) 839 4880

COOKING 1
COST £26–£50

If the Haymarket theatres or Leicester Square cinemas are on your evening agenda, Café Fish offers a more inspiring way to dine than the steakhouse and pizza chains that proliferate round about. The atmosphere is just as bustly, but the piscatorial menus are about more than just formula eating. Marinated squid with tomatoes and fennel, lobster Newburg, monkfish skewer on Creole sauce, and river trout with beetroot and orange chutney, are all on the large menu cards, supplemented by daily specials. The plateau de fruits de mer is the real deal, a good combination of palpably fresh seafood with mayo and Tabasco, basketloads of bread and an aeroplane-style finger-wipe in a sachet. Poached halibut with wild mushrooms produced 'a pleasant balance of flavours' for one reporter, but the scallops with Thai vegetables and lemon grass didn't live up to their promise. 'Zingy' raspberry mousse sandwiched between shortbread biscuits has made a good dessert. The imaginative wine list has some high points: Sauvion's Muscadets are the best in town. Prices are from £8.25.

CHEF: Andrew Magson PROPRIETOR: Groupe Chez Gérard OPEN: Mon to Fri L 12 to 3, Mon to
Sat D 5.45 to 11.30 MEALS: alc (main courses £7.50 to £15). Cover £1.25 SERVICE: 12.5%
(optional), card slips closed CARDS: Access, Amex, Diners, Switch, Visa DETAILS: 94 seats. 6
seats outside. Private parties: 20 main room. Vegetarian meals. Children welcome. No
cigars/pipes in dining-room. No-smoking area. Wheelchair access. Music

Café Japan £

NEW ENTRY map 12

626 Finchley Road, NW11 7RR
TEL: (0181) 455 6854

COOKING 1
COST £19–£36

Low prices are a significant part of the draw, reckons an inspector who has eaten his way through most of the raw fish in London. 'Café' sums up the décor: thin wooden slats and 'muslin' on the ceiling, posters on the walls, harsh light from large bare bulbs, continuous Japanese pop coming out of the speakers. The menu focuses on sushi and yakitori – 'the raw and the cooked' – although sashimi, tempura and noodles are also on offer. Call in on Friday for the offer of sushi ad lib for £15. Acceptable dishes from other sections of the menu have included nasu agedashi (deep-fried aubergine strips garnished with ginger, turnip and spring onion), katsudon (fried pork cutlet on a huge bowl of rice) and salmon steak with bean sprouts and a thick garlicky sauce. Drink green tea, Kirin beer or cold saké. House wine is £7.90.

CHEF: Mr K. Konnai   PROPRIETOR: Mr H. Matsuda   OPEN: Mon to Sat D only 5.30 to 10.30   CLOSED: bank hols   MEALS: alc (main courses £3.50 to £9). Set D £8 to £15. BYO £3   SERVICE: not inc   CARDS: Access, Delta, Switch, Visa   DETAILS: 37 seats. Private parties: 37 main room. Vegetarian meals. Children welcome. Smart dress preferred. Music. Air-conditioned

▲ Café Nico   NEW ENTRY   map 15

Grosvenor House, Park Lane, W1A 3AA   COOKING 1*
TEL: (0171) 495 2275   FAX: (0171) 493 3341   COST £38–£46

This is the cheaper and simpler end of Nico's Grosvenor House domain, although it enjoys a more opulent prospect on to Park Lane and Hyde Park by virtue of a sweeping picture window. The eating area is raised slightly above floor level, 'a little island of dining in a sea of hotel drinkers'. For a fixed price, you get to choose from a range that encompasses ham hock in jelly with celeriac rémoulade, cod in sherry vinegar, and maize-fed guinea-fowl with lentils and cream. Nothing is more than the menu says it will be, whether a ballottine of foie gras with green beans, truffle oil and pear, or simple grilled sole with a squeeze of lemon. There is 'decent' lemon crème brûlée to follow, along with other modern standards such as tiramisù and chocolate marquise. Service is good, coffee is excellent. Thirty-plus wines bump up the cost, but 14 are available by the glass from £4.50.

CHEF: Alexis Guillemot   PROPRIETOR: Granada Services Ltd   OPEN: all week 12 to 3, 6 to 11   CLOSED: 2 weeks mid-Jan   MEALS: Set L and D £21 (2 courses) to £26. Light snacks available from 11am to 11pm   SERVICE: net prices   CARDS: Access, Amex, Delta, Diners, Switch, Visa   DETAILS: 110 seats. Private parties: 250 main room. Car park. Vegetarian meals. Children's helpings. Smart dress preferred. Wheelchair access (also WC). Music. Air-conditioned   ACCOMMODATION: 280 rooms, all with bath/shower. TV. Phone. Air-conditioned. B&B £170 to £299. Deposit: 100%. Rooms for disabled. Children welcome. Dogs welcome exc in restaurant. Afternoon teas. Swimming-pool

Café Royal, Brasserie   map 15

68 Regent Street, W1R 6EL   COOKING 1
TEL: (0171) 437 9090   FAX: (0171) 439 7672   COST £27–£47

The brasserie has much of the *fin de siècle* appeal of the Grill Room (see entry, below), with a carved and painted ceiling, pictures of eminent Edwardians, and tables arranged around a central bar. It also has 'Radio 2-style croony music' and welcoming and helpful staff. Set menus with two choices per course work well, and there is a more extensive *carte*. The food is at the comfortable end of the modern brasserie spectrum, offering baked potato with smoked salmon and quail's eggs, and 'pleasantly chewy' barley risotto 'made with a well-flavoured stock and assorted mushrooms'. Simpler dishes include seared salmon, or grilled liver and bacon, and the cooking can produce impressive items such as pink breast of woodpigeon, and desserts of rhubarb tart with clotted cream, or pear and raspberry crème brûlée. A short list of round-the-world wines stays mostly under £20. Prices start at £12.50.

CHEF: Herbert Berger   PROPRIETOR: Granada Group   OPEN: all week L 12 to 3, Mon to Sat D 6 to 11   MEALS: alc (main courses £10 to £15). Set L and D £14.50 (2 courses) to £17.50. Afternoon tea and bar D available   SERVICE: not inc   CARDS: Access, Amex, Diners, Switch, Visa   DETAILS: 170 seats. Private parties: 50 private room. Vegetarian meals. Children's helpings. Smart dress preferred. Wheelchair access (also WC). Music. Air-conditioned

Café Royal, The Grill Room ▼

map 15

68 Regent Street, W1R 6EL
TEL: (0171) 437 9090   FAX: (0171) 439 7672

COOKING 2*
COST £36–£84

'It would be easy to be carried away by the glamour of the place,' suggested one first-time visitor, which may be exactly why some people love it: gilt, cherubs and plush red velvet all add up to one of London's more spectacular dining-rooms. The reason that first-timer had not eaten here before was because he was put off by the idea of a menu consisting entirely of grills. Nothing could be further from the facts, however. True, fillet of beef en croûte is wheeled round in a trolley, rendering it susceptible to the inherent timing difficulties of this old-fashioned treatment, but the repertoire is as broad as at any other smart address.

Foie gras, wild mushrooms and truffles appear in various guises, and the modern European style offers up red mullet with basil and black olives, lamb with provençale vegetables, and ravioli of langoustines with a suitably light buttery sauce. An inspector found that the beautifully presented desserts of bitter chocolate mille-feuille, and a caramel mousseline with mango compote and lime were 'less satisfying in substance'. Ancillary items such as bread and coffee are of the highest standard, prices are 'moderately breathtaking', and among staff 'the wine waiter was a lone oasis of competence'. Wines take in a vast roll-call of classics, including many noble vintages from Bordeaux and Burgundy. New World listings are shorter, yet sound. Don't miss the fine cognacs and armagnacs. French house wines start at £16.50. CELLARMAN'S CHOICE: Chablis premier cru 1992, Fourchaume, £32; Pauillac 1986, Ch. Haut Bages Libéral, £55.

CHEF: Herbert Berger   PROPRIETOR: Granada Group   OPEN: Mon to Fri L 12 to 2.30, Mon to Sat D 6 to 10.30   CLOSED: bank hols   MEALS: alc (main courses £18.50 to £24). Set L £24, Set D £39   SERVICE: not inc   CARDS: Access, Amex, Diners, Switch, Visa   DETAILS: 50 seats. Private parties: 8 main room. Children welcome. Smart dress preferred. No pipes in dining-room. No-smoking area. Wheelchair access (also WC). No music. Air-conditioned

Canteen

map 12

Unit G4, Harbour Yard, Chelsea Harbour, SW10 0XD
TEL: (0171) 351 7330   FAX: (0171) 351 6189

COOKING 3
COST £38–£58

Some would argue that the Canteen is the one bright spot in 'that great 1980s folly', Chelsea Harbour. Tim Powell arrived at the Canteen shortly before Marco Pierre White sold his stake in it, just as the last edition of the *Guide* was going to press, and the main shift seems to have been away from a brasserie philosophy towards a more relaxed restaurant with a slightly shorter but still generous menu. The playing-card motif (not universally appealing) remains stamped on everything, and service is 'unhurried', which can also translate as 'painfully slow', but the changes seem to have had little effect on the quality of the food. If it has sacrificed some inventiveness for consistency, that is considered a gain.

'Mostly very simple classical dishes rendered with great aplomb and the best of ingredients,' summed up an inspector who dined on expertly cooked pappardelle pasta with field mushrooms, with pungent truffle oil enriching the thin creamy sauce: simple, but 'an absolute dream. It just got richer as it went on.' If one dish divides the men from the boys it is risotto, here made with 'fat, soft and luscious' grains, containing crab and colourful vegetables, and timed perfectly: a flavourful and satisfying affair. Other successes have included sea bream with a stir-fry of oriental vegetables, and a fillet of smoked haddock with poached egg and grain-mustard sauce that was considered 'a triumph'.

Consistency extends to desserts of lemon tart with 'super pastry and a well-balanced filling', and a trio of 'sensational' ice-creams – chocolate, pistachio and vanilla – that 'I could say were the best ice-creams I've eaten in a month of sundaes'. The first half of the wine list is entirely French, followed by a fair New World section. Some good names appear, but you'll have to head for the French country wines if you want to drink well for under £15. House wines are £12.

CHEF: Tim Powell   PROPRIETORS: Michael Caine and Claudio Pulze   OPEN: Mon to Fri L 12.30 to 3, Mon to Sat D 6.30 to 11 (12 Fri and Sat)   MEALS: alc (main courses £12). Cover £1   SERVICE: not inc   CARDS: Access, Amex, Visa   DETAILS: 140 seats. Private parties: 140 main room. Car park. Vegetarian meals. Children welcome. Smart dress preferred. No pipes in dining-room. Wheelchair access (also WC). No music. Air-conditioned

Cantina del Ponte

map 13

36C Shad Thames, Butlers Wharf, SE1 2YE
TEL: (0171) 403 5403   FAX: (0171) 403 0267

COOKING 1
COST £25–£48

The Cantina shares more than just a riverside frontage with neighbouring Le Pont de la Tour (see entry). The same mixture of Mediterranean modes is available here, with pasta and pizza options occupying their own niches on the menu between starters and main courses. Simplicity is the fervently observed principle, and, when the raw materials are good, dishes such as bresaola with sweet mustard dressing and spring onions, or spinach and ricotta ravioli work well enough.

The more interesting-sounding pizza toppings (smoked salmon, goats' cheese and basil, for one) may not quite come off in the event, and it is a curious version of Italian food that offers a separately priced salad quite innocent of dressing. Red fruit pavlova and chocolate cheesecake offer readier indulgence. Caffè corretto and rosehip tea broaden the range of after-dinner beverages. Service has been described as 'unhelpful' and 'careless'. A well-crafted Italian wine list is fully in keeping with the food. Prices start at £10.95.

CHEF: Mark O'Brien PROPRIETORS: Sir Terence Conran, Joel Kissin and David Burke OPEN: all week L 12 to 3, Mon to Sat D 6 to 11 MEALS: alc (main courses £9.50 to £14). Set L and D £20 to £24 SERVICE: 12.5% (optional), card slips closed CARDS: Access, Amex, Diners, Switch, Visa DETAILS: 95 seats. 44 seats outside. Private parties: 20 main room. Vegetarian meals. Children welcome. Wheelchair access (also WC). No music

▲ The Capital ▼

map 14

Basil Street, SW3 1AT
TEL: (0171) 589 5171 FAX: (0171) 225 0011

COOKING 4
COST £37–£105

LONDON HOTEL RESTAURANT 1997

'A grand hotel in miniature' is how the Capital sees itself, a view confirmed by reporters: 'Unusually for a London hotel, everything seems on a personal scale.' Being a mere 50 yards from Harrods, and close to many other outlets where cash seems to disappear like light into a black hole, it should come as no surprise that shopping refugees head for the 'excellent-value' set lunch at £25. This is appropriately light, rather simpler than the *carte*, but done with as much panache as everything else, and reporters are grateful to find such value in the civilised surroundings of a small dining-room with mirrors, etched glass, a lot of beige and comfortable padded chairs.

The menu is an extraordinary document, offering six- and nine-course meals for £55 and £75 respectively, as well as a long *carte* revelling in all sorts of ideas, from a savoury trio of vegetable crème brûlées to a tulip of artichokes with a six-herb mousse. Marmite of lobster is a pastry-sealed crock which one reporter considered 'a splendid way to package a small amount of milky-creamy lobster soup' that was aromatised with lemon grass and lime leaf. Innovation seems to be the motor that keeps the kitchen running, yet dishes are 'thoughtfully assembled, not contrived'.

The quality of materials is evident in roast rack of lamb with 'sweet and juicy kidneys' and a glossy red wine sauce, and in simple 'farmyard chicken' that is 'full of free-range flavour'. Vegetarians who give advance notice do very well indeed. The kitchen's professionalism never misses a beat when it comes to timing; seasonings are sufficient to be noticed, but not so strong as to overpower; and textures constitute a significant part of the enjoyment.

Some of the flavour combinations can be as unsurprising as a chocolate mousse with a crème de menthe sorbet, but the effect is still electric. Indeed, superlatives queue up for the puddings, including a 'sensational' assiette of vanilla, a very superior apple and blackberry crumble, and 'trembling' turned-out soufflés such as banana with butterscotch sauce. Service is generally informative, well rehearsed but responsive, with mercifully 'no pomp or grovelling servility'. The wine list is a cosmopolitan one, with such fashionable bottles as Italian Sassicaia, Le Cigare Volant from California's Bonny Doon, and Coldstream Hills reds from Australia. Prices are down to earth by London hotel standards. House wines from the Loire are £14.50.

'The old ladies around us were mainlining on ham cornets with asparagus, which I thought had gone out with Fanny Cradock.' (On eating in Dorset)

CHEF: Philip Britten PROPRIETOR: David Levin OPEN: all week 12 to 2.30, 7 to 11.15 (10.30 Sun) CLOSED: D 25 Dec MEALS: alc (main courses £23.50 to £25.50). Set L £25, Set D £55 to £75 SERVICE: none, card slips closed CARDS: Access, Amex, Delta, Diners, Switch, Visa DETAILS: 40 seats. Private parties: 8 main room, 12 and 24 private rooms. Car park. Vegetarian meals. Children's helpings. Jacket and tie. No cigars/pipes in dining-room. Wheelchair access (no WC). No music. Air-conditioned ACCOMMODATION: 48 rooms, all with bath/shower. TV. Phone. Air-conditioned. Room only £196 to £231. Deposit: 1 night's stay. Children welcome. Baby facilities. Dogs by arrangement. Afternoon teas (*The Which? Hotel Guide*)

Le Caprice

map 15

Arlington House, Arlington Street, SW1A 1RT
TEL: (0171) 629 2239 FAX: (0171) 493 9040

COOKING 2*
COST £27–£71

Despite the fine reputation of Le Caprice, reporters genuinely seem surprised to have such a good time when they eat here. If they think that the Mayfair address – it is down a side-street behind the Ritz – means it will be snooty, they are absolutely charmed by the discovery that it isn't. A certain smartness prevails, of course, but all comers receive a degree of attention that makes them feel special. The stylish room is a trim L-shape, wears its tinted windows like a pair of dark glasses, and is on the go twice a day for 362 days a year. This is about as attractive a way of packaging a bistro as you will find.

Tim Hughes has a penchant for tried and tested ideas that are as simple as they are effective, and the menu is arranged to accommodate both trenchers and grazers. Eggs Benedict or risotto nero can be taken as either a first or a main course, and there is every reason to make a meal of dressed Cornish crab, followed by sauté foie gras with a Sauternes *jus*. Main courses concentrate on fish, from salmon fish-cake to deep-fried cod to roast skate, and avoid the more usual cuts of meat in favour of calf's liver with grilled bacon, or braised pork cheeks served Tuscan-style with beans and cabbage. Desserts may include 'deliciously gooey' Scandinavian iced berries with hot white chocolate sauce poured over. Wines are sophisticated but come at sensible prices, and there's plenty to choose from by the glass or half-bottle. The French and Italian sections start at £8.75.

CHEF: Tim Hughes PROPRIETORS: Christopher Corbin and Jeremy King OPEN: all week 12 to 3, 6 to 12 CLOSED: 25 and 26 Dec, 1 Jan MEALS: alc (main courses £9 to £22.50). Cover £1.50 SERVICE: not inc CARDS: Access, Amex, Delta, Diners, Switch, Visa DETAILS: 85 seats. Vegetarian meals. Children's helpings. Wheelchair access (no WC). No music. Air-conditioned

Charco's

map 14

1 Bray Place, SW3 3LL
TEL: (0171) 584 0765 FAX: (01932) 851600

COOKING 2
COST £24–£45

From outside it might not look the most chic of the small clutch of restaurants in this narrow lane, but the basement restaurant is smartly furnished with a light wood floor, old prints and potted palms. The menu adopts a trendy scatter-gun approach, listing risotto, rocket, salsa, tabbouleh, black beans, and saffron and honey ice-cream. It was 'so hip', one reporter remarked, that 'it actually excluded the passé sun-dried tomato'. But the cooking is a long way from 'just slinging everything on a charcoal grill and throwing a tomato salsa over it'.

Instead it produces effective combinations such as 'well-flavoured' sweet onion and Welsh rarebit served with cherry tomato salad, or rocket partnered with 'perfectly cooked' asparagus and given a pungent dressing of blue cheese and basil. A dish of soy-glazed duck with avocado and black-bean salsa was considered by an inspector to be 'an excellent adaptation of Chinese ingredients to fit a Western-style main course', while timing of fish from John Dory to monk has also impressed. Gary Pavitt's good sense of workable partnerships has included mascarpone and yoghurt terrine with strawberries and caramel sauce. Around a dozen wines by the glass feature on the well-priced round-the-world list. House French starts at £10.50.

CHEF: Gary Pavitt   PROPRIETOR: Pillarcrest Ltd   OPEN: Mon to Sat 12.30 to 2.30, 6 to 10.30 CLOSED: 24 Dec to 2 Jan, 15 Aug to 1 Sept   MEALS: alc (main courses £8 to £12). Set L £8.50 (2 courses)   SERVICE: not inc   CARDS: Amex, Diners, Switch, Visa   DETAILS: 60 seats. 8 seats outside. Private parties: 35 main room. Vegetarian meals. Children welcome. Music. Air-conditioned

Cheng-Du
map 13

9 Parkway, NW1 7PG
TEL: (0171) 485 8058   FAX: (0171) 794 5522

COOKING 1
COST £20–£49

'For once the background music was acceptable, perhaps because it was good jazz,' observes a satisfied customer about this attractive restaurant. Cheng-Du deals in mainly Peking and Szechuan specialities, with an occasional nod to the Cantonese repertoire. Bang-bang chicken in peanut sauce is an ever-popular appetiser, while the long menu also includes favourably reported dishes such as 'delightfully spicy' prawns in chilli sauce with walnuts, and duck in plum sauce. Raw materials are of a high quality (some interesting fish are offered at market price, which confirms that the kitchen buys fresh) and seasoning is reckoned to be 'superb'. Chinese toffee apples pass the test, and even the cappuccino is good. Service is efficient and speedy. Drink Chinese beer or the Italian house wine.

CHEF: Tony Lam   PROPRIETOR: Redfern Enterprises Ltd   OPEN: all week 12 to 2.30, 6.30 to 11.30   MEALS: alc (main courses £4.50 to £18). Set L and D £18.50   SERVICE: 12.5%   CARDS: Access, Amex, Delta, Visa   DETAILS: 75 seats. Private parties: 80 main room. Vegetarian meals. Children welcome. Smart dress preferred. Wheelchair access (no WC). Music

Chez Bruce
map 12

2 Bellevue Road, SW17 7EG
TEL: (0181) 672 0114

COOKING 2*
COST £26–£46

Bruce Poole appears to have settled into a comfortable stride at this well-known Wandsworth address opposite the Common. The room is light, with modern art posters, and reporters praise the warm welcome, relaxing atmosphere, and service that for the most part pleases. French-inspired cooking, with a choice of half a dozen items per course on the fixed-price menus, brings forth a seamless combination of modern and traditional ideas, from poached egg on toast with Bayonne ham and onion sauce, to pot-au-feu of lambs' offal with peas and mint.

'These boys really can *cook*,' claimed one visitor. Confidence and assurance are evident in the kitchen's handling of fish, in lamb served in various ways (most notably with couscous and aubergine) and in puddings such as chocolate brownie with a 'superb, crunchy' praline parfait, and a 'wonderfully caramelised' pear tarte Tatin that puts others to shame. Value is considered good, although 'I don't like the idea of an "optional" gratuity of 12.5 per cent being added to the bill', wrote one, 'which makes it more or less obligatory'. A short, savvy wine list includes a dozen by the glass. House French is £9.95.

CHEFS: Bruce Poole and Anthony Dimeck PROPRIETOR: Bruce Poole OPEN: Mon to Sun L 12 to 2.15 (3 Sun), Mon to Sat D 7 to 10.30 CLOSED: Christmas MEALS: Set L £10.50 (1 course) to £16.50, Set Sun L £18.50, Set D £20.50 (2 courses) to £24.50. BYO by arrangement only, corkage £10 SERVICE: 12.5% (optional), card slips closed CARDS: Access, Amex, Delta, Diners, Switch, Visa DETAILS: 75 seats. Private parties: 60 main room, 20 private room. Children's helpings L. No children D. No cigars/pipes in dining-room. Wheelchair access (no WC). No music. Air-conditioned

Chez Liline

map 12

101 Stroud Green Road, N4 3PX
TEL: (0171) 263 6550 and 272 9719

COOKING 1*
COST £25–£45

A couple of blocks north of Finsbury Park tube station may seem an unlikely spot to find exotic fish, but here it is none the less. Chez Liline is a cheerfully hectic place specialising in Mauritian food, though the kitchen is open to other influences too. An inspection meal began with a 'haunting, ultra-subtle' dish of marinated halibut in a 'gritty but creamy' sauce of mustard and saffron. New Zealand mussels are given a powerful brandy and garlic potion, with which they cope admirably. Anything cooked à la mauricienne, such as sea bream or lobster, comes with a high-octane tomato and chilli sauce. Service has been described as 'bumbling', but the menu does announce that delays are the result of preparing and cooking fish strictly to order. Ice-creams and sorbets are good bets for dessert. The largely French white wines are well sourced, with Sauvignon and Chardonnay dominating. House French is £9.25.

CHEFS: Mario Ho Wing Cheong and Pascal Doudrich PROPRIETOR: Mario Ho Wing Cheong OPEN: Mon to Sat 12.30 to 2.30, 6.30 to 10.30 CLOSED: bank hols MEALS: alc (main courses £9.50 to £17). Set L and Set D Mon to Thur £12.75 SERVICE: not inc CARDS: Access, Amex, Delta, Switch, Visa DETAILS: 50 seats. Private parties: 35 main room. Children's helpings. Music

Chez Max

map 13

168 Ifield Road, SW10 9AF
TEL: (0171) 835 0874 FAX: (0181) 947 4461

COOKING 2*
COST £26–£63

Ownership has now reverted to one of chez Max's initial backers and, although the name remains, Max Renzland has now departed. Regular visitors unaware of the new regime may not have noticed the difference. The sepulchral green basement is still reached by a spindly spiral staircase and the cooking remains firmly in French bistro mould. That said, the Relais & Châteaux background of new chef Gilles Chirat has brought a certain artistry to the presentation.

Turbot is sauté with asparagus, artichoke heart and tiny morels, and served in an 'excellent' fish stock with chives. A wedge of Brie de Meaux is briefly cooked on a layer of puff pastry and served on a Dijon mustard sauce with pine-nuts – a highly satisfying first course. An inspection dish of duck breast, cooked pink and accompanied by pot-roasted foie gras, was 'very rich but superb'. Technique comes into its own in show-off desserts such as a strawberry mille-feuille with strawberry ice-cream and coulis, or a powerfully intense chocolate praline gâteau in a coffee-bean sauce. If you're expecting only Bordeaux and Burgundy on the wine list, think again: Dry Creek, Yarra Valley and Stellenbosch are there too. Prices may seem nearly as steep as the staircase, but if you take your own, note that the corkage has been cut from £7.50 to £5. Otherwise, house wines are £11.50.

CHEF: Gilles Chirat   PROPRIETORS: Graham Thomson and Steven Smith   OPEN: Mon to Fri L 12.30 to 2.30, Mon to Sat D 7 to 11   CLOSED: Christmas, Easter, bank hols   MEALS: alc (main courses £11.50 to £20). Set L £14.50, Set D £19.50 (2 courses) to £24.50. BYO £5   SERVICE: 12.5% (optional), card slips closed   CARDS: Access, Amex, Delta, Switch, Visa   DETAILS: 60 seats. Private parties: 40 main room. Children welcome. Smart dress preferred. No cigars/pipes in dining-room before 11pm. No music. Air-conditioned

Chez Moi
map 12

1 Addison Avenue, W11 4QS   COOKING 3
TEL: (0171) 603 8267   FAX: (0171) 603 3898   COST £24–£50

By way of a 30th birthday present to itself, Chez Moi has been refurbished. Warm red walls are given extra dash by black door surrounds and dramatic dashes of tiger-skin fabric. It has spent almost all of that time in the *Guide*, satisfying reporters with some of the most consistent cooking around. Part of its appeal has to do with a customer-centred approach. Most good restaurants take their lead from the seasons or the market, but Richard Walton changes his menu every two or three weeks 'depending on how many regulars we have in'. He juggles a wide variety of dishes on both the main and 'Something Different' menu, although a casual visitor might be hard pressed to guess that tuna tataki or chicken and prawn dhosa are both mainstream, while baby chicken stuffed with sage and onion is meant to be an exotic excursion.

This does not matter a bit, since he appears equally at home with a Japanese dish of seared scallops served with a complex nori-wrapped rice roll, or a gamey saddle of hare with a honey and vinegar sauce. Some customers appear to be less adventurous. One reporter noticed that of the eight people lunching that day, all chose omelette Arnold Bennett to start, and escalope of salmon to follow: all plates were cleared. 'Scrummy' coffee ice-cream or 'wonderful' apple tart are good ways to finish. Delicate flavours, original ideas, intricate workmanship, but above all accurate cooking and workable combinations are the stuff of enthusiastic reports. This is bench-mark cooking of the kind that *Guide* inspectors prefer when off duty. Quietly professional service is at least the equal of the food, which is considered 'excellent value for money'. Good French wines dominate the list.

CHEF: Richard Walton PROPRIETORS: Richard Walton and Colin Smith OPEN: Mon to Fri L
12.30 to 2, Mon to Sat D 7 to 11 CLOSED: bank hols MEALS: alc (main courses £12.50 to £17).
Set L £15 SERVICE: not inc CARDS: Access, Amex, Diners, Switch, Visa DETAILS: 45 seats.
Private parties: 16 main room. Vegetarian meals. Children's helpings. Smart dress preferred. No
pipes in dining-room. Wheelchair access (no WC). No music. Air-conditioned

Chez Nico at Ninety Park Lane

map 15

90 Park Lane, W1A 3AA   COOKING 5
TEL: (0171) 409 1290   FAX: (0171) 355 4877   COST £42–£94

Nico himself characteristically describes this as 'an unpretentious family-run
French restaurant', as if it were some auberge in the country. The rectangular
dining-room is well proportioned, with some luxury chintzy fabrics, but it has to
fight hard to escape the feel of 'international luxury corporate entertaining'.
Service is plentiful, quiet, well orchestrated, professional rather than personable, and as often as not Nico stands near the entrance, arms folded, eyeing
his customers having a good time.

'Without doubt a *tour de force*,' summed up an inspector of his April meal. This
is a superlative-defying restaurant with an extraordinary consistency and total
mastery of technique. Of course it relies on luxury ingredients, producing a
'gorgeous creamy' langoustine soup with truffle sabayon, and a 'wonderfully
rich' salad of haricot beans with boudin of foie gras. But it also turns out a
'faultlessly executed Nico classic' of goats' cheese wrapped in pasta on a red
pepper coulis, and a single large grilled scallop, served simply with shredded
leek and a chive velouté: an 'unforgiving' dish that was 'cooked to perfection'.

The very success of the cooking, however, may have brought a degree of
predictability and conservatism. One inspector wrote of the food 'cruising along
effortlessly in top gear', which prompts the view that while it is impeccable, it
may also lack passion, as if the operation might be weighed down with the
burden of being exemplary. This is not a criticism, just a musing on what a top
restaurant is all about. To illustrate, a dish of marinated salmon, carefully
trimmed and fanned to form a circle, was partnered with a light fluffy blini, a
dollop of soured cream and a spoon of caviare: probably as good as you'll get, but
in the end an assembly of ingredients that lacked surprise.

Contrast this with a ravioli of langoustine, 'one of Ladenis's best ever dishes'
according to a Nico-watcher: a square of ravioli holds a deliciously sweet, plump
langoustine that tastes 'stunningly fresh' with firm yet soft texture, partnered by
an emulsion of herb-infused oils, and vegetables diced into tiny cubes. 'It is a
dish that grows and develops from the first mouthful, and is followed by small
explosions of sweet-and-sour tastes, and soft and crunchy textures.' Perhaps the
press of international custom demands the blinis, but the boundary-extending
langoustine ravioli has more of the Nico flair.

The set-price lunch, as ever, is a bargain, although it is worth doing the
arithmetic and noting that a ten-course dinner for £65 is a mere £6.50 per course:
we are talking about some of the best cooking in the country at virtually
bar-snack prices. It even includes a mini assiette gourmande, with a tuile – 'one
of the finest and most delicate pastries imaginable' – containing a distinctive
vanilla ice-cream. Otherwise lemon tart remains a classic, and the warm
chocolate tart is 'simply divine'. A few Italian and New World wines complement the fine French ones, but prices are heart-stoppingly high.

CHEFS: Nico Ladenis and Paul Rhodes PROPRIETORS: Nico and Dinah Jane Ladenis OPEN: Mon to Fri L 12 to 2, Mon to Sat D 7 to 11 CLOSED: 10 days Christmas, 4 days Easter, bank hols MEALS: Set L £29 to £65, Set D £51 (2 courses) to £65 SERVICE: net prices, card slips closed CARDS: Access, Amex, Diners, Visa DETAILS: 80 seats. Private parties: 10 main room, 20 private room. No children under 7. Smart dress preferred. No pipes in dining-room. Wheelchair access (also WC). No music. Air-conditioned

Chiaroscuro

map 15

24 Coptic Street, WC1A 1NT
TEL: (0171) 636 2731   FAX: (0171) 580 9160

COOKING 1
COST £22–£45

Ideally placed a stone's throw from the British Musuem, Chiaroscuro makes much of its arty connotations. The downstairs dining-room is spare yet comfortable, and seems to have picked up a quota of regulars: 'witness one man next to us reading his paper all the way through while devouring a steak, asparagus and an enormous bowl of mashed potatoes.' Tiny tables are laid with strips of coloured cloth, bread comes in a protective napkin. The cooking is described as modern European, and Sally James is capable of producing some lively and stylish dishes. Mixed antipasto contains all the right ingredients for colour and contrast, pork fillet is wrapped in pancetta and set on a bed of beans, while mushroom and ricotta ravioli come in a pleasing light broth tinged with lemon and garlic. Cheeses from Neal's Yard are served at the correct temperature. The downside is that there can be lapses of concentration in both kitchen and service. Sunday brunch brings in the families. Prices on the short wine list start at £8.

CHEF: Sally James PROPRIETORS: Carl and Sally James OPEN: Mon to Fri L 12 to 3.30, Sun L 11.30 to 4, Mon to Sat D 6 to 11.45 CLOSED: Christmas MEALS: alc (main courses £7 to £13). Set L £12.50 (2 courses), Set D 6 to 8 £10 (2 courses) SERVICE: not inc CARDS: Access, Amex, Delta, Switch, Visa DETAILS: 65 seats. Private parties: 30 main room, 14 and 30 private rooms. Vegetarian meals. Children's helpings. Smart dress preferred. Wheelchair access (no WC). No music

Chinon

map 12

23 Richmond Way, W14 0AS
TEL: (0171) 602 5968   FAX: (0171) 602 4082

COOKING 2*
COST £25–£52

'Chinon is a treasure,' maintains one supporter of this very individual restaurant. Behind the blue awning is a bright lemon-yellow room on two levels with a picture window at the back. Attempts to classify the cooking inevitably founder on dishes such as scallop ravioli oriental with toasted Chinese leaves, but it is refreshing to see Jonathon Hayes following his own nose. It leads him through a simple compilation of smoked ham, celeriac rémoulade and black olives 'of excellent quality', to roast saddle of hare with creamed lentils, to a meringue sandwich containing bananas, passion-fruit and cream.

He takes care over presentation, often piling things into towers capped by deep-fried shredded vegetables, and may use the same device – tempura batter, for instance – in more than one dish. Sauces have varied between a less than successful curry oil accompanying tempura of prawns, to a good stock-based reduction partnering a 'nicely undercooked' pigeon breast. On one occasion a 'moist, tender, flavoursome' rack of lamb came with three sauces, two too many for its reporter. 'Service can be a bit erratic or quirky, but it is highly personal and never bad,' wrote one regular. The wine list is very French and lacks much of the necessary information for people to make a sensible choice.

CHEF: Jonathon Hayes   PROPRIETORS: Barbara Deane and Jonathon Hayes   OPEN: Mon to Sat D 7 to 10.45   CLOSED: Christmas, but check   MEALS: alc (main courses £9 to £14.50). Set D £15. Minimum £20   SERVICE: 12.5% (optional), card slips closed   CARDS: Access, Amex, Delta, Switch, Visa   DETAILS: 60 seats. 6 seats outside. Private parties: 30 main room, 30 private room. No children under 10. No cigars/pipes in dining-room. Music. Air-conditioned

Chiswick

map 12

131 Chiswick High Road, W4 2ED
TEL: (0181) 994 6887

COOKING 1*
COST £21–£41

This offshoot of the Brackenbury (see entry, London) runs according to the same formula. The sparsely decorated, large modern room is done up in neutral tones and furnished with basic bentwood chairs. The food is bang up to date, and the atmosphere is bustling: people enjoy the sense of 'cool'. Service – 'frenetic, but in control' – knows what it's doing. One reporter ate four slices of 'moderately hung' woodpigeon on a potato pancake painted with garlic oil, then a hake fillet roasted and bedded on spinach with an 'intense but over-peppered' sauce of tomatoes, olives and haricot beans. He finished with plum clafoutis with a scoop of orange ice-cream and emerged a satisfied customer. Others have enjoyed neck end of lamb with artichokes and broad beans, and chocolate pot. Imaginatively chosen wines offer plenty of encouragement for the food in terms of big, racy flavours. House French is £9.50.

CHEF: Ian Bates   PROPRIETORS: Adam and Kate Robinson   OPEN: Mon to Fri and Sun L 12.30 to 2.45, Mon to Sat D 7 to 11.30   CLOSED: 1 week Christmas, bank hols   MEALS: alc (main courses £6.50 to £13). Set L £8.50 (2 courses), Set D 7 to 8 £8.50 (2 courses). BYO £4   SERVICE: not inc   CARDS: Access, Amex, Delta, Switch, Visa   DETAILS: 70 seats. 20 seats outside. Private parties: 12 main room. Vegetarian meals. Children's helpings. No cigars/pipes in dining-room. Wheelchair access (no WC). No music

Christopher's

map 15

18 Wellington Street, WC2E 7DD
TEL: (0171) 240 4222   FAX: (0171) 240 3357

COOKING 1
COST £26–£63

'An enjoyable place for a noisy lunch or a late casual dinner after the opera or theatre' is a fair summary of this establishment's appeal. 'It really saved the day,' wrote a grateful reporter who otherwise despaired of Covent Garden. The site is a former bank and the food is American, and mainly East Coast at that. Eat a Caesar salad, BLT or buffalo wings in the café on the busy ground floor, or climb the dramatic sweeping staircase to the relative peace and quiet of the restaurant proper, where Maine lobster, and Maryland crab-cakes with red-pepper mayo, figure alongside fried oysters with olive oil mash, and lamb steak béarnaise. Häagen-Dazs ice-creams and New York cheesecake are ways to finish. Service has been willing, though has also 'left much to be desired'. Well-chosen wines balance the Old and New Worlds, and £20-£25 secures a good bottle. House wine is £14.

CHEF: Adrian Searing PROPRIETOR: Christopher Gilmour OPEN: restaurant Mon to Fri L 12 to 2.30, Mon to Sat D 6 to 11.45; café Mon to Sat 11.30 to 10, Sun 12 to 4 CLOSED: 25 Dec, 1 Jan, bank hols MEALS: alc (main courses £9.50 to £21). Set pre- and post-theatre D £15 (check times when booking) SERVICE: not inc CARDS: Access, Amex, Delta, Diners, Switch, Visa DETAILS: 120 seats. Private parties: 32 main room. Children welcome. Smart dress preferred. No pipes in dining-room. No music

▲ *Claridge's* 🍷 ✱

map 15

Brook Street, W1A 2JQ
TEL: (0171) 629 8860 FAX: (0171) 499 2210

COOKING 1
COST £38–£94

Like the Changing of the Guard or the Tower of London, Claridge's is a very British institution. It is a timeless place for dining in the grand style, for feeling pampered in a beautiful art deco dining-room with impeccable service. Waiters appear as if by magic, footmen in knee breeches bring drinks, chandeliers glitter, sliver gleams, domes are lifted by white-gloved hands, and every cliché in the book is trotted out to describe the comfort and cosseting.

Large amounts of smoked salmon, oysters, lobster, caviare, steaks and Dover soles are tenderly placed on plates and eaten with pleasure. The *carte* is not cheap, though attempts at more serious cooking do not match the surroundings. An inspection meal proved disappointing on several counts, though it did register properly cooked salmon in a main course and a 'wonderful' gratin of raspberries. The nearest Claridge's gets to 'fast food' is a 'three-course lunch in 59 minutes'. The wine list is surprisingly well-balanced for such a grand place, rocketing up to the heights of Ch. Lafite '61 at £1,200, but also providing something palatable around £20. Don't miss the wide range of whiskies at the back of the list, near the smokes. House wines are £17.50. CELLARMAN'S CHOICE: Mâcon-Lugny, Les Genièvres 1994, Louis Latour, £21; St Emilion, Ch. St Christophe 1990, £28.50.

CHEF: John Williams PROPRIETOR: Savoy Group plc OPEN: all week 12.30 to 3, 7 to 11.30 MEALS: alc D (main courses £16 to £35). Set L £24 (2 courses) to £36, Set D Sun to Thur £38, Fri and Sat £40 to £45 SERVICE: net prices, card slips closed CARDS: Access, Amex, Diners, Switch, Visa DETAILS: 120 seats. Private parties: 14 main room, 20 to 210 private rooms. Vegetarian meals. Children's helpings. Jacket and tie. No smoking in 1 dining-room. No pipes in dining-room. Wheelchair access (also WC). Music. Air-conditioned ACCOMMODATION: 192 rooms, all with bath/shower. TV. Phone. Air-conditioned. Room only £195 to £295. Rooms for disabled. Children welcome. Baby facilities. Afternoon teas

Clarke's 🍾 ✱

map 13

124 Kensington Church Street, W8 4BH
TEL: (0171) 221 9225 FAX: (0171) 229 4564

COOKING 3
COST £31–£50

This comfortable, elegant Kensington landmark with its adjoining shop is an immensely civilised place at which to eat, and everybody seems happy to be surprised by whatever the no-choice dinner menu offers: 'It forces me to eat things I would not normally choose,' admitted one reporter. At its best the food is well thought out, artfully constructed, and carefully made with fine ingredients. Some items have engendered a slight feeling of disappointment due to a small oversight, imbalance or misjudgement, but when things go well there is no doubting the 'style and confidence' that have long been the hallmarks of Sally Clarke's cooking.

Dishes are simple in conception, with no fireworks or gimmicks. At one meal grilled fillet of sea bass with a light brushing of olive oil was surrounded by 'mousserons with a wonderful intensity of flavour' and a strewing of vegetables. 'When you concentrated on what you were eating, you realised how much care had gone into it.' Part of that care has to do with ingredients, perhaps at their most transparent in something like crab salad. Techniques are assured, producing a skewer of 'fat, light-textured' scallops that were timed to the second at inspection.

The flip-side of the 'simple' coin is that the food might be considered unadventurous, and one reporter was conscious of a regimented feel stemming from the identical portions and contents of everybody's plate. Two contrasting cheeses come with a ration of two 'truly excellent' oatmeal biscuits, followed by what is usually a cleverly conceived dessert: for example a spiced baked pear doused in syrup, served with a dessertspoon of lightly whipped cream and fingers of two different biscuits. Service is well drilled and paced, though somewhat remote. Prices have remained commendably unchanged for a long time, and include home-made bread, biscuits, pasta and so on. Lunch, which also offers a small choice, is considered a relative bargain. Wines are a scrupulously chosen, fairly priced and fashionable bunch. California is particularly well represented, and there are 15 wines by the glass, including three Tokais. CELLARMAN'S CHOICE: Acacia Brut 1989, Carneros, California, £38; Bonny Doon Old Telegram 1993, California, £30.

CHEFS: Sally Clarke and Elizabeth Payne PROPRIETOR: Sally Clarke OPEN: Mon to Fri 12.30 to 2, 7 to 10 CLOSED: 10 days Christmas, 2 weeks Aug, bank hols MEALS: Set L £22 (2 courses) to £26, Set D £37. BYO £10 still, £20 sparkling SERVICE: net prices, card slips closed CARDS: Access, Amex, Switch, Visa DETAILS: 90 seats. Private parties: 12 main room. Children welcome. No smoking in 1 dining-room; no cigars/pipes. Wheelchair access (no WC). No music. Air-conditioned

Coast ▼

NEW ENTRY map 15

26B Albemarle Street, W1X 3FA
TEL: (0171) 495 5999 FAX: (0171) 495 2999

COOKING 2*
COST £34–£58

This is what you get if you cross the Atlantic with the Canteen (see entries, both London). Oliver Peyton owns the former, and Stephen Terry used to cook at the latter. The ex-car showroom has been made to look like 'a 1970s vision of the twenty-first century', with curved walls and 'breast-like protuberances' for lights. The first test is to find the front door, cleverly disguised as a plate-glass window, thence into a single large high-ceilinged room with polished wooden floor and pale green surfaces that are 'a cross between after-dinner mint and eau-de-nil'.

The kitchen produces classy, good-looking, complex dishes, with a praiseworthy emphasis on lightness and fish. Every ingredient that should be here *is* here, including, on one menu, beetroot risotto, risotto cake, pavé of tomato risotto, and apple risotto for dessert. 'Is this a record outside Italy?' Far Eastern flavours are equally prominent, and overall the choice is wide and full of interest: ham dumplings in potato and cabbage soup, oxtail ravioli, or discs of crisp potato sandwiching a creamy crab filling.

'In striving for originality, some of the cooking misses its mark,' felt an inspector, but good buying and careful timing are evident, and textures are well handled. Presentation gets full marks too: 'Even rhubarb and custard looked exciting: quite an achievement.' Service is young and pleasant, although time-limits on tables can interfere with enjoyment. Wines are a varied, stylish and cosmopolitan range at fairly steep mark-ups. France is taken seriously, and top-notch New World whites fill out the list. The house selection starts at £11.50. CELLARMAN'S CHOICE: Mâcon-Uchizy, Dom. Talmard 1994, £20; St-Aubin premier cru 1993, Dom. Larue, £25.

CHEF: Stephen Terry   PROPRIETOR: Oliver Peyton   OPEN: all week 12 to 2.30, 6 to 11.30 (10.30 Sun)   CLOSED: bank hols   MEALS: alc (main courses £12 to £16.50)   SERVICE: not inc; 12.5% for parties of 6 or more   CARDS: Access, Amex, Delta, Switch, Visa   DETAILS: 150 seats. Private parties: 8 main room. Vegetarian meals. Children welcome. Wheelchair access (no WC). Music. Air-conditioned

The Collection

NEW ENTRY   map 14

264 Brompton Road, SW3 2AS
TEL: (0171) 225 1212   FAX: (0171) 225 1050

COOKING 1*
COST £27–£44

The latest Mogens Tholstrup venture is some kind of homage to the fashion world, a point made by the long glass-floored entrance catwalk that leads over a sea of silver-sprayed pebbles. A capacious room, once a warehouse, now boasts a long bar where the sharpest suits stand and chat. The restaurant itself is on the upper level, and no prizes for guessing where the culinary inspiration comes from: everywhere, and never mind the terminological precision on the rationale. Items from the spring collection included seared tuna sashimi, aubergine and feta salad, and grilled beef with tortilla, avocado, tomato, soured cream and coriander. Salmon ceviche at inspection was good and acidic, a dish of fresh crabmeat sandwiched between wun-tuns even better. Puddings can be as homely as the fairly solid orange and honey cake served with yoghurt, or as high-falutin as an exemplary passion-fruit tart with its own coulis. Staff float about in martial-arts gear, the swish of loose fabric imparting a laid-back San Francisco feel rather than anything war-like. Wines are as snappily tailored as the food: a bright selection that picks up unusual bottles from the US, the southern hemisphere, Spain and Italy, starting with Vin de Pays d'Oc at £11.50.

CHEFS: Chris Benians and Christian Sanderfeld   PROPRIETOR: Mogens Tholstrup   OPEN: Mon to Sat 12 to 3, 7 to 11.30   CLOSED: Christmas to New Year   MEALS: alc (main courses £9.50 to £14)   SERVICE: 15% restaurant, 12.5% ground floor (optional), card slips closed   CARDS: Access, Amex, Diners, Switch, Visa   DETAILS: 160 seats. Private parties: 160 main room. Vegetarian meals. Smart dress preferred. Wheelchair access (also WC). Music. Air-conditioned

'The response to our preference for a no-smoking area was to put a handwritten sign on our table, saying: "Please, no smoking at this table."' (On eating in Yorkshire)

Como Lario

map 14

22 Holbein Place, SW1W 8NL
TEL: (0171) 730 2954   FAX: (0171) 244 8387

COOKING 1
COST £25–£42

Stargazers should head for Como Lario. 'It is frequented,' say the owners, 'by figures from film, entertainment, politics and the aristocracy.' Venetian blinds and a translucent glass ceiling give the place a feeling of coolness and chic, and the Italian cooking is equally bright. Artichokes lend piquancy to a starter of charcoal-roasted ham, while crustacea make for glamorous pasta dishes – lobster with spaghetti, spider-crab with tagliolini. Dishes from the Lake Como area are dear to the kitchen's heart: rabbit stewed with olives and white vinegar, for example. Otherwise, calf's liver, 'cooked as you like', is highly regarded, and lamb is sauced with red wine and grain mustard. Ice-creams and sorbets are up to the mark, and the kitchen has been known to do crème brûlée for those suffering withdrawal symptoms. The wine list has been rewritten, and now names producers (some very good ones too) but still no vintages. House Sicilian is £8.95.

CHEF: Giancarlo Moeri   PROPRIETORS: Guido Campigotto, Giancarlo Moeri and Roberto Colussi   OPEN: Mon to Sat 12.30 to 2.45, 6.30 to 11.30   MEALS: alc (main courses £7 to £14). Cover £1.25   SERVICE: not inc   CARDS: Access, Amex, Delta, Switch, Visa   DETAILS: 100 seats. Private parties: 22 main room, 22 private room. Vegetarian meals. Children's helpings. Smart dress preferred. No pipes in dining-room. Wheelchair access (no WC). Music. Air-conditioned

▲ Connaught

map 15

Carlos Place, W1Y 6AL
TEL: (0171) 499 7070   FAX: (0171) 495 3262

COOKING 3*
COST £42–£126

The *Guide*'s longest-serving restaurant is an institution, perhaps even a relic of a bygone era, cooking in a steadfastly Edwardian hotel style. The place is as smart and club-like as anywhere in Mayfair, with an army of retainers who produce whatever is needed with a sleight of hand that Paul Daniels might envy. It is difficult to begrudge the 15 per cent service charge because there is nothing they have not done. Food arrives from the kitchen on a chafing dish and is transferred from there to your plate. Is this necessary or 'just a habit that goes on because nobody has thought to switch it off'? wondered one diner. After the main course, a fresh tablecloth is rolled into position with solemn ritual, and the food seems to be produced in much the same careful spirit: a haven of immutability in a world of change.

Dishes are half-English, half-French (with some fantasy names to boot), but the menu divides across this grain into fish, grills and so on. The cooking works well in a beautifully prepared and utterly classical duck-based terrine, tasting 'wonderfully deep and long', and in such standards as a pastry barquette filled with mushroom duxelle, topped with squirtingly soft-boiled quail's eggs and covered in a light hollandaise sauce. At one meal, by contrast, a 'thermidor' treatment did 'absolutely nothing' for the fine scallops underneath.

The dessert trolley is loaded with mousses, trifles, syrupy fruits, pastries and creams, and there might be a crumble of the day from the kitchen, all seemingly very nice. But a regular who has been eating here 'for most of my adult life' noticed something of a decline over the past year or so, and other reporters have echoed the doubts. Although the wine list is indisputably aristocratic, some of the mark-ups are 'wicked', in a few cases nearly four times the retail price. House wine is £16.50 per 75cl carafe.

CHEF: Michel Bourdin PROPRIETOR: Savoy Group plc OPEN: restaurant all week 12.30 to 2.30, 6.30 to 10.45; Grill Room Sun to Fri L 12.30 to 2.30, all week D 6 to 10.45 CLOSED: Grill Room bank hols exc 25 and 31 Dec MEALS: alc (main courses £10 to £40). Set L Mon to Sat £25, Set L Sun £30, Set D £35. Minimum £25 SERVICE: 15% (optional), card slips closed CARDS: Access, Amex, Diners, Visa DETAILS: 75 seats restaurant, 35 seats Grill Room. Private parties: 12 and 22 private rooms. Car park. Vegetarian meals. Children welcome. Jacket and tie. Wheelchair access (also men's WC). No music. Air-conditioned ACCOMMODATION: 90 rooms, all with bath/shower. TV. Phone. Air-conditioned. Room prices on application. Rooms for disabled. Children welcome. Baby facilities. Afternoon teas (The Which? Hotel Guide)

Cookhouse

NEW ENTRY map 12

56 Lower Richmond Road, SW15 1JT
TEL: (0181) 785 2300

COOKING 2
COST £26–£34

Minimalist in conception and Lilliputian in scale, Cookhouse succeeds by getting the basics right. The setting is a ten-table dining-room painted blue, with the kitchen in one corner and 'the spirit of IKEA hanging over it', observed one reporter. Tim Jefferson cooks unaided, Amanda Griffiths serves with confidence and good humour. They change their menu every month and keep it deliberately short and to the point: four starters, four mains, four puddings. To begin there might be something as robust as bruschetta with grilled vegetables, or as refined as spanking-fresh carpaccio of tuna with strips of cucumber and coriander leaves. Main courses could range from skewered monkfish (again, ultra-fresh) with cloves of roasted garlic and lemon peel, to calf's liver in a creamy sauce with broad strands of pasta and sugar-snap peas ('I'd be happy to eat that every day of my life,' confessed one contented soul). As for desserts, there might be Muscat cake with fresh nectarines, or a single cheese served with two dates and two biscuits. Cookhouse is unlicensed, but corkage is included in the cover charge.

CHEF: Tim Jefferson PROPRIETORS: Tim Jefferson and Amanda Griffiths OPEN: Tue to Sat D only 7 to 11 CLOSED: 2 weeks after Christmas, 2 weeks summer MEALS: alc (main courses £11.50 to £13). Cover £1.50, inc corkage. Unlicensed, BYO (no corkage) SERVICE: not inc CARDS: Access, Delta, Switch, Visa DETAILS: 28 seats. Private parties: 32 main room. Children welcome. No cigars/pipes in dining-room. Wheelchair access (no WC). Music. Air-conditioned

Criterion Brasserie

LONDON 1997 NEWCOMER

NEW ENTRY map 15

224 Piccadilly, W1V 9LBP
TEL: (0171) 930 0488
FAX: (0171) 930 8190

COOKING 3*
COST £30–£80

'The building is great, the food is modern, the service efficient: it is a great package in a central location,' concluded one reporter. Of the several contenders for London's best-looking dining-room, this must come very near the top of the list. Gold tiles reflect the candlelight without seeming gaudy or brash, and Arabic pictures lend an exotic note. 'At last a dining-room to match those historic monuments in Paris' was the view of a reporter. It is particularly heartening to see it put to such effective use, and there is no doubt the cooking benefits enormously from association with Marco Pierre White. Consistency of output is impressive, timing is accurate, and flavours are true. What's more, it is done successfully on a large scale, making the Criterion the kind of brasserie to which others must aspire. The flexible list of dishes sounds unfussy and interesting; many are culled from the White repertoire, and some may be familiar from his days at Harvey's and Canteen, including an accomplished, glistening black squid-ink risotto with calamari, produced with apparently effortless skill. Foie gras and chicken liver parfait, another Marco input, is as good here as anywhere.

There are no frills or fancy footwork, just excellent materials properly and intelligently handled, from first-rate scallops, briefly and accurately seared, resting on tasty chopped tomato flesh, to smoked haddock with poached egg, potatoes and mustard sauce: 'a classic brasserie-style dish done just as you hope it will be.' Simplicity is a characteristic, from soups, salads and pasta dishes through to excellent, unadorned lemon tart. Pear tart with crème anglaise, and a chocolate marquise have 'disappeared into grinning mouths'. Early staff problems seem to have been ironed out, and at its best service is pin-sharp and professional from a largely French team dressed in black. The sound list of modern wines is very sharp, cherry-picking its way around the world, though prices tend to be high.

CHEFS: Peter Reffell and Timothy Payne   PROPRIETOR: Marco Pierre White   OPEN: all week 12 to 2.30, 6 to midnight (10.30 Sun)   MEALS: alc (main courses L £11.50 to £15, D £11.50 to £28), Set L £14.95 (2 courses) to £17.95   SERVICE: 12.5% (optional)   CARDS: Access, Amex, Delta, Switch, Visa   DETAILS: 196 seats. Private parties: 11 main room. Vegetarian meals. Children welcome. Smart dress preferred. Wheelchair access (no WC). No music. Air-conditioned

Crowthers

map 12

481 Upper Richmond Road West, SW14 7PU
TEL: (0181) 876 6372

COOKING 2
COST £25–£38

'A good local restaurant,' summed up an inspector, 'although the décor and atmosphere need rethinking.' Perhaps 'a few pots of jolly paint' and a change from the dim lighting and 'numb bum' seating would be enough to bring the converted shop into line, although another visitor thought the small dining-room 'cosy'. The Crowthers have been here for 15 years, and the food remains basically French, with a few modern twists and turns: grilled aubergine with tomato, for instance, or feta cheese and pesto, or grilled cod with Savoy cabbage.

One reporter, to whom filo pastry is normally a bête noire ('it becomes soggy, and people use wads of the stuff') found it a strikingly crisp success when wrapped around mushrooms and served with a wild mushroom sauce. Indeed, saucing is a strong point, borne out by pink lambs' kidneys in a rich sauce sharpened with mustard, and by the lime that cuts the richness of a sauce served with roast breast of duck. Seasoning is well judged and desserts delight, including 'exceptional' hazelnut dacquoise with nutty meringue and a hot chocolate sauce, and a poached pear between layers of crisp biscuit pastry in crème anglaise. 'Sweet' service and three dozen fairly priced wines complete the deal.

CHEFS: Philip Crowther and Justin Gellatly PROPRIETORS: Philip and Shirley Crowther OPEN: Tue to Fri L 12 to 2, Tue to Sat D 7 to 10; Sat and Sun L and Mon D by arrangement CLOSED: Christmas to New Year, 2 weeks Aug MEALS: Set L £14.85 (2 courses) to £18.50, Set D £18.50 (2 courses) to £22.50. BYO £3.50, champagne £5 SERVICE: not inc CARDS: Access, Visa DETAILS: 32 seats. Private parties: 32 main room. Vegetarian meals. Children's helpings. Smart dress preferred. Wheelchair access (no WC). No music. Air-conditioned

Cucina

NEW ENTRY map 13

45A South End Road, NW3 2QB
TEL: (0171) 435 7814 FAX: (0171) 435 7815

COOKING 2
COST £22–£45

Cucina is in a row of shops at South End Green, midway between Belsize Park and Hampstead, while its culinary focus is sited indeterminately in southern Europe. The atmosphere is that of a modern brasserie with wooden-backed banquette seating and eccentric chairs with diagonal back-rests. The simplest dishes become 'sensationally good' by virtue of fine ingredients and spot-on execution. Bruschetta with roasted tomatoes and pesto scored highly with one reporter for careful amalgamation of flavours, while a salad of spinach, bacon, pear and pecan was 'light, clean and clever'. Immaculate desserts have included a poached pear that came as a bright yellow whole (poached with saffron) accompanied by a 'well-judged and exciting' ice-cream made with Chinese five-spice powder. The reasonably priced international wine list has some canny choices. House French is £10.50.

CHEFS: Andy Poole and Steve Baker PROPRIETORS: Vernon Mascarenhas, Andy Poole and Steve Baker OPEN: all week L 12 to 2.30, Mon to Sat D 7 to 10.30 (11 Fri and Sat) CLOSED: 3 days Christmas MEALS: alc (main courses £8 to £14). Set L Mon to Sat £10 (2 courses), Set L Sun £12.95 (2 courses) to £15.95, Set D £14.95 SERVICE: not inc CARDS: Access, Amex, Delta, Switch, Visa DETAILS: 86 seats. Private parties: 60 main room. Vegetarian meals. Children welcome. No cigars/pipes in dining-room. Music. Air-conditioned

Daphne £

map 13

83 Bayham Street, NW1 0AG
TEL: (0171) 267 7322

COOKING 1
COST £19–£33

A pleasantly unpretentious ambience is part of the draw in this likeable family-run restaurant, with its white candles stuck in saucers and photographs of old Cyprus on the walls. A printed menu runs the gamut of Greek-Cypriot staples, from hummus to baklava, but it pays to consider the regularly changing blackboard of specials. At one dinner it produced some excellent offerings, including brilliant koukia anginares (fresh artichoke hearts casseroled in a 'super' stock with broad beans), louvi (black-eyed beans with spinach), marinated octopus, fresh anchovies, and leek rolls served with mint chutney. Main dishes are more refined than in some comparable places: kleftiko is a perfectly cooked knuckle of 'young pale lamb' served with decent plain rice. The two-course lunch for a fiver remains one of the bargains of the neighbourhood. Coffee hits the spot, and the Greek-Cypriot wines are quaffable. There's a short selection of French wines, with house wine £9.50 a litre.

CHEF: Lambros Georgiou   PROPRIETORS: Panikos and Anna Lymbouri   OPEN: Mon to Sat 12 to 2, 6 to 11.30   CLOSED: 25 and 26 Dec   MEALS: alc (main courses £6 to £11). Set L £5 (2 courses)   SERVICE: not inc   CARDS: Access, Switch, Visa   DETAILS: 85 seats. 30 seats outside. Private parties: 30 main room. Vegetarian meals. Children's helpings. Wheelchair access (also WC). Music

Daphne's

map 14

112 Draycott Avenue, SW3 3AE
TEL: (0171) 589 4257 and 584 6883
FAX: (0171) 581 2232

COOKING 1
COST £24–£62

One of Chelsea's more stylish eateries, long frequented by the figure-conscious smart set, Daphne's is a tiled and foliage-filled refuge from the hubbub of traffic nearby. Chefs come and go, but the menus are straight from Central Casting, the Mediterranean mode done with suave restraint. The bread selection is especially good; remember to get your fill. Wild mushroom risotto at inspection was appropriately creamy in texture, if bland in seasoning. Pasta ranges from safe-and-sound spaghetti with tomatoes and basil to pappardelle with duck, walnuts and thyme. The fish of the day may be a large fillet of halibut, reported on one occasion as 'a bit dried out through overcooking', but served with softly roasted peppers and tiny pools of rocket salsa. Desserts such as pear and nut crumble, and chocolate brownie with apricot cream are competently rendered. Grumbles this year concern the non-segregation of smokers and the trance-like service. The wine list is evenly divided among Italy, France and the New World, with mark-ups you can expect for this area.

CHEF: Chris Benians   PROPRIETOR: Mogens Tholstrup   OPEN: all week 12 to 3 (4 Sun), 7 to 11.30 (10.30 Sun)   CLOSED: Christmas   MEALS: alc (main courses £6.50 to £19.50)   SERVICE: 15%, card slips closed   CARDS: Access, Amex, Delta, Diners, Switch, Visa   DETAILS: 110 seats. Private parties: 8 main room. Vegetarian meals. Children welcome. Smart dress preferred. Wheelchair access (no WC). No music. Air-conditioned

Del Buongustaio ♥

map 12

283 Putney Bridge Road, SW15 2PT
TEL: (0181) 780 9361   FAX: (0181) 789 9659

COOKING 1
COST £19–£45

The business of Del Buongustaio is rustic Italian peasant food. It bills itself as an osteria and serves plain gutsy dishes, many made from humble materials. With this kind of food, it is not the skill of cooking that impresses so much as the juggling with simple ingredients to produce a never-ending variety of interesting dishes. Inspiration comes mainly from Piedmont but moves outwards in summer, taking in a Trentino vegetable strudel, a Ligurian thin pastry pie stuffed with sausage and mozzarella, and a Puglian version of lamb with asparagus, lemon and egg. The wine list is a happy mix of Italian and Australian producers, with most bottles coming in at less than £20. There are just four half-bottles, but nine wines are available by the glass. House wines start at £8.80. CELLARMAN'S CHOICE: Soave Classico Superiore 1995, Anselmi, £14.50; Charles Melton Rose of Virginia 1995, Barossa Valley, South Australia, £15.50.

CHEFS: Antonio Strillozzi and Aurelio Spagnuolo   PROPRIETORS: Rochelle Porteous and Aurelio Spagnuolo   OPEN: Sun to Fri L 12 to 3, all week D 6.30 to 11.15 (10.30 Sun)   CLOSED: 10 days Christmas to New Year, Sun L June and July, all day Sun Aug   MEALS: alc (main courses £6.50 to £12.50). Set L £7.50 (2 courses), Set D £22.50. Cover 90p. Minimum £15 D   SERVICE: not inc, card slips closed; 10% (optional) for parties of 5 or more   CARDS: Access, Amex, Visa   DETAILS: 55 seats. Private parties: 60 main room. Vegetarian meals. Children's helpings. No cigars/pipes in dining-room. Wheelchair access (no WC). Music. Air-conditioned

dell'Ugo 🍴

map 15

56 Frith Street, W1V 5TA

COOKING 1

TEL: (0171) 734 8300   FAX: (0171) 734 8784

COST £26–£48

Dell'Ugo epitomises the appeal of Soho and tries to be all things to all comers, with a ground-floor café-bar open to the street and open all day, a busy first-floor bistro with packed tables, and a more spacious and quieter second floor with bright Mediterranean colours. A standard core menu with variations serves the lot, and deals in snappy cooking techniques that pull together disparate ingredients: chargrilled lamb steak with cold bean salad and an aubergine and roast pepper salsa, for example. Individual dishes change with the merry-go-round of materials, but the breezy Antony Worrall-Thompson style rolls on under Matthew Fanthorpe, who arrived in March 1996. The trendy trawl might take in chicken and almond tajine, hot and sour duck breast, and home-made ice-creams with coconut biscotti, while the wine list makes a similar stab at a wide range of grape varieties, including Viognier, Zinfandel, and house Trebbiano and Merlot at £8.95.

CHEF: Matthew Fanthorpe   PROPRIETOR: Simpsons of Cornhill plc   OPEN: Mon to Fri L 12 to 3, Mon to Sat D 5.30 to 12; café-bar all week 11am to 11.30pm   CLOSED: bank hols   MEALS: alc (main courses £7 to £14.50). Pre- and post-theatre D £19.95 (2 courses) to £12.95 (available 5.30 to 7 and 10.30 to 12)   SERVICE: not inc   CARDS: Access, Amex, Delta, Diners, Switch, Visa   DETAILS: 190 seats. 12 seats outside. Private parties: 30 main room, 12 and 16 private rooms. Vegetarian meals. Children welcome. No cigars/pipes in dining-room. Music. Air-conditioned

▲ Dorchester, Grill Room 🍷

map 15

Park Lane, W1A 2HJ

COOKING 2

TEL: (0171) 317 6336   FAX: (0171) 317 6363

COST £35–£87

The Terrace is now used entirely for banqueting, but that still leaves three restaurants for Willi Elsener to keep his eye on: the Oriental (see entry, below), the Bar, with its cocktails and Italian dishes, and the Grill Room, looking pre-War Spanish but tasting British, and very traditional British at that. Lunchtime specials vary with the day – saddle of lamb on Tuesday, braised beef in Guinness on Saturday – and virtually anything that can be wheeled round on a trolley will be; there's one for bread, one for roast beef and Yorkshire pudding, one for smoked salmon, one for salads, one for cheese, and one for puddings.

About the only Olde English items they don't appear to serve are Brown Windsor soup and bangers and mash, although there is a brown onion soup alongside cream of lobster and cock-a-leekie. Alternatively, begin with Morecambe Bay potted shrimps or Cornish dressed crab. Simple grills of Dover

81

sole or liver and bacon back up old oven-cooked favourites of shepherd's pie or braised oxtail.

Wines are taken terribly seriously, but mark-ups are high; suffice it to say that house wines are £19.50. None the less, quality looks assured, and the Italian and Californian sections are assembled with as much scrupulous care as the major French regions. Half-bottles and magnums abound. CELLARMAN'S CHOICE: Pouilly-Fumé 1992, Dézat, £29.50; Côtes du Rhône 1991, Guigal, £17.

CHEF: Willi Elsener PROPRIETOR: Dorchester Hotel Ltd OPEN: all week 12.30 to 2.30, 6 to 11 (7 to 10.30 Sun and bank hols) MEALS: alc (main courses £16 to £25.50). Set L £25.50, Set D £34 SERVICE: net prices, card slips closed CARDS: Access, Amex, Delta, Diners, Visa DETAILS: 81 seats. Private parties: 14 main room. Vegetarian meals. Children's helpings. Smart dress preferred. Wheelchair access (also WC). No music. Air-conditioned ACCOMMODATION: 244 rooms, all with bath/shower. TV. Phone. Air-conditioned. B&B £225 to £280. Rooms for disabled. Children welcome. Baby facilities. Afternoon teas

▲ Dorchester, Oriental
map 15

Park Lane, W1A 2HJ
TEL: (0171) 317 6328 FAX: (0171) 317 6363

COOKING 3
COST £33–£133

Eating Chinese food in the environs of a top-flight hotel may seem an affectation too far, but transplant the operation to Hong Kong and no one would bat an eyelid. There, people eat out in hotel dining-rooms quite as readily as they do in restaurants, if not more so. The attempt to re-create that ambience at the Dorchester in this chic room on the mezzanine floor has been helped along by lush carpeting, swaths of silk and antique vases.

A long menu, under the aegis of Simon Yung, is composed largely of Cantonese dishes, and ingredients like abalone and shark's fin are flown in direct from Hong Kong. The former appears braised and sliced with broccoli or black mushrooms, while the fin is shredded in soups with other mixed seafood or boiled with chicken and Chinese cabbage. Fried pigeon in orange sauce, and deep-fried sole with chilli beans and asparagus extend the range, but there are echoes of old Guangdong in there, too, in prawns and cashew-nuts in lemon sauce, and a good assortment of stir-fried dishes (although nothing stoops to describing itself as sweet-and-sour). Objections surface at the prices, a world away from those in Chinatown, but at least this is an MSG-free zone. Home-made coconut ice-cream and refreshing chilled mango pudding are the best ways to finish. Wines are the same as in the Grill Room; for details and CELLARMAN'S CHOICE, see previous entry.

CHEFS: Willi Elsener and Simon Yung PROPRIETOR: Dorchester Hotel Ltd OPEN: Mon to Fri L 12 to 2.30, Mon to Sat D 7 to 11 CLOSED: Aug, bank hols MEALS: alc (main courses £12 to £45). Set L £23.50 to £25.50, Set D £34 to £77 SERVICE: net prices, card slips closed CARDS: Access, Amex, Delta, Diners, Switch, Visa DETAILS: 81 seats. Private parties: 7, 10 and 16 private rooms. Car park. Vegetarian meals. Children's helpings. Smart dress preferred. Wheelchair access (also WC). No music. Air-conditioned ACCOMMODATION: see entry above for details

'I was very brave to choose crispy squab with honey and ginger, since it was a couple of days after the pigeons went missing from Trafalgar Square.' (On eating in London)

La Dordogne

map 12

5 Devonshire Road, W4 2EU
TEL: (0181) 747 1836   FAX: (0181) 994 9144

COOKING 1
COST £27–£49

This aims to be 'a corner of France in Chiswick'. French pictures hang on the green walls, producing an 'old-fashioned' feel for one reporter and 'the atmosphere of a distinguished French bistro' for another. The cooking is not distinctively regional, although a little foie gras might appear in a salad or sauce. Its strength is seafood, from Irish rock oysters, and lobster done four ways, to fish soup, and an 'elegant' scallop mousse with lobster sauce. Salads and terrines set the ball rolling, main courses take in a few meat dishes such as lamb with ratatouille, and desserts top the billing with a feuilleté of apples with cider sabayon, or crêpes soufflés. Six French cheeses are 'all just right for eating', and the French staff provide 'caring service'. Wines from the south-west head up the fairly priced and entirely French list, beginning with house Pécharmant and Bergerac at £9.50.

CHEF: Jean-Luc Morcellet   PROPRIETOR: La Dordogne Ltd   OPEN: Mon to Fri L 12 to 2.30, all week D 7 to 11   CLOSED: bank hols   MEALS: alc (main courses £8.50 to £12.50). Cover £1   SERVICE: 10%   CARDS: Access, Amex, Delta, Diners, Switch, Visa   DETAILS: 80 seats. 6 seats outside. Private parties: 30 main room, 20 to 50 private rooms. Children's helpings. Smart dress preferred. Wheelchair access (also WC). Music

Drones

NEW ENTRY   map 14

1 Pont Street, SW1X 9EJ
TEL: (0171) 259 6166   FAX: (0171) 259 6177

COOKING 1
COST £22–£57

This 'very appealing makeover of an old favourite' now sports Tuscan colours of orange and powder blue, an indoor tree and clever flower arrangements. An imposing half-open gate separates the front room's café/brunch menu (eggs Benedict, crab- and corn-cakes with chilli relish) from the 'villa architecture' of the rest, while a small shop next door sells take-away dishes. In typical Antony Worrall-Thompson fashion, the flexible food caters for all sorts, with options for healthy eating, some tapas, 'style nibbles' and big blow-outs.

It may sometimes feel like Victoria Coach Station cuisine, where ingredients come together, mingle about, then go off again in all directions, as in pumpkin and feta ravioli with coriander and Pecorino shavings, but despite sometimes inaccurate menu descriptions there have been impressive rustic hand-thrown gnocchi with mussels and coppa cracklings, light tempura of courgette flower and asparagus, and chocolate and macadamia nut tart with vanilla ice-cream. Service is open, welcoming, calm and professional. Wines are varied, interesting and a bit pricey, the cheapest £11.95.

CHEF: Chris Millar   PROPRIETOR: Simpsons of Cornhill plc   OPEN: restaurant all week 12 (9.30 Sat and Sun brunch) to 3.30, 7 to 11.30; café all week 9 to 6   MEALS: alc (main courses £9 to £16). Set L £9.95 (2 courses) to £12.95. BYO £4. Light meals available   SERVICE: not inc   CARDS: Access, Amex, Delta, Diners, Switch, Visa   DETAILS: 100 seats. Private parties: 100 main room. Vegetarian meals. Children's helpings. Smart dress preferred. Music. Air-conditioned

Eagle £

map 13

159 Farringdon Road, EC1R 3AL
TEL: (0171) 837 1353

COOKING 1*
COST £19–£29

The Eagle has been doing its thing for longer than most other born-again London 'food pubs'. Little changes, apart from the fact that the place is now open on Saturdays, when lunch meanders on leisurely until four o'clock. 'Everything from the spicy Italian sausages to the grilled fish benefits from the noisy, infectious, spontaneous atmosphere and the casual yet still rather hip charm this smoke-filled room has always maintained,' observes a regular. The chargrill is used fiercely to sear prime ingredients, and timing is impeccable. Lots of influences crop up: warm duck salad comes with pancetta, radicchio, new potatoes, capers and a balsamic dressing; squid is stewed the Spanish way with saffron; and there may be Portuguese custard tart to finish. Draught beer from Charles Wells and Ruddles, cider from Westons and a motley collection of imported brews supplement the tiny list of affordable wines (all of which can be bought by the glass). Prices start at £8.50 the bottle.

CHEF: David Eyre   PROPRIETORS: Michael Belben and David Eyre   OPEN: Mon to Sat 12.30 to 2.30 (4 Sat), 6.30 to 10.30   CLOSED: 2 weeks Christmas, Easter Sat, bank hols   MEALS: alc (main courses £6.50 to £10.50)   SERVICE: none   CARDS: none   DETAILS: 60 seats. 20 seats outside. Vegetarian meals. Children's helpings. Wheelchair access (no WC). Music

English Garden

map 14

10 Lincoln Street, SW3 2TS
TEL: (0171) 584 7272   FAX: (0171) 581 2848

COOKING 2
COST £23–£62

This period Chelsea town house conveys a sense of the Gothic, especially in the plant-strewn conservatory, which is naturally at its best in summer. The food deals in both traditional – pea soup, grilled calf's liver, rice pudding – and more contemporary interpretations of English cooking, such as spiced red-pepper mousse or red-plum tarte Tatin. The Brian Turner here is not the 'Ready, Steady, Cook' chef, as one couple discovered, but he nevertheless provided them with entertainment in the form of halibut mousse, followed by pigeon with warm blackcurrant vinaigrette.

Mastery of the mousse (crab, for one reporter) and a sure technique with the tart (asparagus and Brie, for example) combine with accurate roasting and grilling to produce both a varied menu and a successful array of tastes and textures, as in melt-in-the-mouth pastry and tender lamb. Service was 'eccentric' for one, 'attentive and cheerful' for another. Classic French wines dominate the list (curiously there is nothing from England), and Ch. Reynier house wine at £11 is considered exemplary.

CHEF: Brian Turner   PROPRIETOR: Roger Wren   OPEN: all week 12.30 to 2.30 (2 Sun) 7.30 to 11.30 (7 to 10 Sun)   CLOSED: 25 and 26 Dec   MEALS: alc (main courses £8 to £19.50). Set L Mon to Sat £15.75, Sun £18.75   SERVICE: not inc   CARDS: Access, Amex, Delta, Diners, Switch, Visa   DETAILS: 70 seats. Private parties: 30 main room, 8 and 22 private rooms. Vegetarian meals. Children's helpings. No pipes in dining-room. Wheelchair access (no WC). Music. Air-conditioned

L'Escargot

map 15

48 Greek Street, W1V 5LQ
TEL: (0171) 437 6828 and 2679
FAX: (0171) 437 0790

NEW CHEF
COST £28–£49

The kitchen at this landmark Soho restaurant serves two masters: a self-styled 'brasserie' on the ground floor, and a first-floor dining-room that has traditionally dealt in more elaborate cooking at rather higher prices. As we went to press, Garry Hollihead left, and Billy Reid and David Hawkesworth were in the process of taking over. They may nudge the cooking in a new direction, but L'Escargot has long existed on a diet of comforting modern food such as scallop and lobster terrine, foie gras with rösti potatoes, and lamb shank. As for pudding, one man who brought his whole family down from Lancashire for the day had 'no complaints about the world's most expensive tarte Tatin.' It took 30 minutes to make, so they missed the last train home and took a cab that cost £375. A wide-ranging list includes some excellent wines, but mark-ups are high. House Vin de Pays d'Oc is £10.50.

CHEFS: Billy Reid and David Hawkesworth   PROPRIETOR: Jimmy Lahoud   OPEN: Mon to Fri L 12.15 to 2.15, Mon to Sat D 6 to 11.15   CLOSED: dining-room: Aug, bank hols; brasserie: bank hols   MEALS: dining-room: Set L £21 (2 courses) to £25, Set D £25 (2 courses) to £30; brasserie: alc (main courses £12.50), Set L £14 (2 courses) to £17.50   SERVICE: dining-room: 15%; brasserie: 12.5%; card slips closed   CARDS: Access, Amex, Delta, Diners, Switch, Visa   DETAILS: 120 seats. Private parties: 20 main room, 10 and 60 private rooms. Vegetarian meals. Children welcome. No cigars/pipes in dining-room. Wheelchair access (also men's WC). Music. Air-conditioned

L'Estaminet

map 15

14 Garrick Street, WC2E 9BJ
TEL: (0171) 379 1432

COOKING 1
COST £27–£47

Plumb in the heart of Covent Garden, opposite the Garrick Club, L'Estaminet keeps the tricolour flying for rustic French (specifically provençale) cooking in cheerily informal surroundings. Staff wear 'splendidly embroidered' waistcoats and recite the day's specials, of which there may be half a dozen, so pay attention. An excellent starter of herring with warm potato salad encouraged one spring diner, while crab tart with 'wonderfully crisp' pastry did the same for his companion. Bangers and mash, a speciality of at least one sort of inhabitant of Provence, has interpolated its way among the main courses, which otherwise offer grills and casseroles – seafood, and rabbit, say – in the expected way. At dinner's end, chariots bear down on you, one full of little tartlets, the other of cheeses. Chocolate tart comes highly commended. Wines are standard French bistro fare at slightly uncomfortable prices. Vins de maison are £9.

CHEF: Philippe Tamet   PROPRIETORS: Christian Bellone and Maria Echevarrie   OPEN: Mon to Sat 12 to 2.30, 6 to 11   MEALS: alc (main courses £8 to £16). Set L Sat £14.99, Set pre-theatre D £9.99. Cover £1.50   SERVICE: 12.5% (optional), card slips closed   CARDS: Access, Amex, Switch, Visa   DETAILS: 70 seats. Private parties: 30 private room. Vegetarian meals. Children welcome. Smart dress preferred. No cigars/pipes in dining-room. Music

Euphorium

NEW ENTRY map 13

203 Upper Street, N1 1RQ
TEL: (0171) 704 6909   FAX: (0171) 226 0241

COOKING 2
COST £23–£44

Upper Street goes on accumulating good restaurants, this one owned by a man who once appeared on Lloyd Grossman's 'Masterchef'. Custard-coloured sand-blasted walls and a huge Peter Doig canvas make the interior forever Islington, and the menu speaks the same language. Dishes are not so much entitled as represented by terse lists of their components joined by plus signs, as in chemical equations, and some seriously good food emerges from the semi-exposed kitchen. Ox-tongue, capers, gherkins, shallots + flat-leaf parsley was 'very fine indeed', noted an inspector, the tongue astonishingly tender, the poignant accompaniments in 'perfect balance'. Black beans added interest to a dish of roast cod with chargrilled tomatoes, spring onions and basil leaves. Vegetarian dishes show up well, as in fried okra with chickpeas and asparagus on a delectably oily lump of focaccia, enlivened with coriander, chilli and garlic, while meats have taken in braised salt-beef with broad beans and mash, and neck end of lamb with courgettes. Desserts should inspire too – 'very rich and perfumed' sesame and rose-water parfait served with half a quince certainly does. The wine list is very short and goes in for Languedoc Viognier and red Sancerre for fear of dealing in anything too mainstream, but the choices are good, starting at £9.50.

CHEF: Paul Tweedie   PROPRIETOR: Marwan Badran   OPEN: all week L 12.30 to 2.30, Mon to Sat D 6 to 10.30   CLOSED: 1 week Christmas, 1 week Easter, 2 weeks Aug   MEALS: alc D (main courses £8.50 to £13.50). Set L £10 (2 courses) to £15   SERVICE: 12.5% (optional), card slips closed   CARDS: Access, Amex, Delta, Switch, Visa   DETAILS: 40 seats. Private parties: 40 main room. Vegetarian meals. Children welcome. Smart dress preferred. Wheelchair access (no WC). No music. Air-conditioned

Exxo

NEW ENTRY map 15

33–34 Rathbone Place, W1 1AD
TEL/FAX: (0171) 255 1120

COOKING 1*
COST £21–£38

A staircase leads down to black double-doors at this newcomer just off Charlotte Street. Inside is a monument to New Brutalism, with undressed frosted-glass tabletops, a mélange of chair styles and everything from the plumbing pipes to the kitchen on public view.

Mark Williamson speaks a language London understands. It's feta, bruschetta, pancetta and spicy pork wun-tun soup all the way. A positively old-fangled starter of lamb sweetbreads with wild mushrooms in a capacious pastry case delivered plenty of richness at one meal, though a more à la mode main course of crispy duck with noodles and gingery soy sauce seemed short on zing. Cod gremolata with braised fennel, fondant potato and garlic sauce is the sort of thing done with fish. A thin slice of cinnamon custard tart comes with a whole pear poached in red wine that resonates with flavour. Service is casual but capable; 'there was a set of bongos in the service-area but we were spared.' The short wine list trips lightly from Oregon Pinot to Puligny-Montrachet, starting with house red at £9.75.

CHEF: Mark Williamson PROPRIETOR: A.A. Khan OPEN: Mon to Fri 12 to 3, 6 to 10.30
CLOSED: 24 and 25 Dec MEALS: alc (main courses £8 to £11). Bar food available SERVICE: not
inc, 12.5% for parties of 6 or more CARDS: Access, Amex, Delta, Switch, Visa DETAILS: 120
seats. Private parties: 300 main room. Vegetarian meals. Children welcome. Music

Fables

NEW ENTRY map 12

839 Fulham Road, SW6 5HQ
TEL: (0171) 371 5445 FAX: (0171) 371 5545

COOKING 2*
COST £29–£42

After relinquishing Pied-à-Terre (see entry, London), Richard Neat took on the
role of executive chef at this newly opened restaurant in Parsons Green, with his
former sous-chef James Kirby doing the day-to-day hands-on cooking. This may
not be the poshest part of Fulham Road, but the design is modern enough: pale
wood, just a little chrome, and black and white 'strip cartoon' walls depicting a
La Fontaine fable.

The food is modestly inventive, not outlandish but certainly intriguing,
producing rillettes of home-smoked whiting with a poached egg and chive
sauce, for example, or a terrine of skate and potatoes bound together with parsley
sauce. Not all combinations work equally well. A dish of 'exquisite cod' at one
early meal was unbalanced by powerful chorizo, but a warm ballottine of
braised and de-boned oxtail wrapped in roasted aubergine, and a dish of crab
surrounded by a shellfish jelly were both distinguished. Professional execution
shows throughout, not least in an excellent plum tart, and a pistachio ice-cream
filled with runny chocolate fondant. A bright, modern, two-page wine list turns
up some interesting flavours, from Alsace Muscat to Argentinian Malbec, and
prices are fair. House French is £10.

CHEF: James Kirby PROPRIETOR: Alexandria Fields OPEN: Mon to Sat 12.15 to 2.30, 7 to 11
MEALS: alc (main courses £10 to £14). Set L £12 (2 courses). Set D £22 SERVICE: 12.5%
CARDS: Access, Amex, Delta, Diners, Switch, Visa DETAILS: 65 seats. Private parties: 35 main
room, 35 private room. Vegetarian meals. Children welcome. Weelchair access (no WC). Music.
Air-conditioned

Fifth Floor 🍷

map 14

Harvey Nichols, 109–125 Knightsbridge, SW1X 7RJ
TEL: (0171) 235 5250 FAX: (0171) 823 2207

COOKING 2
COST £30–£81

The fifth floor is one store's answer to a whole Soho street. A wonderfully
well-stocked shop and delicatessen shares the space with a wine shop, a busy
bar, and a café serving trendy 1990s salads, pasta, grilled fish and unusual
ice-creams to 'a bustling mix of lunching ladies and tired shoppers'. Food in the
restaurant is up to the minute, British, and as chic as it comes, with a line-up of
dishes running from poached goats'-cheese dumpling and chorizo in leek broth,
to 'admirable' saffron risotto with squid and oysters. There may be roast wild
rabbit, or a 'light, moist and tangy' leek and Roquefort tart for non-meat eaters.

A glass of dessert wine is recommended with each option at pudding:
Hungarian Tokai with pain perdu, or Australian Liqueur Muscat with warm
chocolate tart and pistachio ice-cream. Minus-points have included the general
environment – acoustics and smoking – and the cost. Service was 'fantastic' for

one reporter, but has lacked sharpness for others. One of the biggest attractions is the wine list, which reads like a roll-call of some of the best bottles in the world. Happily, prices are kept well in check, and half-bottles abound. France is dealt with thoroughly, while Italy, Spain, California and Australia provide strong competition. CELLARMAN'S CHOICE: Harvey Nichols Bourgogne Blanc Reserve 1994, £14.95; Côtes du Rhône 1993, Jean-Luc Colombo, £17.

CHEF: Henry Harris   PROPRIETOR: Harvey Nichols & Co Ltd   OPEN: all week L 12 to 3 (3.30 Sat and Sun), Mon to Sat D 6.30 to 11.30   CLOSED: 25 and 26 Dec, bank hol D   MEALS: alc D (main courses £10 to £29.50). Set L £17.50 (2 courses) to £21.50. Bar food available   SERVICE: 12.5% (optional), card slips closed   CARDS: Access, Amex, Delta, Diners, Switch, Visa   DETAILS: 110 seats. Private parties: 12 main room. Car park. Vegetarian meals. Children's helpings. No pipes in dining-room. Wheelchair access (also WC). No music. Air-conditioned

Fire Station 🍴 £

map 13

150 Waterloo Road, SE1 8SB
TEL: (0171) 620 2226   FAX: (0171) 633 9161

COOKING 1
COST £16–£32

Waterloo's Edwardian fire station provides a big space for South Bankers to meet and mill around in after work and before the theatre. They spill on to the pavement from the two-roomed 'noisy boozer' that supplies newpapers to read in quieter moments. Wooden tables and 'jumble sale chairs' herald a no-frills approach to the food, and given a view of the open-plan kitchen 'you can see that you will be getting chargrills, stir-fries and short-order cooking'. So it proves. Food and drink are chalked on not-easy-to-see blackboards, and service keeps up with those who just want a starter and a pud: chicken liver salad with couscous to begin, plum ice-cream or banana brûlée to finish, for example. In between might be lamb cutlets with a Mediterranean twist, or steamed sea bass with Thai vegetables. There is nothing higher than £20 on the short wine list, with quite a few bottles around £8 to £10. House wine is £7.95.

CHEF: Paul Bloxham   PROPRIETOR: Regent Inns plc   OPEN: all week 12.30 to 2.30 (11 to 3.30 Sun), 6 to 11   CLOSED: 25 and 26 Dec, Easter   MEALS: alc (main courses £4 to £10). BYO £5   SERVICE: not inc; 10% for parties of 6 or more   CARDS: Access, Amex, Delta, Diners, Switch, Visa   DETAILS: 100 seats. Private parties: 20 main room, 80 private room. Vegetarian meals. Children's helpings. Wheelchair access (also WC). Music. Air-conditioned

First Floor ♛

map 13

186 Portobello Road, W11 1LA
TEL: (0171) 243 0072   FAX: (0171) 221 9440

COOKING 1*
COST £27–£53

A first visit to the First Floor, a throbbing heart of trendiness in the middle of Portobello market, is a crash course in post-modern design. You pick your way along a gravel-strewn corridor, up a dingy wooden staircase and arrive in a wide, curving space described by one visitor as 'sumptuous 1990s baroque'. If you imagined for one minute the food couldn't live up to its context, try seared emu with grilled aubergine and tamarillo relish: 'a perfect confluence of bitter-sweet flavours'. Visuals are accorded a high premium, as in risotto that brings together slivered black olives and balls of orange pumpkin in a vivid display of colour, and palates are put through their paces when duckling is partnered with fennel, prunes and dried cranberries. Desserts subside into tried and tested sticky toffee pudding, impeccably sharp lemon tart, or banana ice-cream with chocolate pecan cookies. Service is by 'well-informed and interested' staff.

The wine list brings together an impressive selection under £20, supplemented by a few fine bottles. Highlights are from Petaluma and Rockford in Australia, Hunter's and Matua Valley in New Zealand, and Antinori in Italy. House wines are £9.75. CELLARMAN'S CHOICE: Kushushu Creek Chardonnay 1994, Paarl, South Africa, £19.50; Bellingham Estate Pinotage 1994, Frankschhoek, South Africa, £12.50.

CHEF: Nilton Campos PROPRIETOR: R.J. Blundell OPEN: Mon to Sat 10 to 4, 7 to 11 (7.30 Sat), Sun noon to 10 CLOSED: 25 Dec MEALS: alc (main courses £7 to £17). Set L £10.50 (2 courses), Set D £26.50. Bar D available SERVICE: 12.5% (optional), card slips closed CARDS: Access, Amex, Delta, Diners, Switch, Visa DETAILS: 130 seats. Private parties: 65 main room, 55 and 100 private rooms. Vegetarian meals. Children welcome. No cigars/pipes in dining-room. Music

---

▲ Four Seasons ▌ map 15

Hamilton Place, Park Lane, W1A 1AZ
TEL: (0171) 499 0888 FAX: (0171) 493 6629

COOKING 3
COST £33–£91

There is no general traffic along Hamilton Place, just the sleekest of limos and fleets of black cabs depositing the international glitterati outside either one of the five-star hotels that face each other across its narrow gauge. In summer 1996 Shaun Whatling arrived as head chef from the kitchen at Les Saveurs (see entry, London) to succeed Jean-Christophe Novelli, and the enterprising style looks set to continue. At an inspection meal, a moist and chunky terrine of quail and foie gras, with baby onions, confirmed that execution was up to the mark. Herb-crusted fillet of sea bass with a turmeric-tinged beurre blanc showed a positive way with fish, while smoked beef fillet on celeriac with mashed potatoes and a red wine sauce offered a 'satisfyingly rich' treatment of tip-top raw materials. The simpler dishes, in a reversal of accepted wisdom, tend to be less successful. Nostalgic flavours abound, as in a white chocolate mousse topped with lemon-curd ice-cream.

Wines are on the grand side and pricey with it; rather more choice under £20 would be welcome. Still, the list makes an impression for its sheer quality, particularly in Bordeaux and Burgundy. House wines are good too, offering a mixed bag of 11, including wines by Penfolds, Antinori and Alsace's Muré. Here prices start at an encouraging £15. CELLARMAN'S CHOICE: Chablis 1992, Dom. de l'Eglantière, J. Durup, £26; St-Estèphe, Ch. La Commanderie 1990, £26.

CHEF: Shaun Whatling PROPRIETOR: Four Seasons, Regent Hotels and Resorts OPEN: all week 12.30 to 3, 7 to 10.30 MEALS: alc (main courses £21 to £35). Set L £19.50 (2 courses, Mon to Fri) to £25, Set D 7 to 10 £45 SERVICE: net prices, card slips closed CARDS: Access, Amex, Diners, Visa DETAILS: 60 seats. 30 seats outside. Private parties: 12 main room, 16 private room. Car park. Children's helpings. Jacket and tie. No pipes in dining-room. Wheelchair access (also WC). Music. Air-conditioned ACCOMMODATION: 227 rooms, all with bath/shower. TV. Phone. Air-conditioned. Room only £265 to £329. Rooms for disabled. Children welcome. Baby facilities. Small dogs welcome. Afternoon teas. Garden

French House Dining Room

map 15

49 Dean Street, W1V 5HL
COOKING 2
TEL: (0171) 437 2477   FAX: (0171) 287 9109
COST £26–£49

The French House is a single room above the French House pub, an unself-conscious reminder of old Soho. Coloured brown, and with no frills beyond white table coverings, it serves a particular style of modern English food not a million miles removed from that of its sibling restaurant, St John (see entry, London). The menu generally features an offal dish, such as lambs' tongues and horseradish dumpling in a mushroom and beetroot broth. Equally likely, though, is a meatless dish of mushrooms with potato pie and rocket, or fishy things along the lines of whole crab with mayonnaise, or grilled lemon sole and chips with tartare sauce. Portions can be generous.

The essence of the style is to use ingredients that don't cost the earth, so prices are kept within reason. Margot Clayton and Harvey Cabaniss tend to do straightforward things, producing a thick and savoury chestnut and apple soup, or wood pigeon and celeriac with 'deep flavour and lively texture'. Steamed treacle pudding or quince blancmange continue the English theme right to the end. One New Zealand wine looks lonely, but not out of place, among the three-dozen fairly priced French offerings. House French is £9.50.

CHEFS: Margot Clayton and Harvey Cabaniss   PROPRIETORS: Melanie Arnold, Margot Clayton, Fergus Henderson and Jon Spiteri   OPEN: Mon to Sat 12 to 3, 6 to 11.15   CLOSED: Christmas, Easter, bank hols   MEALS: alc (main courses £7.50 to £16)   SERVICE: not inc   CARDS: Access, Amex, Delta, Diners, Switch, Visa   DETAILS: 30 seats. Private parties: 30 main room. Vegetarian meals. Children's helpings. No music

Fulham Road ♥

map 14

257–259 Fulham Road, SW3 6HY
COOKING 2
TEL: (0171) 351 7823   FAX: (0171) 376 4971
COST £34–£52

Staff come and go at a rate of knots these days, all part of the increasing pace at which the more fashionable London restaurants seem to operate. Richard Corrigan has moved to Searcy's Brasserie (see entry, London), Adam Newell was chef for a time, then Craig Thomas moved up from sous-chef. In the middle of all this, prices have come down in line with Stephen Bull's stated intentions. He has always aimed for a light touch – putting fish and poultry centre stage, for instance, and keeping portion size under control – while his combination of thrift and inventiveness can make a meal of risotto with 'an interesting mix of five juicy snails and a few artichoke hearts' followed by rabbit with polenta.

Sometimes the partnerships can be as 'well mannered' as fillet of lamb with wild garlic tortellini in a broth of smoked bacon and tomato, and sometimes as loud as a fillet of John Dory with foie gras and mango. 'Strangely, it all worked amazingly well,' concluded an inspector of the latter, although other aspects of the same meal – seasoning and timing particularly – fell short of ideal. 'Tart and creamy' lemon soufflé is worth the wait, sorbets are good, and crème brûlée is a dense version 'of artery-blocking strength'. An 80-strong wine list focuses on interest and quality, with some fine Burgundy and an appealing range of grape varieties across four continents. CELLARMAN'S CHOICE: Pacherenc du Vic-Bilh sec, Ch. Bouscassé 1994, Brumont, £18; Coteaux du Languedoc, Ch. Lascaux 1993, £17.50.

CHEF: Craig Thomas   PROPRIETOR: Stephen Bull   OPEN: all week D only 7.00 to 10.45
CLOSED: 1 week Christmas, bank hols   MEALS: alc (main courses £11 to £15). BYO £5
SERVICE: not inc, card slips closed   CARDS: Access, Amex, Visa   DETAILS: 80 seats. Private
parties: 80 main room, 16 private room. Vegetarian meals. Children's helpings. No cigars/pipes
in dining-room. Wheelchair access (no WC). No music. Air-conditioned

Fung Shing £

map 15

15 Lisle Street, WC2H 7BE
TEL: (0171) 437 1539   FAX: (0171) 734 0284

COOKING 2
COST £20–£68

After a fire in 1995, Fung Shing rose again from the ashes with stylish contemporary décor but the same team in the kitchen. Most visitors thoroughly approve of the French-blue shop-front, the yellow-washed walls adorned with floral prints, and the light oak panelling. Plans are also afoot to extend the back of the restaurant into Gerrard Street. 'The menu and cooking have thankfully not been tampered with,' notes a devotee. Many fixture dishes continue to be enthusiastically endorsed: soft-shell crab is encrusted with salt laced with green chilli pepper ('a stimulating blend of contrasting flavours, leaving the crab mainly as a texture'), scallops are cooked tenderly in their shells and served with black-bean sauce, while stewed duck with yam in a hot-pot remains 'a truly stunning dish' suffused with deep flavours. Even staples such as crispy beef and sweet-and-sour chicken are given a new dimension here. At its best, Fung Shing has few rivals in the capital. A Western-style wine list covers a lot of ground at fair prices. Try Chinese wine (hot or cold) or house French at £9.

CHEF: Kwun Fu   PROPRIETOR: Forum Restaurant Ltd   OPEN: all week 12 to 11.15   MEALS: alc
(main courses £6.50 to £23). Set L and D £12.50 to £13.50. Minimum £8.50 after 6.30   SERVICE:
not inc   CARDS: Access, Amex, Delta, Diners, Switch, Visa   DETAILS: 85 seats. Private parties:
50 main room, 28 and 30 private rooms. Vegetarian meals. Children welcome. Music.
Air-conditioned

Le Gavroche ♟

map 15

43 Upper Brook Street, W1Y 1PF
TEL: (0171) 408 0881 and 499 1826
FAX: (0171) 491 4387 and 409 0939

COOKING 4
COST £38–£131

Few restaurants feel more traditional than this, even in London. Ties are required for gentlemen, ladies are handed menus without prices, and if you want an English translation you have to ask for it. Le Gavroche's currency is utterly classical French cooking, though at prices that can make grown men wince. The money pays for haute cuisine, smooth service and pleasant surroundings. Start at ground level with canapés, aperitifs and a choice of à la carte, menu exceptionnel or one entitled 'hommage à mon père' (the repository for soufflé Suissesse, assiette du boucher and omelette Rothschild). Despite lobster, foie gras and truffles, the offerings were 'a little ordinary' for the price in one reporter's view.

The food is very competently crafted as in a cold first course of sculpted artichoke heart containing two soft-boiled gull's eggs topped by smoked salmon mousse, caviare and a slice of smoked salmon. Everything was of first-class quality, and the execution and assembly were perfect, but 'it remained a luxury restaurant confection that neither surprised nor excited', which rather summarises the general approach. Nevertheless, there are heartier and more flavourful moments reminiscent of the country, in a dish of pork cheek with Puy lentils and foie gras, and in a pigeon with tender breast and bloody legs baked with black truffle. 'Brilliant, full of strong complementary flavours' was the verdict on this.

Perhaps because of changing tastes, reporters are finding the desserts particularly sweet these days, but the cheeseboard is one of the best, with more than a dozen specimens all in prime condition. Service, from an army of staff, is notably slick, and although a service charge is included in the price, 'the canvassing for an additional tip' by leaving the credit card slip open was 'the final straw' for one reporter. Another called it 'extremely annoying and pressurising'. For value, the set lunch beckons, and at £38 includes a half-bottle of wine per head. Many wines on the extensive list are illustrious, as the price tags make abundantly clear. There is little under £20 and much over £100, but for the sheer range of French vintages, and for opening with over 60 champagnes, it succeeds in its main aim: to impress. House wines are £16.50. CELLARMAN'S CHOICE: Chablis, St Martin Cuvée Albert Roux 1993, Dom. Laroche, £34; Pomerol 1990, Ch. La Croix des Moines, £32.

CHEF: Michel Roux   PROPRIETOR: Le Gavroche Ltd   OPEN: Mon to Fri 12 to 2, 7 to 11   CLOSED: bank hols, Christmas to New Year   MEALS: alc (main courses £27 to £39). Set L £38 (inc wine) to £80, Set D £55 to £80. Minimum £50 D   SERVICE: net prices   CARDS: Access, Amex, Diners, Switch, Visa   DETAILS: 60 seats. Private parties: 80 main room, 20 private room. Children welcome. Jacket and tie. No cigars/pipes in dining-room. No music. Air-conditioned

Gay Hussar

map 15

2 Greek Street, W1V 6NB
TEL: (0171) 437 0973   FAX: (0171) 437 4631

COOKING 2
COST £26–£50

If you're after pressed boar's head (and these days, who isn't?), or 'bored with pointless innovation and scared of sky-high West End prices', go to the Gay Hussar. This old Soho stager has been in the *Guide* for 40 years, and Laszlo Holecz has been cooking his gutsy Hungarian food here for 20 of them. 'Attentive' service, gigantic portions, and demonstrable value that astonishes still in the heart of London: all are undimmed by time's passage. Wild cherry soup or casino eggs are among the off-beat starters, or there is cold pike with beetroot sauce and a cucumber salad. Fish dumplings with dill sauce and rice is ethnically unimpeachable, while roast duck with potatoes, red cabbage and apple sauce offered one reporter good moist meat and masses of vegetables – 'the sort of cooking I'd expect from a Hungarian grandmother, if I had one'. Pancakes stuffed with walnut purée and streaked with chocolate sauce are an 'undeniably authentic' way to finish. The brief Franco-Hungarian wine list just about suffices in the circumstances, prices starting at £10.

CHEF: Laszlo Holecz PROPRIETOR: Restaurant Partnership plc OPEN: Mon to Sat 12.30 to 2.30, 5.30 to 10.45 CLOSED: bank hols MEALS: alc (main courses £12 to £15). Set L £16 SERVICE: 12.5% (optional), card slips closed CARDS: Access, Amex, Delta, Diners, Switch, Visa DETAILS: 70 seats. Private parties: 23 main room, 12 and 23 private rooms. Vegetarian meals. Children's helpings. Smart dress preferred. Wheelchair access (no WC). Music. Air-conditioned

Golden Dragon

NEW ENTRY map 15

28–29 Gerrard Street, W1V 7LP
TEL: (0171) 734 1152 FAX: (0171) 734 1073

COOKING 2
COST £20–£39

Soho is buzzing, Chinatown is in top gear and this 200-seater culinary stadium is full to bursting at evenings and weekends. Menus are tellingly printed not only in English and Chinese but also in Japanese: it is rumoured that karaoke takes place in the upstairs room. 'The combination of good dim-sum, ordinary Cantonese dishes and roast meats is very rare in Chinatown,' noted one correspondent, and on a good day the kitchen can produce 'the best roast pork (char siu) and duck ever in London'. A dim-sum lunch yields a wealth of skilful and authentic delights: prawn dumplings with chives in a glutinous casing 'shaped like a goldfish head', taro croquettes 'made with real taro', sweet egg custards that knock spots off most of their European counterparts. Occasionally a curiosity doesn't come off: lobster dumplings with 'salad cream', for example. Elsewhere, braised udon noodles (another Japanese echo) with stir-fried seafood and oyster sauce have been pitched exactly right in terms of flavour and balance. Some say that service and management are adequate, others that it is notably good by Chinatown standards. House wine is £8.50. A sister operation, Royal Dragon, is at 30 Gerrard Street, (0171) 734 0935.

CHEF: Y.C. Man PROPRIETORS: Charlie Tsui and Lawrance Cheng OPEN: all week noon (11 Sun) to 11.15pm (11.45 Fri and Sat) CLOSED: 25 Dec MEALS: alc (main courses £7 to £14). Set L £9.50 (2 courses) to £11.50, Set D £12.50 to £20. Minimum £5 SERVICE: 10% CARDS: Access, Amex, Delta, Diners, Switch, Visa DETAILS: 230 seats. Private parties: 300 main room, 15 and 40 private rooms. Vegetarian meals. Children welcome. Smart dress preferred. Wheelchair access (also WC). Music. Air-conditioned

Gourmet Garden 🎧✳ £

NEW ENTRY map 12

59 Watford Way, NW4 3AX
TEL: (0181) 202 9639

COOKING 1
COST £17–£45

Marooned in a row of shops, fronted by an urban dual carriageway, the Gourmet Garden survives on loyal followers seeking some of London's most authentic and rustic Singaporean and Chinese cookery. The interior may be the Chinese equivalent of chintz, but the separate 'chef's recommendation' menu pulls no punches. Unusual dishes such as pig's trotters cooked in vinegar and soy sauce, crab with belacan, or assam fish beckon. Deep-fried chicken livers with spicy salt and chilli come piping hot, the livers perfectly fried, spicy salt giving them an agreeable crunch without overwhelming the flavour. The main menu lists standard Cantonese and South-east Asian dishes, among which is Hainanese chicken rice, 'spot on' with a velvety, just-cooked texture. If you like the unusual textures and colours of Malaysian-style desserts, some of these are sublime. Service is efficient and friendly. House wines are £7.50.

CHEF: Kia Lian Tan   PROPRIETOR: Annie Tan   OPEN: Wed to Mon 12 to 2.15 (3 Sun and bank hols), 6 to 11.15 (11 Sun and bank hols)   MEALS: alc (main courses £5 to £10.50). Set L and D £10.80 to £14.80   SERVICE: not inc   CARDS: Access, Amex, Delta, Switch, Visa   DETAILS: 70 seats. Private parties: 70 main room. Vegetarian meals. Children welcome. Smart dress preferred. No smoking in 1 dining-room. Wheelchair access (no WC). Music. Air-conditioned

Granita

map 13

127 Upper Street, N1 1QP
TEL: (0171) 226 3222   FAX: (0171) 226 4833

COOKING 2
COST £22–£39

'Granita is my local, and I like it for being straightforward and sensible,' writes a reporter who has put her finger on what matters here. There are no decorative frills – just a long, narrow, bare room with modern pine tables and chairs – and the cooking is as plain, and as good, as you might expect from the simple, frank descriptions: crispy fried squid with spicy peanut sauce, or chargrilled calf's liver with mushroom mash, sage and grilled courgettes. Tastes and spicing are upbeat, and flavoured mash is something of a trademark: made with olive oil, or perhaps with basil to accompany marinated chump of lamb. Warm rice pudding with plum compote continues the 'sensible' theme, and rich chocolate mousse works well. Service is cheerful and attentive and prices are fair, particularly at lunch-time. The compact wine list offers an international selection at level-headed prices. House French is £8.50.

CHEF: Ahmed Kharshoum   PROPRIETORS: Ahmed Kharshoum and Vicky Leffman   OPEN: Wed to Sun L 12.30 to 2.30, Tue to Sun D 6.30 to 10.30 (10 Sun)   CLOSED: 1 week Christmas, 1 week Easter, 2 weeks Aug   MEALS: alc (main courses £7 to £12). Set L £11.95 to £13.95. Minimum £11.95 L   SERVICE: not inc   CARDS: Access, Visa   DETAILS: 65 seats. Private parties: 65 main room. Vegetarian meals. Children welcome. No cigars/pipes in dining-room. Wheelchair access (no WC). No music. Air-conditioned

Great Nepalese £

map 13

48 Eversholt Street, NW1 1DA
TEL: (0171) 388 6737

COOKING 1*
COST £16–£33

'If you are on your own, there are few better ways of investing a £10 note and lifting your spirit,' observes an enthusiast. The place is run with benign good humour by Gopal Manandhar and his three sons, the latter often sporting flashy black 'Great Nepalese' waistcoats. There isn't much in the way of décor – apart from a few prints and Gurkha memorabilia – but the kitchen continues to put other, 'showier places to shame'. Bypass the dhansaks and birianis (although these are fine in their own way) and focus on the line-up of authentic Nepalese specialities. Bhutuwa chicken and toriko sag are bestsellers; also look for masco bara (black lentil pancakes), gundruko tarkari (Tibetan preserved vegetables), and dhaniya achar (coriander pickle). Duck and pork show up alongside mutton, chicken and fish. Drink Nepalese Iceberg beer and finish with a slug of Coronation rum. House wine is £6.75.

CHEF: **Masuk Manandhar** PROPRIETOR: **Gopal Manandhar** OPEN: all week 12 to 2.30, 6 to 11.30 (11.15 Sun) CLOSED: 25 and 26 Dec MEALS: alc (main courses £3 to £9.50). Set L £5.75, Set D £11.50. Minimum £5. BYO £1.50 SERVICE: 10% CARDS: Access, Amex, Delta, Diners, Visa DETAILS: 48 seats. Private parties: 30 main room. Vegetarian meals. Children's helpings. Wheelchair access (no WC). Music

Greenhouse 🍴

map 15

27A Hays Mews, W1X 7RJ
TEL: (0171) 499 3331 and 3314
FAX: (0171) 449 5368

COOKING 2*
COST £29–£65

Having made himself famous as a television chef, Gary Rhodes left the restaurant where he had spent the past five years and opted for a job with a lower profile. His acting successor, Wayne Tapsfield, has come up through the ranks, and carries on championing the cause of British cooking until a more permanent head chef is appointed. A covered walkway leads into a cool, cream-coloured dining-room decorated with dried flowers and prints, and a generous menu arrives along with a basket of good breads. Given pistou salad, tuna carpaccio, and a tomato and spinach risotto, it is clear that the thrust is not entirely traditional British, but the mix is an appealing one.

Ideas can be interesting: a pressed terrine of pork and black pudding, for instance, or grilled halibut perched on a flaky pastry tartlet of smoked haddock. Dishes are well turned out, from a rich soup of red mullet, to 'delightfully sticky' braised oxtails with just the right texture sitting in a deep-flavoured sauce. Vegetables are charged extra and are the same for all dishes (now that's traditionally British), and afters include a moist, eggy version of bread-and-butter pudding: 'more like a bread omelette'. Twenty wines include house red and white at £10.50.

CHEF: **Wayne Tapsfield** PROPRIETORS: **David and Margaret Levin** OPEN: Mon to Fri L 12 to 2.30, Sun L 12.30 to 3, all week D 7 to 11 (10 Sun) CLOSED: Christmas, bank hols MEALS: alc (main courses £9 to £18.50). Set L Sun £19.50. Cover £1 SERVICE: not inc CARDS: Access, Amex, Delta, Diners, Switch, Visa DETAILS: 96 seats. Private parties: 95 main room. Vegetarian meals. Children's helpings. Smart dress preferred. No pipes in dining-room. Music. Air-conditioned

Green Olive

NEW ENTRY map 13

5 Warwick Place, W9 2PX
TEL: (0171) 289 2469

COOKING 1
COST £23–£44

'What a transformation!' notes a local reporter who remembers this place in its previous incarnations. Gone is the 'dingy Laura Ashley clutter'; now the décor is understated, with a few large prints on bare brick walls. Downstairs is a bar with a sun roof that can be drawn back for balmy evenings. Daniel Gobet used to cook at Mon Plaisir (see entry, London), and his style is French provincial – pistou soup, caviare of aubergine with tomato coulis, bouillabaisse, casseroled rabbit, dark chocolate mousse and so on. Sometimes the cooking is seriously rustic (as in chunks of Barbary duck breast in a fine savoury broth with assorted beans), sometimes swish and flashy (roasted scallops with skeins of two-coloured pasta

95

surrounded by a garlic and parsley sauce). Olive oil, naturally, flows freely. Among desserts, look for the 'wondrously sharp' passion-fruit sorbet. The mainly French wine list features a few enterprising names, although prices are not cheap. House wines start at £11.95.

CHEF: Daniel Gobet   PROPRIETOR: Bijan Behzadi   OPEN: Sat and Sun L 12 to 3, all week D 7 to 10.45   MEALS: Set L £13.95, Set D £17.50 (2 courses) to £21   SERVICE: not inc   CARDS: Access, Amex, Delta, Switch, Visa   DETAILS: 55 seats. Private parties: 35 main room, 22 private room. Vegetarian meals. Children's helpings. Smart dress preferred. No cigars/pipes in dining-room. Wheelchair access (no WC). Music. Air-conditioned

Gresslin's

NEW ENTRY map 13

13 Heath Street, NW3 6TP
TEL: (0171) 794 8386   FAX: (0171) 433 3282

COOKING 2
COST £18–£45

Hampstead, once a gastronomic Sahara, becomes more verdant by the year. Gresslin's opened its doors at the beginning of 1996, adding further enticement hardly a stone's throw from the tube station. It is a long, thin room painted buttery yellow and decorated with monochrome photographs by Mrs Gresslin. Chef Michael trained with Anton Mosimann, as may be seen by the drifts of paprika or icing sugar that adorn the plates, but the mostly confident Eurasian cooking shows some inspired personal touches too. Thai barbecued chicken salad began one lunch in fine style, the moist chicken and exciting dressing judged 'spot on' by its recipient. Grey mullet with peppers and tapénade is 'a handsome dish in every way', a fashionable stack of ingredients on a base of crisply cooked fennel, while salmon fish-cakes with a lemon thyme sauce are both palpably fresh and quite bulky. Caesar salad is less convincing than either the 'creamiest, wobbliest' bread and butter pudding, or 'splendidly tart' lemon tart with raspberry coulis. Fine espresso comes in teacups. The wine list is largely French, and not especially imaginative. House wines are £9.50.

CHEF: Michael Gresslin   PROPRIETORS: Mr and Mrs Michael Gresslin   OPEN: Tue to Sun L 12.30 to 2.45, Mon to Sat D 7 to 10.45   CLOSED: bank hols   MEALS: alc (main courses £9 to £13). Set L Tue to Sat £7 (2 courses) to £10, Set L Sun £13.95 (2 courses) to £16.95   SERVICE: 12.5% (optional), card slips closed   CARDS: Access, Switch, Visa   DETAILS: 56 seats. Private parties: 30 main room, 18 private room. Vegetarian meals. Children's helpings. Smart dress preferred. Music. Air-conditioned

Grill St Quentin

map 14

3 Yeoman's Row, SW3 2AL
TEL: (0171) 581 8377   FAX: (0171) 584 6064

COOKING 1*
COST £25–£51

The Grill is a spacious basement brasserie just off Knightsbridge, complete with paper cloths and brass-railed wooden partitions to divide it all up. A happy hubbub prevails at busy times, and the relaxed style of cooking – mostly grilling, of course – is uncomplicatedly French. Five enormous juicy prawns in pungent garlic butter are an agreeably messy way to start, and there are goose rillettes or a Roussillon-style anchovy salad. Among the grills, sea bream shows well, retaining firmness of texture and helped along with a fresh tomato sauce, while côte de boeuf comes with a fine béarnaise. Rabbit is served on the bone, a huge portion in a strong mustard sauce with Agen prunes. Meals might end with warm apple tart with vanilla ice-cream, or 'very rich' truffe au chocolat with crème anglaise. Extraneous frills are avoided, and service is commended by all. The wine list sticks to French classics, including a few older clarets, and prices are kept well in check. House wine is £9.20.

CHEF: Nigel Davis PROPRIETOR: Savoy Group plc OPEN: all week 12 to 3 (3.30 Sun), 6.30 to 11.30 (10.30 Sun) MEALS: alc (main courses £8.50 to £17.50). Set L £10 (2 courses), Set D 6.30 to 7.30 £10 (2 courses) SERVICE: 12.5% (optional), card slips closed CARDS: Access, Amex, Delta, Diners, Switch, Visa DETAILS: 140 seats. Private parties: 30 main room. Vegetarian meals. Children welcome. Smart dress preferred. No music. Air-conditioned

▲ *Halcyon Hotel* 🍷

map 13

129 Holland Park Avenue, W11 3UT — COOKING 2

TEL: (0171) 221 5411 FAX: (0171) 229 8516 — COST £41–£75

Despite the relative opulence of the hotel itself, the coolly appointed basement restaurant, known as the Room, is an unexpectedly relaxed venue. A majority of the diners on a Saturday evening in spring looked far more laid-back than would be the jacket-and-tied norm at similar places. Martin Hadden's culinary style opts for substance and earthiness, rather than the ethereal leafiness of Cal-Ital, using roots, fungi and offal to good effect. Noisettes of pig's trotter with bacon and a cream sauce are accompanied by heaps of truffle-oiled leaves, a rich and inventive dish, while enormously plump grilled scallops are shoehorned into lidded pastry boxes on a beurre blanc. Nevertheless, the overall effect is 'lightness of touch and no feeling of having had too much food'. Fish is generally supported by something starchy: celeriac purée with sea bass, or vegetable cannelloni with herb-crusted salmon, for example.

Chocolate marquise edged with ground pistachio on a fine crème anglaise is one way to finish, or there may be a gratin of red fruits, or lemon tart. Good strong coffee is partnered by a whole regiment of 'absolutely first-class' petits fours. Wines are a bright and fashionable set, with a reasonable number under £20 as well as more grand offerings. The New World is well represented. Six house wines start at £11 a bottle, £3 a glass. CELLARMAN'S CHOICE: Hamilton Russell, Chardonnay 1994, Walker Bay, South Africa, £19.50; Rioja, Ygay Reserva Especial 1989, Marqués de Murrieta, £22.

CHEF: Martin Hadden PROPRIETOR: Halycon Hotel Corporation Ltd OPEN: Sun to Fri L 12 to 2.30 (3 Sun), all week D 7 to 10.30 (11 Fri and Sat, 10 Sun) CLOSED: bank hols MEALS: Set L £23 (2 courses), Set D £29 (2 courses) to £35 SERVICE: not inc CARDS: Access, Amex, Diners, Switch, Visa DETAILS: 55 seats. 25 seats outside. Private parties: 50 main room, 12 private room. Vegetarian meals. Smart dress preferred. No pipes in dining-room. Music. Air-conditioned ACCOMMODATION: 44 rooms, all with bath/shower. TV. Phone. Air-conditioned. Room only £165 to £550. Rooms for disabled. Lift. Children welcome. Baby facilities. Afternoon teas. Garden

'There was a cheese tray full of British cheeses, but I was somewhat puzzled by the response to my question "Do you have a local cheese?" to be informed, "Yes, there is, but whenever we put it on the dish, everyone asks for it and the other cheeses don't get eaten".'
(On eating in Northumberland)

▲ The Halkin

map 14

5–6 Halkin Street, SW1X 7DJ
TEL: (0171) 333 1234   FAX: (0171) 333 1100

COOKING 2
COST £39–£75

A reporter has remarked that seemingly everything is done for you at the Halkin:
the glass doors open automatically to admit you to the faultlessly attentive
service that is alert to the merest raising of eyebrows. It is a smart hotel just off
Belgrave Square, furnished with elegant restraint throughout, and if the airy
dining-room and marble floors don't make you imagine you've arrived in
heaven, the harpist probably will. Stefano Cavallini cooks in what the restaurant
describes as the 'new Italian' style, and current impressions are that the kitchen
is on something of an upswing. Visuals are accorded maximum priority: picture
a black plate of creamy-white risotto flavoured with 'tangy and very rich' goats'
cheese, rippled through with red wine and garnished with a courgette flower.
Langoustine and asparagus salad with sun-dried tomato and olive vinaigrette
marries fine ingredients and contains an added bonus of herb-flecked quail's
eggs.

Substantial main courses might encompass salt-crusted saddle of venison
with blueberry sauce, or stuffed hare with celeriac, black truffle sauce and white
polenta. Yoghurt mousse with sauté berries makes an agreeably light way to
finish. Good coffee comes with heaps of petits fours. The fine Italian-led wine list
displays some excellent growers, though some prices, which start at around £15,
may well intimidate. Non-vintage Moët & Chandon at £49 sets the tone.

CHEF: Stefano Cavallini   PROPRIETORS: Mr and Mrs B.S. Ong   OPEN: Mon to Fri L 12.30 to 2.30,
all week D 7.30 to 11 (7 to 10 Sun)   CLOSED: 25 and 26 Dec   MEALS: alc (main courses £12.50 to
£25). Set L £18 (2 courses). Bar food available   SERVICE: net prices, card slips closed   CARDS:
Access, Amex, Delta, Diners, Switch, Visa   DETAILS: 45 seats. Private parties: 8 main room, 30
private room. Vegetarian meals. Children welcome. Smart dress preferred. No cigars/pipes in
dining-room. Wheelchair access (also WC). Music. Air-conditioned   ACCOMMODATION: 41
rooms, all with bath/shower. TV. Phone. Air-conditioned. Room only £220 to £275. Children
welcome. Baby facilities. Afternoon teas (The Which? Hotel Guide)

Hilaire ▼

map 14

68 Old Brompton Road, SW7 3LQ
TEL: (0171) 584 8993   FAX: (0171) 581 2949

COOKING 3*
COST £34–£66

'Everything is operating at a high level,' summed up an off-duty inspector, who
considers this 'an understated but classy place, with friendly and knowledgeable service.' A pleasant buzz and good-humoured staff have made a
favourable impression on several reporters, who consider the atmosphere a
fitting one for Bryan Webb's food. He has clocked up a decade in Hilaire's
kitchen, all the while moving easily with the times and trends. He is guided by
sure judgement and a cook's good sense of which combinations of ingredients
and techniques work best. As so often, the simplest ideas are most effective, and
his cooking has a directness and clarity that are much appreciated.

Dishes are in contemporary mould, from risotto of leeks with black truffle, or
potato pancake with smoked eel and horseradish cream, to oxtail faggot with a
red wine sauce and mashed potato. The handwritten carte lists around eight to
ten choices per course, and has included first-rate sea bass with Puy lentils and

'an intense blob of salsa verde', as well as breast of chicken served with a potato pancake and fresh ceps simply fried in butter. 'Three small slices of cheese, with no cheeseboard and no choice' in an otherwise excellent meal left one reporter wondering if it was the thin end of a cost-cutting wedge. There is no such problem with puddings, judging by steamed sponge 'with plenty of pungent ginger flavour, served with a classic custard'. Wines are a cosmopolitan selection, with a good spread of grape varieties and interesting flavours, focused mainly in the mid-price range, and helpfully arranged by style. The final page of dessert wines is particularly appealing. House wines start at £11. CELLARMAN'S CHOICE: Mulderbosch Sauvignon Blanc 1995, Stellenbosch, South Africa, £24; Penley Estate Shiraz/Cabernet 1991, Coonawarra, S. Australia, £28.

CHEF: Bryan Webb PROPRIETORS: Bryan Webb and Dick Pyle OPEN: Mon to Fri L 12.15 to 2.30, Mon to Sat D 6.30 to 11.30 CLOSED: bank hols MEALS: alc (main courses £14 to £19). Set L £16.50 (2 courses), Set D (not available 7.30 to 10) £16.50 (2 courses) to £29.50 SERVICE: not inc CARDS: Access, Amex, Delta, Diners, Switch, Visa DETAILS: 60 seats. Private parties: 50 main room, 30 private room. Children's helpings. No cigars/pipes in dining-room. No music. Air-conditioned

▲ Hyde Park Hotel, The Restaurant   map 14

66 Knightsbridge, SW1X 7LA   COOKING 5
TEL: (0171) 259 5380   FAX: (0171) 235 4552   COST £46–£160

Perhaps a hotel dining-room always feels like a hotel dining-room. This one has been considered 'a little bit dull, but very reassuring'. An impressive display of huge white spring tulips and a collection of modernish paintings perk it up, while tables that might seat about ten elsewhere are reserved for groups of three or four. There is even 'enough spare space for a dance floor, should one have felt the urge, and one could well have, being so happy and content'. That came from a reporter, fresh off Eurostar, who found Marco Pierre White's food more French than a week's worth of eating in Paris.

Shellfish and liver dominate first courses, most of which (apart from soups) are served cold, while main courses balance dark meats (lamb and pigeon) against white (rabbit for example) and include braises of oxtail or pig's trotter, together with lots of fish. Meals typically begin with an appetiser version of a classic Marco dish: a one-inch thick scallop lightly criss-crossed on the chargrill, 'immaculate, brilliantly fresh, gorgeously sweet, perfectly timed', and served with crisp squid tentacles and blobs of ink.

Dishes are full of flavour, with interesting textures, and sometimes vivid colours. They impress for more than their virtuosity, increasing simplicity and technical accomplishment. 'I found this food very sensuous,' wrote one reporter. Among many highlights has been an impressively simple arrangement of three fillets of red mullet with a small moulded tower of ratatouille and a 'sensational' sauce made from olives and shellfish, aromatised with truffle oil. Others have raved over calf's liver, and a sensational large veal sweetbread served with a gelatinously sticky reduction.

The term 'mashed potatoes' proved inadequate for one reporter: 'sieved, puréed, squeezed through silk stockings might be a better description of the extreme fineness of this sensation.' At dinner either cheese or a small crème caramel precedes a classic range of desserts from Roger Pizey and Thierry Busset:

tarte Tatin of pineapple with black pepper, a caramel pyramid containing a brace of ice-creams, or the unbeatable lemon tart. Despite (or perhaps because of) the extraordinary number of formal staff, most reporters have a gripe. 'If too many cooks spoil the broth, perhaps too many waiters spoil the service,' mused one. The £6 charged for coffee is considered fair largely thanks to the excellence of the accompanying chocolates and petits fours, as is the overall food price, although aperitifs, water and wine soon bump it up. The wine list was in the process of being revised as we went to press. House French is £25.

CHEF/PROPRIETOR: Marco Pierre White   OPEN: Mon to Fri L 12 to 2.15, Mon to Sat D 7 to 11.15   MEALS: Set L £29.50, Set D £70   SERVICE: not inc, card slips closed   CARDS: Access, Amex, Diners, Visa   DETAILS: 50 seats. Vegetarian meals. Children welcome. No music. Air-conditioned   ACCOMMODATION: 186 rooms, all with bath/shower. TV. Phone. Air-conditioned. Room only £250 to £325. Rooms for disabled. Children welcome. Baby facilities. Pets welcome. Bedrooms only. Afternoon teas

Inaho
map 13

4 Hereford Road, W2 4AA   COOKING 1*
TEL: (0171) 221 8495   COST £13–£44

Inaho occupies what is in effect the front room of a terraced house. Its quaint, charming mood seems to evoke everyday Japan: noren curtains hang in the windows, stripped wooden walls are decorated with 'folkloric stuff' and tables are bunched together. What attracts customers is reliable, workmanlike food that is entirely in keeping with this unpretentious setting: 'Everything is as it should be,' observed one who knows. Sashimi is a robust, homespun version (diagonally halved raw scallops have been 'wonderful'), and the printed menu also takes in seaweed salad served in a glass bowl, and rich salmon teriyaki, in addition to tempura and noodles. A few specials, such as raw pounded tuna tataki marinated in rice vinegar, are listed on a slatted wooden stand on each table, and sushi is on offer from Wednesday to Saturday evening. Service may be European but is pleasantly efficient. Saké comes in a selection of different cups accompanied by little snacks, and there is a minimal list of mostly French wines. House wine is £7.

CHEF: S. Otsuka   PROPRIETOR: H. Nakamura   OPEN: Mon to Fri L 12.30 to 2.30, Mon to Sat D 7 to 11   CLOSED: 2 weeks Christmas and New Year, 1 week late summer   MEALS: alc (main courses £6.50 to £10). Set L £8 to £10, Set D £20 to £22   SERVICE: 10%   CARDS: Access, Delta, Visa   DETAILS: 20 seats. Private parties: 20 main room. No children under 10. Smart dress preferred. No cigars/pipes in dining-room. Music

L'Incontro
map 14

87 Pimlico Road, SW1W 8PH
TEL: (0171) 730 6327 and 3663   COOKING 1*
FAX: (0171) 730 5062   COST £33–£76

Antique shops pavilioned in splendour round about, expensive gentlemen with cigars within: L'Incontro fits seamlessly into the Pimlico scene. A mirrored wall and monochrome photographs are intended to provide a tastefully muted backdrop to the vivid Venetian cooking of Danilo Minuzzo. Some things work well: the 'aggressively peasant style' of bigoli pasta with anchovy and onion, or a 'splendidly simple' main dish of monkfish tail in an impressively garlicky sauce, lightly spiked with chilli, 'gentled with butter'. Very smooth, ripe pear sorbet makes a pleasing dessert. Then again, 'slimy' polenta is worrying in a Venetian restaurant, and two women encountering shruggy wine treatment is a familiar tale not worthy of a place like this. Strong, fresh-tasting espresso ends things on a high note. Fine Italian wines are offered at get-your-wad-out prices, adding to an already imposing bill. House wines from Friuli are £16.50.

CHEF: Danilo Minuzzo   PROPRIETOR: Gino Santin   OPEN: Mon to Fri L 12.30 to 2.30, all week D 7 to 11.30 (10.30 Sun)   MEALS: alc (main courses £16 to £23.50). Set L £14.50 (2 courses) to £18.50. Cover £1.50   SERVICE: not inc   CARDS: Access, Amex, Delta, Diners, Switch, Visa   DETAILS: 65 seats. Private parties: 65 main room, 35 private room. Vegetarian meals. Children's helpings. Smart dress preferred. No pipes in dining-room. Wheelchair access (no WC). Music. Air-conditioned

▲ Inter-Continental, Le Soufflé ♥   map 14

1 Hamilton Place, W1V 0QY   COOKING 2*
TEL: (0171) 409 3131   FAX: (0171) 491 0926   COST £41–£88

The location is pretty central – the Intercontinental is one of a clutch of hotels overlooking Hyde Park Corner – but given what else is happening within a mile radius, the food these days can look a bit old-fashioned. 'If it wants to remain a fly in amber and cook soufflés for ever, then it is succeeding,' suggested one reporter. Menus are in a mixture of English and French, and luxuries are the stock-in-trade, from lobster bisque through sauté foie gras to oysters in a champagne and caviare sauce.

'The food looks great on paper,' ventured one reporter, as it does on the plate. A pale blue-fin tuna steak, for example, is turned into 'a clever visual joke' by having a plug of lobster inserted to make it resemble an osso buco veal bone. 'If this had worked it would have been something of a triumph,' suggested an inspector, but the taste didn't quite live up to the promise of the picture. A lot of workmanship obviously goes into the preparation, although both lamb (pains-takingly covered with a tarragon-flecked mini-soufflé) and venison at inspection lacked conviction. Set-price menus all offer a sweet soufflé, and the carte lists three. Service is polite, and generally keeps a discreet distance. Wines are taken seriously, and range widely from the down-to-earth sommelier's suggestions (15 wines, nearly all under £20) to the flashier stars of the rare vintage collection. Eleven varied wines are available by the glass. CELLARMAN'S CHOICE: St-Véran 1994, Dom. des Deux Roches, £26; Graves, Ch. de Seuil 1991, £28.

CHEF: Peter Kromberg   PROPRIETOR: Inter-Continental Hotels and Resorts   OPEN: Tue to Fri L 12.30 to 3, Sun L 12 to 3.30, Tue to Sat D 7 to 10.30 (11.15 Sat)   CLOSED: 2 weeks after Christmas   MEALS: alc (main courses £17.50 to £27). Set L £29.50 to £34.50, Set D £41.50 to £47   SERVICE: not inc   CARDS: Access, Amex, Delta, Diners, Switch, Visa   DETAILS: 80 seats. Car park. Vegetarian meals. Children welcome. Smart dress preferred. No pipes in dining-room. Wheelchair access (also WC). Music. Air-conditioned   ACCOMMODATION: 460 rooms, all with bath/shower. TV. Phone. Air-conditioned. B&B £210 to £270 (double rooms). Rooms for disabled. Children welcome. Afternoon teas

Interlude de Chavot

map 15

5 Charlotte Street, W1P 1HD
TEL: (0171) 637 0222   FAX: (0171) 637 0224

COOKING 4
COST £46–£61

'It was worth buying the *Guide* just to find this place,' claimed one reporter. The two rather sparsely decorated rooms, deliberately understated, have a provincial air about them. Neither they nor the service comes anywhere near to matching the food, but Eric Crouillere-Chavot's 'quite outstanding' cooking more than makes up for them both. The 'modern French' tag is apparent in a 'superb' tarte Tatin of endive with pan-fried foie gras, or snail ravioli with pesto.

Flavours throughout are strong and (generally) finely balanced, the combinations bright and dramatic. 'Adventurous yet well judged' is one reporter's view, although they can sometimes strike an 'eccentric' note, as with a roast leg of rabbit stuffed with squid on a pearl barley risotto. Not everyone would jump at this prospective partnership of fur and cephalopod, but it does at least indicate a lively kitchen. Superlatives pepper reports – 'the best I have ever eaten' is not uncommon – reflecting the quality of ingredients, accurate timing, admirable textures, the careful construction of dishes, and the remarkable consistency of standards throughout a meal.

Appetisers, which have included perfectly cooked mackerel served variously on fresh leaves or pickled vegetables, fulfil their purpose in arousing interest and anticipation. From then on, for one reporter, 'each dish was a complete experience which kept one intrigued and satisfied till the last mouthful'. An indication of the scope is given by tender woodpigeon breast with beetroot, and by monkfish in a caper sauce on a bed of polenta that 'must have been soaked in a langoustine reduction' and was 'unrecognisable from the normal stodge'.

Classic desserts such as crème brûlée are consummately executed. A gelée of citrus fruit made a 'perfect, refreshing end' to one meal, and chocolate soufflé has been of the highest calibre, with a 'supremely fluffy texture' into which is poured a rich, dark chocolate sauce. Service has been 'willing, helpful and knowledgeable' as well as 'slow', 'over-zealous' and 'disorganised'. Communication can be a problem for English-speakers. Prices 'have now caught up with the cooking', as early reporters predicted. 'Why does a 40p bottle of water cost £3?' one reporter wanted to know. Wine prices too are on the high side, though the quality is impressive. House Vins de Pays d'Oc are £14.50.

CHEF/PROPRIETOR: Eric Crouillere-Chavot   OPEN: Mon to Fri L 12.15 to 2.30, Mon to Sat D 7 to 11   MEALS: alc (main courses £18 to £20). Set L (2 courses) £18.50   SERVICE: not inc   CARDS: Access, Amex, Delta, Diners, Switch, Visa   DETAILS: 50 seats. Private parties: 8 main room, 10 and 16 private rooms. Children welcome. Smart dress preferred. No pipes in dining-room. No music. Air-conditioned

Ivy

map 15

1 West Street, WC2H 9NE
TEL: (0171) 836 4751   FAX: (0171) 240 9550

COOKING 2*
COST £29–£69

The Ivy is perfectly geared to its theatreland environment, opening in plenty of time for a pre-show meal, and buzzing with luvvies who flock in afterwards. In between, who knows how many times the tables change hands, but it remains a well-organised operation with quick and friendly service. Even if there is barely time to lay up tables between bookings, nobody seems to feel pressurised, which is a tribute to the front-of-house management and staff.

The menu successfully suits all comers too, combining light leafy salads of rocket and Parmesan, or spinach and Roquefort, with rich dishes of Cumberland sausage and mash, or calf's liver and bacon. It covers a range from foie gras to shepherd's pie, from steamed mussels with coconut and lemon grass, to corned beef hash with fried egg. Dishes may be as simple as scrambled eggs with smoked salmon, but they are done with supreme skill. Among desserts that have hit the mark is a plate of Scandinavian berries (also praised at the sister restaurant Le Caprice – see entry, London) consisting of an irresistible combination of wild strawberries, pale yellow cloudberries, bilberries and raspberries, with a creamy white chocolate sauce. Wines on the simple modern list have been picked with an eagle eye, and a dozen wines by the glass are particularly welcome.

CHEF: Des McDonald   PROPRIETORS: Jeremy King and Christopher Corbin   OPEN: all week 12 to 3, 5.30 to 12   CLOSED: 25 and 26 Dec, 1 Jan   MEALS: alc (main courses £7 to £9). Set brunch Sat and Sun £14.50 Cover £1.50   SERVICE: not inc   CARDS: Access, Amex, Delta, Diners, Switch, Visa   DETAILS: 100 seats. Private parties: 6 main room, 15 to 60 private room. Vegetarian meals. Childrens helpings. Wheelchair access(no WC). No music. Air-conditioned

Iznik £

map 13

19 Highbury Park, N5 1QJ
TEL: (0171) 354 5697

COOKING 1*
COST £18–£27

By day Iznik offers English fry-ups (and the papers to read), plus a few authentic Middle Eastern delights for the famished. In the evening the place becomes seductively enticing, with gentle light from innumerable candles and soft Turkish music in the background. What it offers is realistically priced Turkish food with 'beautifully judged' flavours. There is plenty for vegetarians among the starters, which range from falafel and piyaz (haricot bean salad) to ispanak (spinach braised in olive oil). Among the carnivorous main courses, kuzu firin (oven-baked lamb) is a favourite. Sticky pastries and fruit compotes round things off, and bramble mousse and bread pudding are renowned. House wines, at £7.95, are Turkish; others are gathered from the usual international crop.

CHEF: Ahmet Poyraz   PROPRIETORS: Adem and Pirlanta Oner   OPEN: Mon to Fri 10 to 4, 6.30 to 11, Sat and Sun 9 to 4, 6.30 to 12   CLOSED: 25 to 28 Dec   MEALS: alc (main courses £6.50 to £9.50)   SERVICE: 10%   CARDS: none   DETAILS: 66 seats. Vegetarian meals. Children welcome. Music

Joe's

map 14

126 Draycott Avenue, SW3 3AH
TEL: (0171) 225 2217

COOKING 1
COST £28–£53

If the famous dictum that 'location, location and location' are the three most important things for a hotel or restaurant to have, then this site near the junction of Draycott Avenue, Walton Street and Fulham Road would seem to score on all counts. The restaurant is part of the Joseph fashion group, and takes the trendy side of its character seriously; if it isn't heaving with smartly dressed actors and celebs, then it is having a bad day.

The food is naturally in the swim, too, usually in the Mediterranean. Several lunchtime items come in a choice of large or small portions, and the repertoire takes in busy soups and salads, simple grills of steak, cod or chicken, as well as deep-fried rice pudding with cinnamon and honey. Service is 'friendly, helpful, cheerful and professional', in exchange for an 'optional' 15 per cent of the takings. About half the 30 wide-ranging wines are under £20.

CHEF: Dave Hodgins PROPRIETOR: Joseph Ettedgui OPEN: all week L 12 to 3 (4 Sat, 5 Sun), Mon to Sat D 7 to 11 MEALS: alc (main courses £7 to £15.50). Cover £1. Minimum £12 SERVICE: 15% (optional), card slips closed CARDS: Access, Amex, Diners, Visa DETAILS: 70 seats. 5 seats outside. Private parties: 50 main room. Vegetarian meals. Children's helpings. Smart dress preferred. Music. Air-conditioned

Kalamaras 🍞 £

map 13

76–78 Inverness Mews, W2 3JQ
TEL: (0171) 727 9122 FAX: (0171) 221 9411

COOKING 1*
COST £18–£39

This bastion of genuine Greek – as opposed to Greek-Cypriot – cooking has seen a number of changes over the last year. The décor has received a minor face-lift – one visitor was bowled over by the maroon satin napkins and matching tablecloths – and the chef has changed, but service remains 'positively cheerful'. There's no doubting the quality of the mezedes and starters in particular: among the highlights have been Greek salad with excellent feta cheese incorporating fresh herbs, casseroled artichokes with broad beans and dill, and grilled octopus gently flavoured with oregano and parsley. Main courses such as chicken with spinach and avgolemono sauce have been slightly less impressive. Bread is topped with sesame seeds, Greek 'delights' are well flavoured. The wine list includes some inexpensive Greek names. House wine is £8.90. Micro-Kalamaras, at 66 Inverness Mews, is unlicensed (BYO) and is open for dinner all week.

CHEF: Antonio Jiminez PROPRIETOR: Mr F.J. Ridha OPEN: Mon to Fri L 12.30 to 2.30, Mon to Sat D 5.30 to 12 MEALS: alc (main courses £7 to £10) SERVICE: 10%, card slips closed CARDS: Access, Amex, Diners, Visa DETAILS: 90 seats. Private parties: 60 main room, 30 private room. Vegetarian meals. Children's helpings. Smart dress preferred. Wheelchair access (no WC). Music. Air-conditioned

Kastoori £

map 12

188 Upper Tooting Road, Tooting, SW17 7EJ
TEL: (0181) 767 7027

COOKING 1
COST £13–£25

'Highly recommended,' enthuses one reporter; 'our favourite Indian restaurant', claim others. The Thanki family clearly know how to keep their customers satisfied with unerringly helpful service and food that is outstanding value. What they offer is 'pure vegetarian' cooking based on 'Indo-African and pan-Indian recipes' drawn from the regional cuisine of Kathia Wadi. Most intriguing of all are the family specials, which include exotic vegetables such as green bananas and karela. Assorted green leaves are blended in a yoghurt, onion and chilli sauce; spring onions are 'cushioned in sev, tomato and Kastoori masala sauce'. Also look for the bizarre 'Thanki européenne' (a 'Euroveg special' that takes in such things as rhubarb and leeks). Elsewhere, there are votes for corn bhel poori, home-made pickles and 'all the breads'. Drink Kingfisher beer or choose from the modest wine list. House wine is £7.25.

CHEF: Manoj Thanki   PROPRIETOR: Dinesh Thanki   OPEN: Wed to Sun L 12.30 to 2.30, all week D 6 to 10.30   MEALS: alc (main courses £3 to £5). Minimum £4   SERVICE: not inc, card slips closed   CARDS: Access, Visa   DETAILS: 84 seats. Private parties: 20 main room. Vegetarian meals. Children's helpings. Wheelchair access (no WC). No music. Air-conditioned

Kensington Place ♟   map 13

201–205 Kensington Church Street, W8 7LX   COOKING 3
TEL: (0171) 727 3184   FAX: (0171) 229 2025   COST £23–£60

Whatever signs of age the design may now be showing – and it can feel like a living, breathing monument to the 1980s – Kensington Place is still capable of making a 'full-frontal impact'. As dusk falls over Kensington, the huge glass façade 'seems to project its contents – people, colour, noise and hustle-bustle – on to the street outside'. This is a stance the 1990s have come to define as Attitude, and this place had it in spades from the start.

Rowley Leigh, it bears reiterating, delved into the treasure-chest of rustic country cooking when others were still stuffing courgette flowers with fish mousse. Newcomers to Kensington Place might find the menus these days indistinguishable from nearly everywhere else in offering bruschetta with truffled mushrooms, Parma ham and rocket, or chicken breast with black pudding and apple, but this is one of the places where it all began and is still one of the places where it is done best. The perennial griddled scallops with pea purée and mint vinaigrette continue to be lauded: half a dozen sweetly juicy, lightly seared specimens with a creamy but appealingly gritty purée. Sea bass with Puy lentils and a blob of salsa verde was 'beautifully cooked' at one meal, while chocolate sponge pudding has evoked rhapsodic memories for some.

Wines are handled with confidence, producing a list full of bright and lively flavours. New Zealand's Cloudy Bay, Argentina's Alamos Ridge, Piedmont's Mascarello, and Thelema from South Africa are among those lending a cosmopolitan air. French house wines start at £9.75. CELLARMAN'S CHOICE: Quincy 1994, Denis Jaumier, £14.50; Pomerol, Ch. la Croix 1989, £32.50.

CHEF: Rowley Leigh   PROPRIETORS: Nick Smallwood and Simon Slater   OPEN: all week 12 to 3, 6.30 to 11.45 (10.15 Sun)   MEALS: alc (main courses £10 to £16). Set L Mon to Fri £14.50, Set L Sun £16.50. BYO £9.75   SERVICE: not inc   CARDS: Access, Delta, Switch, Visa   DETAILS: 130 seats. Private parties: 90 main room. Vegetarian meals. Children's helpings. Wheelchair access (also WC). Music. Air-conditioned

'The braised thigh I was given came from a chicken which had been working out intensively, so bulging it was almost spherical. The sort of chicken you would not wish to meet in a vest and Lycra shorts down the gym. A gladiator amongst chickens.'
(On eating in Hampshire)

Lahore Kebab House £

map 13

2 Umberston Street, E1 1PY
TEL: (0171) 488 2551

COOKING 1
COST £10–£17

If you are expecting turbanned waiters, classical ragas and florid menus, you have come to the wrong place. This place is a café, there's no décor to speak of, and most of the dishes on offer are displayed in large serving-dishes. Orders are not written down, and neither is the bill. Chicken and lamb tikka have been praised, vegetable curries, nan bread and rice are fine, and there is rice-pudding to finish. Lahore is unlicensed, but you can bring your own wine or lager.

CHEFS: M. Din and M. Azeem   PROPRIETOR: M. Siddique   OPEN: all week noon to midnight   MEALS: alc (main courses £3 to £4). Set L and D £6 to £10. Unlicensed, BYO (no corkage)   SERVICE: not inc   CARDS: none   DETAILS: 80 seats. Private parties: 60 main room. Car park. Vegetarian meals. Wheelchair access (no WC). No music. Air-conditioned

▲ Landmark London

map 13

222 Marylebone Road, NW1 6JQ
TEL: (0171) 631 8000   FAX: (0171) 631 8080

COOKING 1
COST £39–£63

The historic ex-British Railways Board building has been lovingly restored, with a spectacular eight-storey atrium as its centrepiece: well worth a gander over afternoon tea. Since Ken Hom became consultant chef in May 1996, the elegantly furnished dining-room's preoccupation has been with 'fusion food', a broad canvas that stretches from Italy to Japan by way of Thailand, and which has included such oddball items as pickled mangosteen (served with lobster salad), and deep-fried lychees with chocolate. An inspector found that dishes from the Ken Hom section of the menu worked best: orange Peking duck, and a filo purse of finely sliced vegetables, for instance. Colourful plates lend drama to the presentation, although rice pudding with mango sorbet appeared outclassed by its stage scenery of coconut husk and banana leaf. French, Italian and Californian wines get thorough treatment on the long wine list, but prices are high and there is little choice under £20. French house wines are £16.50.

CHEF: Georg Heise   PROPRIETOR: Lancaster Landmark Hotel Co Ltd   OPEN: all week 12 (12.30 Sun) to 3, 7 to 11   MEALS: alc (main courses £14.50 to £19.50). Set L £21.50   SERVICE: not inc   CARDS: Access, Amex, Diners, Switch, Visa   DETAILS: 85 seats. Private parties: 36 main room. Car park. Vegetarian meals. Children welcome. No-smoking area. Wheelchair access (also WC). No music. Air-conditioned   ACCOMMODATION: 304 rooms, all with bath/shower. TV. Phone. Air-conditioned. Room only £205 to £270 plus VAT. Rooms for disabled. Lift. Children welcome. Afternoon teas. Swimming-pool

▲ Lanesborough, The Conservatory

map 14

1 Lanesborough Place, SW1X 7TA
TEL: (0171) 259 5599   FAX: (0171) 259 5606

COOKING 2
COST £31–£78

'The Conservatory is attractive, the décor is interesting, and staff could not be faulted,' began one report. There is no doubt about the appeal of the sugar-pink walls, Chinese statues and trickling fountain, a setting capable of enhancing almost any special occasion. Paul Gayler continues the 'twin track' style of cooking, serving fillet of venison, or roast rump of lamb with ratatouille alongside vegetarian options such as a cappuccino soup of wild mushrooms ('full of flavour') or lemon risotto with peas and asparagus ('a little bit stodgy').

His favoured Euro-Asian strand surfaces in spice-roasted duckling, and in lettuce spring rolls with crab, soy and ginger, while other ideas have ranged from fish and chips with tartare sauce, via terrine of foie gras with a parfait of morels, to lobster salad with mango. The wine list deals mostly in fine bottles at high prices: out of some 200 bins, a mere handful cost less than £20. House wine starts at £15.

CHEF: Paul Gayler   PROPRIETOR: Rosewood   OPEN: all week 12 to 2.30, 6.30 to 12   MEALS: alc (main courses £8.50 to £26.50). Set L £19 (2 courses) to £23.50, Set D £24.50 to £28.50. BYO £15. Bar food available   SERVICE: net prices, card slips closed   CARDS: Access, Amex, Delta, Diners, Switch, Visa   DETAILS: 110 seats. Private parties: 110 main room, up to 100 private room. Car park. Vegetarian meals. Children's helpings. Smart dress preferred. Wheelchair access (also WC). Music. Air-conditioned   ACCOMMODATION: 98 rooms, all with bath/shower. TV. Phone. Air-conditioned. Room only £175 to £310. Deposit: 75%. Rooms for disabled. Children welcome. Baby facilities. Dogs welcome. Afternoon teas

Langan's Brasserie

map 15

Stratton Street, W1X 5FD
TEL: (0171) 491 8822   FAX: (0171) 493 8309

COOKING 1*
COST £31–£52

Langan's is testament to the enduring appeal of the British brasserie, and proof that the genre is not a 1990s phenomenon. It is 20 years since Richard Shepherd and Michael Caine brought their wide-ranging menu to Mayfair, and the place has never lost its gloss. So fashionable is it that food may not appear to be the focus – 'watch out for 40-foot stretched limousines outside the door,' warned one reporter – yet it delivers square meals with a degree (and sometimes a blob) of relish. The ground floor is littered with stardust, the upstairs Venetian Room quieter and more formal, but apart from the everlasting spinach soufflé in one and a roast from the trolley in the other, the food is the same: a long list of timeless classics, from poached eggs with smoked haddock to bangers and mash, from cod and chips to trifle and rice pudding. Service is everywhere and friendly, the wine list brief and to the point, and the shorter afternoon menu perfectly good. House wine is £9.50.

CHEFS: Richard Shepherd, Roy Smith and Dennis Mynott   PROPRIETORS: Richard Shepherd and Michael Caine   OPEN: Mon to Fri L 12.30 to 3, Mon to Sat D 6 to 11.30 (11.45 Fri, 12.45 Sat); afternoon menu 3 to 6   MEALS: alc (main courses £11 to £14). Cover £1   SERVICE: 12.5% (optional)   CARDS: Access, Amex, Visa   DETAILS: 250 seats. Private parties: 12 main room. Vegetarian meals. Children's helpings. Music. Air-conditioned

Lansdowne £

map 13

90 Gloucester Avenue, NW1 8HX
TEL: (0171) 483 0409

COOKING 1
COST £17–£26

Expect crowds, noise and smoke in this revamped Primrose Hill watering-hole. The advice is to keep your eyes peeled for a vacant seat while you order at the bar.

The menu is lively, prices are low and you can expect to find such multi-ethnic offerings as chorizo, rice and saffron soup, pasta with chilli and garlic, confit of duck, and grilled mackerel with tomato salsa as well as home-made bangers and mash. Recent highlights have also included grilled langoustines on couscous, and whole roast brill with aïoli and roasted chips. If you are lucky there may be a home-made sorbet, pear and almond tart or Dunsyre Blue cheese to finish. 'There is no longer West Indian food to accompany the live jazz on Sunday night,' laments a reporter. Draught beers and cider are alternatives to the minimal wine list. House wine is £8.

CHEF/PROPRIETOR: Amanda Pritchett   OPEN: Tue to Sat L 12.30 to 2.30, Sun L 1 to 3, all week D 7 to 10   MEALS: alc (main courses £6 to £8). Set L Sun £15   SERVICE: none, card slips closed   CARDS: Access, Switch, Visa   DETAILS: 80 seats. 30 seats outside. Private parties: 12 main room, 30 private room. Vegetarian meals. Music

Launceston Place ▼

map 14

1A Launceston Place, W8 5RL
TEL: (0171) 937 6912   FAX: (0171) 938 2412

COOKING 2
COST £27–£51

The leafy Kensington street feels like somewhere much more rural, and Launceston Place, with its restful sea-shaded carpets and plain wooden chairs, does its best to suit that mood, coming over as the unflurried country cousin of its brash cosmopolitan sibling, Kensington Place (see entry). 'Eclectic' was the name of the game here before many others had even looked the word up. Soups may be Thai or Tuscan in style, from mixed fish, coconut milk and lemon grass to cannellini beans with gremolata. Main courses play off bold treatments of fish (steamed halibut with ceps, shaved truffle and chervil) against more obvious meat preparations, as in grilled lamb cutlets served on pea and mint purée. An extra order of vegetables will bring three: a trio of greens, or three ways with potato (mash, chips and dauphinois). The predominantly British desserts may include upside-down pear pudding or egg-custard tart. Service appears to be a creature of many moods, at its best 'friendly, efficient, relaxed, a delight'.

The fairly concise list of wines manages to pack in a wide range of styles and grapes. Try English white from Chiltern Valley or Argentinian red if stuck for new ideas. The dessert wines available by the glass are a lively lot too. House wines start at £10. CELLARMAN'S CHOICE: Frog's Leap Sauvignon Blanc 1994, Napa Valley, California, £21; Lussac-St-Emilion, Ch. Lyonnat 1990, £22.50.

CHEF: Derek Francis   PROPRIETORS: Nick Smallwood and Simon Slater   OPEN: Sun to Fri L 12.30 to 2.30 (3 Sun), Mon to Sat D 7 to 11.30   CLOSED: bank hols   MEALS: alc (main courses £12.50 to £16). Set L £14.50 (2 courses) to £17.50, Set D Mon to Fri 7 to 8 £14.50 (2 courses) to £17.50   SERVICE: not inc   CARDS: Access, Amex, Delta, Switch, Visa   DETAILS: 80 seats. Private parties: 50 main room, 12 private room. Vegetarian meals. Children's helpings. Smart dress preferred. No cigars/pipes in dining-room. Wheelchair access (no WC). No music. Air-conditioned

'Like policemen, chefs seem to be getting younger these days as I get older. They also seem, like supermodels, to be increasingly thin, pale and frail. The poor guy looked whacked. He had only had one day off in the last three months and had the pallor of the kitchen. Bet he wishes he was a junior doctor.' (On eating in Somerset)

Laurent £

map 13

428 Finchley Road, NW2 2HY
TEL: (0171) 794 3603

COOKING 1
COST £18–£28

Couscous is the name of the game in Laurent Farrugia's family eating-house. Five versions of this great stew dominate the tiny menu, and all of them are gastronomically addictive. One couple with a serious craving for the stuff 'carefully sidestepped' the brique a l'oeuf starter (fried egg in filo pastry) so that they could gorge themselves on 'huge lumps of extremely tender pieces of leg of lamb, veg with some bite left, and wonderful fluffy couscous', plus some extra merguez sausages on the side. Cassis sorbet makes a refreshing finale, the coffee is fine, and there are a few punchy North African wines. House wine is £8.20.

CHEF/PROPRIETOR: Laurent Farrugia   OPEN: Mon to Sat 12 to 2, 6 to 11   CLOSED: last 3 weeks Aug   MEALS: alc (main courses £6.60 to £10.50). Minimum £6.60   SERVICE: not inc   CARDS: Access, Amex, Delta, Visa   DETAILS: 36 seats. Private parties: 45 main room. Vegetarian meals. Children's helpings. No cigars/pipes in dining-room. Wheelchair access (no WC). No music

Leith's 🍷

map 13

92 Kensington Park Road, W11 2PN
TEL: (0171) 229 4481

COOKING 3
COST £34–£74

Dinner at Leith's used to begin with the rolling around of an hors d'oeuvre trolley, but when the new partnership took over in 1995 this was one of the first things to go. None the less, this is, in the opinion of a senior reporter, 'a time-warp restaurant', and Leith's is certainly still proud of its Old World courtesies.

The cooking, let it be said, is not at all tied to the past. True, there is a vein of English tradition here, particularly in the offering of plain roasts, but Alex Floyd is constantly refining and developing the kitchen's operations. Layered terrines of confit (sometimes duck, sometimes rabbit) with spinach and a plum chutney work well, and sound judgement is shown in a grilled and herbed turbot steak sitting on cep cannelloni in a richly sticky meat stock reduction. Feuilleté of pigeon with pancetta comes in a vol-au-vent case filled with cream sauce, in turn resting on another meat stock. The separate vegetarian menu is worth a look, whatever your principles, while desserts range from simple sorbet selections to an 'ovoid scoop of rice-pudding' adorned with tropical fruits and a passion-fruit sauce. There may be trendier places in the vicinity, but Leith's is able to draw on a formidable wealth of skill in what it does.

It is worth lingering over the excellent wine list, which does its best to encourage good drinking. Each regional section has been chosen with impeccable taste, but champagne, Spanish red, Burgundy and Bordeaux stand out in particular. A house selection of six wines starting at £14.50 provides some relief under £20. CELLARMAN'S CHOICE: Thelema Chardonnay 1994, Stellenbosch, South Africa, £19.50; Nebbiolo delle Langhe, Mascarello 1992, £19.50.

🍷 *denotes an outstanding wine cellar;* 🍷 *denotes a good wine list, worth travelling for.*

CHEF: Alex Floyd   PROPRIETORS: Sir Christopher Bland, Caroline Waldegrave, Nick Tarayan and Alex Floyd   OPEN: Tue to Fri L 12.15 to 2.15, Mon to Sat D 7 to 11.30   CLOSED: 24 Dec to 7 Jan, 10 to 25 Aug, bank hol Mons   MEALS: alc D (main courses £18.50 to £23.50). Set L £16.50 (2 courses) to £19.50, Set D £26.50 (2 courses) to £33   SERVICE: 12.5% (optional), card slips closed   CARDS: Access, Amex, Diners, Switch, Visa   DETAILS: 80 seats. Private parties: 24 main room, 4 to 40 private rooms. Vegetarian meals. Children's helpings. No children under 7. Smart dress preferred. Wheelchair access (no WC). No music. Air-conditioned

Livebait

NEW ENTRY   map 13

43 The Cut, SE1 8LF
TEL: (0171) 928 7211

COOKING 1
COST £21–£47

'We came upon this by chance when looking for a pre-theatre restaurant near the Old Vic,' began one reporter, unlikely to be the last to stumble upon it in this fashion. Rejuvenation of the area is bringing a vitality to restaurant life, and few are as effervescent as this dedicated seafood specialist. A counter displays fresh fish and shellfish – bought daily at auction – an open kitchen entertains with lots of activity, and seating is diner-style with shoulder-high booths and plastic-topped tables. The green and white tiled room is not spacious, and informality reigns.

The food stands or falls by its freshness, best served by plain cockles, whelks, winkles, Poole crab, Oban razor clams, Rossmore oysters, grilled langoustines, or king scallops in a butter sauce. Attempts to incorporate okra gumbo, or coconut curry sauce have met with mixed success, but there are votes for 'moist and tasty' sea bass, and 'just wonderful' red mullet with a red pepper coulis, garlic and couscous. Desserts are straightforward, bread is baked on the premises, 'very pleasant girls' provide helpful service, and a short modern list of wines includes nine by the glass from £2.45.

CHEF/PROPRIETOR: Theodore Kyriakou   OPEN: Mon to Fri L 12 to 3, Mon to Sat D 5.30 to 11   MEALS: alc (main courses £7.50 to £16). Set D 5.30 to 7.30 and 10 to 11 £12 (2 courses)   SERVICE: not inc   CARDS: Access, Switch, Visa   DETAILS: 48 seats. Children welcome. Wheelchair access (also WC). No music

Lobster Pot

map 13

3 Kennington Lane, SE11 4RG
TEL: (0171) 582 5556   FAX: (0171) 582 9751

COOKING 1*
COST £22–£58

The Régents (originally from Brittany) have taken the maritime theme about as far as it will go, captaining what feels like a boat with a lounge on the upper deck; an aquarium overlooks the dining-room, but sound effects are not overlooked. It is 'all sea shanties and fog horns', wrote one, adding 'it only needed distress flares'. The food hasn't altered course since the restaurant set sail, offering generous portions of fresh fish as a centrepiece. Poaching and grilling work well, and saucing is as commendably simple as lemon or garlic butter, perhaps, or a spicy creole sauce for a slab of tuna. A platter of seafood contains all the usual components, lobster is cooked however you want it, and fish soups run to a superior bouillabaisse Bretonne. Smoked or marinated fish are likely ways to begin, with profiteroles or tarte Tatin to finish, and there are main-course meat alternatives for landlubbers. A short French wine list includes house wine at £10.50.

CHEF: Hervé Régent   PROPRIETORS: Hervé and Natalie Régent   OPEN: Tue to Sat 12 to 2.30, 7 to 10.45   CLOSED: 24 Dec to 3 Jan   MEALS: alc (main courses £14.50 to £24.50). Set L Tue to Fri £15.50, Set D £22.50. Minimum £15.50 L, £23.50 D   SERVICE: net prices, card slips closed   CARDS: Access, Amex, Delta, Diners, Switch, Visa   DETAILS: 28 seats. Private parties: 30 main room. No children under 8. Smart dress preferred. No cigars in dining-room. Music. Air-conditioned

Lou Pescadou

map 13

241 Old Brompton Road, SW5 9HP

COOKING 1
COST £18–£50

TEL: (0171) 370 1057   FAX: (0171) 244 7545

'Is it my imagination or have they put more things on the walls?' enquired one reporter. The whole place is decorated from top to bottom with 'nautical kitsch', just in case anyone should forget that this is a French restaurant specialising in fish. Lou Pescadou's formula is so simple and so successful: you come here to devour the fruits of the sea cooked without frills or embellishments. One typically enjoyable dinner featured juicy, sweet prawns with a powerful but uncomplicated garlic butter sauce followed by perfectly timed brill with a spot-on beurre blanc. If fish is not to your liking, there are always pizzas, salads and steaks. The manager likes people and service is 'jovially Gallic'. The modest wine list generally produces a few winners. House wine is £9.90.

CHEF: Laurent David   PROPRIETORS: Daniel Chobert and Laurent David   OPEN: all week 12.15 to 2.30, 7 to 11.30   MEALS: alc (main courses £6 to £14). Set L £9. Cover £1   SERVICE: 15% (optional), card slips closed   CARDS: Access, Amex, Delta, Diners, Switch   DETAILS: 68 seats. 21 seats outside. Private parties: 35 main room, 35 private room. Vegetarian meals. Children welcome. Smart dress preferred. No music

Magno's

map 15

65A Long Acre, WC2E 9JH

COOKING 1
COST £26–£50

TEL: (0171) 836 6077   FAX: (0171) 379 6184

Emmanuel Coliadis's proud boast is that his buzzy French brasserie is within 15 minutes' walk of no fewer than 33 theatres. Not surprisingly, his no-nonsense pre-theatre menu (served from 5.30 to 7.15) is a bestseller, and it succeeds because service is sharp enough to get the punters to the show on time. The kitchen mixes traditional French with new Italian, and also flirts with in-vogue victuals such as ostrich and wild boar. One reporter commented favourably on a supper that included seafood tagliatelle and turkey escalope with vegetables, but the repertoire extends to Caesar salad, wild mushroom ravioli, 'free-range' coq au vin, and roast pork with prunes. Desserts feature crème brûlée, and iced coffee and rum parfait, for example. The value for money is appreciated, and France dominates the affordable wine list, which also accommodates a few interlopers from the New World. House wine is £9.75.

The Guide always appreciates hearing about changes of chef or owner.

CHEF: Gilbert Rousset   PROPRIETOR: Emmanuel Coliadis   OPEN: Mon to Fri L 12 to 2.30, Mon to
Sat D 5.30 to 11.30   CLOSED: 25 Dec, bank hols   MEALS: alc (main courses £9 to £14). Set L
£13.50 (2 courses) to £16.50, Set pre-theatre D £10.95 (2 courses), Set D £13.50 (2 courses) to
£16.50   SERVICE: 12.5%   CARDS: Access, Amex, Delta, Diners, Switch, Visa   DETAILS: 50
seats. Private parties: 60 main room. Vegetarian meals. Children welcome. Smart dress
preferred. No cigars/pipes in dining-room. Wheelchair access (no WC). Music. Air-conditioned

Maison Novelli   **NEW ENTRY**   map 13

29 Clerkenwell Green, EC1R 0DU   COOKING 2
TEL: (0171) 251 6606   FAX: (0171) 490 1083   COST £26–£63

Although Jean-Christophe Novelli is not the first chef to desert a West End hotel
– he was at the Four Seasons (see entry) – he is certainly part of a trend towards
unpretentious and modest restaurants with rip-roaring kitchens. The transformation of Café St Pierre into Maison Novelli began in the summer of 1996 and was
incomplete as the *Guide* went to press, but the corner site near Farringdon Road
enables him to serve both the City and Central London. A 'Rapido' menu aims to
get lunch over and done with in the space of an hour, and faxing of menus and
orders is also designed to streamline proceedings.

Upstairs becomes a restaurant with an ambitious menu, while the
ground-floor is a brasserie – with seats outside under the awning on fine days –
that deals in homely braised onion filled with cubed lamb, mackerel and
lemon-grass kebab, and waffles with coconut ice-cream. An early inspection
meal turned up perfectly sound cooking of home-made country-style pâté, warm
goats'-cheese terrine, and roast fillet of grey mullet sitting on an excellent
aubergine base. The wine list was being extended as we went to press.

CHEF/PROPRIETOR: Jean-Christophe Novelli   OPEN: restaurant Mon to Fri 12 to 3.30, 6.30 to
10.30; brasserie Mon to Fri 11am to 11pm   CLOSED: bank hols   MEALS: alc (main courses
brasserie £6.95 to £8.40, restaurant £10 to £20), Set L and D £25 to £40   SERVICE: 15%
DETAILS: 45 seats, 35 seats outside. Private parties: 45 main room, 45 private room. Vegetarian
meals. Children's helpings. Wheelchair access (no WC). Music.

Mandarin Kitchen   map 13

14–16 Queensway, W2 3RX   COOKING 2
TEL: (0171) 727 9012 and 9468   COST £23–£67

The reason why people throng to this large Chinese restaurant opposite
Queensway tube station is to feast on some of the freshest seafood around. Stars
of the show are wild Scottish lobsters, which almost everybody seems to order.
They are served six ways, including steamed, baked with ginger and spring
onions, or with garlic and chilli. Crabs from the south coast are also much in
demand – a knowledgeable reporter singled out the 'pots of crab' with bean
noodles and dried shrimps in chilli sauce. The catalogue of aquatic species also
extends to eels, carp, Chinese pomfret, yellow croaker, and the euphemistically
named 'sea cucumber'. A full complement of meat, poultry and vegetarian dishes
also fleshes out the menu, from great bowls of stuffed bean curd soup (enough
for four people), or braised duck with 'eight treasures', to veal chop in
black-bean and chilli sauce, and beef with preserved hot cabbage. The food

remains 'really interesting', although two reporters found the welcome rather frosty. Coffee may be served 'grudgingly in wine glasses', or you can drink tea, beer or something from the workmanlike wine list. House wine is £7.90.

CHEF: Mr Man   PROPRIETOR: Helen Cheung   OPEN: all week 12 to 11.30   CLOSED: 25 and 26 Dec   MEALS: alc (main courses £6 to £25). Set L and D £9.90 (2 courses)   SERVICE: not inc CARDS: Access, Amex, Diners, Switch, Visa   DETAILS: 100 seats. Private parties: 20 main room. Vegetarian meals. Children welcome. Wheelchair access (no WC). Music. Air-conditioned

Mantanah
map 12

2 Orton Buildings, Portland Road, SE25 4UD
TEL: (0181) 771 1148   FAX: (0181) 771 2341

COOKING 2
COST £21–£41

Mantanah sits in what the owners describe as 'an arid culinary area of South London' within earshot of Norwood Junction railway station. It is a family business through and through, with Mrs Tym Srisawatt-Yeoh in charge of the kitchen. The menu is lengthy and livened up by a few family inventions that sound as if they ought to be cocktails: Dragon Dance is sliced beef cooked with green beans, bean sprouts, red wine and chillies; Pink Lady consists of deep-fried aubergine with chilli sauce; Cinderella's Best Friend turns up in the shape of shredded pumpkin in coconut batter with sweet plum sauce. And who could resist the meaty prospect of Hot Pork ('mother's recipe') with young jackfruit, tomato and kaffir lime leaves.

Elsewhere you will find all the staples of the cuisine, from satays and fish-cakes to fiery salads, stir-fries and noodle dishes, plus a selection of specialities drawn from the north and north-east of Thailand: sai ooa Chiang Mai (spicy curried pork sausage with fresh ginger) sounds intriguing. In addition to tea and Thai beer, there is a short but sensibly chosen wine list, with house wine £7.50.

CHEF: Mrs Tym Srisawatt-Yeoh   PROPRIETORS: Mr and Mrs K.S. Yeoh   OPEN: Tue to Sun D only 6.30 to 11   CLOSED: 25 and 26 Dec, 1 Jan   MEALS: alc (main courses £5 to £6.50). Set D £12.95 to £16   SERVICE: not inc, card slips closed   CARDS: Access, Amex, Visa   DETAILS: 40 seats. Private parties: 40 main room. Vegetarian meals. Children's helpings. Smart dress preferred. No cigars/pipes in dining-room. Wheelchair access (no WC). Music. Air-conditioned

Matsuri ✻
NEW ENTRY   map 15

15 Bury Street, SW1Y 6AL
TEL: (0171) 839 1101   FAX: (0171) 930 7010

COOKING 2*
COST £40–£95

Next door to Quaglino's (see entry) in an extremely expensive part of St James's, this posh Japanese restaurant is stylish without being overpoweringly formal. A three-metre-high papier mâché visage of a warrior watches from the stairs by the entrance; the main dining areas are below. 'Matsuri' means 'festivals', and the light, attractive interior is decorated with photographs of celebrations; lanterns and other red objects are tastefully arranged around the gleaming white walls. Service could not be more polite or gracious, the atmosphere is 'great' and the food is 'pretty flawless'.

The cooking focuses on two great culinary styles, ancient and modern. On the one hand is the traditional high art of sushi, on the other the Westernised theatrical flamboyance of teppanyaki. The quality of the sushi is outstanding: huge scallops ('we've never had fresher or better') cut in a tent shape over a tiny finger of rice, and vivid orange-coloured tobi-ko (flying fish roe) served in a nori roll are just two examples.

To sample the full teppanyaki experience, order the kaiseki teppan. Amazing appetisers are followed by chawan-mushi (steamed egg custard), while the centrepiece seafood or first-rate Scotch beef is cut into cubes and cooked before your eyes. Two dips are provided, along with grilled vegetables of various kinds. Steamed rice, light miso soup and pickles signal that proceedings are drawing to a close, but not before some 'super' green-tea ice-cream has arrived. At lunch-time it is possible to eat affordably from one of the bento box assemblies, or even drop in for a bargain-price okonami-yaki (Japanese pizza). Mark-ups on the wine list are steep, but there are some reasonably priced New World offerings to keep the bill in check. Chilean house white is £16.50.

CHEF: Kanehiro Takase   PROPRIETOR: JRK UK Ltd   OPEN: Mon to Sat 12 to 2.30, 6 to 10   CLOSED: bank hols   MEALS: alc (main courses L £5.50 to £20, D £8.50 to £29). Set L £14 (2 courses) to £35, Set D £34 to £55   SERVICE: 12.5% (optional), card slips closed   CARDS: Amex, Diners, Visa   DETAILS: 133 seats. Private parties: 100 main room, 8 private room. Vegetarian meals. Children welcome. Smart dress preferred. No smoking in 1 dining-room. Wheelchair access (also WC). Music. Air-conditioned

Melati
map 15

21 Great Windmill Street, W1V 7PH
TEL: (0171) 437 2745 and 734 6964
FAX: (0171) 434 4196

COOKING 1
COST £24–£46

'Make sure your companions are adventurous eaters,' advises an expert, because Melati is the real thing. The location may be X-certificate Soho, but the kitchen delivers probably the most genuine and tantalising Indonesian and Malaysian food in London. A brigade of good-humoured waiters keeps things ticking over, and the 140-dish menu offers plenty of classic stuff with gutsy flavours: lumpia sayur (spring rolls), opor ayam (mild chicken curry), gado-gado salad and 'brilliant' achar (pickled vegetables in a sweet-and-sour sauce) have all been applauded. One-plate rice and noodle dishes and bowls of laksa soup offer the best value for anyone eating alone. Melati also has a range of authentic multi-coloured desserts, or you could finish with banana fritters. The food remains really good value, although the practice of offering un-itemised bills is a potential niggle. Drink jasmine tea or imported beer. House wine is £8.45.

CHEF: Sjamsir Alamsjah   PROPRIETORS: Sjamsir Alamsjah and Margaret Ong   OPEN: all week noon to 11.30 (12.30 Fri and Sat)   CLOSED: 25 Dec   MEALS: alc (main courses £5.50 to £7.50). Set L and D (min 2) £16.50 to £21.25 (inc wine)   SERVICE: not inc, card slips closed   CARDS: Access, Amex, Diners, Visa   DETAILS: 120 seats. Private parties: 40 main room. Vegetarian meals. Children welcome. Smart dress preferred. Wheelchair access (no WC). Music. Air-conditioned

---

'Whenever I asked the waiter anything he didn't know, he went and found out the answer from the kitchen, and dropped it at my feet like a happy dog with a stick.'
(On eating in the West Country)

▲ *Le Meridien Hotel, Oak Room* map 15

21 Piccadilly, W1V 0BH
TEL: (0171) 734 8000 and 465 1640
FAX: (0171) 437 3574

COOKING 3*
COST £36–£110

Here is a grand hotel with a beautifully appointed dining-room, decorated in limed oak with large mirrors, gilt mouldings, big chandeliers and art deco lights dangling from the lofty ceiling. Generous-sized tables are well spaced and immaculately set, and service is 'impeccable'; but despite all the trappings the Oak Room still has a rather cool and somewhat 'impersonal' atmosphere. The food is equally grand, determinedly French with a modern outlook, and with enough options to accommodate anything from two courses on the *carte* to seven on the menu gourmand.

There is also freedom to opt for relatively light crab ravioli or lobster salad, or to indulge in the richness of foie gras two ways: pan-fried with cooking juices, and a confit rolled into a sausage shape, sliced, and served with a port jelly. Seafood is well treated, as an inspector found. 'Five of the softest, plumpest, most beautifully cooked scallops it has been my pleasure to eat' came with a creamy sauce flavoured with fish stock and thyme. Five seems to be the chef's lucky number when it comes to lamb fillet too: 'five small slices of perfection', together with five small heaps of aubergine purée and an intricate 'box' of provençale vegetables.

Despite the change of chef, some dishes remain in the repertoire, including a dessert of thin pineapple slices and pineapple sorbet served with mashed banana and little blobs of lime mousse dusted with chocolate. Both presentation and flavour remain impressive at this stage, not least in soft ovals of chocolate ganache with a praline sauce that contrived to look like two small mice: 'very rich, very very good'. A token New World showing heads the predominantly French list of fine wines at sometimes daunting prices. Half-bottles, and bottles under £20, are buried among the classed growths and grand cru Burgundy. House wine is £15.50.

CHEFS: Mark Leach and Pascal Villain   PROPRIETOR: Granada Group plc   OPEN: Mon to Fri L 12 to 2.30, Mon to Sat D 7 to 10.30   CLOSED: first 3 weeks Aug   MEALS: alc (main courses £21 to £38). Set L £24.50, Set D £28 (inc wine) to £49   SERVICE: not inc   CARDS: Access, Amex, Delta, Diners, Switch, Visa   DETAILS: 45 seats. Children welcome. Jacket and tie. No smoking in 1 dining-room. No cigars in dining-room. Wheelchair access (also WC). Music. Air-conditioned   ACCOMMODATION: 266 rooms, all with bath/shower. TV. Phone. Air-conditioned. Room only £200 to £252. Rooms for disabled. Children welcome. Baby facilities. Afternoon teas. Swimming-pool

Le Mesurier   map 13

113 Old Street, EC1V 9JR
TEL: (0171) 251 8117   FAX: (0171) 608 3504

COOKING 2
COST £29–£41

'A haven from the noise of lunchtime Old Street', Le Mesurier is generally populated by suited City types. Gillian Enthoven's curiously idiosyncratic little venue is open for lunches only, and you need to ring the bell to gain admittance. The interior is welcoming, cool and somewhat cramped, with a motley collection of old posters on the walls and a short but imaginative menu that is intended to resuscitate flagging spirits. One reporter's lasting memory is of splendid fungi: oyster mushrooms with asparagus in Gewurztraminer sauce, and morels swimming in a sherry-based sauce with a juicy pork chop that clearly had its provenance as 'part of a real pig'. Also praiseworthy have been 'magnificent' pieces of hot-smoked wild salmon hidden beneath slices of the cold variety, not to mention young crunchy vegetables, buttery sauces, and ripe cheese. Others have singled out twice-baked cheese soufflé, sardine and potato terrine, baked cod, and grilled chicken breast with lemon sauce. The short wine list is satisfactory, although some half-bottles might suit the lunchtime trade. House wine is £9.

CHEFS: Gillian Enthoven and Loic Le Pape   PROPRIETOR: Gillian Enthoven   OPEN: Mon to Fri L only 12 to 3; D by arrangement for private parties only   CLOSED: 1 week Christmas, 3 weeks Aug   MEALS: alc (main courses £9.50 to £12)   SERVICE: 12.5% (optional), card slips closed   CARDS: Access, Amex, Diners, Switch, Visa   DETAILS: 25 seats. Private parties: 25 main room. No children under 10. Smart dress preferred. No pipes in dining-room. Wheelchair access (no WC). No music

Mezzo   NEW ENTRY   map 15

100 Wardour Street, W1V 3LE   COOKING 2
TEL: (0171) 314 4000   FAX: (0171) 314 0124   COST £25–£79

'Another Conran cracker,' reckoned one reporter of this glamorous 700-seater. 'A bit like a school canteen for adults,' volunteered another. Whatever else, a restaurant that can feed upwards of 14,000 people a week is certainly a sign of a successful business, not to mention a healthy industry. The ground-floor Mezzonine takes no bookings and is the more casual of the two eating-areas, specialising in South-east Asian flavours from stir-fried pork with green beans and chilli paste, to sour yellow vegetable curry; only desserts take a different tack with crème brûlée, or pavlova.

Mezzo itself is in the basement, more European in outlook, with a view into the glassed-in kitchen, and a menu that takes in shellfish and grills beside jambon persillade, saddle of lamb, or 'wonderful' crisp-skinned, just-cooked roast cod, with first-rate chips 'crisp outside and fluffy inside'. The atmosphere is part of the appeal, provided this sort of atmosphere appeals to you: it can be noisy, it is possible to feel 'processed', and there is no designated no-smoking area. In addition, the telephone booking system has not always appeared to work effectively. Early-evening deals in both Mezzo and Mezzonine are fair, and the wine list is interesting, sensibly chosen and tolerably marked up, beginning with Vin de Pays d'Oc at £11.75.

CHEF: John Torone   PROPRIETORS: Sir Terence Conran and Joel Kissin   OPEN: all week 12 to 3, 5.30 to 12.30 (2.30am Thur to Sat, 11 Sun); Mezzo closed Sat L   CLOSED: 25 and 26 Dec   MEALS: alc (main courses £7 to £25). Mezzo Set L Mon to Fri £19.50, Mezzo Set L Sun £14.50, Mezzo Set D 6 to 7 £14, Mezzonine Set D 5.30 to 7 £7 (2 courses). Music cover £5 Mezzo after 10.30 Thur to Sat   SERVICE: 12.5% (optional), card slips closed   CARDS: Access, Amex, Diners, Switch, Visa   DETAILS: 700 seats. Private parties: 350 main room. Vegetarian meals. Children welcome. Smart dress preferred. Wheelchair access (also WC). Music. Air-conditioned

Mirch Masala £

NEW ENTRY   map 12

1416 London Road, SW16 4BZ
TEL: (0181) 679 1828 and 765 1070

COOKING 1
COST £10–£32

Norbury's answer to a Birmingham balti house is this authentic eating-place in a parade of shops. Queues form outside the door, a large proportion of the clientele are Asian families, and cooking takes place in an open kitchen at the back, in full view of the customers. An army of casually dressed waiters maintain a frenetic pace. Ignore the menu categories ('warmers', 'steamers', 'coolers') and concentrate on the food itself. Most dishes are stir-fried in iron 'woks', and the spicing is what counts: methi chicken receives a dose of fenugreek and green chillies, while jeera aloo is laced with cumin. Vegetable masala tikki makes a good starter, while rice and accompanying nan bread are better than average. The premises are unlicensed, but you can drink lassi or buy alcohol from the off-licence opposite.

CHEFS: Raza Ali and Harjit Jutla   PROPRIETORS: Raza Ali and Raiz Ali   OPEN: Tue to Sun and bank hol Mon 12 to 12   CLOSED: Tue after bank hol Mon   MEALS: alc (main courses £2.50 to £8). Unlicensed, BYO (no corkage)   SERVICE: not inc, card slips closed   CARDS: Access, Delta, Switch, Visa   DETAILS: 70 seats. Private parties: 150 main room. Vegetarian meals. Children's helpings. Wheelchair access (also WC). Music. Air-conditioned

Mr Kong £

map 15

21 Lisle Street, WC2H 7BA
TEL: (0171) 437 7341 and 9679

COOKING 2*
COST £20–£40

Since 1984 Mr Kong and his team have turned this into one of the most reliable and enduring addresses in Soho's Chinatown. A first-timer here confirmed that the kitchen delivers 'distinctive and distinguished cooking'. There is also agreement about the value for money: prices are very reasonable, given that many dishes are 'labour intensive, carefully prepared and decorated with vegetable sculptures'.

A vast range of chef's specials adds an extra pinch of variety and zest to the long, mainly Cantonese menu. Chunks of crispy duck are deep-fried, surrounded by yam paste and served with two sauces (oyster and sweet-and-sour); Szechuan-style braised scallops and king prawns are heaped into a lattice of crisp potato shreds; stuffed fish maw appears with baby clams and prawn paste. Lobster and crab are cooked every which way, and the main repertoire also includes such things as bean curd and fish soup, roasted salted chicken, braised belly-pork with preserved vegetables, and earthy hotpots and casseroles. Service is efficient if 'slightly uninterested'. House wine is £7.

CHEFS: K. Kong and Y.W. Lo   PROPRIETORS: K. Kong, Y.W. Lo, M.T. Lee, K.C. Tang and C.Y. Chan   OPEN: all week 12 to 1.45am   CLOSED: 4 days Christmas   MEALS: alc (main courses £5.50 to £11). Set L £8.80 to £11 (all 2 courses), Set D £16 to £22 (all minimum 4). Minimum £7 after 5   SERVICE: net prices   CARDS: Access, Amex, Diners, Visa   DETAILS: 115 seats. Private parties: 40 main room, 40 private room. Vegetarian meals. Children welcome. Music. Air-conditioned

Mitsukoshi

map 15

Dorland House, 14–20 Regent Street, SW1Y 4PH
TEL: (0171) 930 0317   FAX: (0171) 839 6714

COOKING 2*
COST £31–£99

Mitsukoshi is principally the domain of 'the Japanese salaryman on expenses', and no wonder. The location is the basement of a department store, the mood is serene and understated, the cost is intimidating. Most people opt for one of the set menus or ceremonial kaiseki banquets, although a *carte* provides alternatives. What impresses is the freshness of ingredients, the painstaking visual artistry and the sheer variety within each meal. One of the cheaper options is the nihonbashi dinner, which kicks off with two appetisers before moving on to chawan mushi (steamed egg custard) and beef teriyaki. The obligatory trio of rice, miso soup and multicoloured pickles precedes fruit, which one reporter observed often take more calories to eat than they contain.

Elsewhere, there are meals based around sushi (the price includes a glass of wine), bento delicacies served in lacquered boxes, shabu-shabu, sukiyaki and sashimi. A few slightly more affordable options are also available at lunch-time. Drink green tea, unless you can afford to plunge into the heady world of rare malts and vintage clarets. The cheapest bottle on the list is a 1989 Liebfraumilch at £15, the most expensive a 1982 Dom. de la Romanée-Conti at £600.

CHEF: Jiro Shimada   PROPRIETOR: Mitsukoshi (UK) Ltd   OPEN: Mon to Sat 12 to 2, 6 to 9.30   MEALS: alc (main courses £4.50 to £27). Set L £15 to £60, Set D £30 to £60; minimum 2 for some set meals. Cover £1.50   SERVICE: 15%, card slips closed   CARDS: Access, Amex, Diners, Visa   DETAILS: 80 seats. Private parties: 24 main room, 12 and 24 private rooms. Jacket and tie. Music. Air-conditioned

Miyama

map 15

38 Clarges Street, W1Y 7PJ
TEL: (0171) 499 2443   FAX: (0171) 493 1573

COOKING 2
COST £24–£80

The whisky bottles labelled 'Bank of Tokyo' instantly tell you, in the words of one experienced reporter, that Miyama is a Japanese businessmen's 'expense account lair', with few Westerners in evidence. Having said that, it remains one of the better restaurants of its kind in the capital. Downstairs is a teppanyaki bar; upstairs is the main dining-room, with minimalist three-dimensional art and tables discreetly divided by lattice screens.

A standard *carte* covers everything from zen-zai to tempura, but the most exciting food is the separate selection of what a reporter described as 'home-cooked-type dishes': highlights have included nasu dengaku (a cylinder of deep-fried aubergine with sweet miso paste), 'very traditional' thick udon noodles, and exquisite-looking ebi shumae (steamed prawn dumplings) served on a bamboo mat with a blob of yellow mustard. Even better is unagi kabayaki – meaty fillets of the finest chargrilled eel with a 'wonderful' sauce of soy and mirin: 'utter heaven,' wrote one recipient. While some dishes are 'a real shock of taste in the mouth', at inspection there were some unforgivable mistakes: indifferent sushi made with lamentably 'mushy' rice, for example, slow service and disappointing saké. House French is £10. There is a second branch, City Miyama, at 17 Godliman Street, EC4; tel: (0171) 489 1937.

CHEFS/PROPRIETORS: Mr T. Miura and Mr F. Miyama OPEN: Mon to Fri L 12 to 2.30, Mon to Sat D 6 to 10.30 MEALS: alc (main courses £8.50 to £26). Set L £12 to £18, Set D £34 to £42 SERVICE: 15% CARDS: Access, Amex, Delta, Diners, Switch, Visa DETAILS: 64 seats. Private parties: 32 main room, 4 and 8 private rooms. Vegetarian meals. Children welcome. Wheelchair access (no WC). Music

Monkeys

map 13

1 Cale Street, Chelsea Green, SW3 3QT
TEL: (0171) 352 4711 and 5120

COOKING 2
COST £23–£53

The elegance of this former town house in a quiet corner of Chelsea is such that visitors may feel they have been welcomed into a well-to-do family home. You will, moreover, dine in the company of a fair few of the ancestors, as the name indicates; pictures and carvings of everything from lumbering anthropoid apes to impish little marmosets abound.

Tom Benham cooks in the grand manner, shades of Escoffier stealing across a starter portion of lobster Thermidor and a grilled châteaubriand béarnaise. A rather powerful gratinated topping covered the former, but the steak was great – 'well-hung meat with good texture and lots of flavour'. Dead-simple presentation of grilled sea bass has allowed the fish to speak for itself, without relying on either a rich sauce or the ubiquitous oriental seasonings. Rack of lamb is robustly devilled, and has a light layer of crisp fat left on. Treacle tart with gently acidulated syrup and real vanilla ice-cream impressed an aficionado, but lemon tart was thought a bit 'timid' in terms of acidity. Wines are French first and foremost, with cursory selections from elsewhere. There are some good Burgundy growers and mature clarets but mark-ups reflect the postcode. House wines start at £11.

CHEF: Tom Benham PROPRIETORS: Tom and Brigitte Benham OPEN: all week L 12.30 to 2.30 (1 to 3.30 Sun), Mon to Sat D 7.30 to 11 CLOSED: 1 week Christmas, 2 weeks Easter, 3 weeks Aug MEALS: Set L Mon to Sat £15, Set L Sun £20, Set D £20 to £30 SERVICE: not inc CARDS: Access, Switch, Visa DETAILS: 40 seats. Private parties: 10 main room. Children welcome. Smart dress preferred. No pipes in dining-room. No music. Air-conditioned

Mon Plaisir

map 15

21 Monmouth Street, WC2H 9DD
TEL: (0171) 836 7243 and 240 3757
FAX: (0171) 379 0121

COOKING 1*
COST £21–£52

Alain Lhermitte's constantly crowded, unimpeachably French Covent Garden bistro is getting back into its stride of late. New chef David Joly arrived in the New Year, and has already made an impact. Everything, from the 'tall, dark and handsome' waiters to the menu that takes a bit of working out, is designed to make you feel you've floated across the Channel, and the food is rightfully the strongest pointer. Gratinée à l'oignon is a 'deep, delicious broth with plenty of onion, thick bread and gooey Gruyère'. Duck confit is the real thing too, a 'great hunk' sitting on a mound of lentils in an intensely reduced sauce. Black and white puddings with apples and mash are there, as well as the occasional more modern note, such as John Dory with baby artichokes and balsamic vinegar.

Desserts take in profiteroles, tiramisù and crème brûlée, and French cheeses offer exemplary value. The wine list spins democratically through the classic regions, with house wines from £8.95.

CHEFS: David Joly and Daniel Valay   PROPRIETOR: Alain Lhermitte   OPEN: Mon to Fri L 12 to 2.15, Mon to Sat D 5.50 to 11.15   CLOSED: 25 Dec to 1 Jan, bank hols   MEALS: alc (main courses £8.50 to £16). Set L £13.95, Set pre-theatre D £10.95 (2 courses) to £13.95, Set D £19.95. BYO £8   SERVICE: 12.5% (optional), card slips closed   CARDS: Access, Amex, Delta, Diners, Switch, Visa   DETAILS: 96 seats. Private parties: 28 main room, 28 private room. Vegetarian meals. Children welcome. Smart dress preferred. Wheelchair access (no WC). Music. Air-conditioned

Montana

NEW ENTRY   map 12

125–127 Dawes Road, SW6 7EA
TEL: (0171) 385 9500   FAX: (0171) 386 0337

COOKING 1
COST £25–£48

Chipotle, mulatto, pasilla and other key names from the chilli encyclopedia are Montana's touchstones. Eclectic, American-style food seems to have found its niche in this off-the-wall Fulham venue with wood floors, navy-blue ceilings, and curious classical Greek allusions on one wall. The mood is laid back, the music is often live. For the inhabitants of SW6, here is a taste of that relatively New World across the water: blackened prawn and sweet pepper fajita with soured cream, a splendidly peppery Rhode Island fish chowder with water biscuits, and cumin-roasted vegetables in a large conical tortilla. Specials provide added interest: chargrilled salmon with blackeye-bean salsa has hit the button. Desserts include a 'competent' coconut-flavoured crème caramel. The modern wine list is totally in keeping. House wine is £12.

CHEF: Dan McDowell   PROPRIETORS: Drew Barwick and Kevin Finch   OPEN: Sat and Sun brunch 12 to 3.30, all week D 7 to 11 (11.30 Fri and Sat)   MEALS: alc (main courses Sat and Sun brunch £5 to £14, D £10 to £15). Set D £15.95 to £21   SERVICE: 12.5% (optional), card slips closed   CARDS: Access, Amex, Delta, Switch, Visa   DETAILS: 65 seats. Private parties: 70 main room, 30 and 35 private rooms. Vegetarian meals. Children's helpings. Smart dress preferred. No cigars before 11pm. Wheelchair access (also WC). Music. Air-conditioned

Moshi Moshi Sushi ⁵✳ £

map 13

Unit 24, Liverpool Street Station, EC2M 7QH
TEL/FAX: (0171) 247 3227
7–8 Limeburner Lane, EC4M 7HY
TEL: (0171) 248 1808   FAX: (0171) 248 1807

COOKING 1*
COST £12–£21

Caroline Beckett has opened a second branch of her Liverpool Street Station sushi bar, which is proving just as popular. The idea – the same in both – is simplicity itself: a long line of dishes trundling past on a conveyor belt. Pick up a plate of anything you like the look of: salmon, tuna, grey mullet, squid and so on. The food is cheaper than at most other sushi bars, and different colours and patterns on the plates indicate the price.

'Only the cheap dishes are put on the belt, and you can, if unwary, wait for ages for something good to pass by,' reckoned one knowledgeable reporter. Another, familiar with the conveyor-belt sushi bars of Tokyo and able to 'gobble down raw fish with the best of them', also found that a display of knowledge brought results. But there is a simple short-cut: the à la carte lists the whole range in English, from sea-water eel through flounder and horse mackerel to toro (the fatty belly part of the tuna) and uni (sea urchin). Drink one of the half-dozen wines, saké or Japanese lager.

CHEF: Roland Ongcoy   PROPRIETOR: Caroline Bennett   OPEN: Mon to Fri 11.30 to 9   CLOSED: Christmas, Easter, bank hols   MEALS: alc (main courses £1 to £2). Set L and D £4.50 to £9 SERVICE: not inc, card slips closed   CARDS: Access, Delta, Switch, Visa   DETAILS: 54 seats (Liverpool Street Station), 60 seats (Limeburner Lane). Private parties: 30 main room (Liverpool Street Station), 25 main room (Limeburner Lane). Vegetarian meals. Children welcome. No smoking in dining-room. Wheelchair access (also WC Limeburner Lane). Music. Air-conditioned (Liverpool Street Station)

Museum Street Café ▼ ✸

map 15

47 Museum Street, WC1A 1LY
TEL: (0171) 405 3211

COOKING 2*
COST £23–£37

'It's the kind of small operation one could become very fond of, and not wish to tell the world about,' mused one reporter, capturing the feel of the Café. It manages to be a haven of intimacy despite being on the tourist trail to the British Museum. Gail Koerber and Mark Nathan have not only judged the atmosphere to a T, but their cooking too is in tune with what a metropolitan audience wants.

First courses are simply a pair of alternatives: a salad of goats' cheese with leaves and trimmings from organic Appledore Farm with 'refreshing, mouth-cleansing' flavours, or a crustacean-rich fish soup enhanced by a thick blob of saffron mayonnaise, for example. Main courses, from a choice of three, have included skewered chargrilled monkfish with pancetta, subtly scented with rosemary, and 'moist and tender' guinea-fowl with raisins and Muscat sauce. At one meal, almond sponge cake, fresh from the oven, was judged 'a triumph of the baker's art' and came with praline ice-cream and prunes that were 'heavily steeped in armagnac'. Service remains calm even when the place is full. Good judgement shines through on the compact wine list. Every one of the 21 wines has thoroughly earned its place, be it a bright Californian or an elegant Burgundian. Five are available by the glass. House wine is £8.50. CELLARMAN'S CHOICE: Chablis Fourchaume 1994, Jean-Claude Bessin, £21.50; Frog's Leap Zinfandel 1993, Napa Valley, California, £19.50.

CHEFS/PROPRIETORS: Gail Koerber and Mark Nathan   OPEN: Mon to Fri 12.30 to 2.15, 6.30 to 9.30   CLOSED: 1 week spring, 2 weeks summer, 1 week Christmas   MEALS: Set L £12.50 (2 courses) to £15.50, Set D £17.50 (2 courses) to £21.50. BYO £5   SERVICE: not inc   CARDS: Access, Amex, Delta, Switch, Visa   DETAILS: 35 seats. Vegetarian meals. Children welcome. No smoking in dining-room. Wheelchair access (also WC). No music

Neal Street Restaurant

map 15

26 Neal Street, WC2H 9PS
TEL: (0171) 836 8368   FAX: (0171) 497 1361

COOKING 2
COST £43–£74

The varied styles of London's Italian restaurants are richer for this Neal Street fixture, now into its second decade. The early Conran dining-room, with tiled floor and cream-brick walls, is decked out with some exotic blooms, and gets pretty busy, mostly with Americans and Italians. Its individuality derives from owner Antonio Carluccio, whose passion for mushrooms is as evident throughout the menu as it is on television. Fungi might appear as a mixed sauté of the day ('interesting selection and a generous portion'), in soup, with pasta, or perhaps pickled and served with roast skate.

Where many modern Italian restaurants aim for lightness, the Neal Street kitchen seems more at home with a richer style: in a morel and foie gras sauce for roast quail, for instance, or in a 'sensational'-looking dish of black angel hair pasta with 'huge scallops' and a scraping of bottarga. 'You must love olive oil' to eat here, reckoned one reporter, and a penchant for ice-cream also helps: saffron and pistachio are among the flavours. An 'optional' charge of 15 per cent pays for 'efficient, attentive, polite' service. Prices are considered high, not least among the interesting line-up of mostly Italian wines, although several likeable bottles under £15 help ease the situation, and there are lots of halves. House wines are £13.

CHEF: Nick Melmoth-Coombs   PROPRIETOR: Antonio Carluccio   OPEN: Mon to Sat 12.30 to 2.30, 7.30 to 11   CLOSED: 1 week Christmas to New Year, bank hols   MEALS: alc (main courses £14 to £19.50)   SERVICE: 15% (optional), card slips closed   CARDS: Access, Amex, Delta, Diners, Switch, Visa   DETAILS: 60 seats. Private parties: 26 private room. Vegetarian meals. Children welcome. Smart dress preferred. Wheelchair access (no WC). No music. Air-conditioned

Nico Central

map 15

35 Great Portland Street, W1N 5DD
TEL/FAX: (0171) 436 8846

COOKING 3
COST £33–£56

As we went to press Nico Central transferred to the Restaurant Partnership, but the name stays, Nico Ladenis continues to oversee the operation, and André Garrett remains in the kitchen. Within walking distance of Oxford Circus, the restaurant is light and modern, with flowers, prints and close-set tables. The food has a consistent style and approach, supported by high-quality materials and generally accurate cooking. 'Technical execution could be taken pretty much for granted,' maintained one reporter, comforted by the fact that 'one is not likely to be surprised by any dramatic bravura strokes from the kitchen.'

The Anglo-French approach might produce a meal of fish soup with rouille and croûtons, ribeye of beef with horseradish sauce, and crème brûlée. A variety of cooking techniques contributes to the palette of colours, flavours and textures: anything roasted or grilled, from chicken livers to squid to guinea-fowl, usually arrives crisp outside and juicy within, while main courses can range from braised oxtail with roast parsnips to skate with lentils. Risotto of ceps is a stalwart, as is the caramelised lemon tart.

Supplements are imposed for foie gras and a couple of the main courses, plus potatoes (chips or mash) and coffee, but the set price includes service charge, and the general perception is of good value. Service is the main thing that gets up reporters' noses: it is out of kilter with the food, ranging from 'neglectful and patronising' to 'polite but somewhat offhand in the Gallic fashion'. An intelligent, up-to-date and mid-priced selection of fifty wines is bolstered by ten half-bottles, with house wine from £3.50 a glass.

CHEF: André Garrett   PROPRIETORS: Restaurant Partnership plc   OPEN: Mon to Fri L 12 to 2,
Mon to Sat D 7 to 11   CLOSED: 10 days Christmas   MEALS: Set L £20 (2 courses) to £24.50, Set
D £27   SERVICE: net prices, card slips closed   CARDS: Access, Amex, Diners, Visa   DETAILS:
55 seats. Private parties: 55 main room, 12 private room. Vegetarian meals. No children under
10. Smart dress preferred. No cigars/pipes in dining-room. Wheelchair access (no WC). No
music. Air-conditioned

Nicole's

map 15

| 158 New Bond Street, W1Y 9PA | COOKING 1* |
| TEL/FAX: (0171) 499 8408 | COST £34–£54 |

The fact that Nicole's is in the basement of a smart dress shop has nothing to do
with its success as a restaurant, at least as far as reporters are concerned. The
room is bright, cool and 'beautifully appointed'. Despite such things as a raw
mushroom salad with Parmesan, and a nice line in fish – roast monk with
spinach and mash – the uncomplicated menu is not geared particularly to
weight-watchers. Simplicity and a lightness of touch are what drive it along:
grilled tuna with a hot chickpea salad, or chicken with black olive relish, each
served with a different selection of vegetables. Soups have included spiced
butternut squash, and smoked haddock chowder, while braised lamb shank
with cannellini beans, and hot mocha fudge pudding are among the weightier
offerings. Pre-meal nibbles and coffee are rated highly, service is attentive and
friendly, and most of the three dozen wines are available by the glass for around
£2.50 to £6.

CHEF: Annie Wayte   PROPRIETOR: Stephen Marks   OPEN: Mon to Sat L 12 to 3.30 (4 Sat), Mon
to Fri D 6.30 to 11; bar meals available Mon to Sat 11.30 to 5.30   CLOSED: 25 and 26 Dec
MEALS: alc (main courses £13 to £17.50). Cover £1. Minimum £12   SERVICE: 12.5% (optional),
card slips closed   CARDS: Access, Amex, Delta, Diners, Switch, Visa   DETAILS: 70 seats.
Private parties: 70 main room. Vegetarian meals. Children's helpings. No cigars/pipes in
dining-room. Music. Air-conditioned

Noughts 'n' Crosses

map 12

| 77 The Grove, W5 5LL | COOKING 2 |
| TEL: (0181) 840 7568   FAX: (0181) 840 1905 | COST £24–£36 |

The converted corner shop just off Ealing High Street has been home to Anthony
Ma's inspiring East–West crossover food for a decade now, long before such
mixing and matching had occurred to many West End entrepreneurs. There may
be reports of ups and downs from time to time, almost inevitable when you work
at the cutting edge, but the ideas are often stimulating and the good news is that
the balance is mostly up. The stylistic range can be illustrated by a meal that
began with half a dozen plump prawns on a sauce of lime, tomato and coriander,
went on to duck breast of great taste and tenderness in soy, ginger and plum
sauce, and closed with bread-and-butter pudding filled with apple and raisins
parcelled up neatly in filo.

Flavours stand up well, and experiments work: an impressive and labour-
intensive main course involved stuffing loin of pork with black pudding and
then wrapping it in bacon, the sauce a rich tomato- and herb-based stock. The
menu always features a variety of fish options, and further interest might be

added by pan-fried ostrich fillet. Finish with Russian pear tart, Caledonian whisky parfait, or French farmhouse cheeses. Service has been described as 'distrait' and 'efficient but not over-friendly'. Some fine growers appear on the wine list, and the geographical compass is pleasingly wide. House Bergerac is £9.80.

CHEF: Anthony Ma PROPRIETORS: Jörgen Kunath and Anthony Ma OPEN: Sun L 12 to 2, Tue to Sat D 7 to 10 CLOSED: 26 Dec to 5 Jan, Aug MEALS: Set L Sun £12.50 (2 courses) to £16.10, Set D £16.30 (2 courses) to £20.50 SERVICE: not inc CARDS: Access, Amex, Switch, Visa DETAILS: 55 seats. 10 seats outside. Private parties: 25 main room, 25 private room. Vegetarian meals. Children's helpings. Smart dress preferred. Wheelchair access (no WC). Music

L'Odéon ♥ 　　　　　　　　　　NEW ENTRY map 15

65 Regent Street, W1R 7HH　　　　　　　　　　COOKING 3
TEL: (0171) 287 1400 FAX: (0171) 287 1300　　COST £28–£60

When it opened in November 1995 L'Odéon may have given the impression of being simply another large restaurant for trend-spotters to add to their collection, but Bruno Loubet's involvement ensured that the food would be taken seriously. He has operated traditionally on a small scale, where his own cooking invariably has been excellent, often stunning. His style may not translate directly or easily to a larger format, but after all the hype and first impressions have settled down we are left with a very individual addition to the Central London eating options.

The building follows the curve of Regent Street, with a bar at the top of the stairs, and a dining-area broken up with low-level partitions to create a degree of privacy. The menu is generous, ingredients are generally sound, and components are appropriately cooked, though a question mark occasionally surfaces about whether the elements of a dish really hang together. Supporters, however, are more than happy to revel in the sheer invention and excitement of beetroot tarte Tatin, rabbit in coconut milk, or the signature dish of roast scallops with black pudding and mash. Among undisputed successes have been seared tuna 'of a freshness to please the most fastidious Japanese', served with a well-balanced salsa, and délices du sud-ouest: a plate of duck done five ways – as foie gras, tartare, sausage, wind-dried and in a terrine – which one reporter found 'just bliss on a plate'.

Desserts often get rave notices, too, and have included a refreshing grapefruit jelly with green aniseed ice-cream, and mascarpone and basil ice-cream with prune sauce. Service is matter-of-fact and efficient. A well-spread, modern wine list picks up some exciting bottles while keeping prices at a reasonable level. Wines are grouped by grape variety and style so that, for example, Italian, Californian and Burgundian Chardonnays are listed together, a ruse that may lead drinkers to try new regions. Prices start at £10.50. CELLARMAN'S CHOICE: Pommery Champagne Brut NV, £20; Firesteed Pinot Noir 1994, Oregon, £20.50.

'The reason vegetables are served undercooked is simply that what is left, untouched, in the serving dish can be re-used for the next customer – as I am sure the GFG knows even if it doesn't say so.' (On eating in Dorset)

CHEFS: Bruno Loubet and Anthony Demetre PROPRIETORS: Pierre and Kathleen Condou, and Bruno Loubet OPEN: Mon to Fri L 12 to 2.45, Mon to Sat D 5.30 to 11.30 CLOSED: 25 and 26 Dec, 1 Jan, bank hols MEALS: alc D (main courses £12.50 to £18). Set L £14.50 (2 courses) to £21. Cover £1.50 SERVICE: not inc; 12.5% for parties of 6 or more CARDS: Access, Amex, Delta, Diners, Switch, Visa DETAILS: 290 seats. Private parties: 220 main room, 20 private room. Vegetarian meals. Children's helpings. Smart dress preferred. No cigars/pipes in dining-room. Wheelchair access (also WC). Music. Air-conditioned

Odette's 🍷

130 Regent's Park Road, NW1 8XL
TEL: (0171) 586 5486 and 8766

map 13

COOKING 3
COST £19–£56

This is the best kind of neighbourhood restaurant, offering informality and value for money, a choice of rooms and eating options, and enough variety to keep regulars intrigued. The front dining-room opens up to the street on warm days, the garden room at the back feels light and fresh all year round, and the wine bar is exemplary. Here is thoroughly modern cooking that bristles with ideas: chargrilled ox tongue with black kidney-bean salad, fried eggs and black pudding, and chocolate espresso tart. Accompaniments are as bright as a button too: lime pickle and coriander to go with mackerel fillets, or a barley and chorizo pilaff with a leg of guinea-fowl.

The three-course set lunch is incontestably a bargain; there is no choice, but one example shows the kind of thing to expect for £10: a mousse-like chicken liver parfait with toast and chutney, home-smoked salmon on black olive risotto, and rhubarb and pistachio crème brûlée. The kitchen is careful with timing, sensitive to textures and alive to interesting but not outlandish flavour combinations. Almost any dish demonstrates this; for example, one reporter's thick fillet of roasted cod with a 'light crust and succulent flakes', served with lightly cooked spinach and streaks of 'just enough black olive and chilli sauce to give zest to the dish'. A limited menu may be in place during August.

Service is friendly and relaxed, and the ambience busy and cheerful. The wine list is long but well annotated, easy to negotiate, and arranged by style and in price order. Half-bottles take up two pages and, overall, there is a judicious balance between down-to-earth offerings under £12 and expensive classics. House wines start at £8.95. CELLARMAN'S CHOICE: Madfish Bay Chardonnay 1995, Denmark, Western Australia, £17.75; Au Bon Climat Pinot Noir 1994, Santa Maria, California, £28.50.

CHEF: Paul Holmes PROPRIETOR: Simone Green OPEN: all week L (Sat wine bar only) 12.30 to 2.30, Mon to Sat D 7 to 11 CLOSED: 1 week Christmas, bank hols MEALS: alc (main courses restaurant £8.50 to £15, wine bar £5.50 to £9). Set L £10. BYO £5 SERVICE: not inc CARDS: Access, Amex, Delta, Diners, Switch, Visa DETAILS: 60 seats. 9 seats outside. Private parties: 30 main room, 8 private room. Vegetarian meals. Children's helpings. No music

Olivo

21 Eccleston Street, SW1W 9LX
TEL: (0171) 730 2505

map 13

COOKING 1
COST £24–£47

There cannot be many British restaurants claiming to specialise in Sardinian cooking, and a first glance at Olivo's menu might suggest it is one of the many thousands which don't, what with lentil and carrot soup, artichoke risotto, and fillet of venison with red wine. The small, busy dining-room near Victoria Station runs along trattoria lines, using chargrilling as its main weapon, applying it to a plate of mixed vegetables, escalope of veal, tuna with rocket, and Italian sausages among others. A second distinguishing feature of the Sardinian approach appears to be an even-more-generous-than-usual use of olive oil, and a third is the occasional speciality such as stuffed baby squid with tomatoes, pork neck slices served with Sardinian bread, and spaghetti served with botarga (grated grey mullet roe). Prices are fair, lunch is good value, and the short, well-chosen wine list includes a handful from Sardinia, including house Monica and Nuragus varietals at £9.

CHEF: Sandro Medda   PROPRIETORS: Mauro Sanna and Jean-Louis Journade   OPEN: Mon to Fri L 12 to 2.30, Mon to Sat D 7 to 11   MEALS: alc D (main courses £9 to £15). Set L £13.50 (2 courses) to £15.50. Cover £1.30   SERVICE: not inc   CARDS: Access, Amex, Delta, Switch, Visa   DETAILS: 42 seats. Vegetarian meals. Children's helpings. No cigars in dining-room. Music. Air-conditioned

---

192 ♥

map 13

192 Kensington Park Road, W11 2ES   COOKING 3
TEL: (0171) 229 0482   FAX: (0171) 727 7133   COST £24–£45

'It was Sunday night and still the place was hopping as if in tribal celebration of this hot April evening,' observed a reporter, plunging bravely into the whirlpool of cool that is 192. Most nights it is peopled by a West London tribe straight out of Martin Amis: 'crop-tops, French accents, blonds of indeterminate sex speaking into sleek mobile phones', while the lighting makes its own statement, lurking beneath the seating, and playing over the ceiling in mauve and pink.

In the hands of Albert Clark the cooking has established what for the venue is a rare continuity. Stylistically, it remains close to the 1980s original, with a firm Mediterranean bias, though latterly refined to the nth degree. As a result, things are now probably better than ever. Combinations are not as reckless as at some other places, but the quality of ingredients and honesty of presentation are highly commended. Three fat scallops dribbled with pungent olive oil surround a mound of cubed ratatouille on rocket leaves to make a 'simple but really excellent' starter. Jambon persillé with celeriac rémoulade will similarly stimulate most appetites, or one might opt for a sweet pepper, broccoli and Gruyère tart. An inspector was impressed by a main-course pyramid of 'succulently rare' chicken livers intermingled with pancetta, spinach and chunks of mushroom in a thickly reduced poultry stock. Good vegetable accompaniments include leeks and chanterelles with sea bass, and curly kale and flageolets with roast lamb chump. Tarte Tatin with crème fraîche is A1, and is joined on the dessert list by most of today's favourite puddings.

The wine list travels around the world in 82 bottles; there's plenty to choose from below £20, as well as pricier sections headed 'grand reds and whites'. A commendable number are available by the glass, both large and standard. CELLARMAN'S CHOICE: Vin de Pays d'Oc Chardonnay 1994, Pierre Vidal, £12.75; Ravenswood Vintner's Blend Zinfandel 1993, California, £16.75.

CHEF: Albert Clark   PROPRIETORS: Anthony Mackintosh, John Armit and Tchaik Chassay
OPEN: all week 12.30 to 3 (3.30 Sat and Sun), 7 to 11.30 (11 Sun)   CLOSED: 25 and 26 Dec, Aug
bank hol   MEALS: alc (main courses £9 to £13). Set L Mon to Fri £9.50 (2 courses), Set L Sun
£12.50 (2 courses)   SERVICE: not inc; 12.5% for parties of 6 or more   CARDS: Access, Amex,
Diners, Switch, Visa   DETAILS: 105 seats. 30 seats outside. Private parties: 14 main room, 25
private room. Vegetarian meals. Children welcome. No cigars/pipes in dining room. Wheelchair
access (no WC). Music

L'Oranger ♥

NEW ENTRY   map 15

5 St James's Street, SW1A 1EF
TEL: (0171) 839 3774   FAX: (0171) 839 4330

COOKING 3
COST £32–£44

Short of opening a restaurant in Downing street, addresses do not come much
more establishment than this. St James's Palace is across the way, and some of
the neighbouring businesses have been trading for centuries. L'Oranger is the
most recent of three new openings in St James's Street since the last edition of
the *Guide*, which collectively seems to be telling us that it is all right to consume
conspicuously once again. Thanks to a team from Aubergine (see entry, London)
– including chef and front-of-house staff – L'Oranger has hit the ground running.
A bar leads to a two-part dining-room and, during summer, a small hidden
square for outside eating (evenings only). A conservatory roof lets in light and
mirrors increase the perception of space.

There is a sense of luxury and ease, and the carefully constructed menu backs it
up with appropriate ingredients (smell the truffle oil), but interest and variety
are high too, not least among fish: marinated tuna, sea bream with saffron risotto,
or brill cleverly coated with crispy potato slices. Expertly made pasta is formed
into a single raviolo containing chopped wild mushrooms (or perhaps duck
confit), and fashionable braised ox cheek makes an appearance. Flavours can be
wonderfully strong – in cream of celeriac soup, for instance – although the
tendency to chop things like ratatouille or fruit salad into tiny bits can reduce
their intensity. Nevertheless, techniques are accomplished, and the food
succeeds because it is relatively simple, well considered and accurately cooked.

Puddings have outshone cheeses, in particular banana parfait, fine plum tart,
and passion-fruit crème brûlée. Service is multi-layered and mostly French, as is
the wine list, which majors in the classics: Bordeaux, Burgundy and champagne.
A handful of New World and Italian bins lend support. The list concentrates on
quality, and those looking for a bargain may be disappointed. French house
wines are £15. CELLARMAN'S CHOICE: Cape Mentelle Chardonnay 1994,
Margaret River, W. Australia, £22; Coteaux des Baux, Dom. de Trévallon 1991,
£34.

CHEF: Marcus Wareing   PROPRIETORS: Claudio Pulze and Gordon Ramsay   OPEN: Mon to Sat
L 12 to 3, all week D 6.30 to 11.15 (10.30 Sun)   CLOSED: 1 week Christmas   MEALS: Set L £16 (2
courses) to £19.50, Set D £18 (2 courses) to £22   SERVICE: not inc   CARDS: Access, Amex,
Delta, Diners, Switch, Visa   DETAILS: 64 seats. 20 seats outside. Private parties: 25 private
room. Vegetarian meals. Children welcome. Smart dress preferred. No music. Air-conditioned

*The Guide is totally independent, accepts no free hospitality, and survives on the number
of copies sold each year.*

Orsino ♟   map 12

119 Portland Road, W11 4LN   COOKING 1
TEL: (0171) 221 3299   FAX: (0171) 229 9414   COST £21–£48

The Holland Park sibling of Covent Garden's Orso (see entry below) may sound like a more diminutive member of the family but caters for just as many covers in a full house. In the clinically white and bright surroundings, its repertoire of regional Italian food is out of the same mould. Meals may kick off with a plate of dandelions, broad beans, tomato and Pecorino, or one of the pasta dishes that aim for maximum flavour impact, such as penne with smoked salmon, mascarpone, leeks and radicchio. Substantial entrées run a gamut from the meatier kinds of fish to roast suckling pig with spinach and roast celeriac. Chargrilled sea bass, and a rich and generous seafood pasta, have won praise.

A glass of vin santo with cantucci biscuits may be a better bet than the chocolate and hazelnut cake, described by one diner as 'dry and hard'. Specialists will appreciate the range of Italian coffees. 'Service', noted a reporter, 'is quick and efficient, but not hectic', allowing everybody to relax. The wines are a lively bunch of Italians from some of the trendiest and best producers, supplemented by two champagnes. Umbrian house wine at £10.50 a litre is one of the dozen or so bottles listed at under £15.

CHEF: Annie Kettle   PROPRIETOR: Orsino Restaurants Ltd   OPEN: all week noon to 11   CLOSED: 24 and 25 Dec   MEALS: alc (main courses £6.50 to £14). Set L £11.50 (2 courses) to £13.50   SERVICE: not inc   CARDS: Access, Delta, Switch, Visa   DETAILS: 100 seats. Private parties: 8 main room, 30 private room. Vegetarian meals. Children welcome. No cigars/pipes in dining-room. No-smoking area. No music. Air-conditioned

Orso ♟   map 15

27 Wellington Street, WC2E 7DA   COOKING 1
TEL: (0171) 240 5269   FAX: (0171) 497 2148   COST £21–£47

Monochrome photographs of Italian theatrical types from days gone by light up the apricot walls of Orso, over a decade old now and fast approaching the status of West End institution. Regional Italian cooking – on offer all over London these days, of course – has a longer track record here than in most other places. Black spaghetti with crisp-cooked cuttlefish, tomato and garlic has been 'sensational', and the cheerfully jumbly first-course salads are usually good too. Main courses are typically grills and roasts, and while lamb fillet with chickpeas and olives, or rabbit with spinach and balsamic, might not ignite the palate, amaretto-flavoured mousse of white and dark chocolate delivers 'a lovely combination of flavours and textures' to finish. Service is 'jolly', though delays can occur. Italian wines rise to the lofty heights of Antinori's Solaia at £70, but there is plenty under £20 and quality is consistently high. Umbrian house wines are £10.50 a litre.

CHEF: Martin Wilson   PROPRIETOR: Orso Restaurants Ltd   OPEN: all week noon to midnight   CLOSED: 24 and 25 Dec   MEALS: alc (main courses £10.50 to £13). Set L Sat and Sun £11.50 (2 courses) to £13.50   SERVICE: not inc   CARDS: Access, Delta, Switch, Visa   DETAILS: 100 seats. Private parties: 8 main room. Vegetarian meals. Children welcome. No-smoking area. No music. Air-conditioned

Osteria Antica Bologna ♟

23 Northcote Road, SW11 1NG
TEL: (0171) 978 4771   FAX: (0181) 789 9659

map 12

COOKING 1*
COST £21–£35

The correspondent who described eating at the Osteria as 'like sitting in a wine barrel' was referring not to the bibulous atmosphere but to the heavy wooden ceiling beams that soften the interior shape of the restaurant. Aurelio Spagnuolo has worked assiduously to create the feel of his native Bologna, the point pressed home by the framed old photographs of that city which adorn the walls. Bucolic robustness is the style, dishes such as lamb roasted with prunes and barley leading the charge.

Hand-made stuffed pastas are a speciality, and include tortellacci with radicchio and rucola, while a bowl of sardine soup with tomatoes and tarragon shows that a lighter hand can be equally assured. Crostini di milza – a Sicilian snack involving fried pork spleen with garlic and rosemary – demonstrates that this is not a kitchen content to trot out Italian standards. That said, the chef is very proud of his tiramisù, which eschews cream but uses plenty of mascarpone, strong espresso and chocolate liqueur. The wine list successfully conveys the wide variety and appeal of Italian drinking. Wines are grouped by region, with brief notes supplied for each, and prices are sensible. Sicilian house wines are £7.90 or £2.95 for a large glass. CELLARMAN'S CHOICE: Biancolella dell'Isola d'Ischia 1994, D'Ambra, £14.90; Cabernet Franc 1993, De Tarczal, £16.50.

CHEF: Aurelio Spagnuolo   PROPRIETORS: Rochelle Porteous and Aurelio Spagnuolo   OPEN: Mon to Fri 12 (10 bank hol Mons) to 3, 6 to 11 (11.30 Fri), Sat and Sun 10am to 11.30pm (10.30pm Sun)   CLOSED: 10 days Christmas to New Year   MEALS: alc (main courses £6 to £10). Set L Mon to Sat £7.50 (2 courses). Cover 70p   SERVICE: not inc; 10% for parties of 5 or more   CARDS: Access, Amex, Switch, Visa   DETAILS: 75 seats. 15 seats outside. Vegetarian meals. Children's helpings. No cigars/pipes in dining-room. Wheelchair access (no WC). Music. Air-conditioned

Osteria Basilico £

29 Kensington Park Road, W11 2EU
TEL: (0171) 727 9957 and 9372
FAX: (0171) 229 7980

map 13

COOKING 1
COST £19–£35

Invariably noisy and utterly informal, the Osteria thrives on reasonably priced Italian café-style food served to a youngish crowd. 'The hubbub and simple furnishings were appealing, although the high volume of music discouraged conversation,' observed one reporter. Service is fast, baskets of gutsy bread appear from nowhere and are quickly replenished, and variously shaped pasta is home-made. Pizzas are a staple (there is a take-away service), risotto varies by the day, and chicken, fish and meat are simply chargrilled. Desserts include tiramisù and cantucci biscuits with Vin Santo. 'The house wine (£7.90) appeared in a hand-painted carafe, and was served in simple Duralex glasses.' Many of the 30 or so Italian wines now specify vintages and producers, which is a big improvement; interesting bottles, fair prices and a handful of grappas add to the fun.

CHEF: Alex Palano PROPRIETORS: Adolfo Tiraboschi and Alex Palano OPEN: all week 12.30 to 3 (4 Sat), 6.30 to 11 (10.30 Sun) CLOSED: 25 Dec and 1 Jan MEALS: alc (main courses £5.50 to £9.50). BYO £7 SERVICE: 10% (optional) CARDS: Access, Delta, Switch, Visa DETAILS: 80 seats. 20 seats outside. Private parties: 20 main room. Vegetarian meals. Children welcome. Smart dress preferred. No cigars in dining-room. Music. Air-conditioned

Le Palais du Jardin

map 15

136 Long Acre, WC2E 9AD
TEL: (0171) 379 5353 FAX: (0171) 379 1846

COOKING 1
COST £23–£44

'Having braved the rough seas of noisy folk around the bar, one climbs up to a raised platform to view them beyond rails as if on the deck of a ship,' observed one couple. Le Palais is part French brasserie with a liking for seafood – everyone raves about the oysters – and part metropolitan restaurant: the décor still looks bright and new and the mood is 'elegant without being intimidating'. A trio of marinated salmon, baby scallops and red mullet appears in the style of sushi, halibut is poached and served on pea purée with a saffron sauce, and there are bangers and mash for the die-hards. Other successes have included crab bisque, grilled goats' cheese with a hazelnut crust and pickled pear, prune and armagnac ice-cream, and an assiette of chocolate. Service may be stretched at peak times. The rudimentary wine list does its job affordably. House wine is £8.50.

CHEF: Winston Matthews PROPRIETOR: Le Palais du Jardin Ltd OPEN: all week 12 to 3.30, 5.30 to 12 (11 Sun) CLOSED: 25 and 26 Dec MEALS: alc (main courses £7 to £12.50) SERVICE: 12.5% (optional), card slips closed CARDS: Access, Amex, Delta, Diners, Switch, Visa DETAILS: 250 seats. 26 seats outside. Vegetarian meals. Children's helpings. Wheelchair access (also WC). Music. Air-conditioned

People's Palace

map 13

Royal Festival Hall, SE1 8XX
TEL: (0171) 928 9999 FAX: (0171) 928 2355

COOKING 1
COST £22–£41

Level 3 of the Royal Festival Hall plays host to this vast, sweeping modern brasserie with fine views through trees to the river traffic and the skyline beyond. Gary Rhodes has left, and the cooking is now supervised by Stephen Carter. The RFH itself may hark back to the Festival of Britain, but the menu encompasses feta, pimento and red onion salad, and Moroccan mackerel as well as multi-ethnic pigeon breasts with sauerkraut and chorizo. A reporter commented that there is a feeling of ingredients being combined more in hope than expectation of success, but a first course ballottine of 'deliciously succulent' salmon with a herb coating and chive crème fraîche, and a follow-up spinach-stuffed rabbit leg with little gnocchi and pine-nuts gave cause for rejoicing. A huge chunk of chocolate and hazelnut brownie with a quenelle of vanilla ice-cream is a satisfying way to conclude. The good spread of modern wines at friendly prices suits the People's Palace well. House wines are £9.50, and there is plenty available by the glass.

CHEF: Stephen Carter   PROPRIETORS: the Levin family   OPEN: all week 12 to 3, 5.30 to 11
CLOSED: 25 Dec   MEALS: alc (main courses £6.50 to £12.50). Set L £10.50 (2 courses) to £14.50,
Set D 5.30 to 6.30 £10.50 (2 courses) to £14.50. BYO £9.50   SERVICE: not inc   CARDS: Access,
Amex, Delta, Diners, Switch, Visa   DETAILS: 240 seats. Private parties: 240 main room.
Vegetarian meals. Children's helpings. Wheelchair access (also WC). Music. Air-conditioned

Le P'tit Normand

map 12

185 Merton Road, SW18 5EF
TEL: (0181) 871 0233 and 877 0996

COOKING 1
COST £18–£35

'More authentically French than many a French restaurant' was the verdict of a
pair of newcomers to Philippe Herrard's Normandy bistro in Southfields.
Checkered cloths on the jammed-in tables, the distant strains of Edith Piaf, and a
menu that opens with soupe à l'oignon should provide most of the cultural
signifiers even before the first waiter has opened his mouth. Normandy
specialities predominate, so prawns come in calvados, boudin noir is served
with apples, and crêpes dieppoise are bursting with seafood and properly
browned under a cheesy gratin top. Good sauces add depth to main courses such
as côte de veau and guinea-fowl forestière, although seasoning can be reticent. A
salad may well be a better option than the 'sélection de légumes'. Crème brûlée
and tarte Tatin anointed with flamed calvados are tried and tested crowd-
pleasers, and the crowd that packs the place certainly looks mighty pleased.
House wines at £8.95 are supported by a smattering from Bordeaux, Burgundy
and the Loire.

CHEF/PROPRIETOR: Philippe Herrard   OPEN: Sun to Fri L 12 to 2.30, all week D 7 to 10.30 (11 Fri
and Sat)   MEALS: alc (main courses £9 to £9.50). Set L Mon to Fri £9.95, Set L Sun £11.95
SERVICE: 12.5% (optional)   CARDS: Access, Amex, Delta, Diners, Switch, Visa   DETAILS: 40
seats. Private parties: 24 main room. Children's helpings. Smart dress preferred. No pipes in
dining-room. Wheelchair access (no WC). Music. Air-conditioned

Pied-à-Terre

map 15

34 Charlotte Street, W1P 1HJ
TEL: (0171) 636 1178   FAX: (0171) 916 1171

COOKING 3
COST £35–£82

'Top London chef retires...at 29,' ran the shock-horror headline around Easter
1996 as Richard Neat announced that he was leaving. His old colleague Tom
Aikens, recently at Jamin in Paris with Joël Robuchon, took up the reins a
couple of months later, and the cooking continues in a rich and earthy vein. The
top-end set-price dinner menus are now joined by a somewhat less expensive
option, though this isn't ever going to be the place for cheap eats.
   A pair of fat scallops atop mounds of fondant potato – covered with pea purée
and strips of ventreche bacon – is classic Pied-à-Terre fare. Langoustines in a
salad with asparagus, artichoke and truffle-oiled new potatoes make another
spot-on starter, though as the components of a dish proliferate, there may be a
slight sense of confusion: as in a main course of turbot on creamy potato purée
with creamed leeks, trompettes-de-mort, deep-fried potato cubes and deep-fried
mussels; and a deep-fried scallop, too. A pre-dessert, perhaps a smooth vanilla

cream, comes before your menu choice, which may be caramel and banana parfait accompanied by fine banana ice-cream and caramel sauce. Meals can feel remorselessly richer as they progress, but the technique is of an indisputably high order, so pace yourself carefully to get the best from the experience. Service might be improved. The wine list is excellent, with a host of star producers from most important regions, but mark-ups are steep. Regional France offers the best value, and the fine dessert wines are tempting. House vins de pays are £14.

CHEF: Tom Aikens   PROPRIETOR: David Moore   OPEN: Mon to Fri L 12.15 to 2.15, Mon to Sat D 7 to 10.15   CLOSED: Christmas week, 1 Jan, last 2 weeks Aug, bank hols   MEALS: Set L £22 to £46, Set D £38 (2 courses) to £52   SERVICE: not inc   CARDS: Access, Amex, Delta, Diners, Switch, Visa   DETAILS: 40 seats. Private parties: 8 main room, 12 private room. Children welcome. Smart dress preferred. No music. Air-conditioned

Pizzeria Castello £

map 13

20 Walworth Road, SE1 6SP
TEL: (0171) 703 2556   FAX: (0171) 703 0421

COOKING 1
COST £14–£21

After a decade of eating at this lively pizzeria, a devoted fan is happy to let the memories linger: there is the 'consistent reliable quality of the pizzas, the same familiar faces serving, the bustling atmosphere and the heady waft of garlic that hits you as you emerge from the underground network in Elephant & Castle'. Its reputation and success are clearly defined by the output of the pizza oven. Starters are tried-and-tested staples from the old days – prawn cocktail, avocado vinaigrette – rather than faddish bruschetta and carpaccio. Pasta dishes are filling and hearty and the garlic bread lives up to its name. Drink imported beer or one of the cheap-and-cheerful Italian wines. House wine is £7.20.

CHEF: F. Arrigoni   PROPRIETORS: Renzo Meda and Antonio Proietti   OPEN: Mon to Fri noon to 11, Sat 5 to 11   MEALS: alc (main courses £3.50 to £6). BYO £3   SERVICE: not inc; 10% for parties of 7 or more   CARDS: Access, Amex, Delta, Switch, Visa   DETAILS: 150 seats. Private parties: 50 main room, 30 private room. Vegetarian meals. Children welcome. Smart dress preferred. Wheelchair access (also WC). Music. Air-conditioned

Le Pont de la Tour 🍾

map 13

36D Shad Thames, Butlers Wharf, SE1 2YE
TEL: (0171) 403 8403   FAX: (0171) 403 0267

COOKING 3
COST £30–£73

Everyone admires the view. One of London's most attractive and under-used features – a riverside setting – is enhanced in this case by Tower Bridge, which also serves as a conduit for punters from the City. The gastrodrome attempts to cater for a variety of needs with a busy bar, a shop and a clutch of restaurants (see entries for neighbouring Butlers Wharf Chop House, Cantina del Ponte and Blue Print Café). The feel of Pont de la Tour is 'smart but not stuffy', and fine weather brings outside tables into operation, though these are not bookable.

   The food is a well-considered mixture of fish and shellfish (a Conran speciality), contemporary Franco-Italian marriages (risottos and salads among them), and a good range of fowl, including perhaps woodpigeon with red wine risotto, or roast stuffed quails. Luxuries such as foie gras or cep tart add comforting ballast, and the cooking, to its credit, never gets too tricksy or convoluted. A charge of 'blandness' has been levelled at one or two dishes, but simple buttery accompaniments to lobster or Dover sole are sensible, and bursts of flavour in other instances arise from accompaniments such as a mustard vinaigrette for roast saddle of rabbit.

One reporter experienced 'slick service' while another found it so bad that he vowed never to return. It is not unfriendly, but appears to lack care and proper organisation at times. Then there may be chain-smokers at some tables; with a room this size, it should be possible to sort something out. Then there are the prices: 'When we asked for two glasses of champagne to start, we received a recommendation and took it: we hardly expected a bill for £25.50 for the privilege!' It was Billecart-Salmon 1986, but even so, the resentment it caused is understandable. The wine list astounds with its high prices, but there are many noble wines that deserve them. The champagne section alone is awesome, with vintages dating back to 1962. Dessert wines are another strong suit, with a good number available by the glass. Quality is sky-high. Lottery losers or those in a rush are saved by the inclusion of two house selections, one for bottles under £20, the other under £50. CELLARMAN'S CHOICE: Tim Adams Riesling 1994, Clare Valley, S. Australia, £22.25; Côte de Beaune Maranges 1993, Dom. Vincent Girardin, £29.50.

CHEF: David Burke PROPRIETORS: Sir Terence Conran, Joel Kissin and David Burke OPEN: restaurant all week 12 to 3, 6 to 12 (11 Sun); bar and grill all week noon to midnight (11 Sun) CLOSED: 23 to 27 Dec, Good Fri MEALS: alc (main courses £15.50 to £20). Set L £27.50, Set D Mon to Sat 6 to 6.45 and 10.30 to 11.30 £19.50 SERVICE: 12.5% (optional), card slips closed CARDS: Access, Amex, Diners, Switch, Visa DETAILS: 165 seats. 102 seats outside. Private parties: 8 main room, 20 private room. Car park. Vegetarian meals. Children welcome. Wheelchair access (also WC). Music

Poons £

map 15

4 Leicester Street, WC2H 7BL
TEL: (0171) 437 1528

COOKING 1
COST £15–£41

All three floors of this Chinatown institution teem with life in the evening. The attractions are the central location, low prices and 'interesting, authentic Cantonese' cooking. The smart interior is only just starting to show signs of wear and tear a couple of years after complete refurbishment. The translated menu makes deciphering dishes tricky, but takes in 'rather good' siu mai (steamed pork and prawn dumplings) and boneless chicken sandwiched between wind-dried pork. This is 'interesting, authentic Cantonese food cooked with gusto' – try the deep-fried squid with chilli and garlic – using good ingredients. Drink jasmin tea, tsingtao beer, or house wine at £6.50.

CHEF: Yuan Jin He PROPRIETOR: W.N. Poon OPEN: all week 12 to 11.30 CLOSED: 24 to 28 Dec MEALS: alc (main courses £4 to £25). Set L and D (minimum 2) £13 to £17 SERVICE: not inc CARDS: Access, Switch, Visa DETAILS: 120 seats. Private parties: 60 main room, 20 private room. Vegetarian meals. Children welcome. Music. Air-conditioned

'We were given a plateful of deep-fried parsnip chips which were not a success: a bit like those liquorice sticks we used to chew as kids which looked like tree bark before chewing, and like a mass of hamster bedding afterwards.' (On eating in the West Country)

Quaglino's

map 15

16 Bury Street, SW1Y 6AL
TEL: (0171) 930 6767   FAX: (0171) 839 2866

COOKING 2
COST £24–£67

It is impossible not to be impressed by the subterranean splendour of this dramatic and beautiful dining-room, with its painted pillars, intermittently flaming grill, and shellfish counter at the far end all adding colour. There is lots of movement, and a buzz that only such a big room at full stretch can produce, although the time allocation for a table (one and three-quarter hours) might militate against leisurely enjoyment. Seafood is a strong suit, and its simple freshness has been commended: crab, lobsters and langoustines are typically served with mayonnaise; oysters and caviare by themselves. The fish in fish and chips is better than the chips.

Otherwise there might be roast rabbit with leeks and mustard sauce, or shoulder of pork with crackling and apple sauce. Given the scale of the operation, it is perhaps understandable that a few things slip through the quality net, as a pale liver parfait and a veal escalope saltimbocca did at an inspection dinner, but the meal also produced perfectly good goats' cheese and caramelised onion tart, and a potato pancake spiked with smoked haddock and served with asparagus and hollandaise sauce. Service deals tolerably well with the time constraint, and wines are both varied and interesting; a dozen or so are served by the glass from £3.25 upwards. House french is £11.75 a bottle.

CHEF: Paul Wilson PROPRIETORS: Sir Terence Conran, Joel Kissin, Keith Hobbs and Tom Conran OPEN: all week 12 to 3, 5.30 to 12 (1am Fri and Sat, 11 Sun) CLOSED: 25 and 26 Dec MEALS: alc (main courses £11 to £20). Set L £13.95, Set D 5.30 to 6.30 £13.95 SERVICE: 12.5% (optional), card slips closed CARDS: Access, Amex, Diners, Switch, Visa DETAILS: 350 seats. Private parties: 10 main room, 40 private room. Vegetarian meals. Wheelchair access (also WC). Music. Air-conditioned

Quality Chop House

map 13

94 Farringdon Road, EC1R 3EA
TEL: (0171) 837 5093

COOKING 2
COST £21–£48

Although the Victorian working-class origins of the building may no longer be strictly relevant, the chop house has an informality and a broad enough repertoire to attract all comers. It is small, with shared bench seating, a view into the kitchen, and a menu that takes in artichoke vinaigrette, grilled calf's liver and bacon with 'a mountain of chips', and salmon fish-cake with sorrel sauce. It stays open late enough for suppers of eggs, bacon and chips, corned beef hash, or scrambled eggs with smoked salmon, and also turns out a few French staples such as Toulouse sausage, black pudding with apple compote, and a rouille-laden fish soup with a 'strongly accented but sweet fishy flavour with bags of garlic'. Comforting nursery desserts might include rice pudding or spotted dick. Around 30 mostly French wines (five available by the glass) are supplemented by a few beers. House wine is £9.

CHEF/PROPRIETOR: Charles Fontaine OPEN: Sun to Fri L 12 to 3 (4 Sun), all week D 6.30 (7 Sun) to 11.30 CLOSED: around 22 Dec to 3 Jan MEALS: alc (main courses £6 to £14) SERVICE: not inc CARDS: none DETAILS: 40 seats. Vegetarian meals. Children's helpings. No cigars/pipes in dining-room. No music. Air-conditioned

Quincy's
map 13

675 Finchley Road, NW2 2JP
TEL: (0171) 794 8499

COOKING 1*
COST £31–£38

Finchley Road may surge past outside the window, but Quincy's feels a world away from London blather. It is not grand, nor even especially comfortable, but the unforced warmth extended to everybody who steps through the door is what turns a place like this into a genuine neighbourhood restaurant. David Philpott cooks on, this year filling field mushrooms with salmon mousseline, adding gin and juniper berries to venison and offering vegetarians pumpkin dumplings with tomato, orange and cinnamon. Dinners are fixed-price and represent real value for the level of thought involved. Puddings are of the soothingly indulgent school: sticky toffee, pear Belle Hélène, chocolate and pistachio truffle cake. The well-selected wines are mainly French, with a healthy scattering from the southern hemisphere to add depth. House Duboeuf is £9.

CHEF: David Philpott   PROPRIETOR: David Wardle   OPEN: Tue to Sat D only 7 to 11   CLOSED: 1 week Christmas   MEALS: Set D £24   SERVICE: not inc   CARDS: Access, Amex, Visa   DETAILS: 30 seats. Private parties: 10 main room, 12 private room. Vegetarian meals. Children's helpings. No cigars/pipes in dining-room. Wheelchair access (no WC). Music. Air-conditioned

Ragam £
map 15

57 Cleveland Street, W1P 5PQ
TEL: (0171) 636 9098

COOKING 1
COST £13–£33

Consistency is Ragam's strong point and 'old faithful dishes are turned out very well', according to one seasoned reporter who knows his way round London's ethnic restaurants. The location – opposite Middlesex Hospital Medical School – helps to keep the modest dining-room ticking over, and service remains friendly in an unhurried sort of way. South Indian and Keralan vegetarian specialities are handled with plenty of zip: witness masala dosa and uthappam (a cross between a pizza and a pancake loaded with chillies). Elsewhere the kitchen wins over carnivores with chicken dopiaza and chilli chicken ('more often seen in Southall than the West End', but 'confidently produced' here). Vegetable dishes such as aloo peas are spot on, although breads are reckoned to be 'nothing out of the ordinary'. Lassi suits the food, otherwise drink lager. House wine is £9.

CHEFS: J. Dharmaseelan, G.K.C. Nair and N. Moideen   PROPRIETORS: J. Dharmaseelan, T. Haridas and S. Pillai   OPEN: all week 12 to 3, 6 to 11.15 (11.45 Fri, 11.00 Sun)   CLOSED: 25 and 26 Dec   MEALS: alc (main courses £2.50 to £7). Minimum £6.50. BYO £3   SERVICE: 10%, card slips closed   CARDS: Access, Amex, Diners, Visa   DETAILS: 34 seats. Private parties: 40 main room, 20 private room. Vegetarian meals. Children welcome. Smart dress preferred. Wheelchair access (also WC). Music. Air-conditioned

Rani ✻
map 12

7 Long Lane, N3 2PR
TEL/FAX: (0181) 349 4386

COOKING 1*
COST £22–£34

In a converted shop not far from Finchley Central tube station, Rani offers Gujarati home cooking that can sometimes be a match for anything in London,

135

although one reporter found the unchanging repertoire a little 'boring'. Pickles and chutneys are one of its trademarks, vegetables are genuinely ethnic, and there are daily starters, curries and rice dishes. The plate of mixed bhajias continues to win praise, as does fiery banana curry methi, although one correspondent complains that 'fenugreek turns up far too often on the menu'. Masala dosai is served as a main meal for one person, and there is an enterprising menu for children. Breads include 'delicious' stuffed paratha. Service has been called 'friendly' and 'poor'. On the plus side the menu is available in braille. Drinks range from lassi and falooda to Cobra beer and a handful of affordable wines. House wine is £8.60. A newish branch has opened in Richmond (see Round-up entry).

CHEF: Sheila Pattni   PROPRIETOR: Jyotindra Pattni   OPEN: all week D only 6 to 10.30   CLOSED: 25 Dec, 1 Jan   MEALS: alc (main courses £6.50 to £11). Set D £12.90 to £16.50. Minimum £10 Sat. BYO £5   SERVICE: not inc; 10% for parties of 7 or more   CARDS: Access, Amex, Delta, Switch, Visa   DETAILS: 90 seats. Private parties: 56 main room, 23 private room. Vegetarian meals. Children's helpings. Smart dress preferred. No smoking in 1 dining-room. No cigars/pipes in dining-room. Wheelchair access (no WC). Music

Ransome's Dock ♥ ⅚✳   map 12

35–37 Parkgate Road, SW11 4NP
TEL: (0171) 223 1611 and 924 2462   COOKING 2*
FAX: (0171) 924 2614   COST £25–£51

No sooner had last year's *Guide* appeared with its comment that some found the window tables overlooking the river a little draughty in winter than the installation of double-glazing had been completed. Shiver no more. Martin Lam's waterside restaurant has a 'lived-in feel', according to one reporter, although the menu does its best to keep things fresh and new, rustling up first courses of Thai chicken soup with lemon grass and coconut, or watercress salad with Gorgonzola, walnuts and blood orange. Grilled new season's lamb with fondant potatoes, spinach and pine-nuts has impressed hugely, not least for the 'first-class tender meat'.

Desserts offer some diverting flavours, such as baked banana with cardamom, orange and rum, ricotta cheesecake with blueberries, and good old rhubarb fool. Strong coffee and excellent service are commended. Exciting bottles litter the wine list, including sparkling Shiraz from Australia, Lustau Almacenista sherries, and a lively and ever-changing set of wines by the glass. Wines are grouped by style, taking in some fashionable and unusual grape varieties. Dessert wines are a strong suit. House wines start at £11.50. CELLARMAN'S CHOICE: Mitchelton III 1993, Goulburn Valley, Victoria, Australia, £15; Côtes du Rhône, Coudoulet de Beaucastel 1990, £21.

CHEF: Martin Lam   PROPRIETORS: Martin and Vanessa Lam   OPEN: Mon to Fri noon to 11, Sat noon to midnight, Sun 11.30 to 3.30   CLOSED: Christmas, Easter Mon, Aug bank hol   MEALS: alc (main courses £9 to £16.50 not available Sat and Sun L). Set L Mon to Fri £11.50 (2 courses). Brunch menu L Sat and Sun. BYO £5.50   SERVICE: not inc   CARDS: Access, Amex, Delta, Diners, Switch, Visa   DETAILS: 84 seats. 25 seats outside. Private parties: 14 main room, 30 private room. Car park. Vegetarian meals. Children's helpings. Smart dress preferred. No smoking in 1 dining-room. Wheelchair access (also WC). Music. Air-conditioned

Rasa 🌢❋ £ map 12

55 Stoke Newington Church Street, N16 0AR	COOKING 1*
TEL: (0171) 249 0344 FAX: (0181) 802 6695	COST £18–£29

'The food really shines' at this quietly civilised Indian restaurant. Since opening in 1994, chef Sivadas Padmanabhan has not only introduced a new audience to the freshness and delicacy of Keralan vegetarian cuisine, but has made Rasa a local focus for Indian cultural life. The menu features a few familiar dishes such as mysore bonda (spicy deep-fried potato balls) and bhel pooris, but moves quickly into enthralling uncharted territory. Even the dazzlingly good home-made relishes are 'quite unlike the luminous gloop served in many Indian restaurants'. Kappa and kadala curry – spiced chickpeas with a separate dish containing chunks of whole tapioca root – is endorsed regularly, along with idiappam (steamed rice noodles) with vegetable korma. The back-up is equally impressive: stir-fried green banana thoran, 'excellent' lemon rice, sensational parathas 'coiled in the shape of a coir mat', 'super' kulfi. Big bottles of Cobra beer suit the food, or you could opt for one of the workaday wines. House wine is £7.25.

CHEF: Sivadas Padmanabhan   PROPRIETOR: Rasa Ltd   OPEN: Tue to Sun L 12 to 2.30, all week D 6 to 11 (12 Fri and Sat)   CLOSED: 25 and 26 Dec   MEALS: alc (main courses £4.50 to £5.50) SERVICE: not inc   CARDS: Access, Amex, Delta, Diners, Visa   DETAILS: 42 seats. Private parties: 20 main room. Vegetarian meals. Children welcome. Smart dress preferred. No smoking in dining-room. Wheelchair access (no WC). Music. Air-conditioned

Red Pepper **NEW ENTRY** map 13

8 Formosa Street, W9 1EE	COOKING 1*
TEL: (0171) 266 2708	COST £22–£33

Red Pepper is a thoroughly Italian restaurant in Maida Vale, full of hustle-bustle and centred on a magnificently domed wood-fired pizza oven. You eat cheek by jowl with your neighbours in a world of stripped pine against a 'dashing' colour scheme, the tables attended by efficient boiler-suited waitresses. Pizzas are the speciality, and include an 'absolutely first-rate' version of quattro stagioni using baby artichoke, mushrooms, black olives and shaved ham. Grilled marinated vegetables as a starter capture the atmosphere, a laden plateful of well-oiled peppers, aubergine, celeriac and so forth. Other dishes include a salad of octopus with French beans and roasted onions, ink-black tagliolini with scallops and saffron, and linguine with clams and chilli. Garlic bread uses a pizza base and plenty of olive oil. Finish with tiramisù, chocolate mousse, or frozen yoghurt. The short wine list impressively crams in as many Italian regions as it can at manageable prices. House wines are £9.

CHEFS: Manni Pasqual and Franco Parisi   PROPRIETORS: Mr and Mrs B. Behzadi   OPEN: Sat L 12.30 to 2.30, Sun L 12.30 to 3.30, all week D 6.30 to 10.45 (10.30 Sun)   MEALS: alc (main courses £6 to £8.50)   SERVICE: not inc; 12.5% for parties of 5 or more   CARDS: Access, Delta, Switch, Visa   DETAILS: 50 seats. 15 seats outside. Private parties: 25 main room. Vegetarian meals. Children's helpings. No cigars in dining-room. Wheelchair access (no WC). Music. Air-conditioned

Riva

map 12

169 Church Road, SW13 9HR
TEL: (0181) 748 0434

COOKING 2
COST £25–£49

'An interesting menu, good food and helpful service,' summed up one reporter of this uncompromising Italian restaurant. The long, narrow, mirrored room is thrown open on warm evenings to accommodate a couple of tables on the pavement. Andrea Riva's food is based on that of north-east Italy, a region bounded by the Alps, the River Po and the Adriatic Sea. The Po provides rice for risotto (here served with porcini if you are lucky), and the sea inspires a whole range of dishes from grilled squid with herbs, to sea bass baked in a bag.

In true Italian style, variety and invention are trade marks of a kitchen that turns out gnocchi alla Friulana (potato and prune dumplings served with sage butter), roast goose stuffed with cotechino (served with cabbage and lentils), and a dessert of toasted bread, Gorgonzola, chestnut-flavoured honey and pears. Riva continues to divide readers: some will never return, others cannot get enough. 'Very simple, very rustic, very tasty,' concluded one reporter, impressed by the heart-on-sleeve honesty of the place. The short, serviceable wine list includes excellent wines from Jermann in Friuli, as well as an intelligent sampling from other regions. House wine is £9.75.

CHEF: Francesco Zanchetta PROPRIETOR: Andrea Riva OPEN: Sun to Fri L 12.15 to 2.30, all week D 7 to 11 (11.30 Fri and Sat, 9.30 Sun) CLOSED: Christmas, Easter, last 2 weeks Aug, bank hols MEALS: alc (main courses £7 to £14.50) SERVICE: 10%, card slips closed CARDS: Access, Amex, Delta, Switch, Visa DETAILS: 50 seats. 8 seats outside. Private parties: 40 main room. Vegetarian meals. Children welcome. Smart dress preferred. No cigars/pipes in dining-room. Wheelchair access (no WC). Music. Air-conditioned

River Café ▼

map 12

Thames Wharf Studios, Rainville Road, W6 9HA
TEL: (0171) 381 8824 FAX: (0171) 381 6217

COOKING 3
COST £34–£67

The River Café may be difficult to find, but the car is valet-parked and ready and waiting on departure: standard procedure, perhaps, for the showbiz customers. Inside, all is glass and chrome, and the whole operation has a clean and purposeful feel. Work goes on behind a long stainless-steel counter, while bowls of colourful vegetables sit on top waiting to be spooned on to plates as an antipasto, or to accompany predominantly fishy main-course grills and roasts. Food and décor are both state-of-the-art.

Reliance on chargrilling and the wood-burning oven inevitably limits variety, but these simple techniques expose the excellence of ingredients. What is served is extremely good of its kind, including perhaps a spiedino of 'brilliantly fresh and juicy' scallops and monkfish, skewered on a twig of thyme. Fruit and vegetables abound among the listed ingredients: fennel tops, artichokes, boiled and salted Sicilian lemons, Swiss chard, black and green figs. Dishes may be served warm rather than hot, and rocket appears to garnish 'nearly everything on offer'.

All in all, reporters are happy with the food, including lemon tart with crisp pastry and a sharp filling, ricotta cake, and the regular chocolate nemesis, not to mention the tiny glasses of strong espresso. Problems occur elsewhere. 'Overcrowded and overpriced' sums up the views of more than one reporter, and it seems that a degree of tolerance (towards smokers, for example) is required to get the best out of the River Café. Planning restrictions require the premises to be vacated by 11 o'clock, and two sittings are the penalty of a last-minute booking. Staff may lack expertise, but the welcome is friendly, intentions are good, and they go out of their way to be helpful. Wines reflect the wide variety of styles and flavours that Italy, particularly northern Italy, produces. Fine dessert wines include Recioto della Valpolicella, Moscato d'Asti and Torcolato. It would be easy to splash out on many of the top Italian bottles featured, but Bianco di Custoza kicks off at a sensible £9.50.

CHEFS: Rose Gray, Ruth Rogers and Theo Randall   PROPRIETORS: Richard and Ruth Rogers, and Rose Gray   OPEN: all week L 12.30 (1 Sun) to 3, Mon to Sat D 7.30 to 9.30   CLOSED: Christmas to New Year, Easter   MEALS: alc (main courses £12 to £24)   SERVICE: 12.5%, card slips closed   CARDS: Access, Amex, Delta, Switch, Visa   DETAILS: 90 seats. 60 seats outside. Car park D. Children's helpings. No cigars/pipes in dining-room. Wheelchair access (also WC). No music

Royal China   map 13

13 Queensway, W2 4QJ	COOKING 2*
TEL: (0171) 221 2535	COST £24–£70

At weekends the queues start well before opening time for arguably 'the best dim-sum in London'. This is a well-tuned operation: names are taken outside, allowing you to be whisked to your table promptly, waitresses bring dishes of stir-fried greens to whet the appetite, and tea awaits. Delicate scallop dumplings, deep-fried prawns, cheung-fun and glutinous rice are first-rate, but 'the pinnacle of achievement' is reckoned to be 'divine' prawn dumplings with coriander.

Intense popularity has led to the enlargement of this most opulent of Chinese restaurants, with its dramatic black and gold décor and motifs of soaring birds. The menu shows influences from much of the provincial repertoire, with Cantonese dishes to the fore. The 'house soup', which varies daily and only appears on the 'Chinese menu', is worth enquiring about: on one occasion this was a brilliant limpid consommé with chunks of papaya and pork knuckle arranged separately on a plate. Other fine renditions have included boned spare ribs with spicy salt, rich steamed eel in black-bean sauce, and 'outstanding' Singapore noodles. Service is smart and cool. Drink jasmine tea or something from the carefully assembled wine list. House wine is £8.50. A second branch is in Putney, at 3 Chelverton Road, SW15; tel: (0181) 788 0907

CHEFS: Wai-Hung Law and Simon Man   PROPRIETOR: Playwell Ltd   OPEN: all week noon to 11 (10.30 Sun)   CLOSED: 23 to 25 Dec   MEALS: alc (main courses £5.50 to £18). Set D (minimum 2) £22 to £28. Dim-sum available noon to 4   SERVICE: 12.5%   CARDS: Access, Amex, Diners, Switch, Visa   DETAILS: 100 seats. Private parties: 80 main room, 12 private room. Vegetarian meals. Children welcome. Smart dress preferred. Music. Air-conditioned

'Our suspicions should have been aroused before our arrival, for the brief letter acknowledging our booking contained eight spelling errors.' (On eating in Cumbria)

▲ Royal Garden Hotel, The Tenth

| NEW ENTRY | map 13

2–24 Kensington High Street, W8 4PT
TEL: (0171) 361 1910 and 937 8000
FAX: (0171) 361 1991

COOKING 3*
COST £31–£55

Take a lift to the tenth floor and emerge to enjoy a beautiful panorama of Kensington Palace Gardens. Once the effect of the view begins to wear off, the dining-room seems increasingly bizarre, partly thanks to a series of back-lit panels against one wall that change colour every few seconds, giving the impression of a 1970s disco, to which live and taped music add their own contribution. But don't go away. The restaurant contradicts one reporter's usually reliable finding that 'food gets worse as you go higher: witness revolving restaurants, ski lodges and airline food'.

Paul Farr's menu is an accomplished marriage of classical tehniques and contemporary ideas, ranging from crab and saffron soufflé pudding with watercress butter, to braised pork knuckle with lentils. A piece of mustard-crusted halibut at inspection was 'timed to perfection, full of flavour', and with delightful texture, served on a bed of mashed potato, with salsify and a butter sauce. The food may suffer a little from the let's-just-add-one-more-flavour kind of cooking that can dog grand-hotel dining, but treatment of components has been exemplary in a breast of corn-fed chicken with flavour 'like it used to have', served on a lattice of fennel, with deep-fried aubergine, a salsa verde, a garlic-flavoured stuffing, potato chips, and carrots cooked with thyme. Cheeses arrive in good condition, and desserts have kept up the standard with hot lemon meringue tart, and baked pear (succulent and still firm) into which two leaves of dark chocolate were melting, on a well-made almond ice-cream in a pool of honey. Instead of the expected tome of clarets, a short, sharp modern wine list does the food proud. House wines are £12.50.

CHEF: Paul Farr PROPRIETOR: Goodwood Group OPEN: Sun to Fri L 12 to 2.30 (3 Sun), Mon to Sat D 5.30 to 11.30 CLOSED: bank hols MEALS: alc (main courses £10.50 to £18). Set L and D (before 7pm) £15.95 (2 courses) to £19.95 SERVICE: not inc CARDS: Access, Amex, Delta, Diners, Switch, Visa DETAILS: 90 seats. Private parties: 200 main room. Vegetarian meals. Children welcome. Smart dress preferred. No-smoking area. Wheelchair access (also WC). Music. Air-conditioned ACCOMMODATION: 402 rooms, all with bath/shower. TV. Phone. Air-conditioned. Room only £170 to £999. Rooms for disabled. Lift. Children welcome. Baby facilities. Afternoon teas

RSJ ▐

map 13

13A Coin Street, SE1 8YQ
TEL: (0171) 928 4554

COOKING 1*
COST £23–£44

RSJ continues more or less serenely on its way, clocking up 17 years on the site. The appeal is wonderful Loire wines and a sensibly modern menu that makes as much noise about fish and vegetable main courses as it does about meat ones. Inside, it is light, bright and welcoming, and service adjusts comfortably to those with other business on the South Bank. Soups are well reported, including gazpacho and chicken consommé, risotto (of wild musrooms) is properly executed, and a leek and crab tart impresses for its crisp pastry and creamy filling. At inspection a good-quality fillet of beef, cooked pink, with leeks, shallots and a red wine sauce was a great success.

As for wines, Loire is the speciality, and it is heart-warming to see this much-underrated region given due recognition. Fifteen pages of wines flow along every curve in the Loire river; four pages are devoted entirely to sweet wines from the area. Highlights include a dozen Vouvrays from Huet and a pair of wines from cult vineyard Clos de la Coulée-de-Serrant. Halves are plentiful. Should you choose to reject the Loire, head for the small range of wines from Australian Adam Wynn. House wines from Anjou are £9.95. CELLARMAN'S CHOICE: Touraine, Sauvignon 1995, J.M. & T. Puzelat, £12.95; Bourgueil Les Galichets 1993, Pierre Breton, £15.95.

CHEF: Ian Stabler   PROPRIETOR: Nigel Wilkinson   OPEN: Mon to Fri L 12 to 2, Mon to Sat D 6 (5.45 Sat) to 11   CLOSED: 4 days Christmas, bank hols   MEALS: alc (main courses £11 to £15). Set L and D £14.50 (2 courses) to £15.95   SERVICE: 10%, card slips closed   CARDS: Access, Amex, Delta, Switch, Visa   DETAILS: 95 seats. 12 seats outside. Private parties: 20 main room, 16 private room. Vegetarian meals. Children's helpings. No cigars/pipes in dining-room. Music. Air-conditioned

Rules   map 15

35 Maiden Lane, WC2E 7LB   NEW CHEF
TEL: (0171) 836 5314   FAX: (0171) 497 1081   COST £32–£47

At London's oldest restaurant there is a genuine feeling of days gone by, as crisply proper as the damask tablecloths, but with a diverting sense of camp, too, in the portraits of legendary actor-managers that crowd the walls. The fare is traditional British in the most enjoyably unreconstructed way: winged and quadruped game in season, from ptarmigan to roe-deer, mighty pies and native oysters.

As we went to press Rory Kennedy (ex-Hanbury Manor, Thundridge) was appointed head chef, ready to take up his duties in the autumn of 1996, which is why we are unable to award a cooking mark. Wines 'from the former colonies', as the list puts it, include claret; but of Burgundy (customary partner to game) there is not a drop. House wines are £9.75.

CHEFS: Rory Kennedy and Frank Wilkinson   PROPRIETOR: John Mayhew   OPEN: all week noon to 11.30 (10.30 Sun)   CLOSED: 4 days Christmas   MEALS: alc (main courses £13 to £16). Set L Sat and Sun 12 to 4 £14.95 (2 courses), Set pre-theatre D Mon to Fri 3 to 6 £14.95 (2 courses) SERVICE: not inc, card slips closed   CARDS: Access, Amex, Delta, Diners, Switch, Visa DETAILS: 230 seats. Private parties: 18 to 55 private rooms. Vegetarian meals. Children's helpings. Wheelchair access (no WC). No music. Air-conditioned

Sabras £   map 12

263 High Road, Willesden Green, NW10 2RX   COOKING 2
TEL: (0181) 459 0340   COST £19–£31

A world away from 'the average high-street Indian restaurant', Sabras remains a beacon in a desolate neighbourhood close to Willesden bus garage. It is a tiny, brightly lit, civilised place, sometimes virtually deserted, sometimes so crowded that the owners may have to turn people away unless they have booked. The kitchen cooks to order – which can mean delays – but the food is genuinely fresh and worth the wait. What it offers is, quite simply, some of the best Gujarati vegetarian food in the capital – yet it seems to survive on a knife-edge.

The backbone of the menu is a heady mix of blisteringly good home-made pickles and chutneys, farsan snacks, excellent dosai, and a great harvest of ethnic vegetables seldom found in comparable establishments. As the *Guide* went to press, many new dishes were about to be unleashed on the public: red onion raita, sakkariya (slow-cooked sweet potato with spices), orange pumpkin with gowar (green cluster beans), and mamaji's patish (fried gram flour savouries and 'ten selected ingredients' covered with mashed potato), for example. Thalis are served until eight o'clock. Drink lassi, or explore the remarkable range of imported beers. House wine, from Australia, is £9.50.

CHEFS/PROPRIETORS: Hemant and Nalinee Desai   OPEN: Tue to Sun D only 6.30 to 10.30   MEALS: alc (main courses £4 to £6.50). Set D 6.30 to 8 £10 to £15   SERVICE: not inc   CARDS: none   DETAILS: 32 seats. Private parties: 32 main room. Vegetarian meals. Children welcome. Smart dress preferred. Wheelchair access (no WC). Music

Saga
map 15

43–44 South Molton Street, W1V 1HB   COOKING 1*
TEL: (0171) 408 2236   FAX: (0171) 629 7507   COST £19–£89

'Our guests are almost 80 per cent Japanese,' note the proprietors of this swish venue in the heart of big-money Mayfair. The ground floor of Saga is mostly taken up with a sushi bar, where Mr Kikuchi slices fish with confidence and moulds parcels of vinegared rice. Downstairs is a labyrinthine hive of discreetly screened dining areas where guests can sample traditional Japanese cuisine. The menu of many sections covers everything from sashimi to sukiyaki, taking in soups, salads, simmered nimono dishes, yakitori and much more. A glance at the list of side-dishes will reveal many curiosities, such as aradaki (a 'gourmet dish' described as 'heads and bony part of fish simmered in special sauce'), ika shiokara (pickled squid with grated mooli), and hatsu shio yaki (grilled chicken heart with salt). For slurping, there are also bowls of udon and soba noodles. Scores of whiskies and sakés bolster the wine list; house French is £12.90.

CHEFS: Mr Kikuchi and Mr Tominaga   PROPRIETOR: Mr K. Hashimoto   OPEN: Mon to Sat 12.30 to 2.30, 6.30 to 10   CLOSED: 24, 25 and 31 Dec, 1 Jan   MEALS: alc (main courses £6.50 to £22). Set L £7.50 to £18, Set D (to 9.30) £35 to £55. Cover £1. Minimum £7.50   SERVICE: not inc L, 15% D   CARDS: Access, Amex, Delta, Diners, Switch, Visa   DETAILS: 100 seats. Private parties: 30 main room, 6 and 12 private rooms. Vegetarian meals. No cigars/pipes in dining-room. Music. Air-conditioned

Saint
NEW ENTRY   map 15

8 Great Newport Street, WC2H 7JA   COOKING 2
TEL: (0171) 240 1551   FAX: (0171) 240 0829   COST £23–£47

Saint is the reincarnation of the Newport, with new owners and a new attitude to things. 'We have a dress code – no suits allowed,' one reporter was informed when booking. At this stylishly modern basement, where the bar operates right through the day, expect noisy music, a young crowd and exceptionally agreeable service. Co-chef Kerwin Browne worked at Fulham Road (see entry, London), and the pedigree shows.

The menu 'reads wonderfully', and the short list of 'amuse' (light appetisers) tells you how the kitchen thinks: charred squid with olives and samphire, palm hearts and asparagus wrapped in nori with chilli dip, and potted shrimps with sweet cucumber salad suggest some serious alchemy between East and West. Warm salads are superbly executed, and soups are unashamedly oriental. Roast corn-fed chicken is served in a soup-bowl on a bed of mash surrounded by steamed spring vegetables ('the simplicity and restraint were masterly,' noted one correspondent). Fish is similarly handled: sea bass, for example, is pan-roasted and served with fennel salad, roasted plum tomatoes and red pepper. Desserts such as a meringue of Muscavado sugar and roasted banana are unexpected but highly enjoyable. New York martinis and imported beers bolster the short, modern wine list. House wines start at £9.50.

CHEFS: Kerwin Browne and Neale White   PROPRIETORS: Eric Yu and Connie O'Donovan   OPEN: Mon to Fri L 12 to 3, Mon to Sat D 6.30 to 11   CLOSED: 25 Dec, 1 Jan, bank hols   MEALS: alc D (main courses £7 to £15). Set L £13.50 (2 courses) to £16.50. Bar food available   SERVICE: not inc   CARDS: Access, Amex, Delta, Diners, Switch, Visa   DETAILS: 50 seats. Private parties: 250 main room. Vegetarian meals. No children under 18. Smart dress preferred. Wheelchair access (also WC). Music. Air-conditioned

---

▲ St George's Hotel, The Heights 🍴   map 15

Langham Place, W1N 8QS
TEL: (0171) 636 1939   FAX: (0171) 436 7997

COOKING 2
COST £36–£61

The view from the fifteenth floor is equally well suited to business lunches as to enjoying a 'superb' if largely sodium-coloured vista at night. Face the other way for clean lines and a white grand piano in an otherwise rather plain and elongated room. Nick Evenden, new since last year, produces modern European dishes of pumpkin ravioli, or a carpaccio of scallops and tuna with a dandelion and lime dressing. He is fond of serving things with pancetta or 'bits of bacon', as one correspondent found in consecutive dishes of pigeon salad and rump of lamb, and obviously enjoys pasta.

Reporters agree that the food is best when at its most straightforward, as in roast monkfish with a herb risotto, or in layers of flat pasta around a lobster mousse, both dishes reflecting the kitchen's sympathy with fish. Materials are good, though the food can fall over itself in an effort to make a splash with, say, a mango tarte Tatin that seems to miss the point of the original dish. Water adds to the already substantial cost, as do many of the wines, though six house wines and around twenty others are under £20.

CHEF: Nick Evenden   PROPRIETOR: Forte Hotels (UK) Ltd   OPEN: Mon to Fri L 12 to 2, Mon to Sat D 7 to 10   CLOSED: D 25 Dec, 1 Jan   MEALS: alc (main courses £17 to £18.50). Set L £17.50 (2 courses) to £23. Light meals available   SERVICE: not inc, card slips closed   CARDS: Access, Amex, Delta, Diners, Switch, Visa   DETAILS: 75 seats. Private parties: 75 main room, 10 and 30 private rooms. Vegetarian meals. Children welcome. Smart dress preferred. Wheelchair access (no WC). Music   ACCOMMODATION: 86 rooms, all with bath/shower. TV. Phone. B&B £140 to £170. Children welcome. Baby facilities. Dogs welcome by arrangement. Afternoon teas

St John

map 13

26 St John Street, EC1M 4AY
TEL: (0171) 251 0848 and 4998
FAX: (0171) 251 4090

COOKING 2*
COST £27–£45

The converted smokehouse just north of Smithfield Market is painted white, old chimneys surround the bar, and the busy canteen-like dining-room has industrial lighting and a view of the kitchen. Fergus Henderson likes to describe his food as New English, although the foundation is an old idea that goes to the very heart of the restaurant's purpose. Why kill a whole animal and just use the fillet or the leg? What about the cheeks, the muzzle, the marrow in the bones, the tail, kidneys, liver, heart, neck? All these find their way on to the menu, and the effect is one of earthiness and simple variety, producing grilled ox-heart with rocket and pickled shallots, duck neck and gizzard terrine, and the signature dish of roast bone-marrow and parsley salad.

The restaurant also deals in non-meat dishes – carrot with boiled egg and aïoli, or potato pie – as well as fish (cod and lentils) and fowl (pheasant with black cabbage). Puddings reminded one reporter of school dinners, though thankfully in name only: rhubarb and custard tart, or a sophisticated queen of puddings, made from ginger and fig. It is not necessary to eat three courses – the bar serves half a dozen rock oysters and a pint of Guinness for £5. Service is 'efficient but eccentric with antipodean informality'. Wines are entirely French, with an appropriate emphasis on reds to match offal, a Tokai for dessert, and five sherries available by the glass from £2.10.

CHEF: Fergus Henderson   PROPRIETORS: Trevor Gulliver, Fergus Henderson and Jon Spiteri   OPEN: restaurant Mon to Fri L 12 to 3 (3.30 Sun), Mon to Sat D 6 to 11.30. Bar food available Mon to Fri 11am to 11pm,   MEALS: alc (main courses £8 to £12.50).   SERVICE: not inc   CARDS: Access, Amex, Delta, Diners, Switch, Visa   DETAILS: 120 seats. Private parties: 150 main room, 22 private room. Vegetarian meals. Children's helpings. No music

Salloos

map 14

62–64 Kinnerton Street, SW1X 8ER
TEL: (0171) 235 4444

COOKING 2
COST £27–£60

The Salahuddins (Salloos to their friends) opened a restaurant in Pakistan in 1969, based on a blend of Mogul and home cooking, and moved to London in 1976. Abdul Aziz has been with them since the very beginning. What sets the food apart is quality and freshness, making it some of the finest of its kind in London. Tandoori dishes are the mainstay, including lamb chops ('the most popular starter') and quails. Good marinating helps, and the fresh spicing – 'no curry powder or paste in our kitchen,' writes Mr Salahuddin – is what separates it from the also-rans.

Among the 'specialities' are whole leg of lamb, and chicken with ginger and chillies served sizzling in a karahi. Care extends to incidentals: home-made chutneys, excellent nan, rice, and properly cooked lentil and chickpea dishes. 'For those of us who dine regularly in Southall,' writes one reporter, 'the bill comes as a bit of a shock,' although this is Belgravia, and it is fair to say that some other restaurants of a similar standard in the *Guide* can cost more. Look to the Corney & Barrow section of the wine list for best value. House French is £12.50.

CHEFS: Abdul Aziz and Humayun Khan PROPRIETORS: Mr and Mrs M. Salahuddin OPEN: Mon to Sat 12 to 2.30, 7 to 11.15 CLOSED: Christmas MEALS: alc (main courses £11 to £17). Set L £16, Set D £25. Cover £1.50 SERVICE: 12.5% (optional), card slips closed CARDS: Access, Amex, Delta, Diners, Switch, Visa DETAILS: 65 seats. Private parties: 65 main room. Vegetarian meals. Children welcome. No children under 6 after 8. Smart dress preferred. No music. Air-conditioned

Les Saveurs 🦐
map 15

37A Curzon Street, W1Y 7AF   COOKING 4
TEL: (0171) 491 8919   FAX: (0171) 491 3658   COST £37–£98

With the departure of Joël Antunès in mid-1996 Marco Pierre White took over the running of this smart Mayfair address, installing a team from The Restaurant (see entry, Hyde Park Hotel, London). The style may have changed, but the standard of cooking remains extremely high. Entry from Curzon Street is through a hallway, past a display of white lilies, and down a flight of stairs into an elegant basement dining-room with light wood-panelled walls and discreet lighting. The menu is that modern enigma, a set-price à la carte, which in effect means a generous and well-balanced choice of about eight items per course.

Among trade-mark dishes might be a chicken liver and foie gras parfait with Poilâne bread, or oysters in a light jelly with watercress. The White preoccupation with fish is also reflected in the general tilt of the menu, taking in marinated salmon in a pool of beurre blanc, or well-timed herb-crusted cod, or a dish of three lightly grilled scallops 'cooked to perfection' on a garlic purée with a carefully judged sorrel-flecked sauce. Accurate timing, fine judgement and balance are impressive characteristics of the cooking.

One reporter considered his saddle of rabbit with a pea risotto 'a work of art'. Moist meat and creamy risotto in which 'all the tastes rang loud and clear' were helped along by a novel and finicky addition of mange-tout stuffed with pea purée. Another's Bresse chicken was 'full of the wonderful flavour that chicken never seems to have these days', served with a few girolles and a simple *jus* of the chicken's own cooking juices. Mint-flavoured chocolate marquise has come in for praise, and The Restaurant's 'pyramid' desserts have been quick to make the short hop across Mayfair, producing one of liquorice and pistachio, and a successful variation on the theme of nougat glacé and passion-fruit. Meals begin with a first-rate appetiser and end with excellent coffee and petits fours. Two things took the shine off an otherwise 'exemplary' inspection meal: some very poor cheeses, which should be easy enough to fix, and some 'surly, arrogant' service that was at odds with the maître d's air of charm and gentility. House wine is £17.50.

CHEF: Richard Stewart PROPRIETOR: Marco Pierre White OPEN: Mon to Fri 12 to 2.30, 7 to 10.30 CLOSED: 2 weeks Christmas to New Year, 2 weeks Aug MEALS: Set L £17 (2 courses) to £47, Set D £38 to £47 SERVICE: not inc CARDS: Access, Amex, Delta, Diners, Switch, Visa DETAILS: 50 seats. Private parties: 10 main room, 10 private room. No children under 5. Jacket and tie. No pipes in dining-room. No music. Air-conditioned

'By now it was snowing extremely hard, Nature's laudable attempt to decrease the temperature outside to that suffered inside.' (On eating in Dorset in December)

▲ The Savoy, Grill Room

map 15

Strand, WC2R 0EU   COOKING 3
TEL: (0171) 836 4343   FAX: (0171) 240 6040   COST £46–£83

'Our overriding impression was one of excellence,' summed up a reporter who
appeared to enjoy the service as much as the food. The Grill doesn't have the
River Restaurant's view, nor the sympathetic Upstairs pricing (see entries
below), but it does have the best food of the three. Classic Franco-British fare is
the substance, and we use the word 'substance' advisedly since it can run to beef
Wellington, kidneys and bacon, or roast breast of pigeon stuffed with truffle,
shiitakes and celeriac.

The appeal lies in comforting pea and ham soup, omelette Arnold Bennett, or
one of the daily options: sausage and mash for Monday lunch, steak and kidney
pudding on Tuesday. Dinner also has its weekly cycle. The French end of things
is represented as much by the language as anything, which is used to describe
crab risotto, tagliatelle, and even Les Fromages Britanniques Variés, if you
please. But the food is not all dyed-in-the-wool, judging by black-bean soup
with coriander relish, and poached lobster with mango salsa. A two- or
three-course pre-theatre option is seriously priced.

We get so used to the contemporary idea of 'service' – a student who brings
plates to table, carries them away, then pockets an 'optional' 12.5 per cent for his
trouble – that 'traditional' service can come as something of a surprise. Here it is
apparently no trouble to carve, slice, arrange and flambé when necessary, using
service skills that are a true extension of the kitchen. The wine list, similar to the
River Restaurant's, runs about energetically, scooping up bottles from here,
there and everywhere, though prices (over £20 for a bottle of English wine, for
example) seem to have little contact with reality. Around half a dozen house
wines begin at £16.50.

CHEF: David Sharland   PROPRIETOR: Savoy Group plc   OPEN: Mon to Fri L 12.30 to 2.15, Mon
to Sat D 6 to 11.15   CLOSED: Aug, bank hols   MEALS: alc (main courses £12.50 to £23). Set
pre-theatre D 6 to 7 £28 to £31.50   SERVICE: not inc, card slips closed   CARDS: Access, Amex,
Delta, Diners, Switch, Visa   DETAILS: 100 seats. Car park. Vegetarian meals. Children welcome.
Jacket and tie. No pipes in dining-room. Wheelchair access (also WC). Music. Air-conditioned
ACCOMMODATION: 202 rooms, all with bath/shower. TV. Phone. Air-conditioned. B&B £180 to
£750. Rooms for disabled. Children welcome. Baby facilities. Afternoon teas. Swimming-pool
(The Which? Hotel Guide)

▲ The Savoy, River Restaurant

map 15

Strand, WC2R 0EU   COOKING 2
TEL: (0171) 836 4343   FAX: (0171) 240 6040   COST £33–£95

The gent in the topper bids you good evening as you pass through the doors.
Carry on through the lounge area, towards the light coming through large
south-facing windows. The dining-room is a huge space with views of the
Thames (provided you are not behind a pillar), where illuminated boats go
gliding by as night descends.

The food is of another era, but embellished with touches of London fashion. A
pair of red mullet fillets sandwiching a layer of fresh herbs makes a fine starter, as
does a brace of portly scallops on a vivid broad-bean purée encircled by a tomato
coulis. Would it be pedantic to point out that the scallops were not wrapped in

bacon, as advertised? Classic main courses might include mignon of veal, or sauté calf's liver with potato purée and apple. The assiette de nôtre pâtissier is the dessert selection for those who can't choose, or who don't fancy anything from the trolley; nôtre pâtissier lets rip with a trio of puddings, over which towers a kind of gingerbread mask with chocolate features. Service during an inspection was 'totally charmless'. Wines are a predictable treasure trove of luxuries, at appropriate prices. House wines start at £16.50.

CHEF: Anton Edelmann PROPRIETOR: Savoy Group plc OPEN: all week 12.30 to 2.30, 6 (7 Sun) to 11.30 (10.30 Sun) MEALS: alc (main courses £22.50 to £24). Set L Mon to Sat £28, Set L Sun £25, Set D Sun to Thur £32.90 to £59 (inc wine), Set D Fri and Sat £39.50 to £64 (inc wine) SERVICE: net prices, card slips closed CARDS: Access, Amex, Delta, Diners, Switch, Visa DETAILS: 160 seats. Private parties: 50 main room, 6 to 60 private rooms. Car park. Vegetarian meals. Children's helpings. Jacket and tie. No pipes in dining-room. Music. Air-conditioned ACCOMMODATION: 202 rooms, all with bath/shower. TV. Phone. Air-conditioned. B&B £180 to £750. Rooms for disabled. Children welcome. Baby facilities. Afternoon teas. Swimming-pool (*The Which? Hotel Guide*)

▲ *The Savoy, Upstairs* map 15

Strand, WC2R 0EU COOKING 2
TEL: (0171) 836 4343 FAX: (0171) 240 6040 COST £30–£61

Upstairs is not way up top, but on the first floor: a long, thin room with a bar counter running the full length, and overlooking the busy-as-a-station courtyard with taxis arriving and uniformed staff shepherding folk in and out. It is a good place to pop into for a casual meal from the short printed card, perhaps at lunch-time or either side of the theatre: Drury Lane and Covent Garden are not far away. Long opening hours and a flexible format that majors on fish are the principal attractions.

Among these might be kedgeree with a perfectly timed poached egg, or perhaps fish-cakes served with a tomato sauce and fried potatoes. Traditionalists can swallow half a dozen oysters with a choice of Chablis or a half-pint silver tankard of champagne, and other shellfish have included 'three enormous fat scallops tasting sweet and succulent', crammed into a bowl with bacon, sage, leeks and butter. As a change, perhaps try baked goats' cheese or grilled chicken, and finish with raspberry brûlée or chocolate tart. Prices on the short wine list are high, but ten good wines are sold by the glass.

CHEF: David Sharland PROPRIETOR: Savoy Group plc OPEN: Mon to Fri L 12 to 3, Mon to Sat D 6 (5 Sat) to 12 CLOSED: bank hols MEALS: alc (main courses £8 to £14.50) SERVICE: not inc, card slips closed CARDS: Access, Amex, Delta, Diners, Switch, Visa DETAILS: 36 seats. Car park. Vegetarian meals. Children's helpings. Smart dress preferred. No music. Air-conditioned ACCOMMODATION: 202 rooms, all with bath/shower. TV. Phone. Air-conditioned. B&B £180 to £750. Rooms for disabled. Children welcome. Baby facilities. Afternoon teas. Swimming-pool (*The Which? Hotel Guide*)

'We asked one of the waitresses for details of the house wine but she just giggled, saying she didn't know the answer (and she didn't go and find out).' (On eating in East Sussex)

Searcy's Brasserie 👍✱

| | NEW ENTRY | map 13 |

Level 2, Barbican Centre, Silk Street, EC2Y 8DS   COOKING 3
TEL: (0171) 588 3008   FAX: (0171) 382 7247   COST £27–£57

Whatever else the Barbican has achieved, it has not exactly been a recommended conversational gambit in the game of gastronomic one-upmanship. 'You ate where?' Now, Richard Corrigan (formerly at Fulham Road; see entry) has changed that. The site belongs to the Corporation of London, and is operated under contract by Searcy Tansley (suppliers of posh nosh to Ascot and Hurlingham, among others), which has had the foresight to put Corrigan in charge of the brasserie kitchen. It is a bit of an adventure for both of them, and refurbishment is expected to pull the long-windowed room more into line with the new ambition.

Traditionally a source of fuel before or after the main evening event, Searcy's Brasserie now offers a viable alternative to it. A small team turns out dishes of bankable quality in impeccably modern mode. Small savings are to be gained by opting for the weekly-changing fixed-price menu rather than the monthly-changing *carte*, but both share a satisfyingly gusty quality in poached gammon with split-peas, or ox-tongue with roast beetroot and shaved horseradish. Even lighter dishes of dandelion salad or white turnip soup have a solid foundation: the former served with bacon, poached egg and hollandaise, the latter containing Toulouse sausage and chilli.

Gutsiest of all might be a casserole of pig's head: not the banqueting kind with an orange in its mouth, but fashioned into a 'gloriously sticky' cotechino-like sausage and served with pink veal kidney and sweetbread in a dark winey sauce. Perhaps due to pressure on the kitchen at peak times, desserts tend not to rely too much on last-minute preparation, and might include crème brûlée cappuccino, or pear and almond tart. Fifty varied wines span an appropriate range of prices, beginning at £9.95 for house French.

CHEF: Richard Corrigan   PROPRIETOR: Searcy Tansley   OPEN: Mon to Fri and Sun L 12 to 3, all week D 5 to 11.15 (7 Sun)   CLOSED: 25 and 26 Dec   MEALS: alc (main courses £10.50 to £17.50). Set L and D £14.95 (2 courses) to £17.50   SERVICE: not inc   CARDS: Access, Amex, Delta, Diners, Switch, Visa   DETAILS: 130 seats. Private parties: 30 main room, 20 private room. Car park. Vegetarian meals. Children's helpings. Smart dress preferred. No smoking in 1 dining-room. Wheelchair access (also WC). Music. Air-conditioned

Shaw's ♥

map 14

119 Old Brompton Road, SW7 3RN   COOKING 2
TEL: (0171) 373 7774   FAX: (0171) 370 5102   COST £32–£59

Old Brompton Road has seen fewer comings and goings over the past year or two than nearby Fulham Road and its environs, and Shaw's reflects a sense of ease, tranquillity and continuity in its smart, pastel décor and amiable service. Staff are 'well trained, but with a sense of humour', and Gerald Atkins supervises with gentle diplomacy and old-fashioned charm. The food certainly scores high for interest. Frances Atkins is resourceful enough to produce a camomile sauce, for example, to partner a crab soufflé, as well as a dish of scallops and prawn dumplings marinated in lime, served in a broth containing spinach and oyster mushrooms.

This is light and sensitive invention, without the distraction of coarsely exotic flavours, although bright Thai spicing takes its place alongside more muted basil aïoli (with salmon) or saffron mash (with steamed sea bass). The work that goes into producing dishes can be complicated, but the end result is generally clear in its intention and straightforward in its appeal. A classical foundation is put to good use in desserts too, such as queen of puddings or nougatine glacé with apricots. A well-balanced wine list is clearly set out with helpful tasting notes, and quality is high throughout. Prices are fair, particularly by London standards. A generous 15 wines are offered by the glass and house Beaujolais is £14. CELLARMAN'S CHOICE: St Aubin premier cru 1993, Gérard Thomas, £23; Acacia Pinot Noir 1993, Carneros, California, £25.

CHEFS: Frances Atkins and Julian Williams PROPRIETORS: Gerald and Frances Atkins, Sir Neil and Lady Shaw, David Banks and Torunn Fieldhouse OPEN: Mon to Fri L 12 to 2, Mon to Sat D 7 to 10, pre-theatre supper 6 to 7, post-theatre supper 10.30 to 11 CLOSED: Christmas and New Year, Easter, last 2 weeks Aug MEALS: Set L £15 (2 courses) to £18.50, Set D £29.95 (2 courses) to £32.95. Pre-and post-theatre D £15 (2 courses) to £18.50. Minimum £15 SERVICE: not inc L and pre- and post-theatre suppers, 12.5% D CARDS: Access, Amex, Delta, Diners, Switch, Visa DETAILS: 46 seats. 10 seats outside. Private parties: 46 main room. Vegetarian meals. Children welcome. Smart dress preferred. Wheelchair access (no WC). No music. Air-conditioned

Simply Nico

map 13

48A Rochester Row, SW1P 1JU

TEL: (0171) 630 8061

COOKING 3

COST £33–£54

Like its sibling Nico Central (see entry, London), Simply Nico has been acquired by the Restaurant Partnership, but continues to produce up-market brasserie food in the smart surroundings of a long, thin dining-room with closely set tables. Although near Victoria, it is more properly considered a Westminster restaurant. A few luxury items are trotted out, including foie gras either sauté in a piece or made into a mousse, and the general effect is of food that gratifies rather than challenges. Despite the 'journeyman level of food', as one reporter describes it, the generally high level of execution ensures that the package works successfully.

Just how comforting the food is can be gauged from a warm tartlet of salmon with poached egg and béarnaise sauce, or croustade of lambs' sweetbreads in a cep sauce. The kitchen has little time for exotic herbs and spices, concentrating instead on more traditional Anglo-Mediterranean favourites, including risotto, rich duck confit, salt-cod in various guises, lamb shank with caramelised vegetables, and guinea-fowl with lentil purée. Standards of the repertoire continue to please: fish soup with rouille and croûtons is a good version.

A classic French approach continues into puddings of pear tart 'bourdaloue', and terrine of prune and armagnac with a plum sauce. Cheeses have been considered 'too cool, too similar, too unadventurous', but a fair conclusion of the overall deal is 'very good food at relatively reasonable prices', bearing in mind that these include service. The wine list includes 50 well-chosen bottles from around the world.

CHEF: Tim Johnson PROPRIETORS: Restaurant Partnership plc OPEN: Mon to Fri L 12 to 2,
Mon to Sat D 7 to 11 CLOSED: 10 days Christmas, 4 days Easter, bank hols MEALS: Set L £22
(2 courses) to £25, Set D £27 SERVICE: net prices, card slips closed CARDS: Access, Amex,
Diners, Visa DETAILS: 45 seats. Private parties: 8 main room. No children under 8. Smart dress
preferred. No cigars/pipes in dining-room. Wheelchair access (no WC). No music. Air-
conditioned

Singapore Garden Restaurant
map 13

83–83A Fairfax Road, NW6 4DY
TEL: (0171) 328 5314 FAX: (0171) 624 0656
COOKING 1*
COST £25–£57

There is a vibrancy about the Lim family's brightly decorated restaurant that
suits perfectly the style of food on offer. This is one of the most authentic places
for Singaporean and Straits cooking in London, and it pays to be adventurous.
The menu has a fair sprinkling of familiar Chinese dishes – chicken and
sweetcorn soup, Szechuan beef, prawns in oyster sauce – but the real treasures
are on the list of specialities. Here you will find such delights as whole crab sauté
in black pepper and butter; braised duck with soy, garlic and star-anise; kwa
tiow rice-sticks; and kang kong blachan (Chinese spinach fried with a fiery
prawn and chilli paste). Service from young waitresses is 'super, efficient'. Drink
Singapore Tiger beer, saké or something from the carefully chosen wine list.
House wines start at £9.50. A second branch is at 154 Gloucester Place, London
NW1; tel: (0171) 723 8233.

CHEF: Mrs S. Lim PROPRIETORS: the Lim family OPEN: all week 12 to 2.45, 6 to 10.45 (11.15 Fri
and Sat) CLOSED: 4 days Christmas MEALS: alc (main courses £4.50 to £25). Set L and D (min
2) £16. Minimum £10 D SERVICE: 12.5% (optional), card slips closed CARDS: Access, Amex,
Diners, Visa DETAILS: 100 seats. 10 seats outside. Private parties: 50 main room. Vegetarian
meals. Children welcome. Smart dress preferred. No cigars in dining-room. Music. Air-
conditioned

Snows on the Green
map 12

166 Shepherd's Bush Road, W6 7PB
TEL: (0171) 603 2142 FAX: (0171) 602 7553
COOKING 1
COST £26–£45

Sebastian Snow's attempt to split himself in two and cook both here and at B
Square (see entry, London) has been partially successful. This is a good local
restaurant, with rag-rolled walls, bright lighting, wicker chairs and bare tables.
Reporters seem to miss the zip and crackle the food used to provide when it had
his undivided attention, though the kitchen still turns out creditable dishes of
duck magret with flageolet beans and baked garlic, and a Mediterranean
vegetable spring roll with garlic mayonnaise.

The style appeals for its plain, down-to-earth way with materials and its
straightforward presentation: 'country toast, bone-marrow, rock salt' is one
dish; 'saddle of rabbit en croûte, coriander gravy, gnocchi' is another. 'Any
colour you like, so long as it's blue,' was one reporter's experience of the cheese
course, though it (Cashel Blue) was in good condition. Lemon tart with clotted
cream, or spiced poached pears with praline custard are likely ways to finish.
Three dozen modern wines at fair prices include five by the glass; prices start at
£9.95.

CHEF/PROPRIETOR: Sebastian Snow   OPEN: Sun to Fri L 12 to 2.30, Mon to Sat D 7 to 11
CLOSED: 24 Dec to 2 Jan   MEALS: alc (main courses £9 to £12). Set L Mon to Fri £12 (2 courses)
SERVICE: not inc; 12.5% for parties of 6 or more   CARDS: Access, Amex, Delta, Diners, Switch,
Visa   DETAILS: 90 seats. Private parties: 60 main room, 25 private room. Vegetarian meals.
Children's helpings. No cigars/pipes in dining-room. Music. Air-conditioned

Soho Soho

map 15

11–13 Frith Street, W1V 5TS

TEL: (0171) 494 3491   FAX: (0171) 437 3091

COOKING 1

COST £26–£51

Soho Soho opts for 'mildly arty' comfort without ever seeming too trendy. There is plenty of unrestrained action in the all-day rôtisserie and bar, while the upstairs restaurant is more sober, 'ideal for businessmen or parents who want to feel themselves part of the Soho scene without the risks'. The food is in keeping: a safe, typically 1990s mixture of provençale and Mediterranean assemblies in the shape of a tartlet of grilled scallops on a courgette coulis, aubergine purée and goats' cheese layered with 'discs of brittle poppadom lookalike', and sliced loin of pork with couscous. Classic desserts include delicate pear sorbet, and a 'seriously over-the-top' crème brûlée. Service keeps things rolling along nicely. The wine list is short and carefully judged to reflect the restaurant's 'Mediterranean identity'. House wines begin at £9 a bottle.

CHEF: Laurent Lebeau   PROPRIETOR: Groupe Chez Gérard   OPEN: restaurant Mon to Fri L 12 to 2.30, Mon to Sat D 6 to 11.45; rôtisserie all week noon to 12.45am (10.30 Sun); café-bar all week 11 to 11 (noon to 10.30 Sun)   MEALS: alc (main courses £7.50 to £15). Set D £13.50 (2 courses) to £15.95. Cover £1.50   SERVICE: 12.5%, card slips closed   CARDS: Access, Amex, Delta, Diners, Switch, Visa   DETAILS: 62 seats. Private parties: 30 main room, 60 private room. Car park for restaurant customers after 6.30pm. Vegetarian meals. Children welcome. No cigars/pipes in dining-room. Music. Air-conditioned

Sonny's

map 12

94 Church Road, SW13 0DQ

TEL: (0181) 748 0393   FAX: (0181) 748 2698

COOKING 2

COST £19–£42

The dining-room stretches back a long way and seems to get cosier the further in you go, although one couple sitting by the window felt they had a prime spot too. The room has developed over the years, rather than arriving newly formed like Milton Keynes, and so has a mixture of styles, not unlike the food. Croissants and BLT are available all day, while lunch offers smoked salmon and scrambled egg, or steak sandwich with frites, in addition to the same Anglo-Med *carte* as dinner.

The *carte*'s business is Parmesan mash, sweet potato ravioli, fish soup, and Caesar salad, alongside more British ideas such as eggy potato pancake served with smoked eel and crispy bacon bits. Peter Harrison makes his own bread, pasta and pickles: try the salt-beef with pickled cucumber. Cod (whoever thought it would be a fashionable fish?) comes with couscous salad, while plaice (more neglected than it should be) might be steamed and served with spinach and shelled cockles. Puddings tend to be homely: pear and ginger crumble, or baked citrus cheesecake. The short wine list is geared to the food and fairly priced, bottles starting at £8.95.

CHEF: Peter Harrison PROPRIETOR: Rebecca Mascarenhas OPEN: restaurant all week L 12.30 to 3, Mon to Sat D 7.30 to 11.30 MEALS: alc (main courses £8 to £12). Set L Mon to Sat £10 (2 courses) to £12.50, Set L Sun £16.50. Light meals available in café Mon to Sat 10 to 6. SERVICE: not inc CARDS: Access, Amex, Delta, Switch, Visa DETAILS: 90 seats. Private parties: 24 private room. Vegetarian meals. Children's helpings. No cigars/pipes in dining-room. Music. Air-conditioned

Sree Krishna £

map 12

192–194 Tooting High Street, SW17 0SF
TEL: (0181) 672 4250 and 6903

COOKING 1
COST £14–£31

The South Indian presence in Tooting has created a score of inexpensive restaurants and cafés, but grandaddy of them all is Sree Krishna, established in 1973. The interior still dates from the era of brown and beige, but prices have barely crept up. The menu has also changed little, with over a dozen consistently good South Indian snacks given prominence, and a few others hidden among the more conventional and mostly mundane meat and vegetarian choices. You won't find better renditions of classics such as masala dosai: a roll of rice and lentil pancake, correctly crisp, filled with a paste of spicy mashed onions and potatoes. Seek out the Keralan dishes – aromatic lemon and coconut rice are delightfully fluffy and scattered with little mustard seeds. Service is usually pleasant but can occasionally be brusque. House wine is £7.

CHEF: Terab Ali PROPRIETORS: the Haridas family OPEN: all week 12 to 3, 6 to 11 (12 Fri and Sat) CLOSED: 25 and 26 Dec MEALS: alc (main courses £2 to £6.50). Minimum £5. BYO £1.50 SERVICE: 10%, card slips closed CARDS: Access, Amex, Diners, Visa DETAILS: 120 seats. Private parties: 60 main room, 60 private room. Vegetarian meals. Children welcome. Smart dress preferred. Wheelchair access (also WC). Music. Air-conditioned

Sri Siam

map 15

16 Old Compton Street, W1V 5PE
TEL: (0171) 434 3544 FAX: (0171) 287 1311

COOKING 2
COST £19–£50

Sri Siam remains on course. The move to adjoining premises has not generated anything in the way of adverse reports and the cooking is – likewise – safe and sound. A striking modern dining-room is divided by a thick wall with oblong unglazed 'windows' set into it. Stencilled designs of abstract leaves and fish brighten up the stone-grey walls; tapestries and Thai artefacts are dotted around to catch the eye. The full menu has a strong vegetarian contingent ('the only Thai restaurant whose vegetarian menu is approved by The Vegetarian Society,' claims the blurb), and it promises some nice-sounding stuff: deep-fried sweetcorn cakes are served with cucumber salad and a sweet-and-sour peanut dressing, crispy crêpes are filled with coconut and bean sprouts.

Those with carnivorous inclinations have a whole repertoire to choose from, including deep-fried chicken wings, tom yum soups, curries of various colours, stir-fried beef with black fungus, ginger and spring onions, and pla nueng salmon (steamed and served with preserved plum and ginger). The wine list has been thoughtfully assembled to match the food, and there is Singha Thai beer. House wine is £8.95.

CHEF: W. Rodpradith   PROPRIETOR: Thai Restaurants plc   OPEN: Mon to Sat L 12 to 3, all week D 6 to 11.15 (10.30 Sun)   CLOSED: 25 Dec, 1 Jan   MEALS: alc (main courses £6 to £10). Set L £11, Set D £15.90   SERVICE: 12.5% (optional), card slips closed   CARDS: Access, Amex, Delta, Diners, Switch, Visa   DETAILS: 130 seats. Private parties: 30 main room, 20 and 30 private rooms. Vegetarian meals. Children welcome. Music. Air-conditioned

Sri Siam City map 13

85 London Wall, EC2M 7AD	COOKING 2
TEL: (0171) 628 5772 FAX: (0171) 628 3395	COST £24–£53

During the week this younger sibling of Sri Siam (see entry above) caters admirably for hungry City workers and visitors soaking up cultural attractions at the nearby Barbican. The setting is a modern office block, and you pass an impressive throne before reaching the dining-areas. At the front is the bar, where snacks can be consumed (note the 'happy hour' from 5 to 7 when there is a 25 per cent reduction in prices). Beyond is the main restaurant, done out in pleasant shades of peachy pink.

The menu of around 70 dishes is virtually identical to the Soho branch (although prices are generally a shade higher), with a strong vegetarian presence, good-value set meals, and a broad sweep of authentic specialities culled from the mainstream of the Thai repertoire. Typical offerings include hoi malag phoo (green-lipped mussels cooked with Thai herbs), homok kai (steamed chicken with spicy coconut gravy served in banana leaf baskets), 'jungle curry', and phad makeur yao (stir-fried aubergine with yellow beans and sweet basil). The wine list deserves proper consideration, or go for Singha Thai beer. House wine is £9.50.

CHEF: Pongchan Lerdjirakul   PROPRIETOR: Thai Restaurants Ltd   OPEN: Mon to Fri 11.30 to 8.30   CLOSED: bank hols   MEALS: alc (main courses £7 to £10.50). Set L and D £14.95 to £24.95   SERVICE: 12.5% (optional), card slips closed   CARDS: Access, Amex, Delta, Diners, Switch, Visa   DETAILS: 140 seats. Private parties: 250 main room. Vegetarian meals. Children welcome. Wheelchair access (also WC). Music. Air-conditioned

▲ *Stafford Hotel* **NEW ENTRY** map 15

St James's Place, SW1A 1NJ	COOKING 2
TEL: (0171) 493 0111 FAX: (0171) 493 7121	COST £30–£75

Against a background of chefs fleeing hotel dining-rooms to set up their own places, it comes as rather a surprise to find Christopher Oakes, once a chef-patron in Stroud, doing the journey in reverse. The Stafford is a top-notch hotel on the cosy scale, tucked into a traffic-free back street in St James's, which holds a special place in the affections of American visitors. Its bar is festooned with American college scarves, football pennants and the like, while the refurbished dining-room adds a sense of grande luxe with its gilded columns, crystal chandelier and ceiling fresco of azure sky.

A set-price menu is supplemented by a long list of 'Stafford Classics' (British heritage stuff), and a *carte* that majors in fish: a slice of sole and gurnard terrine, for example, offering a whole fillet of the latter wrapped around a cream-cheesed mousse of the former in a lime vinaigrette. Main courses tend to be rich: fillet of

Aberdeen Angus on spinach with dauphinois and Madeira sauce, perhaps, or moist and flavourful guinea-fowl breast with mushrooms, smoked bacon and parisienne potatoes. Desserts might include blueberry and cream tart with honey ice-cream, and Cambridge burnt cream with a heap of raspberries and a lake of coulis. Punctilious service is relaxed enough to chat. The wine list is a very classical assemblage mostly at classical prices, but the odd bargain can be unearthed by those with a will to forage. House French is £14.50.

CHEFS: Christopher Oakes and Peter Williams   PROPRIETOR: Thwaites Brewery, Shire Inns   OPEN: Sun to Fri L 12.30 to 2.30, all week D 6.30 to 10.30 (9.30 Sun)   MEALS: alc (main courses £14.50 to £26). Set L £19.50 (2 courses) to £22.50, Set D £25. Bar food available   SERVICE: net prices, card slips closed   CARDS: Access, Amex, Delta, Diners, Switch, Visa   DETAILS: 50 seats. Private parties: 12 main room, 2 to 44 private rooms. Vegetarian meals. Children welcome. Jacket and tie. No pipes in dining-room. Music. Air-conditioned   ACCOMMODATION: 80 rooms, all with bath/shower. TV. Phone. Air-conditioned. Room only £200 to £529. Rooms for disabled. Children welcome. Afternoon teas

Stephen Bull ▼

map 15

5–7 Blandford Street, W1H 3AA
TEL: (0171) 486 9696   FAX: (0171) 490 3128

COOKING 2*
COST £34–£50

Although Stephen Bull might seem like a brand name, he is not some grand absentee proprietor. This is his original central London restaurant (if you consider Marylebone central), smartened up with a lick of turquoise and primrose-yellow paint, and bears a personal stamp. There is never a hint of staleness or tiredness; more a feeling that what you eat here today others may be cooking tomorrow. Mercy Fenton is well adapted to the Bull way of doing things, emphasising fish, vegetables and fowl, making just about everything interesting and rewarding to eat, and yet retaining a sense of proportion and balance.

A seemingly inexhaustible fund of variations rolls out, producing cep dumpling with salsify and a soft-poached egg, chickpea fritters, or sea bass with a beetroot and black-bean salsa. Cooking relies on pan-frying, grilling and roasting, sauces are often a simple *jus*, perhaps perked up with a herb or a squeeze of lime, while salsas, confits and pesto add a spark of vitality. Puddings offer a generous choice. This is some of the most attractive cooking of its kind going: informal, modern, brisk, simple and direct. Service is on the ball, as is the wine list: around 100 bottles jostle for space on two crowded pages. France takes up the most room, but Australia, New Zealand and California get a good look in. Fourteen house wines start at £14 a bottle and £3.25 a glass. CELLARMAN'S CHOICE: Jurançon sec, Cuvée Marie 1993, Charles Hours, £22.50; Bourgogne Grande Ordinaire 1991, J. Roty, £17.50.

CHEF: Mercy Fenton   PROPRIETOR: Stephen Bull   OPEN: Mon to Fri L 12 to 2.15, Mon to Sat D 6.30 to 10.45   CLOSED: 1 week Christmas, bank hols   MEALS: alc (main courses £11.50 to £14.50). BYO £4   SERVICE: not inc, card slips closed   CARDS: Access, Amex, Switch, Visa   DETAILS: 53 seats. Private parties: 50 main room. Vegetarian meals. Children's helpings. No cigars/pipes in dining-room. Wheelchair access (no WC). No music. Air-conditioned

Stephen Bull's Bistro ♥ 🍮 ✸

map 13

71 St John Street, EC1M 4AN

TEL: (0171) 490 1750   FAX: (0171) 490 3128

COOKING 1*
COST £29–£46

New chef Danny Lewis arrived at this primary-coloured bistro in the summer of 1996. It is a popular place, and tables are obligingly small enough to pack in the crowds. Some dishes from the previous regime remain, such as the platter of Spanish appetisers, and the seafood bar still decants its cornucopia of rock oysters, sushi, and langoustines with mayo. Earthy dishes of suckling pig faggots with champ and sage sauce might be followed by chocolate tart with blood orange sauce, or blueberry cake with lemon syrup. Service is mostly efficient and dextrous. Most of the lively and cosmopolitan wines are pitched comfortably between £15 and £20 a bottle. Italy's Ca' del Frati and Isole e Olena, Spain's Viñas del Vero and Catena's Argentinian wines reveal a leaning towards modern, fashionable tastes. A generous 18 wines are available by the glass, while house French starts at £11.50. CELLARMAN'S CHOICE: Vouvray Sec, Vieilles Vignes 1994, Bourillon d'Orléans, £18.50; Côtes du Rhône 1993, Jean-Luc Colombo, £16.

CHEF: Danny Lewis   PROPRIETOR: Stephen Bull   OPEN: Mon to Fri L 12 to 2.30, Mon to Sat D 6 to 10.45   CLOSED: 1 week Christmas, bank hols   MEALS: alc (main courses £9.50 to £11.50). BYO £3.50   SERVICE: not inc, card slips closed   CARDS: Access, Amex, Visa   DETAILS: 125 seats. Private parties: 60 main room. Vegetarian meals. Children's helpings. No smoking in 1 dining-room. Wheelchair access (no WC). Music. Air-conditioned

Stepping Stone ✸

map 12

123 Queenstown Road, SW8 3RH

TEL: (0171) 622 0555   FAX: (0171) 622 4230

COOKING 2
COST £24–£36

The Stepping Stone calls its style 'urban rustic', and although the chances of rusticity on the Queenstown Road may sound slim, the kitchen looks to Hampshire and Kent for meat and salads rather than just the usual London supply lines. In fact, the food in this needle-sharp, clean-lined Battersea restaurant is distinctly metropolitan, judging by chargrilled ox tongue with broad-bean purée, or onion and Parmesan cheesecake with red wine sorbet and caraway crackers. That said, a domestic feeling shows itself too, in rack of lamb with braised red cabbage, or home-made sausages with mash and onion gravy.

Comforting desserts of pecan pie with clotted cream, or 'rich and tasty' brandy-snaps of lemon syllabub win admirers, as does the 'friendly and very cheery' service. The enterprising wine list is full of thought-provoking possibilities at scrupulously fair prices. A dry Hungarian Furmint opens the batting at £8.75, with house red just a little more.

CHEFS: Laura Greenfield, Tom Illic and Gary Levy   PROPRIETORS: Gary and Emer Levy   OPEN: Mon to Fri and Sun L 12 to 2.30 (3 Sun), Mon to Sat D 7 to 11 (10.30 Mon)   CLOSED: 1 week Christmas, bank hols   MEALS: alc (main courses £9 to £12). Set L Mon to Fri £10 (2 courses). Set L Sun £11.75 (2 courses). BYO £5   SERVICE: not inc   CARDS: Access, Amex, Delta, Diners, Switch, Visa   DETAILS: 56 seats. Private parties: 30 main room. Vegetarian meals. Children's helpings. No smoking in 1 dining-room. Wheelchair access. No music. Air-conditioned

LONDON

Sugar Club ✷

NEW ENTRY map 13

33A All Saints Road, W11 1HE
TEL: (0171) 221 3844 FAX: (0171) 229 2759

COOKING 2
COST £22–£49

Peter Gordon hit the ground running when the Sugar Club opened in 1995.
From a see-into kitchen, in a cramped but agreeable basement dining-room, he
serves up a soup of spicy plantain, tamarind and coconut with coriander and
chicken dumplings, and a dish of pan-fried John Dory with soba noodles and
sugar snaps. Until somebody comes up with a niftier phrase, this is Southern
Hemisphere Pacific Rim Modern Mediterranean Cosmopolitan British cooking.
Superficially it may sound as if a roulette wheel has chosen the ingredients, but
in fact the dishes are well conceived, gutsy and appetising, delivering most of
what they promise in terms of vibrant flavours.

Gordon is from New Zealand, which may explain why he enjoys cooking
Australia's national symbol. Four thick strips of grilled kangaroo loin,
'exquisitely tender, and full of deep, rich, though not emphatically gamey
flavour', might be served with a sweet and piquant salsa, while a 'perfectly
conceived relish, sharp with coriander and unctuously oily' has helped along a
wing of skate. Crème fraîche offsets some of the spicier flavours, and has worked
a treat with a dessert of 'sensuously quivery citrus jelly, cloudy and full of zesty
bits'. Cheery service is from 'mostly young male waitpersons, full of the right
sort of attitude, aproned, unshaved, Antipodean'. Italy, North America and the
southern hemisphere supply most of the wines, though not at giveaway prices,
which start at £10.50.

CHEF: Peter Gordon PROPRIETORS: Ashley Sumner and Vivienne Hayman OPEN: all week
12.30 to 3, 6.30 to 11 CLOSED: Notting Hill Carnival MEALS: alc (main courses £9.50 to £15).
Set L £10.50 (2 courses) to £13.50 SERVICE: not inc CARDS: Access, Amex, Delta, Switch,
Visa DETAILS: 70 seats. 20 seats outside. Private parties: 45 main room. Vegetarian meals.
Smart dress preferred. No smoking in 1 dining-room. Wheelchair access (no WC). No music

Suntory ⌲

map 15

72–73 St James's Street, SW1A 1PH
TEL: (0171) 409 0201 FAX: (0171) 499 0208

COOKING 3
COST £31–£128

'At £80 a head including drinks (beer), this is not a cheap restaurant' must be one
of the understatements of the year. A visit to this most moneyed of Japanese
establishments is not for those with a little ready cash to dispose of: 'Only the
cheapest set lunch is a (relative) bargain.' Stratospherically high prices (though
happily inclusive of service) induce great expectations, and hopes are generally
fulfilled. The ground-floor (shabu) room is formal yet faintly rustic, with some
intriguing asymmetrical touches, but the works of art are 'stunning'. Against this
backdrop, service is impeccable: 'there when wanted, invisible when not
wanted'.

What the kitchen delivers is an assured version of Japanese haute cuisine
based on spectacularly fresh ingredients. Zensai appetisers show the quality:
two broad beans standing up, a single shrimp covered in green herbs, two pieces
of 'outstanding' lobster mousse in a cylinder of vegetables. Other fine points are
juicy yakitori and a great assortment of sushi, although the zenith of one

156

reporter's meal was wakasagi: three whitebait-sized fish fried in the lightest dusting of flour and served in a delicate vinegar dressing.

Proceedings in the downstairs teppanyaki room are scarcely less impressive, as chefs prepare a 'devastating succession' of superlative dishes in front of customers. The Westernised accent of this experience is clear from a report that eulogises about 'delicious amuse-gueules', 'delightful clam miso soup', 'a plate of the freshest sashimi I have ever tasted in London', not to mention foie gras, fillet steak, and ice-cream. Drink brown tea, or gaze in trepidation at prices on the wine list. House French is £16.

CHEF: N. Hoshino   PROPRIETOR: Suntory Ltd   OPEN: Mon to Sat 12 to 2, 6 to 10   CLOSED: Christmas and Easter   MEALS: alc (main courses £15 to £45). Set L £15 (2 courses) to £35, Set D £49.80 to £69.40   SERVICE: net prices, card slips closed   CARDS: Access, Amex, Delta, Diners, Switch, Visa   DETAILS: 120 seats. Private parties: 100 main room. Vegetarian meals. Children's helpings. Smart dress preferred. Wheelchair access (no WC). No music. Air-conditioned

Le Suquet
map 14

104 Draycott Avenue, SW3 3AE
TEL: (0171) 581 1785

COOKING 1*
COST £20–£54

Like many fish restaurants, Le Suquet is timeless. The tide of trends has washed in and out several times, leaving it pretty well untouched over the 20-odd years of its existence. In good weather tables spill on to the pavement, increasing the French-café feel, and the press of people can make it seem like holiday time. Shut your eyes and you could be in Brittany. Bowls of winkles and shrimps arrive with the menu, which majors in langoustines, scallops, mussels and clams done various ways from marinière to Madras, and in oysters, sea urchin, crab and lobster served up straight. The market delivers anything from cod to sea bass, and freshness ensures that most things work well, including the ever-popular *plateau de fruits de mer*. The brief French wine list is short on detail, and starts with house wine at £9.50.

CHEF: Phillipe Moron   PROPRIETOR: Pierre Martin   OPEN: Mon to Fri 12 to 2.30, 7 to 12, Sat and Sun 12.30 to 11.30   MEALS: alc (main courses £9.50 to £17). Set L £12, Set D £30. Cover £1   SERVICE: 15%, card slips closed   CARDS: Access, Amex, Delta, Diners, Switch, Visa   DETAILS: 70 seats. 6 seats outside. Private parties: 16 main room, 16 private room. Children welcome. Smart dress preferred. No pipes in dining room. Music

Tabac
map 13

46 Golborne Road, W10 5PR
TEL/FAX: (0181) 960 2433

NEW CHEF
COST £20–£41

Tabac is the sort of place that, perhaps a decade hence, people will look back on as epitomising the busy, chirpy appeal of the 1990s restaurant. First, it is in the right place, a 'newly arrived' West London street. Second, it looks the part, with rich, bright colours countering the bare wooden floors and tables. Nineties food is distinguished by its unashamed borrowings from here, there and Italy, by the general simplicity of technique, particularly chargrilling, and by upbeat it's-amazing-what-salsa-will-do flavours. Rosie Bowdrey (ex-All Saints, see entry, London), who shares an enthusiasm for this kind of cooking with Pip

Wylie (who has now left), arrived too late for us to award a cooking mark, but zingy flavours – whether Pacific Rim or Mediterranean – are her stock-in-trade. A short, sharp wine list matches the diversity of the food; house wines are £9.

CHEF: Rosie Bowdrey   PROPRIETOR: Benny Neville   OPEN: Tue to Sun L 11 to 4, Mon to Sat D 7.30 to 11 (12 Fri and Sat)   MEALS: alc (main courses £5 to £12)   SERVICE: 12.5% (optional) CARDS: Access, Diners, Switch, Visa   DETAILS: 80 seats. Private parties: 50 main room, 40 private room. Vegetarian meals. Children's helpings. Wheelchair access (no WC). Music. Air-conditioned

Tamarind
map 15

20 Queen Street, W1X 7PS
TEL: (0171) 629 3561   FAX: (0171) 499 5034

COOKING 2
COST £24–£48

Tamarind looks every inch the epitome of glamorous ethnic chic. An Indian doorman directs customers down the spiral staircase, past a 'distressed' tree and into the 'hard-edged' 1980s-style dining-room. Panels of silk enliven the walls, gold pillars break up the space and the chairs are heavyweight steel. The cooking is north Indian with esoteric flourishes, and the results can be outstanding: 'Quite the tastiest Indian food I've had for years,' enthused one reporter.

Recent highlights have included sunheri khasta (crispy spring rolls with mint chutney), bhuna gosht and excellent jhinga tawamasala, but the real star is hari machli – a thick piece of marinated cod topped with crisp, deep-fried spinach cooked 'the Italian way'. Vegetables are fine, although not always wildly exciting; breads, too are a mixed bag. Service is by a brigade of attentive waiters 'dressed casually in chinos and blue shirts'. Prices are gilt-edged Mayfair. Bottled water and Cobra beer are expensive, but the wine list has some decent and reasonably priced choices from around the world. House wine is £10.

CHEF: Atul Kochhar   PROPRIETOR: Indian Cuisine Ltd   OPEN: Sun to Fri L 12 to 3, all week D 6 to 11.30 (10.30 Sun)   CLOSED: 1 week Christmas, 1 week Easter   MEALS: alc (main courses £4.50 to £13). Set L £16.50   SERVICE: 12.5%, card slips closed   CARDS: Access, Amex, Delta, Diners, Switch, Visa   DETAILS: 90 seats. Private parties: 90 main room. Vegetarian meals. Children's helpings. Smart dress preferred. Music. Air-conditioned

La Tante Claire ♥
map 14

68 Royal Hospital Road, SW3 4HP
TEL: (0171) 352 6045 and 351 0227
FAX: (0171) 352 3257

COOKING 5
COST £33–£85

Pierre Koffmann celebrates 20 years at Tante Claire in 1997, with a remarkable record as one of the country's foremost, and most consistent, chefs. He has deliberately eschewed glamour in favour of dedication to his craft, turning out some of the finest French cooking imaginable. The food is not showy, but accessible – he leaves a chink in the prices for lunchers to pay with their own money, thus providing 'a wonderful introduction to top-quality dining in a superb restaurant' – and the setting is unassuming rather than grand. 'You don't feel intimidated by the surroundings' is a typical view of the light, bright, sophisticated, elegant room, with pastelly colours and modern prints. Service is a rare amalgam of informality and utter professionalism, treating all comers to equal attention, yet not in the least intrusive.

The food's ability to impress transcends fashion. It evolves very slowly, if at all, but uses ingredients of a quality that many can only dream of, and the technical accomplishment is such that good cooks have gone home asking, 'How on earth do they do that?' Nobody ever asks, 'Why do they do that?', which demonstrates the easy, unaffected yet refined style of a cuisine that has developed naturally from its French roots. The kitchen rather assumes you like lobster, foie gras and truffles, but Koffmann is also a past master at the earthier end of the spectrum, whether in the classic pig's trotter or a peasanty ox-cheek braised in red wine served with 'stunning polenta'. Needless to say, anybody who can make polenta stunning isn't half motoring.

Disappointments are rare, and most of our reports are a succession of superlatives: faultless, terrific, perfectly judged, spot on, I have never eaten anywhere better, and so on. Meals begin with a small cup of intensely flavoured soup (which can arrive before the aperitif at lunch) and might progress to snails with 'the lightest and possibly the most buttery puff pastry I have ever eaten', or a small galette of loosely woven potato strands topped with a slice of impeccable foie gras and crisp roast shallots, in a Sauternes sauce. Textures make an impact – duck breast so meltingly tender it might have been liver – as do fish of all sorts. Sweet soufflés (of Grand Marnier or pistachio, maybe) have a blob of ice-cream spooned in at table, and apple is a regular dessert ingredient, perhaps in a *tarte fine* topped with a mound of vanilla ice-cream.

Unsurprisingly, the wine list homes in on classic France, with a fine selection within as well as outside Bordeaux and Burgundy. While there's plenty to splash out on, French regions, including the south-west, offer humbler bottles. House wines are Ch. de Lastours from Corbières at £17.80 and Sauvignon from Côtes de Duras at £13.90.

CHEF/PROPRIETOR: Pierre Koffmann   OPEN: Mon to Fri 12.30 to 2, 7 to 11   CLOSED: 10 days Christmas, 10 days Easter, 3 weeks Aug   MEALS: alc (main courses £24.50 to £26.50). Set L £26. Minimum £45 D   SERVICE: net prices   CARDS: Access, Amex, Diners, Visa   DETAILS: 48 seats. Private parties: 48 main room. Children's helpings. Jacket and tie D. No cigars/pipes in dining-room. No music. Air-conditioned

Tate Gallery Restaurant ♟ 🍴   map 13

Millbank, SW1P 4RG   COOKING 1
TEL: (0171) 887 8877   FAX: (0171) 887 8902   COST £27–£49

This large booming basement room operates a bit like a production line. Whistler's landscape mural relieves the stark black and white décor, sound echoes off the parquet floor, tables are packed close together, and prices are on the high side, but it provides a useful service in the locality, and is 'vital if you are visiting the Tate (which you should anyway)'. The set-price menu doesn't differ much in either style or price from the *carte*, and a fondness for British standards prevails in sausage and mash, and bread-and-butter pudding.

Well-timed fish main courses are considered a high point, including moist pan-fried salmon trout with a tangy, crisp exterior, and seared fillet of sea bass brushed with oil, lemon, salt and herbs. Service is functional, and can be stretched when busy. After a long period in the doldrums, the wine list seems to be on an upward curve again. Good vintages abound, and value is now excellent, especially for London, where champagne at £3.50 a glass is a rarity. Several other lively examples are offered by the glass, as well as a host of halves. House wines are £11.50.

CHEF: Shaun Rowlands   PROPRIETOR: Trustees of the Tate Gallery   OPEN: Mon to Sat L only 12 to 3   CLOSED: 24 to 26 Dec, 1 Jan, Good Fri, May Day bank hol   MEALS: alc (main courses £8.50 to £15). Set L £17 (2 courses) to £23. Minimum £10   SERVICE: not inc, card slips closed   CARDS: Access, Delta, Switch, Visa   DETAILS: 100 seats. Private parties: 12 main room. Vegetarian meals. Children's helpings. Wheelchair access (also WC). No music. Air-conditioned

Tatsuso
map 13

32 Broadgate Circle, EC2M 2QS   COOKING 3
TEL: (0171) 638 5863   FAX: (0171) 638 5864   COST £30–£111

The area around Broadgate Circle is 'suit city', and the corporate name is more highly valued to this restaurant than the cash of the 'private customer'. In the view of one inspector, Tatsuso plays to the moneyed gallery: prices are painfully high, and staff are relentless in their pursuit of large drinks orders. Through the door and past reception is a teppan room; the main eating-area, devoted to the high art of Japanese cuisine, is downstairs. The bill may hurt, but the kitchen is able to deliver 'good, though not really amazing' food.

Set menus are named after places in Japan: Fuji, Momoyama, and so on. The Azuchi version shows the style: a tiny appetiser of two spinach rolls served on an altar-like piece of stoneware, sashimi presented on a fresh shizo leaf, a Lilliputian piece of grilled salmon with teriyaki sauce, a nimono dish of boiled vegetables and fish, light miso soup with 'rubber bands' of tofu floating in it, and more. Elsewhere, the range of zensai appetisers has been good, and kaiso salad of four seaweeds served with a 'tahini-like dip' was reckoned to be 'brilliant'. Kirin beer is topped up and served quickly, but you may need to ask for tea. House wine is £12.

CHEFS: Mr Yamanaka and Mr Maehara   PROPRIETOR: T. Fujii   OPEN: Mon to Fri 11.30 to 2.30, 6 to 9.45   CLOSED: bank hols   MEALS: alc (main courses £8.50 to £31). Set L and D £20 to £75. Minimum £25   SERVICE: 14%, card slips closed   CARDS: Access, Amex, Delta, Diners, Switch, Visa   DETAILS: 140 seats. Private parties: 30 main room, 8 and 6 private rooms. Children's helpings. Smart dress preferred. No pipes in dining-room. Music. Air-conditioned

Thai Bistro
NEW ENTRY   map 12

99 Chiswick High Road, W4 2ED   COOKING 1
TEL: (0181) 995 5774   COST £20–£36

Vatcharin Bhumichitr can lay claim to being one of the founding fathers of Thai cuisine in London, and readers may remember his time at Chiang Mai in Soho. In 1994 he took over this no-frills, canteen-style place in media-rich Chiswick. Wooden benches are arranged in rows, blue lights dangle from blue chains in the window. The menu is a three-way affair: around two dozen conventional dishes, a full repertoire for vegetarians and a monthly selection of regional specialities. From the north-east might come nan tak gung (a spicy warm salad of prawns with rice grains), from the central region you might encounter haw muk (steamed curried pork). Soups such as cauliflower-based tom ka gai are well balanced (as are the 'red' curries), while other staples including papaya salad, noodles, and egg-fried rice are capably handled. Service is 'jeans and T-shirt'. Drink tea or Thai beer; house wine is £7.95.

CHEF/PROPRIETOR: Vatcharin Bhumichitr OPEN: Mon, Wed and Fri to Sun L 12 to 3, all week D 6 to 11 (10.30 Sun) CLOSED: bank hols MEALS: alc (main courses £3.50 to £7) SERVICE: not inc CARDS: Access, Visa DETAILS: 60 seats. 20 seats outside. Private parties: 12 main room. Vegetarian meals. Children welcome. No music

Thai Garden ⅝ £

map 12

249 Globe Road, E2 0JD
TEL: (0181) 981 5748

COOKING 2
COST £18–£33

Jack Hufton's notion of a Thai restaurant devoted solely to fish and vegetarian dishes seems to have paid off. His intimate, 'nicely decorated' venue a few minutes' walk from Bethnal Green tube station ('take the Roman Road exit,' advises one) continues to please, partly because it has remained true to its principles: 'It was lovely to eat in a restaurant without the worry of MSG,' noted one lady after her first visit. Although meat and poultry are out, the 60-dish menu still manages to provide bags of variety and subtlety at every turn.

Set meals span the full repertoire: prawns in filo pastry with a fierce chilli dip, hot-and-sour seafood salad with 'extremely large' mussels and an authentic whiff of fish sauce, pomfret with vegetables, and more prawns – this time fried with ginger, tomatoes and spring onions. The kitchen's star turn, however, is undoubtedly tom khar: 'the most delicious cauliflower soup I've ever eaten' was the verdict of one convert. Desserts include a moreish Thai custard cake as well as bananas in warm coconut milk. Service is provided by waitresses dressed in blue Thai skirts and lacy blouses. Drink jasmine tea or the house wine (£6.50); also try a shot of Thai whisky.

CHEF: Mrs N. Duff PROPRIETORS: Suthinee and Jack Hufton OPEN: Mon to Fri L 12 to 2.45, Mon to Sat D 6 to 10.45 CLOSED: bank hols MEALS: alc (main courses £4.50 to £7). Set L £7.50 (2 courses), Set D (min 2) £16 to £21 SERVICE: 10%, card slips closed CARDS: Access, Delta, Visa DETAILS: 32 seats. Private parties: 20 main room, 14 private room. Vegetarian meals. Children welcome. No smoking in 1 dining-room. Wheelchair access (1 step). Music

Thailand

map 12

15 Lewisham Way, SE14 6PP
TEL: (0181) 691 4040

COOKING 2*
COST £26–£52

'Still for my money the best Thai place in London,' writes a regular. Any shortcomings in the location are more than compensated for by food that is often outstanding. Chef/proprietor Mrs Herman was born in northern Thailand, and her food is shot through with the authentic flavours of regional home cooking. The 90-dish menu is spelt out clearly in plain English: look for the section devoted to Laotian specialities, which are generally intended to be eaten with the fingers, along with morsels of delicately perfumed sticky rice.

There is a finesse and confidence about the cooking, and it doesn't need heavy doses of chilli to impress. 'Lovely' soups, marinated chicken wings, fish-cakes with a clear herby sauce, and green papaya salad have all impressed. Curries of all complexions are in a class of their own, but the high point of one meal was crab shell stuffed with crabmeat and minced chicken which showed just how fine and delicate Thai cooking can be. As a finale, try the soothing effects of black sticky sweet rice. Tiger beer or tea suits the food, and the restaurant has a remarkable line-up of malt whiskies. The short wine list is not at all bad, either. House Italian is £8.50.

CHEF/PROPRIETOR: Mrs Gong Kambungoet Herman   OPEN: Tue to Sat D only 6 to 10.30 CLOSED: 2 weeks Aug, 2 weeks Easter   MEALS: alc (main courses £6.50 to £11). Set D £20 SERVICE: not inc, card slips closed   CARDS: Access, Visa   DETAILS: 25 seats. Private parties: 25 main room. Vegetarian meals. Children welcome. Music. Air-conditioned

33

NEW ENTRY map 15

33 St James's Street, SW1A 1ND

TEL: (0171) 930 4272   FAX: (0171) 930 7618

COOKING 2
COST £38–£65

It's all happening on St James's Street, what with the Avenue, L'Oranger (see entries) and this too. Winning 'Masterchef' is clearly a lucrative career-move, for that is how owner Derek Johns shot into the restaurant world. Pale-primrose walls form the backdrop for a dramatic truncated pillar and several giant brooding still-lifes by Paul Howard Carslake.

Sean Davies's food ventures somewhat beyond the 'Masterchef' idiom into a full-blown modern restaurant Esperanto that may be teetering towards parody in some dishes. Are you ready for rhubarb and walnut ravioli with caramelised rhubarb broth (for pudding, that is)? But the kitchen delivers: a quail pithiviers with mousserons, for example, full of 'richly savoury gunge'. Scallops are fashionably seared, and accompanied by braised carrots, leeks and some garlic cloves 'browned to near-bitterness', a striking counterpoint of flavours supporting 'positively the best scallops I have ever had'. Meats are given the plainer treatment, and the only offal is calf's liver with bacon. A seriously glazed crème brûlée is value-added with peach slivers, scoring highly for 'eggy, creamy softness'. 'Very professional' service ensures things go with a swing. A browse through the wine list reveals a good spread of producers, especially within France, and 14 appealing wines served by the glass. However, there is little to choose under £20, and the first glassful comes in at £3.50. House French is £16.

CHEF: Sean Davies   PROPRIETORS: Derek Johns and Vince Defeo   OPEN: Mon to Fri L 12.30 to 2.30, Mon to Sat D 6 to 11   MEALS: alc (main courses £12 to £22). Set L £16.95 (2 courses) to £21.90, Set D £27.85. Cover £1. BYO £5   SERVICE: 12.5% (optional), card slips closed   CARDS: Access, Amex, Delta, Switch, Visa   DETAILS: 70 seats. Private parties: 40 main room. Vegetarian meals. Children welcome. Smart dress preferred. Wheelchair access (no WC). Music. Air-conditioned

'Service was pathetically slow, full of misplaced preciosity that involves placing your plate before you as if it were the Ark of the Covenant, turning it through half a centimetre to get the angle just so, and then murmuring in mortal sorrow, 'The tart,' as if the sous-chef had just run off with the sommelier.' (On eating in London)

Tokyo Diner ⁵✳ £

map 15

2 Newport Place, WC2H 7JJ

TEL: (0171) 287 8777   FAX: (0171) 434 1414

COOKING 1
COST £8–£18

'I'm in danger of getting addicted to this place!' confesses a fan. The obvious appeal of Richard Hills's converted Chinatown launderette is its theatreland location, its low, low prices (cash only) and its vibrant atmosphere. Hills and his chefs aim for streetwise authenticity, offering the kinds of textures and flavours you might find in cafés near Japanese railway stations. Most people pack in for the fun of eating from arty lacquered 'bento' boxes, with their compartments of cold noodles, rice, sashimi, potato salad, powerful wasabi and perhaps pork croquettes or salmon in Japanese breadcrumbs. Also look for 'don' dishes – variations on soft-cooked eggs, with spring onions and 'dashi' stock flavoured with meat, fish or chicken. Miso soup is the real thing and you can also order sushi if you don't mind waiting. Drink tea, beer or saké; house wine is £6.90.

CHEF: T. Fujiama   PROPRIETOR: Richard Hills   OPEN: all week noon to midnight   MEALS: alc (main courses) £4 to £13   SERVICE: none   CARDS: none   DETAILS: 90 seats. Private parties: 30 main room. Vegetarian meals. Children welcome. No smoking in 1 dining-room. No music. Air-conditioned

La Truffe Noire ⁵✳

map 13

29 Tooley Street, SE1 2QF

TEL: (0171) 378 0621   FAX: (0171) 403 0689

COOKING 1
COST £25–£79

If its location opposite the London Dungeon doesn't inspire, proximity to London Bridge is certainly convenient. The atmosphere is 'stark' with functional furniture but the 'friendly, efficient' welcome gives it a relaxed feel, and the flexible eating options include a ground-floor restaurant, a subterranean jazz bar that attracts a younger crowd, plus tapas for a quick snack. Some of the evening functions conclude with breakfast. Staff are French, as is the thrust of the cooking, although it also explores the former colonial world in the shape of Vietnamese spare ribs, and North African lamb with couscous. Given the City as its catchment area, it is wise to offer such luxuries as lobster and foie gras, though the highlights of an inspection meal were lightly cooked scallops in lime and ginger butter, and simply grilled goats' cheese with spinach. The largely French wine list is conservative, and the few New World wines offer the best value. House French is £8.

CHEF: Philippe Roth   PROPRIETORS: Mohini and Murshed Alam-Ahmed   OPEN: Mon to Fri (Sat and Sun by arrangement) 11.45 to 2.30, 6.30 to 10.30   MEALS: alc (main courses £10 to £25). Set L and D £10 to £21   SERVICE: 12.5% (optional), card slips closed   CARDS: Access, Amex, Delta, Diners, Switch, Visa   DETAILS: 40 seats. 50 seats outside. Private parties: 40 main room, 10 to 40 private rooms. Vegetarian meals. Children welcome. Smart dress preferred. No smoking in 1 dining-room. No pipes/cigars in dining-room. Wheelchair access restaurant only. Music. Air-conditioned

'There may not be Muzak but the air conditioning – welcome as it was – sounded like the mating cry of a hovercraft.' (On eating in Kent)

Turner's

map 14

87–89 Walton Street, SW3 2HP

COOKING 4

TEL: (0171) 584 6711   FAX: (0171) 584 4441

COST £26–£65

Brian Turner's sleek, civilised restaurant on style-conscious Walton Street generates one of the largest annual postbags to the *Guide* of any London entry. Some might say that's testimony to the power of television: Turner's bluff Yorkshire manner gives him one of the more accessible media profiles. Most nights, he perambulates through the dining-room in chef's whites, but not to encourage awe-struck genuflexion so much as to have a good natter with whoever's in. It is a refreshingly grass-roots approach that somehow chimes harmoniously in the moneyed environs of Knightsbridge.

Fixed-price menus probably account for most of the support Turner's receives. They have long been beacons of exemplary value at this level of cooking. A man who ate veal and wild mushroom terrine with a green bean salad, corn-fed chicken with baby turnips and roast garlic, and 'scrummy' chocolate marquise, was a well-satisfied customer. Panaché of steamed fish on another occasion brought together sea bream, plaice and salmon on an al dente saffron risotto with herb butter, the fish cooked 'simply and sensitively' for optimum flavour impact. Some may find certain of the cheaper dishes a little simple in construction, but execution is equally assured across the board. John Dory fillets with foie gras mousseline and artichokes was a 'class act', according to one reporter impressed by the 'precise judgement of flavours'; not far behind was a main course of seared calves' kidneys that came on a cake of mashed celeriac with a grain-mustard sauce. Lime bavarois with apple slices, or raspberry and white chocolate torte sit comfortably alongside apple crumble and chocolate sponge in the pudding line-up. Most reports commend the service: 'a well-trained and assiduous young brigade that avoids over-formality'. Wines are predominantly French. Quality is high, but then so are the prices. House Bordeaux are £13.50.

CHEFS: Brian Turner and Charlie Curran   PROPRIETOR: Brian Turner   OPEN: Sun to Fri L 12.30 to 2.30, Mon to Sat D 7.30 to 10.30, Sun D 6 to 8.30   CLOSED: 1 week Christmas, bank hols   MEALS: Set L Mon to Fri £9.95 (2 courses) to £39.25, Set L Sun £19.50 to £39.25, Set D Mon to Sat £23.50 (2 courses) to £39.25, Set D Sun £32.50   SERVICE: not inc, card slips closed   CARDS: Access, Amex, Delta, Diners, Switch, Visa   DETAILS: 52 seats. Private parties: 52 main room. Vegetarian meals. Children's helpings. Smart dress preferred. Wheelchair access (no WC). Music. Air-conditioned

Two Brothers £

map 12

297–303 Regents Park Road, N3 1DP

COOKING 1*

TEL: (0181) 346 0469

COST £16–£43

The brothers in question are Leon and Tony Manzi, who are the main men at this swanky fish-and-chip restaurant on Regents Park Road. They pride themselves on the freshness and quality of their fish, which extends beyond the staples into Rossmore rock oysters, sea bass and Mediterranean prawns. In addition to the basics, the menu offers such things as Arbroath smokies, sauté sardines and home-made fish-cakes, while the blackboard of specials moves into the eclectic world of baked cod Chinese-style and salmon teryaki. Starters might feature jellied eels and marinated herrings, while puddings include home-made bread-and-butter pudding, cheesecake, and a host of ice-cream extravaganzas. The wine list is quite a surprise in terms of its range and knowledge. House wine is £8.95.

CHEFS/PROPRIETORS: Leon and Tony Manzi   OPEN: Tue to Sat 12 to 2.30, 5.30 to 10.15   CLOSED: last 2 weeks Aug, bank hols exc Good Fri   MEALS: alc (main courses £6.50 to £14)   SERVICE: not inc, card slips closed   CARDS: Access, Amex, Switch, Visa   DETAILS: 90 seats. Children welcome. Music. Air-conditioned

Union Café   map 15

96 Marylebone Lane, W1M 5FP   COOKING 1*
TEL: (0171) 486 4860   COST £24–£41

'This is better than its café name suggests.' It is as plain as a canteen, spacious, with big windows that let in lots of light, and an open-plan kitchen to show there is nothing to hide. The accent is on fresh ingredients and simple daily-changing dishes, and an accommodating schedule makes food available 12 hours a day, beginning with breakfast from 10am. Soups are a forte and have included a 'substantial and robust' tomato version with white beans, potatoes, herbs and Parmesan: 'not subtle, but warming and filling on a cold day'. And there is good bread to dunk into it. Salads also feature prominently, and non-meat dishes might range from a roast vegetable and mozzarella pizza to 'correctly made' risotto of wild mushrooms with rocket and Parmesan. Tropical fruit salad, chocolate cake, and a tart such as rhubarb and ginger are typical puddings. Service is 'efficient, friendly and relaxed', and a short list of drinks includes thick, fruity 'smoothies' and around 15 decent wines from £9.75, half of them available by the glass.

CHEFS/PROPRIETORS: Caroline Brett and Sam Russell   OPEN: Mon to Fri 10 to 12, 12.30 to 3.30, 6.30 to 10. Light meals available all day   CLOSED: 2 weeks Christmas, 1 week end Aug   MEALS: alc (main courses £9 to £12). Minimum £10 L and D   SERVICE: 12.5% (optional), card slips closed   CARDS: Access, Delta, Switch, Visa   DETAILS: 68 seats. Private parties: 80 main room. Vegetarian meals. Children welcome. Wheelchair access (no WC). No music

Upper Street Fish Shop £   map 13

324 Upper Street, N1 2XQ   COOKING 1
TEL/FAX: (0171) 359 1401   COST £12–£23

'A hugely successful mom and pop operation; long may they prosper,' enthused a reporter. The Conways have been doing their own thing in Islington since 1981 and have become something of an institution. The attractions are clear: fresh fish, good chips, a great neighbourhood atmosphere, and that indefinable personal touch are what draw the crowds. There have been strong votes for rock oysters, deep-fried mussels on a skewer, grilled Dover sole, and poached halibut with herb sauce. Others have been disappointed by 'tough' tempura prawns and 'tasteless' scampi, but the balance is firmly in the Conways' favour. Round things off with home-made Bakewell tart with custard, or treacle tart. The place is unlicensed, but its BYO policy (no corkage) is known and appreciated by all who come here.

CHEFS: Alan Conway and Stuart Gamble   PROPRIETOR: Alan Conway   OPEN: Tue to Fri L 12 to 2.15 (3 Sat), Mon to Sat D 6 (5.30 Fri and Sat) to 10.15   CLOSED: bank hols   MEALS: alc (main courses £6.50 to £10). BYO (no corkage)   SERVICE: not inc   CARDS: none   DETAILS: 50 seats. Children welcome. Wheelchair access (no WC). No music. Air-conditioned

Vegetarian Cottage ⅔✳ £

map 13

91 Haverstock Hill, NW3 4RL
TEL: (0171) 586 1257

COOKING 1
COST £14–£36

'A commendable effort in trying to bring Chinese vegetarian dishes to the masses' is one Oriental verdict on this spick-and-span restaurant. Black-framed prints hang from the white walls, and Chinese classical music provides a soothing accompaniment. The menu may be tilted towards 'meatlessness', but the presence of seafood would be frowned upon by devout Buddhist monks. Signs of one-dimensional similarity can creep in, especially with the variations on gluten employed to mimic animal protein, but there is also plenty to enjoy. Spring rolls, winter melon and bean curd soup, and Buddha's Cushion (an assemblage of black moss, fungi and well-timed greens) are skilfully done, and stir-fried scallops with 'beautifully cooked' vegetables suggest that the kitchen can also handle fish. Desserts range from sago and yam pudding to red-bean pancakes. The wine list is a shade above the Chinese norm; house Australian is £6.80.

CHEF: C.K. Wong   PROPRIETORS: Y.K. Tsui and S.W. Chu   OPEN: Sun L 12 to 3, all week D 6 to 11   CLOSED: 25 and 26 Dec   MEALS: alc (main courses £4.50 to £15.50). Set L Sun £8, Set D £11.80 to £13.50. Minimum £8   SERVICE: not inc   CARDS: Access, Delta, Switch, Visa   DETAILS: 50 seats. Private parties: 30 main room. Vegetarian meals. Children welcome. Smart dress preferred. No smoking in 1 dining-room. Wheelchair access (no WC). Music. Air-conditioned

Village Bistro

NEW ENTRY   map 12

38 Highgate High Street, N6 5JG
TEL: (0181) 340 5165 and 0257
FAX: (0181) 347 5584

COOKING 1*
COST £23–£42

A narrow and unevenly paved passageway leads into the small converted shop premises that the Village Bistro inhabits. Inside, an unexpected vision of fake beams and flounced curtains greets the eye. The culinary focus is French, the menus bilingual, the translations unashamedly approximate, but the cooking shows more than a hint of real flair. 'Impressively large' helpings add to the sum of human happiness. Lightly cooked, tender squid sauté with garlic and herbs comes awash with pungent juices, and well-marinated barbecued belly-pork with stir-fried vegetables is 'nicely sticky, the best set-meal meat I've been offered in ages'. Apple fritters in cider batter is a good dessert, as is full-throttle blackcurrant sorbet, a masterpiece of vivid intensity. Courtesy distinguishes the service. A short, predominantly French wine list keeps prices considerate, kicking off with house wines at £9.95.

CHEF: Nicholas Rochford PROPRIETOR: Darela Ltd OPEN: all week 12 to 3, 6 to 11 MEALS: alc (main courses £9 to £12.50). Set L £14.95, Set D Sun to Wed £10.95 (2 courses) SERVICE: not inc CARDS: Access, Amex, Delta, Switch, Visa DETAILS: 45 seats. Private parties: 30 main room, 18 and 30 private rooms. Vegetarian meals. Children's helpings. Smart dress preferred. No cigars/pipes in dining-room. Music. Air-conditioned

Villandry Dining Room ¦✳ map 15

89 Marylebone High Street, W1M 3DE
TEL: (0171) 224 3799 and 487 3816   COOKING 1
FAX: (0171) 486 1370   COST £24–£36

One reporter who turned up in spring was intrigued to find the front window entirely covered in chocolate, with an outline 'Happy Easter' waiting for a chocolate engraver to complete. As publicity this is modest by London standards, but then so is the restaurant. Its gentle eccentricity wins friends quickly. 'Since I discovered it last month, I eat here whenever I am in town.' The front half is a delicatessen selling breads, oils, vinegars, cheeses – a browser's collection to whet the appetite on the way to the dining-room at the back. Adornment and decoration are obviously frowned on, and the food is as simple and basic as the furniture: vegetarian flan, a plate of charcuterie, or kedgeree. It might also stretch to a lamb stew with couscous, but the pitch is towards light lunches, with lemon tart or chocolate cake (if there's any left over from the window) to finish. 'I enjoy the noise and bustle,' writes one, and 'even though madly busy the staff are still delightful.' Around 30 wines are imported directly from France. House wine is £11.90.

CHEF: Rosalind Carrarini PROPRIETORS: Jean-Charles and Rosalind Carrarini OPEN: Mon to Sat L only 12.30 to 3 CLOSED: 1 week Christmas MEALS: alc (main courses £8 to £11) SERVICE: net prices, card slips closed CARDS: Access, Amex, Switch, Visa DETAILS: 50 seats. Private parties: 40 main room. Vegetarian meals. Children's helpings. No smoking in dining-room. Wheelchair access (no WC). No music. Air-conditioned

Vong [NEW ENTRY] map 14

Wilton Place, SW1X 7RL   COOKING 2*
TEL: (0171) 235 1010 FAX: (0171) 235 1011   COST £32–£73

New York hits London. Jean-Georges Vongerichten is the new kid on the block, exchanging the hubbub of East 54th Street and 3rd Avenue for some flashy premises at the corner of Wilton Place and Knightsbridge. Anything not smartly turned out around here wouldn't last five minutes, hence the spruce entrance, shiny bar, and dashing, mirrored basement dining-room with a glass-fronted kitchen that enables customers and chefs to eye each other up. The subject of the razzmatazz is a much-hyped combination of classical French cooking and Thai flavours. Here is a chef with a clear message, although since respectable numbers of British chefs have been successfully ploughing a similar furrow for the best part of a decade, its novelty value may have less impact than the PR machine would like.

The Franco-Thai meetings occur at different levels: hardly at all in puddings, such as an excellent warm Valrhona chocolate cake with a runny centre; slightly more when sauté foie gras is expertly partnered with ginger and mango; and rather more again in a dish of squab pigeon breasts on egg noodle pancakes. Fish features prominently and is well treated, some tastes are cleverly contrasted, and sauces and dips are well judged: a rosemary and ginger one for lobster and daikon rolls, for example. Despite highish mark-ups, the wine list manages to produce some drinkable bottles under £20. 'Silly money' is one reporter's view of the overall cost, but then who comes to Knightsbridge for a cheap night out? House wine starts at £14.50.

CHEF: Jean-Georges Vongerichten   PROPRIETOR: Savoy Group plc   OPEN: Mon to Sat 12 to 2.30, 6 to 11.30   MEALS: alc (main courses £11.50 to £26.50). Set L £20   SERVICE: 12.5% (optional), card slips closed   CARDS: Access, Amex, Delta, Diners, Switch, Visa   DETAILS: 140 seats. Car park. Vegetarian meals. Children welcome. Smart dress preferred. Wheelchair access (also WC). Music. Air-conditioned

Wagamama ⅝✳ £   map 15

4A Streatham Street, WC1A 1JB	COOKING 1
TEL: (0171) 580 9365 FAX: (0171) 323 9224	COST £17–£28

Wagamama's philosophy of 'positive eating + positive living' is a real crowd-puller. It's ironic that the avowed intention of affordable fast food has resulted in such long queues: if you want to sample the experience, expect to take time out. Legions of students, tourists and office workers sit in regimented rows on hard benches while waiters and waitresses whirl around in top gear. The decibel level is unerringly high. The menu – which is 'long and complicated' to most people – is built around ramen noodle soups and pan-fried soba noodles with myriad toppings. Added to these are little side-dishes – which can also be eaten as starters – such as edamame (salted soya beans in the pod), and chicken yakitori. Drinks range from frothy raw juices and free green tea to plum wine and super-dry Asahi lager. House wine is £7.90. The second branch at 10A Lexington Street, W1R 3HS, is run along identical lines.

PROPRIETOR: Wagamama Ltd   OPEN: all week noon to 11 (10.30 Sun)   CLOSED: Christmas   MEALS: alc (main courses £6 to £7)   SERVICE: not inc   CARDS: Access, Delta, Switch, Visa   DETAILS: 104 seats. Vegetarian meals. Children welcome. No smoking in dining-room. No music. Air-conditioned

Waltons   map 14

121 Walton Street, SW3 2HP	COOKING 1*
TEL: (0171) 584 0204 FAX: (0171) 581 2848	COST £24–£70

'Swish' and 'handsome' are words that spring to mind when describing Waltons. It occupies a prime site in a well-heeled Chelsea street, and owner Roger Wren tells us that much of his business is still from the neighbourhood. He is a champion of old-fashioned English food, and raw materials are often home-produced. Sauté Cornish scallops come with squid-ink vinaigrette, slices of roast Gressingham duck are topped 'bizarrely' with deep-fried seaweed, and roast rack of Southdown lamb is accompanied by parsnip purée and rosemary gravy. To finish, mille-feuille of raspberries contains superb fruit. The kitchen performs competently, although there's a feeling that the results lack excitement. Service is 'well above par'. The wine list is long, but there is a helpful mini-selection at the front; prices are generally fair. House wine is £11.

CHEF: Jonathan Coxon   PROPRIETOR: Roger Wren   OPEN: all week 12.30 to 2.30 (2 Sun and bank hols), 7.30 to midnight (7 to 10 Sun and bank hols)   CLOSED: D 25 Dec, 26 Dec   MEALS: alc (main courses £12 to £18). Set L Mon to Sat £16.75, Set L Sun £18.75, Set D £17.50 (2 courses) to £30 (prices vary daily; ring to cheque). BYO by arrangement   SERVICE: not inc   CARDS: Access, Amex, Delta, Diners, Switch, Visa   DETAILS: 90 seats. Private parties: 45 main room, 6 to 20 private rooms. Vegetarian meals. Children's helpings. No pipes in dining-room. No music. Air-conditioned

Wilsons
map 12

236 Blythe Road, W14 0HJ	COOKING 1
TEL: (0171) 603 7267	COST £24–£39

'What a jolly place,' commented a couple, clearly much taken with the Gaelic goings-on in Bob Wilson's eponymous restaurant. If you are looking for signs of Scottishness on the menu, you will find them in Finnan haddock pudding, rack of lamb with a haggis crust, and Atholl brose with caramelised oranges; otherwise it's something of a lucky dip into the European larder, pulling out leek, tomato and mozzarella tart, confit of duckling, escalope of salmon with basil and vermouth, and sauté guinea-fowl with Chartreuse and hazelnuts. Reliably good salmon fish-cakes with parsley sauce, and first-rate summer pudding keep England in the frame. Service and atmosphere are charming: 'there is even a stone cat just by the door to make you feel at home'. The wine list is modest, keenly priced and dependable. House French is £8.95.

CHEF: Robert Hilton   PROPRIETORS: Robert Wilson and Robert Hilton   OPEN: Sun to Fri L 12.30 to 2.30, Mon to Sat D 7.30 to 10   CLOSED: bank hols   MEALS: alc (main courses £8 to £12). Set L Sun £14.95   SERVICE: 12.5% (optional), card slips closed   CARDS: Access, Amex, Delta, Switch, Visa   DETAILS: 44 seats. Private parties: 44 main room. Vegetarian meals. Children's helpings. Wheelchair access (no WC). Music. Air-conditioned

Wiltons
map 15

55 Jermyn Street, SW1Y 6LX	COOKING 3
TEL: (0171) 629 9955 FAX: (0171) 495 6233	COST £30–£84

'If you don't have a club to go to, come and eat here,' seems to be one of the messages that Wiltons conveys. The building – and indeed the à la carte menu – has an Edwardian feel about it, and the atmosphere is very English and genteel. Politeness and decorum reign, with matron-like ladies and waiters in striped trousers setting the tone.

Seafood dominates, and there is no messing about with, say, gurnard or whelks. This is blue-blooded stuff – oysters, lobster and langoustines, Dover sole and turbot – all helped along with foie gras pâté and beluga caviare, plus lamb chop and Scotch fillet steak for the red-blooded. There is, some overlap between the *carte* and 'today's specialities', although the latter may also run to skate wing in black butter, or baked cod with herb butter. Part of Wiltons' success lies in keeping the cooking simple. Poaching and grilling are the principal techniques, and very few dishes are diverted by strident intrusions of salsas or Thai flavourings. It is impervious to gastro-fashion, but the food is by no means lacklustre. Fish is 'in the peak of condition', and the attitude is one of 'generous and uncomplicated style'. A choice of four savouries adds to the

Edwardian feel. Nursery sweets (and they can be sweet) include sherry trifle. Aristocratic French wines at appropriate prices dominate the list, and house wine is £13.50.

CHEF: Ross Hayden   PROPRIETORS: Rupert, Richard and James Hambro   OPEN: Sun to Fri 12 to 2.30, 6 to 10.30   CLOSED: Easter and Christmas   MEALS: alc (main courses £10 to £28). Set L Sun £19.75. Cover £1. Minimum £12.50   SERVICE: not inc   CARDS: Access, Amex, Diners, Visa   DETAILS: 90 seats. Private parties: 40 main room, 18 private room. Vegetarian meals. Children welcome. Jacket and tie. Wheelchair access (no WC). No music. Air-conditioned

---

Zafferano |NEW ENTRY| map 14

15 Lowndes Street, SW1X 9EY   COOKING 2
TEL: (0171) 235 5800   FAX: (0171) 235 1971   COST £27–£51

'This is a serious restaurant with a talented and thoughtful chef,' summed up one reporter of Giorgio Locatelli's Italian restaurant in Belgravia. The deep saffron-yellow paint is responsible for the name, and the cooking appeals for its 'unfamiliar dishes and simple but original presentation'. A fairly lengthy menu delivers food of great verve and freshness: a salad of French beans for instance, with chunks of artichoke and slivers of nutty Parmesan on a layer of red onion. Bushy little turnip tops cooked with chilli-dressed orechiette pasta – a speciality of Apulia – make a dish full of subtle contrasts, while recommended main courses have included chargrilled grey mullet with tomatoes and basil, cod with lentils in a parsley purée sauce, and 'delicious, rustic' rabbit wrapped in Parma ham on non-gooey polenta. Lemon and mascarpone tart, or copiously garnished rum baba, are typically rich ways to finish, although a rhubarb and amaretto tartlet with frozen yoghurt has been described as 'unsweet and surprisingly refreshing'. Espresso is grade A, and an Italian wine list rounds up some of the more illustrious names, including an impressive run of top-flight Barolo, Barbareco and Brunello, at hefty prices. House wines from Sicily and Abruzzi are £10.50.

CHEF/PROPRIETOR: Giorgio Locatelli   OPEN: Mon to Sat 12 to 2.30, 7 to 11   MEALS: Set L £14.50 (2 courses) to £17.50, Set D £18.50 (2 courses) to £25.50   SERVICE: not inc, card slips closed   CARDS: Access, Amex, Delta, Visa   DETAILS: 65 seats. Vegetarian meals. Children welcome. Smart dress preferred. Wheelchair access (no WC). Music. Air-conditioned

---

Zen Central   map 15

20 Queen Street Mayfair, W1X 7PJ
TEL: (0171) 629 8089 and 8103   COOKING 2
FAX: (0171) 493 6181   COST £41–£81

The Zen chain set the tone for a new ultra-chic approach to Chinese food in London, and this Mayfair branch is typical. Cool and smart 'in a retro-1970s sort of way' sums up the décor; designer clothes are *de rigueur* for the clientele. The menu draws freely from most Chinese regions, isn't afraid to borrow, and deals in dishes that sound instantly appealing to Westerners. The food is generally well judged and finely tuned. Soft-shell crab is 'tenderly cooked' in a crust of salt, perfectly timed sea bass is steamed and served with an understated black-bean sauce. Away from fish, the menu advertises such things as cold pig's trotter, genuine Peking duck, deep-fried chicken with Yunnan ham and nuts, and sea-spiced lamb.

High-quality sorbets round things off refreshingly. Service is outstanding: 'Many top French restaurants could learn a great deal from the front-of-house here,' observed one. Even so, prices are 'silly even for Mayfair', and the extras quickly mount up. You need to look hard to uncover bargains among the vintage clarets and champagnes on the 'tolerable' wine list. House wine is £12.

CHEF: Wai Hong Ho   PROPRIETOR: Tealeaf Ltd   OPEN: all week 12.15 to 2.30, 6.30 to 11.15 (10.45 Sun)   CLOSED: 4 days Christmas   MEALS: alc (main courses £10 to £22.50). Set L £28, Set D £35 to £50 (minimum 4 for all set meals). Cover £1   SERVICE: 15% (optional)   CARDS: Access, Amex, Delta, Diners, Switch, Visa   DETAILS: 90 seats. Private parties: 70 main room, 18 private room. Vegetarian meals. Children welcome. Smart dress preferred. Wheelchair access. Music. Air-conditioned

London Round-ups

Eating out in London is largely a question of picking the location that offers the right kind of food for the occasion. To assist *Guide* readers, the Round-up section provides details of a range of restaurants, bistros, and cafés that are well worth a visit but do not merit a full entry. Each is included for a specific reason: you may find lunchtime bolt-holes for shoppers, good hotel dining-rooms, chippies, Cantonese soup kitchens, up-and-coming brasseries, even a new star or two in the making. Entries are based on readers' recommendations, often backed up by inspectors' reports. In some cases we have put an establishment in the Round-ups rather than in the main-entry section because there are changes in the air or because there has been a dearth of votes in its favour. Reports on these places are especially welcome, as they enable us to extend our overall coverage of good food in the capital.

Akasaka   NW11
10A Golders Green Road   map 12
(0181) 455 0676
'Honest, simple, rustic' Japanese place run by a husband-and-wife team. He hand-rolls the excellent sushi, she does the rest. Salads, noodles and tempura are particularly good; specials are written on paper and pinned to the walls. Good value and highly popular with the local Japanese community. Drink tea, beer or saké. More reports, please.

Albero and Grana   SW3
Chelsea Cloisters   map 14
(0171) 225 1048
The glitzy face of regional Spanish cooking in the metropolis. The décor is as dazzlingly brilliant as a matador's costume and the food tries to thrill. Tapas draws a huge noisy crowd, while the restaurant at the back of the place offers ambitious-sounding dishes culminating in Segovian-style suckling pig. Service may disappoint.

Atrium   SW1
4 Millbank   map 13
(0171) 233 0032
Modish Mediterranean laced with a drop of hard-core Irish is the mix in this outpost of the Antony Worrall-Thompson empire, set in the atrium of a vast office block, the seductively soothing atmosphere enhanced by a tinkling pianist. Soda bread is authentic, smoked salmon comes on a potato pancake, and black pudding makes a comforting plateful with baked apples and tarragon sauce. The wine list is a racy, fashionable slate.

Avenue West Eleven   W11
157 Notting Hill Gate   map 13
(0171) 221 8144
Neighbourhood bar and restaurant with a short global menu. Recommended dishes have included a salad of moist capon with rocket, pine-nuts and basil, cod baked in a crust on a bed of spinach, and a wedge of very 'intense' chocolate tart. The short wine list is predominantly French. Service needs a lift.

Balzac Bistro   W12
4 Wood Lane   map 12
(0181) 743 6787
A favourite retreat for staff from the BBC Television Centre just down the road. Classic French bistro cooking is the kitchen's stock-in-trade, and the menu scores highly on value for money. Examples from the hand-scrawled menu are fish soup with rouille, moules provençale, venison with black cherries, and beef bourguignon.

Belgo Centraal WC2
50 Earlham Street map 15
(0171) 813 2233
Bigger and brasher than its North London
relative Belgo Noord (see main entry),
but run along similar lines. Gargantuan
helpings of mussels in different guises, a
back-up of authentic specialities, and
scores of Belgian beers are the big
attraction. 'The monks keep smiling
under pressure.'

Beotys WC2
79 St Martin's Lane map 15
(0171) 836 8768/8548
Fifty years is a long time in the restaurant
business, but Beotys continues to
flourish, eschewing fashions and staying
true to its roots. It offers Continental
cooking with an affection for things
Greek, happily making seasonal detours
for gazpacho in summer or steak and
kidney pudding in winter. The kitchen
crew knows exactly how to time meals
for pre-theatre audiences in a hurry.

Big Night Out NW1
148 Regent's Park Road map 13
(0171) 586 5768
Amazingly popular neighbourhood
restaurant that a reporter likened to 'a
butter-coloured squash court', hung with
massive paintings. The food is new-wave
Italian, prices are low. Choices might
include mussels with pesto, grilled squid
and rocket salad, calf's liver with
pancetta, cabbage and balsamic vinegar,
and osso buco with risotto. Wines are
cheap and cheerful.

Bistrot 190 SW7
190 Queen's Gate map 14
(0171) 581 5666
Next door to the Albert Hall, so ideal for
pre-concert dining, Bistrot 190 is
emblazoned with all the trademarks of
Antony Worrall-Thompson: bare tables,
noisy pop music, trendy staff and a menu
seemingly ladled out of a global melting
pot with a Mediterranean spoon. Fish-
cakes on spinach, and poached pear with
Gorgonzola have earned praise, and the

chips are 'absolutely marvellous'. Great
fun if you fancy Sunday brunch with the
Sloanes.

Books for Cooks W11
4 Blenheim Crescent map 13
(0171) 221 1992
You have browsed through the books,
now taste some of the recipes in the café
at the back of this most renowned haunt
of foodie bibliophiles. The lunch menu is
tiny, but the cooking is sound (provided,
of course, that the published recipes
actually work!). Bargain-basement prices.

Bruno Levantine W1
63 Frith Street map 15
(0171) 734 4545
Formerly Bistrot Bruno, this restaurant
acquired a new name shortly before the
Guide went to press. It also changed its
style: the bistro and café have merged,
and the cooking has taken on a distinct
North African and Middle Eastern
complexion. Pierre Khodja remains at the
stoves. Reports, please.

Buchan's SW11
62–64 Battersea Bridge Road map 12
(0171) 228 0888
Casual neighbourhood wine bar-cum-
restaurant where the Sloanes come to
unwind or let off steam and the cooking
shows allegiance to the Auld Alliance.
Warm chicken-liver salad, pea soufflé,
and casseroled lamb shank share the
billing with kipper fish-cakes, haggis with
neeps, and Scotch rump steak flamed in
whisky. Thirty-nine wines (including 13
by the glass), 39 malts and Caledonian
Ales are the alcoholic stand-bys.

Café Spice Namaste E1
16 Prescot Street map 13
(0171) 488 9242
The move from the original premises in
Alie Street was greeted with much hype.
The atmosphere and mood are much
livelier, service is pretty sharp, and Cyrus
Todiwala's idiosyncratic menu reads well.
Goan dishes loom large, but there are also
specialities from Bombay and even Nepal,

and the kitchen takes on board everything from wild rabbit to goat fish. Prices are by no means cheap, and results have been inconsistent.

Caffè Italia   SE3
107 Humber Road   map 12
(0181) 858 7577

A useful neighbourhood address in slightly bereft Blackheath. Owned and run by Domenico and Sarah Lovecchio, it offers broadly based Italian cooking with a few Continental detours. Expect aubergine and tomato salad, braised lamb shank with white wine and herbs, and breast of guinea-fowl with leeks and mustard fruit chutney. Pasta and fish vary each day. The Sardinian wine is good stuff. Can be pricey.

Cambio de Tercio   SW5
163 Old Brompton Road   map 14
(0171) 244 8970

Really exciting tapas are the great attraction in this comfortable, minimalist venue. Garlicky calamares a la plancha, a 'stunning' three-layered vegetable terrine with sweet onion sauce, and scrambled eggs with prawns, tomato and toasted country bread have been enthusiastically devoured. Main dishes focus on the cuisine of the Basque region. Top-drawer Spanish wines.

Chapel   NW1
48 Chapel Street   map 13
(0171) 402 9220

Another former pub converted into bare-tabled, come-as-you-are eating-house. The short blackboard menu offers rough-hewn dishes such as pappardelle with meatballs, excellent griddled salmon, and herb-flecked lamb-burgers. Take a tip from the regulars and drink Shepherd Neame Spitfire, or the guest ale; or opt for wines chalked on a board.

Chez Gérard   W1
8 Charlotte Street   map 15
(0171) 636 4975

Part of a mini-chain, but distinctive in style and highly popular. Bread, anchovy butter and olives are 'the best', steaks are invariably good and the cheeseboard is worth exploring. Other bonus points are the onion soup, brilliant frites and espresso coffee. Service maintains its Gallic sense of efficiency. The branch in the Covent Garden Piazza, WC2, tel. (0171) 379 0666, is perfectly placed to view the mime, music and jugglers. Other branches are at 31 Dover Street, W1, tel. (0171) 499 8171; and 119 Chancery Lane, WC2, tel. (0171) 405 0290.

Clerkenwell Restaurant & Bar   EC1
73 Clerkenwell Road   map 13
(0171) 405 4173

Carpaccio comes to Clerkenwell in the shape of this lively restaurant with grey-tiled floors and metallic artwork on the walls. The menu is undiluted '90s Italian, offering red mullet with marinated aubergine, pine kernels and coriander salad, or chicken breast stuffed with crabmeat and served with hand-made taglioni verde. 'Wicked' orange, mint and ricotta zuccotto rounds things off in style. Good-value, fairly priced Italian wines.

Condotti   W1
4 Mill Street   map 15
(0171) 499 1308

Arguably the most reliable independent pizza place in the West End, and a very handy pit-stop for shoppers. The mood is up-beat, service is razor-sharp and the pizzas themselves are timed to a T. Reliable back-up arrives in the form of garlic bread, espresso, Peroni beer and a few quaffable Italian wines.

Conrad London, Brasserie   SW10
Chelsea Harbour   map 12
(0171) 823 3000

Modern hotel brasserie overlooking the Marina with harbour views from all vantage points. Enjoy a salad on the terrace when the sun shines or delve into the internationally inclined *carte*. Specialities include warm potato pancake with crème fraiche and deep-fried leeks, plank-roasted lamb with mango salsa and barley risotto, and goats'-cheese galette with pineapple confit as a dessert. Fish dishes are best sellers.

Cork & Bottle WC2
44–46 Cranbourn Street map 15
(0171) 734 7807
Still a great little wine bar despite the up-and-coming competition around Leicester Square. It succeeds because it has worked out a user-friendly formula and sticks to it. Crowds pack the cellar for the happy-go-lucky atmosphere and the good drinking on Don Hewitson's impressive wine list. The menu offers anything from oysters to cheese, with terrines, pies, grills and casseroles along the way. The Hanover Square Wine Bar & Grill, 25 Hanover Square, W1, tel. (0171) 408 0935, is also out of the Don Hewitson stable.

Diwana Bhel Poori NW1
121 Drummond Street map 13
(0171) 387 5556
The most consistent Indian vegetarian food in the Drummond Street enclave. Favourites such as samosas, bhel pooris, dosas and aloo papri chat rarely disappoint, and lassi is some of the best in town. Thalis and daily specials are also up to the mark, as is the home-made kulfi. Lunchtime buffets are outstanding value.

Ebury Wine Bar SW1
139 Ebury St map 13
(0171) 730 5447
Near-legendary wine bar with a bright new image. Australian chef Josh Hampton has been around, and has given the menu a shake-up. Out goes steak and kidney pie, in come grilled tuna with sweet noodle chilli salad, sea bass with Lebanese cucumber salad, and chargrilled kangaroo with Bloody Mary sauce. The wine list contains a few New World gems.

Efes Kebab House W1
80 Great Titchfield Street map 15
(0171) 636 1953
'Amazingly popular and a good place to take a carnivore' is the verdict on this long-serving Turkish warhorse. Crisp, puffy boreks, and cubes of deep-fried lamb's liver outshine the taramasalata, while main courses consist mostly of capably handled high-protein grills. Sticky baklava, genuinely thick Turkish coffee, plus Efes beer and a handful of Turkish wines provide an authentic back-up. Efes II is at 175–177 Great Portland Street, NW1, tel. (0171) 436 0600.

Enoteca SW15
28 Putney High Street map 12
(0181) 785 4449
Simply decorated south London Italian with an enticing regional menu. Broad-bean purée with roasted peppers, crostini of focaccia with duck liver, pine-nuts and raisins, and risotto of red onion and cuttlefish show the style. Pasta appears in the shape of pappardelle with artichokes and garlic, and taglierini neri with seafood. Plentiful bread, gutsy wines, and courteous, well-trained staff.

L'Escargot Doré W8
2–4 Thackeray Street map 13
(0171) 937 8508
A long-time favourite with the denizens of Kensington, this popular restaurant continues to win praise for its renditions of French culinary classics, though 'prices are not cheap'. The 'very, very substantial' menu takes in everything from filet mignon, and snails in garlic butter to goats'-cheese salad with honey, and salmon marinated in Armagnac and dill. Modesto Sanchez and his wife are extremely amicable hosts.

Formula Veneta SW10
14 Hollywood Road map 14
(0171) 352 7612
A flash setting for 'a very civilised supper'. The full-frontal-Italian cooking includes wild mushroom and cannellini bean soup, a fair assortment of pasta and 'decent' tiramisù. Wines are a promising Italian collection; otherwise set your pulse racing with cappuccino and Sambuca. Good territory for star-spotters.

Frederick's N1
Camden Passage map 13
(0171) 359 2888
An old-stager among the curio and
antique shops of Camden Passage.
Andrew Jeffs (ex-Nico Central; see main
entry, London) now heads the kitchen,
although reports suggest he has yet to
find top form. His menu covers a lot of
ground, from brilliant pan-seared foie
gras with caramelised oranges, and glazed
guinea-fowl with mushrooms, spinach
and spätzle, to steamed fillet of sea bass
with spiced aubergine, coriander and
tagliolini. Praiseworthy house wines.

Geales W8
2 Farmer Street map 13
(0171) 727 7969
Grand old fish and chip restaurant that
has had mixed fortunes over the years,
but is now back on course. Mighty
portions of excellent fresh cod, haddock,
skate and so on overlap the plate, and
well-cooked chips are copious. Rapid,
friendly service is combined with a
professional welcome. Cheap and
cheerful wines.

Gilbert's SW7
2 Exhibition Road map 14
(0171) 589 8947
Superb home-baked breads and a wine
list loaded with exciting bottles at bargain
prices are two attributes of this charming
little restaurant. Recent successes on the
plate include Roquefort and walnut salad,
salmon and avocado sushi, loin of lamb
with haricot beans, and lemon tart with
raspberry coulis. Handy for the Albert
Hall and the museums.

Gopal's of Soho W1
12 Bateman St map 15
(0171) 434 1621/0840
This up-market Soho Indian pre-dates the
café society explosion and used to hold its
own by offering what were called new-
wave dishes, acknowledging the regions
of the Sub-continent. Times change:
Gopal has extended his little empire into
the City and Fitzrovia, and there's a

feeling that the cooking here has lost
some of its orginal charge. 'It's a useful
place', but not particularly cheap.

Le Gothique SW18
Royal Victoria Patriotic map 12
Building, Fitzhugh Grove
(0181) 870 6567
Way off the beaten track at the back of
council flats in the Royal Patriotic
Building (an extraordinary Gothic edifice
that was once an orphanage and later the
wartime home of MI5 and MI6). The
restaurant offers French cooking along
the lines of goats'-cheese and artichoke
salad, casseroled venison, and heavenly
Grand Marnier ice-cream. Don't leave
without seeing the enchanting cloistered
garden.

Greek Valley NW8
130 Boundary Road map 13
(0171) 624 3217
Family-run, neighbourhood taverna
offering a reasonable assortment of
mostly familiar Greek-Cypriot dishes.
Recent successes have included tender,
fresh kalamari, 'excellent' swordfish
kebabs with 'Cyprus greens', and nicely
herbed 'fall off the bone' kleftiko. Greek
wines are fairly priced, service is speedy
and the atmosphere is very jolly.

Green Cottage NW3
9 New College Parade, map 13
Finchley Road
(0171) 722 5305/7892
Useful local restaurant that attempts to
bring a taste of Soho Chinatown to Swiss
Cottage. Wun-tun and vegetable soup,
steamed duck with plum sauce, and stir-
fried scallops have been recommended.
There are also regular votes for fish-
flavoured aubergine with garlic and chilli.

La Grignote NW3
77 Heath Street map 13
(0171) 433 3455
A tiny Gallic gem run by a charming
French couple. The style is simple bistro,

fixed-price menus are good value, and the wine list is sound. Dishes range from 'excellent' fish soup to tarte Tatin, with salads in between and main courses that could include pink rack of lamb, or 'well-judged' turbot and salmon.

Kartouche   SW10
329–331 Fulham Road   map 14
(0171) 823 3515
Loud colours, high decibels and a menu that surfs wildly over the Pacific Rim are the ingredients of this glitzy Chelsea address. Style counts, and virtually anything goes in the kitchen, where tom yum soup and Thai fish-cakes rub shoulders with emu steak and kangaroo sausages. Squid salad comes with green mango, chillies and peanuts, while brill is served boldly with a spicy beurre blanc and crisp parsnip shavings. Wines are 'pricey'.

Kym's   SW1
70–71 Wilton Road   map 13
(0171) 828 8931
Extremely useful Chinese restaurant in a neighbourhood not teeming with addresses where you can eat drunken fish and sizzling beef. The surroundings are pleasing, service is helpful, and there are special deals for those taking in performances at the nearby theatres. Chef's specials include carp, fresh from their pond, braised with ginger and spring onion.

Lavender   SW11
171 Lavender Hill   map 12
(0171) 652 7502
'A hip meeting place for twenty-somethings' serving lively bistro food with Californian and Mediterranean overtones. Smoked haddock and salmon come in a tomato-based daube-like stew; Mozzarella, spinach and red onion tart is served with 'rocket ravioli of balsamic turnip' and a mushroom vinaigrette. Sweets might include raspberry and white chocolate tart. The wine list provides good value.

London Hilton,
Windows Rooftop Restaurant   W1
22 Park Lane   map 15
(0171) 493 8000
Glitzy international hotel with a de luxe address and brilliant views over London from the Windows Rooftop Restaurant. Jacques Rolancy's cooking is in the modern mould of tartare of sea bream with avocado, roast fillet of hare with a ragoût of fennel and chestnuts, and iced nougat and bitter chocolate pyramid. More down-to-earth food is also available in the Park Brasserie and Trader Vic's.

Mandalay   W2
444 Edgware Road   map 13
(0171) 258 3696
Tiny Burmese cafe that tries very hard in an unpromising Edgware Road location. The menu is a straightfoward run through starters, salads, and variations on curries, rice and noodles. Sound bets are the weird-looking 'leafy green fritters' with dips, assertive chicken, shrimp and lime soup, and spiced lamb with rice. Very cheap and cheerful, good fun and a boon to the area.

Mas Café   W11
6–8 All Saints Road   map 13
(0171) 243 0969
If you can put up with the noise and smoke, there is plenty to enjoy from a menu that dives headlong into the Mediterranean, but also embraces fish cassoulet, and grilled sirloin steak with porcini butter. Flavours and spicing come through forcefully and dishes are attractively presented. Among desserts you might find orange crème renversée and some interesting sorbets. Open for brunch at weekends. The wine list is reasonably priced.

Mezzanine   SE1
National Theatre   map 13
(0171) 928 3531
'A perfect prologue to Richard II', or any other performance being staged at the National. The setting is wonderfully restful (even though you can hear the

entertainment), and the cooking is reckoned to be 'splendid'. There has been applause for hot spinach mousse with Parmesan sauce, a salad of ham, asparagus and artichokes, for praline ice-cream, and a 'marvellous' compote of fruit.

New Mayflower   W1
68–70 Shaftesbury Avenue   map 15
(0171) 734 9207
The new incarnation of this long-established venue on Shaftesbury Avenue has yet to return to its former stature. The large 'Cantonese Soho menu' is a mixed bag, although reporters have approved of deep-fried milk balls, belly pork with preserved vegetables, brisket of beef hot-pot, and grilled chicken with honey and lemon. Note it is open until 4am, and has a minimum charge of £8 a head.

New World   W1
1 Gerrard Place   map 15
(0171) 434 2508
'Go early on Sunday (before noon) and watch the show.' This is the front-runner in Soho Chinatown for 'trolley' dim-sum, served by brigades of waitresses who tour the tables. Separate trolleys are loaded with steamed dumplings, deep-fried morsels, and roasted meats. Soups and items such as stuffed aubergine with black-bean sauce are prepared in front of you. Huge entertainment value, consistent standards.

Panda Si Chuen   W1
56 Old Compton Street   map 15
(0171) 437 2069
'Excellent pickles' kick off proceedings in this likeable Szechuan restaurant. Stay with the genuine regional dishes for best results: tea-smoked duck with a subtle jasmine flavour, double-cooked pork, excellent red-cooked aubergine, and prawns in the shell with chilli and garlic have been recommended. As a finale, try almond bean curd with fresh fruit salad. Service is friendly and leisurely.

Patisserie Valerie   W1
R.I.B.A., 66 Portland Place   map 15
(0171) 580 5533
Established in Soho in 1926, Patisserie Valerie now has several branches dotted around central London, including this outlet in the Royal Institute of British Architects. All are renowned for their cappuccino, cakes and pastries, not to mention fast, light lunches.

Phoenix   SW15
162 Lower Richmond Road   map 12
(0181) 780 3131
Noisy, airy, but pleasant place opened by Rebecca Mascarenhas and James Harris, of Sonny's fame (see main entries, London and Nottingham). The décor is monochromatic, the short menu is straight out of the global melting pot. Thai crab soup sits alongside Spanish charcuterie, sea bream comes with rocket and chillies, beef teriyaki is served with vegetable noodles. Also note that groovy newcomer to London – the lobster club sandwich. Reasonably priced wines. The actual restaurant entrance is in Pentlow Street.

Pierre Victoire   SW1
William Street   map 14
(0171) 823 1414
The favoured branch of Pierre Levicky's ever-expanding empire of ultra-cheap Parisian-style bistros. Crowds pack in for the 'unbelievable' set lunches. Quality and consistency throughout the chain are mixed, presumably because most are franchised.

Poons   WC2
27 Lisle Street   map 15
(0171) 437 4549
Internationally renowned as the original branch of the Poons empire, and a fixture of the Lisle Street scene. Order hefty platefuls of classic wind-dried duck, sausages and bacon on rice, bowls of soup, or one of the peasant-style hot-pots. Tea is the recommended drink.

Porte des Indes   W1
32 Bryanston Street   map 13
(0171) 224 0055
Heavily hyped sibling of the Blue
Elephant (see main entry, London),
specialising in Indo-French cuisine. The
setting is a lavishly converted Edwardian
ballroom, complete with marble stairs
and a waterfall. Vegetable samosas,
parsee fish (sole fillets steamed in a
banana leaf), and spicy prawns with
chillies have been mentioned favourably,
as have desserts. Prices are high.

Rebato's   SW8
169 South Lambeth Road   map 12
(0171) 735 6388/582 8089
Rebato's is not as fashionable as it used to
be, but is still a great neighbourhood
venue offering excellent value for money.
The tapas bar is authentic, and the 'very
formal' restaurant at the back goes in for
mainly Continental cooking with an
emphasis on fish. Soft roes on toast, skate
with black butter, and grilled sea bream
have been enjoyed. Arrive early and
there may be suckling pig on offer. Drink
Torres and enjoy the jolly atmosphere.

Ritz Hotel   W1
Piccadilly   map 15
(0171) 493 8181
It is hard not to be seduced by the
voluptuous, magical setting of the Louis
XVI dining-room, where you can sample
David Nicholl's confident, de luxe
cooking. Beef Wellington is a must,
soufflés are worth the wait, and some
cheeses are ripe enough to eat with a
spoon. Boned roast grouse, truffled
chicken, and grilled turbot with asparagus
have also been commended. Service is
beyond reproach.

Rotisserie   W12
56 Uxbridge Road   map 12
(0181) 743 3028
'An oasis of calm and civilised cooking,'
says one reporter of this solidly reliable
venue. Aberdeen Angus steak cooked on
a genuine rotisserie is the star; otherwise
try top-quality rack of lamb with

excellent french fries. 'Don Pedro' – a
milkshake spiked with Kahlua – makes a
luscious finish. A second branch has
opened at 134 Upper Street, Islington,
N1, tel. (0171) 226 0122

Spread Eagle   SE10
2 Stockwell Street   map 12
(0181) 853 2333
Very appealing old coaching-inn almost
next door to the Greenwich Theatre, well
placed for meals before and after the
show. The mood is that of 'a small
opulent club' and the cooking has an
unmistakable French accent.
Recommendations include marinated
salmon with dill, duck terrine with plum
chutney, lamb cutlets provençale,
panaché of cod and salmon with
samphire, and poached pear with
cinnamon ice-cream. Decent wines.

The Square   SW1
32 King Street   map 15
(0171) 839 8787
As we went to press, this restaurant was
about to move to Bruton Street, just off
Berkeley Square, but should be open by
the time the *Guide* is published. Expect
food of a similar pedigree, backed up by
an upper-crust, high-class wine list.
Reports on the new set-up would be most
welcome.

Sun and Doves   SE5
61 Coldharbour Lane   map 12
(0171) 733 1525
Once the unofficial watering-hole for
staff at nearby Kings College Hospital, this
stripped-bare Victorian pub is now
fashionably food-conscious. The menu
contains a bit of everything, from Spanish
charcuterie, and Thai mussels, to
sauerkraut with sausages, and salmon
with red pepper sauce and pesto noodles.
Rump steak and chips has been right on
target. The two-course early-evening deal
(6.30 to 7.30, Mon to Sat) is great value.
Pub beers and some youthful modern
wines.

Toffs NW10

38 Muswell Hill Broadway map 12
(0181) 883 8656

'Fresh fish, good batter, decent chips and
excellent gherkins and tartare sauce –
what more could a hungry person ask?'
writes a reporter extolling the virtues of
this ultra-reliable Muswell Hill chippy.
There are tables at the back if you want to
sit down to eat; otherwise queue at the
takeaway counter.

Vasco & Piero's Pavilion W1

15 Poland Street map 15
(0171) 437 8774

Long-serving, unpretentious, family-run
Italian that continues to please as the
years roll by. The superb-value set-dinner
menu has featured courgettes stuffed
with sea bass, roast pigeon on a pile of
fresh pappardelle, and chocolate mousse.
Antipasti, bruschetta, and tiramisù have
also been praised. Look out for interesting
regional and seasonal specials, and
quaffable Italian wines.

Vincent's SW15

147 Upper Richmond Road map 12
(0181) 780 3553

Echoes of the eponymous artist loom
large in the prints and colour schemes of
this neighbourhood restaurant. David
Healey offers an excellent-value menu of
bistro dishes along the lines of bresaola
with roasted vegetables, rib-eye steak
with wild mushrooms, and spinach and
cheese tartlet. Rhubarb tart with rhubarb
sauce makes a pretty dessert. The wine
list is unusual.

Wodka W8

12 St Albans Grove map 14
(0171) 937 6513

Admirable Kensington address promising
an irresistible combination of
atmospheric buzz, serious food and brain-
jangling flavoured vodkas. The menu is
Polish with fashionable diversions: blinis
with assorted toppings, golabki (cabbage
stuffed with pork and wild rice), roast
suckling pig with olive paste, and salad of
warm salt beef with pickles. To finish, try
a sorbet, or chocolate truffle cake with
vodka-marinated cherries.

England

▲ Elms ⅍✷   NEW ENTRY

Abberley WR6 6AT
TEL: **(01299) 896666**   FAX: **(01299) 896804**
on A443, between Worcester and Tenbury Wells, 2m   COOKING **1**
W of Great Witley   COST £25–£51

There is general agreement that the Elms is much improved since the arrival of
Marcel and Corinna Frichot (formerly of Knockinaam Lodge, Portpatrick; see
entry, Scotland). This auspicious Queen Anne mansion in the Teme Valley
recently celebrated 50 years as a country hotel, and now feels and looks more
stylish than ever. Andrew Palmer's menus are interesting and to the point,
although you may be distracted by the wildlife paintings used as a background.
An early inspection revealed good buying, sure timing and plenty of modern
ideas, although there were quibbles about freshness and sauces. A typical meal
might kick off with feuilleté of mussels with Noilly Prat and leeks before new
season's lamb coated with a classic tapénade, or caramelised duck breast with
apple marmalade. Vegetables are appropriate, and desserts could include crispy
apple tart with home-made cinnamon ice-cream. Service is well informed and
pleasantly unstuffy. Ten house wines start at £10.50.

CHEF: Andrew Palmer   PROPRIETORS: Marcel and Corinna Frichot   OPEN: all week 12.30 to 2,
7.30 to 9   MEALS: alc D (main courses £15 to £17). Set L £12.50 (2 courses) to £15, Set D
£22.50   SERVICE: not inc, card slips closed   CARDS: Access, Amex, Delta, Diners, Switch,
Visa   DETAILS: 75 seats. 15 seats outside. Private parties: 80 main room, 32 and 50 private
rooms. Car park. Children's helpings. Smart dress preferred. No smoking in dining-room.
Wheelchair access (also men's WC). No music   ACCOMMODATION: 16 rooms, all with
bath/shower. TV. Phone. B&B £75 to £135. Children welcome. Dogs welcome. Afternoon teas.
Garden

Lighthouse ⅍✷

77 High Street, Aldeburgh IP15 5AU   COOKING **2**
TEL/FAX: **(01728) 453377**   COST £17–£37

The Lighthouse is a converted shop, decorated with sensible understatement, a
magnet for festival-goers and those with holiday homes as much as the faithful
local clientele. The fishing fleet is a matter of yards away, and its wares are put to

ENGLAND

good use, particularly in first courses, as in a fine version of rich fish soup with grated mozzarella and croûtons, while smoked haddock may be fashioned into 'a little custard' and served with grilled pancetta and leaves. One party who plumped for cod and chips all round admired the 'wonderful freshness' of the fish. Salade niçoise made with salmon becomes a main course, served with Jersey Royals in season. Meat-eaters may go for grilled duck with apple and ginger compote, or roast lamb on celeriac mash. 'Wicked bread-and-butter pudding', as the menu puts it, is rendered 'immoral' with a shot of Scotch. Wines are from Adnams, the list marked by great catholicity and value. House selections start at £8.

CHEFS: Sara Fox, Guy Welsh and Gavin Battle   PROPRIETORS: Sara Fox and Peter Hill   OPEN: all week 12 to 2.30, 7 to 10   CLOSED: 2 weeks Jan   MEALS: alc L (main courses £5.50 to £11). Set L £13.50 (2 courses) to £15.75, Set D £13.50 (2 courses) to £15.75. BYO £3 to £5. Light meals available 9 to 3.30   SERVICE: not inc, card slips closed   CARDS: Access, Delta, Switch, Visa   DETAILS: 90 seats. 36 seats outside. Private parties: 50 main room, 20 and 30 private rooms. Vegetarian meals. Children's helpings. Smart dress preferred. No smoking in 1 dining-room. Wheelchair access (no WC). Music. Air-conditioned

Regatta ⅝✷

171–173 The High Street, Aldeburgh IP15 5AN   COOKING 1*
TEL/FAX: (01728) 452011   COST £21–£34

This branch of Robert Mabey's East Anglian gastro-empire is on the main street of fashionably cultured Aldeburgh: you can't mistake the building, with its nautical pennants flying and its sky-blue paintwork. The man himself cooks part of the time, when he is not behind the stoves at Mabey's Brasserie (see entry, Sudbury), but Nigel Ramsbottom is more than just a stand-in. The kitchen is loyal to local seafood, yet treats most things with global dexterity: 'beautifully cooked' salmon might be served with new potatoes and vinaigrette, while cod is more likely jazzed up with with steamed rice and Thai curry sauce. Smoked prawns come with a missable dipping sauce. Otherwise, the excellent-value menu straddles hand-thrown pizzas, grilled fillet of beef, and roast chicken with a red wine sauce, Puy lentils, and 'perfect' chips. Puddings have included spotted dick with vanilla custard. Families are welcomed and children have their own proper menu. Courteous staff and an absence of music are assets. House French wine is £7.50.

CHEF: Nigel Ramsbottom and Robert Mabey   PROPRIETORS: Robert and Johanna Mabey   OPEN: June to Sept all week and Oct to May Wed to Sun 12 to 2.30, 6 to 10   MEALS: alc (main courses £8 to £12)   SERVICE: not inc, card slips closed   CARDS: Access, Amex, Switch, Visa   DETAILS: 80 seats. Private parties: 30 main room. Vegetarian meals. Children's helpings. Smart dress preferred. No smoking in 1 dining-room. Wheelchair access (also men's and women's WC). No music

'[The waiter] sported a hilarious tie: plastic, part translucent, part luminescent, ending in a bikini-clad female reclining on a beach of real sand. I enquired whether he used it as an egg timer.' (On eating in Hereford & Worcester)

ALTRINCHAM Greater Manchester   map 8

Juniper √8/3/97   NEW ENTRY

21 The Downs, Altrincham WA14 2QD   COOKING 3
TEL: (0161) 929 4008   FAX: (0161) 929 4009   COST £23–£44

'The most exciting new restaurant to open in Cheshire for a long time,' reckoned one reporter. 'The Aubergine of the North' another called it, and a feeling of 'not before time' runs through several reports. The wooden floor and ceiling and white walls of the converted shop are enlivened by a Tuscan motif from the Siena palio, producing a 'clean and modern' feel. Paul Kitching cooks much as he did at Nunsmere Hall (see entry, Sandiway), using prime cuts, stock reductions and stylish layered presentation.

Fish is a strong suit. Brill or sea bass are typically fresh, grilled to a tee, and set on a small mound of creamy leek and saffron risotto, or maybe celeriac purée, or perhaps beside a shellfish raviolo. Several reporters have used the word 'nouvelle' in their descriptions, aware of the food's neatness and precision, but it is not backward-looking; there is too much generosity in roast duck with cabbage, bacon and black pudding, or in three succulent pink nuggets of lamb arranged around a creamy mousse of mushrooms on a sticky truffled stock reduction.

'Elegant presentation and robust flavours' make a winning combination, especially when allied to first-class raw materials and impressive technique. Perhaps a few slow-cooked dishes, plus some game or offal, and a soup, might help to round out the menu, but there is no doubt that what appears on the plate is impressive. Skilful pastry-work shows in a glazed lemon tart, and an early star among desserts was a 'sensational' hot rice pudding soufflé. The alternative is a selection of 'unpasteurised British cheeses in good condition served at room temperature'.

Pricing is sensible and reasonable, appetisers and bread are good, and 'very sharp, very switched-on' service is efficiently supervised by Katie O'Brien. The wine list is a bit uneven, and prices jump about a bit, but there are some good bottles and a fair selection by the glass. Prices start at £12 a bottle.

CHEF: Paul Kitching   PROPRIETORS: Nora and Peter Miles   OPEN: Mon to Fri L 12 to 2, Mon to Sat D 7 to 9.30 (10 Fri and Sat)   MEALS: alc (main courses L £7 to £8, D £13). Set D £20 SERVICE: not inc, card slips closed   CARDS: Access, Amex, Delta, Switch, Visa   DETAILS: 46 seats. Private parties: 40 main room. Children welcome. Smart dress preferred. Music. Air-conditioned

ALVECHURCH Hereford & Worcester   map 5

The Mill

Radford Road, Alvechurch B48 7LD   COOKING 2
TEL: (0121) 447 7005   FAX: (0121) 447 8001   COST £19–£39

The heavy beams, dark interior and preserved mill wheel confirm that this was a working mill at one time. Carl Timms cooks in what feels a little like the textbook Anton Mosimann style of the 1980s, offering duck confit with mixed leaves, monkfish with red pepper sauce, and pork fillet with Roquefort. He wishes he could persuade Midlanders to eat more fish, but a man who ate a puff pastry case of salmon, cod and prawns with a good cream sauce was certainly a satisfied customer, and his tagliatelle with tomatoes and bacon to start was pretty nifty too. If you ever thought you'd hanker for chicken breast stuffed with mango all over again, here it is – sauced with Malibu. Flashy desserts, such as white and dark chocolate mousse with coffee sauce, and poached pear in a brandy-snap receptacle with chocolate sauce have been 'much enjoyed'. The fixed-price menus are reckoned to be notably good value, and 'attentive and pleasant' is what the service is all about. An enterprising wine list is supplemented by a good showing of bin-ends, plus a fine-wine list containing mainly mature clarets at not unreasonable prices. House wines are from £7.50.

CHEF: Carl Timms   PROPRIETORS: Stefan, Geoffrey and Vivienne McKernon   OPEN: Sun L 12.30 to 2, Tue to Sat D 7 to 9 (9.30 Sat)   CLOSED: 2 to 3 days after Christmas, first week Jan, first 2 weeks Aug   MEALS: alc (main courses £11 to £14.50). Set L £13.50, Set D £13.50 (2 courses) to £15   SERVICE: not inc   CARDS: Access, Amex, Visa   DETAILS: 34 seats. Private parties: 38 main room. Car park. Vegetarian meals. Children's helpings. Smart dress preferred. Music

---

AMBERLEY   West Sussex   map 3

▲ Amberley Castle, Queen's Room ⅚✳

Amberley BN18 9ND
TEL: (01798) 831992   FAX: (01798) 831998   COOKING 2*
on B2139, between Storrington and Bury Hill   COST £30–£74

As themed restaurants go, this takes some beating. The manor house and Queen's Room are twelfth-century, the battlements and great hall are fourteenth-century. Elizabeth I was a tenant, Cromwell knocked it all about a bit, and Charles II stayed here. As a diner you can hardly ask more of history. Extensive renovations, meanwhile, have brought it up to date with Jacuzzis, and Simon Thyer has done a similar job in the victualling department. An idea of the aspirations can be gleaned from a main-course assiette of lamb, consisting of the kidney in suet, a cutlet, plus liver and sweetbreads, all served with couscous flavoured with black olives and sun-dried tomatoes.

The kitchen is well managed, and there is genuine skill to back up the clear intentions. A classical foundation underlies the operation, yet with enough flexibility to add its own individual dash. Hence, a terrine of duck breast, lentils and foie gras is served with a sour cherry jelly, for instance. A bulgar salad containing red onion, mango and mint (to accompany tuna fillet) shows a lively sense of adventure, while desserts can be as involved as a dark chocolate puff pastry layered with lemon and white chocolate mousse, with a raspberry compote. The wine list is well set out with helpful hints on food matchings, a page of wines selected for their good value, and plenty by the glass. Quality is high throughout, but beware: so are the prices.

Dining-rooms where music, either live or recorded, is never played are signalled by No music *in the details at the end of an entry.*

CHEF: Simon Thyer   PROPRIETORS: Martin and Joy Cummings   OPEN: all week 12 to 2, 7 to 9.30   MEALS: alc D (main courses £17 to £22.50). Set L £18.10, Set D £27.50   SERVICE: not inc, card slips closed   CARDS: Access, Amex, Diners, Switch, Visa   DETAILS: 36 seats. Private parties: 48 main room, 12 and 48 private rooms. Car park. Vegetarian meals. Children's helpings weekdays. No children under 10. Jacket and tie. No smoking in dining-room. No music ACCOMMODATION: 15 rooms, all with bath/shower. TV. Phone. B&B £130 to £275. Deposit: 50%. Children welcome weekdays. Dogs welcome. Afternoon teas. Garden

---

AMBLESIDE Cumbria   map 8

Glass House 🔔✳

	NEW ENTRY

Rydal Road, Ambleside LA22 9AN   COOKING 2
TEL: (01539) 432137   FAX: (01539) 431139   COST £15–£38

'Nearly everyone who visits Ambleside passes within 20 feet of the Glass House.' Next door to the National Trust's House on the Bridge, this multi-level sixteenth-century mill has been restored to working order by glassmaker Adrian Sankey, using local materials to make furniture, oak beams, flooring and wrought ironwork. Open fires and mullioned windows add to the already strong appeal, though you might need a head for heights: 'Set in the floor below our table was a perspex "window" immediately above the moving wheel.'

At the moment the café part of the café/restaurant predominates, serving teas, coffees, snacks and light lunches, but the kitchen certainly has enough going for it should it decide to become a serious restaurant. Dinner offers 'an interesting choice at a fair price', beginning perhaps with 'dainty mounds' of pimento filled with aubergine, or garlicky Portuguese sausage with polenta. Main-course fish and vegetable dishes outnumber meats, and roasts and grills predominate, from saddle of rabbit to a generous steak of firm, white roasted brill sitting on a bed of braised celery, and topped with a crisp potato waffle. Desserts come in the form of apple and fig strudel, or a first-rate rum and raisin crème brûlée. Service is friendly and brisk, and good bottled beers supplement the short and reasonably priced wine list. Reds start at £8.75, whites at £8.95.

CHEF: Stuart Birkett   PROPRIETOR: Adrian Sankey   OPEN: all week 12 to 3, 6.30 to 10   CLOSED: 25 and 26 Dec   MEALS: alc (main courses L £4 to £5.50, D £7 to £13). Snacks available 10am to 10pm.   SERVICE: not inc, card slips closed   CARDS: Access, Switch, Visa   DETAILS: 75 seats. 20 seats outside. Private parties: 50 main room. Vegetarian meals. Children's helpings. No smoking in dining-room. Wheelchair access (no WC). Music

---

▲ *Rothay Manor* 🍷 🔔✳

Rothay Bridge, Ambleside LA22 0EH
TEL: (01539) 433605   FAX: (01539) 433607   COOKING 1*
off A593 to Coniston, ½m W of Ambleside   COST £22–£44

The elegant Regency house near the head of Windermere was built in 1825 as a private residence and has been run as a hotel by the Nixon family for 30 years. The dining-room sports embossed Regency wallpaper and candlelit tables, and although dinner offers limited choice it is more flexible than the Lakeland norm in terms of the number of courses available: anything from two to five. The 'home-made' impression of the food, from soups to poached char with hollandaise to banoffi flan, reflects the unpretentious country-house style, although the cooking could be sharper than it is. 'The feeling was of an old friend trying hard to keep standards up and not quite making it,' is one reporter's view. Lunch can be a cold buffet, or soup followed by a hot dish such as a large, home-made puff pastry vol-au-vent filled with sweetbreads, onion and mushroom: 'good, simple, farmhouse fare' was the verdict.

The unpretentious wine list is full of good producers, from Germany and Australia as well as the Loire, Rhône and Burgundy, and includes many half-bottles. Four house wines are £11. CELLARMAN'S CHOICE: Catena Agrelo Vineyard Chardonnay 1993, Argentina, £18.80; Dom. Leasingham Shiraz 1993, Clare Valley, S. Australia, £13.

CHEFS: Jane Binns and Colette Nixon   PROPRIETORS: Nigel and Stephen Nixon   OPEN: all week 12.30 (12.45 Sun) to 2 (1.30 Sun), 7.45 to 9   CLOSED: 3 Jan to 7 Feb   MEALS: alc L (main courses £8). Set L £13, Set D £22 (2 courses) to £28   SERVICE: not inc, card slips closed   CARDS: Access, Amex, Delta, Diners, Switch, Visa   DETAILS: 70 seats. Private parties: 32 private room. Car park. Vegetarian meals. Children's helpings. Smart dress preferred. No smoking in dining-room. Wheelchair access (also WC). No music. Air-conditioned   ACCOMMODATION: 18 rooms, all with bath/shower. TV. Phone. B&B £76 to £160. Deposit: £60. Rooms for disabled. Children welcome. Baby facilities. Afternoon teas. Garden (The Which? Hotel Guide)

Sheila's Cottage 🐾✕

NEW ENTRY

The Slack, Ambleside LA22 9LE   COOKING 1
TEL: (01539) 433079   FAX: (01539) 434488   COST £16–£37

People have been coming to this all-day tea-room in a side-street in the centre of Ambleside for cakes, snacks and light lunches for over 30 years. The arrival of David Clay has upped the ambition, especially at dinner, when the first-floor barn extension with pine furniture, bright cushions and candelight turns into a bistro-like restaurant. Given the aspirations, it benefits from a small menu of around five items per course, beginning perhaps with chicken, ham and ox tongue terrine, or a vegetable soup topped with a 'very light and extremely tasty' twice-baked ewes'-milk cheese soufflé.

Dishes such as chargrilled chicken breast with roasted provençale vegetables and aïoli are 'full of interesting contrasts of flavours'. Despite the somewhat elaborate approach, raw materials are good and the cooking is effective; an inspector was particularly impressed by loin of local lamb covered with a light mousseline of chicken and tarragon, for example. To finish, British cheeses offer an alternative to lemon surprise or timbale of strawberries. Around 40 wines are well chosen and fairly priced, starting with house South African at £10.50

CHEF: David Clay   PROPRIETORS: Stewart and Janice Greaves   OPEN: Mon to Sat L 12 to 2.30, Tue to Sat D 7 to 9.30 (10 Sat)   CLOSED: Jan   MEALS: alc L (main courses £7.50 to £12). Set D £7.75 (Thurs only) to £15. Light lunches available   SERVICE: not inc   CARDS: Access, Amex, Diners, Visa   DETAILS: 68 seats. Private parties: 46 main room, 28 private room. Vegetarian meals. Children's helpings. Smart dress preferred. No smoking in dining-room. Wheelchair access (no WC). Music. Air-conditioned

AMERSHAM Buckinghamshire   map 3

King's Arms

30 High Street, Old Amersham HP7 0DU   COOKING 1
TEL: (01494) 726333   FAX: (01494) 433480   COST £19–£44

Quintessentially English, half-timbered and of venerable pedigree, the King's Arms fits Old Amersham to a tee. To the left of the courtyard is the darkly timbered pub, where bar meals are served and pints of ale are supped. To the right is the beamed dining-room, with mullioned windows looking out on to the street. Gary Munday changes his menus every few weeks and enlivens his Anglo-French repertoire with a few fashionable inventions: tangy lime pickle with chicken and mango salad, tender braised venison with shiitake mushrooms, or a deeply flavoured basil and tomato sauce with roast fillet of lamb. Sweets such as cold banana crème brûlée have been excellent. Service can be 'matter of fact'. Seafood bonanzas and gastronomic events are a regular feature. France is the main contributor to the reasonably priced wine list. House wine is £8.75.

CHEF: Gary Munday   PROPRIETOR: John Jennison   OPEN: Tue to Sun L 12 to 2, Tue to Sat D 7 to 9.30   CLOSED: 25 to 30 Dec   MEALS: alc (main courses £14 to £16.50). Set L Tue to Sat £8.50 (2 courses) to £11.50, Set L Sun £14.50, Set D Tue to Fri £17, Set D Sat £25. Minimum £8.50 L, £13 D. BYO £5. Bar food available   SERVICE: not inc   CARDS: Access, Amex, Delta, Diners, Switch, Visa   DETAILS: 30 seats. Private parties: 48 main room, 12 to 48 private rooms. Car park. Vegetarian meals. Children's helpings. Smart dress preferred. No cigars/pipes in dining-room. Wheelchair access (no WC). No music

APPLETHWAITE Cumbria   map 10

▲ Underscar Manor 🍴✶

Applethwaite CA12 4PH
TEL: (01768) 775000   FAX: (01768) 774904   COOKING 3
off A66, 1½m N of Keswick   COST £26–£58

A pair who associate the Lake District only with tourist crowds and foul weather found their cynicism stilled as they gazed down on Derwent Water and the mountains beyond from this Italianate villa. To be sure, the heavens had opened as soon as they crossed the county line, but the show that Underscar puts on – red squirrels and strutting guinea-fowls patrolling the grounds in numbers – is hard to resist.

The same has often been said of Robert Thornton's cooking these past few years. Menu descriptions are of the wordier sort, requiring a certain mental agility in imagining dishes while choosing, as in corn-fed chicken breast filled with a mousse of sweetcorn and Westphalian ham accompanied by green pasta, morels, creamed leeks and a Sauternes sauce with tomato and basil. Got that? On the plate, though, it all usually makes sense. A salad of Parma ham with roasted tomatoes and toasted focaccia, decorated with Parmesan shavings and lovage leaves, was considered 'a bit of a hodgepodge but full of flavour'. A slender chargrilled pork chop that came with a sausage (a garlic- and sage-scented affair) and prune compote added up to a superbly accomplished main course, while fish from the Fleetwood boats offers a lighter alternative. Great panache is evident in a dessert of red fruits and kiwi in a sharp syrup topped with a sort of soufflé that discharges a flood of vanilla custard when pierced. For all that the owners abjure the word 'hotel' in describing the manor, preferring the ambience of a private home, it is a home run on surprisingly formal lines, with main courses hidden beneath silver domes and a printed request that diners 'maintain an atmosphere of occasion and decorum'. Elbows in, then.

Pages of opulent French bottles, including a good spread of fine wines, are supplemented by more affordable offerings from elsewhere on the list. This is not really the place for New World fans. Prices open at £10.50 for red Bergerac.

CHEF: Robert Thornton   PROPRIETORS: Pauline and Derek Harrison, and Gordon Evans   OPEN: all week 12 to 1, 7 to 8.30 (9 Sat)   MEALS: alc D (main courses £17 to £18.50). Set L £18.50, Set D £28   SERVICE: not inc, card slips closed   CARDS: Access, Amex, Switch, Visa   DETAILS: 60 seats. 20 seats outside. Private parties: 40 main room. Car park. No children under 12. Jacket and tie. No smoking in dining-room. No music   ACCOMMODATION: 11 rooms, all with bath/shower. TV. Phone. D,B&B £75 to £250. No children under 12. Garden (*The Which? Hotel Guide*)

ARNCLIFFE North Yorkshire   map 8

▲ *Amerdale House* ⅝✳

Arncliffe, Littondale BD23 5QE	COOKING 2
TEL/FAX: (01756) 770250	COST £32–£39

The fact that Paula and Nigel Crapper are warm and polite adds to the appeal of their Victorian country house overlooking the Dales. Nigel buys judiciously from local sources: lamb is from his butcher's own farm, fish comes from the Yorkshire coast as well as Aberdeen and Brixham, while herbs, soft fruit and salad vegetables are grown in the hotel garden. Dinner is a daily-changing, four-course affair that might begin with an Italian salad, or roast chicken livers with bacon, before moving on to spiced lentil soup, or salmon fish-cake. Main courses inhabit the sensible world of confit of duck with caramelised onions, and grilled fillet of halibut with wild mushroom sauce. To finish, there is always a brace of contrasting desserts (chocolate tart, or prune and armagnac ice-cream, for example) and good North Country cheeses with home-made oatcakes. The wine list offers plenty of dependable drinking from around the world at prices that won't intimidate. House wines start at £8.85.

CHEF: Nigel Crapper   PROPRIETORS: Paula and Nigel Crapper   OPEN: all week D only 7 to 8.30   CLOSED: mid-Nov to mid-Mar   MEALS: Set D £25   SERVICE: not inc, card slips closed   CARDS: Access, Switch, Visa   DETAILS: 24 seats. Private parties: 14 main room. Car park. Children's helpings. Smart dress preferred. No smoking in dining-room. No music   ACCOMMODATION: 11 rooms, all with bath/shower. TV. D,B&B £64.50 to £119. Rooms for disabled. Children welcome. Baby facilities. Garden (*The Which? Hotel Guide*)

'"It's a soup you could serve on board a ship," said one old lady, and I strained to hear what it was about mushroom soup that made it particularly appropriate for a maritime setting. "Because it is too thick to spill over," was her explanation.'
(On eating in Wales)

---

map 9

Crab & Lobster

Dishforth Road, Asenby YO7 3QL
TEL: (01845) 577286   FAX: (01845) 577109   COOKING 1
off A168, between A19 and A1   COST £21–£50

The busy bar of this thatched pub just off the A1 looks like a 'granny's attic', with wall-to-wall, floor-to-ceiling clutter. Food is ordered at the counter amid lobster-pots, fairground slot machines, a wooden crocodile and much else besides, while the bookable waitress-service dining-room is calmer. Despite calf's liver, roast duck and the like, fish is what most reporters eat: typically turbot, halibut or scallops, served with a creamy sauce that for one senior reporter obscured the excellence of the raw materials. Simply cooked and first-rate vegetables accompany.

An inspector who ordered hot Loch Fyne oysters served with leeks was surprised to find himself served with lumpfish roe instead of the advertised beluga caviare. Resisting a cash refund, he sampled instead an attractively flavoured provençale fish soup. Puddings are filling, with more cream for those who just can't get enough. Service has been described as 'informed, polite and slow'. The general view is that reporters would happily return, though they wish it were less expensive. The sensible wine list spans a good range of styles and prices, starting at £7.95.

CHEF: Michael Pickard   PROPRIETORS: David and Jackie Barnard   OPEN: all week L 12 to 2.30, Mon to Sat D 7 to 9.30   CLOSED: 25 Dec   MEALS: alc (main courses £11.50 to £19.50). Set L Mon to Sat £11.50 (2 courses) to £13.50. BYO £5   SERVICE: not inc, card slips closed   CARDS: Access, Amex, Delta, Switch, Visa   DETAILS: 100 seats. Private parties: 60 main room, 6 to 50 private rooms. Car park. Vegetarian meals. Children's helpings. Smart dress preferred. Music

map 8

▲ Callow Hall ♥ ⁑ ✓ 14/2/97

Mappleton Road, Ashbourne DE6 2AA
TEL: (01335) 343403   FAX: (01335) 343624
m NW of Ashbourne, turn left off A515 at crossroads
with Bowling Green pub on left; Mappleton Road is   COOKING 2
first on right   COST £23–£50

The Spencer family have been caterers of one sort or another since 1724. The present generation acquired this handsome hall in 1983 and has turned it into a successful country-house enterprise. Within the dining-room that one reporter likened to 'a primitivist's dream of a boudoir' (rich red walls beneath a pink ceiling), the English shires cooking impresses more and more. Dishes that stand out have included a generously crammed bowl of precisely seasoned moules marinière, 'very pleasing' grilled halibut sauced with Pernod, butter and chives, and brandy-snapped pistachio and white chocolate ice-creams. Meats may be subjected to bolder treatments than fish, as in venison with woodland berries and bitter chocolate, or a variation on wiener schnitzel that incorporates smoked salmon as well as veal, and sauces it with lime butter. Service is warmly friendly without taking liberties.

Wines are grouped by country, but no further order has gone into the list, which is a jumble of vintages and prices. However, the French selection is commendable, and variety is provided by solid entries from around the world and by a generous number of half-bottles. French house wines are £9.95. CELLARMAN'S CHOICE: Vouvray, Ch. Gaudrelle 1993, Vignobles Monmousseau, £13.75; Montagne-St-Emilion, Ch. Roudier 1986, £18.25.

CHEFS: David and Anthony Spencer PROPRIETORS: David, Dorothy and Anthony Spencer OPEN: Sun L 12.15 to 1.30, Mon to Sat D (Sun residents only) 7 to 9.15 CLOSED: 25 and 26 Dec, 1 week Jan or Feb MEALS: alc D (main courses £13.50 to £17). Set L Sun £15.50, Set D £30 SERVICE: not inc CARDS: Access, Amex, Diners, Switch, Visa DETAILS: 60 seats. Private parties: 40 main room, 30 and 40 private rooms. Car park. Vegetarian meals. Children's helpings. Smart dress preferred. No smoking in dining-room. No music ACCOMMODATION: 16 rooms, all with bath/shower. TV. Phone. B&B £65 to £140. Rooms for disabled. Children welcome. Baby facilities. Dogs by arrangement. Garden. Fishing (*The Which? Hotel Guide*)

ASTON CLINTON Buckinghamshire map 3

▲ *Bell Inn*

Aston Clinton HP22 5HP
TEL: (01296) 630252 FAX: (01296) 631250 COOKING 2*
on A41, between Tring and Aylesbury COST £27–£70

The seventeenth-century coaching-inn has been in the Harris family for over half a century, and retains its distinctive character thanks to a flag-floored bar and an imposing 'four seasons' mural of birds and trees in the dining-room. For one couple, 'in spite of the slightly faded elegance, this restaurant remains first-class'. Michael Keenlyside has come up from sous-chef, and brought some of the fixtures with him, including Bell Inn smokies and roast Aylesbury duck: the crisp-skinned breast cooked pink, thickly sliced, and served with Savoy cabbage leaves rolled around shredded duck confit.

Good quality ingredients underpin the cooking, and Keenlyside applies an accurate sense of timing to fresh-tasting vegetables, and to meats such as fillet of new season lamb served with ratatouille, and goes in for well-reduced sauces. Desserts tend to be cold – strawberry shortbread, for instance – but might also include a hot cherry soufflé. Service is polished, with napkins unfurled on to knees, domes lifted and 'Sir' and 'Madam' popping up here and there, but is also genuinely friendly and helpful.

'The idea of having a glass of different wine with each course is an excellent one': three glasses, one a port or a pudding wine, costs £13.95 per person. The main list is long and packed with fine names from the classic regions. Half-bottles are a strong feature, and there's a list of 22 house recommendations. Mark-ups can be high. CELLARMAN'S CHOICE: Sancerre, Côte de la Roche 1994, Michel Brock, £26.50; Haut-Médoc, Ch. Cissac 1989, £33.

indicates a change of chef since last year's Guide.

CHEF: Michael Keenlyside PROPRIETOR: Michael Harris OPEN: all week 12.30 to 1.45, 7.30 to 9.30 MEALS: alc (main courses L £8, D £19.50 to £27.50). Set L Mon to Sat £12 (2 courses) to £16, Set L Sun £19.75, Set D £17.95 (2 courses) to £39. BYO by arrangement SERVICE: not inc CARDS: Access, Amex, Delta, Switch, Visa DETAILS: 100 seats. 48 seats outside. Private parties: 100 main room, 14 and 20 private rooms. Car park. Vegetarian meals. Children's helpings. Smart dress preferred. No smoking in dining-room. Wheelchair access (also WC). Music ACCOMMODATION: 20 rooms, all with bath/shower. TV. Phone. B&B £50 to £120. Rooms for disabled. Children welcome. Baby facilities. Dogs welcome. Afternoon teas. Garden (*The Which? Hotel Guide*)

AYLESBURY **Buckinghamshire**   map 3

▲ *Hartwell House* ♟ ⅋✳

Oxford Road, Aylesbury HP17 8NL
TEL: (01296) 747444 FAX: (01296) 747450   COOKING 2*
on A418, 2m from Aylesbury towards Oxford   COST £30–£63

The place is fit for a king, which is just as well since Louis XVIII of France lived here for a time in the early nineteenth century. While a little local difficulty, called Napoleon, prevented him from assuming the throne in France, he paid £500 a year for this modest Buckinghamshire pad in 90 acres of landscaped parkland, a sum which would barely get a him a long weekend these days. The fact that commoners can now stay here at all, never mind in such unashamed luxury, is a tribute to the sympathetic restoration and maintenance by Historic House Hotels.

The rooms are truly regal in scale, as are the prices, although one reporter reckoned that the occasional afternoon harp recital with champagne and canapés for £22.50 was not a bad deal. At meal-times there is no menu, but there is a bill of fare which, maintains director Jonathan Thompson, is the correct British way of referring to it, and which might include ravioli of smoked chicken, roulade of goose liver with a Tokai wine jelly, or roast sea bass with a vegetable and bean cassoulet. Freshness, vitality and good timing set the cooking apart, and the sense of indulgence engendered by the fabric is echoed in rich chocolate desserts and hot soufflés.

The wine list is wide-ranging and includes some lovely Loire wines, older vintages of Penfolds Grange, plus half a dozen appealing Californian bottles from the Fetzer winery. French house wines are £11.90. CELLARMAN'S CHOICE: Montagny premier cru, Dom. de la Cheneraie 1993, £28.50; Syrah 1988, Luigi Bosca, Argentina, £23.

CHEF: Alan Maw PROPRIETOR: Historic House Hotels Ltd OPEN: all week 12.30 to 1.50, 7.30 to 9.45 MEALS: Set L £18.25 (2 courses) to £24.50, Set D £39.50. BYO £10 SERVICE: net prices, card slips closed CARDS: Access, Amex, Switch, Visa DETAILS: 80 seats. 15 seats outside. Private parties: 60 main room, 18 to 60 private rooms. Car park. Vegetarian meals. No children under 8. Jacket and tie D. No smoking in dining-room. Wheelchair access (also WC). Music ACCOMMODATION: 45 rooms, all with bath/shower. TV. Phone. B&B £107 to £187. Rooms for disabled. No children under 8. Dogs welcome. Afternoon teas. Garden. Swimming-pool. Fishing (*The Which? Hotel Guide*)

See inside the front cover for an explanation of the symbols used at the tops of entries.

BARNARD CASTLE Co Durham

map 10

Blagraves House ⁝✳

30–32 The Bank, Barnard Castle DL12 8PN
TEL: (01833) 637668

COOKING 1
COST £21–£37

After five centuries – this is the oldest surviving house in Barnard Castle – one reporter felt it was now 'in need of a facelift', although the beamed ceilings, plaster crests, log fires and mullioned windows all add enormously to the character. An attractive-looking *carte* offers generous choice along the lines of duck sausages, cannelloni of rabbit, and undyed smoked haddock on a thick buckwheat blini with a creamy sauce. Saucing, however, has rather let the side down, producing at inspection a 'jammy' port and redcurrant sauce for rare, tender, pan-fried breast of pigeon. An individual beef Wellington looking 'like a large Cornish pasty' with good meat and puff pastry was also better then its accompanying 'old-fashioned, thickened brown gravy'. Desserts have included 'moreish' cinder toffee ice-cream, and a well-made tart of cocoa pastry with a creamy, sharp lemon filling and a fudgy topping. Forty-plus varied wines do the business, and house French is £8.25.

CHEFS/PROPRIETORS: Kenneth and Elizabeth Marley   OPEN: Tue to Sat D only 7 to 9.30   MEALS: alc (main courses £8.50 to £14). Set D Tue to Fri £13.50   SERVICE: not inc, card slips closed   CARDS: Access, Delta, Switch, Visa   DETAILS: 24 seats. Private parties: 24 main room, 40 private room. Vegetarian meals. No children under 8. Smart dress preferred. No smoking in dining-room. Music

BARNET Hertfordshire

map 3

Mims

63 East Barnet Road, Barnet EN4 8RN
TEL/FAX: (0181) 449 2974

COOKING 3
COST £23–£35

Ali Al-Sersy's little neighbourhood restaurant in New Barnet seemingly goes from strength to strength. The simple, even minimal décor and the location in a main-road shopping parade do nothing to announce the class of cooking that is on offer. A glance at the menu reveals the culinary backbone to be provincial French, but there is also room for crab ravioli (an 'excellent' crab mousse within tenderly light pasta), and potted shrimps. Presentation is thought elaborate: lambs' tongues in Madeira sauce at a Sunday lunch came with turned carrots and roast parsnips standing on end. A main course of 'very fresh' grilled red mullet comes topped with a potato galette, the ensemble crowned with crisp-fried cabbage leaves. A certain homeliness characterises many of the dishes, as in pot-roasted hake with sauté potatoes and deep-fried green beans, or roast lamb with sweetbreads, served with mashed potato and mushrooms.

'Enterprising and delicious' puddings may include white chocolate mousse in a dark chocolate cone, 'excellent' sorbets with 'tropical fruits of all kinds', or banana and coconut tart. Service can seem a little bashful, but gets things done in an unhurried sort of way. The wine list has a strong French bias but is sadly lacking information on vintages. House wine is £9.50.

CHEF/PROPRIETOR: Ali Al-Sersy   OPEN: Sun noon to 10.30, Tue to Fri L noon to 2.30, Tue to Sat D 6.30 to 11 CLOSED: 1 to 15 Sept   MEALS: Set L £9.50 (2 courses) to £13.50, Set D £15 (2 courses) to £19   SERVICE: not inc   CARDS: Access, Visa   DETAILS: 45 seats. Private parties: 45 main room. No children under 7. Smart dress preferred. No cigars/pipes in dining-room. Wheelchair access (also WC). Music

---

BARNSLEY South Yorkshire map 9

Armstrongs ♟

102 Dodworth Road, Barnsley S70 6HL	COOKING 1*
TEL: (01226) 240113 and 244990	COST £20–£41

Armstrongs has moved out of the town centre and taken over the Victorian house once occupied by Peano's. A lick of paint from the National Trust paint collection and some dramatic photographs and fabrics have helped to smarten it up. Simon Shaw has spent time in some good kitchens, and combines a sure hand with a sensible menu that harks back to a few traditional ideas (salad of pear with blue cheese, coq au vin) and offers the solid reassurance of ample protein in a modern context. Thick, creamy onion soup is made with good stock and dribbled with truffle oil, while seared fillet of salmon is served with couscous and a spring onion crème fraîche. Sauces can be strongly flavoured, and desserts have included banoffi cheesecake and a 'brilliant, tangy, fresh' lemon tart. The wine list is relatively concise yet spans a good range of styles. Prices remain fair, with six house wines starting at £9.50. CELLARMAN'S CHOICE: Vouvray Sec 1992, Gaston Huet, £19.25; Qupé Syrah 1994, Santa Maria Valley, California, £18.75.

CHEF: Simon Shaw   PROPRIETORS: Nick Pound and Deborah Swift   OPEN: Tue to Fri L 12 to 2, Tue to Sat D 7 to 10   CLOSED: 2 weeks Aug   MEALS: alc (main courses £9 to £15). Set L £10.50 (2 courses) to £12.50, Set D Tue to Fri £14.50. BYO £3.50   SERVICE: not inc   CARDS: Access, Amex, Delta, Switch, Visa   DETAILS: 55 seats. Private parties: 30 main room. Car park. Vegetarian meals. Children's helpings. Wheelchair access (no WC). Music

---

BARNSTAPLE Devon map 1

▲ *Lynwood House* ⚡✳

Bishop's Tawton Road, Barnstaple EX32 9DZ	
TEL: (01271) 43695 FAX: (01271) 79340	COOKING 1*
1m S of town centre, before A377 roundabout	COST £30–£64

This family-run business occupies a Victorian house in a residential area on Barnstaple's outskirts, and fish is understandably the main business, although not all of it is local. Creamy smoked haddock pancakes and Loch Fyne's hot-smoked Bradan Rost are typical first courses, alongside either a vegetable or chunky fish soup, while main courses are likely to feature plainly grilled Dover sole, poached salmon, or a skewer of local scallops wrapped in bacon. Good ingredients are carefully handled and simply presented. Salads make the most of crab and local lobster, while roast duck or fillet steak ring the changes. Finish with cream caramel, an ice-cream-filled meringue with a hot butter and rum sauce, or perhaps a savoury. Lighter bar lunches are largely taken from the main menu's first courses, and a wide-ranging respectable wine list is careful to allow for all pockets. French or German house wines are £9.05.

CHEFS: Ruth and Matthew Roberts   PROPRIETORS: John, Ruth and Matthew Roberts   OPEN: Mon to Sat 12 to 1.45, 7 to 9.30, and L Easter and Mothering Sun   MEALS: alc (main courses £13.50 to £27). Light lunches available   SERVICE: not inc, card slips closed   CARDS: Access, Amex, Delta, Diners, Switch, Visa   DETAILS: 60 seats. Private parties: 60 main room, 20 private room. Car park. Vegetarian meals. Children's helpings. Smart dress preferred. No smoking in dining-room. Wheelchair access (also WC). Music   ACCOMMODATION: 5 rooms, all with bath/shower. TV. Phone. B&B £47.50 to £67.50. Children welcome. Pets welcome (not in public rooms)

BARTON-UPON-HUMBER   North Lincolnshire   map 9

Elio's ⁵✳

| 11 Market Place, Barton-upon-Humber DN18 5DA | COOKING 1 |
| TEL: (01652) 635147 | COST £15–£42 |

Elio Grossi says that work is under way to extend his efficiently manned trattoria into the adjacent premises, which should alleviate any cramped feelings, and there are plans to provide accommodation. As ever, people come here for Italian favourites. There is a printed menu with pages of pasta and pizzas, but Elio's reputation hinges on his blackboard of daily specials. Spanking-fresh fish is the star, and the talk is all of 'luscious' fish soup, grilled sea bass, turbot with agrodolce sauce, and red sea bream with a spiky Mexicana sauce. Others have singled out pigeon breast with two sauces, wild duck with plum sauce, and aubergine parmigiano as non-fishy alternatives. Vegetables and puddings could do with a lift, but the freshness of the fish and the cost make amends. House wine is £8.95.

CHEFS: Elio Grossi, Nick Lyon and Louise Kuyath   PROPRIETOR: Elio Grossi   OPEN: Tue to Fri L 12 to 2, Mon to Sat D 6 to 10.30 (11 Sat)   CLOSED: last 2 weeks Aug   MEALS: alc (main courses £7 to £16). Set L £7.95, Set D (to 8pm) £10   SERVICE: not inc   CARDS: Access, Amex, Delta, Visa   DETAILS: 60 seats. Private parties: 20 main room, 8 private room. Vegetarian meals. Children's helpings. Smart dress preferred. No smoking in 1 dining-room. Wheelchair access (no WC). Music

---

BARWICK   Somerset   map 2

▲ Little Barwick House ⁵✳

Barwick BA22 9TD	
TEL: (01935) 423902 FAX: (01935) 420908	COOKING 3
off A37, take second left opposite Red House pub	COST £34–£41

'I shall return and stay longer next time,' concluded one typical reporter, pleased to have discovered this congenial and welcoming Georgian dower house. Well-equipped rooms with large comfortable beds, good food, and hard-to-beat value for money make this 'the epitome of a place to be cosseted for a short break'. There is a naturalness about the cooking that owes much to simple treatment of British produce. Local supplies are the foundation, and dishes reflect the seasons. 'Excellent ingredients, well cooked and very well presented,' summed up a reporter, noting that 'the easy approach hides a high degree of professionalism'.

A short but varied menu treats roast poussin to no more than herbs and garlic, and serves Lyme Bay sole à la meunière. Fillet and game pie is a highlight: 'a fine range of different meats, beautifully tender, succulent and tasty, with a gamey taste and good pastry'. There is usually something spicier too, such as sauté strips of duck breast marinated in soy and ginger and served with a confit of the leg. In all this, flavour is paramount. Vegetarians are not forgotten; meatless dishes might include popeye pancake (spinach and cream cheese with herbs), a grilled vegetable tartlet, or a warm salad of quail's eggs.

Puddings range from an indulgent steamed treacle sponge to an interesting fennel-flavoured crème brûlée. 'One dessert which particularly impressed was a meringue filled with fresh lemon curd and cream, served with a lime sauce.' The wine list makes a reasonable job of trawling the vinous globe; highlights include Alsace whites from Turckheim and award-winning Penfold's Coonawarra Cabernet. House wines are £9.60.

CHEF: Veronica Colley   PROPRIETORS: Christopher and Veronica Colley   OPEN: Mon to Sat D only 7 to 9, Sun D residents only   MEALS: Set D £18.90 (2 courses) to £24.90   SERVICE: not inc CARDS: Access, Amex, Delta, Switch, Visa   DETAILS: 40 seats. Private parties: 30 main room, 16 private room. Car park. Vegetarian meals. Children's helpings. Smart dress preferred. No smoking in dining-room. No music. Air-conditioned   ACCOMMODATION: 6 rooms, all with bath/shower. TV. Phone. Air-conditioned. B&B £35 to £78. Deposit: £20. Children welcome. Dogs welcome. Garden (*The Which? Hotel Guide*)

BASLOW Derbyshire   map 9

▲ *Fischer's Baslow Hall* ♀ ⁵⁄✳ ✓ /6/96

Calver Road, Baslow DE45 1RR   COOKING 4
TEL: (01246) 583259   FAX: (01246) 583818   COST £29–£63

Baslow Hall has an Edwardian feel. Ceilings are ornate, logs smoulder in the stone fireplace, and soft furnishings and wall coverings are 'un-designerish but assembled by someone with a good eye'. Tables are smartly set, but there is nothing pompous about either the place or the food. A sense of generosity pervades, from luxury ingredients to the wonderful array of appetisers and a pre-meal course at table. Overall, Baslow 'has the spark that separates excellence from the merely competent'.

Hereford beef comes from an organic farm, lamb is local, and venison finds its way from nearby Chatsworth estate. Even more intriguing is wild hare cooked in a blood-thickened sauce, or locally shot grouse. Humble ingredients are carefully bought too: 'as one who bemoans the lack of flavour in tomatoes available in Britain, and who spends much time seeking out the most promising species and source countries, I was particularly impressed by these,' wrote an inspector. The cooking is not especially innovative, but the composition is well thought out, as in roast loin of lamb, pink and delicately flavoured, served with couscous and a well-flavoured stock, or roast squab pigeon breasts on a mound of red cabbage containing pieces of the leg meat and foie gras for extra-rich gameyness.

Complexity and flavour contrast are well handled, many things enhanced by liberal use of fresh herbs, and despite much 3-D stacking of components one above the other, 'there is no over-elaboration, no confusion, just perfect ingredients and perfect technique,' according to one who enjoyed lobster tails wrapped in spinach in a 'wonderfully pungent' bisque. Some reporters have felt that the operation may be so dazzled by its own artistry that it fails to pick up on elementary faults – a lack of flavour here, some poor timing there – but these seem to be rare lapses. Pastry work from Luke Dalton is excellent, and among puddings that have impressed is a kind of tall paper bag fashioned out of thin dark chocolate, holding a layer of dark chocolate truffle then a layer of creamy white chocolate mousse. Susan Fischer, 'reserved but kind, informative and efficient', runs front-of-house. Café Max serves simpler, lighter food. The high standards are maintained on the wine list, which majors in good-quality bottles over £20. Tasting notes are concise and helpful. French house wines start at £9.50. CELLARMAN'S CHOICE: Dry River Sauvignon Blanc 1995, Marlborough, New Zealand, £23; Marsannay 1989, Dom. Fougeray de Beauclair, £22.

CHEFS: Max Fischer, Paul Coy and Eddie Gray PROPRIETORS: Max and Susan Fischer OPEN: all week L 12 to 1.30 (2.30 Sun), Mon to Sat D 7 to 9.30 (Sun D residents only) CLOSED: 25 and 26 Dec MEALS: Set L Mon to Fri £16.50 (2 courses) to £19.50, Set L Sun £21.50, Set D £42 SERVICE: not inc CARDS: Access, Amex, Delta, Diners, Switch, Visa DETAILS: 76 seats. Private parties: 40 main room, 12 and 24 private rooms. Car park. No children under 12 after 7pm. Smart dress preferred. No smoking in dining-room. Wheelchair access (also WC). No music ACCOMMODATION: 6 rooms. all with bath/shower. TV. Phone. B&B £75 to £120. Deposit: £50. Children welcome. Baby facilities. Afternoon teas. Garden (The Which? Hotel Guide)

BATH Bath & N.E. Somerset   map 2

▲ Bath Spa Hotel, Vellore Restaurant ⬥✳

Sydney Road, Bath BA2 6JF   COOKING 1*
TEL: (01225) 444424 FAX: (01225) 444006   COST £28–£75

The colossal house – a little apart from the town itself, close to the Holburne Museum – isn't overflowing with character. Drinks are served in a bar 'hardly bigger than a cupboard', or in a restful drawing-room, while dining takes place in what was once obviously the ballroom, a vast space with pillars, chandeliers and a grand piano. Jonathan Fraser's ambitious round-the-world menu stops off at crispy duck with daikon and pickled ginger, mozzarella wrapped in basil and Parma ham with a tomato and chilli salsa, and all stations to loin of lamb with rogan josh spices and almond biriani. Timing is good, but garnishing can be elaborate, as if it were an end in itself rather than a means to getting the best from the palpably good raw materials. A classical wine list is prefaced by a sommelier's selection offering plenty of choice in itself. Prices are high, with house vin de pays at £18.50.

'The restaurant is certainly better than when old Mrs X owned it. She got so ga-ga, bless her, that she used to forget the soup powder, and customers just got bowls of hot water (which was a lot more palatable than some of the other stuff she served up).'
(On eating in Dorset)

CHEF: Jonathan Fraser PROPRIETOR: Forte Hotels OPEN: Sun L 12.30 to 2, all week D 7 to 10
MEALS: alc (main courses £17 to £23). Set L £16.50, Set D £35. BYO £10 (champagne £15)
SERVICE: not inc, card slips closed CARDS: Access, Amex, Diners, Switch, Visa DETAILS: 100
seats. Private parties: 140 main room, 8 to 140 private rooms. Car park. Vegetarian meals.
Children's helpings. Jacket and tie. No smoking in dining-room. Wheelchair access (also WC).
Music. Air-conditioned ACCOMMODATION: 98 rooms, all with bath/shower. TV. Phone. Room
only £119 to £189. Rooms for disabled. Children welcome. Baby facilities. Dogs welcome in
bedrooms only. Afternoon teas. Garden. Swimming-pool

Clos du Roy

1 Seven Dials, Saw Close, Bath BA1 1EN	COOKING 2*
TEL: (01225) 444450 FAX: (01225) 460218	COST £17–£39

Philippe Roy sets out to fill the eyes as well as the ears with music: the
furnishings are awash with leaping crotchets and quavers, and a pianist
generally tinkles through dinner. The jovial M. Roy acknowledges the Theatre
Royal's proximity – it's next door – by offering pre- and post-theatre deals in
addition to the *carte* and the fixed-price menus. Lentil and bacon soup, boeuf
bourguignonne with pasta, and raspberry nougat glacé on a passion-fruit coulis
should set you up nicely for watching Ibsen. Those with more time may relax
over vol-au-vent stuffed with Cornish seafood, or boned quails stuffed with
apricots with a curry sauce, although the kitchen is also broad-minded enough to
offer more eyebrow-raising stuff such as pork cassolette with pineapple and soy.
When on song, this is highly competent cooking, though grumbles surface from
time to time over portion sizes: even several years on, any hint of nouvelle
cuisine is enough to alienate the British eater-out. Pear Belle-Hélène, Paris-Brest
filled with praline cream, and Cointreau crêpe soufflé keep the tricolour flying,
while service is hailed as both 'discreet and efficient'. The overwhelmingly
French wine list is arranged by style, offering a fair selection under £20 and a
healthy showing of halves. House wines are £8.95.

CHEF/PROPRIETOR: Philippe Roy OPEN: all week 12 to 2.30, 6 to 11 MEALS: alc (main courses
£11.50 to £14). Set L Mon to Sat £8.95 (2 courses) to £11.95, Set L Sun £9.95, Set D 6 to 7 and
post-theatre £8.95 (2 courses) to £11.95, Set D Sun to Fri £14.50, Set D all week £18.50
SERVICE: not inc, card slips closed; 10% for parties of 8 or more CARDS: Access, Amex, Delta,
Diners, Visa DETAILS: 85 seats. 24 seats outside. Private parties: 90 main room. Vegetarian
meals. Children's helpings. Smart dress preferred. No cigars/pipes in dining-room. Wheelchair
access (no WC). Music. Air-conditioned

Hole in the Wall 🍷 🍮 ⁵⁄ₓ

16 George Street, Bath BA1 2EN	COOKING 3
TEL/FAX: (01225) 425242	COST £18–£39

Christopher and Gunna Chown also jointly own Plas Bodegroes (see entry,
Pwllheli, Wales). In practice, he looks after the Welsh end of things while she is
in charge here. In addition, Matthew Benson-Smith arrived from the Capital
Hotel (see entry, London) in the summer of 1996 to replace Adrian Walton. The
style, however, has hardly changed at all. Pricing remains reasonable in the two
rooms – a relatively spartan one for smokers, more colourful and modern for

non-smokers – and cooking under the new regime seems 'calm, confident and accomplished'.

It is a place for 'offal and strong flavours', with gutsy cooking of calf's liver 'half an inch thick', surrounded by caramelised whole cloves of garlic, in a dark brown Madeira *jus* with so many contributing flavours that 'it was hard to know where one stopped and another started'. Some ideas – such as pan-fried red mullet with sauerkraut and a herb nage – can sound challenging, but recognisable combinations are the norm, as in a variation on the scallop and lentil partnership reminiscent of Shaun Hill: three fat, sweet Cornish scallops sitting on a bed of salad greens dressed with lime and coriander, surrounded by cold, earthy Puy lentils. Duck rilletes with sauce gribiche is another classic, with thick strands of meaty, peppery duck and 'subtle flavourings of cumin and caraway'.

Accompaniments can be exceptionally good: for example, a spicy, lime-flavoured riesling jelly 'to die for' that partnered a foie gras and chicken liver parfait. Wherever possible, components of a dish are stacked on top of each other, richness is a characteristic, and contrasts continue into desserts of, perhaps, searingly cold apple parfait and searingly hot apples infused with calvados; 'where the two met was like true love.' The wine list is compact and meticulously crafted. The major wine regions of the world are each represented by a small number of highly fashionable and exciting producers, and 16 of these wines are available by the glass. Prices start at £9.50 for regional French, and head up to over £50 for big names from the Rhône, Bordeaux and Champagne.

CHEF: Matthew Benson-Smith PROPRIETORS: Christopher and Gunna Chown OPEN: Mon to Sat 12 to 2, 6 to 11 MEALS: alc (main courses £12). Set L £9.50 (2 courses) to £11.50 SERVICE: not inc CARDS: Access, Amex, Switch, Visa DETAILS: 60 seats. Private parties: 16 main room. Vegetarian meals. Children welcome. No smoking in 1 dining-room. No music

No. 5 Bistro

NEW ENTRY

5 Argyle Street, Bath BA2 4BA
TEL: (01225) 444499

COOKING 1*
COST £19–£39

Situated a stone's throw from Pulteney Bridge in the heart of the city, No. 5 does a great job in feeding the denizens of Bath. The interior pleases with its profusion of plants, polished elm floorboards and Continental prints, and the cooking hits the button. Lunch is tailored to quick, one-course meals such as vegetable spring rolls, smoked trout salad with coriander dressing, and chicken with pesto sauce. The evening menu is more ambitious, and best choices are from the list of specials: reporters have singled out innovative Thai-style gravlax, neatly timed calf's liver with port and raisin sauce, and roast duck breast with orange, cardamom and kumquat sauce. Wednesday night is fish night. Desserts range from bread-and-butter pudding to poached pears filled with caramelised nuts in filo pastry. The wine list is strong on value-for-money and you can bring your own on Monday and Tuesday evenings (no corkage). House wine is £7.95.

If a restaurant is new to the Guide *this year (did not appear as a main entry in the last edition),* NEW ENTRY *appears opposite its name.*

CHEFS: Stephen Smith, Paul Hearne and Sarah Grantins   PROPRIETORS: Stephen Smith and Charles Home   OPEN: Tue to Sat L 12 to 2.30, Mon to Sat D 6.30 to 10 (10.30 Fri, 11 Sat) CLOSED: 25 to 29 Dec   MEALS: alc (main courses L £4 to £10, D £9 to £14). BYO Mon and Tue D (no corkage)   SERVICE: not inc; 10% for parties of 7 or more   CARDS: Access, Amex, Delta, Diners, Switch, Visa   DETAILS: 35 seats. Private parties: 16 main room. Vegetarian meals. Children's helpings. No cigars in dining-room. Wheelchair access (no WC). Music

▲ Queensberry Hotel, Olive Tree ⅚✳

Russel Street, Bath BA1 2QF   COOKING 2*
TEL: (01225) 447928   FAX: (01225) 446065   COST £22–£43

The restaurant is in a basement, and started life as a bistro, but is 'more sophisticated than that implies'. Low ceilings, close tables and scattered rugs help to create an impression of intimacy, and yet the room feels light and spacious. Reporters appreciate the combination of 'imaginative cooking in pleasant surroundings'. The style is of no particular fixed abode but, like most kitchens in modern British mould, benefits from all sorts of contributory ideas and ingredients. Native input is represented by hot Cornish crab and saffron tart, Norfolk samphire (served with poached turbot), and loin of venison with chestnut dumplings. Spätzli with morel mushrooms is reminiscent of Austria, and the menu has its share of Mediterranean dishes, from roasted vegetables to provençale fish soup, plus a fair number of pasta dishes. The *carte* offers a generous selection, and the kitchen's marshalling and handling of all these assorted components is impressive.

'I started with the largest glass of dry sherry I have seen, and green olives,' began a reporter who went on to enjoy a bowl of gazpacho followed by baked sea bass in a shellfish sauce. Indeed, fish has come in for more than usual praise, including 'robust and very satisfying' cod with sun-dried tomatoes. Vegetables are left on the table to help yourself from, and the dauphinoise potatoes constitute (for one reporter) 'unctuous, cream-laden nursery food with a crusty brown top, like savoury crème brûlée'. Both hotel and restaurant staff operate 'a level of service and courtesy above normal' – single diners are offered a selection of reading material, for instance – and the whole package is considered good value for money. The wine list has expanded since last year, embracing some serious bottles as well as wines that are approachable in both taste and price, especially from the New World. House French is £10.50.

CHEFS: Mathew Prowse and Garry Rosser   PROPRIETORS: Stephen and Penny Ross   OPEN: Mon to Sat L 12 to 2, all week D 7 to 10 (9 Sun)   CLOSED: 1 week Christmas   MEALS: alc (main courses £7.50 to £13.50). Set L £10.50 (2 courses) to £12.50, Set D Mon to Fri £18   SERVICE: not inc, card slips closed   CARDS: Access, Amex, Delta, Switch, Visa   DETAILS: 45 seats. Private parties: 30 main room, 20 and 30 private rooms. Car park. Vegetarian meals. Children's helpings. Smart dress preferred. No smoking in dining-room. Music. Air-conditioned ACCOMMODATION: 22 rooms, all with bath/shower. TV. Phone. B&B £66.50 to £164. Rooms for disabled. Children welcome. Baby facilities. Afternoon teas. Garden (*The Which? Hotel Guide*)

'*Most fish was frozen, and although fresh fish was in a tank the waiter didn't know what it was.*' (On eating in Manchester)

▲ *Royal Crescent Hotel, Dower House* ⚡✖

16 Royal Crescent, Bath BA1 2LS	COOKING 2*
TEL: (01225) 739955 FAX: (01225) 339401	COST £27–£71

'Our guests are people who enjoy being spoilt,' claims the restaurant. Hands up who doesn't. The hotel is in the centre of a great pillared curve looking down on the inner city, and the Dower House restaurant is reached across a serene and pretty garden. It is posh, with stiff table linen, giant plates and two sizes of dome (one for first courses), and charges accordingly. Steven Blake's food is characterised by good raw materials and some quite complex detail, from the appetisers right through to petits fours with coffee. The various menu options range from light lunches of salad and fish to a three-course dinner for £42.50.

An inspector dining off the latter found much to praise, particularly a starter of scallops ('wonderful taste, excellent timing'), a small venison steak of 'superb quality', and a coarse-textured sausage of guinea-fowl with 'amazing flavour'. A slab of banana parfait sandwiched between slices of coconut tuile and partnered by a sharp lime syrup also impressed. A lot of work goes into the food, and some of the dishes are 'decidedly fussy', including a trio of chestnut desserts with three sauces, 'two of which were pointless'. What the cooking really needs is more guts, less in the way of decorative flourish, and something lopping off the price. There is lots of service, which is not as stiff or formal as the surroundings might suggest. Wines are generous in scope and arranged by style, but hardly a bargain, though there are some decent bottles under £20. House wine starts at £12.65.

CHEF: Steven Blake   PROPRIETOR: Queens Moat Houses plc   OPEN: all week 12 to 2, 7 to 9.30 (10 Sat)   MEALS: Set L £14.50 (2 courses) to £18.50, Set D £33.50 to £42.50. Light L available   SERVICE: not inc   CARDS: Access, Amex, Diners, Switch, Visa   DETAILS: 66 seats. 20 seats outside. Private parties: 80 main room, 40 to 80 private rooms. Car park. Vegetarian meals. Children's helpings. No children under 7 D. Smart dress preferred. No smoking in dining-room. Music   ACCOMMODATION: 46 rooms, all with bath/shower. TV. Phone. Room only £98 to £145. Rooms for disabled. Lift. Children welcome. Baby facilities. Afternoon teas. Garden. Swimming-pool (*The Which? Hotel Guide*)

Woods

9–13 Alfred Street, Bath BA1 2QX	COOKING 1
TEL: (01225) 314812 FAX: (01225) 443146	COST £16–£33

Close to the Assembly Rooms in the Georgian centre of Bath, Woods is an expansive brasserie in the modern city idiom. That means buzz, bustle and goats'-cheese timbale with yellow pepper purée. Antony Edwards is responsible for the last of those, returning as head chef here in 1995 after a more junior stint a few years ago. Filo parcels of spinach, cheese and pine-nuts on a warm gazpacho sauce merit praise for their clarity of flavour, as does baked cod with sauté sweet peppers and a light curry sauce, the fish well timed and the supporting elements adding depth to the dish. Smoked haddock in parsley sauce, and steak served with a sun-dried tomato butter sauce have pleased others, while puddings such as 'smooth, rich, yet delicate' chocolate marquise with mint crème anglaise end things on an upbeat note. Service is courteous but keen to get things done quickly. Ten wines available by the glass bolster the largely French list, bottle prices opening at £9.

CHEFS: Antony Edwards, Leigh Davidson and David Price   PROPRIETORS: David and Claude Price   OPEN: all week L 12 to 3, Mon to Sat D 6 to 11   CLOSED: 24 to 26 Dec   MEALS: alc (main courses L £3 to £11, D £7 to £11). Set L Mon to Sat £5 (2 courses), Set L Sun £12, Set D Mon to Fri £10 (2 courses) to £13.50, Set D Sat £19.95   SERVICE: not inc   CARDS: Access, Visa   DETAILS: 130 seats. 12 seats outside. Private parties: 70 main room, 40 private room. Vegetarian meals. Children's helpings. No cigars/pipes in dining-room. Wheelchair access (also WC). Music

---

BEAMINSTER Dorset   map 2

▲ *Bridge House* ⅚✳

3 Prout Bridge, Beaminster DT8 3AY   COOKING 2
TEL: (01308) 862200   FAX: (01308) 863700   COST £20–£43

The house is thirteenth-century, stone built, with beams, large fireplaces and a pink-suffused dining-room that leads out through a conservatory to the garden. What struck one reporter was 'the very pleasant atmosphere and attitude of the staff, who were friendly without being overly chummy'. Lunch is along simple bistro lines, offering pancakes with smoked haddock in cheese sauce, or cider-baked ham with salad, plus variations on a theme of Welsh rarebit.

At dinner the generous choice of dishes – some carrying a supplement – allows plenty of variety, including salmon marinated in orange and lime or tagliatelle with ham and mushrooms in a cream sauce to begin, followed by pork tenderloin in mustard sauce or confit of duck with an onion marmalade. Plaice appears among the fish, rabbit among the meats, and saucing benefits from being kept simple. Vegetables are the same for all main courses. Puddings play with traditional ideas: snow eggs with crème anglaise, or chocolate and banana strudel. Enthusiastic notes liven up the wine list, which is a merry mixture of nationalities and styles. Five house wines, including two from Penfolds, kick off the proceedings at £8.90.

CHEF: Jacky Rae   PROPRIETOR: Peter Pinkster   OPEN: all week 12.30 to 2, 7 to 9   MEALS: Set L £11.95 (2 courses) to £13.95, Set D £16.95 (2 courses) to £18.95. BYO £8   SERVICE: not inc, card slips closed   CARDS: Access, Amex, Delta, Diners, Switch, Visa   DETAILS: 40 seats. 4 seats outside. Private parties: 48 main room, 16 private room. Car park. Vegetarian meals. Children's helpings. ACCOMMODATION: 14 rooms, all with bath/shower. TV. Phone (most rooms). B&B £53 to £99. Deposit: £25. Rooms for disabled. Children welcome. Baby facilities. Dogs welcome in bedrooms only. Afternoon teas. Garden (*The Which? Hotel Guide*)

'Try as you may, you cannot please everyone. We had to disappoint a lady who could not see why we did not have a strict kosher menu, and we had to refuse to open a fourth bottle of Puligny-Montrachet for a gentleman who rejected three on the grounds that they weren't good enough (the wine merchant came over next morning and declared all three perfect).' (Cumbria restaurateur)

BECKINGHAM Lincolnshire

map 6

Black Swan ✦✗

Hillside, Beckingham LN5 0RQ
TEL: (01636) 626474
off A17 to Sleaford, 6m E of Newark-on-Trent

COOKING 2
COST £18–£44

You are scarcely out of the car before the front door of this seventeenth-century coaching-inn is opened as if by telepathy, and the warmest of welcomes has begun. Little dining-rooms seem to proliferate as space is sought to accommodate everybody.

Anton Indans's complex-sounding dishes always keep one foot on the ground of classical British technique, however rarefied the embellishments may sound. A home-made spicy lamb sausage is a dare in a county that reckons to know a thing or two about sausages ('Lincolnshire folk prefer a coarser grind,' a reporter informs us), but it was enjoyable none the less and cleverly dressed with thinly sliced onions, dried, dipped in chilli flour and deep-fried. Chicken breast rolled around dried apricots scores highly for flavour, as do puddings of poached fruits with mango sauce, and hazelnut parfait with an 'intense' fruit coulis. Service is on the silver side, and everything adds up to a 'relaxed place with a sense of occasion'. Wines (which are dispensed with the full schemozzle of cork-sniffing and wrist flourishes) are a standard, mainly French bunch, and still lack some producers' names – 'Chardonnay Réserve' covers a multitude of sins these days. House French is £8.40.

CHEFS: Anton Indans and Claire Rogers PROPRIETORS: Alison and Anton Indans OPEN: Tue to Sun L 12 to 1.30, Tue to Sat D 7 to 9.30 CLOSED: end Jan, last 2 weeks Aug MEALS: alc (main courses £7.50 to £14.50). Set L £10.50 (2 courses) to £13.50, Set D £15.50 to £25. BYO £3 SERVICE: not inc CARDS: Access, Visa (5% surcharge) DETAILS: 40 seats. 25 seats outside. Private parties: 28 main room, 14 and 28 private rooms. Car park. Vegetarian meals. Children's helpings. Smart dress preferred. No smoking in dining-room. Wheelchair access (also WC). Music

BECKINGTON Somerset

map 2

▲ Woolpack ✦✗

Beckington BA3 6SP
TEL: (01373) 831244 FAX: (01373) 831223
off A36, in centre of village

COOKING 2
COST £22–£44

This sixteenth-century former coaching-inn, with flagstoned bar and inglenook fireplace, functions as both pub and restaurant, serving the same menu throughout. Fish has a pretty strong showing – skate wing with salsa verde, grilled lemon sole, or roast cod with a mussel and saffron sauce – and shares the billing with game (venison sausages with braised lentils, perhaps) plus the customary beef, chicken and maybe honey-glazed duck breast. Dishes such as marinated sea bass and smoked tuna, or game terrine with Cumberland sauce can be taken as either a first or main course, and a typical pub generosity produces overflowing plates with lots of ingredients and salad components.

The quality of raw materials has been apparent in a warm chicken and bacon salad, the poultry 'nicely timed, nicely sauté', although not helped by a sharp dressing. Likewise a dish of 'beautifully textured' lamb fillets cooked pink, as requested, and full of flavour was better than the accompanying ratatouille, which lacked the amalgamation brought about by long, slow cooking. Puddings include cheesecakes, mousses, a two-tone chocolate terrine, and various ice-creams. Service can be attentive, although it has upon occasion lacked the cohesion to be properly responsive. Fifty-odd bins and a dozen half-bottles include house wines at £9.50.

CHEF: David Woolfall   PROPRIETOR: West Country Village Inns Ltd   OPEN: all week 12 to 2, 7 to 10 (9 Sun)   MEALS: alc (main courses £6 to £16). BYO £5   SERVICE: not inc, card slips closed   CARDS: Access, Delta, Switch, Visa   DETAILS: 100 seats. 30 seats outside. Private parties: 55 main room, 20 and 55 private rooms. Car park. Vegetarian meals. Children's helpings. No children under 5. No smoking in 1 dining-room. No music   ACCOMMODATION: 12 rooms, all with bath/shower. TV. Phone. B&B £54.50 to £84.50. Deposit: £20. No children under 5. Dogs by arrangement. Afternoon teas. Garden

---

BIBURY Gloucestershire   map 2

▲ *The Swan* 🍷 ⁑✳ ✓ 28/1/97

Bibury GL7 5NW   COOKING 2
TEL: (01285) 740695   FAX: (01285) 740473   COST £23–£58

The ivy-covered hotel has bagged a prime spot by the bridge over the shallow River Coln, with a private fishing stretch to boot. Inside, a ghostly automatic piano plays away to itself in reception, while visitors progress through the lounge and a copious number of appetisers *en route* for the grand mustard and crimson dining-room. Edward Portlock's well-balanced menu adopts some French and Mediterranean ways with ingredients, from foie gras parfait to sweet, fresh-tasting, lightly seared scallops, crowned with circular parsnip 'chips' in a good pesto sauce.

Although one couple felt that 'for the price, the menu somehow lacked sparkle', it might nevertheless include a fleshy fillet of lightly cooked brill served with a generous pile of black olive couscous. Portions are generous, including one first course of pink calf's liver wrapped in puff pastry, and vegetables are 'fresh, carefully cooked and presented'. At inspection some promised ingredients did not materialise, more care might have been taken to keep pastry crisp, and ice-creams placed on top of warm puddings melted all too quickly, but the flavours of the ice-creams were good: pistachio with a prune tart, and yoghurt with a glazed lemon tart. Wines are well chosen, and sweet ones are generous in scope, but prices are high. House wines are £13.25.

CHEF: Edward Portlock   PROPRIETORS: Mr and Mrs J.A. Furtek   OPEN: Sun L 12.30 to 2.30, all week D 7.30 to 9.30   MEALS: alc D (main courses £14 to £22). Set L £15.95, Set D Mon to Fri £21.50. Brasserie meals available   SERVICE: net prices, card slips closed   CARDS: Access, Amex, Delta, Switch, Visa   DETAILS: 80 seats. Private parties: 100 main room, 10 private room. Car park. Vegetarian meals. Children's helpings. Smart dress preferred. No smoking in dining-room. Wheelchair access (also WC). Music   ACCOMMODATION: 18 rooms, all with bath/shower. TV. Phone. B&B £89 to £155. Deposit: £50. Rooms for disabled. Children welcome. Baby facilities. Afternoon teas. Garden. Fishing (*The Which? Hotel Guide*)

BIGBURY-ON-SEA Devon   map 1

▲ Burgh Island   NEW ENTRY

Bigbury-on-Sea TQ7 4BG   COOKING 1
TEL: (01548) 810514   FAX: (01548) 810243   COST £33–£50

When the tide is high, guests are ferried over to Burgh Island by a giant sea
tractor. Nothing is predictable at this astonishing 'art deco palace' where Agatha
Christie once wrote thrillers, Edward and Mrs Simpson hid from the press, and
music was provided by the likes of Harry Roy. The magic lives on, as today's
visitors sip extravagant cocktails in the Palm Court and dress for dinner. By
contrast, Tony Murphy is a modernist, cooking 1990s food based on local
supplies. Successes from his daily fixed-price menu have included a slab of
baked goats' cheese wrapped in Parma ham and served with pickled walnuts,
seared scallops on a bed of samphire, and roast loin of lamb cooked pink with
garlic, thyme and port. Desserts are in keeping, while cheeses are from the West
Country. The whole place is run with supreme efficiency and personable good
humour. House wine is £12.

CHEF: Tony Murphy   PROPRIETOR: Tony Vernon Porter   OPEN: all week 12.30 to 2, 7.30 to 9
CLOSED: Mon to Fri Jan and Feb   MEALS: Set L £18.50 (2 courses) to £22.50, Set D £32. BYO £6
(sparkling £9)   SERVICE: not inc   CARDS: Access, Amex, Delta, Diners, Switch, Visa   DETAILS:
60 seats. 20 seats outside. Private parties: 70 main room, 50 private room. Car park. Vegetarian
meals. Children's helpings. Children under 6 by arrangement. Jacket and tie D. Music
ACCOMMODATION: 14 rooms, all with bath/shower. TV. Phone. D,B&B £168 to £238 (double
room). Deposit: 33.3%. Children welcome. Afternoon teas. Garden. Swimming-pool. Fishing
(The Which? Hotel Guide)

BILLESLEY Warwickshire   map 5

▲ Billesley Manor 🍷

Billesley B49 6NF
TEL: (01789) 279955   FAX: (01789) 764145   COOKING 2*
off A46, 3m W of Stratford-upon-Avon   COST £23–£66

Billesley is a grand Cotswold stone house, built in the sixteenth century. Its
main business appears to be the conference trade, no doubt drawn by the 'olde
worlde' appeal of oak panelling and log fires, and the chance to unwind between
meetings with a swim or a game of tennis. There is a distinct old-fashioned air
about the whole experience, with 'domes and mid-meal sorbets left over from
before the Flood', and prices are high, but Roger Barstow's broadly European
menu puts an appealing emphasis on fish and game.

Attempts to update the style include a cappuccino of lentil soup with good
body if rather fugitive flavour. 'Why would anybody want to put a frothy white
head on a bowl of soup?' enquired one reporter. Nevertheless, the kitchen's
ability to deliver is evident in a saffrony risotto of mussels, in baked sea bass
with garlic potatoes and a dribble of tangy olive 'salsa', and in pink roast squab
pigeon with a tiny and refined 'cassoulet' underneath it, moistened by a good
stock and Madeira sauce. The big let-down for reporters is the slow and
ponderous service, a problem that can be exacerbated by the difficulties of
mixing corporate and private customers. The wine list is sound, with impressive

forays into Burgundy and Bordeaux, good back-up from Australia and California and 28 half-bottles. French house wines are £11.75. CELLARMAN'S CHOICE: Dalwood Chardonnay 1994, S.E. Australia, £15.95; Margaux Ch. Cantenac Brown 3ème Cru Classé 1991, £38.

CHEF: Roger Barstow PROPRIETOR: Queens Moat Houses plc OPEN: all week 12.30 to 2, 7.30 to 9.30 (10 Sat) MEALS: alc (main courses L £9.50 to £12.50, D £21 to £23). Set L £10 (2 courses) to £15, Set D £29.50 SERVICE: not inc CARDS: Access, Amex, Delta, Diners, Switch, Visa DETAILS: 80 seats. 20 seats outside. Private parties: 100 main room, 14 to 100 private rooms. Car park. Vegetarian meals. Children's helpings. Smart dress preferred. No smoking in dining-room. Wheelchair access (no WC). No music ACCOMMODATION: 41 rooms, all with bath/shower. TV. Phone. B&B £76 to £250. Children welcome. Baby facilities. Afternoon teas. Garden. Swimming-pool (*The Which? Hotel Guide*)

BIRCH VALE Derbyshire   map 8

▲ *Waltzing Weasel*

New Mills Road, Birch Vale SK12 5BT
TEL/FAX: (01663) 743402   COOKING 2
on A6015, ½m W of Hayfield   COST £20–£39

'A good, reliable, honest eating house' sums up this pub-cum-restaurant-with-rooms. The atmosphere is one of easy-going courtesy, with friendly yet professional service, and menus offer a typically generous choice. Unlike many pubs that have turned into restaurants, the Weasel retains its role as a traditional inn, with sporting prints, wooden tables and chairs in the bar, and a simple menu of garlic mushrooms, egg mayonnaise, lasagne, and fruit crumble. Lunches revolve around a hot and cold carvery in both bar and restaurant: baked ham, salt beef, or perhaps seafood tart.

The dining-room has wonderful views of Kinder Scout, and serves food as straightforward as hot buttered shrimps or Barnsley chop, or as hearty as jugged hare or osso buco. Fish arrives daily, game appears in season and vegetables are always a strong point. Bread-and-butter pudding comes with Grand Marnier as an optional extra, or there might be treacle tart or Welsh rarebit to finish. Unpretentious wines match the food, with one or two special bottles for those with boats to push out, and prices are very reasonable. House French is £8.75.

CHEF: George Benham PROPRIETORS: Linda and Michael Atkinson OPEN: all week 12 to 2, 7 to 9 MEALS: alc (main courses £7 to £12). Set D £20.50 (2 courses) to £24.50 SERVICE: not inc, card slips closed CARDS: Access, Delta, Switch, Visa DETAILS: 30 seats. 12 seats outside. Private parties: 35 main room, Car park. Vegetarian meals. No children under 5. Smart dress preferred. Wheelchair access (no WC). Music ACCOMMODATION: 8 rooms, all with bath/shower. TV. Phone. B&B £45 to £95. Deposit: £20. No children under 12. Dogs welcome. Garden (*The Which? Hotel Guide*)

'*The tables are widely spread, so you find out absolutely nothing at all about the sex lives of the illicit couple on the next table, which makes you concentrate on the food no end.*'
(On eating in London)

205

BIRDLIP Gloucestershire   map 2

▲ Kingshead House ⚟

Birdlip GL4 8JH
TEL: (01452) 862299
on B4070 towards Stroud ½m off A417 between   COOKING 2
Gloucester and Cirencester   COST £25–£46

The Knocks' restaurant-with-room (singular) in the tiny community of Birdlip
has reached its tenth anniversary. The unforced domestic atmosphere typified by
worn wooden floors, the amicable Warren Knock, and Judy Knock's modern
country cooking have combined to make this one of the hardier survivors in the
shires. The formula is à la carte for lunch, save on Sundays, and fixed-price for
dinner, where the three-course framework may expand to four for an extra £2.

Pride is taken in sauce-making, whether it be the saffron potion that comes
with seafood tagliatelle, or the curry cream that enriches an aubergine pilaff.
'The cooking allows ingredients and flavours to speak for themselves without
unnecessary over-elaboration,' explain one couple, whose summer Sunday
lunch took in leek and sorrel soup, escalope of salmon in a dill cream sauce, and
strips of turkey breast with Paris mushrooms and green tagliatelle. 'And the
gooseberry ice-cream was memorable,' they add. Otherwise, floral notes are
much favoured at pudding stage, as in the lime blossom syrup in which
nectarines and raspberries are steeped. The substantial wine list includes
intelligent notes on each wine and a wide range of half-bottles. Prices are very
reasonable, starting with sound house wines at £9.80. CELLARMAN'S CHOICE:
Givry, Clos St Paul premier cru 1989, Dom Silvestre, £21.50.

CHEF: Judy Knock   PROPRIETORS: Judy and Warren Knock   OPEN: Tue to Fri and Sun L 12.30
to 1.45, Tue to Sat D 7.30 to 9.45   CLOSED: 10 to 12 days in summer   MEALS: alc L (main
courses £8 to £12.50). Set L Sun £17.50, Set D £25 to £27   SERVICE: not inc; 10% for 6 or
more   CARDS: Access, Amex, Diners, Visa   DETAILS: 34 seats. 12 seats outside. Private
parties: 34 main room. Car park. Vegetarian meals. Children's helpings. Smart dress preferred.
No smoking while others eat. Wheelchair access (no WC). Music   ACCOMMODATION: 1 room,
with bath/shower. TV. B&B £35 to £60. Deposit: £20. Children welcome. Small dogs by
arrangement. Garden

BIRKENHEAD Merseyside   map 8

Beadles

15 Rosemount, Oxton, Birkenhead L43 5SG   COOKING 1
TEL: (0151) 653 9010   COST £23–£37

Roy and Bea Gott's eminently civilised restaurant is a fixture of eating out on
Merseyside, and the place continues in its own way. Bea's monthly menus are a
mixture of accumulated culinary wisdom and new ideas culled from travels
hither and yon. The repertoire ranges far and wide for warm salad of home-made
black pudding and ham hock with crostini and mulberry vinegar, mussels
masala, and tartare of oak-smoked haddock with avocado. And they are just
starters. Move on and you might find medallions of venison with Seville orange
sauce, seared tuna on Puy lentils with basil and caper sauce, and Singapore-style
chicken breast with Thai noodles. As a finale, try steamed kumquat pond

pudding, or pears poached in Muscat with honey and lavender ice-cream. Roy's wine list is in harmony with the food, and his enthusiasm for little-known gems shows no signs of flagging. House wine is £8.

CHEF: Bea Gott   PROPRIETORS: Roy and Bea Gott   OPEN: Wed to Sat D only 7.30 to 9   CLOSED: 2 weeks Feb, 2 weeks Aug to Sept   MEALS: alc (main courses £9.50 to £12.50)   SERVICE: not inc; 10% for parties of 6 or more   CARDS: Access, Delta, Switch, Visa   DETAILS: 32 seats. Private parties: 30 main room. No children under 7. Smart dress preferred. No smoking before coffee. Wheelchair access (no WC). Music

---

BIRMINGHAM West Midlands   map 5

Chung Ying

16–18 Wrottesley Street, Birmingham B5 4RT   COOKING 1
TEL: (0121) 622 5669   FAX: (0121) 666 7051   COST £21–£39

This long-serving Cantonese warhorse in the heart of Birmingham's revitalised Chinese quarter continues to find favour with its buzzy atmosphere and gutsy, peasant-style food. The kitchen delivers mighty portions of authentic food that are generally big on flavour, even if the execution may seem a bit 'rough hewn'. Pan-fried Shanghai dumplings, stuffed green pepper and other dim-sum are reliably good, and the monumental 300-strong menu holds a vast assortment of specialities ranging from good casseroles (such as braised brisket with spices), hotpots and one-plate rice and noodle dishes, to steamed eel with black-bean sauce, stuffed crispy duck with crabmeat, and shredded pork with preserved vegetables. Service by a veritable army of waiters is 'fast, friendly and no-nonsense'. House wine is £10. A sister restaurant, Chung Ying Garden, is at 17 Thorp Street; Tel: (0121) 666 6622.

CHEF/PROPRIETOR: Siu Chung Wong   OPEN: all week noon to 11.30 (10.30 Sun)   CLOSED: 25 Dec   MEALS: alc (main courses £5.50 to £9.50). Set D £25 (serves 2) to £96 (serves 6)   SERVICE: not inc   CARDS: Access, Amex, Delta, Diners, Switch, Visa   DETAILS: 250 seats. Private parties: 120 main room, 120 private room. Vegetarian meals. Children welcome. Smart dress preferred. Wheelchair access (no WC). Music. Air-conditioned

---

Leftbank   [NEW ENTRY]

79 Broad Street, Birmingham B15 1QA   COOKING 1
TEL/FAX: (0121) 643 4464   COST £21–£42

One of the signs occasionally seen in restaurants reads: 'We have an arrangement with the bank. They don't sell food; we don't cash cheques.' Now this once-upon-a-time bank does – sell food, that is. The restaurant occupies the ground floor of a grand Victorian building close to Birmingham Rep, and is less Bohemian than its name might suggest: 'John Lewis meets Marie Antoinette' suggested one reporter of the décor. Service is friendly and unstuffy.

   Bill Marmion, formerly of Charingworth Manor, cooks a modish menu that takes in a boudin of chicken and black pudding with wild mushrooms, the ubiquitous fish soup with rouille, rump of lamb with flageolet beans, and confit of duck with chilli salsa and wild rice. He may even have scored a first with 'couscous risotto', which accompanies juicy chargrilled chicken. Good buying, timing, presentation and judgement were evident in an inspector's pink flavourful venison served with creamed parsnips. Sticky toffee pudding has been 'pretty good'. The short, up-to-date wine list is fairly priced, with house wines £9.90.

CHEF: William Marmion   PROPRIETOR: Caroline Benbrook   OPEN: Mon to Fri L 12 to 2, Mon to Sat D 7 to 10.30 (11 Sat)   CLOSED: bank hols   MEALS: alc (main courses £9.50 to £14). Set L £10 (2 courses) to £12.50   SERVICE: not inc   CARDS: Access, Amex, Delta, Diners, Switch, Visa   DETAILS: 80 seats. Private parties: 65 main room, 16 private room. Vegetarian meals. Children's helpings. Smart dress preferred. No pipes in dining-room. Music

Maharaja £

23–25 Hurst Street, Birmingham B5 4AS
TEL: (0121) 622 2641   FAX: (0121) 622 3113

COOKING 1*
COST £17–£31

Nothing seems to change in this very agreeable little restaurant a few doors from the Birmingham Hippodrome. 'The same staff, the same courtesy and civility, the same cultured feel to the whole set-up' noted a reporter who knows the place. Indian prints, paintings and framed fragments of cloth decorate the delightfully unshowy ground-floor and basement dining-rooms, sitar music soothes the spirit and the clientele seems to be drawn equally from East and West. The menu focuses on North Indian and Mughlai cuisine, and dishes are notable for their fresh, acute spicing. Butter chicken is the speciality of the house, dhal varies from day to day, and vegetables (such as earthy lotus roots with peas) are a strong point. Other good dishes include aloo tikkian (deep-fried potato balls spiked with green chillies), and king prawn bhuna masala. Drink lassi or Kingfisher beer. House wine is £7.15.

CHEF: Bhupinder Waraich   PROPRIETOR: N.S. Batt   OPEN: Mon to Sat 12 to 2, 6 to 11   CLOSED: last week July, bank hols   MEALS: alc (main courses £6 to £7.50)   SERVICE: 10%, card slips closed   CARDS: Access, Amex, Diners, Switch, Visa   DETAILS: 62 seats. Private parties: 30 main room. Vegetarian meals. Children welcome. Smart dress preferred. Wheelchair access (also WC). Music. Air-conditioned

---

BIRTLE   Greater Manchester

map 8

▲ Normandie

Elbut Lane, Birtle BL9 6UT
TEL: (0161) 764 3869 and 1170
FAX: (0161) 764 4866
off B6222, 3m NE of Bury

COOKING 3
COST £20–£45

There have been some changes since last year. Gillian Moussa has moved elsewhere, son Max and his wife run the show, and Pascal Pommier's sous-chef Paul Bellingham has taken control of the kitchen. Something else has changed too. The house is still at the top of a winding lane, still looking out over the metropolis, but the dining-room has been painted 'violent' yellow, with bright cornflower-blue woodwork and matching chairs, 'like a trattoria on speed' in one reporter's view. The laudable aim of the changes – staff now wear jazzy ties, and the menu has been simplified – is to make everything more approachable.

The repertoire is still built around a combination of modern French dishes on a traditional bourgeois base, beginning with interesting soups (white bean with bean-cakes), terrines such as mackerel and potato, or a hot and delicately savoury sausage of chicken and lambs' sweetbreads on a crisp potato pancake with Madeira sauce. Although an inspector was disappointed with the timing, seasoning and indeed conception of a modish-sounding monkfish with ginger salsa and saffron noodles, the general impression is of 'simple, clear and robust' flavour combinations that have a natural air about them, including a dish of thickly sliced pork loin coated in chopped herbs, in a caramelised sauce with sweet and smoky shallots.

Desserts vary in accomplishment, too, one of the more sophisticated being a dark chocolate ganache with a vividly flavoured passion-fruit sorbet that proved both 'masterly and exciting'. There may be fewer extras these days, but the admirable policy of no service charge being made or expected continues, and although the set-price menus offer more limited choice they are considered 'terrific value'. The wine list is 'as good as ever', according to a reporter – a broad sweep of top producers from around the world. Despite the plethora of fine names, it is possible to keep your feet firmly on the ground with plenty of bottles costing under £20. French house wines are £11.95. CELLARMAN'S CHOICE: Sauvignon de St-Bris 1994, William Fèvre, £15; Montgras Merlot 1994, Chile, £13.50.

CHEF: Paul Bellingham   PROPRIETORS: Mr and Mrs Max Moussa   OPEN: Mon to Fri L 12 to 2, Mon to Sat D 7 to 9.30   CLOSED: 2 weeks from 26 Dec, 1 week Easter, bank hols exc 25 Dec MEALS: alc (main courses £10 to £17.50). Set L £12.50, Set D £15   SERVICE: none, card slips closed   CARDS: Access, Amex, Delta, Diners, Switch, Visa   DETAILS: 50 seats. Car park. Vegetarian meals. Children welcome. Smart dress preferred. No cigars/pipes in dining-room. Wheelchair access (also WC). Music   ACCOMMODATION: 23 rooms, all with bath/shower. TV. Phone. B&B £49 to £79. Rooms for disabled. Children welcome. Baby facilities. Garden

---

BISHOP'S TACHBROOK Warwickshire   map 5

▲ Mallory Court 🍷 ✗

Harbury Lane, Bishop's Tachbrook CV33 9QB
TEL: (01926) 330214   FAX: (01926) 451714   COOKING 3
off B4087, 2m S of Leamington Spa   COST £36–£84

Formal gardens, a bright floral lounge strewn with glossy magazines, and an oak-panelled dining-room with well-spaced tables provide a comfortable and persuasive setting for Stephen Shore's cooking. One lunching couple 'were delighted to sit on the terrace overlooking the enchanting garden, drinking champagne', though later were less enamoured of an entrecôte steak that proved tough. Aside from such lapses, the cooking is accomplished and technically sound.

The fixed-price menus and a generous *carte* cover a lot of ground, mostly in a modern European style with solid footing in the French repertoire. The variety in the cooking is appealing for a number of reasons: it offers classical renditions such as a casserole of squab pigeon with smoked bacon and lentils, as well as the simplicity of, say, grilled Dover sole with lemon butter. It stirs up interest with poached quenelle of game mousseline with onion rösti, or a wild mushroom soufflé with roasted artichoke, and it comforts with parfait of foie gras, or roast fillet of lamb in a potage of pearl barley.

Soufflés are singled out for recommendation among desserts such as chocolate teardrop filled with cherry mousse, and lemon crème brûlée. One reporter pointed out that 'the plush luxury and good food come at a price', in which context the light two-course lunch is particularly attractive. Polite but unstuffy service is a plus, as is the absence of a charge for it. Wines are a shrewd collection of lively flavours and top producers, with strong entries from California and Australia as well as France. It is an appealing list, although mark-ups are high in places. Nine house wines start at £14.25. CELLARMAN'S CHOICE: Wairau River Sauvignon Blanc 1994, Marlborough, New Zealand, £22.50; Cabernet Sauvignon 1993, Dom. Paul Bruno, Chile, £31.

CHEF: Stephen Shore   PROPRIETORS: Allan J.G. Holland and Jeremy R. Mort   OPEN: all week 12.30 to 2, 7 to 9.45   CLOSED: first 2 weeks Jan   MEALS: alc D (main courses £24 to £28). Set L £19.50 (2 courses) to £25, Set D £30 to £60. BYO £10   SERVICE: none, card slips closed   CARDS: Access, Amex, Delta, Diners, Switch, Visa   DETAILS: 50 seats. 6 seats outside. Private parties: 25 main room. Car park. Vegetarian meals. No children under 9. Smart dress preferred. No smoking in dining-room. Wheelchair access (no WC). No music   ACCOMMODATION: 10 rooms, all with bath/shower. TV. Phone. B&B £115 to £220. Children welcome. Afternoon teas. Garden. Swimming-pool

---

BLACKPOOL Lancashire   map 8

September Brasserie

15–17 Queen Street, Blackpool FY1 1PU	COOKING 2
TEL: (01253) 23282 FAX: (01253) 299455	COST £26–£41

'The gem in Blackpool's culinary crown', as a reporter describes it, cuts bravely against the local grain. Where most places dish up chips with almost everything, September offers samphire, wild garlic and sweet peppers. The place itself is a curious hybrid: its logo is a surrealist pair of scissors with lobster claws for handles. On the ground floor is a hairdressing studio, above is the brasserie with views of the promenade.

The cooking is based around a monthly-changing three-course menu plus a short *carte*. Fish gets a good airing, although local produce of all kinds is called into play. The style is emphatically modern. Reporters have liked English asparagus with lemon butter, lambs' kidneys in a 'lip-tingling' chilli sauce, and noisettes of lamb with lentils and sliced aubergine. Otherwise, you can expect such things as tartare of tuna with sushi rice, saddle of rabbit stuffed with Parma ham, ricotta and sun-dried tomato, or brochette of monkfish and scallops marinated in Thai spices. To finish, try baked egg custard jazzed up with red grapefruit and pear compote. The wine list has a strong organic bias, and a few more venerable bottles are offered 'for connoisseurs'. House wines start at £11.50.

CHEF: Michael Golowicz   PROPRIETORS: Michael Golowicz and Pat Wood   OPEN: Tue to Sat 12 to 2, 7 to 9.30   CLOSED: 2 weeks summer, 2 weeks winter   MEALS: alc (main courses £10 to £14). Set L £6.50 (2 courses), Set D £15.95   SERVICE: not inc, card slips closed   CARDS: Access, Amex, Diners, Visa   DETAILS: 40 seats. Private parties: 40 main room. Vegetarian meals. Children's helpings. Smart dress preferred. Music

BOLLINGTON Cheshire   map 8

Mauro's ✓ 1993

88 Palmerston Street, Bollington SK10 5PW   COOKING 1
TEL: (01625) 573898   COST £20–£37

Given the distance that Italian food has covered in Britain over the last decade,
Mauro's might appear slightly old-school. It is a family-run village restaurant
with a convincing Italian atmosphere that does chicken five ways, and wheels
around a trolley full of antipasti. But it has more going for it than the high-street
trattorias of old. For a start the pepper-pots are normal size (and the waiters leave
them alone), and fresh ingredients make a real impact. Pasta is made in-house
and might include linguine with pesto, or ravioli filled with goats' cheese and
ham, while veal is breadcrumbed, or served with butter and lemon, or topped
with Parma ham saltimbocca-style. A couple of daily specials broaden the scope
a little – calf's liver or kidneys may appear from time to time – and fish is well
worth asking about. Another trolley brings around the sweets, and
grappa-lovers are well served. Wines are all Italian (except for three
champagnes), many from renowned producers. House red and white are £8.80.

CHEF/PROPRIETOR: Vincenzo Mauro   OPEN: Mon to Fri L (and first Sun L in month) 12 to 2, Mon
to Sat D 7 to 10   CLOSED: 25 and 26 Dec   MEALS: alc (main courses £8.50 to £13)   SERVICE:
not inc; 10% for parties of 6 or more   CARDS: Access, Amex, Delta, Switch, Visa   DETAILS: 45
seats. Private parties: 60 main room. Vegetarian meals. Children welcome. Smart dress
preferred. No cigars/pipes in dining-room. Wheelchair access (also WC). Music

BOLTON ABBEY North Yorkshire   map 9

▲ Devonshire Arms, Burlington Restaurant £✳

(DALES STAR 1997)

Bolton Abbey BD23 6AJ
TEL: (01756) 710441 FAX: (01756) 710564   COOKING 3
at junction of A59 and B6160, 5m NW of Ilkley   COST £27–£59

Do not be misled by the name. This is no mere pub with a good line in bar
snacks. The house dates back to 1753, and the dining-room, which overlooks the
Yorkshire Dales National Park, is named after the eighteenth-century patron of
the arts Lord Burlington (one of the Devonshire family), some of whose
architectural drawings grace the walls. If the furnishings look impressive, that is
because they have come from the Devonshires' other home: Chatsworth House.

Balanced menus (with supplements for such things as foie gras and Dover
sole) change on a monthly basis, while lunches vary daily. Some of the starters
sound like scaled-down main courses: pink sauté calf's liver, for example,
served on mashed potato with glazed shallots in a red wine sauce. Overall,
though, portions are well judged, and timing is accurate. Andrew Nicholson
does not rely on exotic flavours for effect, but works in a modern classical style,
producing a chicken and truffle boudin, or ravioli of crab with 'lightly griddled,
wonderfully fresh' scallops. His 'flavour enhancers' might include a little truffle

oil for the turbot or roast garlic for the lamb, and he gets some of the vegetables, and all of his herbs, from the garden.

The place is immaculately kept, with well-spaced tables, starched linen, matching napkins and sparkling glassware, and incidentals are good, from bread to 'intensely flavoured' sorbets. Friendly and helpful staff provide 'oustanding service, and the entire operation flows without a hitch'. Mark-ups are rather high on the largely French wine list, but there are some good bottles, and Italy and the New World get a look in too. Half a dozen house wines run from £11.50 to £14.50.

CHEF: Andrew Nicholson   PROPRIETORS: Duke and Duchess of Devonshire   OPEN: all week 12 to 2, 7 to 10 (9.30 Sun)   MEALS: Set L £18.95, Set D £32.50   SERVICE: not inc, card slips closed   CARDS: Access, Amex, Diners, Switch, Visa   DETAILS: 75 seats. Private parties: 12 main room, 12 to 100 private rooms. Car park. Vegetarian meals. No children under 12. Jacket and tie. No smoking in dining-room. Wheelchair access (also WC). No music ACCOMMODATION: 41 rooms, all with bath/shower. TV. Phone. B&B £95 to £250. Rooms for disabled. Children welcome. Baby facilities. Dogs welcome. Afternoon teas. Garden. Swimming-pool. Fishing (*The Which? Hotel Guide*)

BOUGHTON LEES   Kent   map 3

▲ *Eastwell Manor* ⁺✳

Eastwell Park, Boughton Lees TN25 4HR
TEL: (01233) 219955   FAX: (01233) 635530   COOKING 2
on A251, 3m N of Ashford   COST £32–£68

Eurostar travellers alighting at the new Ashford International Station may like to know that the comforts of this Jacobean-style manor are close to hand. Bought from the Queens Moat Houses group in late 1995, Eastwell has started afresh, but Ian Mansfield remains at the stoves. The full panoply of formal service – white-gloved hands brandishing silver domes – may seem dated, but the food has a modern, light touch that reporters appreciate. A clever first course of shredded crab and salt-cod with avocado and curry oil is 'subtle and addictive', its various flavours well balanced, while a main course of loin of hare matches good gamey meat with 'earthy' diced beetroot and a juniper sauce. Oriental seasonings appear in cardamom-scented sauce with sea bass, and again in gently perfumed lemon grass ice-cream with blueberry tart. There is plenty to mull over on the expansive French-led wine list, but prices are fairly stiff, opening at £14.50 for a white Côtes de Gascogne (albeit a good one).

CHEF: Ian Mansfield   PROPRIETOR: T.F. Parrett   OPEN: all week 12.30 to 2, 7.30 to 9.30 (10 Sat)   MEALS: Set L £19.50, Set D £28.50 to £42. Bar snacks available   SERVICE: not inc, card slips closed   CARDS: Access, Amex, Delta, Diners, Switch, Visa   DETAILS: 75 seats. Private parties: 95 main room, 40 and 95 private rooms. Car park. Vegetarian meals. Children's helpings. Smart dress preferred. No smoking in dining-room. Wheelchair access (no WC). Music   ACCOMMODATION: 23 rooms, all with bath/shower. TV. Phone. B&B £130 to £260. Rooms for disabled. Children welcome. Dogs welcome. Afternoon teas. Garden (*The Which? Hotel Guide*)

BOWNESS-ON-WINDERMERE Cumbria   map 8

▲ Linthwaite House ⚡✗

Crook Road, Bowness-on-Windermere LA23 3JA   COOKING 3
TEL: (01539) 488600   FAX: (01539) 488601   COST £25–£46

Quite who has the best location in an area where natural splendour is the norm
may be a moot point, but Linthwaite House has a pretty strong claim. A mile or
so on from Windermere Golf Club, it sits on a hilltop overlooking the lake within
14 acres of gardens and woods, including a tarn where the splash of brown trout
rising to the bait is the only sound. Old cabin trunks fitted with glass tops make
tables for drinks, while the dining-room is informal in the sense that tables are
clothless and the dress code is relaxed.

Fixed-price dinner menus of four courses with coffee form the centrepiece of
the operation. Ian Bravey's cooking style is identifiably English country-house,
but while there is a fondness for artful presentations (such as salmon mousseline
studded with pistachios poached en quenelle, or seafood served in a filo purse),
there is no shying away from absolute simplicity if that is what is called for.
Slices of four varieties of melon come with an 'exceptionally good' red wine
granita that rapidly melts down into a rather good sauce. Whole Dover sole is
skilfully cooked to retain its 'freshness and fragrance', served unsauced with
simple vegetable garnishes. Then again, ink pasta and a saffron cream sauce
provide the dramatic backdrop for an escalope of salmon. Ambitious meat dishes
take in the likes of Barbary duckling breast with olive oil mash and a sauce of
forest berries and gin. Desserts range from the sumptuously rich, such as
chocolate truffle and praline cake with white chocolate sauce, to particularly
good lemon tart that has more citric bite than most. Cheeses are a speciality. The
carefully constructed wine list is arranged stylistically. There are many inspired
choices from around the world, the notes are helpful and mark-ups are not
greedy. Halves are plentiful. Prices start at £13.

CHEF: Ian Bravey   PROPRIETOR: Mike Bevans   OPEN: Sun L 12.30 to 1.30, all week D 7.15 to
8.45   MEALS: Set L £14.95, Set D £31. Minimum £19.50. Bar L available   SERVICE: net prices,
card slips closed   CARDS: Access, Amex, Delta, Switch, Visa   DETAILS: 40 seats. 18 seats
outside. Private parties: 8 main room, 18 private room. Car park. Vegetarian meals. Children's
helpings. No children under 7 D. Smart dress preferred. No smoking in dining-room. Wheelchair
access (also women's WC). Music   ACCOMMODATION: 18 rooms, all with bath/shower. TV.
Phone. D,B&B £100 to £210. Deposit: £80. Rooms for disabled. Children welcome. Afternoon
teas. Garden. Fishing (The Which? Hotel Guide)

Porthole Eating House 🍾

3 Ash Street, Bowness-on-Windermere LA23 3EB   COOKING 2
TEL: (01539) 442793   FAX: (01539) 488675   COST £17–£49

'Bowness,' commented one couple, circulating balefully in the car, 'is a pig of a
place for parking.' Indeed, the Porthole is in the pedestrianised part of town,
which at least makes the tables outside a pleasanter prospect than they might be.
A dramatic colour scheme brightens the low-ceilinged interior, black beams
standing out from vivid red gloss overhead, the roughcast walls cleanly
whitewashed.

Mike Metcalfe has been in the Porthole galley for 20 years now, his cooking characterised as a cocktail of Italian, French and English. That means that chicken breast saltimbocca, and fillet of brill Paul Bocuse, may be as much a part of the repertoire as breaded deep-fried scampi with tartare sauce. 'It is the day's specials that tend to whet the appetite,' according to one report. Pasta is well handled, the meatless dishes in particular impressing for resonance of flavour. A main course of lightly cooked moist salmon came in a cream sauce given 'tingling zip' by a touch of ginger, while pot-roasted lamb was tender as anything and enriched with a hearty, garlicky red wine gravy. Creamy desserts include raspberry pavlova, zuppa inglese and tiramisù. Coffee is jubilantly praised for quasi-Turkish intensity: 'The best we have had for many a long day.' The breadth and variety of the wine list is deeply impressive, from myriad mature clarets through the fine sections on Alsace and Italy, to a fascinating collection of old and rare digestifs. Italian house wines are £9.50.

CHEF: Mike Metcalfe PROPRIETORS: Gianni and Judy Berton OPEN: Wed to Mon (exc Sat L) 12 to 3, 6.30 to 11 CLOSED: last 2 weeks Dec, Jan and Feb MEALS: alc (main courses L £4 to £8.50, D £8.50 to £14). Set L £9.50 SERVICE: not inc, card slips closed CARDS: Access, Amex, Delta, Diners, Switch, Visa DETAILS: 34 seats. 32 seats outside. Private parties: 30 main room, 16 and 20 private rooms. Vegetarian meals. Children's helpings. Smart dress preferred. Music

---

BRADFIELD COMBUST Suffolk   map 3

▲ *Bradfield House* 💷✳

Bradfield Combust IP30 0LR
TEL: (01284) 386301 FAX: (01284) 386177   COOKING 1
on A134, 4m S of Bury St Edmunds   COST £29–£34

A seventeenth-century timbered house set in pleasingly informal gardens, Bradfield has been the preserve of the Green family for the past couple of years. Douglas Green's cooking is often characterised by a feeling of experimentation, so that smoked eel mousse may be paired with beetroot and apple as a starter, while chicken breast is crammed with king prawns and sauced with plums and brandy. One may wonder what marinating in vodka can possibly do for monkfish, but caramelised duck magret in a sauce of green peppercorns and orange strikes more familiar chords. Puddings offer the likes of apple and cinnamon strudel, or poached pears in a Marsala sabayon. The workmanlike wine list is geographically expansive and prices don't get silly. A quartet of New World house wines are all around £10.

CHEF: Douglas Green PROPRIETORS: Gordon, Moya and Douglas Green OPEN: Tue to Sun L 12 to 2, Tue to Sat D 7 to 9 MEALS: Set L and D £15.50 (2 courses) to £19.50. Bar L available SERVICE: not inc CARDS: Access, Delta, Diners, Switch, Visa DETAILS: 30 seats. 12 seats outside. Private parties: 20 main room, 15 private room. Car park. Vegetarian meals. Children's helpings. Smart dress preferred. No smoking in dining-room. Music ACCOMMODATION: 4 rooms, all with bath/shower. TV. Phone. B&B £45 to £80. Deposit: £25. Children welcome. Baby facilities. Dogs welcome. Afternoon teas. Garden (*The Which? Hotel Guide*)

'My friend had the wild mushroom and chicken terrine: one wild mushroom dutifully inserted in a stodgy terrine.' (On eating in Scotland)

BRADFORD West Yorkshire   map 8

▲ *Restaurant Nineteen* ♥

North Park Road, Heaton, Bradford BD9 4NT   COOKING 3
TEL: (01274) 492559   FAX: (01274) 483827   COST £40–£49

'The difficulties of maintaining a restaurant of this standard and integrity, in an area not always wholly appreciative, remain,' in the view of one reporter thankful for its survival. The interior looks classy, with lavishly draped curtains and blinds, but the two small dining-rooms are modest in scale. A fixed-price format, with four or five choices per course, allows the kitchen ample scope to develop its ideas.

Sophisticated handling of classic dishes is a hallmark, as in pheasant breast on Savoy cabbage with a sausage of the leg meat on 'superb' mashed potato: 'full of flavour, one of the best game dishes I have eaten,' according to one reporter. Some first courses can contribute to the feeling of richness and weight – for example, roast teal with lardons of bacon, mushrooms and sauté polenta, all in a red wine sauce – but there are lighter alternatives: salad, pasta or perhaps an 'exceptionally smooth' artichoke and pumpkin soup. The exactness of the cooking is in no way clinical, thanks to gutsy dishes such as fillet of beef with oxtail sauce and horseradish dumpling, and all manner of interesting part-nerships: a mustard pudding to accompany rabbit, or crusted cod with a well-judged coriander sauce on a bed of okra, for example.

'Desserts never disappoint here,' reckoned one reporter, and a lemon tart served as part of a trio of citrus puddings 'demonstrated the chef's ability to delight with apparently simple dishes'. At the other end of the scale might be a chocolate pot filled with frozen coffee parfait served with pear compote. Service is 'relaxed and charming'. Wines are well-chosen, and include mature clarets and Burgundies, several fine Rhônes and a concise but exemplary New World choice. House wines start at £12.50. CELLARMAN'S CHOICE: Hautes Côtes de Nuits Chardonnay 1993, Devevey £19.50; Ribera del Duero Crianza 1989, Bodegas Felix Callejo, £18.50.

CHEFS: Stephen Smith and Mark Wood   PROPRIETORS: Stephen Smith and Robert Barbour
OPEN: Tue to Sat D only 7 to 9.30 (10 Sat)   CLOSED: 1 week Christmas, 2 weeks Aug to Sept
MEALS: Set D £28   SERVICE: not inc   CARDS: Access, Amex, Switch, Visa   DETAILS: 36 seats.
Private parties: 30 main room. Car park. No children under 8. Smart dress preferred. No cigars/pipes in dining-room. Music   ACCOMMODATION: 4 rooms, all with bath/shower. TV. Phone. B&B £70 to £85. No children under 8. Garden (*The Which? Hotel Guide*)

BRAITHWAITE Cumbria   map 10

▲ *Ivy House* ♥ ⅚✳

Braithwaite CA12 5SY
TEL: (01768) 778338   FAX: (01768) 778113   COOKING 1*
just off B5292 Keswick to Braithwaite road   COST £25–£30

Braithwaite is pretty enough to be a Hollywood version of the quintessential Lakeland village, and dark-green Ivy House, dating from the seventeenth century, stands in hard-edged relief at its centre. The Shills, according to a report,

ENGLAND

are 'two of the most delightful hoteliers we have met', combining warmth and vivacity in equal measure. Menus experiment in unpretentious fashion along recognised Cumbrian lines. A ripe pear, for instance, is sliced and interleaved with delicately smoked chicken and dressed to impress with balsamic. The famous pea soup is 'a real rib-sticker', pale khaki in colour and based on good strong stock. A local supplier provides excellent lamb, the rack roasted pink and generously herbed, the sauce a very sweet redcurrant reduction. Hosts of vegetables are provided in the northern way, not forgetting creamy dauphinois, and the pudding list is enough to 'horrify dietary tyrants'. Our inspectors led the resistance with sticky toffee and tiramisù, commending both for richness that didn't cloy. Some excellent wines feature on a list that is not afraid to stray away from the classic regions into lesser-known territory: Argentina, Chile, Tasmania and England. House wines are French and German, and start at £5.95 for a half-litre carafe.

CHEFS: Wendy Shill and Peter Holton PROPRIETORS: Nick and Wendy Shill OPEN: all week D only 7.30 (1 sitting) CLOSED: Jan MEALS: Set D £18.95. BYO £5 SERVICE: not inc, card slips closed CARDS: Access, Amex, Delta, Diners, Switch, Visa DETAILS: 32 seats. Private parties: 10 main room. Car park. Children's helpings. Smart dress preferred. No smoking in dining-room. Music ACCOMMODATION: 12 rooms, all with bath/shower. TV. Phone. D,B&B £44 to £88. Children welcome. Baby facilities. Dogs by arrangement. Afternoon teas (The Which? Hotel Guide)

BRAMPTON Cumbria   map 10

▲ Farlam Hall

Brampton CA8 2NG
TEL: (01697) 746234 FAX: (01697) 746683   COOKING 2
on A689, 2½m SE of Brampton (not at Farlam village)   COST £38–£47

'The loveliest of country hotels' is how one observer described this mellow stone house just a few leagues from Hadrian's Wall. 'Vastly overdone,' countered another. A manor of some sort has been on the spot for centuries, but the Victorian imprint is strongest, both on the house and on the landscaped, ornamental garden. This is a two-family affair that benefits from a hands-on approach. Mrs Quinion presides over a dining-room with large windows and enough crisply starched linen 'for a state banquet', and 'almost bends backwards to make sure that all is well'.

Some starters on the short-choice menu – such as confit of duck leg on winter leaves, or fillet of sea bass with creamed spinach – can feel like mini-versions of main courses, but there is usually a soup as well. Main courses, of perhaps turbot or guinea-fowl, are often sauced using wine and cream. Vegetables, bread and cheeses are good, while puddings might include grape and banana trifle, or nut fudge pie with praline sauce. Forty-odd serviceable wines, and a respectable number of half-bottles, are reasonably marked up. House French is £12.75.

Restaurateurs justifiably resent no-shows. If you quote a credit card number when booking, you may be liable for the restaurant's lost profit margin if you don't turn up. Always phone to cancel.

CHEF: Barry Quinion PROPRIETORS: the Quinion and Stevenson families OPEN: all week D only 8 to 8.30 CLOSED: 26 to 31 Dec MEALS: Set D £28.50 to £29.50 SERVICE: not inc, card slips closed CARDS: Access, Amex, Switch, Visa DETAILS: 45 seats. Private parties: 25 main room. Car park. No children under 5. Smart dress preferred. No cigars/pipes in dining-room. Wheelchair access (no WC). No music ACCOMMODATION: 12 rooms, all with bath/shower. TV. Phone. D,B&B £95 to £220. No children under 5. Dogs welcome. Afternoon teas. Garden (*The Which? Hotel Guide*)

BRAY Berkshire   map 3

Fat Duck

NEW ENTRY

1 High Street, Bray SL6 2AQ   COOKING 3*
TEL: (01628) 580333 FAX: (01628) 776188   COST £28–£56

Heston Blumenthal has hit the ground running, having opened for business in August 1995 after working with, well, hardly anybody. He learnt about food by eating in most of France's top restaurants, and merely had a short spell with Marco Pierre White before diving straight into the thick of things. The beamed and listed building, formerly the Bell & Ringers, was a pub for some 200 years, and is now open-plan and stylishly decorated with a beaten copper bar, painted wall-panels and dried twigs and teasels. The combination of seriousness and informality is epitomised by the smart Riedel wine glasses and bare wooden tables.

The menu is short, the skills classical, the cooking modern. It is difficult to get more simple and direct than a conical mound of herb and leaf salad, or steak and chips with sauce moelle. What these plain-sounding dishes hide is a serious concern with the science of food and cooking that leads Heston Blumenthal to re-jig many of the techniques that others might take for granted, from preparing lentils to making stock. Chips, for instance, are blanched, refrigerated, cooked in ground-nut oil, refrigerated, and cooked again in oven-rendered veal fat. Petit salé of duck, perhaps destined to become a signature dish, is a Franco-Chinese collaboration involving brining, spicing, poaching and roasting, and comes with especially fine potato purée.

All this activity heightens and concentrates flavours, putting the focus squarely where it belongs, in smooth Marco-style parfait of foie gras and chicken livers with its compote of figs, or in chicken breast with a stuffing of herbs underneath its skin. Lemon tart, and a dish of nuts enclosed in salted butter caramel served with a gooey, chocolatey sorbet are recommendable desserts. Forty-odd wines soon escalate in price, there are no half-bottles, but around ten are available by the glass. House wines start at £13. Parking can be a problem.

CHEFS: Heston Blumenthal and Jason Gilmore PROPRIETORS: Heston and Susanna Blumenthal OPEN: Tue to Sun L 12.15 to 2.30, Tue to Sat D 7 to 9.30 (10.30 Fri and Sat) MEALS: alc (main courses £13.50 to £17). Set L Tue to Fri £14.50 (2 courses) to £17.50. BYO £13 SERVICE: not inc CARDS: Access, Amex, Delta, Switch, Visa DETAILS: 50 seats. 30 seats outside. Private parties: 50 main room. Children's helpings. Wheelchair access (no WC). Music

---

The Guide always appreciates hearing about changes of chef or owner.

▲ *Waterside Inn* ♀ ✓ 6/3/97

Ferry Road, Bray SL6 2AT
TEL: (01628) 20691 FAX: (01628) 784710   COOKING 4*
off A308 Maidenhead to Windsor road   COST £39–£140

Michel Roux chose an enviable spot for his restaurant 25 years ago. There is little more beguiling than a riverside location with a picture-book weeping willow and assorted wildfowl providing free entertainment. 'Customers are warmly greeted and treated with the proper hint of formality' as they are led through the bar with its 'countless certificates of gastro-proficiency', autographed cookery books and other tourist souvenirs, and into the pale green dining-room or on to the terrace. The appeal is classic French cooking of an exceptionally high order, organised around a *carte* and a *menu exceptionnel*, with other options sometimes available.

Everything is done 'very much in the grand French manner', and luxury ingredients are conspicuous by their presence. 'Croesus-rich' terrine of foie gras is served with a feather-light buttery brioche and a tiny salad of lambs' tongue and rocket smartly dressed in a vinous reduction emulsified with truffle oil. The cooking is unquestionably polished, laborious, disciplined and 'almost impervious to fashion', and is refined by constant rehearsal. A velouté de coquillages aux huîtres, enriched with cream and egg yolks, was 'almost like drinking fish-flavoured satin', while at the same inspection meal a main course of delicate, precisely cooked lamb combined saddle with tender, sweet neck-end chops, and briskly chargrilled liver. It came with a clear, heavily reduced *jus* 'bursting with meaty flavour', plus a pool of hollandaise sauce with freshly cut mint swirled into it.

Precision and 'almost faultless technical know-how' are clear. Although timing has produced 'very undercooked' salmon that was cold in the middle, it has also turned out plump, lightly pan-fried scallops, crisp outside and 'like mother-of-pearl' inside. Occasional lapses of clumsy or intrusive spicing are generally outweighed by excellence elsewhere, such as the 'perfect' hot soufflé of mirabelles. 'We found all the staff to be charming and helpful,' reported one couple of the solicitous service, although another couple who had been asked 'about 15 times in all' whether they were enjoying the food judged it 'well intentioned but *de trop*'. That a restaurant of this quality allows smoking to interfere with the food remains beyond belief, while the 'quaint, old-fashioned' custom of giving ladies a menu without prices is considered 'ridiculous in this day and age'. 'I was surprised that they left the credit card slip total open in view of the bill saying "VAT and service included",' complained a reporter.

The wine list is 'par for the course in an establishment with such lofty aspirations,' according to another reporter, with 'some very fine wines but not a bargain to be had'. It's all French, except for the vintage ports, and the quality is unimpeachable. The Sauternes and Barsac, champagne and Loire sections deserve an enthusiast's attention. House wines are £19. CELLARMAN'S CHOICE: Mercurey, Ch. de Chamirey, Dom. du Marquis de Jouennes 1992, £33; Santenay Beaurepaire 1989, Joseph Drouhin, £32.50.

CHEFS: Michel Roux and Mark Dodson PROPRIETOR: Michel Roux OPEN: Wed to Sun L 12 to 2
(2.30 Sat and Sun), Tue to Sun D 7 to 10 CLOSED: Sun D mid-Oct to mid-Apr, 5 weeks from 26
Dec MEALS: alc (main courses £24 to £37). Set L Wed to Fri £29.50 to £66.50, Set L Sat and Sun
£42.50 to £66.50, Set D £49.50 (winter only) to £66.50. Minimum £30 SERVICE: net prices
CARDS: Access, Amex, Delta, Diners, Switch, Visa DETAILS: 75 seats. Private parties: 80 main
room, 8 private room. Car park. Vegetarian meals. No children under 12. Smart dress preferred.
No cigars in dining-room. Wheelchair access (no WC). Music ACCOMMODATION: 7 rooms, all
with bath/shower. TV. Phone. B&B £130 to £205. Deposit: £60. No children under 12

BRIGHOUSE West Yorkshire

map 8

Brook's ✿✱   ✓ *1995*

6–8 Bradford Road, Brighouse HD6 1RW
TEL: (01484) 715284 FAX: (01484) 712641

COOKING 1*
COST £19–£38

Darrell Brook's lively and informal restaurant has a bar, a couple of smoking
lounges upstairs, and a dining-room with bare floorboards and taped jazz. A set
menu (with an 'early-bird' price before seven o'clock) offers cream of pea and
ham soup with a poached egg, game pie, and perhaps hot summer pudding with
custard. Among the regular specials are a 'money-bags' of filo pastry filled with
mushrooms and Brie, and smoked haddock prepared gravlax-style, but equally
likely to turn up are grilled ostrich or kangaroo fillet. When everything is cleared
away, wax crayons are provided for anyone wishing to express themselves on
the paper table-covers, and the best ones are framed on the wall. There are no
reports so far of these works being sufficient to pay for the meal. The short and
fairly priced wine list might help with the creative process. Prices start at £7.95.

CHEF: Richard Ullah PROPRIETOR: Darrell Brook OPEN: Mon to Sat D only 6 to 11; open L
during Dec CLOSED: 2 weeks Jan MEALS: Set D £15.95 (2 courses) to £19.95; early-bird menu
Mon to Fri 6 to 7 £11.95 SERVICE: not inc CARDS: Access, Switch, Visa DETAILS: 70 seats.
Private parties: 70 main room, 20 private room. Vegetarian meals. Children welcome. Smart
dress preferred. No smoking in dining-room. Wheelchair access. Music

---

BRIGHTON East Sussex

map 3

Black Chapati

12 Circus Parade, New England Road,
Brighton BN1 4GW
TEL: (01273) 699011

COOKING 2
COST £23–£33

The weirdly named Black Chapati is no ordinary restaurant. Half hidden in a
shopping arcade away from the centre of things, it is a brightly lit, monochromatic dining-room with cramped tables that reminded one visitor 'of a
school canteen – but painted black'. If the décor is wayward, the food is seriously
nonconformist. Stephen Funnell and Lauren Alker live dangerously: they
plunder Asia for inspiration, adapt ideas and create some outrageously risky
mixed marriages. What underpins their maverick view of cooking is the power
of chillies. From India might come 'pungently delicious' lamb samosas and
vegetarian thalis; the rest of the short menu is harder to pin down. Grilled pigeon
breast with stir-fried noodles and shiitake mushrooms, salad of preserved

guinea-fowl with peanuts, baked haddock with coconut milk, and Malaysian braised mutton with cucumber sambal throw down the gauntlet to convention. Desserts offer European reassurance in the shape of caramelised apple tart, and chocolate truffle cake with cinnamon ice-cream. Service is helpful but 'sparse'. Dunkerton's Royal Court cider and Staropramen Czech lager are alternatives to the minimal wine list. House wine is £8.95. Payment by cheque is not accepted.

CHEFS/PROPRIETORS: Stephen Funnell and Lauren Alker   OPEN: Tue to Sat D only 7 to 10.30   CLOSED: 1 week Christmas, 1 week June   MEALS: alc (main courses £8.50 to £11)   SERVICE: 10%, card slips closed   CARDS: Access, Amex, Delta, Switch, Visa   DETAILS: 30 seats. 8 seats outside. Private parties: 12 main room. Vegetarian meals. Children welcome. Wheelchair access (no WC). Music

One Paston Place

1 Paston Place, Brighton BN2 1HA	COOKING 1*
TEL: (01273) 606933 FAX: (01273) 675686	COST £23–£46

Mark and Nicole Emmerson are now monarchs of all they survey at what was, until 1995, the Brighton outpost of Langan's (see entry, London). Regulars noted that the paintings had been removed, and a cheery new mural commissioned in their stead, but all else remains unchanged. Mark Emmerson's cooking takes its inspiration from southern French modes, delivering substance and flavour without undue fuss. Fish is very capably handled: a bowl of classic fish nage, brimming with many species and alive with anise, showed up well at inspection, while a summer party found both the red mullet and tuna 'strikingly fresh'. Game is enthusiastically used, so much so that hare and venison appeared on the same plate one night, accompanied by a sauce poivrade and pasta. A version of bubble and squeak, made with sweet potato, may be used to partner either calf's liver or guinea-fowl. Orange, coffee and coconut have been the value-added twists on crème brûlée, and there is always a tart such as fig or prune with appropriate ice-cream. A few 'vins du nouveau monde' and some fine French classics have been introduced to add depth to the list. House French is £8.80.

CHEF: Mark Emmerson   PROPRIETORS: Mark and Nicole Emmerson   OPEN: Tue to Sat 12.30 to 2, 7.30 to 10   CLOSED: first 2 weeks Jan, first two weeks Aug   MEALS: alc (main courses £14 to £16). Set L £14.50 (2 courses) to £16.50   SERVICE: 10%, card slips closed   CARDS: Access, Amex, Delta, Diners, Switch, Visa   DETAILS: 45 seats. Children welcome. No babies D. No pipes in dining-room. Wheelchair access (no WC). Music. Air-conditioned

Terre à Terre 🍴✳ £

7 Pool Valley, Brighton BN1 1NJ	COOKING 1*
TEL: (01273) 729051 FAX: (01273) 327561	COST £19–£31

Half-hidden just off the sea-front, this splendid vegetarian café offers round-the-world cooking of confidence and flair. The flimsy folding chairs and undeniably cramped feeling when the place is full are small prices to pay for the vividly exuberant food. Sumptuous Glamorgan sausages are fashioned from Welsh cheese, leek and fresh herbs, anointed with truffle oil and cracked black pepper, and served with onion marmalade and mash. Rice noodles and vegetable threads are dressed with tamarind juice and mustard seeds and served in a miso broth garnished with hoisin tofu. Flavour is at a premium throughout, as is a genuine feeling of substance. Riviera rabbit isn't bunny, but a rarebit variation using ciabatta topped with cheeses, Worcester sauce (a strictly vegetarian version) and beer and crowned with a poached egg. Shamelessly rich desserts include chocolate and praline mousse with caramelised orange, and apple and cinnamon charlotte with calvados custard. Dishes suitable for vegans are helpfully noted on the menu. The short wine list has done a commendable job in sourcing many organic offerings. House French is £7.75.

CHEFS: Philip Taylor, Amanda Powley, Julio Estevot, Ricky Hodgkins and Laurence Glass
PROPRIETORS: Philip Taylor and Amanda Powley   OPEN: Tue to Sun L 12 to 5.30, all week D 6 to 10.30 (booking essential D)   CLOSED: 4 days Christmas   MEALS: alc (main courses £4.50 to £7)   SERVICE: not inc; 10% for parties of 6 or more   CARDS: none   DETAILS: 40 seats. Private parties: 20 main room. Vegetarian meals. Children's helpings. No smoking in 1 dining-room. Wheelchair access (no WC). Music

Whytes

33 Western Street, Brighton BN1 2PG	COOKING 1*
TEL: (01273) 776618	COST £27–£33

'A dinky cottage in a street full of dinky cottages,' a reporter writes of Ian and Jane Whyte's popular two-hander just off the sea-front on the Hove side of Brighton. Cheerful bustle prevails when the place is full, as do oohs and aahs of quiet approbation. This is a neighbourhood restaurant, centred on a kitchen that knows its clientele. 'Creamy, full-flavoured, exemplary' Jerusalem artichoke soup may kick off a meal, perhaps followed by deftly cooked salmon in a saffron and chive cream sauce, or good best end of neck of lamb cooked rare and served with a purée of red pepper and garlic. Sweetish accompaniments characterise some savoury dishes: a pair of crisp filo parcels, for example – one of Roquefort and leek, the other of ricotta and olives – is sauced with redcurrant and orange, while the duck-with-citrus variation has been caramelised grapefruit. Custardy desserts, such as lemon posset and crème caramel, are agreeably rich. Prices on the wine list look fair, but the information offered is too general, with producer names and vintages omitted in many cases. House Côtes du Lubéron, white and red, is £8.50.

CHEF: Ian Whyte   PROPRIETORS: Ian and Jane Whyte   OPEN: Tue to Sat D only 7 to 9.30, and some Mons (phone to check); also open L Mothering Sun and by arrangement   CLOSED: end Feb to early Mar, bank hol Mons   MEALS: Set D £15.95 (2 courses) to £19.50.   SERVICE: not inc   CARDS: Access, Amex, Visa   DETAILS: 36 seats. Private parties: 24 main room, 12 private room. Vegetarian meals. Children welcome. Smart dress preferred. No cigars/pipes in dining-room. Music

'One dish was "pavé". When we asked what it was, the waiter said, "It's a slab, but we couldn't put that on the menu."' (On eating in London)

An asterisk (*) after the 1 to 5 cooking mark at the top of an entry signifies that the Guide and its readers think that the restaurant is a particularly fine example within its rating.

▲ *Roebuck, Poppies* ♼

Brimfield SY8 4NE
TEL: (01584) 711230   FAX: (01584) 711654   COOKING 3*
on A49, 4m S of Ludlow   COST £30–£56

The Roebuck is a village pub within the orbits of Ludlow and Leominster, with accommodation and a dining-room. Informality is a cherishable part of a meal here, but what reporters come for is Carole Evans's spin on British country cooking, whether in the bar or restaurant. 'Bar snacks' is hardly the term to describe a menu that takes in moist, tasty rabbit terrine with rhubarb chutney, Bury black pudding on a purée of potato, apple and celeriac, or smoked chicken pudding with bacon and leeks, although prices are commendably low.

The dining-room's serious intentions are evident in ravioli of calves' sweetbreads and truffles, or in peppered hake with spinach served with a frothy champagne sauce. Simple dishes are made memorable by fresh ingredients sensitively cooked, as in one reporter's glazed scallops served in their shells with garlic, parsley, butter and mushrooms, and another's 'superb' salmon fish-cakes. The care that goes into the food shows on the plate, and reporters find the results hugely enjoyable. Sauces have been 'perfectly matched to the main ingredient', and there is the added advantage that 'instead of a bowl of overcooked vegetables which bear little relationship to the dish you are eating, you get a variety of beautifully cooked and presented fresh produce'.

To follow, caramel pyramid with brown-bread ice-cream looks and tastes 'spectacular', and the cheeseboard has been rated 'exceptional'. The wide range of half-bottles which kicks off the wine list is tempting; it makes way for a good choice from the classic French regions and sound representatives from the New World. House wines are £11.50. CELLARMAN'S CHOICE: Pouilly Vinzelles 1994, Dom. Jean Mathias, £17.50; Sancerre Rosé 1994, Dom. Pierre et Alain Dezat, £20.

CHEF/PROPRIETOR: Carole Evans   OPEN: Tue to Sat 12 to 2, 7 to 10   CLOSED: 25 and 26 Dec
MEALS: bar menu L (main courses £6 to £9); alc restaurant D (main courses £16 to £19.50). Set
bar L and D £16 (2 courses) to £20   SERVICE: not inc   CARDS: Access, Delta, Switch, Visa
DETAILS: 40 seats. 16 seats outside. Private parties: 30 main room, 14 private room. Car park.
Vegetarian meals. Children welcome. Smart dress preferred. No music   ACCOMMODATION: 3
rooms, all with bath/shower. TV. Phone. B&B £45 to £60. Deposit: 50%. Children welcome.
Dogs welcome (*The Which? Hotel Guide*)

Bell's Diner ⅀✸

1 York Road, Montpelier, Bristol BS6 5QB
TEL: (0117) 924 0357
take Picton Street off Cheltenham Road (A38) – runs   COOKING 2
into York Road   COST £15–£36

Bustling Bell's has built up a solid reputation over the years. 'It just shows that it is possible to pack a non-smoking restaurant if the food is good,' noted a reporter. The building was formerly a grocer's shop, and many of the original fittings have been retained, although one visitor thought the cutlery had seen better days.

Menus are fixed-price, but there are so many supplements you might think you were ordering from a *carte*. The cooking is modern, seasonal and ingredients-led. Autumn might bring carefully seasoned cream of Jerusalem artichoke and celeriac soup, and a main course of red spinach and Gruyère soufflé; other successes have included 'luscious' pan-fried scallops, beetroot soup, 'superb' chargrilled salmon marinated in ginger on a bed of noodles, and 'outstanding' chocolate tart. The kitchen also takes on board meaty offerings along the lines of rabbit and tarragon rillettes, and roast confit of duck with colcannon. Cheeses are British and Irish. Wines are keenly chosen from some of the most forward-looking growers; house wines start at £8.

CHEFS: Peter Taylor, Shirley Anne Bell and Jason Bright   PROPRIETORS: Shirley Anne Bell, Peter Taylor and Mark Hall   OPEN: Tue to Fri and Sun L 12.15 to 2, Tue to Sat D 7 to 10 (10.30 Sat) CLOSED: L Sun June to Sept   MEALS: Set L £7 (2 courses) to £9.50, Set D £13.50   SERVICE: not inc; 10% on parties of 8 or more   CARDS: Access, Switch, Visa   DETAILS: 60 seats. Private parties: 26 main room, 18 private room. Vegetarian meals. Children's helpings. No smoking in dining-room. Music

Glass Boat

NEW ENTRY

Welsh Back, Bristol BS1 4SB
TEL: (0117) 929 0704   FAX: (0117) 929 7338

COOKING 2
COST £25–£43

A restaurant on a boat moored in the centre of a city is not a common sight, but Bristol has one. The vessel in question is a renovated timber barge that once unloaded freight in the Severn Estuary and is now home to Arne Ringner's brasserie-style operation. Decoration is kept 'spare but elegant', the walls filled with displays of Matisse-like prints by the owner's wife.

An inspection dinner suggested that the kitchen, under Roux-trained chef Michael Lemoine, is capable of accomplishing great things. Scallop mousse parcelled in spinach leaves with an 'impeccable, velvety' saffron-tinged seafood sauce set the tone. It was followed by a dish of rabbit cooked in a Mexican-style dark brown sauce containing bitter chocolate giving it something of the character of a 'pungent civet – a risk that paid off handsomely'. The accuracy of cooking in a piece of wild salmon was admirable indeed: seared quickly so that it was crisped on the surface but still soft and fondant within. Baking skills were on parade in a slice of simple almond tart with light pastry and a 'subtle but dense' filling. White chocolate mousse with a sorbet of dark chocolate garnished with cherries, or orange and cardamom parfait with mango sauce can be other uplifting desserts. A good modern wine list offers a useful spread of choice, with clarets and Burgundies the centrepieces. Prices open at £9.50.

CHEF: Michel Lemoine   PROPRIETOR: Arne Ringner   OPEN: Mon to Fri L 12 to 2.30, Mon to Sat D 6.30 to 10.30   CLOSED: 25 and 26 Dec, and L 27 and 28 Dec   MEALS: alc (main courses £11 to £16). Set L £9.95 (2 courses), Set D £16.50   SERVICE: not inc   CARDS: Access, Amex, Delta, Switch, Visa   DETAILS: 130 seats. 8 seats outside. Private parties: 100 main room, 40 private room. Vegetarian meals. Children's helpings. Smart dress preferred. Wheelchair access (no WC). Music. Air-conditioned

Harveys 🍾

12 Denmark Street, Bristol BS1 5DQ
TEL: (0117) 927 5034 FAX: (0117) 927 5003

NEW CHEF

COST £22–£57

A wine museum (worth a visit) and huge sherry casks add their bit to the character of these medieval wine cellars. The sense of history is not diminished by bright modern artwork, and all is helped by strategic lighting. This is 'an up-market, stylish restaurant' with shining white walls, comfortable chairs, and large tables set well apart, all matched by staff who greet customers by name, deliver everything deftly and pleasantly, and time things perfectly. For an inspector, 'everything Harveys sets out to do was achieved with imagination, flair and craft'.

And maybe still is, but as we went to press Ramon Farthing announced his departure. He is to set up shop at 36 on the Quay in Emsworth, Hampshire. In his place comes Daniel Galmiche, who used to cook at Knockinaam Lodge, Portpatrick, Scotland (see entry), but who unfortunately arrived too late for us to make an assessment. As one might expect in a restaurant owned by wine merchant John Harvey and Sons, the wine list is impressive, plundering old stocks from the extensive cellars. Sherries, ports and clarets dazzle for their range and maturity, and many fortified wines are available by the glass. French house wines are £12. CELLARMAN'S CHOICE: Sancerre Rosé, Paul Prieur 1993, £18; Pauillac, Les Forts de Latour 1986, £32.

CHEF: Daniel Galmiche PROPRIETOR: John Harvey and Sons OPEN: Mon to Fri L 12 to 1.45, Mon to Sat D 7 to 10.45 CLOSED: 25 to 27 Dec, bank hols MEALS: alc (main courses £16 to £21). Set L £16, Set D £26 to £29 SERVICE: net prices, card slips closed CARDS: Access, Amex, Delta, Diners, Switch, Visa DETAILS: 100 seats. Private parties: 100 main room, 50 private room. Valet parking D. Vegetarian meals. No children under 8. Smart dress preferred. Music. Air-conditioned

Howards

1A–2A Avon Crescent, Hotwells, Bristol BS1 6XQ
TEL: (0117) 926 2921

COOKING 1

COST £20–£40

This three-storey Georgian building by the dockside has a view of Brunel's Clifton Suspension Bridge and occupies a handy corner spot. It is family run, feels more like a bistro than a restaurant, and serves a short seasonal *carte* supplemented by a couple of blackboards, one of fish, one of vegetarian dishes. The food is modish enough to include a salad of marinated prawns and mussels with coriander and lime, and old-fashioned enough to serve hot cheese beignets. Flavours are helped along by a beetroot and balsamic vinaigrette (applied to flaked duck in a filo tartlet) and a beer and onion gravy that accompanies marinated venison, while desserts have included hot chocolate fudge cake, and a lime and mascarpone torte. A sensibly chosen and fairly priced list of around 50 wines includes house French at £7.50.

'Stick clear of the puddings unless you have fond memories of school dinners, and a spare set of false teeth.' (On eating in London)

CHEF: David Short PROPRIETORS: Christopher and Gillian Howard OPEN: Mon to Fri L 12 to 2.30, Mon to Sat D 7 to 11.30 CLOSED: 25 and 26 Dec, some bank hols MEALS: alc (main courses £10.50 to £14.50). Set L £13, Set D Mon to Fri £15 SERVICE: not inc; 10% for parties of 8 or more CARDS: Access, Amex, Delta, Diners, Visa DETAILS: 65 seats. Private parties: 40 main room, 12 and 25 private rooms. Vegetarian meals. Children's helpings. Smart dress preferred. Wheelchair access (no WC). Music

Hunt's

26 Broad Street, Bristol BS1 2HG
TEL/FAX: (0117) 926 5580

COOKING 3
COST £22–£52

'I lunch regularly at Hunt's, and standards are absolutely consistent,' confirms a reporter who enjoys eating here most in summer 'with the door open and gulls crying outside, as though one were in the centre of Bristol of old, with ships moored a few yards down the road'. This part of Bristol does that to people: the restaurant is in a former tea and coffee merchant's in a characterful corner of the city. Or perhaps it is lunch that does it. Jerusalem artichoke soup, boiled ham with turnip and parsley cream, and hazelnut parfait all for £13.50 is good going.

Andrew Hunt's cooking is confident, and flavour combinations show that he knows his way around the powerful primary taste sensations. Sometimes a little fruitiness or sweetness accompanies a dish – spiced plums with a breast of Trelough duck, or sweet onion marmalade with baked goats' cheese, for example – but is never allowed to get out of hand. The sense of balance and clarity is helped by careful herbing and spicing, as in a smoked haddock soufflé with ground coriander and dill cream, or baked Cornish sea bass with a simple sorrel sauce. Pasta is made in-house (perhaps tagliatelle with smoked bacon and pesto), and among other dishes that have pleased are baked cod with artichokes, venison and beef suet pudding, and diplomat pudding.

Desserts are taken seriously, from a made-to-order prune and armagnac tart to a dish of toasted marshmallow with saffron ice-cream and caramel oranges encased in a spun sugar veil. British and Irish cheeses might include Wigmore and Gubbeen. Service is impeccable and friendly. The wine list majors on France, with an engaging selection at under £20 a bottle. Several wines are available by the glass and half-bottle, and the house selection starts at £9.75.

CHEF: Andrew Hunt PROPRIETORS: Andrew and Anne Hunt OPEN: Tue to Fri L 12 to 2, Tue to Sat D 7 to 10 (10.30 Sat) CLOSED: 1 week Easter, 1 week after Aug bank hol, 24 Dec to 3 Jan MEALS: alc (main courses £13.50 to £16). Set L £11.50 (2 courses) to £13.50 SERVICE: not inc, card slips closed CARDS: Access, Amex, Delta, Switch, Visa DETAILS: 35 seats. Private parties: 26 main room. Children's helpings. Smart dress preferred. Wheelchair access (no WC). Music

Lettonie ♥

9 Druid Hill, Stoke Bishop, Bristol BS9 1EW
TEL: (0117) 968 6456 FAX: (0117) 968 6943

BRISTOL 1997 INDIVIDUAL

COOKING 4*
COST £30–£67

The contrast between food and surroundings is striking. Sandwiched between a dry-cleaner's and a vet's, Lettonie puts a brave face on it, but it is 'no wonder Siân and Martin Blunos are looking for a small manor-house in the country'. Once inside, though, 'the Tardis element takes over', and it is easy to forget the world beyond the heavily shrouded windows and concentrate instead on the dark colours, simply set tables and fixed-price three-course menus of planet Blunos.

The famous Fabergé-like starter of scrambled duck eggs and caviare arrives with the top neatly hewn off a pale blue shell which rests in a golden egg-cup, the ensemble surrounded by flaming vodka like a Christmas pudding. It is 'creamy, sloppy, decadent, naughty and nurseryish as only good scrambled egg can be', but the generous dollop of sevruga caviare makes the whole thing 'very grown up and sophisticated'. Accompanied by a glass of iced vodka, it is all very dramatic and well worth the £3.50 supplement.

An astonishing amount of intricate workmanship goes into some dishes. In one first course, minced and cumin-spiked quail meat had been re-formed into a thigh shape around a quail drumstick and served with a livery chicken mousse flavoured with caraway and wrapped in a spinach leaf, plus a gamey quail sausage and a light but intense stock-based sauce. Martin Blunos seems to revel in taking an element and exploring its potential by presenting it several ways. Assiette of pork consists of a rib, trotter, bacon fillet and black pudding, while a pigeon dish impressed an inspector as 'one of the best main courses I have ever had'. Tender, gamey breast was served with an intense meatball of livers, minced pigeon meat and barley 'like a pigeon haggis', while other bits of the bird had gone into making a pale pink chipolata and a small pool of reduced broth.

'After the main course came an amusing frou-frou' in which a hen's eggshell mimicked the duck egg starter, with white vanilla cream, and mango purée for a yolk. Crunchy sticks of shortbread acted as toast soldiers, and little piles of sugar and finely grated chocolate stood in for pepper and salt. Among desserts, kümmel parfait with buttermilk ice-cream and blueberries incorporates a favourite Blunos combination of cumin and caraway. Exceptional materials are passionately sourced for quality, intense but light stock reductions 'are a revelation', and the food is both innovative and stylish. A well-balanced wine list is enhanced by short fine-wine and bin-end sections and half a dozen appealing house bottles which start at £12.85. CELLARMAN'S CHOICE: St-Véran Cuvée Prestige 1993, Roger Lasserat, £23.80; Givry, La Grande Berge 1992, Gérard Mouton, £26.05.

CHEF: Martin Blunos   PROPRIETORS: Siân and Martin Blunos   OPEN: Tue to Sat 12.30 to 2, 7 to 9   CLOSED: 2 weeks Christmas, 2 weeks Aug   MEALS: Set L £17.95 to £36.50, Set D Tue to Thur £17.95 to £36.50, Set D Fri and Sat £36.50   SERVICE: not inc   CARDS: Access, Amex, Diners, Switch   DETAILS: 24 seats. Private parties: 24 main room. Children welcome. Smart dress preferred. Wheelchair access (no WC). Music

---

Markwicks 🍷

43 Corn Street, Bristol BS1 1HT
TEL/FAX: (0117) 926 2658

COOKING 3*
COST £24–£48

'Markwick's is a very special experience,' claims one reporter, though that is obviously true for others too. Everything is of a piece, from the coolly smart dining-room in a converted bank to Stephen Markwick's estimable food, and the way Judy Markwick and her staff look after guests. Art deco furnishings, bright modern pictures and generous table spacings all help to induce a feeling of ease and comfort, while a sensible approach to preliminaries made an inspector feel that 'the very pleasant tone of the evening was already set' before he had eaten a thing.

If the kitchen has a preference, it is for fish (which depends on the market), game and offal, from rare and succulent loin of venison 'with plenty of flavour' to a plate of lambs' kidneys, liver and plentiful sweetbreads with a mustard sauce. Do not be misled by the apparent modesty of the menu. 'House charcuterie' may not sound much, but it consists of two exquisitely light pâtés (one coarse, one smooth), accompanied by two small brioche slices served with frisée and lambs'-tongue lettuce, and a distinctive but not overpowering spiced apricot chutney.

The common thread running through reports is that components taste of what they should, cooking gets the best out of materials, and combinations are well judged. The style is mercifully free of empty gesture, and concentrates on essentials, even when these are as simple as a caramelised rice pudding with rhubarb compote. The high point of the meal for one reporter was a prune and armagnac tart with fine crispy pastry and plump prunes soaked in brandy, 'the whole bound in an eggy mousse with a vanilla sauce'. The wine list is littered with reputable producers at each turn of the page and from every major country. Prices are eminently fair, and there's a new house selection at the front with 16 wines, all under £15. CELLARMAN'S CHOICE: Pacherenc du Vic-Bilh, Ch. Bouscassé 1994, Brumont, £14.50; St Hallett Old Block Shiraz 1992, Barossa Valley, S. Australia, £19.

CHEFS: Stephen Markwick and Sara Ody   PROPRIETORS: Stephen and Judy Markwick   OPEN: Mon to Fri L 12 to 2, Mon to Sat D 7 to 10.30   CLOSED: 1 week Christmas, 1 week Easter, 2 weeks Aug, bank hols   MEALS: alc (main courses £15 to £17). Set L £12.50 (2 courses) to £15, Set D £21.50   SERVICE: not inc, card slips closed   CARDS: Access, Amex, Delta, Switch, Visa   DETAILS: 40 seats. Private parties: 8 main room, 6 and 20 private rooms. Vegetarian meals. Children's helpings. No music

Melbournes

74 Park Street, Bristol BS1 5JX   COOKING 1*
TEL: (0117) 922 6996   COST £16–£27

Handy for the university, brightly decorated with colourful prints, and buzzing with life, Melbournes attracts the crowds. They are drawn by the atmosphere as much as the food, and their sheer numbers and the pace of eating dictate the format, which relies on quick grilling and roasting for effect – of sirloin steak, chicken leg, or whatever fish the market has to offer – plus a simple sauce of garlic and herb butter, or basil and cream. Lunch is flexible, with starters at £2.25 and desserts at £2, although the set-price options are good value, and a daily blackboard of specials adds to the breezy feel. Pastas and salads set the ball rolling, the vegetarian main course might be a ratatouille-filled pancake with cheese sauce, and puddings regress to the nursery with apple pie and custard, or treacle tart with vanilla ice-cream. A short, modern wine list does its best to stay under £15, and there is no corkage charge for BYO. A sister restaurant, Redcliffs, is at Redcliff Quay, 125 Redcliff Street, down by the waterfront.

CHEFS: C. Cowpe and R. Smith   PROPRIETORS: Tony Wilshaw and Nick Hennessy   OPEN: Tue to Fri and Sun L 12 to 2 (2.30 Sun), Mon to Sat D 7 to 10.30   CLOSED: 24 to 30 Dec   MEALS: Set L £8 (2 courses) to £10, Set D £13.50 (2 courses) to £15.50. BYO (no corkage)   SERVICE: 10%, card slips closed   CARDS: Access, Amex, Delta, Diners, Switch, Visa   DETAILS: 100 seats. Vegetarian meals. Children's helpings. No cigars/pipes in dining-room. Wheelchair access (no WC). Music

Muset ✎

16 Clifton Road, Clifton, Bristol BS8 1AF
TEL/FAX: (0117) 973 2920

COOKING 1
COST £23–£33

'Bristol's original BYO restaurant', as Muset describes itself, occupies an L-shaped slice of a block of flats and shops, with entrances on two sides of a street corner. It is in effect a big, bustling, modern brasserie, offering a thoroughly up-to-date menu in surroundings that don't encourage anyone to stand on ceremony. Some ideas may sound a little alarming (hands up for chicken livers with mange-tout and raspberries) but the saner dishes generally satisfy. Caesar salad uses notably good Parmesan, while main courses of pheasant breast with 'a slosh of bacon, lentil and tarragon sauce', and accurately cooked beef fillet with a sauce of horseradish, cognac and peppercorns do exactly what's required of them. Puddings include profiteroles filled with raspberry mousse and coated with almond chocolate sauce. Service by young staff is 'second to none'. If you don't bring your own wine, the short selection offered is perfectly sound and inexpensive. House French is £8.25. Two sister restaurants are Hullaballoos, at 46 Whiteladies Road, tel: (0117) 923 9212, and Colston Street Bistro and Grill, at 19–23 Colston Street, tel: (0177) 922 7757.

CHEF: Dave Wheadon   PROPRIETOR: Muset Ltd   OPEN: all week D only 7 to 10.30   CLOSED: 3 or 4 days at Christmas, 1 week Aug   MEALS: Set D £13.95 (2 courses) to £14.95. BYO (no corkage)   SERVICE: 10% (optional), card slips closed   CARDS: Access, Amex, Delta, Diners, Switch, Visa   DETAILS: 120 seats. Private parties: 50 main room. Vegetarian meals. Children welcome. Smart dress preferred. Music. Air-conditioned

Rocinantes

85 Whiteladies Road, Bristol BS8 2NT
TEL: (0117) 973 4482

COOKING 1*
COST £23–£37

On a hot summer's night Rocinantes is jammed with scores of noisy young bloods eyeing the streetlife and table-hopping behind the huge glass frontage. The place bills itself as 'café/bar' with tapas as its main stock-in-trade, but there is an increasing tilt towards formal restaurant meals now that refurbishment is complete. The kitchen delivers some of the 'greenest' food in the city and the cooking continues to improve. Olives, tortillas and calamares are top-quality, as are the carefully nurtured Spanish cheeses. Other recent successes have included crisp salt-cod fish-cakes, and home-made Italian-style sausages that any professional charcutier would be proud of. Confit of duck has impressed, and the short *carte* may also list warm butter-bean salad, and monkfish with pesto. Service is young and capable. Trendy beers are drunk from the bottle, jugs of sangria flow freely and some quaffable tipples show up on the short wine list. House wines start at £7.95.

CHEF: Barny Haughton   PROPRIETORS: Barny Haughton and Matthew Pruen   OPEN: Mon to Sat 12 to 3, 6 to 11, Sun 10 to 3, 6 to 10.30   CLOSED: 25 and 26 Dec, 1 Jan   MEALS: alc (main courses £9.50 to £12.50). Light meals available   SERVICE: not inc, 10% for parties of 6 or more   CARDS: Access, Amex, Delta, Switch, Visa   DETAILS: 90 seats. 40 seats outside. Private parties: 30 main room, 30 private room. Vegetarian meals. Children welcome. Wheelchair access (no WC). Music

---

BROADHEMBURY Devon   map 2

Drewe Arms

Broadhembury EX14 0NF
TEL/FAX: (01404) 841267   COOKING 2*
off A373, between Cullompton and Honiton   COST £28–£38

Nigel Burge reckons that Broadhembury is 'Devon's quintessential thatched village', and it is hard to deny the charms of the place. In their quixotically decorated pub, the Burges have hung an eel-catcher's basket, walking-sticks and farming implements: 'a delightful place' was the opinion of one reporter, who added, 'Please move it to Surrey.'

Freshest fish and seafood are the order of the day, prepared in a variety of more or less classical ways, from crab thermidor and langoustines with garlic mayonnaise to whole griddled Dover sole and turbot with hollandaise. A reporter who started with a bowl of pea and ham soup – the stock made from simmered ham bone, the portion packed with whole peas and pieces of ham – and went on to a laden platter of gravad lax, prawns and smoked salmon followed by ripe Brie with bread, came away feeling he certainly had his money's worth. Fish even gets a look-in in fillet steak with anchovy butter, but to insist on meat here is to miss the point. There's hazelnut meringue to finish, or perhaps a pudding that manages to combine toffee, chocolate and banana. The wine list works from a broad palette, offering reds almost as plentifully as whites. House wines are £9.50.

CHEFS/PROPRIETORS: Kerstin and Nigel Burge   OPEN: all week L 12 to 2, Mon to Sat D 7 to 10   CLOSED: L 25 Dec   MEALS: alc (main courses £14). Set L and D £19. BYO £4. Bar food available   SERVICE: not inc   CARDS: none   DETAILS: 40 seats. 60 seats outside. Private parties: 25 main room. Car park. Children's helpings. Wheelchair access (also WC). No music

---

BROADWAY Hereford & Worcester   map 5

▲ Dormy House ♥ ⅝✷

Willersey Hill, Broadway WR12 7LF
TEL: (01386) 852711   FAX: (01386) 858636   COOKING 2
on A44, 1m NW of Broadway   COST £24–£63

The modernised seventeenth-century farmhouse sits on a wooded escarpment above the touristy village, with big armchairs crowding the lounge, and a reproduction medieval tapestry acting as a backdrop to the dining-room. An awful lot of cooking goes on here. Dinner in particular seems to give the kitchen brigade a mountain to climb, having to serve 22 dishes on the *carte*, plus a table d'hôte, plus a 'gourmet' menu, with very little overlap between them. Why do chefs put themselves through it? one wonders. Cuts of meat, fowl and fish are prime – suprêmes and fillets of everything – in typically smart country-house style, and ideas are inviting: polenta with pigeon, a fig and ginger confit to accompany duck, or a creamy cumin sauce for red mullet.

Lovers of fish and vegetables do well, and a brightness in the seasonings and accompaniments gives the whole show a lift, as in steamed mousseline of scallops and crayfish with a cucumber and lime sauce, or a tart of mushrooms, baby spinach and Jerusalem artichokes on a coriander cream sauce. The dessert department works as hard as any, whipping up a hot chestnut soufflé with nutmeg ice-cream, or fashioning meringue mushrooms and a chilled cinnamon custard to accompany an iced coffee and rum parfait. The well-annotated wine list is generally high quality with a strong line in the French classics and good back-up from the rest of the world. Three Swiss wines help to ring the changes. French house wines are £11.50. CELLARMAN'S CHOICE: Gavi di Gavi 1993, Vigneti Lugarara, Tenuta la Giustiniana, Rovereto di Gavi, £15.40; Chianti Classico Riserva 1990, 'Il Grigio', Da San Felice, £17.95.

CHEFS: Alan Cutler and Colin Seymour   PROPRIETOR: Ingrid Philip-Sorensen   OPEN: Mon to Fri and Sun L 12.30 to 2, all week D 7 to 9.30 (9 Sun)   CLOSED: 25 and 26 Dec   MEALS: alc (main courses L £8.50 to £12, D £15 to £21). Set L Sun £17, Set D £26.50 to £34. BYO £8. Bar food available   SERVICE: not inc   CARDS: Access, Amex, Delta, Diners, Switch, Visa   DETAILS: 80 seats. Private parties: 40 main room, 8 and 14 private rooms. Car park. Vegetarian meals. Children's helpings. Smart dress preferred. No smoking in 1 dining-room. Music ACCOMMODATION: 49 rooms, all with bath/shower. TV. Phone. B&B £60 to £145. Rooms for disabled. Children welcome. Baby facilities. Dogs welcome in bedrooms only. Afternoon teas. Garden (*The Which? Hotel Guide*)

▲ *Lygon Arms* ▼ ✳

High Street, Broadway WR12 7DU   COOKING 2*
TEL: (01386) 852255   FAX: (01386) 858611   COST £34–£66

This sixteenth-century coaching-inn is Broadway's most celebrated building. As a country outpost of the Savoy it naturally goes in for a degree of luxury in the appointments and a certain amount of pampering in the service, as well as vigorously embracing the health spa idea. You don't eat in a mere dining-room but in the Great Hall, with its barrel-vaulted ceiling, heraldic frieze and minstrels' gallery. At its simplest there might be smoked salmon, and char-grilled fillet steak, but Roger Narbett's menus also have a lively and appealingly inventive streak.

A meal might begin with a pressed terrine of mustard-spiced ham hocks served with rocket and a parsley pesto, or a charlotte of goats' cheese and red onion served with marinated grilled vegetables and toasted brioche. This is British cooking in its broadest sense, taking in a pithiviers of smoked Cotswold game with peas and roasted tomatoes, or serving porcini and crab ravioli beside a salmon fillet. 'Slick, very sophisticated and very clever' was one view of the style. Desserts might vary from a traditional jam roly-poly to pineapple parfait with kadaifi.

The consistently high-quality wine list spans the globe, taking in Lebanon, Argentina, Madeira and England. It makes a welcome point of highlighting organics. French house wines are £12. CELLARMAN'S CHOICE: Barrel-fermented Chardonnay 1993, Rothbury Estate, Hunter Valley, Australia, £25; Late-harvest Orange Muscat & Flora 1994, Brown Brothers, Victoria, Australia, £14.75 a half-bottle.

CHEF: Roger Narbett PROPRIETOR: Savoy Group plc OPEN: all week 12.30 to 2, 7.30 to 9.15 (9.30 Sat) MEALS: alc (main courses £15.50 to £20.50). Set L £21.75, Set D £33.75. BYO £10 (champagne £15). Bar food available SERVICE: not inc, card slips closed CARDS: Access, Amex, Diners, Visa DETAILS: 120 seats. 10 seats outside. Private parties: 95 main room, 12 to 95 private rooms. Car park. Vegetarian meals. Children welcome. No children under 5 D. Smart dress preferred. No smoking in dining-room. Wheelchair access (also WC). Music ACCOMMODATION: 65 rooms, all with bath/shower. TV. Phone. B&B £95 to £195. Rooms for disabled. Children welcome. Baby facilities. Dogs welcome. Afternoon teas. Garden. Swimming-pool (*The Which? Hotel Guide*)

BROCKENHURST Hampshire   map 2

Le Poussin ❦ ✻

The Courtyard, Brookley Road,
Brockenhurst SO42 7RB   COOKING 4
TEL/FAX: (01590) 623063   COST £28–£46

On 2 January 1996 a fire destroyed the kitchen, but the Aitkens were back in business within a couple of months, a tribute to their grit and determination. The experience did nothing to diminish their enthusiasm which, if anything, is even greater than before. An inspector dining in May felt that the cooking was 'at an all-time high at the moment' although, curiously, another reporter felt the reverse. The dining-room was not damaged by fire, though blackened by smoke, and now sports a new livery of dark-green upholstery and a plum-coloured carpet. Out in the courtyard sit one or two tables for summertime eating, or for desperate smokers: the restaurant is defiantly non-smoking.

Alex Aitken cooks with minimal assistance, and even though dinner might offer only a choice of two items at each stage (with cheese as an alternative to dessert), there is freedom to opt for two, three or four courses. The lack of elaborate presentation, the concentration on local foods, and the brevity of the menu are all 'exactly what restaurants should aim for', in our inspector's view. Alex Aitken's dishes have always provided exciting contrasts and sensations: the rich soft creaminess of foie gras, mousses and purées set beside the crisp, sharp clarity of salad leaves, dressings, fruits and vegetables, or the sequence of poached foods followed by grills. But now there is 'an added dash and brilliance'.

Richness is typified by salmon cooked in duck confit juices, served on a bed of chopped ratatouille vegetables, and at its best the food can be as seductive as grilled woodpigeon, the breast, grilled rare, laid on 'the softest, creamiest, most mushroomy risotto' containing morels, Jew's ear and oyster mushrooms, the whole topped with a slice of foie gras. First-rate and often local ingredients are enhanced by popular flavours of the day, as in a rich hunk of rare griddled tuna with a sweet-and-sour sauce of soy and ginger. Stalwarts such as a trio of meats owes its success to lamb, beef and pork that are 'perfect examples of their kind'.

Meals might end with the indulgence of chocolate – white and dark on contrasting sauces – or with a refreshing combination of fresh fruits and distinctively flavoured sorbets. The only cloud on the horizon appears to be service, described variously as 'frosty' and 'sour', but then again as 'not obtrusive, and well paced'. A sensible wine list emphasises quality and includes many fine producers. Mature vintages abound, and a dozen wines are available by the glass. Australian house wine is £12.50. CELLARMAN'S CHOICE: St-Véran 1994, J.-M. Drouin, £17.50; Cabernet Sauvignon 1985, Bodegas Weinert, Argentina, £18.

CHEF: Alex Aitken and Angus Hyne   PROPRIETORS: Alex and Caroline Aitken   OPEN: Wed to Sun L 12 to 2, Tue to Sat D 7 to 10   MEALS: Set L Wed to Sat £12.50 (2 courses) to £17.50, Set L Sun £15 (2 courses) to £20, Set D £22.50 (2 courses) to £27.50. BYO £10   SERVICE: not inc   CARDS: Access, Switch, Visa   DETAILS: 24 seats. 10 seats outside. Private parties: 24 main room. Car park. Vegetarian meals. Children welcome. Smart dress preferred. No smoking in dining-room. Wheelchair access (also WC). No music

---

BROMSGROVE Hereford & Worcester   map 5

▲ *Grafton Manor* ⁞✴

Grafton Lane, Bromsgrove B61 7HA
TEL: (01527) 579007   FAX: (01527) 575221   COOKING 2
off B4091, 1½m SW of Bromsgrove   COST £29–£52

Conference facilities and easy access to the M5 take nothing away from the appeal of this largely eighteenth-century red-brick manor-house. It boasts a private fifteenth-century chapel, and a herb and vegetable garden round the back, while ornate plasterwork, a coat of arms and a grand piano add up to a very stylish interior. Links with India are strong – Simon Morris spends a few weeks there each year – although the Indian influence does not dominate the menu. A parsnip and roasted cumin soup served with mint raita illustrates the degree to which the two cuisines are intertwined. There are still plenty of European flourishes, from gravlax to duck confit.

That strand of British cooking that combines the savoury and the fruity appears in 'beautifully balanced' pear, pea and tarragon soup, and in pheasant with medlar jelly. Accurate timing and punchy flavours are characteristics of the cooking, as in pink fillet of beef with a honey-infused sauce. Unusual 'regional puddings' might include Worcestershire pear pudding; an accompanying shot of the house pear liqueur is considered £2 well spent. The maître d' was considered 'intrusive' by one reporter, but service is otherwise pleasant and polite. Wines are thought to be too highly priced for the modest quality. House French is £10.95

'I thought it indelicate that, when I presented my credit card, the waitress asked as she took it for processing, "Would you like me to add any service to that?"'
(On eating in London)

CHEF: Simon Morris   PROPRIETORS: the Morris family   OPEN: Sun to Fri L 12.30 to 1.30, Mon to Sat D 7 to 9   MEALS: Set L £18.50 to £20.50, Set D £24.95 to £31.50   SERVICE: not inc, card slips closed   CARDS: Access, Amex, Diners, Switch, Visa   DETAILS: 80 seats. Private parties: 60 main room, 60 private room. Car park. Vegetarian meals. Children's helpings. Smart dress preferred. No smoking in dining-room. No music   ACCOMMODATION: 9 rooms, all with bath/shower. TV. Phone. B&B £85 to £150. Children welcome. Garden. Fishing (*The Which? Hotel Guide*)

BROXTED Essex   map 3

▲ *Whitehall Hotel*

Church End, Broxted CM6 2BZ
TEL: (01279) 850603   FAX: (01279) 850385   COOKING 2*
off B1051, 3m SW of Thaxted   COST £28–£61

A luxuriously appointed Elizabethan manor may be precisely where you want to be whisked to if you have just jetted in to Stansted, and here is one ready and waiting. Hugely professional service will help smooth away the jet-lag, while the muted tones of the dining-room, all pink and beige and cream, provide an elegant backdrop for Stuart Townsend's accomplished country-house cooking.

Menus are formatted every which way, from simple fixed-price to à la carte, via the chef's six-course menu surprise. Gravlax and beef carpaccio are perhaps expected starters, a robust soup of lamb shank and celery less so. A couple impressed by a winter lunch found the tone grandly set by a smoked haddock soufflé that rose from its bowl like an airy cauliflower. Thai chicken breast was 'a little more curried than expected, but none the less enjoyed'. They finished with banoffi pie in a brittle pastry case with toffee custard and a 'magnificent selection of mainly French cheeses in ace condition'. The wine list contains some good growers within its concise regional sections. Six house wines start at £12.

CHEF: Stuart Townsend   PROPRIETORS: Sisyrinchium Ltd   OPEN: all week (exc Sat L) 12.30 to 2, 7.30 to 9.30   CLOSED: 27 to 30 Dec   MEALS: alc (main courses £10 to £18.50). Set L £13.50 (2 courses) to £16.50, Set D £13.50 (2 courses) to £37.50   SERVICE: not inc   CARDS: Access, Amex, Delta, Diners, Switch, Visa   DETAILS: 60 seats. Private parties: 120 main room, 16 private room. Car park. Vegetarian meals. Children's helpings. Smart dress preferred. No cigars/pipes in dining-room. Wheelchair access (also WC). No music   ACCOMMODATION: 25 rooms, all with bath/shower. TV. Phone. B&B £80 to £140. Rooms for disabled. Children welcome. Baby facilities. Afternoon teas. Garden. Swimming-pool (*The Which? Hotel Guide*)

BRUTON Somerset   map 2

Truffles

95 High Street, Bruton BA10 0AR   COOKING 2
TEL: (01749) 812255   COST £22–£38

During 1996 Martin and Denise Bottrill celebrated ten years at their converted weavers' cottage, and they continue to love the business. Martin works to an eclectic fixed-price menu that changes each month, as seasonal produce and new ideas come to the fore. France and Italy are the cornerstones, although the kitchen can also come up with spicy Goan-style mussels or filo parcels of smoked chicken and avocado with gazpacho sauce. Somerset game might appear in the shape of stuffed pheasant with wild mushroom sauce. One summer dinner featured a tartare of salmon with marinated scallops and lime vinaigrette, lambs' sweetbreads cooked with mint and peas topped with puff pastry, and a cappuccino mousse served in a chocolate cup with lemon sauce. Midweek visitors can also take advantage of the excellent-value supper menu – although booking is essential. Denise Bottrill's presence out front is always appreciated. The reliable wine list leapfrogs between France and the New World, picking up a bottle or two from Spain and Lebanon on the way. House wine is £9.50.

CHEF: Martin Bottrill   PROPRIETORS: Denise and Martin Bottrill   OPEN: Sun L 12 to 2, Tue to Sat D 7 to 9.30 (Tue to Sat L by arrangement)   MEALS: Set L £13.50, Set D Tue to Thur £12.95, Set D Fri and Sat £21.95. BYO £5   SERVICE: not inc, card slips closed   CARDS: Access, Delta, Visa DETAILS: 20 seats. Private parties: 22 main room. Vegetarian meals. Children welcome. No children under 6. Smart dress preferred. Wheelchair access (no WC). No music

BUCKLAND Gloucestershire

map 2

▲ Buckland Manor ▮ ⁵⁂

Buckland WR12 7LY
TEL: (01386) 852626   FAX: (01386) 853557
off B4632, 2m SW of Broadway

COOKING 2
COST £32–£71

A golden Cotswold stone manor house dating from the thirteenth century, with its own gateway to the equally venerable church of St Michael's alongside, Buckland is well versed in putting on a show for its seriously moneyed international clientele. That translates in the dining-room into long menu descriptions, whisking of silver domes and much lavish cosseting, so that even a slice of brioche accompanying 'very rich' duck terrine arrives swaddled in crispest linen. One reporter's panaché of fish and shellfish was well presented on a correct beurre blanc with good seasonal vegetables, while another praised 'first-class' salmon escalope in a claret sauce, and Aberdeen Angus tournedos crusted with horseradish and mustard. Quantities are such that dessert may seem a formidable challenge. For those with the stamina, mango mousse with a strawberry coulis and a garnish of fresh fruits was found suitably delicate. Tiny cups of coffee come with showers of petits fours.

The weighty tome of a wine list contains hundreds of wines, each one with a lengthy tasting note. Everything is in perfect order: the French section is commendably detailed, Australia is top-rate, Germany gets the attention it deserves and prices are fair. French house wines are £11.50. CELLARMAN'S CHOICE: Henschke Sauvignon/Semillon 1994, Eden Valley, S. Australia, £19.30; Jackson Estate Pinot Noir 1994, Marlborough, New Zealand, £24.70.

CHEFS: Martyn J. Pearn and Martin R. White   PROPRIETORS: Roy and Daphne Vaughan   OPEN: all week 12.30 to 1.45, 7.30 to 9   MEALS: alc (main courses £19 to £23.50). Set Sun L £23.50. Set Mon to Sat L £27.50   SERVICE: not inc   CARDS: Access, Amex, Diners, Visa   DETAILS: 40 seats. 10 seats outside. Private parties: 40 main room. Car park. No children under 12. Jacket and tie. No smoking in dining-room. Wheelchair access (no WC). No music   ACCOMMODATION: 13 rooms, all with bath/shower. TV. Phone. B&B £165 to £325. No children under 12. Afternoon teas. Garden. Swimming-pool (The Which? Hotel Guide)

BUCKLAND Oxfordshire

map 2

▲ *Lamb Inn* ▼ ✳ £

Lamb Lane, Buckland SN7 8QN
TEL: (01367) 870484 FAX: (01367) 810475

COOKING 1
COST £18–£43

Since moving in, the Barnards have turned this eighteenth-century village watering-hole into a high-class eating establishment. Menus are chalked on boards, the line-up changes each session and customers are welcome to eat in the bar or the restaurant. The kitchen deals mainly in Anglo-French dishes with a few detours further afield for such things as chicken and coconut curry. On a typical day, you might find boiled beef and carrots, braised oxtail, and salmon fish-cakes alongside cassoulet, and baked sea bass with Pernod. A superb version of *Hasenpfeffer* (jugged hare) was reckoned by one correspondent to be 'better than my club in London that fancies itself in this dish'. Seasonal puddings range from winter fruit compote to strawberry brûlée. The 70-strong wine list is approachable and user-friendly, with a generous 16 available by the glass. Most styles and classic grape varieties get a look-in and there's an appealing set of five house wines, including two from Penfolds, at £8.95 a bottle or £1.65 a glass.

CHEF: Paul Barnard PROPRIETORS: Peta and Paul Barnard OPEN: all week 12 to 2, 6.30 to 9.30 MEALS: alc (main courses £5 to £15). Set L Sun £15.95 SERVICE: not inc, card slips closed CARDS: Access, Delta, Switch, Visa DETAILS: 65 seats. 45 seats outside. Private parties: 70 main room, 18 private room. Car park. Vegetarian meals. Children's helpings. No smoking in dining-room. Music ACCOMMODATION: 4 rooms, all with bath/shower. TV. Phone. B&B £35 to £45. Deposit: £10. Children welcome. Baby facilities. Afternoon teas. Garden

---

BURNHAM MARKET Norfolk

map 6

Fishes'

Market Place, Burnham Market PE31 8HE
TEL: (01328) 738588

COOKING 1*
COST £19–£45

After more than 23 years serving unfussy local seafood to legions of North Norfolk residents and holidaymakers, Fishes' has become something of an institution. In high season you need to book or queue for a table in the cottagey dining-room; during the relatively quiet winter months you can lounge on a settee by the fire and read a book while waiting to be served. The mood is generally one of happy, informal enjoyment. Reports continue to praise the freshness of fish, whether it be poached salmon in cucumber sauce, skate with capers, or whole Dover sole. Other fixtures such as potted shrimps, garlic mussels, and salmon fish-cakes with rich crab sauce are also mentioned in dispatches. Meat-eaters can enjoy home-baked ham with smoked chicken, while desserts are straightforward offerings such as cheesecake with apricots. The short wine list does its job affordably. House wine is £8.50.

'There was a cheese tray full of British cheeses, but I was somewhat puzzled by the response to my question "Do you have a local cheese?" to be informed, "Yes, there is, but whenever we put it on the dish, everyone asks for it and the other cheeses don't get eaten".'
(On eating in Northumberland)

CHEFS: Gillian Cape and Paula Ayres   PROPRIETOR: Gillian Cape   OPEN: Tue to Sun L 12 to 2,
Tue to Sat D 6.45 to 9.30 (9 Tue to Thur in winter)   CLOSED: 3 days Christmas, last 3 weeks Jan
MEALS: alc (main courses £6 to £14). Set L Tue to Fri £9.40 (2 courses) to £11.95, Set L Sat
£10.95 (2 courses) to £12.95   SERVICE: not inc, card slips closed   CARDS: Access, Amex,
Delta, Diners, Switch, Visa   DETAILS: 42 seats. Private parties: 14 main room. Children's
helpings. No children under 5 after 8.30. Wheelchair access (no WC). No music

---

BURY ST EDMUNDS Suffolk   map 6

Mortimer's ▼ ⁵⨉ £

31 Churchgate Street, Bury St Edmunds IP33 1RG   COOKING 1*
TEL: (01284) 760623   FAX: (01284) 761611   COST £19–£42

Churchgate Street leads up to the Norman gate of the abbey, so aim for that if
Bury's topography confuses. Nearby stands Mortimer's, a well-established and
hugely popular fish restaurant that has a younger cousin in Ipswich (see entry).
In agreeably unpretentious surroundings, with oilclothed tables and counter
seating for lunchers who don't want to linger, some impeccably fresh seafood is
served. The lengthy menus take in all the expected classics as well as one or two
more daring turns, such as tiger prawn satay. Potted shrimps come 'tender,
sweet, perfectly seasoned', while skate with black butter and capers is the real
thing – 'absolutely fresh, meaty and delicious'.

Sorbets to finish are intensely flavoured and given interest by 'pleasing
morsels of fruit', while rum-laced chocolate pots win accolades every time.
Service is 'rapid without being rushed'. The broad-minded wine list roams
beyond Muscadet and Chablis, offering inspired selections of mainly white
wines from all over, carefully chosen to match seafood and fish dishes. Barton &
Guestier house wines are £7.65. CELLARMAN'S CHOICE: Alsace Pinot Blanc
1993, Willm, £11.75; Wolf Blass Chardonnay 1994, Barossa Valley, S. Australia,
£13.75.

CHEFS: Kenneth Ambler and Justin Adams-Newton   PROPRIETORS: Kenneth Ambler and
Michael Gooding   OPEN: Mon to Fri L 12 to 2, Mon to Sat D 6.30 to 9 (8.15 Mon)   CLOSED: 24
Dec to 5 Jan, 2 weeks Aug, bank hol Mons and Tues   MEALS: alc (main courses £7.50 to £17)
SERVICE: not inc   CARDS: Access, Amex, Delta, Diners, Switch, Visa   DETAILS: 76 seats. Private
parties: 16 main room, 16 private room. Children's helpings. Smart dress preferred. No smoking
in 1 dining-room. Wheelchair access (no WC). No music

CALSTOCK Cornwall   map 1

▲ Danescombe Valley ▼ ⁵⨉

Lower Kelly, Calstock PL18 9RY
TEL: (01822) 832414   FAX: (01822) 832446
1m W of Calstock on riverside road   COOKING 2*
                                                               COST £35–£42

The hotel is a white villa occupying one of the more striking settings in the
south-west. It perches on the side of a wooded valley, with the River Tamar
running past the door. The verandahs lend a faintly colonial feel, and the
welcome extended by the Smiths is such that, in the words of one reporter, 'from
the moment we walked in we knew we were going to like it'. Anna Smith cooks

a no-choice four-course dinner menu for a maximum of a dozen people. Her Italian background is worn lightly and thrown into productive relief by the best that Cornwall has to offer.

Rosemary, pine-nuts and Parmesan gave a subtle 'aromatic lift' to a 'wonderful' local goats' cheese one night, and this was followed by duck breast roasted with soy sauce and honey, the crisp-skinned meat brilliantly supported by its simple but piquant sauce. Other main dishes have included Tamar salmon baked en papillote with bacon and rosemary, and herb-crusted lamb fillet. A selection of unpasteurised West Country cheeses, naturally including Cheddar, precedes desserts of chocolate and pear tart with honey ice-cream, or a cake of polenta, almonds and lemon. This is a highly successful formula established over a decade now; 'my first choice for a weekend away', in the words of an experienced reporter. As for wine, 'We would like you to be able to experiment with some unfamiliar wines without fear of breaking the bank,' says Martin Smith, and the highly original wine list bears out this philosophy. The most exciting bottles are Italian, grouped by grape variety; try Marzemino or Aglianico for a change, or stick to classic Nebbiolo, Chardonnay and Sangiovese. The tasting notes are helpful, and the prices are indeed fair. Wines are served by the glass 'according to whim on the evening'.

CHEF: Anna Smith   PROPRIETORS: Martin and Anna Smith   OPEN: Sat to Wed D only 7.30 for 8 (1 sitting)   CLOSED: Nov to Mar   MEALS: Set D £30   SERVICE: net prices, card slips closed CARDS: Access, Amex, Delta, Diners, Switch, Visa   DETAILS: 12 seats. Private parties: 12 main room. Car park. No children under 12. No smoking in dining-room. No music ACCOMMODATION: 5 rooms, all with bath/shower. B&B £72.50 to £125. Deposit: £50. No children under 12. Garden (The Which? Hotel Guide)

CAMBRIDGE   Cambridgeshire map 6

Twenty Two ▾

22 Chesterton Road, Cambridge CB4 3AX COOKING 2
TEL: (01223) 351880   FAX: (01223) 323814 COST £31–£37

Since 1992 David Carter and Louise Crompton have created a highly personable neighbourhood restaurant in their candlelit Victorian dining-room a few minutes' walk from the centre of Cambridge. The fixed-price dinner menu changes monthly and offers four courses, with an extra fish course and cheese both charged as supplements. Everyone agrees that presentation is Ian Reinhardt's forte, although there is a feeling that this is sometimes at the expense of flavour. Modernity rules. You might begin with warm salad of lambs' kidneys, or lemon-scented chicken with sesame and black-bean sauce before moving on to fish (perhaps stuffed squid with black-ink risotto, or Thai-style steamed mussels). After this comes an interlude in the form of a mixed leaf salad. Main courses range from roast rabbit with bubble and squeak, or braised hock of lamb with lima beans, to paupiette of aubergine with caper and bean salsa. Desserts move into the realms of warm mincemeat tart with rum and sultana ice-cream, or chocolate parfait with mint anglaise. Service is attentive, although one correspondent felt that it was slightly 'patronising'.

The wine list is wide-ranging without being over-lengthy, and there are bottles from Lebanon, Hungary and South Africa alongside French classics.

Prices are more than fair, and house wines start at £8.50. CELLARMAN'S CHOICE: Beringer Fumé Blanc 1993, Napa Valley, California, £14.50; Crozes-Hermitage 1992, Cuvée Louis Belle, Albert Belle, £19.95.

CHEF: Ian Reinhardt PROPRIETORS: David Carter and Louise Crompton OPEN: Tue to Sat D only 7 to 9.45 CLOSED: 1 week Christmas MEALS: Set D £22.50 SERVICE: not inc CARDS: Access, Amex, Delta, Switch, Visa DETAILS: 30 seats. Private parties: 34 main room, 12 private room. Vegetarian meals. No children under 11. Smart dress preferred. No smoking while others eat. Music. Air-conditioned

---

CAMPSEA ASHE Suffolk   map 6

▲ Old Rectory 🍷 ⁵⁕

Campsea Ashe IP13 0PU
TEL/FAX: (01728) 746524   COOKING 1
on B1078, 1m E of A12   COST £26–£31

Stewart Bassett's converted rectory looks every inch the part and, 'as if to continue the religious theme, guests seem to have the habit of whispering whenever they converse'. Meals are taken in two dining-rooms that exude 'upper-class olde English gentility'. Bassett now cooks a no-choice, three-course dinner (preferences can be discussed when booking), and the menu leaves plenty to the imagination: grilled grey mullet with herbs, chicken roasted in 'a special sauce', sherry and lemon trifle, for example. Results can be 'patchy', but reporters have been happy with monkfish, prawn and scallops in white wine and cream sauce, and tender stuffed leg of lamb in puff pastry ('stuffed with what I'm not precisely sure'). Vegetables draw little enthusiasm, although desserts such as walnut cake soaked in cinnamon syrup seem to fare better. Wines are wide-ranging and reasonably priced. Highlights are Faller from Alsace, and Jaboulet, Chave and Ch. de Beaucastel from the Rhône, eight vintages of Ch. Musar and a recently expanded list of lovely old clarets. House French is £9.50.

CHEF/PROPRIETOR: Stewart Bassett OPEN: Mon to Sat D only 7.30 to 8.45 CLOSED: Christmas MEALS: Set D £17.50 SERVICE: not inc CARDS: Access, Amex, Diners, Visa DETAILS: 40 seats. Private parties: 36 main room, 12 and 18 private rooms. Car park. Children's helpings. Smart dress preferred. No smoking in dining-room. Music ACCOMMODATION: 9 rooms, all with bath/shower. B&B £35 to £60. Deposit: £15. Children welcome. Dogs welcome. Garden (The Which? Hotel Guide)

CANTERBURY Kent   map 3

▲ County Hotel, Sully's 🍴

High Street, Canterbury CT1 2RX   COOKING 2*
TEL: (01227) 766266   FAX: (01227) 451512   COST £23–£51

Sully's is the restaurant of the County Hotel, a hostelry appreciated by Kentish denizens and others since the sixteenth century. The interiors present a mixed set of messages, from the beamed ceiling of the reception area to the spotlit restaurant, with its wall of exposed brick and the sort of carpet pattern politely referred to as 'busy'. In the autumn of 1995 Ian Hunt was lured from the Savoy (see entry, London) to take over the kitchens, and straight away the cooking acquired a new confidence. The fixed-price menus are built around a generous choice of main courses, with starters and desserts occupying a narrower compass.

A salad of lobster, smoked chicken and quail's eggs might have 'sounded a bit much', but was cleverly balanced in the event, and came with a 'delicately pungent dressing'. Goujons of halibut served in a scooped-out brioche surrounded by pesto 'conjured up warm sunny holidays' for one reporter, while meat dishes tend to the classical, as in lamb noisettes with redcurrants and rosemary, or guinea-fowl with roasted garlic and red wine sauce. You might enjoy a 'moelleux of chocolate ganaja' for pudding if you knew what it was, and toffee parfait with spiced raspberry coulis, with a beguiling waft of cardamom, has a 'delicious intensity' all its own. The principally French wine list isn't overloaded with imagination, but there are some decent Italians and a good spread of halves. House French is £10.50.

CHEF: Ian Hunt   PROPRIETOR: Laughing Water Hotels Ltd   OPEN: all week 12.30 to 2.30, 7 to 10   MEALS: Set L £13.50 (2 courses) to £16, Set D £17 (2 courses) to £25.50   SERVICE: not inc   CARDS: Access, Amex, Diners, Visa   DETAILS: 50 seats. Private parties: 18 main room, 30 to 130 private rooms. Car park. Vegetarian meals. Children's helpings. Smart dress preferred. No pipes in dining-room. Wheelchair access (also women's WC). No music. Air-conditioned   ACCOMMODATION: 73 rooms, all with bath/shower. TV. Phone. Room only £65 to £83. Deposit: 1 night's stay. Rooms for disabled. Children welcome. Baby facilities. Afternoon teas

---

CARLTON North Yorkshire   map 9

▲ Foresters Arms 🕸✷ £

Carlton, nr Leyburn DL8 4BB
TEL/FAX: (01969) 640272   COOKING 1
off A684, 5m SW of Leyburn   COST £19–£49

High on a hill overlooking some gorgeous Dales countryside, this revamped seventeenth-century inn is everything you might expect from a country pub on the up. The beer is 'excellent', the welcome 'impressive' and the food in the restaurant full of surprises. Portions are geared to those with healthy outdoor appetites, the menu is dauntingly long and ingredients jostle for the limelight: Toulouse sausage appears in a salad with smoked duck breast and in an unlikely pairing with sauté king prawns and garlic pasta. Wild boar's liver makes an unexpected but seasonal appearance. Elsewhere, salad of grilled goats' cheese with sun-dried tomatoes, leg of lamb with cassoulet, sea bass with saffron noodles, and bitter chocolate terrine have been applauded. The wine list meanders through France and beyond in search of value; best options are the 18 house selections, which start at £8.95.

CHEF/PROPRIETOR: B.K. Higginbotham   OPEN: Tue to Sun (exc Sun D) 12 to 2, 7 to 9.30   MEALS: alc (main courses £6.50 to £14). Bar meals available   SERVICE: not inc, card slips closed   CARDS: Access, Delta, Visa   DETAILS: 60 seats. 30 seats outside. Private parties: 30 main room. Car park. Vegetarian meals. Children's helpings. Smart dress preferred. No smoking in 1 dining-room. Wheelchair access (no WC). Music   ACCOMMODATION: 3 rooms, all with bath/shower. TV. Phone. B&B £30 to £55. Deposit: £20. Children welcome. Baby facilities by arrangement. Dogs welcome in 1 room only (*The Which? Hotel Guide*)

CARTERWAY HEADS Northumberland   map 10

▲ *Manor House Inn* 🍴✷ £

Carterway Heads, Shotley Bridge DH8 9LX
TEL: (01207) 255268   COOKING 1
on A68, 3m W of Consett   COST £14–£29

Set in the wilds of Northumberland, this stone-built pub appeals for its warm
welcome, prompt service, simple food and good value. A new restaurant
extension is planned to take advantage of the views over Derwent reservoir.
'Food and presentation are closer to the homespun than the sophisticated,'
reckoned one reporter, recognising the unfussy style of a blackboard menu, and
a range of dishes that takes in plain but wholesome soups, stuffed pancakes,
game casserole, Cumberland sausage, and steak sandwich. Quite a few can be
ordered as a first or main course, adding to the flexibility, and the kitchen makes
use of good ingredients, including local salmon, game and cheeses. Simplest
dishes work best. A gooseberry version of Eve's pudding, or lemon cheesecake
may bring up the rear, while the minuscule list of twelve wines manages to
explore six countries.

CHEFS: Jane Pelly, Elizabeth Fielding, Peter Tiplady and Kevin Deakin PROPRIETORS: Anthony
and Jane Pelly, and Elizabeth Fielding OPEN: all week 12 to 2.30, 7 to 9.30 (9 Sun) CLOSED: 25
Dec MEALS: alc (main courses £4 to £10.50). BYO £3 SERVICE: not inc, card slips closed
CARDS: Access, Amex, Delta, Switch, Visa DETAILS: 100 seats. 25 seats outside. Private
parties: 60 main room. Car park. Vegetarian meals. Children's helpings. No smoking in
dining-room. Wheelchair access (also WC). No music ACCOMMODATION: 4 rooms. TV. B&B
£22 to £38.50. Children welcome. Baby facilities. Garden

CARTMEL Cumbria   map 8

▲ *Aynsome Manor* 🍴✷ | NEW ENTRY |

Cartmel LA11 6HH
TEL: (01539) 536653 FAX: (01539) 536016   COOKING 1
off A590, ½m N of village   COST £16–£33

The tranquil sixteenth-century manor-house, with views across to Cartmel
Priory, boasts a spiral staircase, long-case clock, painted wood panelling, and a
moulded plaster ceiling in the Victorian dining-room. The style is comfortable
and restrained, and the traditional Lakeland approach has been adapted slightly,
with a choice of either three or four courses at dinner as well as the customary
five. 'This appears to be working well,' write the Varleys.

Victor Sharratt's cooking is soundly based on fresh local produce, including
game from nearby Holker estate, Morecambe Bay shrimps, locally smoked
bacon and locally grown vegetables. Some ideas work surprisingly well, as with
a first course of savoury banana fritters with creamed Stilton and curried
mayonnaise, and there is a lightness of touch in sauces and in, for example, a
poached timbale of pork mousseline. Vegetables and desserts are variable, but
bread is good. The varied wine list majors on recent vintages at fair prices.

CHEF: Victor Sharratt   PROPRIETORS: Anthony and Margaret Varley   OPEN: Sun L 1 (1 sitting),
Mon to Sat D 7 to 8.30 (residents only Sun D)   CLOSED: 2 to 26 Jan   MEALS: Set L £11, Set D
£15.50 to £19.50   SERVICE: not inc, card slips closed   CARDS: Access, Amex, Delta, Switch,
Visa   DETAILS: 28 seats. Private parties: 28 main room. Car park. Children's helpings. No
children under 5 D. Jacket and tie. No smoking in dining-room. No music   ACCOMMODATION: 12
rooms, all with bath/shower. TV. Phone. D,B&B £52 to £104. Children welcome. Baby facilities.
Dogs welcome in bedrooms only. Afternoon teas. Garden (*The Which? Hotel Guide*)

▲ *Uplands* ⁵✳

Haggs Lane, Cartmel LA11 6HD
TEL: (01539) 536248   FAX: (01539) 536848
2½m SW of A590, 1m up road opposite Pig and   COOKING 3
Whistle   COST £21–£41

After 25 years in the business, half of them at this Victorian house, Tom and
Diana Peter elected to sell up. 'However, after about four weeks we decided we
didn't really want to leave, as we really couldn't think of anything we would
rather do, or anywhere we would rather live, and would also miss our regular
customers, some of whom we have known since our days at Miller Howe. So we
are staying put.' There are many who will be grateful. 'Of all the restaurants we
go to, this is the only one where we have never found anything to disappoint us,'
volunteered an off-duty inspector, though a few dissenting voices have been
raised, perhaps by reporters in search of the excitement of a more cosmopolitan
style. This is gentle country cooking that eschews flamboyance, and one couple
who have been visiting regularly for eight years remain 'amazed' at the
reliability and value.

'Excellent-value' lunch is three courses, dinner four, and in Lakeland style
everybody sits down at the same time. Soup is invariably praised, perhaps rich
tomato and basil served with a hot crusty loaf, and the tureen is left on the table
for second helpings. Breast of woodpigeon and saddle of hare introduce a
welcome gamey note, and supporters find that tastes are distinguishable and
textures varied. Poached salmon has impressed for being moist, firm and
accompanied by a simple but effective chive and vermouth sauce. Successful
puddings have included four large fresh figs laced with Pernod and served with
crème fraîche, and a warm banana, walnut and ginger pie served with
butterscotch sauce. Forty-odd wines from around the world offer commendably
good value.

CHEF: Tom Peter   PROPRIETORS: Tom and Diana Peter, and John Tovey   OPEN: Thur to Sun L
12.30 for 1 (1 sitting), Tue to Sun D 7.30 for 8 (1 sitting)   CLOSED: 1 Jan to 1 Mar   MEALS: Set L
£14.50, Set D £26   SERVICE: not inc, card slips closed   CARDS: Access, Amex, Delta, Visa
DETAILS: 28 seats. Private parties: 12 main room. Car park. No children under 8. Smart dress
preferred. No smoking in dining-room. No music   ACCOMMODATION: 5 rooms, all with
bath/shower. TV. D,B&B £68 to £136. No children under 8. Dogs welcome. Garden (*The Which?
Hotel Guide*)

*'When I ordered teal I was thinking of a juicy little duck, and what I got was more of a dry
gamey sparrow with sunburn.'* (On eating in London)

CASTLE CARY Somerset   map 2

▲ Bond's

Ansford, Castle Cary BA7 7JP
TEL/FAX: (01963) 350464   COOKING 1
on A371, 400yds past station towards Wincanton   COST £20–£34

'Meticulous' and 'caring' are the words that best describe Kevin and Yvonne
Bond's attitude to hotel-keeping. Their establishment – once a stop for coaching
travellers – is run like a private house: everything is on a domestic scale. Dinner
is built around two set menus: a monthly affair and a no-choice daily selection.
Smoked salmon, watercress and pear salad with lime and honey dressing works
because it is fresh and uncomplicated. However, an intriguing crust of coriander
leaf and crushed walnuts did little to redeem one senior reporter's 'bone-dry'
roast rabbit. The repertoire also extends to Cornish crab soufflé, venison
carpaccio, and stuffed breast of chicken served on noodles with tarragon and
orange sauce. Vegetables can be over-embellished, desserts likewise, although
Yvonne Bond makes 'really good tasty custard'. Light one-course lunches are
served in the hotel lounge. The wine list is short, well spread and affordable.
House wines start at around £8.50.

CHEF: Yvonne Bond   PROPRIETORS: Kevin and Yvonne Bond   OPEN: all week D only 7 (7.30
Sun and Mon) to 9.30   CLOSED: 1 week Christmas   MEALS: Set D £12.50 to £19.75. Light L
available   SERVICE: not inc, card slips closed   CARDS: Access, Visa   DETAILS: 20 seats. 8
seats outside. Private parties: 20 main room. Car park. Vegetarian meals. Children's helpings.
Smart dress preferred. No music   ACCOMMODATION: 7 rooms, all with bath/shower. TV. Phone.
B&B £56 to £96. Deposit: £40. No children under 8. Afternoon teas. Garden (*The Which? Hotel
Guide*)

CASTLE COMBE Wiltshire   map 2

▲ Manor House Hotel ¾✳

Castle Combe SN14 7HR
TEL: (01249) 782206   FAX: (01249) 782159   COOKING 3
on B4039, 3m NW of junction with A420   COST £30–£84

This is England at its prettiest. A trout stream, the Bybrook, after which the
dining-room is named, runs through the grounds of this gabled, mullion-
windowed, fifteenth-century house of honey-coloured Cotswold stone. The
estate is big enough to accommodate an 18-hole golf course. A glass cabinet in
the bar offering Manor House toilet-roll holders for sale hardly detracts from the
more reverential and formal tone set by carved oak panelling, huge stone
fireplace and coats of arms.

Everything is taken very seriously here, including supplies of free-range duck,
diver-caught scallops and unpasteurised ewes'-milk cheeses such as Beenleigh
Blue from Totnes. Prices, too, are serious. Those scallops, paired with a mousse
of Jerusalem artichokes, will set you back 'fifteen pounds', as the leather-bound
menu puts it. 'Do you think writing the prices in words exacerbates or
diminishes the financial pain?' asked one perplexed reporter. In return,
however, Mark Taylor's kitchen turns out some technically very accomplished
work. Timing is spot on, textures are impressive, and he is happy to explore all

manner of flavour combinations. A ballottine of chicken and langoustine is 'scented' with basil and mango ('twelve pounds fifty pence'), although a 'classical section' of the menu offers simpler roast duck with vanilla and orange at 'forty five pounds ninety five pence for two persons'. There is a richness to the food that continues into puddings such as vanilla and pear brûlée encased in dark chocolate, or raspberry fool with dark chocolate sorbet (both 'eight pounds fifty pence'), and appetisers and petits fours add to the effect. The wine list harbours many good bottles, and prices are extremely high, but the 'house selection' helpfully picks out a dozen or more bottles at under £20.

CHEF: Mark Taylor PROPRIETOR: Manor House Hotel (Castle Combe) Ltd OPEN: all week 12 to 2, 7 to 10 MEALS: alc D (main courses £21 to £24.50). Set L £16.95 (2 courses) to £18.95, Set D £35 SERVICE: not inc, card slips closed CARDS: Access, Amex, Diners, Switch, Visa DETAILS: 90 seats. 12 seats outside. Private parties: 90 main room, 10 to 20 private rooms. Car park. Vegetarian meals. Children's helpings. Jacket and tie. No smoking in dining-room. Wheelchair access (also WC). Music ACCOMMODATION: 40 rooms, all with bath/shower. TV. Phone. Room only £100 to £350. Rooms for disabled. Children welcome. Baby facilities. Afternoon teas. Garden. Swimming-pool. Fishing (*The Which? Hotel Guide*)

CHAGFORD Devon   map 1

▲ Gidleigh Park 🍷 ✿

Chagford TQ13 8HH
TEL: (01647) 432367 FAX: (01647) 432574
from Chagford Square turn right at Lloyds Bank into
Mill Street, take right fork after 150 yards, follow lane   COOKING 4*
for 1½m   COST £37–£80

The sight of the solid country house is welcome after the mile-and-a-half drive up a narrow country lane. Smoke drifts idly from tall chimneys, a river gushes past the front, and the smell of wood smoke lingers inside. It is a wonder there is no smell of singed cat hair, since several Siamese curl around the logs. If you want peace and quiet, and can afford it, this is as good a place as any to come. It has a generous sense of space, looks serious but isn't in the least oppressive. In 1997 Paul and Kay Henderson celebrate 20 years here, yet it feels as fresh as ever, kept at the peak of condition by a tireless hands-on proprietor who doesn't overlook a thing. They have worked hard to make it so completely relaxing.

The food fits the setting like a glove. It may not be wildly innovative, but it is produced with consummate skill using tip-top materials. 'A superb and memorable meal' is typical of the plaudits for Michael Caines's cooking, which conveys the feeling that 'everything in the dish is cautiously considered and rehearsed'. Fish is a highlight, and spot-on timing contributes to its success, producing 'firm texture, moist flesh and sea-fresh flavour' in a plate of braised turbot with roast queen scallops and a silky smooth chive butter sauce. Crab has appeared in various guises, from an intensely flavoured creamy bisque, to a thin fondant pasta packed with its flavourful meat. Caines has 'the knack of deploying good ingredients to their ultimate advantage'.

Fowl figures almost as prominently as fish, and particularly outstanding has been plump, moist roast partridge 'slightly pink and full of flavour', served with winter vegetables and a gewurztraminer sauce. A degree of intricacy is apparent, as when courgette flowers are stuffed with scallop mousse, to accompany roast sea bass, or when a dish of lamb incorporates well-trimmed rack, fillet, sauté tongue and sweetbreads. The overall effect of even this, however, is still one of lightness. A string of successful desserts has included 'classic' crème brûlée, a 'splendid French apple tart' made with first-class pastry, excellent ice-creams, and an 'absolutely perfect' soufflé of prune and armagnac, while the chocolate tart is 'as fine a chocolate dessert as you are likely to find'.

The professional front-of-house team is 'super-efficient' yet genuinely friendly, and the wine list is famous for its wide scope and fair prices. As one reporter put it, 'You don't need a second mortgage for a good bottle, and the mark-ups definitely reduce as the price of the wine goes up.' France gets the full treatment, with Alsace running close to Burgundy and Bordeaux for quality and depth. Elsewhere, Italy and California are highlights, particularly the latter, since mature West Coast Cabernet is a speciality. Thanks to a Cruvinet machine, which keeps open bottles fresh for weeks, eight wines are offered by the glass, ranging from £4 to £7.25 for Ch. Belair 1985.

CHEF: Michael Caines PROPRIETORS: Kay and Paul Henderson OPEN: all week 12.30 to 2, 7 to 9 MEALS: Set L Mon to Thurs £17.50 (2 courses) to £52.50, Fri to Sun and bank hols £22.50 (2 courses) to £52.50, Set D £52.50 to £57.50. BYO £10. Light L available SERVICE: net prices, card slips closed CARDS: Access, Amex, Diners, Switch, Visa DETAILS: 35 seats. Private parties: 30 main room. Car park. Children welcome. No children under 5. Smart dress preferred. No smoking in dining-room. Wheelchair access. No music ACCOMMODATION: 14 rooms, all with bath/shower. TV. Phone. D,B&B £200 to £385. Children welcome. Baby facilities. Dogs welcome in bedroom only. Afternoon teas. Garden. Fishing

---

CHEDINGTON Dorset   map 2

▲ Chedington Court ♀

Chedington DT8 3HY
TEL: (01935) 891265   FAX: (01935) 891442   COOKING 1
off A356, 4m SE of Crewkerne   COST £31–£44

The Tudor-style casement windows are in fact early Victorian, but no less imposing for that. A balustraded terrace affords good views of sunsets and the rolling Dorset countryside, and rooms are furnished with antiques and Persian rugs. The food has a sensible feel and stability about it, taking in spinach and blue cheese tart, venison with braised red cabbage, and desserts from a trolley. Dinner is four courses plus coffee (residents have the option of an à la carte menu as well) and the kitchen takes a strong stand against imported veal, frogs' legs and foie gras, commendably preferring humanely reared and local meat: organic pork with prune forcemeat and a brandy cream sauce, for example. Service is so good you hardly notice it.

Wine is a strong suit, and the hefty list is well worth taking time over. Burgundy is especially good, and it is encouraging to see so much going into the German, Australian and Beaujolais sections. Seven house wines start at £7.50. CELLARMAN'S CHOICE: Hunter's Sauvignon Blanc 1994, Marlborough, New Zealand, £19.50; Brouilly Ch. des Tours 1995, £15.50.

CHEFS: Lindsay Wakeman and Hilary Chapman   PROPRIETORS: Hilary and Philip Chapman
OPEN: all week D only 6.45 to 9   CLOSED: Jan after New Year   MEALS: Set D £27.50. BYO
£7.50   SERVICE: none, card slips closed   CARDS: Access, Amex, Visa   DETAILS: 24 seats. 6
seats outside. Private parties: 8 main room, 14 private room. Car park. Vegetarian meals. No
children under 8 D. Smart dress preferred. No cigars/pipes in dining-room. Wheelchair access
(also WC). Music   ACCOMMODATION: 10 rooms, all with bath/shower. TV. Phone. D,B&B £82 to
£190. Deposit: £30. High tea for under-8s. Dogs welcome in bedrooms only, and must not be left
on their own. Afternoon teas. Garden (*The Which? Hotel Guide*)

CHEESDEN   Greater Manchester   map 8

Nutters £✳

Edenfield Road, Cheesden, nr Rochdale OL12 7TY	COOKING 3
TEL: (01706) 50167	COST £25–£48

Nutters (formerly called the French Connection) sits alone amid moorland,
distantly surrounded at night by 'the yellow glows of civilisation on three sides'.
Viewed from afar, it might be a modest farmhouse, until the row of fluttering
flags outside announces it to be anything but. The aim is to be 'a top-flight
restaurant without off-putting hauteur'.

Andrew Nutter is a gifted chef, man and boy (he won his first award at the age
of 13), and his modestly Gallicised versions of creative British cookery have
excited many readers' palates this year. There may seem a touch of hauteur, after
all, when menus refer to 'boudin noir de Bury' and 'herbes de Lancashire', but
people forgive it, and there is in any case a perceptibly French influence at work.
Wild mushrooms are well used, whether in a first-course mille-feuille
(pastry-work is particularly lauded) or as a main-course tagliatelle with garlic
bread. Fillet of brill might come under a 'confetti' of mixed vegetables – 'every
mouthful a delight' – and with a ginger and coriander sauce, 'an unusual variant
of hollandaise'. Powerful aromatic messages can be delivered by herbs, as in
beef fillet with 'a deliciously earthy, savoury taste'. Dessert soufflés, such as a
chocolate and pistachio version, win enthusiastic paeans, as does a classic lemon
tart. The atmosphere is warm and professional, the service 'relaxed and
generally efficient'. The wine list has its moments but is peopled by too few
reliable producers. Pick carefully through the mainly French bottles to find some
more famous names at reasonable prices. House wines start at £9.80.

CHEF: Andrew Nutter   PROPRIETORS: the Nutter family   OPEN: Tue to Sun L 12 to 2 (Sun L menu
to 7), Tue to Sun D 7 (6.30 Sat) to 9.30 (9 Sun)   CLOSED: first 2 weeks Aug, bank hol Mons
MEALS: alc (main courses £9.50 to £16). Set L Sun £19.95. Set D £28.50   SERVICE: not inc
CARDS: Access, Delta, Switch, Visa   DETAILS: 52 seats. Private parties: 56 main room. Car park.
Vegetarian meals. Children's helpings. Smart dress preferred. No smoking in dining-room.
Wheelchair access (also WC). Music

---

*'It took me ten minutes to attract the attention of someone who could bring me a glass of
wine. During this period endless staff breezed past, one even waved back at my ever more
frantic attempts to prove that I had not suddenly stumbled into H. G. Wells's* The
Invisible Man.*'* (On eating in London)

Le Champignon Sauvage ♥

24–26 Suffolk Road, Cheltenham GL50 2AQ
TEL/FAX: (01242) 573449

COOKING 3*
COST £27–£55

David Everitt-Matthias set himself an exalted standard when he opened here ten years ago, as befitted an ex-Tante Claire man (see Tante Claire entry, London). The Champignon has since thrived through the best and worst of times economically, with an impressive consistency. While this is not the most attractive part of otherwise lovely Cheltenham, the conversion of a segment of terrace into an intimate restaurant has been done with style, with paintings, floral arrangements and decorative plates adding colour.

Menus are fixed-price according to the number of courses. The bedrock may be contemporary French, but the cooking works in the same idiom as many a top-rated Parisian kitchen, using traditional techniques on an unrestricted range of ingredients. 'He seems keen on exotic grains,' noted a reporter who tucked into spiced quinoa with herb-crusted lamb. Presentation can be dramatic: witness an arrangement of pearl-white scallops and pieces of squid interspersed with twirls of orange pumpkin purée on the blackest squid-ink sauce. But then taste it. The shellfish are superbly timed, the purée smooth and sweet-seeming, the whole effect 'very Mediterranean, sunny and gorgeous'. Great fragrance is achieved in many of the dishes, including woodpigeon breasts on the signature bed of beetroot barley 'risotto'.

A caramel mousse of sensuous wobbliness has been partnered by banana ice-cream brittle with shards of praline and hunks of caramelised banana, an artful exercise in textural contrasts. Even petits fours are mini-masterpieces of the art. This is supremely confident cooking that attracts strong support. Service draws a mixed response, from 'aggressive' and 'rude' to 'very friendly' and 'flawless'. France forms the backbone of an annotated wine list, supported by a short set of New World wines. Quality is the priority, but there's a reasonable choice under £20. House wines are £9.95. CELLARMAN'S CHOICE: Mercurey Blanc 1989, Dom. Menotte, £21.50; Gigondas 1990, Bérard, £19.50.

CHEF: David Everitt-Matthias   PROPRIETORS: David and Helen Everitt-Matthias   OPEN: Mon to Fri L 12.30 to 1.30, Mon to Sat D 7.30 to 9.30   CLOSED: 2 weeks Christmas and New Year, bank hols   MEALS: Set L £12.50 (2 courses, inc wine) to £17.50, Set D £25 to £34   SERVICE: not inc   CARDS: Access, Amex, Diners, Switch, Visa   DETAILS: 28 seats. Private parties: 28 main room. Children welcome. Smart dress preferred. No cigars in dining-room. Wheelchair access (no WC). No music. Air-conditioned

Epicurean ⅝✳

NEW ENTRY

81 The Promenade, Cheltenham GL50 1PJ
TEL: (01242) 222466   FAX: (01242) 222474

COOKING 3
COST £29–£52

This is no longer a McDonald's. Patrick of that ilk left, the restaurant disappeared from the *Guide* last year, and since then Jason Lynas, a former Young Chef of the Year, has captained the stoves. The listed Regency building overlooks Cheltenham's fashionable inner promenade, and the operation remains a three-tiered affair, with a café-bar in the basement, a ground-floor bistro, and first-floor restaurant with a tiny lounge. One visitor felt that an authoritative front-of-house manager in the smart, bleached wood-panelled dining-room might have given it the class and *gravitas* that the food is so obviously aiming for.

There is certainly no mistaking the ambition of a restaurant that serves white truffles in a 'classy and unusual' appetiser of creamy artichoke soup, and inside a first-course chicken ravioli, which is surrounded by a stock containing black truffles. The riches continue with seared fillet of beef, capped with a grilled slice of foie gras and served with a rich onion gravy. Partnerships are enterprising – seared scallops with cinnamon and lemon, poached turbot with Welsh rarebit and a mustard glaze – and reflect an intelligent handling of basically Anglo-French ideas. 'The restaurant aims high and often delivers,' concluded an inspector.

The flair for presentation is perhaps most obvious in desserts: a centrepiece of clotted cream surrounded by vanilla custard and glazed fruits, and a 'Louvre' pyramid of chocolate parfait on a base of cherry parfait with glazed 'walls' that was a *'tour de force* visually'. Incidentals include 'wholesomely home-made' bread, a pre-dessert crème caramel, and an array of tempting petits fours. Service, though cheerful and friendly enough, rather lags behind the kitchen in terms of professionalism. High-quality French wines are the mainstay of the wine list, which might do more to find good drinking under £20.

CHEF: Jason Lynas   PROPRIETOR: Epicurean Restaurants Ltd   OPEN: Mon to Sat L 12.30 to 2.30, Tue to Sat D 7.30 to 9.30 (10 Sat)   CLOSED: last week Dec, first week Jan   MEALS: alc (main courses £17). Set L £15 (2 courses) to £17.50   SERVICE: not inc   CARDS: Access, Amex, Delta, Diners, Switch, Visa   DETAILS: 80 seats. 10 seats outside. Private parties: 40 main room, 24 private room. Children welcome. Smart dress preferred. No smoking in 1 dining-room. Music

Mayflower

32–34 Clarence Street, Cheltenham GL50 3NX
TEL: (01242) 522426 and 511580   COOKING 1
FAX: (01242) 251667   COST £14–£57

'We know all our customers by their first names (if they want us to) and we have watched their families grow up,' reports Mr Kong. His own family have been running this rather grandly appointed Chinese restaurant since 1982 and pay due respect to English traditions: Mothering Sunday is the only day of the year when they open for Sunday lunch. The kitchen is capable of producing a broad range of dishes, taking in deep-fried crispy lamb, and mussels with black beans and chilli, as well as Szechuan seafood hotpot, Cantonese roast duck, and chicken with celery in satay sauce. Vegetarians have plenty to choose from. Wines are taken seriously, and the list of 80-odd bins has been assembled with care. House wine is £8.95.

CHEFS: Mrs M.M. Kong and Mr C.F. Kong   PROPRIETORS: the Kong family   OPEN: Mon to Sat L 12 to 1.45 (and Mothering Sun L), all week D 5.45 to 10.45 (11 Fri and Sat)   CLOSED: 24 to 27 Dec   MEALS: alc (main courses £5 to £10). Set L £6.50, Set D £14.50 to £18.50   SERVICE: not inc   CARDS: Access, Amex, Delta, Diners, Switch, Visa   DETAILS: 120 seats. Private parties: 80 main room, 40 private room. Vegetarian meals. Children welcome. Smart dress preferred. Wheelchair access (no WC). Music. Air-conditioned

Staithes ✸

12 Suffolk Road, Cheltenham GL50 2AQ
TEL: (01242) 260666   COOKING 1
on A40, S of town centre at junction with Bath Road   COST £24–£43

The image is of a 'caring husband-and-wife-run restaurant with the world's best loos'. Paul and Heather Lucas certainly try hard, although chandeliers and heavily swagged curtains seem at odds with the 'insistent' Muzak in their dining-room. Paul's cooking is straightforward – some might say old-fashioned – and simple dishes work best. Although at inspection some timings seemed to go awry – for 'overcooked' duck breast with marinated cherries, and 'variable' vegetables – Cornish mussels in a creamy white wine sauce were spot on, and on another occasion a reporter found everything 'extremely well presented and quite delicious'. Desserts such as baked Alaska come 'wreathed with an arrangement of little puddles, each puddle holding a berry'. Front-of-house is top-class, alert and attentive. Service is not included, and you have to pay extra for bread and 'superb Dutch unsalted' butter. The short wine list is dependable and fairly priced. House wine is £9.95.

CHEF: Paul Lucas   PROPRIETORS: Heather and Paul Lucas   OPEN: Mon to Sat D only 7.30 (7 Sat) to 10; L by reservation only   CLOSED: 1 week Christmas, 2 weeks summer, bank hol Mons   MEALS: alc (main courses £8 to £14)   SERVICE: not inc, card slips closed   CARDS: Access, Amex, Delta, Diners, Visa   DETAILS: 24 seats. Private parties: 24 main room, 10 private room. Vegetarian meals. No children under 8, over-8s by arrangement. Smart dress preferred. No smoking in dining-room. Wheelchair access (no WC). Music

---

CHESTER Cheshire   map 7

▲ Chester Grosvenor Hotel, Arkle ♟

Eastgate Street, Chester CH1 1LT   COOKING 4
TEL: (01244) 324024   FAX: (01244) 313246   COST £31–£82

Few properties in the *Guide* have been in the same hands as long as this one. It became part of the Duke of Westminster's Grosvenor Estate Holdings in 1865, when Arkle was barely a twinkle in some ancestral equine eye. Rather like the building, the restaurant now combines a classical foundation with a modern outlook. Aperitifs begin with somewhat unpromising appetisers in the library bar, amid snackers from the brasserie. Nor does the dining-room, with its columns and a painting of the eponymous horse, lift the spirits much; hotel guests staring enviously through the corridor windows made one reporter feel 'like an exhibit in a zoo'. So it isn't the most elegant dining-room in the country, but welcome changes since last year include the rather sensible ones of writing the menu in English and quoting prices in understandable numerical form.

Expensive materials are never far away. A first-course 'pressing' of maize-fed chicken, sweetbreads, flageolet beans and foie gras with a truffle dressing is a luxury terrine if ever there was. Even turbot has been served with pan-fried foie gras and truffle juices. Dishes can be as intricate as a globe artichoke with a whipped mousseline of crab, roasted Scottish lobster and gazpacho, but the cooking never gets too fancy for its own good. It relies on quality of ingredients and professional execution for impact, rather than on innovative flavour combinations. Grilled breast of duck, for example, is dealt with traditionally (served with orange and green peppercorns) but impresses for its sheer tastiness and for a well-judged and intense sauce. Clarity of flavour is the norm.

The flair for presentation is perhaps most obvious at dessert stage, as in a parfait of aniseed with a 'tiara' of crispy shortbread, surrounded by a circle of finely chopped fruit compote. A well-travelled inspector considered his crème brûlée 'quite the best in a series of inspections'. A master baker takes over the kitchen during the night and produces a variety of excellent loaves, including white with sun-dried tomato and brown with muesli; a waiter reels off the list, then slices the bread of choice and brings it to table. Service is generally 'efficient, courteous and knowledgeable'. The wine list is a 25-page tome, chock full of impressive and mature wines at fairly high prices. French house wines are £10.75. CELLARMAN'S CHOICE: Viognier 1993, Dom. St-Hilaire, £19.50; Stag's Leap Cabernet Sauvignon 1988, Vichon, California, £37.50.

CHEF: Paul Reed   PROPRIETOR: Grosvenor Estate Holdings   OPEN: Tue to Sun L 12 to 2.30, Mon to Sat D 7 to 9.30   CLOSED: 25 to 30 Dec, 1 to 6 Jan, bank hols   MEALS: Set L £22.50 to £42, Set D £35 (2 courses) to £42   SERVICE: not inc   CARDS: Access, Amex, Diners, Visa   DETAILS: 45 seats. Vegetarian meals. Wheelchair access (also WC). Music. Air-conditioned   ACCOMMODATION: 87 rooms, all with bath/shower. TV. Phone. Air-conditioned. Room only £115 to £190. Rooms for disabled. Children welcome. Baby facilities. Afternoon teas

---

CHILGROVE West Sussex   map 3

White Horse Inn ▮

Chilgrove PO18 9HX
TEL: (01243) 535219   FAX: (01243) 535301   COOKING 1
on B2141, between Chichester and Petersfield   COST £20–£57

This country pub has been run by the same family since 1969. Cooking is a hobby, no more, no less, but wines are an even bigger hobby, putting the White Horse squarely on anybody's map of top places to drink at. If the food is of secondary importance, it still has its supporters. There is probably no need to direct attention to the simpler dishes, since drinkers tend to gravitate to them anyway, the better to appreciate the wine they have chosen. Successes have ranged from rich braised oxtail to fish from Selsey, including 'superb' Dover sole meunière, roast sea bass, and halibut with butter and dill sauce. Follow with cheese, or perhaps lemon tart 'with plenty of citrus flavour and a good texture'.

The wine list is justly famous, with its awesome array of mature clarets crowning a fine collection of wine from around the world. Highlights are a fabulous German section, an excellent range of fine dessert wines and a whole page of Domaine de la Romanée Conti. If you can't decide where to start, head for the house selection, which begins with five mixed wines at £11.50. CEL-LARMAN'S CHOICE: Muscadet, Cuvée de Millénaire 1994, Marquis de Goulaine, £11.95; Van Loveren Blanc de Noir 1994, Robertson, S. Africa, £11.50. Neil Rusbridger also owns nearby Forge Cottage, which provides B&B accommodation.

'The whole place lacks pizazz. I don't know how to spell it, but I know what it is.'
(On eating in London)

CHEF: Neil Rusbridger   PROPRIETORS: Barry Phillips and Neil Rusbridger   OPEN: Tue to Sat 12 to 2, 7 to 9.30 (10.30 summer)   CLOSED: 3 weeks Feb, last week Oct   MEALS: alc (main courses L £11.50 to £17.50, D £15 to £19.50). Set L £17.50, Set D £23. BYO (no corkage). Bar meals available Tue to Sun L, Tue to Sat D   SERVICE: 10%, card slips closed   CARDS: Access, Delta, Diners, Switch, Visa   DETAILS: 70 seats. 12 seats outside. Private parties: 70 main room, 10 to 20 private rooms. Car park. Vegetarian meals. No smoking before coffee. Wheelchair access (also WC). No music. Air-conditioned

---

CHINNOR Oxfordshire   map 2

Sir Charles Napier Inn ▮

Sprigg's Alley, nr Chinnor OX9 4BX
TEL: (01494) 483011   FAX: (01494) 485434
off B4009; at Chinnor roundabout, take Spriggs Alley   COOKING 2*
turn, continue straight up hill   COST £31–£50

'Our meal included as a starter a collection of about six or seven different mushrooms picked that morning from the fields near the restaurant – absolutely stunning.' So runs a typically up-beat report on this unashamedly idiosyncratic 'inn'. The setting, on high ground close to Bledlow Ridge, is a joy in summer, especially if you eat lunch outside under vine-entangled pergolas. Otherwise, feast your eyes on the jumble of surreal modern sculptures and, inside, antiques that fill every inch of space in the bar and dining-room. Informality reigns. Julie Griffiths is always on hand, and most people warm to her calm, organised presence.

Batiste Tolu's cooking continues to draw effusive praise, with its bold flavours, subtlety and razor-sharp presentation. His menus are shot through with up-to-the-minute ideas and themes: roasted peppers are served with anchovies, capers and ricotta, crab-cakes (a perennial favourite) come with lime and coriander, and chargrilled salmon is accompanied by salsa verde. But there are also classical, traditional touches, as in black pudding with poached egg, saddle of venison with cranberries, and calf's liver with caramelised onions. Puddings may include chocolate and almond torte, and few could complain about the dazzlingly good British cheeseboard. The vast wine list is a joy to browse through; enthusiastic notes direct the reader towards the latest discoveries, although there are plenty of well-known producers at every turn of the page. It's easy to get carried away, especially on the page of magnums, but mark-ups remain modest and, as well as house wines at £10.75, there's a well-judged 'house selection' of eight top-notch wines priced between £17 and £23.50. CELLARMAN'S CHOICE: Piccadilly Chardonnay 1994, Jeffrey Grosset, Clare Valley, S. Australia, £19.75; Frog's Leap Zinfandel 1993, Napa Valley, California, £18.50.

'I asked for salad with my main course and was told that it was a "quirk of the chef's" that he did not do salads. I replied that it was a quirk of mine that I do not like vegetables with fish: so, no salad, but at least I saved the cost of one helping of veg.'
(On eating in Cambridge)

CHEF: Batiste Tolu and David Jones   PROPRIETOR: Julie Griffiths   OPEN: Tue to Sun L 12 to 2.30 (12.30 to 3.30 Sun), Tue to Sat D 7 to 10   MEALS: alc (main courses £10.50 to £15.50). Set L Tue to Sat £13 (2 courses), Set D Tue to Fri £14 (2 courses). BYO £6   SERVICE: 12.5% (optional), card slips closed   CARDS: Access, Amex, Delta, Diners, Switch, Visa   DETAILS: 80 seats. 60 seats outside. Private parties: 10 to 45 main room, 35 and 45 private rooms. Car park. Vegetarian meals. No children under 7 D. No-smoking area. Wheelchair access (no WC). Music. Air-conditioned

---

| CHOBHAM Surrey | map 3 |

Quails

| 1 Bagshot Road, Chobham GU24 8BP | COOKING 1 |
| TEL/FAX: (01276) 858491 | COST £23–£45 |

Quails was about to get a bigger and better nest as we went to press. The ivy-clad converted shop overlooking the green is being enlarged to cope with an ever-increasing influx from Chobham and beyond. Weekday fixed-price menus continue to offer the best value for dishes such as rillettes of smoked mackerel, Basque-style roast pork cutlets, and chocolate and walnut tart. The mix of stalwart French and modern eclectic is followed through in the *carte*, which has included warm pigeon salad, confit of duck on cassis and green peppercorn sauce, and venison with red wine and juniper. Quail appears as a ballottine with fig and shallot marmalade, wild rabbit comes in a pastry parcel with sun-dried tomato salsa, and fillet of sea trout is roasted with sorrel. Wines are listed by taste and style, with some lesser-known French names putting in an appearance. House wine is £9.50.

CHEF: Christopher Wale   PROPRIETORS: the Wale family   OPEN: Tue to Fri and Sun L 12.30 to 1.30, Tue to Sat D 7 to 10   CLOSED: 26 Dec, 1 Jan   MEALS: alc D (main courses £10.50 to £15). Set L Tue to Fri £11.95 (2 courses) to £14.95, Set L Sun £13.95, Set D Tue to Fri £14.95 (2 courses) to £16.95 (each inc wine)   SERVICE: not inc   CARDS: Access, Amex, Delta, Diners, Switch, Visa   DETAILS: 40 seats. Private parties: 40 main room. Car park. Vegetarian meals. Children welcome. Smart dress preferred. Wheelchair access (no WC). Music. Air-conditioned

---

| CHRISTCHURCH Dorset | map 2 |

Splinters

| 12 Church Street, Christchurch BH23 1BW | COOKING 1* |
| TEL/FAX: (01202) 483454 | COST £25–£43 |

Splinters occupies two listed buildings close to the priory. Number 11 serves snacks and light lunches, number 12 is a restaurant that gives the impression of a private house, its small panelled rooms decorated with old prints and antique china. Eamonn Redden's menus are both modern and generous, delving into a soup of lightly smoked fish with a pungent rouille, and grilled haunch of venison steak with béarnaise sauce. The highlight of an inspection meal showed off some of the kitchen's skills to good effect: guinea-fowl and pigeon, both meats 'succulent and well flavoured', baked under a rich short pastry, and served with a dark, glossy rosemary sauce. A tripartite chocolate pudding also proved something of a triumph: a light sponge, contrasting densely textured bitter mousse, and the sort of smooth, rich sauce 'to which we all aspire in our kitchens'. Five house wines head up a roving list with a good spread of styles and prices. House wine starts at £9.80.

CHEF: Eamonn Redden   PROPRIETORS: Timothy Lloyd and Robert Wilson   OPEN: all week L 10.30 to 2.30, Mon to Sat D (and Sun bank hols) 7 (6.30 Sat) to 10   MEALS: Set L £12 (2 courses) to £15, Set D £20 (2 courses) to £25   SERVICE: not inc   CARDS: Access, Amex, Delta, Diners, Switch, Visa   DETAILS: 40 seats. Private parties: 10 main room, 8 and 20 private rooms. Vegetarian meals. Children welcome. Smart dress preferred. Music

---

CLAYGATE Surrey   map 3

Le Petit Pierrot

| 4 The Parade, Claygate KT10 0NU | COOKING 1* |
| TEL: (01372) 465105   FAX: (01372) 467642 | COST £24–£41 |

Rolling up on a chilly Tuesday lunch-time in March, one couple found themselves claiming the last table and feeling jolly grateful for it. This is eloquent testimony to the success of the Brichots' enterprise, a French restaurant done in vibrant pinks, its cosiness enhanced by swags of tented fabric suspended from the ceiling. Duck rillettes, smoked eel and red lentil terrine, brill fillet in pepper sauce, and calf's liver in raspberry vinegar denote the style, not exactly cuisine de grand-mère but homely enough in its way. A 'heaped plateful of piping-hot oxtail bourguignonne' restored *joie de vivre* to that benumbed pair of lunchers, its rich winey sauce contributing to 'thorough enjoyment'. Crème brûlée is accompanied by a dish of grilled prunes in armagnac, and hot apple tart has been well reported. Friendly service keeps everyone content. The French wine list does well by the big regions, with the Loire, Rhône and Alsace providing price relief. House vin de pays is £9.25.

CHEF: Jean-Pierre Brichot   PROPRIETORS: Jean-Pierre and Annie Brichot   OPEN: Mon to Fri L 12.15 to 2.15, Mon to Sat D 7.15 to 9.30   CLOSED: bank hols   MEALS: Set L £14.45 (2 courses) to £16.95, Set D £19.85   SERVICE: not inc   CARDS: Access, Amex, Diners, Visa   DETAILS: 32 seats. Private parties: 32 main room. No children under 9. Smart dress preferred. Wheelchair access (no WC). Music. Air-conditioned

---

CLITHEROE Lancashire   map 8

Auctioneer 🍴✳

| New Market Street, Clitheroe BB7 2JW | COOKING 2 |
| TEL: (01200) 27153 | COST £21–£47 |

You makes your booking, and you takes your choice: a sense of intimacy in the Cottage Room, with its wood-burning stove, or a window on the outside world in the Garden Room, with views over Clitheroe's proud new piazza and the more distant Waddington Fell. Henk Van Heumen has always been a culinary rover, his themed European menus majoring lately in the Italian regions. A couple lunching one Sunday were regaled with cooking from the Veneto: carpaccio of beef fillet 'cut so thin it looked as though it had been painted on to the plate' and – more improbably – fried sea bream with hot slushy banana (who's ever eaten that in the Veneto?). When the themes abate, there may be game sausage on a potato and turnip rösti, or a 'farmhouse pie' of chicken and smoked bacon. Favourite puddings include well-made vanilla parfait replete with nuts and crumbled macaroons, and Dutch apple flan. Service is well-meaning, and solicitous enough to point out on a Sunday that, as the bakery wasn't open, the bread (though excellent light, fresh and crusty wholemeal) was yesterday's. A fine slate of wines at £10 kicks off a fairly standard list of largely French bottles, ending with a good showing of halves.

CHEF: Henk Van Heumen   PROPRIETORS: Henk and Frances Van Heumen   OPEN: Wed to Sun 12 to 1.30, 7 to 9 (9.30 Sat)   MEALS: alc L Wed to Sat (main courses £7.50 to £10). Set L Sun £13.75, Set D Sun and Wed to Fri £18.75 (2 courses) to £21.75, Set D Sat £21.75. Minimum £6.25 L   SERVICE: not inc   CARDS: Access, Amex, Delta, Switch, Visa   DETAILS: 48 seats. Private parties: 24 private room. Vegetarian meals. Children welcome. Smart dress preferred. No smoking in 1 dining-room. Music

---

COCKERMOUTH Cumbria   map 10

Quince & Medlar ✹✶

13 Castlegate, Cockermouth CA13 9EU   COOKING 1
TEL: (01900) 823579   COST £20–£26

The dining-room of this gently paced vegetarian restaurant has been redecorated (the net curtains have gone) but the style of cooking remains the same. Colin and Louisa Le Voi see themselves as 'avoiding the traditional wholemealy image associated with non-meat dishes', and to this end have devised some arresting combinations, including a smoked tofu, noodle and aubergine charlotte with a tomato, cheese and herb sauce. There are those, it has to be said, who might consider these dishes rather more complicated than they need to be, but reporters have found the food 'well balanced, with good textures and tastes'. Meals are good value, and might begin with parsnip and apple mousse wrapped in spinach, and end with chocolate truffle torte, or warm prune pudding. There's a good selection of wines from around the world, and several are organic.

CHEFS/PROPRIETORS: Colin and Louisa Le Voi   OPEN: Tue to Sun D only 7 to 9.30   CLOSED: Sun 1 Jan to Easter, 2 weeks mid-Jan, 1 week Nov   MEALS: alc (main courses £7.50 to £8). BYO £5 SERVICE: not inc, card slips closed   CARDS: Access, Visa   DETAILS: 26 seats. Private parties: 16 main room. Vegetarian meals. No children under 6. Smart dress preferred. No smoking in dining-room. Music

---

COGGESHALL Essex   map 3

Baumann's Brasserie

4–6 Stoneham Street, Coggeshall CO6 1TT   COOKING 1
TEL: (01376) 561453 FAX: (01376) 563762   COST £16–£39

In calling itself a 'sixteenth-century brasserie', Baumann's hints at the mix within. In a timber-framed building opposite the Victorian clock-tower, it was co-founded with the late Peter Langan, whose legacy remains in the large collection of oil and pastel paintings covering the walls, and in the single-sheet menu of simple, mostly European-based brasserie dishes: Caesar salad, pea soup, loin of lamb with a 'gorgeous, buttery, smooth' purée of white beans, and warm treacle tart. When the flavourings turn oriental they do so with some conviction, producing curried apples with grilled grey mullet, and a spicy Singhalese chutney of tomato and sultana that was 'just what was needed' to accompany a terrine of goose. Basil or sage and onion breads are worth the extra charge, and a dark chocolate and mint marquise has proved a 'splendidly rich' way to finish. Affordable set lunches and a 20-bottle wine list add to the brisk appeal. There is another branch at 19 North Hill, Colchester.

CHEFS: Mark Baumann, Doug Wright and Jason Shaw PROPRIETOR: Baumann's Brasserie Ltd OPEN: Tue to Fri and Sun L 12.30 to 2, Tue to Sat D 7.30 to 9.30 (10 Fri and Sat) CLOSED: 2 weeks Jan MEALS: alc (main courses £8 to £13). Set L £5 (1 course) to £9.95, Set D Tue to Thur £16.50 SERVICE: not inc, card slips closed CARDS: Access, Amex, Delta, Switch, Visa DETAILS: 75 seats. Private parties: 75 main room. Vegetarian meals. Children's helpings. Smart dress preferred. Music

---

COLCHESTER Essex   map 3

Warehouse Brasserie £⅝✳

12 Chapel Street North, Colchester CO2 7AT   COOKING 1*
TEL: (01206) 765656   COST £17–£36

When Anthony Brooks and co opened the Warehouse in 1988, their aim was to serve innovative brasserie food at prices that would not offend the citizens of Colchester. Much of their success is due to a flexible approach and the lively mood that they have created. Fixed-price lunches remain a bargain, while the evening *carte* covers a lot of ground, from duck confit with bubble and squeak to roast monkfish with ratatouille to wild mushroom risotto. The tone of some recent reports suggests that the kitchen may have gone off the boil, but timbale of crab with avocado, and chargrilled fillet of beef have been satisfying, and there are some great puddings, including Belgian chocolate and almond praline marquise, and a trio of sorbets in a brandy-snap. Service is unashamedly informal. Several New World wines make their presence felt on the well-spread list. House wines start at £7.50.

CHEFS: Anthony Brooks, Mark Burley and Cheryl Hilham PROPRIETORS: Mel Burley and Anthony Brooks OPEN: all week L 12 to 2, Mon to Sat D 7 to 9.30 (10 Fri and Sat) CLOSED: 25 and 26 Dec, bank hol Mons MEALS: alc (main courses £7 to £12). Set L £8.95 (2 courses) to £10.95 SERVICE: not inc, card slips closed CARDS: Access, Amex, Delta, Diners, Switch, Visa DETAILS: 110 seats. Private parties: 110 main room. Vegetarian meals. Children's helpings. No smoking in 1 dining-room. Wheelchair access (no WC). No music. Air-conditioned

---

COLERNE Wiltshire   map 2

▲ Lucknam Park ♀ £⅝✳

Colerne SN14 8AZ
TEL: (01225) 742777 FAX: (01225) 743536   COOKING 3*
off A420 at Ford, 6m W of Chippenham   COST £36–£66

The mile-long drive up a beech-lined avenue to this elegant, tranquil Palladian mansion, six miles from Bath, only hints at the extent of the 500-acre estate. It has all the trappings of country housedom, including health spa and equestrian centre, but has been refurbished with respect for the period. There are choice antiques, paintings and deep sofas, and the bow-fronted drawing-room, wood-panelled library, and crystal-chandeliered dining-room, with its painted ceiling, have all been handsomely decorated in soft colours.

A member of staff is always on hand to make sure the comfort-level doesn't slip. There is plenty of good advice, too, for those who need it when ordering food or wine. What the kitchen offers under Alexander Venables is a sound grasp of classical techniques, put to use in a modern context. It handles correctly the cooking and timing of fish, demonstrates a deft hand with saucing – a light shellfish and olive oil dressing for steamed sea bass, for instance – and is comfortable with ancillary items such as a potato cage infused with mint olive oil, constructed to accompany roast Wiltshire lamb. Textures are dealt with carefully, tastes are generally distinctive, and the artful construction of a dish is a job the brigade obviously enjoys, as when it fills a globe artichoke with Jerusalem artichoke and serves it with a poached egg glazed with truffle-flavoured hollandaise.

Pastry-work is good, whether savoury or sweet, and presentation is first-rate, as one Sunday lunching couple concluded when they finished with a 'superb' Malibu and coconut soufflé. They were impressed by the value, although noted that prices on the wine list 'range from the sublime to the ridiculous'. But Lucknam Park takes its wines very seriously, listing the great and glorious at appropriately high prices. Wines are grouped according to vintage within country sections, although headings such as 'Weine aus Deutschland' and 'Les Vins du Liban' add a pretentious note. French house wines are £15. CEL-LARMAN'S CHOICE: Jurançon sec, Cuvée des Casterasses 1992, Dom. Bru-Baché, £28.50; Costières de Nîmes, Ch. de Rozier 1993, £22.50.

CHEF: Alexander Venables PROPRIETOR: Lucknam Park Hotels Ltd OPEN: all week 12.30 to 2, 7.30 to 9.30 MEALS: Set L £25, Set D £42.50. Light meals available SERVICE: not inc, card slips closed CARDS: Access, Amex, Diners, Switch, Visa DETAILS: 85 seats. Private parties: 80 main room, 10 to 40 private rooms. Car park. Vegetarian meals. Children welcome. No children under 12 D. Jacket and tie. No smoking in dining-room. Wheelchair access (also WC). No music ACCOMMODATION: 42 rooms, all with bath/shower. TV. Phone. B&B £105 to £550. Children welcome. Afternoon teas. Garden. Swimming-pool (The Which? Hotel Guide)

COLN ST ALDWYNS Gloucestershire   map 2

▲ New Inn 🍴 ⚡

Coln St Aldwyns GL7 5AN   COOKING 1*
TEL: (01285) 750651   FAX: (01285) 750657   COST £22–£38

The stone-built, creeper-clad Elizabethan inn, along with the owners, customers and kitchen, feels 'very Cotswold', with small rooms and closely packed tables. The bar food still looks pretty much as it did – updated versions of British pub classics such as fish and chips with mushy peas, or liver and bacon – but new chef Stephen Morey, last at Homewood Park (see entry, Hinton Charterhouse), has put his own stamp on the restaurant menu with crisp deep-fried squid rings, and roast fillet of duck and lambs' liver with red cabbage. A 'pointless complexity' was apparent at inspection, leaving flavour in second place, although a dish of chargrilled rabbit fillets stood out for its fine materials and timing, and chocolate tart used good pastry and intense chocolate. The appetiser at inspection wasn't appetising, but the petits fours were 'quite exceptional. Would that the entire meal had been like this.' Service has been a mixture of 'willing' and 'conceited', and two dozen wines stay mostly below £20. House wine starts at £8.75 a bottle.

CHEF: Stephen Morey   PROPRIETORS: Brian and Sandra-Anne Evans   OPEN: Sun L 12 to 2, all week D 7.30 to 9.30 (9 Sun)   MEALS: Set L £13.50, Set D £22.50. Bar food available   SERVICE: not inc; 10% for parties of 6 or more   CARDS: Access, Amex, Switch, Visa   DETAILS: 40 seats. 15 seats outside. Private parties: 20 main room, 20 private room. Car park. Vegetarian meals. Children's helpings. Smart dress preferred. No smoking in dining-room. Wheelchair access (also WC). No music   ACCOMMODATION: 11 rooms, all with bath/shower. TV. Phone. B&B £55 to £79. Deposit: £50. Children welcome. Baby facilities. Afternoon teas. Garden (*The Which? Hotel Guide*)

COLSTON BASSETT   Nottinghamshire   map 5

Martins Arms

School Lane, Colston Bassett NG12 3FN
TEL: (01949) 81361   COOKING 1
off A46 Leicester to Newark road, 4m S of Bingham   COST £24–£49

Built as a farmhouse circa 1690, the Martins Arms is a Grade II listed building that has established a reputation as one of the most reliable pub/restaurants in the Vale of Belvoir. The kitchen makes good use of local ingredients such as Colston Bassett Stilton and Melton Mowbray pork pies, and produces its own pickles, sausages and some breads. The bar menu flits convincingly between Welsh rarebit and brasserie-style dishes of duck breast with pepper sauce, or emperor fish on a bed of samphire with chive and cream sauce, while meals in the dining-room move up a notch for the likes of fillet of beef with chargrilled polenta, and calf's liver with balsamic vinegar and pesto. Belgian chocolate tart is a 'blockbuster' of a pudding. Real ales are an alternative to the short Lay & Wheeler wine list. House wine is £8.95.

CHEFS: Salvatore Inguanta and Mark Yarwood   PROPRIETORS: Lynne Strafford Bryan and Salvatore Inguanta   OPEN: all week L 12 to 2, Mon to Sat D 6 to 10   MEALS: alc D (main courses £13 to £17). Set L £15.95. Bar food available   SERVICE: not inc   CARDS: none   DETAILS: 30 seats. 50 seats outside. Private parties: 30 main room, 24 private room. Car park. Vegetarian meals. No children under 14. Smart dress preferred. Wheelchair access (no WC). No music

---

COOKHAM   Berkshire   map 3

Alfonso's

19–21 Station Hill Parade, Cookham SL6 9BR   COOKING 1*
TEL: (01628) 525775   COST £20–£32

The improbability of the setting – in a modern parade of shops – is compounded by old photographs of Ernie Wise and other 'celebrities' plus an 'over-the-top array of chef's certificates and plaques'. The owners, originally from Galicia, are passionate about the enterprise, and this translates into skilful cooking of first-class ingredients, good value, and warm personal service. The menu changes about three times a year (which explains the 'bouquet of autumn leaves' in March), but daily specials add to the variety.

The cooking follows no style except its own, judging by casserole of chicken livers with a thyme and beer gravy, or belly of Berkshire suckling pig, lightly smoked, with black pudding and pearl barley. Bouillabaisse is a refined rather than rustic version, with notably fresh fish in a tasty broth. Just-cooked fish illustrates attention to timing, and good saucing is evident in, for example, a light creamy sage and onion sauce served with 'Kentucky spiced' chicken. Among desserts, prune and almond tart with crème anglaise is expertly done. Only a few of the 40-odd wines cost over £20.

CHEFS: Richard Manzano and Simon Hall   PROPRIETORS: Mr and Mrs Alfonso Baena   OPEN: Mon to Fri L 12.30 to 2, Mon to Sat D 7 to 10   CLOSED: 2 weeks Aug, bank hols   MEALS: Set L £12.50 to £18.50, Set D £18.50   SERVICE: not inc   CARDS: Access, Amex, Diners, Visa   DETAILS: 34 seats. Private parties: 34 main room. Car park. Vegetarian meals. Children's helpings. Smart dress preferred. Wheelchair access (no WC). Music. Air-conditioned

COPPULL MOOR   Lancashire   map 8

Coppull Moor ⅙✳

311 Preston Road, Coppull Moor PR7 5DU   COOKING 1
TEL: (01257) 792222   COST £23–£40

The artfully decorated former roadside pub has amassed an individual collection of knick-knacks, making it feel 'friendly and cosy', and has two dining-rooms with 'foreground music'. Although well to the south, it follows the Lake District format of one sitting, with either a four- or five-course dinner, depending on the day of the week. In the five-course meal, numbers two and three are fixed: minestrone soup on one occasion followed by a twice-baked fish soufflé. The menu is long on description, the cooking involved, and some dishes find it difficult to live up to the advance publicity of, say, 'tenderloin of local pork coated in fresh breadcrumbs scented with fresh garden rosemary and cheese then gently cooked in clarified butter and served with a mild mustard seed and apple sauce'. It is as if the kitchen is trying too hard to impress. Vegetables are many, and desserts can be as rich as creamy rice pudding or sticky toffee pud. Unusually and generously, any wine on the varied and 90-strong list can be ordered by the glass.

CHEFS: Barry Rea and Mark Pilling   PROPRIETOR: Barry Rea   OPEN: Sun brunch 11.30 for 12 (1 sitting) Tue to Sun D 8 for 8.30 (1 sitting)   MEALS: Set Sun brunch £17.50. Set D £24.50 to £27.50   SERVICE: none, card slips closed   CARDS: Amex, Diners   DETAILS: 26 seats. Private parties: 14 main room, 12 to 14 private rooms. Car park. Vegetarian meals. No children under 14 exc by arrangement. Smart dress preferred. No smoking in dining-room. Wheelchair access (no WC). Music

'Drinks were taken in the bar, which was pleasant enough except for the slab of granite serving as a table which would have looked more at home in a graveyard.'
(On eating in Surrey)

CORSCOMBE Dorset   map 2

Fox Inn £

Corscombe DT2 0NS
TEL/FAX: (01935) 891330   COOKING 1
off A356, 6m SE of Crewkerne   COST £17–£33

This is a pleasant rustic pub with a friendly welcome and a short menu bolstered by blackboard specials. The place certainly looks the part: a seventeenth-century thatched inn with stone floors. Filled pancakes and variously sauced steaks constitute the basic fare, but daily additions might include chargrilled aubergine with cheese and herbs, sausage and lentil casserole, and 'generous portions' of fish pie. Among successful dishes have been fried squid, game casserole, fillets of cod and turbot, marinated grilled lamb steak 'cooked pink and well flavoured', and mashed potato. Real ales add to the appeal, and a short list of good wines stays commendably affordable.

CHEF: Will Longman   PROPRIETOR: Martyn Lee   OPEN: all week 12 to 2, 7 to 9 (9.30 Fri and Sat)   CLOSED: 25 Dec   MEALS: alc (main courses £4.50 to £11.50). BYO £5   SERVICE: not inc
CARDS: none   DETAILS: 60 seats. 20 seats outside. Private parties: 22 main room, 20 and 22 private rooms. Car park. Vegetarian meals. Wheelchair access (no WC). No music

---

CORSE LAWN Gloucestershire   map 2

▲ *Corse Lawn House* ▮ ✻

Corse Lawn GL19 4LZ
TEL: (01452) 780771   FAX: (01452) 780840   COOKING 2*
on B4211, 5m SW of Tewkesbury   COST £27–£58

The house dates from 1745, built in Queen Anne style but with twentieth-century additions, and has been owned since 1978 by the Hine family, a branch of the Cognac Hines, who, as it happens, were originally from Dorset. Denis Hine 'makes a roughish country squire impression', suggested one reporter, 'rather like the food'. More than a touch of 'faded gentility' pervades the house, but redecorating plans are in the pipeline. The cooking retains an affection for old ways of doing things, from quantities of cream and butter, to an industriousness that shows in preserving, baking, smoking fish, gathering wild mushrooms for a feuilleté or nettles for soup, and in sausage-making.

One such was a 'nicely made' boudin blanc with a mousse-like texture, served on a heap of flageolet beans and bacon. Typically materials are good, and timing is appropriate, the two working to good effect in grilled scallops for example. A game or offal dish – such as saddle of hare or lamb kidneys – is as likely to appear as poached halibut or stuffed chicken breast. One correspondent felt the food rather 'heavy-handed', and the repertoire relatively unchanging, sentiments that have echoes in other reports. Puddings tend to the nursery end of the spectrum, such as butterscotch sponge, and 'chocolate indulgence'. Service is willing, and an excellent collection of fine wines has been assembled. Burgundy, Bordeaux and the Rhône make a big impression, although some prices are high. Plenty of choice by the glass and half-bottle is helpful. House vins de pays are £9.95.

CELLARMAN'S CHOICE: Faugères 1992, Cuvée les Bastides, Alquier, £19.30; Quincy 1994, Jaumier, £16.80.

CHEFS: Baba Hine and Tim Earley   PROPRIETORS: the Hine family   OPEN: all week 12 to 2, 7 to 10   MEALS: alc (main courses £16 to £20). Set L Mon to Sat £14.95 (2 courses) to £16.95, Set L Sun £17.95, Set D £24.50. Bar and bistro food available   SERVICE: not inc, card slips closed   CARDS: Access, Amex, Diners, Visa   DETAILS: 50 seats. 48 seats outside. Private parties: 80 main room, 12 and 35 private rooms. Car park. Vegetarian meals. Children's helpings. Smart dress preferred. No smoking in dining-room. Wheelchair access (also WC). No music   ACCOMMODATION: 19 rooms, all with bath/shower. TV. Phone. D,B&B £80 to £135. Rooms for disabled. Children welcome. Baby facilities. Dogs welcome. Afternoon teas. Garden. Swimming-pool (*The Which? Hotel Guide*)

CROSTHWAITE Cumbria   map 8

▲ *Punch Bowl Inn* ✱ £

Crosthwaite LA8 8HR   COOKING 1*
TEL: (01539) 568237   FAX: (01539) 568875   COST £17–£31

'Unostentatious, friendly, excellent food and service, and exceptional value for money' is probably music to most readers' ears, and certainly applies to Steven Doherty's renovated pub at the top end of the Lyth Valley. At these prices, don't expect more than pub tables and informal service from Marjorie Doherty and her team; for many, that is precisely the appeal. Only one reporter has demurred from the view that this is a happy, efficient and well-run restaurant.

'Deceptively sophisticated' is one view of the food; other reporters refer to 'amazingly fluffy' soufflé suissesse, and more rustic tender oxtail with a herby dumpling and a rich wine-laden sauce. The pattern is flexible, and first courses can be taken as a main course if preferred. Non-meat dishes might include a sandwich of aubergine and polenta topped with mozzarella and surrounded by plenty of olive oil and tomatoes. To finish, try hot chocolate pudding: 'a small, light, yet rich delight'. Sunday's set-price lunch is considered exceptionally good value. Guest beers such as Speckled Hen are an alternative to the 20 very reasonably priced wines.

CHEFS: Steven Doherty and Andrew McPherson   PROPRIETORS: Steven and Marjorie Doherty, Alan Bell and Lionel Yates   OPEN: all week 12 to 2, 6 to 9 (Mon to Fri D 6.30 to 9 Nov to Feb)   CLOSED: 10 days end Nov to Dec, and 25 Dec   MEALS: alc Mon to Sat (main courses £6 to £8). Set L and D Sun £7.95 (2 courses) to £9.95   SERVICE: not inc, card slips closed   CARDS: Access, Delta, Switch, Visa   DETAILS: 65 seats. 16 seats outside. Private parties: 30 main room. Car park. Vegetarian meals. Children's helpings. Smart dress preferred. No smoking in dining-room. Music   ACCOMMODATION: 3 rooms, all with bath/shower. TV. B&B £25 to £40. Deposit: £10. Children welcome

---

▲ *This symbol means accommodation is available.*

£ *indicates that it is possible to have a three-course meal, including coffee, a half-bottle of house wine and service, at any time the restaurant is open (i.e. at dinner as well as at lunch, unless a place is open only for dinner), for £20 or less per person.*

CRUDWELL Wiltshire   map 2

▲ *Crudwell Court* ♥ ⁵⚶

Crudwell, nr Malmesbury SN16 9EP
TEL: (01666) 577194   FAX: (01666) 577853   COOKING 2
on A429, 3m N of Malmesbury   COST £18–£51

There is a faint Arcadian Englishness about this seventeenth-century rectory
built of local oolitic Cotswold limestone. When the window shutters are opened,
guests can gaze over low box hedges towards the rose garden, rare magnolias
and lily pond. The interior is in keeping, with its wide oak corridor, and
panelled dining-room full of vases of flowers and comfortable armchairs. Dinner
is a three-course affair priced according to the main course, and Chris Amor's
cooking oozes confidence. Soft herring roes come in an 'utterly delicious' creamy
tarragon sauce, while parcels of seafood are baked in crispy, buttery filo pastry.
Main courses are equally assured: Scotch fillet steak ('perfectly seared yet
wonderfully rare') is served with a red wine sauce spiked with horseradish,
while pigeon breasts with chestnuts and bacon are roasted well beyond pink, a
device that imbues them with an unexpected but entirely convincing texture and
flavour. Vegetables are well timed and tantalising. The kitchen's signature
dessert – warm apricot and almond crumble cake with vanilla sauce –
thoroughly deserves its reputation. Nick Bristow serves impeccably.

The wine list, which spans the globe, has been put together with due care and
attention by a Master of Wine. Choice in France is inspired, but it's worth
browsing the New World section for a lively bottle. There's a wide choice of
half-bottles at the back of the list. Five house wines are under £10. CEL-
LARMAN'S CHOICE: Crozes-Hermitage, Mule Blanche 1993, Jaboulet, £14.25;
Pinotage 1991, Zonnebloem, Stellenbosch, South Africa, £13.50.

CHEF: Chris Amor   PROPRIETOR: Nick Bristow   OPEN: all week 12 to 2, 7 to 9.30   MEALS: Set L
Mon to Sat £7.50 (2 courses), Set L Sun £11.50, Set D £19.50 to £25.95   SERVICE: not inc, card
slips closed   CARDS: Access, Amex, Diners, Switch, Visa   DETAILS: 90 seats. Private parties:
60 main room, 30 and 60 private rooms. Car park. Vegetarian meals. Children's helpings. Smart
dress preferred. No smoking in dining-room. Wheelchair access (also WC). Music
ACCOMMODATION: 15 rooms, all with bath/shower. TV. Phone. B&B £50 to £114. Children
welcome. Baby facilities. Dogs welcome in bedrooms only. Afternoon teas. Garden.
Swimming-pool (*The Which? Hotel Guide*)

CUMNOR Oxfordshire   map 2

Bear & Ragged Staff ⁵⚶

Appleton Road, Cumnor OX2 9QH   COOKING 1*
TEL: (01865) 862329   FAX: (01865) 865366   COST £24–£51

Follow the lane past the duck-pond to reach this ancient 'conglomeration of
Cotswold-stone buildings'. Inside are all the trappings of a country pub –
flagstones, beams, 'unspoilt' décor. Here you can sit and have a plate of
fish-cakes with a couple of glasses of house wine; alternatively, order a pint of
Morrells before proceeding to the picture-filled dining-room. Bruce Buchan's
fish cooking is well regarded, and his menus bristle with lively ideas: skate with
crispy lardons, tomatoes and spring onions, turbot with grilled scallops and

pesto potatoes, or chargrilled monkfish with courgette salad. In the meat and game department there have also been good reports of warm salad of Toulouse sausage and pigeon, chicken teriyaki with spicy noodles, and fillet of beef with foie gras and lentils. Puddings are capably executed without gilding the lily. The mood is relaxing, although one reporter felt that service needed to be more organised. The wine list is short and reliable. House wine is £9.50.

CHEF: Bruce Buchan PROPRIETORS: Bruce and Kay Buchan OPEN: all week 12 to 2.15 (2.30 Sun), 7 to 10 CLOSED: 3 days between Christmas and New Year MEALS: alc (main courses £12 to £17). Set L Mon to Sat £12.50 (2 courses) to £14.50 SERVICE: not inc, card slips closed CARDS: Access, Amex, Delta, Switch, Visa DETAILS: 70 seats. Private parties: 50 main room, 20 and 55 private rooms. Car park. Vegetarian meals. Children's helpings. Smart dress preferred. No smoking in 1 dining-room. Wheelchair access (also WC). Music

---

DARLINGTON Co Durham   map 10

Cottage Thai

94–96 Parkgate, Darlington DL1 1RX   COOKING 1
TEL: (01325) 361717   COST £12–£39

Malinee Burachati's family and friends all seem to lend a helping hand in her unassuming restaurant opposite Darlington's Civic Theatre. As you might expect, the high-ceilinged dining-room is kitted out in true Thai fashion, right down to the carved deities and china elephants occupying much of the vacant space. The kitchen may have modest aspirations, but flavours are clear and dishes are ably executed. Satays, soups, curries, noodles and other staples are the mainstays, with one or two unusual items tossed in for good measure: tod mun pla is fried cod with green beans and curry paste. Set meals provide a useful trailer for the full repertoire. Drink jasmine tea or Singha Thai beer; house wine is £7.75.

CHEF/PROPRIETOR: Malinee Burachati OPEN: Mon to Sat 12 to 1.30, 6.30 to 10.15 CLOSED: first 2 weeks Aug MEALS: alc (main courses £6 to £9.50). Set L £5.50 to £5.95, Set D £14.95 to £23.95 SERVICE: not inc CARDS: Access, Amex, Switch, Visa DETAILS: 40 seats. Private parties: 50 main room. Vegetarian meals. Children welcome. Smart dress preferred. No-smoking area. Wheelchair access (also WC). Music

---

Victor's

84 Victoria Road, Darlington DL1 5JW   COOKING 2*
TEL: (01325) 480818   COST £16–£32

'Definitely a serious establishment,' summed up a reporter, although Victor's seems to thrive without the support that should be its due. It may not be the perkiest of dining-rooms, but the food is 'interesting, tasty and meticulously prepared' as well as 'copious'. Three courses are swelled to four with the addition of soup or sorbet, and coffee and sweets are included in the price. Local and seasonal materials underpin the operation, in which only an occasional Eastern gesture (such as Peking-style pork with bean sprout salad) ruffles the smooth Anglo-French surface. Egg florentine tartlet, or chicken liver pâté might be followed by jugged hare with herb dumplings, or roast bacon with pease pudding and parsley cream.

At Sunday lunch (once a month only, so far) Yorkshire pudding with onion gravy is given its proper place as a first course, and the usual choice of five items per course is followed. Value remains good, and such economies as have to be made in recessionary times are sensible ones. 'One adapts to suit changing times,' writes Jayne Robinson, who has reduced the number of cheeses on offer from fourteen to a more manageable five or six to ensure they are served in prime condition. Almost all of the 26 wines (the majority under £10 a bottle) are available by the glass.

CHEFS/PROPRIETORS: Peter and Jayne Robinson   OPEN: Sun L second Sun in month only 12 to 2, Mon (bookings only) to Sat D 7.30 to 10.30   MEALS: Set L Sun £10.95, Set D £20   SERVICE: not inc, card slips closed   CARDS: Access, Amex, Delta, Diners, Switch, Visa   DETAILS: 30 seats. Private parties: 30 main room. Children's helpings. Wheelchair access (no WC). Music

---

DARTMOUTH Devon   map 1

Billy Budd's

7 Foss Street, Dartmouth TQ6 9DW   COOKING 1
TEL/FAX: (01803) 834842   COST £16–£38

'We have long rated Billy Budd's as a no-nonsense high-value-for-money restaurant,' claim a pair of supporters. The pedestrianised street, one block back from the harbour, erupts into colourful floral displays in summer. Everything is relaxed and informal, and the bistro format is appreciated for its honest and straightforward approach. Local ingredients feature, notably fish, which might appear as grilled fillets of John Dory, or baked hake, and the repertoire runs from traditional salmon fish-cakes with béarnaise, through smoked venison with onion confiture, to fillet of beef with a garlic and pesto crust. Banana brûlée, or lemon icicle with strawberry coulis are typical ways to finish, and service is friendly and unhurried. Lunch is an altogether lighter affair featuring soup, a terrine, perhaps an omelette or chicken breast served with salad and potatoes. Two dozen uncomplicated wines match the style, beginning with house French and Australian at £9.50.

CHEF: Keith Belt   PROPRIETORS: Keith and Lynne Belt   OPEN: Tue to Sat and bank hol Mon 12 to 2, 7 to 10   CLOSED: 1 week Nov, 5 weeks Jan to Feb   MEALS: alc (main courses L £4 to £6, D £10 to £14)   SERVICE: not inc, card slips closed   CARDS: Access, Switch, Visa   DETAILS: 35 seats. Private parties: 25 main room. Vegetarian meals. Children's helpings. No children under 11 D. Smart dress preferred. No cigars/pipes in dining-room. Wheelchair access (no WC). Music

Carved Angel ▮ ✳

2 South Embankment, Dartmouth TQ6 9BH   COOKING 4
TEL: (01803) 832465   FAX: (01803) 835141   COST £37–£63

The bright, airy dining-room overlooks both the harbour and the smooth-running kitchen, as if to emphasise that cooking is not something that happens by magic behind closed doors. 'This is still the bench-mark we use to judge every other restaurant we visit,' claims one reporter, and the freshness of supplies is palpable: 'you feel that everything has been picked in the past 24 hours, not arrived jet-lagged from Zimbabwe.' The food thus follows the seasons. One couple who dined in May were 'longing to visit again at a different time of year, perhaps in autumn, to see how it deals with a different range of seasonal produce'.

Fish demonstrates the effectiveness of applying transparent cooking methods to doorstep supplies, as in a piece of brill steamed on the bone, 'a textbook example of how brill should taste', with a bouncy texture, served with baby clams in their shells and cooking liquor: 'as natural as could be, totally simple, totally wonderful,' enthused an inspector. Lunch and dinner menus offer a generous number of dishes, in each case bolstered by a less-expensive no-choice option. The foundation is Elizabeth David, with other ideas suggested by ingredients, or perhaps the kitchen staff, producing a wide range of dishes, from lobster and lemon-grass soup with crab-cakes, to roast best end of lamb (cooked pink and allowed to rest) with spiced couscous and aubergine.

One of the poorest dishes has been apple and rhubarb crumble, distinguished by rhubarb so undercooked as to be inedible, a pudding that Joyce Molyneux, 'had she been there', would not have allowed out of the kitchen. Therein lies one of the Angel's problems. When it is good, it is very, very good, but there are just a few occasions when it comes off the boil, and which seem to coincide with her absence. Estimates of the food's value naturally yo-yo with judgements of its quality, but it is worth noting that set prices include mineral water, bread, olives, amuse-gueules, and 'endless coffee served with fudge and chocolate truffles'. Service has been 'helpful, supportive, attentive, efficient' but also 'intrusive, indifferent, and not notably friendly'.

The wine list is exceptional in its range, quality and interest. It takes on board the unconventional, and provides good pointers for the non-buff by way of monthly selections and wines by the glass. It is a shame that house champagne has to be £7.50 a glass, though; go for one of the marvellous digestifs, perhaps one of six Madeiras by the glass. French and Italian house wines are £15 a bottle. CELLARMAN'S CHOICE: Ochoa Reserva 1987, Navarra, £15; Meursault 1982, Robert Ampeau, £41.25.

CHEFS: Nick Coiley and Joyce Molyneux   PROPRIETORS: Joyce Molyneux, Meriel Matthews, David Shephard and Nick Coiley   OPEN: Tue to Sun L 12.30 to 2, Tue to Sat D 7.30 to 9.30   CLOSED: 6 weeks from 1 Jan   MEALS: alc L (main courses £16 to £25). Set L Tue to Sat £15 (2 courses) to £29, Set L Sun £35, Set D £40 (2 courses) to £45   SERVICE: net prices, card slips closed   CARDS: Delta, Switch   DETAILS: 50 seats. Private parties: 40 main room, 12 and 20 private rooms. Vegetarian meals. Children's helpings. Children under 5 free of charge. Smart dress preferred. No smoking in dining-room. Wheelchair access (no WC). No music

DEDDINGTON Oxfordshire   map 5

Dexter's   NEW ENTRY

Market Place, Deddington OX15 0SE   COOKING 2
TEL: (01869) 338813   COST £19–£47

Jamie Dexter Harrison has done a great service to Deddington and its neighbourhood by opening this unpretentious village restaurant. Visitors can even enjoy morning coffee and afternoon tea in his stylish dining-room with its foodie prints on custard-coloured walls. Service, like the décor, is spruce. The menu is sensibly short and handwritten each week. Dexter's delivers acceptable versions of French bourgeois classics, such as moules marinière and chocolat St-Emilion, but excites more when the kitchen takes a modern view of things. Excellent ingredients and expert timing are the key to chicken livers on a carrot and turnip rösti with a 'nutty' grain-mustard sauce, and charred swordfish on a bed of Chinese egg noodles with lemon grass and black-bean sauce: 'a dish to write home about' in the words of one who wrote to us instead. Elsewhere, there's a rustic generosity about fricassee of chicken with wild mushrooms and tarragon mash. At inspection, vegetables and some of the incidentals could have been improved, but there is little to criticise when it comes to pear tart served with home-made honey and ginger ice-cream and caramel sauce. The wine list is admirably suited to the food, with plenty of interesting choices at affordable prices. House Vin de Pays d'Oc is £10.50.

CHEF/PROPRIETOR: Jamie Dexter Harrison OPEN: Tue to Sat 12 to 2.15, 7 to 10, and Sun brunch 11 to 3 CLOSED: first 2 weeks Jan MEALS: alc (main courses £6 to £15). Set L £7.50 (2 courses) to £10.50, Set D Tue to Fri £15.95 (2 courses) to £18.95 SERVICE: not inc, card slips closed CARDS: Access, Amex, Delta, Switch, Visa DETAILS: 35 seats. Private parties: 38 main room. Vegetarian meals. Children's helpings. Smart dress preferred. No cigars/pipes in dining-room. Wheelchair access (no WC). No music. Air-conditioned

DEDHAM Essex
map 6

▲ *Fountain House* ▼ ⁵✳

Dedham Hall, Brook Street, Dedham CO7 6AD	COOKING 1
TEL: (01206) 323027 FAX: (01206) 323293	COST £23–£30

This is a family-run restaurant and guesthouse in six acres of Constable country, with walks by the river and Flatford Mill. Dedham Hall also runs painting holidays in a converted barn studio. Lots of small rooms and antique furniture lend a feeling of intimacy to Fountain House, which thrives on plain, wholesome food using good ingredients. 'Generous portions well presented' is how one reporter summed up the fillet and sirloin steaks 'cooked as required'. Fish and vegetable dishes are not forgotten: giant prawns, goujons of plaice, stuffed mushrooms, and pancakes with cream cheese and herbs contribute to a wide choice, and a dozen puddings are not unusual. 'Huge' chocolate fondue for two people is always on the menu. The carefully chosen wines are grouped mainly by grape variety. It's a user-friendly list with an exemplary range of half-bottles and bin-ends at generous prices. Eight house wines start at £9 for Vins de Pays d'Oc. CELLARMAN'S CHOICE: Tim Adams Riesling 1993, Clare Valley, S. Australia, £16; Bourgogne Rouge 1990, Gouberd, £14.

CHEF: Wendy Sarton PROPRIETORS: James and Wendy Sarton OPEN: Sun L 12 to 2, Tue to Sat D 7 to 9.30 MEALS: Set L £16.50, Set D £18.50 SERVICE: not inc, card slips closed CARDS: Access, Delta, Switch, Visa DETAILS: 50 seats. Private parties: 50 main room. Car park. Vegetarian meals. Children's helpings. Smart dress preferred. No smoking in dining-room. Wheelchair access (also women's WC). Music ACCOMMODATION: 6 rooms, all with bath/shower. TV. B&B £34 to £57. Rooms for disabled. Children welcome. Baby facilities. Garden

▲ *Le Talbooth* 🍾

Gun Hill, Dedham CO7 6HP
TEL: (01206) 323150   FAX: (01206) 322309   COOKING **3**
on B1029, off A12, 6m NE of Colchester   COST £26–£61

This timbered-framed, master weaver's cottage by the Stour predates Constable's renowned paintings by more than a century, and it continues to nourish
East Anglia's culture-hungry incomers. 'Log fires in winter and outside dining
in summer make this a restaurant for all seasons,' writes Paul Milsom, son of
Gerald. A few fixtures on the *carte* are unchanging: Talbooth soufflé (Finnan
haddock with mushrooms), calf's liver and bacon with onion gravy, and beef en
croûte, which is carved in the neat and tidy dining-room, all seem set to last.

The style is true to English traditionalism – daily roasts on the lunchtime menu
– but it is also youthfully creative. Terry Barber's repertoire encompasses layered
Cromer crab with a salad of mange-tout, and pan-fried tiger prawns, as well as
duck breast served with a home-made duck sausage, braised cabbage and a
citrus sauce. A butcher's-block quartet of lamb (loin, leg, liver and cutlet) is
served with a mousse of sweetbreads and a rosemary and redcurrant *jus*.
Vegetarians might get a trio on the plate – skewered vegetables in tempura
batter, leek and potato gâteau with wild mushroom sauce, and a ratatouille tart
with pesto.

Vegetables have been highly praised, and desserts are a seductive assortment:
'chocolate tart (warm) with white chocolate ice-cream and Bailey's sauce,
though highly sinful, was excellent, even to one who has not really got a sweet
tooth,' admitted one reporter. As befits an establishment that runs on smooth
ambience and old style, service is dapper but friendly and efficient. Local
merchants Lay & Wheeler provide many of the wines on an excellent, classic list.
Prices rocket in the French section, but the high quality is beyond doubt.
Elsewhere, and especially among the sparkling wines and Italian and New
World sections, the choice is more down to earth. Seven house wines from five
countries start at £11.50. CELLARMAN'S CHOICE: Lugana Vigna I Frati 1994, Dal
Cero, £19.95.

CHEF: Terry Barber   PROPRIETOR: Gerald Milsom   OPEN: all week 12 to 2 (4.30 Sun in winter), 7
to 9.30   CLOSED: Sun D in winter   MEALS: alc (main courses £14 to £20). Set L £14.50 (2
courses) to £17, Set D £19.50 (2 courses) to £22.50   SERVICE: 10%, card slips closed   CARDS:
Access, Amex, Delta, Switch, Visa   DETAILS: 75 seats. 50 seats outside. Private parties: 80
main room, 30 private room. Car park. Vegetarian meals. Children's helpings. Smart dress
preferred. No cigars/pipes in dining-room. Wheelchair access (also WC). Music
ACCOMMODATION: 10 rooms, all with bath/shower. TV. Phone. B&B £85 to £140. Rooms for
disabled. Children welcome. Garden (*The Which? Hotel Guide*)

---

*'A customer of ours asked for an extra portion of mushrooms at the local American diner.
"No sir," said the waitress, "we cannot do that." Not because the kitchen didn't have any,
but because there was no code on her touch pad ordering system for extra portions.'*
(Lancashire restaurateur)

DENMEAD Hampshire   map 2

Barnard's ⅚✳

Hambledon Road, Denmead PO7 6NU
TEL/FAX: (01705) 257788
on B2150, 2m NW of Waterlooville

COOKING 2
COST £17–£52

'Finest fresh cuisine' is what David and Sandie Barnard's menu promises at their pleasing restaurant bedecked with big flower pictures. This is no place for risky gestures in either the kitchen or the dining-room. David's menu changes every few weeks, and there is a comforting familiarity about his French-inspired cooking. He seldom deviates from the straight and narrow, offering reliable dishes along the lines of 'superb' Swiss cheese soufflé baked with celery, or chicken and herb roulade. Fish varies with the market, although lobster is an ever-popular fixture. Among desserts you might find sauté peppered pineapple with caramelised crème de cacao sauce, and kirsch-soaked black cherries with blackcurrant sorbet. Coffee is reckoned to be 'excellent'. The slightly expanded wine list starts at £9 a bottle.

CHEF: David Barnard   PROPRIETORS: David and Sandie Barnard   OPEN: Wed to Fri L 12 to 1.45, Tue to Sat D 7 to 9.45   CLOSED: 1 week Christmas, 1 week Sept   MEALS: alc (main courses £13 to £22.50). Set L £10 to £16, Set D £16. BYO £3.50   SERVICE: not inc, card slips closed   CARDS: Access, Amex, Delta, Diners, Switch, Visa   DETAILS: 38 seats. Private parties: 34 main room, 18 and 34 private rooms. Car park. Vegetarian meals. Children's helpings. No smoking in dining-room. Music

DERBY Derbyshire   map 5

Darleys on the River ⅚✳   [NEW ENTRY]

Darley Abbey Mills, Darley Abbey, Derby DE22 1DL
TEL/FAX: (01332) 364987
off A6, 2m N of Derby city centre

COOKING 1
COST £20–£42

The setting is the converted works canteen of a nineteenth-century mill overlooking a bend in the Derwent where it tumbles dramatically down a steep weir. The interior eschews rugged utilitarianism in favour of voluminous pink and white curtains, wood-grained columns and beams. Don't expect much in the way of culinary pyrotechnics: instead, the kitchen works to its modest strengths. 'There is a decent honesty about it all,' noted one correspondent. The menu has its share of soups, pasta and salads, but branches out for black pudding with poached egg and mustard sauce, herb-crusted fillet of salmon, 'excellent' pan-fried scallops with dill, and roast duck with blueberry and orange sauce. Desserts are a mixed bag, but strawberry crumble, and pear tart with lime sauce have made the grade. Service is young and cheerful. The pleasantly surprising list of over 100 wines shows signs of care and knowledge. House wine is £10.

Dining-rooms where music, either live or recorded, is never played are signalled by No music *in the details at the end of an entry.*

CHEF: David Gillan   PROPRIETOR: David Pinchbeck   OPEN: all week L 12 to 2 (2.30 Sun), Mon to Sat D 7 to 10 (10.30 Sat)   CLOSED: bank hols   MEALS: alc (main courses £9 to £17). Set L £12.95. BYO £3   SERVICE: not inc   CARDS: Access, Amex, Delta, Diners, Switch, Visa   DETAILS: 80 seats. Private parties: 80 main room. Vegetarian meals. Children's helpings. Smart dress preferred. No smoking in dining-room. Wheelchair access (no WC). Music. Air-conditioned

---

DINTON Buckinghamshire   map 3

La Chouette

Westlington Green, Dinton HP17 8UW
TEL/FAX: (01296) 747422   COOKING 2
off A418, 4m SW of Aylesbury   COST £19–£58

'A very impressive lunch in a charming little restaurant situated in a beautiful village,' summed up a long-standing reporter. What is a Belgian restaurant doing in a quiet Buckinghamshire village of thatched houses? It is doing everything from a three-course lunch for £10 to a five-course dinner for £36 that includes 'filet of monkfish with a vodka sauce'. Frédéric Desmette's ornithological interests cover the walls of the former pub, but his culinary interests show a penchant for fish. Apart from monkfish, the set five-course dinner might also include a salad of char, and a fricassee of lobster with leek. The *carte*, meanwhile, adds scallops with chicory, salmon with spinach, and a dish of turbot and lobster with mousseline sauce.

A slight air of secrecy appears to surround some dishes – 'ask Frédéric' it says mysteriously on the menu under calves' sweetbreads with mustard sauce – but there is nothing covert about the results: the food impresses for its freshness, the cooking for its quality. As for service, 'Mr Desmette seemed to do everything', and will serve the £10 lunch in under an hour if requested. Wines tend to be grand, and the list could do with a wider and better selection under £15. House wine is £10, or you could choose from the ten or so Belgian beers, including Chimay and Hoegaarden.

CHEF/PROPRIETOR: Frédéric Desmette   OPEN: Mon to Fri L 12 to 2, Mon to Sat D 7 to 9   MEALS: alc (main courses £9 to £15). Set L £10 to £36, Set D £19.95 to £36. BYO by arrangement   SERVICE: 12.5%, card slips closed   CARDS: Access, Amex, Visa   DETAILS: 30 seats. 12 seats outside. Private parties: 40 main room. Car park. Children's helpings. Smart dress preferred. No cigars/pipes in dining-room. Wheelchair access (also WC). Music

---

DISS Norfolk   map 6

▲ Salisbury House ⁑✳

84 Victoria Road, Diss IP22 3JG   COOKING 2
TEL/FAX: (01379) 644738   COST £20–£48

The garden of this Victorian house (off the main road just outside Diss) turns into an extra dining-room in fine weather. An 'easy, pleasant atmosphere' pervades both restaurant and bistro, the latter geared for any number of courses from one upwards, offering a *carte* that might include terrines, steamed skate, home-made beefburger, pasta and salads, or (in winter) venison with red cabbage and chestnuts. By contrast, the restaurant deals in set-price dinners, the number of courses (minimum three, maximum five) determining the price. Fixed-price lunches are by appointment only.

Barry Davies adops a traditional style that many home cooks might recognise: a pancake filled with smoked haddock and glazed, for example, or goujons of chicken with a sweet-and-sour sauce. It is not too ambitious, and dishes stay comfortably within the kitchen's abilities, from pigeon breasts with brown lentils and a Madeira *jus*, to pork fillet topped with Stilton mousse, to lemon meringue pie or chocolate crème brûlée. Meals register accurate timing, sensible flavour combinations and appropriate saucing. Wines are varied in range and style, sensibly chosen, and priced very fairly, beginning with house vin de pays at under £8.

CHEF: Barry Davies   PROPRIETORS: Barry and Sue Davies   OPEN: restaurant Tue to Sat D only 7.15 to 9; L by appointment only; bistro Tue to Fri L 12.15 to 1.45, Tue to Sat D 7.15 to 9   MEALS: restaurant Set D £24.95 to £32.50; bistro alc (main courses £6 to £7.50). BYO £5   SERVICE: not inc   CARDS: Access, Visa   DETAILS: 36 seats. 10 seats outside. Private parties: 20 main room, 14 private room. Car park. Vegetarian meals bistro. Children's helpings. Smart dress preferred. No smoking in dining-room. Wheelchair access (also WC). Music   ACCOMMODATION: 3 rooms, all with bath/shower. TV. B&B £39 to £70. Deposit: £10 per person. Children welcome. Baby facilities. Garden (*The Which? Hotel Guide*)

Weavers Wine Bar & Eating House

Market Hill, Diss IP22 3JZ   COOKING 1
TEL: (01379) 642411   COST £18–£34

A couple who visited on a frosty February night were immediately enticed by the comforting warmth and friendliness of the place: 'no question of waiting for more bodies to arrive or the food to do its work.' The setting is a converted fifteenth-century chapel with low-ceilinged dining-rooms, high-backed settles, and windows overlooking the street. Lunch is a bargain for shoppers and business people alike, and evening menus are packed with lively ideas from around the world: mushrooms stuffed with celeriac and Roquefort on tagliatelle is an approved starter; main courses could range from skate with black butter and capers to rare poached pigeon breast with pickled cabbage and Dijon mustard sauce. Vegetarians have a big choice, while desserts are mostly hot puddings and sponges. The wine list has a strong New World contingent. House wine is £8.95.

CHEF: William Bavin   PROPRIETORS: William and Wilma Bavin   OPEN: Tue to Fri L 12 to 1.30, Mon to Sat D 7 to 9 (9.30 Sat)   CLOSED: last 2 weeks Aug, 2 weeks Christmas   MEALS: alc D (main courses £9 to £13). Set L £7.95 (2 courses) to £10.75, Set D Mon to Fri £12   SERVICE: not inc, card slips closed   CARDS: Access, Delta, Diners, Switch, Visa   DETAILS: 80 seats. Private parties: 50 main room, 50 private room. Vegetarian meals. Children's helpings. Smart dress preferred. No smoking before 2 L, 9.30 D. No cigars. Music

The Guide *relies on feedback from its readers. Especially welcome are reports on new restaurants appearing in the book for the first time. All letters to the* Guide *are acknowledged.*

DORCHESTER Oxfordshire	map 2

▲ George Hotel ♥

High Street, Dorchester OX10 7HH
TEL: (01865) 340404 FAX: (01865) 341620
on A423, 4m NW of Wallingford

COOKING 2
COST £22–£47

This amenable timber-framed hotel not far from Oxford must be one of the oldest surviving coaching-inns in England, having refreshed the weary traveller since the end of the fifteenth century. The present owners brought in David Allison to cook in 1994, and he has set to with a will in his mission to put the George on the culinary map.

Readers write in praise of the deftly presented and precisely seasoned food available on both the set-price menus and the evening *carte*. Fruit features in a number of dishes, as in pear filled with Stilton and celery mousse and smothered with a tarragon sauce, a brace of roast quail sauced with redcurrant and orange vinegar, and roast Gressingham duck with a cherry and brandy sauce. One couple happily finished a Valentine's Day dinner with 'light and delicate' chocolate mousse in a white chocolate heart surrounded by raspberry coulis. Service is 'consistent, interested and helpful'. Wines are sound and fairly priced; a long list of clarets is followed by the rest of France and a handful of good wines from several other major wine countries. Imaginative touches include an Australian dry Muscat and a Moldovan red. There are 26 half-bottles to choose from, and French house wines are £7.75. CELLARMAN'S CHOICE: Cape Charlotte Dry Muscat 1994, S.E. Australia, £11.10; Frankland Estate Isolation Ridge Shiraz 1993, W. Australia, £13.45.

CHEF: David Allison PROPRIETOR: Neville and Griffin Ltd   OPEN: all week 12 to 2, 7 to 9.30
MEALS: alc D (main courses £14 to £18). Set L £14.95, Set D £17.95. Bar food available
SERVICE: not inc   CARDS: Access, Amex, Delta, Diners, Switch, Visa   DETAILS: 26 seats. 20
seats outside. Private parties: 40 main room. Car park. Vegetarian meals. Children welcome.
Music. Air-conditioned   ACCOMMODATION: 18 rooms, all with bath/shower. TV. Phone. B&B
£52.50 to £75. Rooms for disabled. Children welcome. Baby facilities. Dogs welcome.
Afternoon teas. Garden (*The Which? Hotel Guide*)

DORKING Surrey	map 3

Partners West Street 🐟✳

2–4 West Street, Dorking RH4 1BL
TEL: (01306) 882826

COOKING 2*
COST £25–£48

'There's not much you can do with a heavily beamed Elizabethan room décor-wise, except leave the character to speak for itself.' And so it does, give or take a busy carpet and some cheerful flowery prints. The dining-rooms are on two floors, and set menus offer good value, although the *carte* may sound more interesting: woodpigeon soup with pistachio wun-tun, for example. Gutsy and concentrated flavours derive from good ingredients, and portions are generous. Cornish crab-cakes are an old favourite here – 'probably the best fish-cakes I've ever tasted' – and a huge chunk of tender pork stuffed with sage and onion and served with bubble and squeak is distinguished by 'bags of flavour'.

Well-controlled timing has produced a 'fairly bloody' duck breast, and saucing is good. An inspector felt that a pastry 'trellis' for the duck was redundant, and concluded that 'if they cut out a few trimmings' the package would be even better. Service at inspection could also have been sharper; taking the wine order after the first course has arrived is not ideal practice, nor are long waits for the bill. The wine list includes some good bottles, but at highish prices. Local Denbies Bacchus is £16.95.

CHEF: Paul Boyland   PROPRIETOR: Partners Restaurants plc   OPEN: Mon to Fri and Sun L 12 to 2, Mon to Sat D 7 to 9.30   MEALS: alc (main courses £12.50 to £17). Set L £8.95 (2 courses), Set D Mon to Fri £17.50   SERVICE: not inc   CARDS: Access, Amex, Delta, Diners, Switch, Visa   DETAILS: 50 seats. Private parties: 36 main room, 20 and 36 private rooms. Children's helpings. No smoking in dining-room. Wheelchair access (no WC). No music

---

DORRINGTON Shropshire   map 5

▲ *Country Friends* 🍴✶   ✓ 25/1/97

Dorrington SY5 7JD
TEL: (01743) 718707   COOKING 3
on A49, 5m S of Shrewsbury   COST £34–£45

The Whittakers have run this roadside halt since the early 1980s, and take things at a gentle pace. A log fire burns in the grate, and dishes on the set-price menus (the same at lunch and dinner) are described simply, as in lamb with an olive and caper sauce, or tea-smoked duck with pineapple and date salsa. The style is an unshowy version of English country cooking that evolves slowly. Chicken breast cooked in pastry with smoked chicken mousse is a more sophisticated version of a similar dish (stuffed with cream cheese and herbs) that has featured for years: just-cooked chicken and first-class pastry, helped by an accompanying wild mushroom and Madeira sauce, lift the dish well above the ordinary.

Good materials and accurate timing are the foundation, while a restrained and sensible handling of accompaniments is to be found in pink pigeon breasts served with braised pearl barley, or roasted halibut with a professionally made and exciting sorrel hollandaise. Queen of puddings is something of a signature dish, while bread is described as 'splendid'. All in all, praise has come for 'super cooking, particularly fine puddings and very friendly service'. The wine list has a sharp eye for quality at all levels, and much of it is reasonably priced, beginning with house French and Australian at £10.50.

CHEF: Charles Whittaker   PROPRIETORS: Charles and Pauline Whittaker   OPEN: Tue to Sat 12 to 2, 7 to 9 (9.30 Sat)   CLOSED: 7 to 21 July   MEALS: Set L and D £22 (2 courses) to £28.95. Bar L available   SERVICE: not inc   CARDS: Access, Switch, Visa   DETAILS: 40 seats. Private parties: 40 main room. Car park. Vegetarian meals. Children welcome. No smoking in dining-room. Wheelchair access (no WC). No music   ACCOMMODATION: 3 rooms, 1 with bath/shower. D,B&B £60 to £98. Children welcome. Garden

---

The text of entries is based on unsolicited reports sent in by readers, backed up by inspections conducted anonymously. The factual details under the text are from questionnaires the Guide *sends to all restaurants that feature in the book.*

DREWSTEIGNTON Devon   map 1

▲ *Hunts Tor* ⅚✳

Drewsteignton EX6 6QW   COOKING 2*
TEL: (01647) 281228   COST £26–£36

'We like everything about it,' enthused one couple who stayed a week: 'the art deco china; pictures and objects around the rooms; the service, which is exactly right; the attention to detail; but above all the meals.' Hunts Tor is one of a handful of micro-restaurants around Britain – it only seats eight – the very antithesis of London trends, and much appreciated by reporters.

Organic produce is used wherever possible, and the Harrisons grow some of their own soft fruit, salad ingredients and herbs. Meals are well balanced: for example, chargrilled vegetables with pesto and rocket salad, followed by cod with a herb crust served with borlotti beans, finishing with nougat glacé with a raspberry coulis. There is no choice on the menu, which is the reason it was 'all so perfect' for one reporter who enjoyed double-baked cheese soufflé, maize-fed chicken in ginger and soy sauce, and summer pudding. The short wine list stays mostly under £20, thanks to considerate mark-ups, although there are no half-bottles (except for a champagne) or wines by the glass.

CHEF: Sue Harrison   PROPRIETORS: Sue and Chris Harrison   OPEN: all week D only, 7.30 (1 sitting; 24 hours' notice essential)   CLOSED: end Oct to early Mar   MEALS: Set D £18 to £21 SERVICE: not inc   CARDS: none   DETAILS: 8 seats. Private parties: 8 main room. No children under 10. Smart dress preferred. No smoking in dining-room. Music   ACCOMMODATION: 4 rooms, all with bath/shower. TV in 3 rooms. B&B £30 to £70. Deposit: £10. No children under 10. Dogs welcome in bedrooms only

---

DRYBROOK Gloucestershire   map 5

Cider Press ⅚✳   ✓ 14/e/97

The Cross, Drybrook GL17 9EB   COOKING 2
TEL: (01594) 544472   COST £22–£38

Drybrook lies between the Severn and the Wye, near the Gloucestershire–Herefordshire border, and is home to Bernadette Fitzpatrick's cheerful white-painted roadside restaurant. Knick-knacks of all sorts crowd the dining-room. Organic and free-range are the credo of the kitchen. First courses may include quail stuffed with wild rice, prunes, almonds and sage, while among the main courses may be 'beautifully supple, nicely hung' venison with juniper and allspice, or a signature dish of roast pheasant served with apples, calvados and crème fraîche. Occasionally one strong flavour resounds too stridently in a dish, as in the tang of lemon in a smooth mushroom soup, or apple purée lacing kipper pâté. Those who don't have a sweet tooth may find the cheeses a better bet than the 'very rich, indulgent and delicious' puddings such as caramel meringue ice-cream and pecan toffee cheesecake. The wine list is concise and good, its organic offerings asterisked. House Italian is £7.95.

CHEF: Christopher Stephen Challener   PROPRIETOR: Bernadette Fitzpatrick   OPEN: Wed to Sat
D only 7 to 11; Wed to Sun L and Sun and Mon D by arrangement   CLOSED: first 2 weeks Jan
MEALS: alc (main courses £9 to £14)   SERVICE: not inc   CARDS: Access, Delta, Visa   DETAILS:
24 seats. 8 seats outside. Private parties: 28 main room. Children's helpings. Smart dress
preferred. No smoking in dining-room. Wheelchair access (also WC). Music

---

DURHAM   Co Durham   map 10

Bistro 21 £   NEW ENTRY

Aykley Heads House, Aykley Heads,
Durham DH1 5TS   COOKING 2
TEL: (0191) 384 4354   FAX: (0191) 384 1149   COST £20–£38

It has become standard practice for talented chefs to put themselves about a bit.
Terence Laybourne made a great success of 21 Queen Street (see entry,
Newcastle upon Tyne), opened Café 21 in 1994 (see entry, Ponteland), and then
this in May 1996. The principle is a sound one: good sous-chefs learn their trade
from the master (Adrian Watson was at Queen Street) then want some
independence, but probably can't afford to set up on their own. This way,
Laybourne keeps it all in the family, and is able to oversee their progress.

It is an unusual set-up: a sixteenth-century farmhouse that now finds itself in a
business park, brought into the '90s with a sunny ochre paint job. 'I loved the
country-chic look of the place, and the easy, enthusiastic style and atmosphere,'
declared an early visitor as it got off to a cracking start. The food is full of forceful,
confident ideas, from Mediterranean rustic – grilled polenta with asparagus,
field mushrooms and shaved Parmesan – to a more traditional British style of
potted ham knuckle with piccalilli, or deep-fried plaice with tartare sauce and
chips. The passion for exuberant colour and big flavours is anchored in sound
techniques. Finish with pavlova, crème caramel, or knickerbocker glory, and
drink from a short, varied, well-priced selection of wines, including house
French at £9.50.

CHEF: Adrian Watson   PROPRIETORS: Terence and Susan Laybourne   OPEN: Tue to Sat 12 to
2.30, 6 to 10.30   CLOSED: bank hols   MEALS: alc (main courses £7 to £12.50). Set L £11.50 (2
courses) to £13.50   SERVICE: not inc   CARDS: Access, Amex, Delta, Diners, Visa   DETAILS: 90
seats. 25 seats outside. Private parties: 55 main room, 10 to 20 private rooms. Car park.
Vegetarian meals. Children's helpings. Smart dress preferred. No pipes in dining-room.
Wheelchair access (also WC). Music

EAST BOLDON   Tyne & Wear   map 10

Forsters

2 St Bedes, Station Road, East Boldon NE36 0LE
TEL: (0191) 519 0929   COOKING 2
on main Newcastle to Sunderland road   COST £22–£40

'We have eaten at Forsters perhaps six times in the last 18 months and never had
a poor meal. The menu doesn't change much, but what Mr Forster cooks is
always good.' Barry and Sue Forster aim to serve 'decent food without
snobbery', and they see the restaurant not as a temple of gastronomy, but 'just a

venue for a good night out'. This realistic and straightforward approach is much appreciated and results in dishes as homely as lentil soup, sticky toffee pudding, or a mixed grill of fillet steak, pork escalope, sausage, black pudding, buttered mash and onion gravy. Poached eggs usually crop up, perhaps in a Caesar salad, or on a toasted muffin with smoked salmon and hollandaise sauce. Cheese soufflés are highly praised, and chocolate desserts have impressed for their bitterness, intensity and smoothness. Wines are sensibly priced, with a good selection under £10 a bottle. The majority are from France, and house wine from Duboeuf is £8.15.

CHEF: Barry Forster   PROPRIETORS: Barry and Sue Forster   OPEN: Tue to Sat D only 7 to 9.30
CLOSED: 1 week Christmas, 1 week May, 1 week Aug, bank hols   MEALS: alc (main courses
£11.50 to £14). Set D Tue to Fri £16. BYO £3.50   SERVICE: not inc   CARDS: Access, Amex,
Diners, Visa   DETAILS: 30 seats. Private parties: 30 main room. Car park. Children welcome.
Smart dress preferred. No cigars/pipes in dining-room. Music

EASTBOURNE East Sussex   map 3

▲ Grand Hotel, Mirabelle

Jevington Gardens, Eastbourne BN21 4EQ   COOKING 3*
TEL: (01323) 410771   FAX: (01323) 412233   COST £26–£59

Sitting low in its gardens behind the sea-front, the hotel is an imposing 'haven of peace and tranquillity', quiet and cool, elegantly furnished with a pleasingly extravagant use of space. Here is a chance to eat in the grand manner. Service is formal – there are domes to be lifted – but friendly. Meals are decked out with appetiser soups, mid-meal sorbets, and first-rate petits fours with coffee, all of which contribute to the set menu's good value.

Lunch might begin with soup, pasta or salad, followed by pigeon breast with potato cake, breadcrumbed cod or something from the trolley, then maybe iced pear soufflé with cinnamon cream. The price of the fixed-price dinner varies with the main course: perhaps saddle of rabbit, or a more unusual savoury bread-and-butter pudding with morel cream sauce. A *carte* offers more choice. The food generally runs along classical lines, with a few twists and turns from the lively kitchen brigade, such as a bacon and thyme risotto to accompany guinea-fowl, or rack of lamb perked up with a Cajun spiced crust and a coriander *jus*.

Baked egg custard tart is a rarity these days, and all the more welcome for that, here served with red berries and a mousseline sauce, or there might be a hot mango Tatin with a watermelon and lime sorbet. Cheeses, which might include local Gospel Green and Greenacre Farm goats', are 'arranged in order of strength' and served with walnut and raisin bread. The wine list makes a good stab at appealing to a range of tastes and pockets, with some very decent drinking under £20. House wine is £10.75.

All entries in the Guide *are rewritten every year, not least because restaurant standards fluctuate. Don't rely on an out-of-date* Guide.

CHEFS: Keith Mitchell and Mark Jones   PROPRIETOR: De Vere Hotels   OPEN: Tue to Sat 12.30 to 2, 7 to 10   CLOSED: 1 to 15 Jan, 30 July to 12 Aug   MEALS: alc D (main courses £16.50 to £22). Set L £15.50 (2 courses) to £18.50, Set D £24 to £31   SERVICE: not inc   CARDS: Access, Amex, Diners, Visa   DETAILS: 45 seats. Private parties: 50 main room. Car park. Vegetarian meals. Children's helpings. Jacket and tie. Wheelchair access (also WC). Music. Air-conditioned ACCOMMODATION: 164 rooms, all with bath/shower. TV. Phone. D,B&B £91.50 to £170. Rooms for disabled. Children welcome. Baby facilities. Dogs welcome in bedrooms only. Afternoon teas. Garden. Swimming-pool

---

EAST BUCKLAND   Devon   map 1

▲ *Lower Pitt* 🍴✳

East Buckland EX32 0TD
TEL/FAX: (01598) 760243   COOKING 1*
2m N of A361, 4m NW of South Molton   COST £24–£35

This restaurant-with-rooms (a farmhouse in a previous life) is rather isolated and seems timeless, an impression strengthened by the gentle attentions of Jerome and Suzanne Lyons, and by a menu that changes little in style from one year to the next. Suzanne Lyons has been doing the cooking here, single-handedly, for the last 18 years, using West Country produce in traditional game bourguignonne, but also offering more exotic Thai prawn stir-fry or Moroccan lamb tagine with couscous. This is country cooking at its most contemporary, happy to borrow from any source.

The whitewashed dining-room extends into a conservatory that looks on to an attractive garden, whence come vegetables and herbs in season. Trelough duckling is organically reared in a Herefordshire orchard. Treatments are often simple, yet the results can be as comforting as twice-baked cheese soufflé or sticky toffee banana split. Black Forest cherry roulade is a flour-free sponge. Wines are a sound collection that chart the world from New Zealand to South Africa and Lebanon. Twenty-one half-bottles should suffice. House wines start at £8.90.

CHEF: Suzanne Lyons   PROPRIETORS: Jerome and Suzanne Lyons   OPEN: all week D 7 to 9 (booking essential Sun and Mon), L by arrangement   CLOSED: 25 Dec, 1 Jan   MEALS: alc (main courses £9.50 to £11).   SERVICE: not inc, card slips closed   CARDS: Access, Amex, Delta, Switch, Visa   DETAILS: 32 seats. 12 seats outside. Private parties: 16 main room. Car park. Vegetarian meals. Children's helpings. No children under 5. Smart dress preferred. No smoking in dining-room. No music   ACCOMMODATION: 3 rooms, all with bath/shower. D,B&B £50 to £110. Deposit: 10%. Garden (*The Which? Hotel Guide*)

EAST GRINSTEAD   West Sussex   map 3

▲ *Gravetye Manor* 🍾 🍴✳

Vowels Lane, East Grinstead RH19 4LJ
TEL: (01342) 810567   FAX: (01342) 810080   COOKING 3
off B2028, 2m SW of East Grinstead   COST £37–£91

Gravetye is as secluded as they come, hidden away in a thousand-acre forest. It is a delight, in fine weather, to sit in William Robinson's English Natural Garden, admire the plants, the creepers and mullioned windows of the Elizabethan manor-house, and wander in to the comfortable, relaxing club-like rooms. Mark Raffan's modern Anglo-French repertoire suits the elevated circumstances well. Luxurious gestures abound – for which there is a price to pay – but the kitchen knows how to handle the raw materials, producing warm foie gras pithiviers, pike sausage with cep sauce, and a fricassee of lobster with squid ink noodles.

Buying is manifestly good, the level of skill is high, and the right flavours come through, whether delicate, as in asparagus mousse with quail's eggs, or more robust, as in roast partridge with bread sauce. The earthiness of a braised ham hock salad with lentils nicely balances the refinement of a tian of crab with roast scallops, and well-judged timing results in, for example, 'excellent' pink calf's liver. Saucing is varied, from sorrel butter for wild salmon, to a liquorice-flavoured accompaniment for Gressingham duck, although generous amounts of sauce can make the plated vegetables slightly 'soggy' by the time they arrive at table.

Desserts are 'well above average' in the view of a reporter who enjoyed a caramel mousse with a poached Williams pear and honey ice-cream, and the cheeseboard offers a very respectable alternative. 'Courteous and discreet' service, one reporter noted, 'doesn't speak English', but somebody can usually be found to interpret if required. Quirkily, service is included in the prices but VAT isn't. The wine list is exemplary, full of magnums and halves, fine vintages and yardstick wines. France gets the most thorough treatment, and the German wines are worth poring over. Prices are not uniformly low, but neither are they shocking (although, again, VAT must be added), and the quality is assured. House French is £15.50. CELLARMAN'S CHOICE: Santenay, Clos Rousseau 1992, Dom. Prieur-Brunet, £34.50; Crozes-Hermitage 1989, Paul Jaboulet, £27.

CHEF: Mark Raffan PROPRIETORS: the Herbert family OPEN: all week 12.30 to 1.45, 7.30 to 9.30 (9.45 Sat, 8.45 Sun) CLOSED: D 25 Dec exc for residents MEALS: alc (main courses £16 to £25). Set L Mon to Sat £24, Set L Sun £30, Set D £30; all prices exclusive of VAT SERVICE: net prices, card slips closed CARDS: Access, Visa DETAILS: 55 seats. Private parties: 8 main room, 16 private room. Car park. Children's helpings. No children under 7. Smart dress preferred. No smoking in dining-room. No music ACCOMMODATION: 18 rooms, all with bath/shower. TV. Phone. Room only £85 to £210 – plus VAT. Deposit: 1 night's stay. No children under 7. Baby facilities. Garden. Fishing (*The Which? Hotel Guide*)

EAST WITTON North Yorkshire   map 8

▲ *Blue Lion*

East Witton DL8 4SN
TEL: (01969) 624273   FAX: (01969) 624189
on A6108 Masham to Leyburn road, 2m SE of   COOKING 1
Middleham   COST £26–£43

'Another wonderful Dales pub' is one reporter's verdict on this re-vamped coaching-inn not far from Jervaulx Abbey. Visitors can choose between a short *carte* in the dining-room and an ambitious bar menu chalked on boards above the fireplace. Good ideas abound. Warm onion tart is served with rocket, crispy-skinned confit of duck is accompanied by 'small spicy black-pudding sausages'. Chris Clarke aims for generosity, offering grilled tuna steak, pot-roast pigeon, braised lamb shank with horseradish dumplings, and sauté beef with tarragon cream, paprika and brandy sauce, and creamed gnocchi ('I needed to do a lot of walking to justify this!' admitted the beef-eater). Great helpings of vegetables and puddings such as treacle sponge or raspberry bavarois are also in the trencherman mould. Black Sheep Bitter is on draught, and eight wines are served by the glass from a seriously considered, 100-strong list. House wine is £8.95.

CHEF: Chris Clarke   PROPRIETOR: Paul Klein   OPEN: Sun L 12 to 2, Tue to Sat D 7 to 9.30
MEALS: alc (main courses £11.50 to £14.50). Bar meals L and D all week   SERVICE: not inc
CARDS: Access, Delta, Switch, Visa   DETAILS: 70 seats. 20 seats outside. Private parties: 40 main room, 16 private room. Car park. Vegetarian meals. Children's helpings. No music ACCOMMODATION: 12 rooms, all with bath/shower. TV. Phone. B&B £35 to £80. Children welcome. Baby facilities. Pets welcome. Afternoon teas. Garden

---

EDENBRIDGE Kent   map 3

Honours Mill

87 High Street, Edenbridge TN8 5AU   COOKING 3
TEL: (01732) 866757   COST £23–£50

The comfortable dining-room makes an agreeable setting for Martin Radmall's cooking, and choice on the set-price menus is wide enough to make a *carte* redundant. Prices range from £15.50 (lunch-time only) all the way up to £32.75, but there is no question: the food is worth the price. 'Lunch itself is certainly excellent value,' wrote one, while another agreed that the Mill is to be cherished: 'This is a special place.'

Simpler and often lighter dishes are the preserve of the less-expensive option: English asparagus brushed with truffle oil, followed by stuffed breast of chicken with leeks at lunch, or perhaps moules marinière followed by a sausage of sweetbreads with green lentils at dinner, and then a dessert of the day. The extra time and effort that go into the more-expensive menu are well worth the extra cost. Baron of rabbit might be served with glazed root vegetables, beef fillet with a herb and potato pancake (and a thyme and lemon-grass sauce), while a rich pot-au-feu packs in oxtail, beef, salt pork, lambs' tongue and confit of duck. Sussex pond pudding, or roast pears with meringues and blackcurrants, shows that the kitchen is not stuck in the sticky toffee mould. One reporter would have preferred more knowledgeable service when it came to wine but, on the plus side, the list includes some interesting French regional offerings. A few New World bottles are also available, though mark-ups here are on the high side; house wine is £10.15.

CHEF: Martin Radmall   PROPRIETORS: Neville, Duncan and Giles Goodhew   OPEN: Tue to Fri and Sun L 12.15 to 2, Tue to Sat D 7.15 to 10   CLOSED: 2 weeks after Christmas   MEALS: Set L Tue to Fri £15.50 to £32.75, Set L Sun £23.50, Set D Tue to Fri £26 (inc wine), Set D Tue to Sat £32.75   SERVICE: not inc   CARDS: Access, Visa   DETAILS: 36 seats. Private parties: 40 main room. Children's helpings. Smart dress preferred. No music

---

All main entries are fully indexed at the back of the Guide.

ELLAND West Yorkshire   map 8

La Cachette 🍷

7–10 Town Hall Buildings, Elland HX5 0EU
TEL: (01422) 378833   FAX: (01422) 377899

COOKING 1
COST £19–£41

This was once renowned as Bertie's Bistro but has been radically transformed by
the owners of Sous le Nez en Ville (see entry, Leeds). The place now has a sharper
metropolitan edge, with pine floors, terracotta and buttercup-yellow walls, and
staff who dash about a lot. A blackboard of fish specials augments the lively
menu, which has spoonfuls of sun-dried tomato purée, and pesto in abundance.
The kitchen delivers. Wild mushroom and potato cake, and a spicy aubergine
salad with tsatsiki have been praised as starters, while main courses could
include anything from Cajun monkfish to rabbit with spinach and mustard
sauce, to roast guinea-fowl with sauerkraut. Chips are 'home-made', although
one reporter thought they 'wouldn't have passed muster at Elland Road football
ground'. To conclude, there are a few simple puddings such as French
cheesecake.

The vast wine list is worth spending some time over. A strong all-rounder, it's
good within and without France, provides plenty by the glass and keeps prices
well in check. The large number of drinkable wines under £12 is impressive.
House wines start at £8.50. CELLARMAN'S CHOICE: Soave Classico 1994,
Anselmi, £12.95; Fleurie 1994, Michel Chignard, £17.95.

CHEFS: Mark Audsley and Eric Poli   PROPRIETOR: C&O Partnership   OPEN: Mon to Sat 12 to
2.30, 6 to 10 (11 Fri and Sat)   CLOSED: 25 and 26 Dec, 1 and 2 Jan, L bank hols   MEALS: alc
(main courses £7 to £13). Set D 6 to 7.30 £13.95. BYO £5. Bar meals available   SERVICE: not inc,
card slips closed   CARDS: Access, Amex, Delta, Switch, Visa   DETAILS: 160 seats. Private
parties: 50 main room, 12 to 56 private rooms. Vegetarian meals. Children welcome. Smart
dress preferred. No cigars/pipes in dining-room. Wheelchair access (no WC). Music. Air-
conditioned

ELY Cambridgeshire   map 6

Old Fire Engine House 🍷 ✳

25 St Mary's Street, Ely CB7 4ER
TEL: (01353) 662582

COOKING 1
COST £26–£40

The eighteenth-century brick building just west of the cathedral was once a
farmhouse, and serves food that is not a million miles from its roots: roasts,
casseroles and pies using local asparagus, eels, marsh samphire, pike, zander
and old recipes. There appear to be no secrets. 'You walk into the dining-room
past the kitchen where the jolly cooks are chopping and boiling things up', and
the reliability of the cooking is taken for granted by reporters, perhaps not
surprising after 24 unbroken years in the *Guide* under the same ownership. There
may not be much in the way of technical sophistication, but there is a feeling of
integrity, and the kitchen applies the right skills to the right materials and comes
up with a much underrated lovage soup in season, pigeon casserole, rabbit with
mustard and parsley, and steak and kidney pie with a 'beautiful light crust'.
Finish with syllabub, or apple pie and cream. Service is 'attentive'. Wine is taken

ENGLAND

seriously, and the well-annotated list is a helpful guide to a fine range, particularly from France. Wines by the glass are a strength, and the Chilean house wines are good value at £8. CELLARMAN'S CHOICE: Reiler Moullay-Hofberg Riesling Spätlese 1990, Rudolf Müller, £13.95; Chianti Classico 1988, Isole e Olena, £16.

CHEF: Terri Kindred   PROPRIETORS: Ann Ford and Michael Jarman   OPEN: all week L 12.30 to 2, Mon to Sat D 7.30 to 9   CLOSED: 24 Dec to 5 Jan, bank hols   MEALS: alc (main courses £11.50 to £14)   SERVICE: not inc   CARDS: Access, Delta, Switch, Visa   DETAILS: 36 seats. 24 seats outside. Private parties: 30 main room, 12 and 22 private rooms. Car park. Vegetarian meals. Children's helpings. No smoking in 1 dining-room. No music

---

EMSWORTH Hampshire   map 2

Spencers

36 North Street, Emsworth PO10 7DG   COOKING 2*
TEL/FAX: (01243) 372744   COST £22–£47

Gas-lamps give a clue that the building is Victorian – it dates from around 1850 – while bookshelves and an art deco radio playing soft jazz contribute to the 'homely and cottagey' effect. 'What a treat to go somewhere so unpretentious yet so professional where it matters,' concluded one reporter. Lunch and dinner are taken equally seriously, judging by the length of the menus, and Denis Spencer allows himself to concentrate on main-course cooking-to-order by serving predominantly cold starters along the lines of smoked trout pâté, or wild rabbit and hazelnut terrine. His centre of gravity is somewhere in France, which accounts for roast pork fillet with apple and prunes, and baked duck breast with Puy lentils, but local fishermen supply brill for steaming, and skate wing for grilling. 'If I were at home I'd run my finger round the plate,' was a comment prompted by a fruit-filled meringue nest with mango purée, one of five or six desserts that might also include brioche and apricot pudding, or chocolate and walnut torte. A modest but effective wine list is kind to the pocket, with house wines £9.50. A brasserie, called Downstairs at Spencers, is open all day Monday to Friday from 10am.

CHEF: Denis Spencer   PROPRIETORS: Denis and Lesley Spencer   OPEN: Tue to Fri L 12 to 2, Tue to Sat D 7.30 to 10.30   CLOSED: 25 and 26 Dec   MEALS: alc L (main courses £8 to £10.50). Set D £18.50 (2 courses) to £24.50   SERVICE: not inc, card slips closed   CARDS: Access, Amex, Delta, Switch, Visa   DETAILS: 34 seats. Private parties: 24 main room, 10 private room. Vegetarian meals. Children welcome. Smart dress preferred. No cigars/pipes before 10. Music. Air-conditioned

---

EPWORTH North Lincolnshire   map 9

Epworth Tap £

9–11 Market Place, Epworth DN9 1EU
TEL: (01427) 873333 FAX: (01427) 875020   COOKING 2
3m S of M180, junction 2   COST £20–£36

The Tap opened in 1979, in the heyday of wine bars, which goes some way to explaining the equal importance placed on food and wine in this converted pub.

It is a small and personal enterprise in the middle of a pleasant village, with a hands-on owner from whom 'there is always a warm welcome'. 'A likeable, unpretentious place, deservedly popular in the area' is how one regular reporter sees it. The three-course set menu offers a fair choice and demonstrates an integrity in the sourcing of raw materials, and sound cooking 'without much in the way of fancy presentation'.

Parslied ham in Riesling jelly is a simple and refreshing first course, fish has been 'fresh and well-timed', and a French provincial theme runs through the repertoire, in the form of chicken breast bonne femme, or loin of pork stuffed with prunes. Chocolate nemesis, and sticky toffee pudding might give dessert wines a hard time, but the list is well worth lingering over, for the cellar is a treasure trove of old and rare bottles as well as modern classics. Many of the prices, particularly for mature fine wines, are remarkably low. Anyone with a flagging interest in wine should be instantly revived, and John Wynne's wise advice only adds to the experience. House wines are from £8.50. CELLARMAN'S CHOICE: Coteaux du Languedoc, Dom. Peyre Rose 1993, M. Soria, £12.50; Devil's Lair Pinot Noir 1994, Margaret River, W. Australia, £20.

CHEF/PROPRIETOR: Helen Wynne OPEN: Thurs to Sat D only 7.30 to 9.15 MEALS: alc (main courses £8 to £12.50). Set D £17.95. BYO £5 SERVICE: not inc, card slips closed CARDS: Access, Delta, Switch, Visa DETAILS: 50 seats. Private parties: 30 main room. Children's helpings. Smart dress preferred. No smoking in dining-room. Music

---

ERPINGHAM Norfolk   map 6

▲ *Ark* ❢ ⁵⚹

The Street, Erpingham NR11 7QB
TEL: (01263) 761535
on A140 Cromer road, 4m N of Aylsham

COOKING 2
COST £20–£45

The Kidds have made this modest flint cottage a favourite Norfolk bolt-hole, offering guests country-style accommodation and forthright, earthy food. From their dining-room you may be able to spy not only a croquet lawn but also the kitchen garden which provides the family with some startlingly fresh produce. They make everything from breads to chocolates, and plunder Norfolk suppliers for the best of the rest. Dinner is fixed-price for two, three or four courses, and you can imagine the spirit of Elizabeth David overseeing events at the stoves, although quite what she would have made of smoked haddock mousseline with mango salsa is anybody's guess. For the most part the repertoire is a reassuring mix of Anglo-French and Mediterranean: witness feuilleté of wild mushrooms with broccoli purée, monkfish with celery sauce, and spiced lamb braise. Lobster appears as a fricassee, duck is roasted the old way, and venison steak comes with either pears and cinnamon or onion marmalade. For dessert you might choose anything from 'super' crème brûlée to redcurrant ice-cream with strawberries and shortbread biscuits; otherwise there are prime cheeses from Neals Yard Dairy.

The tally of house wines has moved up to 12, all under £10. Prices are equally well reined in throughout the lengthy list, which pauses at most major regions of the world. Half-bottle and fine wine supplements round things off nicely.

CELLARMAN'S CHOICE: Mulderbosch Sauvignon Blanc 1995, Stellenbosch, South Africa, £14.75; Chianti Rufina, Villa di Vetrice Riserva 1985, £12.50.

CHEF: Sheila Kidd   PROPRIETORS: Mike and Sheila Kidd   OPEN: Sun L 12.30 to 2, Tue to Sat D 7 to 9.30   CLOSED: Tue Oct to Easter   MEALS: Set L £13.25, Set D £18.50 (2 courses) to £24 SERVICE: not inc   CARDS: none   DETAILS: 36 seats. 12 seats outside. Private parties: 36 main room, 8 private room. Car park. Vegetarian meals. Children's helpings. Smart dress preferred. No smoking in dining-room. No music   ACCOMMODATION: 3 rooms, all with bath/shower. TV. D,B&B £60 to £115. Deposit: £25. Rooms for disabled. Children welcome. Baby facilities. Dogs welcome. Garden

---

EVERSHOT Dorset   map 2

▲ *Summer Lodge* 🍷 ✳

Summer Lane, Evershot DT2 0JP   COOKING 3
TEL: (01935) 83424 FAX: (01935) 83005   COST £19–£61

'I went expecting a great deal, and I got it,' began one report. 'Still our favourite haunt,' confirmed a regular visitor. Tim Ford arrived in the kitchen last year as we went to press, leaving us insufficient time to award a score for cooking. He had worked as a sous-chef here previously and seems to have been nothing but good news on his return. The lovely old house of local stone retains a period feel, though the atmosphere is unduly reverential.

'The food is interesting without being too gimmicky' and might include risotto of wild rice with poached cod, or the ever-popular twice-baked cheese soufflé served with fish – pan-fried scallops and monkfish on one occasion, spiced ragoût of smoked haddock and mussels on another – an idea that Tim Ford seems to have borrowed from Sharrow Bay (see entry, Ullswater), where he once worked. Materials are sound, cooking skills are good, timing is as it should be, and the kitchen is capable of turning out an 'outstanding' boudin of chicken and truffle with a sauté of forest mushrooms. An inspector, however, found the individual components of a dish – salad of wild pigeon with black pudding, for instance – were more successful than the ensemble.

Puddings have included mango tarte Tatin, and a hot plum soufflé into which the waiter pours warm plum sauce. The big news over the past year for Evershot-watchers is the three-course lunch, now £10.95, which is reckoned to be excellent value: 'We have found nowhere to match it,' claimed one couple. Service has varied enormously for different reporters, perhaps reflecting high turnover of staff. Any wine list which begins with a page of sherries offered by the glass is likely to have plenty going for it. The cellar here is all-encompassing and offers tip-top quality. Among the highlights, pedigree Italian, Rhône, German and Californian wines deserve special mention. Most bottles are over £15, but a small section at the front helpfully highlights 12 that represent good value, starting with Minervois and Vin de Pays d'Oc Sauvignon Blanc at £11.75.

See the inside of the front cover for an explanation of the 1 to 5 rating system for cooking standards.

CHEF: Timothy Ford   PROPRIETORS: Nigel and Margaret Corbett   OPEN: all week 12.30 to 2, 7.30 to 9   MEALS: alc (main courses £10.50 to £24). Set L Mon to Sat £10.95, Set L Sun £18.50, Set D £32.50   SERVICE: not inc, card slips closed   CARDS: Access, Amex, Delta, Diners, Switch, Visa   DETAILS: 50 seats. 12 seats outside. Private parties: 60 main room, 8 and 20 private rooms. Car park. Vegetarian meals. Children's helpings. No under-5s after 7. Smart dress preferred. No smoking in dining-room. Wheelchair access (also WC). No music   ACCOMMODATION: 17 rooms, all with bath/shower. TV. Phone. B&B £105 to £225. Rooms for disabled. Children welcome. Dogs welcome in bedrooms only. Afternoon teas. Garden. Swimming-pool (*The Which? Hotel Guide*)

EVESHAM Hereford & Worcester   map 5

▲ *Evesham Hotel, Cedar Restaurant* ❦

Coopers Lane, off Waterside, Evesham WR11 6DA   COOKING 1
TEL: (01386) 765566   FAX: (01386) 765443   COST £17–£38

Very little changes here. The owners have been in place for over two decades, the chef has been the same for years, as have the jokes. A high risibility factor is integral and inescapable, and 'there is an endearing quality about the Jenkinsons' sillinesses'. The food is busy and cheerful, and takes a pride in offering a wide choice: normally around 18 main courses, quite apart from all the starters, puddings and vegetarian options. This is a bold stance, though it has obvious drawbacks. The owners call it 'a real test of culinary competence', but one can't help feeling that the same amount of effort applied to fewer dishes might produce better results. At inspection, seasoning see-sawed, salads and vegetables could have been perkier, and the cooking didn't always do justice to the excellence of the raw materials: good fresh seafood, well-hung tender meat, and tasty game.

The Jenkinsons deserve a cheer for making drinks actually seem like fun. Rejecting French and German wines back in 1977, they have developed a wine list full of imagination and flair. Wine from Greece? They've got four. Kenyan paw-paw wine? Irish Reichensteiner? There's a serious side to this: a solid backdrop of top-rate producers, particularly from Australia, California and New Zealand, some mature wines and excellent pricing throughout. Chilean house wines are £9.60. CELLARMAN'S CHOICE: Cape Mentelle Zinfandel 1993, Margaret River, W. Australia, £21.50; Bodega Norton Sangiovese 1993, Argentina, £12.50.

CHEF: Ian Mann   PROPRIETORS: the Jenkinson family   OPEN: all week 12.30 to 2, 7 to 9.30   CLOSED: 25 and 26 Dec   MEALS: alc (main courses £7 to £16.50)   SERVICE: net prices, card slips closed   CARDS: Access, Amex, Delta, Diners, Switch, Visa   DETAILS: 55 seats. Private parties: 10 main room, 12 private room. Car park. Vegetarian meals. Children's helpings. No cigars/pipes in dining-room. Wheelchair access (no WC). No music   ACCOMMODATION: 40 rooms, all with bath/shower. TV. Phone. B&B £57 to £88. Children welcome. Baby facilities. Dogs welcome in bedrooms only. Afternoon teas. Garden. Swimming-pool (*The Which? Hotel Guide*)

'*Although the menu said that credit cards were not accepted, they appeared to be the main means by which people paid.*' (On eating in London)

EXETER Devon   map 1

Lamb's ⅋✳

15 Lower North Street, Exeter EX4 3ET   COOKING 1
TEL: (01392) 54269   FAX: (01392) 431145   COST £21–£47

The eighteenth-century listed house is 200 yards from the cathedral square, right up against the Roman city wall. Dining-rooms are on two floors, and visitors are given 'a nice welcome' from Alison Aldridge. The kitchen does its own smoking and curing as well as making bread and pasta, and Carolyn Seath's bright, contemporary menu draws on a range of tastes from mildly spiced couscous with olives and home-dried tomatoes, to Cajun chicken, to medallions of pork fillet with both a lime and mango salsa and a light curry sauce. Seafood might include Brixham crab in filo pastry, grilled scallops, and chargrilled tuna. Although one reporter thought portions on the small side, another found everything 'beautifully prepared and presented'. A generous selection of half-bottles makes an appreciable contribution to the wide-ranging and fairly-priced wine list. Australian house wines are £9.

CHEF: Carolyn Seath   PROPRIETORS: Ian and Alison Aldridge   OPEN: Tue to Fri L 12 to 2, Tue to Sat D 7 to 10   MEALS: alc (main courses £10 to £16). Set L £10 (2 courses) to £15, Set D Mon to Fri £12 (2 courses) to £17. BYO £10   SERVICE: not inc   CARDS: Access, Delta, Switch, Visa
DETAILS: 42 seats. 8 seats outside. Private parties: 26 main room, 26 private room. Vegetarian meals. Children's helpings. Smart dress preferred. No smoking in 1 dining-room. Wheelchair access (no WC). No music

▲ St Olaves Court Hotel ⅋✳

Mary Arches Street, Exeter EX4 3AZ   COOKING 1
TEL: (01392) 217736   FAX: (01392) 413054   COST £23–£50

This family-run hotel occupies a Georgian building in its own walled garden 400 yards from the cathedral. It is 'a nice old house in need of painting', with a welcome feeling of seclusion in the midst of a city. Cream walls and seats upholstered in gold velvet make an impact, and while the food tries hard to impress, opinions of its success have varied.

At inspection, three 'soggy' filo pastry parcels filled with scallops and artichokes were rescued by a 'fettuccine of vegetables' with a dribble of truffle oil, while a pan-fried fillet of beef ('poor-quality meat, overcooked') came with good ravioli and wild mushrooms. Devon lamb has fared better, the grilled rack served pink, stuffed with sweetbreads and with a buttery sauce. Desserts have successfully combined chocolate and fruit, as in a steamed white chocolate pudding with a coulis of strawberries and chocolate sauce. The sensibly chosen, concise list of wines is fairly priced. House wines are £10.50.

Several sharp operators have tried to extort money from restaurateurs on the promise of an entry in a guidebook that has never appeared. The Good Food Guide *makes no charge for inclusion.*

CHEFS: Jason Horn, John Winstanley and Stephen Prigg   PROPRIETORS: Raymond and Ute Wyatt   OPEN: Mon to Fri L 12 to 2, all week D 6.30 to 9.30   MEALS: alc (main courses £11.50 to £17.50). Set L and D £13.50. BYO £5   SERVICE: not inc, card slips closed   CARDS: Access, Amex, Delta, Diners, Switch, Visa   DETAILS: 63 seats. 20 seats outside. Private parties: 50 main room, 8 to 80 private rooms. Car park. Vegetarian meals. Children's helpings. Smart dress preferred. No smoking in dining-room. Wheelchair access (also WC). No music   ACCOMMODATION: 15 rooms, all with bath/shower. TV. Phone. B&B £60 to £90. Rooms for disabled. Children welcome. Baby facilities. Dogs welcome in bedrooms only. Afternoon teas. Garden

---

FAVERSHAM Kent   map 3

Read's 🍾

Painter's Forstal, Faversham ME13 0EE
TEL: (01795) 535344   FAX: (01795) 591200   COOKING 3*
on Eastling road, 2m S of Faversham   COST £28–£59

One couple who paid a return visit after a gap of three years found 'the old shoe-box appearance' intact, but the place 'more welcoming than we remembered it'. Comfortable sofas and Ronald Searle cartoons help to pass the time before one proceeds to the airy dining-room with its luxuriously spaced tables. After 20 years David Pitchford knows exactly the kind of audience he is aiming for: people who appreciate 'well-judged, conservative cooking of sound ingredients'.

There are plenty of interesting dishes to choose from, and a dazzling array of materials from which to construct them. Individuality and character derive from the kitchen's clarity of purpose, and even complex dishes are well balanced. Concern with detail leads the menu to specify the kind of crumbs (brioche) in which the smoked haddock fish-cakes are rolled, the type of cheese (Montgomery Cheddar) in the soufflé, and the wine (Chardonnay) in the curried sauce that accompanies a seafood sausage. And, just in case there was any doubt, it is nice to know that 'both breasts' of a roasted woodpigeon are served with a galette of Jerusalem artichokes. Fish and fowl are preferred ingredients. Service is 'efficient and knowledgeable without being fussy'.

The impressive wine list kicks off with a mixed bag of 40 'best buys' (many under £15 a bottle), which is helpful for those with neither the time nor the inclination to browse through 38 pages of fine wines that follow. Most of the latter are French, including lots of mature vintages, and halves are numerous. Notable among the best buys are Cuvée Napa by Mumm at £16 and South African Hamilton Russell Pinot Noir 1993 at £16.

CHEF: David Pitchford   PROPRIETORS: David and Rona Pitchford   OPEN: Tue to Sat 12 to 2, 7 to 10   CLOSED: 25 Dec D, bank hols   MEALS: Set L £16.50, Set D £32 to £36   SERVICE: not inc, card slips closed   CARDS: Access, Amex, Diners, Switch, Visa   DETAILS: 40 seats. 12 seats outside. Private parties: 60 main room, 20 private room. Car park. Vegetarian meals. Children's helpings. Music

---

Card slips closed *in the details at the end of an entry indicates that the total on the slips of credit cards is closed when handed over for signature.*

ENGLAND

FELSTED Essex

map 3

Rumbles Cottage 🌟

Braintree Road, Felsted CM6 3DJ
TEL: (01371) 820996
on B1417, between A130 and A120

COOKING 1
COST £20–£37

Now approaching her fourteenth year in this delightful sixteenth-century cottage, Joy Hadley continues to delight visitors with her culinary invention and enterprise. In summer she makes full use of her own farm produce, and has now extended her catalogue to include yellow tomatoes and okra. The renowned 'guinea-pig menu' remains the spawning-ground for new ideas, and it's best to enquire about this when booking. Those who have taken the plunge have been impressed by chilled mulligatawny soup with prawns, and breast of duck coated with sesame seeds served with mango salsa, although they thought the layered banana and ground rice dessert needed more fine tuning. Successes from the main menu have included smoked halibut croquettes, pork in pastry with prune sauce, Arabian lamb casserole, and blueberry and Drambuie syllabub. The selection of English cheeses is not to be missed. Around 60 wines provide sound drinking at affordable prices. House wines start at £8.75.

CHEF/PROPRIETOR: E. Joy Hadley   OPEN: Sun L 12 to 2, Tue to Sat D 7 to 9   CLOSED: 2 weeks Feb   MEALS: alc D (main courses £11 to £13). Set L £13, Set D Tue to Thurs £12.50   SERVICE: not inc, card slips closed   CARDS: Access, Visa   DETAILS: 50 seats. Private parties: 22 main room, 8 and 22 private rooms. Vegetarian meals. Children's helpings. No smoking in 1 dining-room. Wheelchair access (no WC). Music

FOLKESTONE Kent

map 3

Paul's

2A Bouverie Road West, Folkestone CT20 2RX
TEL: (01303) 259697   FAX: (01303) 226647

COOKING 1
COST £24–£41

This long-standing Folkestone fixture has picked up its share of regular custom over the years, mostly locals drawn in by the friendly atmosphere and attractive prices on a wide-ranging menu. Fish is notably fresh, meat is from a butcher in Canterbury who deals in Aberdeen Angus beef, and there is a contribution from 'a little man who picks woodland fungus in season'. Among the attractions are slices of lamb sausage in a Cumberland sauce, and a warm quiche of herring roe topped with anchovy and served with a sherry cream sauce. Sauces tend to be creamy, perhaps also incorporating mushrooms, green peppercorns and Madeira to accompany poached chicken breast. Vegetarians have a choice of main course, puddings are from the trolley, and coffee is 'bottomless'. Good value wines pepper the list (though many essential details are missing), and the mostly mature claret is all but given away. House wine is £8.65.

The Guide *is totally independent, accepts no free hospitality, and survives on the number of copies sold each year.*

284

CHEFS/PROPRIETORS: Penny and Paul Hagger   OPEN: all week 12 to 2.30, 7 to 9.30 (later by arrangement)   CLOSED: Christmas   MEALS: alc (main courses £10 to £11). Set L £4.95 (1 course), Set D minimum 4 people £16 (2 courses) to £27. BYO £5   SERVICE: not inc   CARDS: Access, Delta, Switch, Visa   DETAILS: 120 seats. 50 seats outside. Private parties: 100 main room, 45 private room. Car park D. Vegetarian meals. Children welcome. Wheelchair access (no WC). No music

---

FOWEY Cornwall   map 1

Food for Thought

Town Quay, Fowey PL23 1AT   COOKING 2
TEL: (01726) 832221   FAX: (01726) 832060   COST £24–£47

Stunning views of the harbour, river and sea have been restored following the end of a big construction project in Fowey, and 'all is peaceful again', according to a supporter. The small seaside inn (formerly the Customs House) looks immaculate, and naturally deals in fish and shellfish, though not to the exclusion of rack of lamb with a herb crust, or tournedos of beef with a wild mushroom sauce. The fixed-price menu is considered good value, and the *carte* offers enough choice without inducing a state of quivering indecision.

Moules marinière is a regular standby, or there may be fish soup with the customary rouille and croûtons, ravioli of crab, or a mixed grill of the day's catch, such as red mullet, bass, John Dory, scallops, salmon, monkfish and sole. Wine and cream are well-used saucing ingredients, but so are olive oil, herbs and saffron butter. A 'deft hand' is behind everything, from well-timed pigeon breast to accompanying vegetables to a light chocolate pot dessert. An enjoyable atmosphere makes it a pleasure to linger over dinner, all helped by charming and attentive service. Wines skip between France and a rather more dynamic rest-of-the-world selection, and prices start below £10.

CHEF: Martin Billingsley   PROPRIETORS: Martin and Caroline Billingsley   OPEN: Mon to Sat D only 7 to 8.30 (later at busy times)   CLOSED: Christmas to mid-Mar   MEALS: alc (main courses £12 to £16). Set D £15.95   SERVICE: not inc   CARDS: Access, Switch, Visa   DETAILS: 38 seats. Private parties: 50 main room. Children welcome. Smart dress preferred. No music

---

FRAMPTON ON SEVERN Gloucestershire   map 2

Saverys

The Green, Frampton on Severn GL2 7EA
TEL: (01452) 740077   COOKING 2*
2m NW of M5 junction 13   COST £33–£40

Visit Frampton on a hot summer's day and you might think you had drifted into an English idyll. The village boasts the longest green in the land, swans glide on the pond and you may hear the screech of peacocks as you sit in the shade of ancient horse chestnut trees. Saverys is perfectly comfortable on its home patch. John Savery's fixed-price, three-course dinners are imaginative and enthusiastically conceived, without trying to ape the antics of slick cosmopolitan addresses. Marinated salmon is served as a starter with pickled quails' eggs and whole-grain mustard dressing, while warm Roquefort and walnut tart is coupled with a redcurrant and walnut dressing. A daily fish dish augments the main courses, which range from guinea-fowl with broad beans and bacon to crisply roasted duck breast with orange, honey and ginger sauce. To round things off, you might encounter black cherry and armagnac frangipane tart, fresh mango meringue, or white chocolate and passion-fruit terrine. The wine list is modest, but is a careful cull of sound bottles from reliable sources. House French is £8.50.

CHEF: John Savery   PROPRIETORS: Patricia Carpenter and John Savery   OPEN: Tue to Sat D only 7 to 9   CLOSED: 1 week Feb   MEALS: Set D £23.95   SERVICE: not inc, card slips closed CARDS: Access, Delta, Switch, Visa   DETAILS: 26 seats. Private parties: 28 main room. Smart dress preferred. No pipes in dining-room. Wheelchair access (no WC). No music

---

FRESSINGFIELD   Suffolk   map 6

Fox and Goose ▮

Fressingfield IP21 5PB
TEL: (01379) 586247   FAX: (01379) 588107   COOKING 2
on B1116, 3½m S of Harleston   COST £23–£55

Ruth Watson has produced a version of the idealised country hostelry – 'not at all designerish, slightly beaten up, but comfortable' – in this old inn by the churchyard. She has long been a champion of the 'eclectic' approach, incorporating Italian charcuterie, toad-in-the-hole, and what the menu describes as 'nearly sashimi', consisting of briefly seared and succulent fillets of salmon and scallops, served with pickled ginger and shredded dried bonito for 'brilliant contrast'. One annual visitor, however, noted that 'the repertoire fails to develop', while others have taken up the eclectic baton and run with it: bruschetta, bresaola, tempura and risotto have become modern restaurant clichés since the Fox and Goose first championed them.

Nevertheless, the vitality of oriental flavourings appeals, from black-bean and coconut soup to griddled squid with spring onion and coriander, while the Watson version of Peking duck is a 'succulent, superior bird'. Blood-orange and Campari sorbet offers a refreshing alternative to very sticky toffee pudding. General standards of housekeeping have disappointed, as have prices (bumped up by charges for olives in the bar, and for vegetables) and service, which has seemed uncaring.

The short, serviceable wine list which arrives unsolicited has 30 bottles of mixed provenance, the vast majority under £20. Connoisseurs should put in a request to see the full list, a fine collection sourced from Adnams, Bibendum, and Lay & Wheeler among others. Its strengths include mature clarets, red Burgundies, top Alsace and Californian producers, fine ports and dessert wines. Vintage notes are helpful if you decide to splash out. House wines change regularly, but might include a Provence red at £9.75. CELLARMAN'S CHOICE: Chablis 1994, Dom. de Bois Y'ver, £18.50; Montagne St-Emilion, Ch. de Musset 1992, £18.50.

▮ *denotes an outstanding wine cellar;* ▮ *denotes a good wine list, worth travelling for.*

CHEFS: Ruth Watson and Max Dougal PROPRIETOR: Ruth Watson OPEN: Wed to Sun 12 to 2.15, 7 to 9.30 CLOSED: 2 weeks Christmas, 2 weeks July MEALS: alc (main courses £8 to £15.50). Set L £9.95 (2 courses) to £13.50. Bar food available SERVICE: not inc, card slips closed CARDS: Access, Delta, Switch, Visa DETAILS: 50 seats. 16 seats outside. Private parties: 24 main room, 24 private room. Car park. Vegetarian meals. Children's helpings. No cigars/pipes in dining-room. No music

---

FROME Somerset   map 2

Crofts 🍴✳

21 Fromefield, Frome BA11 2HE   COOKING 1*
TEL: (01373) 472149   COST £18–£28

Margaret Graham's cottagey little restaurant in a listed building does a great service to the local neighbourhood by offering robust food and outstanding value for money. Baking is one of her strengths: breads are 'super', and her skill with pastry shows in dishes such as pork en croûte with apricot and brandy sauce. Elsewhere, she turns her hand to coarse pâté with pickled pears, salad of confit of duck, lamb with coconut, and stir-fried chicken with lime and coriander. Sorbets and ice-creams are good, and chocolate soufflé comes with cappuccino sauce. Service is chatty and knowledgeable: a birthday party of 12 plus two babies 'couldn't have been made more welcome'. The wines are a bargain. House wine is £7.95.

CHEF/PROPRIETOR: Margaret Graham OPEN: Sun L 12 to 2, Wed to Sat D 7 to 9.30 CLOSED: 24 Dec to 2 Jan MEALS: Set L £10.95, Set D £15.50 SERVICE: not inc, card slips closed CARDS: Access, Visa DETAILS: 30 seats. Private parties: 22 main room. Vegetarian meals. Children's helpings. No smoking in dining-room. No music

---

GATESHEAD Tyne & Wear   map 10

▲ Eslington Villa Hotel 🍴✳

8 Station Road, Low Fell, Gateshead NE9 6DR
TEL: (0191) 487 6017 and 420 0666
FAX: (0191) 420 0667   COOKING 1*
on A6127, 2m S of Newcastle city centre   COST £21–£50

'A good-class, comfortable, typically English hotel,' summed up one visitor to this residential bit of Gateshead. The house overlooks the Team Valley, a wooded lawn sweeps down to the railway, and Edwardian mouldings and fireplaces give it all the character it needs. The homely nature of the food is appreciated, and Ian Lowrey's cooking is all the better for not being too ambitious. Choice is generous on all the menus, and a set-price dinner might consist of smoked haddock and spinach tartlet with hollandaise sauce, followed by navarin of spring lamb, and passion-fruit cheesecake. The *carte* offers a bit more excitement in the form of grilled scallops with a mango and red onion salsa, or a boozy chocolate trifle in which Tia Maria and white chocolate custard play supporting roles. One reporter appreciated the 'cheerful welcome', and service is attentive and friendly. An approachable wine list balances Old and New Worlds, and house wine is £8.95.

CHEF: Ian Lowrey PROPRIETORS: Nick and Melanie Tulip OPEN: Sun to Fri L 12 to 2, Mon to Sat D 7 to 10 CLOSED: 1 week Christmas, bank hols MEALS: alc (main courses £16.50 to £18). Set L Mon to Fri £10.95 (2 courses) to £14.95, Set D Mon to Fri £15.95 (2 courses) to £19.95 SERVICE: not inc CARDS: Access, Amex, Delta, Switch, Visa DETAILS: 60 seats. 8 seats outside. Private parties: 40 main room, 20 private room. Car park. Children's helpings. Smart dress preferred. No smoking in dining-room. Wheelchair access (also WC). Music ACCOMMODATION: 12 rooms, all with bath/shower. TV. Phone. B&B £34.50 to £64.50. Rooms for disabled. Children welcome. Dogs welcome. Afternoon teas. Garden (*The Which? Hotel Guide*)

GILLINGHAM Dorset	map 2

▲ *Stock Hill* ⁵⧎

Stock Hill, Gillingham SP8 5NR

TEL: (01747) 823626 FAX: (01747) 825628 COOKING **2***

off B3081, 1½m W of Gillingham COST £31–£49

The Hausers' modestly proportioned, comfortable country house in 11 acres of parkland lends new meaning to the epithet 'idiosyncratic'. Reporters who paused in the hallway to drink in the scene noted the 'Egyptian cats, rearing horses, chinoiserie, English grandeur – the lot', before proceeding to the drawing-room to have their orders taken.

Despite the polyglot nature of the surroundings, Austria is where the Hausers hie from, and Austria is the central focus of the cooking. Menus change daily, but certain dishes and techniques are constant. Thus, a starter of goats'-cheese log comes with a pile of 'exceptionally mild' sauerkraut, while another of sliced octopus has trademark potato noodles, soused with tomatoes and paprika. Other starters may venture further afield: sauté duck liver on polenta would make a Viennese feel a fair way from home. Main courses offer comfort along defiantly untrendy routes. Pork medallions with mustard and brandy sauce, or textbook wiener schnitzel – 'which you could hear being thumped in the kitchen' – served with a *de rigueur* wedge of lemon are the sorts of things to expect, but there may well also be guinea-fowl with mango in Noilly Prat. Desserts such as chocolate and banana pancakes, meringue swans, and the inevitable sachertorte get rave write-ups. Service is 'excellent and friendly'. There is fine breadth of choice on the wine list, although surprisingly few Austrians. House French is £13.50.

CHEFS: Peter Hauser and Lorna Connor PROPRIETORS: Peter and Nita Hauser OPEN: all week 12.30 to 1.45, 7.30 to 8.45 (8.30 Sun) MEALS: Set L £22, Set D £30 SERVICE: not inc, card slips closed CARDS: Access, Amex, Diners, Visa DETAILS: 24 seats. 8 seats outside. Private parties: 12 main room, 12 private room. Car park. Vegetarian meals. Children's helpings. No children under 6. Jacket and tie. No smoking in dining-room. No music ACCOMMODATION: 10 rooms, all with bath/shower. TV. Phone. B&B £75 to £200. Deposit: 20%. No children under 7. Afternoon teas. Garden. Fishing (*The Which? Hotel Guide*)

The 1998 Guide *will be published before Christmas 1997. Reports on meals are most welcome at any time of the year, but are particularly valuable in the spring (no later than June). Send them to* The Good Food Guide, *FREEPOST, 2 Marylebone Road, London NW1 1YN. Or e-mail your report to guidereports@which. co. uk.*

GOLCAR West Yorkshire

map 8

Weavers Shed

Knowl Road, Golcar HD7 4AN
TEL/FAX: (01484) 654284
on B6111, 2m W of Huddersfield from A62

COOKING 2
COST £18–£45

The 'greening' of the Weavers Shed continues. Stephen Jackson reports that the family farm at Holywell Green supplies his restaurant with organic fruit, vegetables, rare herbs and wild plants, ranging from violets, burnet and chickweed to pineapple sage (for turbot) and tansy (for chocolate tarts). Fish arrives daily from Huddersfield, free-range eggs are from a nearby farm and meat is hung by the village butcher. Lunch is robust, while dinner might kick off with 'mouth-wateringly succulent' king scallops sprinkled with crispy local bacon, or sauté chicken livers piled on a polenta cake with a 'carefully reduced' sherry sauce. Main courses generally include well-hung beef (perhaps served with wild mushrooms, or with champ and Burgundy gravy); otherwise, the choice ranges from chargrilled venison to poached sea bass with coriander-scented lentil and potato broth. Among desserts, sticky toffee pudding has proved a winner.

Service is gaining in professionalism, although the guiding light is still Shirley Bramald, whose presence has defined the mood of this converted woollen mill for some 25 years. The wine list is a thorough-going, global slate supported by plenty of invigorating digestifs. House wine is £9.95.

CHEFS: Ian McGunnigle, Robert Jones and Stephen Jackson   PROPRIETOR: Stephen Jackson
OPEN: Tue to Fri L 12 to 2, Tue to Sat D 7 to 10   CLOSED: first 2 weeks Jan, last week July, first week Aug   MEALS: alc (main courses £7 to £15.50). Set L £10.95   SERVICE: not inc   CARDS: Access, Amex, Switch, Visa   DETAILS: 50 seats. Private parties: 40 main room, 30 private room. Car park. Vegetarian meals. Children's helpings. Smart dress preferred. Wheelchair access (also WC). Music

GORING Oxfordshire

map 2

Leatherne Bottel

Goring RG8 0HS
TEL: (01491) 872667   FAX: (01491) 875308

COOKING 2*
COST £32–£53

'A place to relax and hide,' rhapsodises Keith Read, and he's the owner! It enjoys a prime site on the Thames, not far from Reading; high-rollers may rent out *Natasha*, an Edwardian saloon boat that will potter up and down while you knock back the fizzy stuff and contemplate the prospect of dinner.

If the setting is a tranquil time-warp, the cooking certainly isn't: a salad of dandelions and coriander leaves with spiced chorizo and a poached egg is very much the mood of the moment. Strong and aromatic seasonings are the norm, with much Asian input. Tuna is 'flash-seared' with crushed peppercorns and wasabi and garnished with sesame prawn toasts. Wun-tuns of sweetbreads and water-chestnuts are scented with galangal and served on pak choi leaves with deep-fried basil. Appreciation might depend on how familiar you are with the idiom. One couple were nonplussed at marinated halibut with a 'sweetly fishy ice-cream', which turned out to be smoked-salmon flavour. Cheeses are 'a good selection in tip-top condition'. Wines trot briskly through both hemispheres, with some sound choices at mostly reasonable prices, although the French selections will inevitably tug on the purse-strings. All four house wines, however, are French and £10.50.

CHEF: Keith Read PROPRIETORS: Keith Read and Annie Bonnet OPEN: all week 12.15 to 2 (2.30 Sat and Sun), 7.15 to 9 (9.30 Sat, 8.30 Sun) CLOSED: D 24 Dec, 25 Dec MEALS: alc (main courses £12 to £17) SERVICE: not inc CARDS: Access, Amex, Visa DETAILS: 50 seats. 75 seats outside. Private parties: 20 main room, 12 private room. Car park. Vegetarian meals. Smart dress preferred. Wheelchair access (no WC). No music. Air-conditioned

---

GRASMERE Cumbria   map 8

▲ *Michael's Nook*

Grasmere LA22 9RP   COOKING 3*
TEL: (01539) 435496 FAX: (01539) 435645   COST £37–£59

Wordsworth's poem 'Michael' was written in 1800 at Dove Cottage, about a mile from where this early-Victorian house now stands. The hotel was opened in 1969 by Reg Gifford, a former antique dealer, whose collection of prints, rugs and furniture (including dining-tables) gives it a unique English character. It is 'individualistic' rather than eccentric, and feels intimate and comfortable. In the autumn of 1995 Mark Treasure moved here from the Capital Hotel (see entry, London), and seems to have settled seamlessly into the Nook style. 'Much was innovative, and all showed freshness of style and quality, and good presentation,' summed up an early visitor.

Appetisers set the tone: apple beignets, scrambled egg and mushroom tartlets, and smoked haddock in pesto sauce. The menu promises lots of treats, from guinea-fowl and cep terrine, or split-pea and foie gras broth, to smoked salmon soufflé, and daube of beef with horseradish gnocchi. Even ordinary-sounding dishes turn out to be vivid and memorable, as an inspector found with lentil potage whose 'intense creamy taste was a revelation', and with a piece of salmon under whose crispy blackened skin was 'a gradual progression from seared to raw salmon, disintegrating easily with only a slight prod'.

The kitchen focuses on good raw materials and doesn't ask the impossible of them. The 'subtle and delicate taste' of a creamy bouillon with small resistant chunks of langoustine has impressed, as has 'pink, tender, tasty, juicy' boned squab pigeon with 'a lovely uncloying cinnamon sauce'. Desserts again sound straightforward, but owe their success to a high degree of skill, whether a simple baked egg-custard tart or a hazelnut parfait with hot cherry compote. These are followed by 'an excellent choice of cheese in good condition'. Wines are fascinating, sourced from Tasmania, New Zealand, England and Lebanon as well as traditional areas. There's a wide range of prices and much to be recommended among the half-bottles. Don't miss the delicious dessert wines at the back of the list. Australia's Jamiesons Run provides full-flavoured house wines at £12.50. CELLARMAN'S CHOICE: Wollombi Brook Chardonnay 1991, Alexandria, New South Wales, Australia, £17.75; Cabernet Sauvignon 1993, Viña Los Vascos, Rapel, Chile, £10.95.

CHEF: Mark Treasure   PROPRIETORS: Mr and Mrs R.S.E. Gifford   OPEN: all week 12.30 to 1, 7.30 to 8.15   MEALS: Set L £28.50, Set D £39.50   SERVICE: not inc   CARDS: Access, Amex, Diners, Visa   DETAILS: 50 seats. Private parties: 40 main room, 40 private room. Car park. Vegetarian meals. No children under 7; older children by arrangement. Jacket and tie. No smoking in dining-room. Wheelchair access (also WC). Music   ACCOMMODATION: 14 rooms, all with bath/shower. TV. Phone. D,B&B £125 to £280. Deposit: £50. Children by arrangement. Afternoon teas (booking essential). Garden

▲ *White Moss House* ▮ ⁵✳

Rydal Water, Grasmere LA22 9SE
TEL: (015394) 35295   FAX: (015394) 35516   COOKING 3*
on A591, at N end of Rydal Water   COST £36–£43

Those who stay at this Lakeland green-stone house at the foot of White Moss Common are particularly appreciative of the quiet and restful atmosphere. Dinner is at 8 o'clock – five courses plus coffee, with no choice until dessert – and is an unshowy interpretation of English country-house cooking. One reporter's meal was typical of the style: fennel, apple and asparagus soup, followed by a mixed fish soufflé of char, sea trout and smoked salmon with leeks and smoked cheese. Then came suckling pig with mushroom and Madeira sauce. 'Each of the vegetables had been treated differently, and the best coaxed out of them,' although another reporter found his 'disappointing'.

Materials are carefully garnered – including char, pike, Sika venison and Herdwick lamb – and are well publicised on the menu: 'line-caught Wastwater wild sea trout baked in the Aga with fennel from the White Moss herb garden', for instance. Beef, too, these days understandably comes with a note that it is 'Argentinian pampas grass fed'. The highlights of one November meal were 'a wonderfully crisp, ungreasy mallard', and cabinet pudding which was 'rich tasting but light as a feather'. A steamed pudding, ice-cream, and a fruity dessert are usually on offer. Cheese is worthy of serious consideration, though one reporter wondered why his selection seemed to have come straight from the fridge. 'Is this crazy regulation something we have to thank the EU for?' he wondered.

The dazzling array of wines includes many old vintages, arranged initially by the classic regions, with follow-up lists of similarly styled offerings. As a wine collection it just about has the lot, plenty by the glass, including ports and dessert wines, lovely old Burgundy, and mature Riesling from both Germany and Alsace. Prices range from fair to impressively low. House wines start at £9.50. CELLARMAN'S CHOICE: Champagne Pommery Brut NV, £27; Pauillac, Ch. Latour 1987, £39.

CHEFS: Peter Dixon and Colin Percival   PROPRIETORS: Susan and Peter Dixon   OPEN: Mon to Sat D only 8 (1 sitting)   CLOSED: Dec to Feb   MEALS: Set D £27.50   SERVICE: not inc, card slips closed   CARDS: Access, Visa   DETAILS: 18 seats. Private parties: 20 main room. Car park. Children's helpings. No children under 8. Smart dress preferred. No smoking in dining-room. Wheelchair access (no WC). No music   ACCOMMODATION: 6 rooms, all with bath/shower. TV. Phone. D,B&B £134 to £174 (double room). Children welcome. Garden. Fishing (*The Which? Hotel Guide*)

▲ *This symbol means accommodation is available.*

GREAT DUNMOW Essex   map 3

▲ The Starr ♟ ⁵⅙

Market Place, Great Dunmow CM6 1AX
TEL: (01371) 874321 FAX: (01371) 876337   COOKING 1
off A120, 9m E of Bishop's Stortford   COST £28–£53

An ebullient Brian Jones plays the role of jolly host in the beamed dining-room of this village inn, and blackboards offer plenty to eat. There are probably 20 main courses on the various menus, which is a lot for a kitchen to handle. Among them might be poached turbot with pesto, or rump of English lamb with a tarragon mousse crust. France, Italy and Britain are the main national strands running through the repertoire, producing leek and Parmesan risotto, boned pig's trotter with black pudding (that's a starter, by the way), and saddle of venison with morels and horseradish sauce. The wine list reveals an impressive grasp of the subject, particularly in the 'rest of the world' section, which is packed with lively, modern offerings from fashionable producers. The top bins command high prices, but there is quite enough to choose from below £15, and house wines start at £10.50. CELLARMAN'S CHOICE: Riddoch Chardonnay 1994 'The Riddoch Run', Coonawarra, Australia, £15.95; Crozes-Hermitage 1992, Alain Graillot, £17.50.

CHEF: Mark Fisher PROPRIETORS: Brian and Vanessa Jones OPEN: Mon to Fri and Sun L 12.30 to 1.45 (2 Sun), Mon to Sat D 7 to 9.30 (10 Sat) CLOSED: first week Jan MEALS: alc L Mon to Fri (main courses £8.50 to £16). Set L Sun £16.50 (2 courses) to £21.50, Set D £21.50 to £35. BYO £5 SERVICE: not inc; 10% for parties of 8 or more CARDS: Access, Amex, Delta, Switch, Visa DETAILS: 80 seats. Private parties: 46 main room, 12 and 36 private rooms. Car park. Vegetarian meals. Children's helpings. Smart dress preferred. No smoking in dining-room. Music ACCOMMODATION: 8 rooms, all with bath/shower. TV. Phone. B&B £55 to £100. Children welcome. Dogs welcome (The Which? Hotel Guide)

GREAT GONERBY Lincolnshire   map 6

Harry's Place ⁵⅙

17 High Street, Great Gonerby NG31 8JS
TEL: (01476) 561780   COOKING 3*
on B1174, 2m NW of Grantham   COST £45–£70

The ordinary-looking Georgian house sits opposite Great Gonerby Social Club, and is remarkable for its small scale. Eating takes place in a single front room with dark pink walls and a lot of pine in a remarkable mix of ages and colours. One reporter who eats here at least once a year claims that 'it just gets better', and is convinced that 'part of the secret is the small dining-room with only eight to ten covers'. The other part is undoubtedly the professionalism of both Harry Hallam and his wife Caroline, whose 'charming' service adds to the appeal.

Two people can eat the entire menu, there being only two choices per course, plus the option of cheese. Even though some exotic items, such as salt-marsh teal, can turn up, a more typical menu might run as follows: chilled tomato soup au pistou, or terrine of Filey lobster and corn-fed chicken; then River Dee salmon with a champagne beurre blanc, or loin of baby roe-deer in a herb and wine sauce; and finally lemon tart with vanilla ice-cream, or hot damson soufflé.

The advantage of such a tiny operation is that no detail escapes Harry Hallam. 'Ingredients are superb,' notes a supporter, citing Orkney scallops as 'the fattest, most flavoursome I have ever tasted,' and cod from Peterhead 'as I remember it ten to fifteen years ago'. Textures make an impact, baking is exceptionally good, saucing is 'absolutely right in balance, freshness and quantity', and one reporter found the herbs 'so fresh they almost intoxicate'. A short and idiosyncratic wine list begins at just under £20 and soon launches into fine Burgundy and claret. There is no house wine, but three are normally available by the glass.

CHEF: Harry Hallam   PROPRIETORS: Harry and Caroline Hallam   OPEN: Tue to Sat 12.30 to 2, 7 to 9.30   CLOSED: 25 and 26 Dec, bank hols   MEALS: alc (main courses £18.50 to £22.50) SERVICE: not inc   CARDS: Access, Visa   DETAILS: 10 seats. Private parties: 10 main room. Car park. Children's helpings. No children under 5. No smoking in dining-room. Wheelchair access (no WC). No music

---

GREAT MILTON Oxfordshire   map 2

▲ *Le Manoir aux Quat' Saisons* 🍷 ✳

Church Road, Great Milton OX44 7PD
TEL: (01844) 278881   FAX: (01844) 278847   COOKING 5
off A329, 1m from M40 junction 7   COST £41–£105

The gardens are maturing well and providing some of the produce, bedrooms are sumptuous, the cooking can fairly claim to be among the best in the land, and prices can be punishingly high, but Raymond Blanc has achieved a remarkably relaxed and natural dialogue between staff and guests. The conservatory extension to the fifteenth-century manor sports a profusion of greenery and trelliswork, while the original dining-room in the main building is painted a luminous yellow, with colourful and striking modern pictures. Service by an Anglo-French team is 'charming and amiable', and although it can miss out on some of the fine detail, this is no great tragedy since 'they do concentrate on putting customers at their ease, which is the most important thing'.

The 'brilliant, inventive' food concentrates on the most important things too. 'Flavour, intensity, freshness and lightness are words that keep recurring in a description of a meal here.' The impression of lightness derives in part from the incorporation of ideas from the Mediterranean and Japan, which in turn are linked to Blanc's concern that food should be healthy. Meatless dishes have been given a boost, and a health spa is on the way, but any fears that this might signal a re-run of 1970s cuisine minceur or, worse, a new holier-than-thou approach, are not well founded, thanks to a feeling of sensuous enjoyment and indulgence. Admittedly there is a dilemma – anything that costs this much money has to be taken very seriously – but the food itself is meant to give pleasure, not be treated with reverence.

The sheer breadth and variety of dishes can be staggering, from a crimson moulded gâteau of pressed tomato, marinated in balsamic vinegar and sur-rounded by peeled langoustines, to roast suckling pig; from the bouillabaisse terrine of moist marinated fish in saffron jelly, surrounded by crunchy vegetables, to the stickiness of pig's trotters filled with sweetbreads, veal tongue, kidneys and foie gras, with a morel *jus*. Desserts are no less invigorating, whether you are watching the pink champagne being poured into a soup of red fruits, or humming something from *South Pacific* while eating mango on steamed jasmine rice with a pineapple and coconut sauce. There is always a tasting menu of eight small courses, a vegetarian menu, a children's menu at £12 (surely a kid's bargain of the year), as well as the *carte* and a three-course lunch for £29.50, a bargain for adults.

There have been a few niggles over the year – some undoubtedly occasioned by toweringly high expectations – but these are far outweighed by those for whom this is Mecca. Londoners wishing to make the pilgrimage may like to note the luxury coach service for lunch or dinner, from and to Hyde Park Corner, at £35, which includes an aperitif. As to cost, the view is that cooking of such outstanding quality fully justifies the prices. Wines are expensive, but there's no denying the pedigree of a list that includes so much that is fine and venerable, particularly from the classic regions of France. Italy and California are other strong suits, and the half-bottle list is a gem.

CHEFS: Raymond Blanc and Clive Fretwell   PROPRIETOR: Raymond Blanc   OPEN: all week 12.15 to 2.15, 7.15 to 10.15   MEALS: alc (main courses £29 to £32). Set L Mon to Sat £29.50 to £69, Set L Sun and Set D £69   SERVICE: net prices   CARDS: Access, Amex, Delta, Diners, Switch, Visa   DETAILS: 100 seats. Private parties: 46 main room. Car park. Vegetarian meals. Children's helpings. Smart dress preferred. No smoking in 1 dining-room. Wheelchair access (no WC). No music. Air-conditioned   ACCOMMODATION: 19 rooms, all with bath/shower. TV. Phone. Room only £185 to £395. Deposit: £150. Children welcome. Afternoon teas. Garden. Swimming-pool (*The Which? Hotel Guide*)

GREAT MISSENDEN Buckinghamshire   map 3

La Petite Auberge

107 High Street, Great Missenden HP16 0BB   COOKING 1
TEL: (01494) 865370   COST £34–£49

This is the kind of country-town restaurant that inspires confidence. Mr Martel's cooking is unswervingly consistent, while his wife maintains a quiet, careful presence in the clean, unfussily decorated dining-room. The menu is a short *carte* drawing most of its inspiration from the French provincial repertoire, and ingredients are of the highest quality. Asparagus is regularly applauded as a starter (either encased in light puff pastry or 'cooked perfectly' with prawns in a butter sauce). Successes from the main courses have ranged from exactly timed fillet of beef topped with truffles, to turbot in a cream sauce with anchovies and capers. As a finale, hot caramelised apple with cinnamon ice-cream continues to please, as does iced nougat with chocolate sauce. The wine list is short, French and perfectly sound; there is no house wine but prices start at £9.50.

CHEF: Hubert Martel   PROPRIETORS: Mr and Mrs Hubert Martel   OPEN: Mon to Sat D only 7.30 to 10.30   CLOSED: 2 weeks Christmas, bank hols   MEALS: alc (main courses £13.50 to £16) SERVICE: not inc   CARDS: Access, Visa   DETAILS: 30 seats. Private parties: 30 main room. Children welcome. Smart dress preferred. Wheelchair access (also WC). Music

---

'*The only illumination was from candles, but the lighting was still brighter than the waiter.*' (On eating in London)

GREAT YELDHAM Essex   map 3

White Hart ▮ ⁵⭑ £   [NEW ENTRY]

Poole Street, Great Yeldham CO9 4HJ   COOKING 1
TEL: (01787) 237250 FAX: (01787) 238044   COST £19–£41

The sprawling half-timbered Tudor monolith, in acres of grounds, comes with
beams, wooden pillars, an open log fire and a welcoming feel. It shares the
relaxed philosophy of other Huntsbridge pub/restaurants (see Pheasant Inn,
Keyston, and the Three Horseshoes, Madingley) in that the same food is
available throughout – informally in the bar, or in a bookable dining-room with
restaurant-style service – and offers a flexible collection of dishes that can be
taken individually as light meals or combined into the full monty. Essex man
and Master of Wine John Hoskins has installed Roger Jones (formerly of the
Pheasant Inn) in the kitchen. He maintains his broadly modern Italian
momentum with ravioli of Mediterranean vegetables, or a tart of spinach, tomato
and Pecorino cheese. A few short-cuts and shortcomings marred an inspection,
but support was due for an excellent sticky braised lamb shank, and others have
endorsed salmon and courgette in tempura batter, confit of duck leg, and
home-made bread, as well as the unstuffy and congenial service.

The wine list is a lively collection of bottles, grouped by style, and at fair
prices. It includes as much that appeals from outside France as within. House
wines start at £8.95. CELLARMAN'S CHOICE: Mount Langhi Ghiran Riesling
1995, Victoria, Australia, £13.75; Chianti Classico Riserva 1990, Felsina
Berardenga, £22.

CHEF: Roger Jones PROPRIETOR: Huntsbridge Ltd OPEN: all week 12 to 2, 6.30 to 10 MEALS:
alc (main courses £5 to £13.50) SERVICE: not inc, card slips closed CARDS: Access, Amex,
Delta, Diners, Switch, Visa DETAILS: 120 seats. 25 seats outside. Private parties: 80 main room,
24 private room. Car park. Vegetarian meals. Children's helpings. No smoking in dining-room.
Music

GRIMSTON Norfolk   map 6

▲ Congham Hall ⁵⭑ ✓ 1993

Grimston PE32 1AH
TEL: (01485) 600250 FAX: (01485) 601191   COOKING 2
off A148 or B1153, 7m E of King's Lynn   COST £23–£54

Visitors are spotted as soon as they arrive in the car park, and escorted through
the square-cut Georgian manor-house to the Orangery dining-room, which
looks out on to mature trees and a large lawn. Smart rattan and rawhide chairs
combine with well-set tables, elegant glasses and a generous *carte* to instil keen
anticipation. Flexibility is paramount. Lunch can be just a Greek salad, or any
combination of dishes from mushroom risotto or BLT sandwich to deep-fried
plaice with chips and mushy peas.

Dinner is a more serious affair, though first courses can be as attractively light
as sauté mussels with an avocado and tomato salad and chilli salsa. The kitchen
embraces a good range of ingredients and cooking techniques, from tortellini of
oysters in a champagne and rocket sauce to pan-fried loin of venison on creamed

chard with sage and onion polenta. It is also lavish in its use of herbs from the garden, not frightened of intricate desserts and strong on cheese. Mark-ups on the reasonably extensive and generally youthful wine list don't produce any bargains. Around ten wines by the glass, and thirty half-bottles, are helpful. House wine is £12.

CHEF: Jonathan Nicholson   PROPRIETORS: Christine and Trevor Forecast   OPEN: Sun to Fri L 12.30 to 2, all week D 7.30 to 9.30   MEALS: alc L (main courses £7.50 to £15.50). Set D £20 (2 courses) to £35. BYO £10. Light L available Mon to Fri   SERVICE: not inc, card slips closed   CARDS: Access, Amex, Diners, Visa   DETAILS: 50 seats. 30 seats outside. Private parties: 50 main room, 18 private room. Car park. Vegetarian meals. No children under 12. Jacket and tie D. No smoking in dining-room. Wheelchair access (also WC). No music   ACCOMMODATION: 14 rooms, all with bath/shower. TV. Phone. B&B £69 to £189. No children under 12. Dogs in kennels. Afternoon teas. Garden. Swimming-pool (*The Which? Hotel Guide*)

HALIFAX West Yorkshire   map 9

Design House ♥

Dean Clough, Halifax HX3 5AX   COOKING 2
TEL: (01422) 383242 FAX: (01422) 322732   COST £19–£42

'I have been twice in the past month. The food is superb, the atmosphere and service excellent. I cannot wait to go again.' Few restaurants excite this kind of enthusiasm, but the Design House has a clear purpose – to bring good food to a wide audience – and pursues its aim with dedication. Value for money is a part of the attraction, especially the fixed-price lunches, which might offer a choice between roast skate wing, duck salad, and celeriac soup, followed by main courses of chicken, plaice, or a vegetable stir-fry.

There is nothing flashy about the food, just a foundation in good ingredients, with simple partnerings of, say, chargrilled salmon with lemon garlic, and a succession of direct and honest flavours. One conspicuous success has been a silky-smooth, intensely flavoured liver parfait served with toasted brioche and a salad of dandelion, chrysanthemum, basil and lemon balm. Non-meat dishes have included pumpkin and sweet-potato wun-tuns with curry and vanilla, and an indulgent streak runs through puddings, as in a chocolate vacherin with malted white chocolate ice-cream. Wines are grouped according to style with a separate section for Italy. Mark-ups are low, in keeping with the general ethos. House wine is £8.95.

CHEF: David Watson   PROPRIETOR: John Leach   OPEN: Mon to Fri L 12 to 2, Mon to Sat D 6.30 to 10; café/bar all week 10 to 5 (3 Sat)   CLOSED: 25 and 26 Dec, 1 and 2 Jan   MEALS: alc (main courses £6.50 to £13.50). Set L £9.50 (2 courses) to £12.75   SERVICE: not inc   CARDS: Access, Amex, Delta, Switch, Visa   DETAILS: 75 seats. 18 seats outside. Private parties: 75 main room. Car park (D only). Vegetarian meals. Children's helpings. Smart dress preferred. No cigars/pipes in dining-room. Music. Air-conditioned

---

'The clapshot was inedible and tasted rancid. I told [the waitress] that it would be perfectly named if one changed one vowel and one consonant.' (On eating in Scotland)

▲ *Hambleton Hall* 🍷

Hambleton LE15 8TH
TEL: (01572) 756991   FAX: (01572) 724721   COOKING **4**
off A606, 3m SE of Oakham   COST £38–£92

The village is a cul-de-sac: there's nowhere else to go once you have left the main road. At first sight the hall – built of light, weathered local stone – appears relatively modest by country-house standards. The drama of the location is apparent only from the lounge or, on a fine day, the terrace, with a glimpse of Rutland Water over the trees beyond the gently cascading gardens. The bar's bright red walls make it feel warm in winter, while the lounge's open aspect and big display of flowers – 'more Chelsea than Interflora' – suits the summer.

This broad seasonal divide also charts the kitchen's annual progress on a large and generous *carte*, with a couple of contrastingly simple set menus that vary by the day or month. Luxury is never far away. Foie gras crops up in a ballottine of duck, or simply by itself: a round slab of pâté with a 'long-lasting flavour' and a couple of blobs of slightly runny Sauternes jelly, accompanied by a slice of excellent grilled brioche. At one meal a terrine of lobster was set in a 'squishy' fondue of tomato and marinated fennel, decked out with a pretty pink sauce and feathery dill.

Aaron Patterson seems to have moved on from the tall towers and elaborate constructions of previous years, although he still packs a remarkable number of items into a dish. Crisp-skinned honey-roasted breast of 'excellent, dark-red and slightly gamey' Gressingham duck comes with a mound of sweet red onion confit dotted with currants or sultanas, a fondant potato, plus a piece of braised chicory that proved 'one too many' ingredients for an inspector. Materials are generally first-rate and well handled, while saucing ranges from a slick of intense bouillabaisse that surrounds a pan-fried fillet of sea bass, to the dark, rich and sticky reductions 'of a rather old-fashioned kind' that might accompany roasted sweetbread wrapped in Parma ham.

A cheese trolley is wheeled alongside, bearing a large truckle of Cheddar, and perhaps Fougéru and Pont l'Evêque in good condition, while an 'exceptionally fine' caramelised apple tart is well worth the wait. Other desserts might include lemon tart with sliced figs in winter (or with poached pear in summer) served with honey ice-cream and red wine sauce. Young staff may be learning the ropes but are 'unfailingly helpful and discreet'. Wines from all around the world are astoundingly good. If the vast list appears unwieldy, there is a useful section at the front highlighting 'wines of the moment' in various price bands, starting at £14.50. CELLARMAN'S CHOICE: Bordeaux, Ch. de Reignac 1990, £16; St-Véran, Dom. des Valanges 1994, M. Paquet, £17.50.

CHEF: Aaron Patterson   PROPRIETORS: Tim and Stefa Hart   OPEN: all week 12 to 1.30, 7 to 9.30   MEALS: alc (main courses £18 to £30). Set L £14.50 (2 courses), Set D £29.50 to £35   SERVICE: net prices, card slips closed   CARDS: Access, Amex, Delta, Diners, Switch, Visa   DETAILS: 60 seats. Private parties: 40 main room, 15 to 60 private rooms. Car park. Vegetarian meals. Children's helpings. Smart dress preferred. No cigars/pipes in dining-room. No music   ACCOMMODATION: 15 rooms, all with bath/shower. TV. Phone. B&B £110 to £275. Rooms for disabled. Children welcome. Baby facilities. Dogs by arrangement. Afternoon teas. Garden. Swimming-pool (*The Which? Hotel Guide*)

Dijonnais

35 High Street, Hampton Wick KT1 4DA   COOKING 1*
TEL: (0181) 977 4895   COST £23–£47

'Pleasant and rewarding' is how one reporter described his first visit to this
modest-looking French restaurant. It is a family enterprise combining Mrs
Jolivet's consistently amiable presence and good humour with Lionel Jolivet's
largely French repertoire. What strikes the visitor is the wide choice on the *carte*,
bolstered by a short set-price alternative. It seems a lot of cooking for a small
kitchen, and runs from old-fashioned snails and frogs' legs through omelettes
and simply sauced fish to main-course salads. Meats are typically given a sauce
with a dash of alcohol: cider and apple for braised duck, or assorted peppers and
cognac for sirloin steak. Look to the daily menus for variety in the form of moules
waterzooï, or boiled gammon with pease pudding and dumplings. Lemon tart
and crème brûlée with Pernod have been among the recommended puddings.
The short wine list is entirely French, with house wine at £9.25 a bottle and also
available by the half-bottle or glass.

CHEFS: Lionel Jolivet and Jerome Aurejac   PROPRIETORS: Lionel and Jan Jolivet   OPEN: Mon to
Fri L 12 to 2, Mon to Sat D 7 to 10   CLOSED: Easter, bank hols   MEALS: alc (main courses £9.50
to £15.50). Set L £11.50 (2 courses), Set D £19.50   SERVICE: not inc, card slips closed   CARDS:
Access, Amex, Delta, Diners, Switch, Visa   DETAILS: 30 seats. 4 seats outside. Private parties:
25 main room. Vegetarian meals. Children welcome. Smart dress preferred. No music

Petit Max

97A High Street, Hampton Wick KT2 5NB
TEL: (0181) 977 0236

*As the Guide went to press, last-minute changes at this establishment made our review
invalid.*

OPEN: Tue to Sun 12.30 to 2.30 (3 Sun), 7 to 10   MEALS: Set L £10, Set L Sun £25.50, Set D
£25.50. Unlicensed, BYO £2.50   SERVICE: 10%   DETAILS: 35 seats. 20 seats outside. Private
parties: 35 main room. Children welcome. No cigars/pipes in dining-room. No music

HARROGATE North Yorkshire   map 8

La Bergerie ⚡✖

11–13 Mount Parade, Harrogate HG1 1BX   COOKING 1
TEL: (01423) 500089   FAX: (01423) 560837   COST £24–£31

Jaques Giron comes from Harrogate's twin town of Luchon, down in the deep south-west of France, so don't be surprised to encounter a waft of the distant Pyrenees in the ambience of this cosy terraced conversion. A stronger blast comes from the cooking itself which follows the truffle and garlic route to gastro-happiness. Fans of all things smoked might be tempted by a smoked chicken pancake with smoked venison and smoked pigeon; but regional specialities, such as duck and armagnac terrine, Basque seafood fricassee, and 'authentic' cassoulet, are probably where the strength lies. That said, a straightforward meal of smoked salmon cornets filled with prawns, rosemary-scented rack of lamb, and crème brûlée pleased one reporter no end. The generously priced French wines do their job efficiently, leading with house Duboeuf at £8.50.

CHEF: Jaques Giron   PROPRIETORS: Jaques and Juliet Giron   OPEN: Mon to Sat L by appointment only, D 7 to 11   CLOSED: 25 Dec, 1 Jan, bank hols   MEALS: Set L by appointment only £15.50 to £17.50, Set D £15.50 to £17.50. BYO £5   SERVICE: 10% (optional)   CARDS: Access, Delta, Visa   DETAILS: 50 seats. 12 seats outside. Private parties: 25 main room, 15 private room. Children welcome. Smart dress preferred. No smoking in 1 dining-room. Wheelchair access (also WC). Music

The Bistro 🍞

1 Montpellier Mews, Harrogate HG1 2TG   COOKING 2
TEL: (01423) 530708   COST £24–£41

The Bistro has dropped its Millers tag, Simon Gueller has moved to Leeds (see entry Rascasse), and a new owner and chef are installed. Despite all this it looks just as it did before, occupying a pretty mews courtyard – it catches visitors to the nearby antique shops at lunch-time – with small packed-together tables more suitable for a general chinwag than a private conversation. The food continues in modern bistro vein, with fish and meat given equal billing, aided and abetted by such contemporary staples as truffle oil, and wild mushroom risotto. 'Fresh ingredients carefully cooked' was how an inspector summed up the food.

Dishes appeal for their simple heartiness: a hunk of chicken or calf's liver with a lively sauce (sometimes sharpened with a little raspberry or balsamic vinegar), or fresh, moist fillet of turbot with saffron noodles, and pan-fried salmon in a red wine sauce. To begin, a flavoursome, thick broth-like version of Mediterranean fish soup comes with all the trimmings, while desserts (generally cold) have included a generous wedge of very rich chocolate tart made with good shortcrust pastry and accompanied by a clove-scented raspberry sauce. A short, international list of wines stays mostly below £20. House French is £8.95.

CHEF: Dean Sowden   PROPRIETOR: Maurizio Capurro   OPEN: Tue to Sat 12 to 2.30, 7 to 10   MEALS: alc (main courses £9.50 to £14.50).   SERVICE: not inc   CARDS: Access, Visa   DETAILS: 40 seats. 8 seats outside. Private parties: 40 main room. Children welcome. Music

Drum and Monkey £

5 Montpellier Gardens, Harrogate HG1 2TF	COOKING 2
TEL: (01423) 502650 FAX: (01423) 522469	COST £14–£41

The Victorian ex-pub has been a Harrogate fixture for more than a decade and a half, serving little else but seafood. It might be a bit of a squeeze to get four round a table, but the crush all adds to the atmosphere. It has two chefs – Tina Nuttall at lunch, Keith Penny at dinner – who cover much the same ground. For simplicity, begin with half a dozen native oysters, some large prawns in garlic butter, or a soup of whiting, or lobster bisque. Smoked fish pâté and prawn cocktail may be standards, but the Drum thrives on both freshness and a repertoire that holds few surprises. Indeed, a rather old-fashioned approach persists in prawn curry, or fish pie with a strong cheese topping, but there is no denying the popular appeal of satisfyingly fleshy halibut and sea bass, or, in the evening, of lobster cooked in various ways, and of the reasonable pricing, which extends to a short list of mostly young white wines whose prices start at £7.15.

CHEFS: Keith Penny and Tina Nuttall   PROPRIETOR: William Fuller   OPEN: Mon to Sat 12 to 2.30, 6.45 to 10.15   CLOSED: D 24 Dec to L 2 Jan   MEALS: alc (main courses £4.50 to £13.50). BYO £3.50   SERVICE: not inc   CARDS: Access, Delta, Switch, Visa   DETAILS: 50 seats. Private parties: 8 main room. Children's helpings. Wheelchair access (also WC). No music

Grundy's

21 Cheltenham Crescent, Harrogate HG1 1DH	COOKING 1
TEL: (01423) 502610	COST £21–£38

The Grundys, ever aware of the economic climate in which they operate, strive to stay afloat by putting off refurbishment until better times return, concentrating attention on the food and service. Consistency, they say, is the aim of their predominantly British cooking, with 'no off-days, no out-of-character combinations and no wild swings in pursuit of fashion'. Regulars don't take kindly to surprises, yet the menu keeps their interest going with puff pastry parcels of chilli-spiked tuna and watercress, and chickpea and coriander cakes served with a mint and yoghurt dressing. Beef is local, from grass-fed herds, and the fillet might be served with a red wine sauce. A range of sweet wines is offered by the glass to accompany desserts of chocolate mousse or treacle sponge, for example, and 30 wines are briefly annotated and sympathetically priced. House wine is £8.50.

CHEF: Val Grundy   PROPRIETORS: Chris and Val Grundy   OPEN: Mon to Sat D only 6.30 to 10; L by arrangement   CLOSED: 2 weeks Jan/Feb, 2 weeks July/Aug, bank hols   MEALS: alc (main courses £9 to £13.50). Set D £11.95 (2 courses) to £13.95   SERVICE: 10% (optional), card slips closed   CARDS: Access, Amex, Delta, Switch, Visa   DETAILS: 40 seats. Private parties: 32 main room. Vegetarian meals. Children's helpings. No pipes in dining-room. Music

Report forms are at the back of the book; write a letter if you prefer; or if you are on the Internet, e-mail us at guidereports@which. co. uk.

HARROW   Greater London   map 3

Percy's ✻

66–68 Station Road, North Harrow HA2 7SJ   COOKING 1*
TEL: (0181) 427 2021   FAX: (0181) 427 8134   COST £26–£44

Tony and Tina Bricknell-Webb's 40 acres of Devon farmland have long
sustained their kitchen here with organically grown herbs, leaves and vegetables. They have now opened a restaurant-with-rooms down there (see entry,
Virginstow) with its own head chef. Percy's menu continues in the contemporary vein that has underpinned its success so far. Oriental seasonings are
favoured: grilled tiger prawns, for example, are enlivened with chilli, garlic and
ginger and then dressed in a raspberry vinaigrette. Chicken is wrapped in bacon
and partnered with sage and crab apple jelly, but culinary adventurers might try
the conger eel poached in white wine and sauced with mustard and pink
peppercorns. Ice-creams seem to accompany most desserts and the flavours
should entice. Banana baba with ginger ice-cream, or cranberry and coconut
steamed pudding with cardamom ice-cream will keep taste-buds alert to the
end. The wine list provides a concise spread of stimulating choices from here,
there and everywhere. House Chilean is £8.50.

CHEF: Tina Bricknell-Webb   PROPRIETORS: Tony and Tina Bricknell-Webb   OPEN: Mon to Sat
12 to 2.30, 6.30 to 10.30   MEALS: alc (main courses £12 to £16). Set L and D £14.50 (2
courses)   SERVICE: 10% (optional), card slips closed   CARDS: Access, Amex, Delta, Diners,
Switch, Visa   DETAILS: 80 seats. Private parties: 80 main room, 30 and 40 private rooms. Car
park. Vegetarian meals. No children under 10. Smart dress preferred. No smoking in
dining-room. Wheelchair access (no WC). No music

HARVINGTON   Hereford & Worcester   map 5

▲ Mill at Harvington ♟ ✻

Anchor Lane, Harvington WR11 5NR
TEL/FAX: (01386) 870688
S of B439 Evesham to Bidford-on-Avon road; avoid   COOKING 1
village   COST £22–£45

Tradition is the forte of this eighteenth-century malting mill beside the River
Avon. Pasta with pesto sauce is about as modern as the food gets; otherwise it
may be crab pancake, Brie wrapped in puff pastry and deep fried, or medallions
of pork with prune sauce. The food is 'safe', with an Anglo-French tilt that might
take in duck terrine, or wild mushrooms in filo pastry to start, and meals are
priced according to the main course, perhaps rack of lamb with a 'superb'
beer-based sauce, or rabbit pie. Consider vanilla and yoghurt cream with
blackcurrant sauce to finish. Service is willing, and the wine list appeals. Bins
are grouped according to style, and notes on grape varieties will help those with
time to glance through them. House wines are £8.95. CELLARMAN'S CHOICE:
Peteroa Sauvignon Blanc 1995, Chile, £10.95; Ialoveni Cabernet Sauvignon
1988, Moldova, £9.95.

CHEFS: Jane Greenhalgh, Bill Downing and John Hunter   PROPRIETORS: Simon and Jane Greenhalgh   OPEN: all week 11.45 to 1.45, 7 to 9   CLOSED: 24 to 29 Dec   MEALS: Set L £12.25 (2 courses) to £13.95, Set D £21.50 to £29.95   SERVICE: not inc, card slips closed   CARDS: Access, Amex, Delta, Diners, Switch, Visa   DETAILS: 40 seats. 20 seats outside. Private parties: 40 main room, 14 private room. Car park. Vegetarian meals. Children's helpings. No smoking in dining-room. No music   ACCOMMODATION: 15 rooms, all with bath/shower. TV. Phone. B&B £54 to £95. No children under 10. Baby facilities. Garden. Swimming-pool. Fishing (*The Which? Hotel Guide*)

HARWICH Essex   map 6

▲ *The Pier at Harwich* ❢

The Quay, Harwich CO12 3HH	COOKING 1
TEL: (01255) 241212 FAX: (01255) 551922	COST £23–£60

The Pier has marvellous views across the Stour and Orwell estuaries, particularly from the restaurant aloft. It is decorated throughout in nautical fashion with charts, ships' wheels, anchors and suchlike, and understandably majors in seafood: from native and gigas oysters to cold poached lobster, Dover sole meunière, and smoked haddock with poached egg and béarnaise sauce. An inspector enjoyed 'gutsy and tasty' soupe au pistou, and 'a really good, flavoursome' roulade of salmon, sole and watercress. Dishes can sometimes over-reach themselves, however, as on one occasion in an exotic but dry mix of salmon, zander, carp and trout; moister, humbler fish might have impressed more. Cheesecake, chocolate torte and bread-and-butter pudding feature among desserts, balanced by good fruity alternatives including sorbets. The Ha'penny Pier on the lower deck is a family restaurant devoted to fish and chips. Local merchants Lay & Wheeler supply the wines, hence a sound list of several bottles from each major wine country, and a few more from regional France. Twenty half-bottles bring up the rear. CELLARMAN'S CHOICE: Randall Bridge Semillon/ Chardonnay 1995, S.E. Australia, £11.95; Uiterwyk, Cabernet Sauvignon 1991, Stellenbosch, South Africa, £19.50.

CHEF: Chris Oakley   PROPRIETOR: Milsom Hotels (Dedham) Ltd   OPEN: all week 12 to 2, 6 to 9.30   CLOSED: D 25 and 26 Dec   MEALS: alc (main courses £10 to £25). Set L Sun to Fri £9.95 (2 courses) to £13.45, Set D £13.75 (2 courses) to £17.25   SERVICE: 10%, card slips closed   CARDS: Access, Amex, Delta, Diners, Switch, Visa   DETAILS: 80 seats. Private parties: 90 main room, 40 and 50 private rooms. Car park. Children's helpings. Smart dress preferred. Music   ACCOMMODATION: 6 rooms, all with bath/shower. TV. Phone. B&B £50 to £80. Children welcome (*The Which? Hotel Guide*)

HASLEMERE Surrey   map 3

Fleur de Sel

23–27 Lower Street, Haslemere GU27 2NY	COOKING 3
TEL: (01428) 651462 FAX: (01428) 661568	COST £22–£49

'Fleur de Sel is a gem,' claims a supporter. The comfortable knocked-together cottages high on the pavement feel 'relaxed but formal', and a welcome from the proprietor gets things off to a good start. Food and service are all very French, and consistency seems to be a hallmark. The overall impression for one reporter was of 'light, fresh tastes, and satisfaction without overwhelming quantity'. Portions can be on the dainty side, although cream and cheese in some sauces can make them seem slightly heavy by today's standards.

The *carte* offers a generous choice, with a balanced selection across the board from warm pigeon salad with lentils, to roast salmon with honey and pink grapefruit, to lamb cutlets topped with ratatouille. Pistachio-studded duck terrine is a 'fine example of French charcuterie', and even though Michel Perraud is as French as they come, he bows to British taste by serving roast beef and Yorkshire pudding for Sunday lunch. Other timeless dishes might include braised oxtail, or Dover sole meunière.

The fixed-price lunch is considered good value, with a caveat: 'We sometimes don't fancy the single pudding offered and therefore have to pay a supplement.' Temptation is provided by summer pudding, crème brûlée with rum and raisins, or perhaps an 'exquisite' pear tartlet with a tiny biscuit cup of chocolate and nut ice-cream. An extra £4 brings a selection of all five desserts. Service is attentive and polite. Wines are entirely French, rather classy and weighted towards reds, and the list doesn't go out of its way to include bottles under £20.

CHEF/PROPRIETOR: Michel Perraud   OPEN: Tue to Fri and Sun L 12 to 2, Tue to Sat D 7 to 10
CLOSED: 1 week Mar, 2 weeks Aug/Sept   MEALS: Set L Tue to Fri £9.50 (2 courses) to £12.50,
Set L Sun £12.50 (2 courses) to £16.50, Set D £12.50 (2 courses) to £26   SERVICE: not inc
CARDS: Access, Amex, Delta, Switch, Visa   DETAILS: 50 seats. Private parties: 50 main room.
Vegetarian meals. Children's helpings. Smart dress preferred. No cigars/pipes in dining-room.
Wheelchair access (no WC). Music. Air-conditioned

HASTINGS East Sussex   map 3

Röser's 🍷

64 Eversfield Place, St Leonards,
Hastings TN37 6DB   COOKING 3*
TEL: (01424) 712218   COST £26–£57

Find the pier, and Röser's is 100 metres east of it: a terraced house with a 'Swiss tea-room' bow front. Surroundings and location require a degree of tolerance; there is no attempt at grandeur. It is a comforting space, but don't expect too much of the décor; concentrate instead on the food and wine, for both are of high quality, and remember that everything is the product of a husband-and-wife team, plus one apprentice. Their foundation is good ingredients. Gerald Röser is not hung up on flashy, expensive or hard-to-find materials, but when he uses them it is with conviction, with no stinting on quantity just because they happen to be costly. He also goes in for home curing, smoking and pickling, and is a keen collector of mushrooms. Wild mushroom salad (with cep, chanterelle, pied de mouton, wood blewits and a few shavings of truffle) is, in his own words, 'a knockout starter that gets many customers addicted'. Another fine combination is of truffles, mushrooms and potatoes with a périgourdine sauce.

Any tendency to innovate is kept in check. 'To say it is reliable sounds boring, and that it is not.' It is simply very calm cooking, lacking the flamboyance that some might hope for at this level of expenditure. Calf's liver with balsamic vinegar and a sage sauce, for instance, illustrates perfect cooking of a very simple dish, with flavours, textures, appearance all finely judged, as does 'an absolutely classic' crème brûlée. Flavours are 'definite, yet with no resort to high-pitched intensity', as in seared scallops in a creamy sauce 'as saffrony as you can get without becoming crude'. Vegetables are ancillary rather than integral, and cost extra. Strong, and clean flavours, not to mention richness, also characterise desserts of chocolate mousse with coffee sauce, or apple mille-feuille with calvados custard and butterscotch sauce.

Bread and butter are exemplary (the saffron bread has 'taken years to develop', writes Gerald Röser), as was an 'intense' appetiser of scallop soup served cappuccino-style for one reporter. A warm welcome, relaxed atmosphere and cheerful and efficient service round the whole thing off. The wine list is a heavy tome with no fewer than nine pages devoted to Burgundy and five to claret. Quality is high throughout, with plenty of opportunity to push the boat out as well as a good showing around £20. House wines include Louis Latour Chardonnay 1993 at £13.95. CELLARMAN'S CHOICE: Chinon Blanc, Dom. Raymond Raffault 1993, £16.50; Ch. de la Liquière, Vieilles Vignes 1993, Faugères, £15.50.

CHEF: Gerald Röser PROPRIETORS: Gerald and Jenny Röser OPEN: Tue to Fri L 12 to 2, Tue to Sat D 7 to 10 CLOSED: first 2 weeks Jan, last week Aug, first week Sept MEALS: alc (main courses £13 to £18.50). Set L £17.95, Set D £19.95 SERVICE: net prices, card slips closed CARDS: Access, Amex, Diners, Switch, Visa DETAILS: 30 seats. Private parties: 12 main room, 30 private room. Vegetarian meals. Children welcome. No cigars/pipes in dining-room. Wheelchair access (no WC). No music

---

HAWORTH West Yorkshire   map 8

▲ Weaver's ⅚✳

15 West Lane, Haworth BD22 8DU   COOKING 1*
TEL: (01535) 643822 FAX: (01535) 644832   COST £20–£40

Visitors to the Brontë Parsonage at Haworth would do well to take note of Weaver's at the top of the village's main cobbled street. It is open only in the evenings, but reporters tell us it's definitely worth making a trip back for. Cottagey furnishings make everyone feel at home, and so will the Rushworths' cooking. Potted Scarborough crab is well peppered and comes with melba toast and well-dressed leaves, while cheese sausage with apple chutney is a variation on the deep-fried Camembert theme, using Wensleydale and Lancashire to great effect. Roast fillet and belly of pork with brilliant crackling and a cider apple gravy is another flag-waving dish that relies confidently on the palpable quality of the meat. Puddings might include 'moist and chewy' chocolate torte with Amaretto ice-cream, or 'flavoursome' sticky toffee pudding with whipped cream. The surprisingly extensive wine list is built around a core selection of decent international house wines starting at £8.50.

Net prices *in the details at the end of an entry indicates that the prices given on a menu and on a bill are inclusive of VAT and service charge, and that this practice is clearly stated on menu and bill.*

CHEFS/PROPRIETORS: Colin and Jane Rushworth OPEN: Tue to Sat D only 6.45 to 9.15 CLOSED: 2 weeks from Christmas, 2 weeks July, Tue and Wed in July MEALS: alc (main courses £10 to £15). Set D Tue to Fri 6.45 to 7.15 £9.95 (2 courses) to £12.50. BYO £3.50 SERVICE: not inc, card slips closed CARDS: Access, Amex, Delta, Diners, Switch, Visa DETAILS: 60 seats. Private parties: 26 main room, 16 private room. Vegetarian meals. Children's helpings. Smart dress preferred. No smoking in dining-room. Music. Air-conditioned ACCOMMODATION: 4 rooms, all with bath/shower. TV. Phone. B&B £49.50 to £69.50. Children welcome (*The Which? Hotel Guide*)

HAYDON BRIDGE Northumberland   map 10

General Havelock Inn

Radcliffe Road, Haydon Bridge NE47 6ER
TEL: (01434) 684376
on A69, 6m W of Hexham

COOKING 1
COST £18–£32

The Clydes' enviably sited village inn has a restaurant at the back, where diners can look out over one of the River Tyne's prettier stretches and enjoy Angela Clyde's well-wrought home-cooking. Fixed-price menus keep things nice and simple, the dishes often described as a shopping-list of ingredients, in the manner of 'mussels baked – garlic – onion – white wine – cream'. Such admirable restraint should be music to the ears of those seeking refuge from the florid country-house style. Crab is devilled, plaice is baked with lemon, tarragon, prawns and a sprinkling of Parmesan, and pork loin comes with apple, as it has for many a generation. The cream-jug works overtime in desserts, but you could always settle for a lemon sorbet. Wines are arranged by style, and shouldn't put too much of a strain on anyone's pocket, as everything is under £20; house wines are £7.50.

CHEF: Angela Clyde PROPRIETORS: Ian and Angela Clyde OPEN: Wed to Sun L 12 to 1.15, Wed to Sat D 7.30 to 8.45 CLOSED: first 2 weeks Jan and Sept MEALS: Set L £11.75, Set D £19.50. Bar L available SERVICE: not inc CARDS: none DETAILS: 28 seats. 8 seats outside. Private parties: 28 main room. Children's helpings. Smart dress preferred. Wheelchair access (also WC). Music

---

HAYFIELD Derbyshire   map 9

▲ *Bridge End*

7 Church Street, Hayfield SK12 5JE
TEL: (01663) 747321 FAX: (01663) 742121

COOKING 2
COST £26–£45

There is nothing soft-focus about the Derbyshire scenery hereabouts. This enclave of pretty stone terraces huddles close to the majestic severity of the Peak District; hostelries proliferate along the main street. Bridge End is a converted shop done out in simple country style, with much unadorned wood. It is a place where fine modern cooking may be enjoyed at prices that are, according to an inspector, 'below what could be expected elsewhere for the standard'.

Joanne Winch's food is the kind that may appear slightly rough-and-ready, but delivers plenty of flavour. A first-course salad composed of pigeon breast, apple, lardons and spinach looked a bit of a heap, 'but everything tasted wonderful'. Balance is properly understood too, so that classically sweet orange sauce with magret of duck comes agreeably cut with both kumquat and grilled chicory. The extensive range also brings in goats'-cheese and onion tart, and roasted monkfish with deep-fried noodles and celeriac cream sauce. The 'squidgy' and 'sticky' applied to menu descriptions of desserts belies the lightness of touch found, for example, in a fruit sablé with crème patissière. The French-led wine list offers much in the way of sound choice at very keen prices. House Bergerac is £12.50. Given that Bridge End had to cope with Geoffrey Tier's untimely death in a climbing accident in 1995, the consistency of its recent performance is all the more impressive.

CHEF: Joanne Winch   PROPRIETOR: Barbara Tier   OPEN: Tue to Sat D only 7.30 to 10   MEALS: alc (main courses £10 to £15)   SERVICE: not inc   CARDS: Access, Amex, Diners, Visa   DETAILS: 50 seats. Private parties: 36 main room, 20 private room. Car park. Vegetarian meals. Children's helpings. Smart dress preferred. Smoking during coffee only. Music   ACCOMMODATION: 4 rooms, all with bath/shower. TV. Phone. B&B £33 to £40. Children welcome. Baby facilities. Small dogs by arrangement (The Which? Hotel Guide)

HERSTMONCEUX   East Sussex   map 3

Sundial ⅚✳

Gardner Street, Herstmonceux BN27 4LA   COOKING 2
TEL: (01323) 832217   COST £27–£74

In 1997 the Bertolis clock up 30 years at this seventeenth-century auberge, Giuseppe cooking and Laure 'making each diner feel special and at ease' while presiding over a well-maintained dining-room – in fact several rooms knocked together – with busy décor and twiddly patterns everywhere. The menu is long and industrious, too, with two completely separate set menus at lunch, part in French, most with English translations, and a more than generous carte.

The food is not exactly modern, but sound ingredients (some local) are the foundation, with plentiful seafood in the form of Dover sole, langoustines, mussels, skate, and a bowl of bouillabaisse covered with garlic pastry. Pork fillet served with kidney in a strong mustard sauce, with a small pile of glutinous rice, was 'highly enjoyable' at inspection, and crispy duck in strawberry sauce was more successful than it might sound. There may be a lot of window-dressing, but 'once you got past the overwhelming garnish, the terrine of leek and smoked salmon was marvellous'. Desserts are displayed in the centre of the dining-room. Classic French wines are the backbone of a long list, and house Soave and Valpolicella are available by the glass for £2.95.

CHEF: Giuseppe Bertoli   PROPRIETORS: Giuseppe and Laure Bertoli   OPEN: Tue to Sun L 12 to 2 (2.30 Sun), Tue to Sat D 7 to 9.30 (10 Sat)   CLOSED: 25 Dec to 20 Jan, last 3 weeks Aug   MEALS: alc (main courses £15.50 to £25). Set L Tue to Sat £15.50 to £19.50, Set L Sun £22.50, Set D £26.50. BYO (no corkage)   SERVICE: 10%, card slips closed   CARDS: Access, Amex, Delta, Diners, Visa   DETAILS: 50 seats. 30 seats outside. Private parties: 60 main room, 22 private room. Car park. Children's helpings. Smart dress preferred. No smoking in dining-room. Wheelchair access (also WC). Music

---

See inside the front cover for an explanation of the symbols used at the tops of entries.

Angel Inn 🍷 ✁✱

Hetton BD23 6LT
TEL: (01756) 730263   FAX: (01756) 730363   COOKING 2*
off B6265, 5m N of Skipton   COST £25–£38

In the main street of a grey-stone village in the Yorkshire Dales, the Angel is somewhat off the beaten track, or would be had it not created its own beaten track: queues for bar lunches begin long before it opens, 'and then, whoosh, everyone tries to grab a good table'. Reporters enjoy the informality of the bar/brasserie, with its bare wooden tables, Victorian kitchen range and its relatively simple fare of rustic fish soup, terrine of Tuscan vegetables, or rump steak with béarnaise sauce. 'Friday is fish day', when a large selection is displayed on a blackboard – sea bream and sea bass, langoustines and lobster among them – although seafood is a strong suit on other days too.

The bookable dining-room offers a calm refuge and a fixed-price menu with slightly tricksier dishes, such as smoked salmon served with an ice-cream made from tomato, red pepper and chilli. Contemporary accompaniments of couscous with lamb, or risotto with breast of chicken take their place beside the plainer delights of a 'large and delicious' Dover sole fried in butter. Puddings are well reported – rhubarb and custard brûlée, or a sharp, fruity raspberry mousse – and contribute to 'a very pleasing meal at a very reasonable price'. Staff are neatly turned out in black and white, and service is generally brisk and efficient, though with a 'natural Yorkshire friendliness'. The wine list manages to pack some excellent names into just a few pages, with the emphasis on Bordeaux, Burgundy and estate-bottled Italians. Prices are very fair. There is plenty of choice by the glass, starting with house red at £1.75, and a long list of half-bottles. CELLARMAN'S CHOICE: Pouilly-Fumé 1994, Jean-Claude Dagueneau, £16.95; Côtes de Nuits Villages 1993, Groffier, £18.80.

CHEF: John Topham   PROPRIETORS: Denis Watkins, John Topham and Juliet Watkins   OPEN: restaurant Sun L 12 to 2, Mon to Sat D 7 to 9.30; bar/brasserie all week 12 to 2, 6 to 9.30   CLOSED: 25 Dec, third week Jan   MEALS: restaurant Set L Sun £18.50, Set D £24; bar/brasserie alc (main courses from £8)   SERVICE: not inc   CARDS: Access, Amex, Visa   DETAILS: 56 seats. Private parties: 40 main room. Car park. Vegetarian meals. Children welcome. No smoking in 1 dining-room. Wheelchair access (no WC). No music. Air-conditioned

Black House ✁✱

Dipton Mill Road, Hexham NE46 1RZ
TEL: (01434) 604744   COOKING 2*
on Whitley Chapel road, S of Hexham   COST £23–£34

The Black House is at a crossroads on a road leading out of Hexham. It occupies converted farm buildings on a hilltop looking down over what the owners affectionately refer to as 'Hexhamshire'. Hazel Pittock's culinary references tend to be French, so that a meal might be made up of provençale fish soup, coq au vin, and petit vacherin au citron, or a slice of Brie if you prefer.

Then again she is equally at home with more obviously modern British fare. If you ate leek and Stilton soup, cod roasted with a herb and garlic crust and sauced with lemon butter, finishing with pear and ginger upside-down pudding with butterscotch sauce, you would hardly feel you had crossed the Channel. An innovation has been evenings of starters and puddings, where a multi-course menu is offered in which terrines and pasta dishes are followed by a succession of desserts: a novel enough idea that may just catch on. Front-of-house is marshalled by Chris Pittock, who likes things to run with brisk precision. The typed wine list is almost entirely French and contains some mature fine wines at prices that, in context, are not unfair. House wines from Languedoc and Bordeaux are £9.75.

CHEF: Hazel Pittock PROPRIETORS: Christopher and Hazel Pittock OPEN: L last Sun each month 12.30 to 1.30, Fri and Sat D 7.30 to 9.30 CLOSED: 25 to 31 Dec MEALS: Set L Sun £15.50, Set D Fri £14.95, Set D Sat £16.50 to £19.50 SERVICE: not inc, card slips closed CARDS: Access, Delta, Visa DETAILS: 28 seats. Private parties: 28 main room. Car park. No children under 10. Smart dress preferred. No smoking in dining-room. Music

---

HINTLESHAM Suffolk
map 6

▲ Hintlesham Hall ▮ ⅝✳

Hintlesham IP8 3NS
TEL: (01473) 652268 FAX: (01473) 652463
on A1071, 4½m W of Ipswich

COOKING 3
COST £30–£77

The front is Georgian, the rear is Elizabethan, and several other periods are represented within. Whichever way you look at it, this fine and well-maintained country house impresses both for its décor and for its professional service. Staff are 'remarkably competent and pleasant', offering a high degree of assistance, and they don't levy a charge for the privilege. Alan Ford's food moves with the times and seasons, uses local produce and offers a few of the luxuries that the surroundings seem to demand, such as briefly seared foie gras with celeriac rösti.

Contemporary flavourings give a vital lift to quite a few dishes – a refreshing pepper salsa with carpaccio of monkfish, or candied lime with calf's liver – and a high degree of workmanship characterises much of the cooking. According to one reporter, 'Grand hotels seem to feel the need to justify high prices by cramming too much into a dish,' and the words 'unnecessary' and 'superfluous' have cropped up in reports when referring to some of the contents of a dish, suggesting that a more straightforward approach might pay dividends. However, that is not to decry the considerable achievements of, for example, a 'huge' piece of chargrilled tuna, perfectly timed, as part of a first-course salad, a well-reduced and sticky lamb consommé, or a pressed duck terrine with 'meaty, juicy pieces, and the earthy taste of lentils'. Silver domes are lifted, to reveal some striking presentation, and incidentals include good canapés, bread and butter. The huge wine list roams far and wide, taking in many fine producers, and there's an impressive range of half-bottles. House wines are £12.50, otherwise mark-ups are on the high side. CELLARMAN'S CHOICE: Coteaux du Languedoc, Picpoul de Pinet 1993, Dom. St Peyre, £13.30; Claridge Wellington Red 1993, Wellington, South Africa £23.50.

CHEF: Alan Ford   PROPRIETOR: David Allan   OPEN: Mon to Fri and Sun L 12 to 1.45, all week D 7 to 9.30   MEALS: alc (main courses £16 to £23). Set L Mon to Fri £18.50, Set L Sun £19.50 Set D Mon to Thur £24   SERVICE: not inc, card slips closed   CARDS: Access, Arnex, Diners, Switch, Visa   DETAILS: 120 seats. Private parties: 81 main room, 14 to 81 private rooms. Car park. Vegetarian meals. No children under 9D. Jacket and tie. No smoking in dining-room. Wheelchair access (also WC). No Music   ACCOMMODATION: 33 rooms, all with bath/shower. TV. Phone. B&B £85 to £300. Children welcome. Baby facilities. Dogs by arrangement. Garden. Swimming-pool. Fishing (*The Which? Hotel Guide*)

HINTON CHARTERHOUSE   Bath & N.E. Somerset   map 2

▲ *Homewood Park* ☕ ✸

Hinton Charterhouse BA3 6BB
TEL: (01225) 723731   FAX: (01225) 723820   COOKING 3*
off A36, 5m SE of Bath   COST £30–£67

Homewood, a beautiful ivy-covered house, has seen some comings and goings in its kitchen over the past year, but 20-something Gary Jones, who has worked at some of the UK's top-scoring restaurants, looks set to dazzle. 'He would seem to be going for gold,' in the words of an inspector, 'when bronze might be a good place to start.' Enthusiasm is evangelistic, and the thrill-to-spill ratio is gripping. The menu is large, but excellent materials underpin the operation. One reporter who reckons to share the same fishmonger insists that Gary (obviously *the* chef's name these days) doesn't want today's catch, 'he wants fish that was caught tomorrow'.

Once bought, ingredients are skilfully and imaginatively handled, even though a lot can happen to them. Seared red mullet fillets on toasted olive bread with a brandade of salt-cod, roast fennel and artichoke bottom was a 'magical mix of complementary tastes and textures' that brought 'a pretty authentic slice of Mediterranean sun to windy Wiltshire'. Some dishes can be too clever by half, as when marinated tuna is shaved so 'contact-lens thin' that texture is lost, and its flavour overpowered by much bigger shavings of Parmesan. But judgement is sound in other respects. Vegetables, for instance, are 'part of the rationale' of a dish, which impressed an inspector dining on gigot of West Country lamb with peeled broad beans and caramelised chicory.

Desserts often aim for fruit, texture, and visual impact. They may sound frighteningly involved, but they work: a 'surrealist's dream' of three moon shapes combining the brown, beige and yellow colours of chocolate, caramel and banana was considered 'a damn good sweet'. One who has seen the tiny kitchen wonders how all this is possible. Pick your way carefully through the wine list, for there are some odd numbers among the French wines, and high prices here and there. For interesting producers, try the New World sections: Hunter's from New Zealand, Rockford from Australia and Bodega Weinert from Argentina. House wines start at £13.50.

Not inc *in the details at the end of an entry indicates that no service charge is made and any tipping is at the discretion of the customer.*

CHEF: Gary Jones   PROPRIETORS: the Gueuning and Fentum families   OPEN: all week 12 to 1.30 (2 Sun), 7.15 to 9.30 (7 to 10 Sat)   MEALS: alc (main courses £18 to £22). Set L £17.50, Set D £28.50   SERVICE: not inc   CARDS: Access, Amex, Delta, Diners, Switch, Visa   DETAILS: 80 seats. Private parties: 90 main room, 20 and 30 private rooms. Car park. Children's helpings. Smart dress preferred. No smoking in dining-room. Wheelchair access (also WC). No music ACCOMMODATION: 19 rooms, all with bath/shower. TV. Phone. B&B £90 to £170. Rooms for disabled. Children welcome. Baby facilities. Afternoon teas. Swimming-pool (*The Which? Hotel Guide*)

HOLDENBY   Northamptonshire   map 5

▲ *Lynton House* 🐾

Holdenby NN6 8DJ
TEL/FAX: (01604) 770777
between A50 and A428, E of Holdenby towards   COOKING 2
Church Brampton   COST £28–£42

The attractive old brick-built rectory stands on the edge of the village, and drinks are taken in either the bar or the conservatory looking out over gentle Northants countryside. Carlo supervises front-of-house, while his wife and anagram cooks in both English and Italian vein, although one reporter thought the style more Franco-Northamptonshire. It is certainly an individual contribution, offering seafood risotto or Tuscan fish casserole beside rack of lamb with mint sauce, or smoked haddock with mustard sauce. The cooking errs on the provincial side, and adopts a versatile approach with a rolling larder of ingredients, from sardines and shellfish through veal and venison.

The deal at dinner is four courses, one of them a mid-meal choice between sorbet and 'minestra' such as tortellini: thin home-made pasta filled with ricotta and spinach, in an old-fashioned tomato sauce. A similar sauce has accompanied home-made discs of potatoey gnocchi spiked with nutmeg, while pesto and herby salsa verde have been ladled over red mullet and sea bass respectively. Timing of meat and fish could do with sharpening up, but materials are sound and fresh. Finish with crème brûlée, or honey and brandy ice-cream, and drink from a list of around 40 well-chosen Italians or 20 posh clarets. House wines are £10.75.

CHEF: Carol Bertozzi   PROPRIETORS: Carlo and Carol Bertozzi   OPEN: Tue to Fri L 12.30 to 1.45, Mon to Sat D 7.30 to 9.45   CLOSED: Christmas, 1 week spring, 1 week summer, bank hols MEALS: Set L £13.25 (2 courses) to £18.75, Set D £22.25   SERVICE: none, card slips closed CARDS: Access, Amex, Visa   DETAILS: 45 seats. 16 seats outside. Private parties: 80 main room, 20 private room. Car park. Vegetarian meals. Children's helpings. No children under 6. Smart dress preferred. No smoking in 1 dining-room. No cigars/pipes in dining-room. Wheelchair access (also men's WC). Music   ACCOMMODATION: 5 rooms, all with bath/shower. TV. Phone. B&B £49 to £55. No children under 6 (*The Which? Hotel Guide*)

🐾 *indicates that smoking is either banned altogether or that a dining-room is maintained for non-smokers. The symbol does not apply to restaurants that simply have no-smoking areas.*

HOLT Norfolk

map 6

Yetman's ▼ ⚒

37 Norwich Road, Holt NR25 6SA

TEL: (01263) 713320

COOKING 2
COST £28–£45

'An excellent little restaurant' is how one couple described this Norfolk cottage with its pretty yellow and blue dining-room. They might have added that it is a likeably quirky set-up that moves along at its own pace and goes its own way regardless. Peter and Alison Yetman explain: 'We serve food and wine that we enjoy ourselves. We have fun doing it and want our customers to have fun too!' Alison's cooking shows respect for local ingredients, and she makes dedicated use of organic meat, fish from the Norfolk boats and biodynamically grown vegetables. A new menu is written each day (choose two, three or four courses), and the thrust of the cooking shows in potted venison with spiced black figs, grilled fillet of cod with anchovy butter, and roast fillet of beef with tarragon and orange hollandaise. Here and there you will also find something with a Mediterranean accent, as in wild mushroom lasagne with wild garlic pasta, or marinated monkfish with fettuccine and pesto. Proceedings conclude with cheeses from Neals Yard, and desserts ranging from raspberry crème brûlée to French lemon tart.

The wine list launches straight into a fine selection from the New World, with Sauvignon Blanc – Peter's favourite grape – to the fore. More wines follow from Italy and France, and there is always an ever-changing, lively choice by the glass. CELLARMAN'S CHOICE: Dashwood Estate Sauvignon Blanc 1995, Marlborough, New Zealand, £17.25; Parker Cabernet Sauvignon 1991, Coonawarra, S. Australia, £22.75.

CHEF: Alison Yetman PROPRIETORS: Alison and Peter Yetman OPEN: Sun L 12.30 to 2 (bookings only), Wed to Sun D and Mon D in summer 7.30 to 9 MEALS: Set L Sun and Set D £20.75 (2 courses) to £27 SERVICE: not inc CARDS: Access, Amex, Delta, Switch, Visa DETAILS: 30 seats. Private parties: 20 main room, 12 private room. Vegetarian meals. Children welcome. No smoking in dining-room. Wheelchair access (no WC). No music

HONLEY West Yorkshire

map 8

Mustards and Punch ▼

6 Westgate, Honley HD7 2AA

TEL: (01484) 662066

NEW CHEF
COST £16–£37

Squashed into a row of shops next to a travel agent in a village outside Huddersfield, and now in its third year, Mustards and Punch continues in the highly idiosyncratic vein established by Scott Hessel. He opened his second restaurant, Café Pacific (see entry, Huddersfield), in May '96 and bequeathed control of the kitchens here to a former colleague from the Crab & Lobster (see entry, Asenby). As we went to press he left, and Andrew Wood took over, too late for us to confirm the cooking mark. The food has been characterised by sharp ideas such as smoked pigeon tart with shallots and balsamic, as well as more traditional roast rack of lamb with onion and garlic purée, and spotted dick or treacle sponge to finish. The wine list is a paean to contemporary tastes, with its emphasis on the bright, modern and fruity. Needless to say, the New World features heavily, as does Spain. Most bottles are under £20. Chilean house wines are £8.95. CELLARMAN'S CHOICE: Mâcon-Uchizy 1992, R. Sallet, £16.95; Rioja Gran Reserva 1986, Montecillo, £17.95.

CHEF: Andrew Wood PROPRIETOR: Scott Hessel OPEN: Tue to Fri L 12 to 2, Tue to Sat D 6 to 10.30 CLOSED: 25 Dec MEALS: alc D (main courses £8 to £14). Set L £5 (2 courses) SERVICE: not inc CARDS: Access, Amex, Delta, Switch, Visa DETAILS: 60 seats. Private parties: 30 main room. Car park. Vegetarian meals. Children welcome. Smart dress preferred. No cigars/pipes in dining-room. Music. Air-conditioned

---

HORNCASTLE Lincolnshire   map 9

Magpies ⁵⨯

73–75 East Street, Horncastle LN9 6AA	COOKING 2
TEL: (01507) 527004 FAX: (01507) 524064	COST £21–£38

'Magpies is clearly a restaurant that is trying very hard,' commented an inspector about this highly popular local establishment right in the centre of the county. The Lee family are great improvers, always keen to adapt, change and re-vamp things. They have recently redecorated their lounges and pretty dining-room, which now has soft colour schemes, fresh flowers and naive agricultural artwork on the walls. Dinner revolves around a monthly-changing fixed-price menu that makes admirable use of local supplies such as beef from Lincoln Reds and meat from other rare breeds. Dishes are often complex compilations, as in pig's trotter served with black pudding, a baked apple, morels, a macedoine of root vegetables and a Madeira sauce, or extremely photogenic sea bass on a bed of braised fennel with vanilla sauce.

Elsewhere, there's a more robust feel to things: rack of lamb comes with minted pea purée, stuffed pig's trotter appears with baked apple, black pudding, morels and an unctuous, lip-smacking Madeira sauce. Sweets could include anything from nougat glacé pyramid to warm chocolate tart with home-made ice-cream. The wine list has been extensively enlarged and the notes are 'illuminating'. House wine is £9.75.

CHEFS: Matthew and Simon Lee PROPRIETORS: the Lee family OPEN: Sun and Wed to Fri L 12.30 to 2, Tue to Sat D 7.30 to 10 CLOSED: 2 weeks Jan MEALS: Set L £11.50 (2 courses) to £14, Set D £24 SERVICE: not inc CARDS: Access, Diners, Visa DETAILS: 40 seats. Private parties: 40 main room. Children welcome (children's helpings L). Smart dress preferred. No smoking in dining-room. Music

---

HORTON Northamptonshire   map 5

French Partridge ▮ ⁵⨯

Horton NN7 2AP	
TEL: (01604) 870033 FAX: (01604) 870032	COOKING 3
on B526, 6m SE of Northampton	COST £29–£34

As it clocks up 32 years in the *Guide*, this family-run restaurant continues to move gently with the times. The original inspiration was the cooking of south-west France, but David Partridge and son Justin are open to offers from bortsch to omelette Arnold Bennett, from poached egg meurette to Moroccan chicken with couscous. The format remains unaltered: four courses of capital cooking, with wines to match, and good value all round. Guests' arrival times are staggered to allow the kitchen to operate smoothly, meals are ordered in the bar and consumed in the brown and green dining-room. Mary Partridge runs the whole show with aplomb.

A typical meal might begin with soup (game and lentil, perhaps, or asparagus and broad bean), a pâté, or a cold selection of fish or pork meats, followed by a simple piece of very fresh plaice with beurre blanc, or a pastry such as mushroom tartlet with soft-boiled quail's eggs and hollandaise. Part of the appeal is that the usual straightforward cuts of meat are kept to a minimum. Commendably, the Partridges prefer to deal in lambs' sweetbreads and braised tongues, roast pigeon breast (in a sauce of raspberry vinegar and bitter chocolate), or boned and stuffed rabbit leg with a port and prune sauce. Butchering, timing and saucing are all well handled, and the quietly confident style of cooking continues into desserts of fresh raspberry pavlova or chocolate and banana délices, with a savoury such as Welsh rarebit or mushrooms on toast making a welcome appearance. Wines are cleverly chosen to include not only the classics but a wide range of food-friendly bottles such as Beaujolais crus, fine German whites and Loire reds and whites. Grape varieties are carefully explained but names of producers are sometimes strangely absent. Still, prices are keen. CELLARMAN'S CHOICE: Pouilly-Fumé 1995, Domaine Thibault, £16; Crozes-Hermitage 1994, Alain Graillot, £15.

CHEFS: David and Justin Partridge   PROPRIETORS: David and Mary Partridge   OPEN: Tue to Sat D only 7.30 to 9   CLOSED: 2 weeks Christmas, 2 weeks Easter, 3 weeks July to Aug   MEALS: Set D £24   SERVICE: net prices   CARDS: none   DETAILS: 50 seats. Private parties: 25 main room. Car park. Children welcome. Smart dress preferred. No smoking in dining-room. Wheelchair access (also WC). No music

---

HUDDERSFIELD West Yorkshire   map 9

Bradley's

84 Fitzwilliam Street, Huddersfield HD1 5BB	COOKING 1*
TEL: (01484) 516773 FAX: (01484) 538386	COST £15–£45

Andrew Bradley's bouncy presence defines the easy-going, professional mood of this converted Victorian warehouse. 'He treats everyone as a dear friend,' notes a regular. The main menu covers lots of ground, from quirky modern inventions such as warm salad of gammon, egg and chips with balsamic vinegar, or kangaroo fillet accompanied by wild mushrooms and slices of chorizo to skilfully executed classics including suckling pig, and fillet of beef with roasted shallots, foie-gras pâté and Madeira sauce. Among desserts, you might encounter really light treacle and sultana sponge, or cappuccino mousse with a 'syrupy' macadamia nut sauce. The daily 'early bird' menu is a great-value crowd-pleaser, particularly as the price includes half a bottle of house wine (call to check times as they vary each evening). The full list of 50-odd wines is well-chosen and affordable, with France as the front runner. House wines start at £8.25.

CHEF: Jonathan Nichols PROPRIETORS: Jonathan Nichols and Andrew Bradley OPEN: Mon to Fri L 12 to 2, Mon to Sat D 6 to 10 (10.30 Fri and Sat) CLOSED: bank hols MEALS: alc (main courses £7.50 to £16). Set L £7.95 (2 courses) to £9.95, Set early-bird D £12.50 Mon to Sat 6 to 7.30 (9 Mon, 7 Sat). BYO £4 SERVICE: not inc CARDS: Access, Switch, Visa DETAILS: 75 seats. Private parties: 75 main room. Car park. Vegetarian meals. Children's helpings. Smart dress preferred. No cigars/pipes in dining room. Wheelchair access (also WC). Music. Air-conditioned

Café Pacific £

NEW ENTRY

3 Viaduct Street, Huddersfield HD1 5DL
TEL: (01484) 559055 FAX: (01484) 559155

COOKING 2
COST £16–£28

'The hottest place to hit Huddersfield for a long time,' a reporter writes of this new venture from Scott Hessel, owner of Mustards & Punch (see entry, Honley). Hessel himself cooks here, bringing his mix-and-match contemporary offerings to an open-plan slate-floored restaurant beneath a railway viaduct. The periodic rumbling of trains overhead somehow adds the right *frisson* to the atmosphere.

Frisson is what Scott Hessel's menus are about too: China, Provence, Piedmont, Thailand and Spain crop up, and that's (literally) just for starters. Black pudding and sweetbreads in a filo money-bag with home-made piccalilli is a dish with its finger on the pulse, all its elements working together to produce huge satisfaction. Lamb shank comes in the modern way as a great clod of meat on the bone, served in a bowl, with gnocchi, roasted garlic and a rosemary-scented stock reduction. In such a context one would hardly expect fish to be given the kid-glove treatment, and so hake is roasted with plum tomatoes, tuna char-grilled, and there is also 'posh fish 'n' chips'. Finish with fig tart, a trio of vari-flavoured crème brûlées (it had to happen in Yorkshire too), or rhubarb jelly given texture with pieces of rhubarb and stem ginger. Early reports suggest that Huddersfield at least knows full well what's hit it. Café Pacific is running a shorter version of the wine list at Honley, a confident international selection at appealing prices, starting at £7.95.

CHEF/PROPRIETOR: Scott Hessel OPEN: Tue to Sat 12 to 2.30, 6 to late CLOSED: 25 Dec MEALS: alc (main courses £5 to £9) SERVICE: not inc CARDS: Access, Delta, Switch, Visa DETAILS: 45 seats. Private parties: 60 main room. Vegetarian meals. Children welcome. Smart dress preferred. Wheelchair access (no WC). Music. Air-conditioned

▲ Lodge Hotel ⁙✱

48 Birkby Lodge Road, Birkby,
Huddersfield HD2 2BG
TEL: (01484) 431001 FAX: (01484) 421590

COOKING 2
COST £22–£39

This Victorian residence a few miles outside Huddersfield exudes homely luxury: don't miss the art nouveau ceiling and bold colour schemes in the lounge. Local observers reckon that the cooking has moved up a notch of late, with more consistency and a greater sense of adventure in the seasonal fixed-price menus. Colour and freshness are the keys to starters such as home-made tagliatelle topped with mango and sweet-and-sour chicken, or fennel-tinged ragoût of seafood with squid ink risotto. At dinner a soup or sorbet heralds the main course, which could be spicily exotic (tagine of lamb with sweet tomatoes), whacky (kangaroo with chocolate and Cassis) or skilfully modern (oxtail in a crepinette with garlic mash and celeriac purée). Desserts are a sensible blend of hot and cold, ranging from a light-textured 'sandcastle' of sultana and treacle sponge to liquorice and aniseed parfait. A full vegetarian menu is also available. Service is neat and polished. The list of around 120 wines straddles the globe and mark-ups are eminently reasonable. House Bergerac is £9.95.

CHEFS: Garry Birley, Kevin Birley and Richard Hanson   PROPRIETORS: Garry Birley and Kevin Birley   OPEN: Sun to Fri L 12 to 1.45, Mon to Sat D 7.30 to 9.45   CLOSED: 26 to 28 Dec and bank hols   MEALS: Set L £12, Set D £22   SERVICE: not inc, card slips closed   CARDS: Access, Amex, Delta, Diners, Switch, Visa   DETAILS: 80 seats. 20 seats outside. Private parties: 62 main room, 10 to 20 private rooms. Car park. Vegetarian meals. No children under 5 D. Smart dress preferred. No smoking in dining-room. Wheelchair access (also WC). Music   ACCOMMODATION: 11 rooms, all with bath/shower. TV. Phone. B&B £55 to £85. Rooms for disabled. Children welcome. Baby facilities. Small dogs welcome in ground-floor bedrooms only. Afternoon teas. Garden (*The Which? Hotel Guide*)

HUNSTRETE   Bath & N.E. Somerset   map 2

▲ *Hunstrete House* 🏠✳

Hunstrete, Chelwood BS18 4NS
TEL: (01761) 490490   FAX: (01761) 490732   COOKING 3
off A368, 4m S of Keynsham   COST £27–£66

Despite the undoubted grandeur of its setting in 92 acres of deer park, Hunstrete manages to avoid that stifling air of formality that can so easily threaten to suffuse such places. 'You do not get the feeling here of being at the rich man's banquet,' commented a reporter. That said, the stiffly starched napery, cane-backed chairs and the view on to a flower-filled courtyard certainly impart a feeling of the good life.

Robert Clayton's menus have grown more ambitious with the passing of time, and the range of choice is wide. That can unnerve if kitchen resources are limited, but here most things are brought off with convincing panache. Presentational skills are not jettisoned simply because the fashion elsewhere is now for heaped agglomerations. So a creamy lobster risotto comes parcelled up in strips of sea trout garnished with deep-fried ginger strands and sitting on a saffron velouté. And the proof of the pudding (or starter)? 'A delightful and clever mixture of tastes.' Contrasts are well handled, so that the richness of sauté foie gras is offset by a sauce using Cabernet Sauvignon vinegar, while an 'intensely flavoured' mushroom and white wine sauce brings out extra dimensions in a grilled fillet of sea bass. Puddings are perhaps a little over-egged, so to speak, as when white chocolate crème brûlée with a biscuit basket of dark chocolate ice-cream comes with glazed bananas and morello cherries. For all the painstaking attention to detail in the kitchen, service has more than once been found distinctly absent-minded.

The wine list harbours some great bottles, mature clarets and Burgundies as well as a clutch of fine Germans (gold-dust these days in restaurants), but prices are weighted in favour of plutocrats. Still, the house selection offers 17 reds and whites that are mostly under £20.

CHEF: Robert Clayton   PROPRIETOR: Arcadian International plc   OPEN: all week 12.30 to 2, 7.15 to 9.30   MEALS: Set L Mon to Sat £17.50, Set L Sun £19.50, Set D £32.50. BYO £8   SERVICE: not inc, card slips closed   CARDS: Access, Amex, Delta, Diners, Switch, Visa   DETAILS: 50 seats. Private parties: 50 main room, 8 to 32 private rooms. Car park. Vegetarian meals. Children's helpings. Jacket and tie. No smoking in dining-room. No music   ACCOMMODATION: 23 rooms, all with bath/shower. TV. Phone. B&B £125 to £160. Rooms for disabled. Children welcome. Baby facilities. Afternoon teas. Garden. Swimming-pool (*The Which? Hotel Guide*)

HURSTBOURNE TARRANT Hampshire   map 2

▲ *Esseborne Manor* ♟ ⁵✳

Hurstbourne Tarrant SP11 0ER
TEL: (01264) 736444   FAX: (01264) 736725   COOKING 1
on A343, 1½m N of Hurstbourne Tarrant   COST £25–£53

A friendly welcome and good service are part of the appeal of this peaceful hotel on the North Wessex Downs. The house is late Victorian, elegantly decorated and comfortable. A set-price menu changes weekly, the *carte* less often, so residents may feel their options diminishing after a few days, but the overall choice is a fair one: a total of nine per course taking both menus together. A traditional British thread runs through beef Wellington, cod and caper fish-cakes, and steak and kidney pudding, while Cornish crab-cakes and wild mushroom tart add interest. Sticky desserts might include banana and rum pancakes with butterscotch ice-cream, but fresh fruit or a savoury such as Welsh rarebit provide diversions. 'What a change to get free water!' exclaimed one who enjoyed a jug from the manor's own well.

California has joined France, Australia and New Zealand on the wine list; of the four, France and Australia look to be the strongest, with high quality and fair pricing applied stringently. Half a dozen thoughtfully chosen house wines start at £12. CELLARMAN'S CHOICE: Scotchmans Hill Chardonnay 1993, Victoria, Australia, £23.50; St-Emilion grand cru, Ch. Pavie-Décesse 1988, £37.50.

CHEF: Nick Watson   PROPRIETORS: Ian and Lucilla Hamilton   OPEN: all week 12 to 2.30, 7 to 9.30   CLOSED: 24 to 27 Dec   MEALS: alc (main courses £12 to £20). Set L and D £12 (2 courses) to £15   SERVICE: not inc, card slips closed   CARDS: Access, Amex, Delta, Diners, Switch, Visa   DETAILS: 40 seats. 20 seats outside. Private parties: 40 main room. Car park. Vegetarian meals. No children under 7. Smart dress preferred. No smoking in 1 dining-room. Music   ACCOMMODATION: 10 rooms, all with bath/shower. TV. Phone. B&B £84 to £112. Rooms for disabled. No children under 7. Dogs welcome. Afternoon teas. Garden (*The Which? Hotel Guide*)

'Service is crushingly formal, and the topping up of water is solemnly methodical and slow, each twirl of the wrist accompanied by a deferential inclination of the head, eliciting a mumbled "Thank you" from each recipient. After about three rounds of this you resolve to go to a Greek plate-smashing restaurant next time.' (On eating in Lancashire)

HUXHAM Devon   map 1

▲ *Barton Cross* ⅝✳

Huxham, Stoke Canon EX5 4EJ
TEL: (01392) 841245   FAX: (01392) 841942   COOKING 1
at Stoke Canon, 5m N of Exeter on A396   COST £23–£38

'Seventeenth-century charm with twentieth-century luxury,' says the brochure
advertising this personally run hotel in the Exe Valley. The charm in question
emanates from three converted thatched cottages around a courtyard garden and,
inside, a lavish galleried dining-room. Paul Bending cooks with the seasons,
and reports suggest that the kitchen is on course. During the summer you might
begin with minestrone with pesto followed by rack of local lamb with roasted
hazelnuts; in autumn there might be 'excellent' marinated salmon with seared
scallops before pheasant stuffed with chanterelles, or fillet of venison en croûte.
Desserts may include tarte Tatin or summer pudding. Atmosphere and service
add to the pleasure. Nine house wines from £9.25 top the thoughtfully
assembled list.

CHEF: Paul George Bending   PROPRIETORS: Brian and Gina Hamilton   OPEN: Mon to Sat 12.30
to 2, 7 to 9.30 (10.30 Sat)   MEALS: Set L £14.50 to £18.50, Set D £18.50 to £22.50   SERVICE: not
inc, card slips closed   CARDS: Access, Amex, Delta, Switch, Visa   DETAILS: 40 seats. 20 seats
outside. Private parties: 50 main room, 12 private room. Car park. Vegetarian meals. Children's
helpings. Smart dress preferred. No smoking in dining-room. Wheelchair access (also WC).
Music   ACCOMMODATION: 7 rooms, all with bath/shower. TV. Phone. B&B £63.50 to £85.
Rooms for disabled. Children welcome. Baby facilities. Dogs welcome. Afternoon teas. Garden

---

HYTHE Hampshire   map 2

Boathouse Brasserie   [NEW ENTRY]

(logo: SOUTH COAST 1997 BRASSERIE)

29 Shamrock Way, Hythe Marina Village,
Hythe SO45 6DY   COOKING 2*
TEL: (01703) 845594   FAX: (01703) 846017   COST £22–£40

The setting is a modern marina, 15 minutes from the centre of Southampton, in a
late-1970s building that 'anticipates the clock-tower school of supermarket
design'. The long, low room functions as both bar and brasserie, and although
boaty pictures emphasise the nautical theme, it is not the exclusive preserve of
yachties. Regular readers of the *Guide* might remember Ian McAndrew from his
days at Adare Manor in the Republic of Ireland or Restaurant Seventy Four in
Canterbury, and for his cookery books, particularly on fish. He and Jane
McAndrew took over here in 1995, and have been steadily wiping out memories
of its previous pub incarnation.

Menu descriptions are simple, prices are reasonable, and the style is
appealingly informal, from a terrine 'with the courage of its porky convictions' to
a 'Schwarzenegger of a chicken' in a sticky sauce with cabbage and pancetta. The
cooking is way ahead of its surroundings, avoiding the 'safe' options of lamb
chop and steak, preferring fish (salmon fish-cake, or monkfish and scallop
fricassee), vegetables, fruit, and meat dishes along the lines of braised pork belly
served with champ. Friendly service suits the surroundings, and is also

317

informative and professional. 'The wine waiter looked like he knew a lot more than we asked him,' and the short Italian-influenced list is interesting and well priced, beginning at £8.50.

CHEF: Ian McAndrew PROPRIETOR: Oakley Leisure Parks Ltd OPEN: Tue to Sun L 12 to 2.30, Tue to Sat D 7 to 10 CLOSED: 2 weeks late Jan/early Feb MEALS: alc (main courses £8 to £12). Set L Tue to Fri £9.50 (2 courses). BYO £4 SERVICE: not inc, card slips closed CARDS: Access, Visa DETAILS: 75 seats. 28 seats outside. Private parties: 75 main room, 50 private room. Children's helpings. Smart dress preferred. Wheelchair access (also WC). Music

ILKLEY West Yorkshire	map 8

Box Tree ▾ ⁵⁄✳

37 Church Street, Ilkley LS29 9DR	COOKING 4
TEL: (01943) 608484 FAX: (01943) 607186	COST £33–£56

The surroundings of this eighteenth-century Dales farmhouse-in-town seem hardly to have changed in decades, apart from looking older. In fact, the curios and *objets* were restored to their former eccentric glory under the present ownership some five years ago. All may be showing signs of wear, but smartly set tables, good glassware and comfortable high-backed chairs combine to produce a degree of elegance. An inspector who eats here (off-duty) once or twice a year reckons that all his meals have been 'virtually faultless: light, refreshing, full of flavour, inventive and technically impressive'.

The menu is short but interesting. Anybody who makes a confit of pork cheeks, as Thierry LePrêtre-Granet does, or succeeds in making turkey interesting (with the help of a little turkey confit, foie gras and artichoke) has to get an A for effort. The cooking doesn't pile on ingredients or decorative bits for the sake of it, but concentrates on essentials. A generous slab of terrine containing succulent pieces of calves' sweetbreads and pheasant, served with pickled vegetables and a walnut oil vinaigrette, has been 'refreshing and packed with flavour'.

Sheer brilliance shines through in apparently straightforward dishes. Sauté woodpigeon breast is 'melting, mouth-exploding', while accompaniments of, say, an orange and ginger sauce with duck foie gras throw the whole dish into sharp relief. Cuts of meat, freshness and texture of fish, timing, sauces and dressings have all drawn praise. Vegetables arrive on the same plate as the main course, although one reporter, obviously with a Yorkshire appetite, thought these were merely for decoration and waited in vain for a man-sized plate of vegetables to arrive separately. Happily, he found the bread rolls excellent.

While the whole meal is typically of a high standard, desserts are particularly impressive: cold rum parfait, for instance, with a thin biscuit separating it from an intense chocolate sorbet, the whole surrounded by caramelised banana and a clear caramel sauce. Prices are high but 'justified by what appears on the plate'. Service is professional, though few reporters would accuse it of being enthusiastic; some genuine warmth would make a big difference. The exception is the 'charming' French sommelier, who has a wonderful selection of bottles to preside over, particularly top-notch French and Italian. There's a list of half-bottles at the back, and some mature vintage ports. The house selection starts at £9.75 for La Serre Chardonnay. CELLARMAN'S CHOICE: Montagny premier cru 1992, Cave des Vignerons de Buxy, £14; Bourgogne, Hautes-Côtes de Nuit 1994, Les Caves des Hautes-Côtes, £13.

CHEF: Thierry LePrêtre-Granet   PROPRIETOR: The Box Tree Restaurant (Ilkley) Ltd   OPEN: Tue to Sun L 12 to 2.30, Tue to Sat D 7 to 9.30   CLOSED: 1 week Christmas, last two weeks Jan, bank hols   MEALS: alc (main courses £16 to £18). Set L £22.50, Set D £29.50   SERVICE: not inc, card slips closed   CARDS: Access, Amex, Visa   DETAILS: 50 seats. Private parties: 26 main room, 15 private room. No children under 5. Smart dress preferred. No smoking in dining-room. Wheelchair access (no WC). No music

---

IPSWICH Suffolk   map 6

Mortimer's on the Quay £

Wherry Quay, Ipswich IP4 1AS   COOKING 1
TEL: (01473) 230225   FAX: (01284) 761611   COST £19–£44

The fish, the whole fish and nothing but the fish is the order of the day in this friendly dockside venue near the old Customs House. Mortimer watercolours and Mike Hope's carved fish adorn the walls, and the whole place is filled with masses of plants. Main courses change daily depending on the catch and the market, but expect to find anything from baked fillet of hake topped with breadcrumbs, and grilled brill with prawn and dill butter, to lobster salad. All dishes come with new potatoes, although you can order spinach or a salad as well. Starters could include potted shrimps, Loch Fyne oysters, and a full-blown smoked fish platter, while desserts take on board hot apple and almond pudding, chocolate pot spiked with rum, and blackcurrant bavarois. The wine list is naturally tilted towards whites, and prices are fair. House wine is £7.65.

CHEF: Kenneth Ambler   PROPRIETORS: Kenneth Ambler and Michael Gooding   OPEN: Mon to Fri L 12 to 2, Mon to Sat D 6.30 to 9 (8.15 Mon)   CLOSED: 24 Dec to 5 Jan, 2 weeks Aug, bank hol Mon and Tue   MEALS: alc (main courses £7.50 to £17)   SERVICE: not inc   CARDS: Access, Amex, Delta, Diners, Switch, Visa   DETAILS: 60 seats. Private parties: 12 main room, 22 private room. Children's helpings. Smart dress preferred. Wheelchair access (no WC). No music

---

IXWORTH Suffolk   map 6

Theobalds ▼ ⅝✳

68 High Street, Ixworth IP31 2HJ   COOKING 2
TEL/FAX: (01359) 231707   COST £26–£46

Theobalds is a house of character dating from 1650, with wooden beams and pillars, a warm fire in the inglenook in winter, and a patio that comes into its own in summer. It rolls along on a tide of local support, with a *carte* at lunch-time and dinners priced according to the main course, from a vegetarian option to the most expensive, fillet steak. Within the compass of around half a dozen choices per course, Simon Theobald injects a goodly variety of tastes. At one meal, for example, first courses included grilled king prawns with stir-fried vegetables and a spicy Szechuan sauce, a terrine of calves' sweetbreads and ox-tongue, and a twice-baked cheese soufflé, as well as steamed globe artichoke, and a warm mousseline of salmon.

No wonder, as one reporter wrote, 'the choice of dishes is invariably so enticing, inventive without being too tricky, that we find almost every dish appealing'. Fish tends to include thick fillets of halibut or turbot, and there will typically be a gamey dish of hare or partridge in winter. The menu changes every two or three months, and deals in rich puddings along the lines of chocolate mousse with coffee sauce, or crème brûlée.

The wine list is straightforward, with an international bunch grouped simply under white and red, and separate pages which helpfully detail the special recommendations. Quality is high and half-bottles a strong point. House French is £12.50. CELLARMAN'S CHOICE: Muscadet de Sèvre-et-Maine, Le Clos du Pont 1992, Dom. Guilbaud, £21.90; Ruche di Castagnole Monferrato 1992, Bava, Piedmont, £24.90.

CHEF: Simon Theobald PROPRIETORS: Simon and Geraldine Theobald OPEN: Tue to Fri and Sun L 12.15 to 1.30, Tue to Sat D 7.15 to 9.15 CLOSED: 2 weeks Aug MEALS: alc L Tue to Fri (main courses £8). Set L Sun £16.95, Set D £20.50 to £28.50 SERVICE: not inc CARDS: Access, Delta, Switch, Visa DETAILS: 36 seats. 10 seats outside. Private parties: 36 main room. Vegetarian meals. Children's helpings. No children under 8 D. Smart dress preferred. No smoking in dining-room. No music

---

JEVINGTON East Sussex   map 3

Hungry Monk ⅝✶

Jevington BN26 5QF
TEL: (01323) 482178 FAX: (01323) 483989   COOKING 1*
off A22 between Polegate and Frinton   COST £33–£40

The Mackenzies have withstood innumerable changes in fashion, plus a recession or two, over a period of nearly three decades. Some things, notably banoffi pie, remain as they were in the late 1960s, but the kitchen has also taken on board olive-oil mash, tartare of tuna, and peppered carpaccio with truffle oil, rocket and Parmesan. 'If there is such a thing as good dinner-party food,' write the Mackenzies, 'that is what we try to create,' and no doubt many dinner-party guests would be pleased to sit down to oxtail soup with dumplings, poached egg hollandaise on a pea purée tart, or hot mackerel salad with lemon grass and coriander.

The menu offers a wide choice, though supplements from £1.75 to £5 can make the bill rise, in the view of one, 'quite alarmingly'. A glass of port, however, is included in the set price. The mainly French wine list offers a fair choice of half-bottles plus short selections from other countries. House wines include the excellent Errazuriz Cabernet Sauvignon from Chile at £12.

CHEFS: Claire Burgess and Thai La Roche PROPRIETORS: Sue and Nigel Mackenzie OPEN: Sun L Sun 12 to 2.30, all week D 7 to 10.30 CLOSED: 24 to 26 Dec, bank hols MEALS: Set L and D £22.90. Minimum £22.90. BYO £5 SERVICE: not inc, card slips closed CARDS: Amex DETAILS: 40 seats. Private parties: 4 to 16 private rooms. Car park. Vegetarian meals. No children under 3. Smart dress preferred. No smoking in dining-room. Music. Air-conditioned

---

All main entries are fully indexed at the back of the Guide.

KELSALE Suffolk   map 6

Hedgehogs ⁵⨯

NEW ENTRY

Main Road, Kelsale IP17 2RF
TEL: (01728) 604444 FAX: (01728) 604499   COOKING 2
on A12, 1m N of Saxmundham   COST £16–£29

Just follow the hedgehog signs on the A12 between Ipswich and Lowestoft to
find this sixteenth-century thatched house. The Yare brothers arrived with CVs
as long as your arm, having worked in an impressive number of top kitchens,
and their aim is to serve 'good home-cooked food at realistic prices', helped by
Suffolk produce including locally landed fish. Contemporary gestures of chilli
and coriander dressing for shellfish, or couscous with lamb, co-exist happily
beside a simple but effective assembly of melon with smoked salmon and
gravlax, and a hearty cassoulet of pork and black pudding with home-made
sausages.

The regular menu of five or six choices per course is supplemented by
blackboard specials of sirloin steak with garlic butter cooked 'just right',
followed perhaps by queen of puddings or lemon tart. One spring special was a
mixture of fish in a light and crispy filo parcel: 'if it's a starter you get one parcel,
if it's a main course you get two.' Even main courses such as roast pigeon breast
served with penne and spicy chorizo come with a large selection of vegetables,
and puddings can be rich: pancakes filled with bananas and butterscotch with
vanilla ice-cream. A short Adnams-supplied wine list is modestly priced, with
house wines at £7.25.

CHEFS/PROPRIETORS: Stephen and Desmond Yare   OPEN: Tue to Sun L 12 to 2.30 (3 Sun), Tue
to Sat D 7 (6.30 Sat) to 10   MEALS: Set L Tue to Sat £9.95, Set L Sun £10.95, Set D £13.95 (2
courses) to £16.95. BYO £4   SERVICE: not inc   CARDS: Access, Amex, Delta, Diners, Switch,
Visa   DETAILS: 60 seats. Private parties: 24 main room, 24 private room. Car park. Vegetarian
meals. Children's helpings. Smart dress preferred. No smoking in 1 dining-room. Wheelchair
access (also WC). Music

KENDAL Cumbria   map 8

Moon ⁵⨯ £

129 Highgate, Kendal LA9 4EN   COOKING 1
TEL: (01539) 729254   COST £20–£29

This is a handy bistro opposite the Brewery Arts Centre decorated in strong
colours: green chairs, yellow tablecloths, and bold posters that find their
counterpart in some intrepid dishes from around the globe. Hummus, and
Thai-spiced chicken might appear beside a 'fairly pleasant' version of South
African bobotie, or a tasty and well-balanced prawn, monkfish and whiting
thermidor. The atmosphere is lively and informal, and the cooking can be 'rough
and ready', with shortcomings such as a 'tired salad' for one reporter, but
desserts have included 'rich and pleasing' raspberry and elderflower cheesecake, and a 'professionally executed' meringue with vanilla ice-cream and
lightly stewed blackcurrants. They have a 'pudding club' on the first Tuesday of
each month, with one starter and five puddings for £10.95, and a 'starter club' on

the third Tuesday of each month, with five starters and one pudding for the same price. Half a dozen beers supplement the 14-bottle non-French wine list. House wine is £8.50 a litre.

CHEFS: Val Macconnell and Sharon Moreton   PROPRIETOR: Val Macconnell   OPEN: all week D only 6.30 (6 Sat) to 10   CLOSED: 24 to 26 Dec, 1 Jan, 2 weeks Jan, Mons in winter   MEALS: alc (main courses £7.50 to £9.50)   SERVICE: not inc, card slips closed   CARDS: Access, Delta, Switch, Visa   DETAILS: 36 seats. Private parties: 28 main room, 45 private room. Vegetarian meals. Children's helpings. No smoking in dining-room. Wheelchair access (no WC). Music

---

KENILWORTH Warwickshire   map 5

Restaurant Bosquet ♥

97A Warwick Road, Kenilworth CV8 1HP   COOKING 2*
TEL: (01926) 852463   COST £32–£49

Warwick Road is where most of Kenilworth's eating takes place, and Bernard and Jane Lignier have run their distinctively French restaurant since 1981 in two rooms of this ordinary-looking net-curtained terraced house. The domestic appearance is no guide to some of the luxuries the kitchen revels in. More useful is the knowledge that M. Lignier hails from south-west France: hence the truffles, foie gras, duck confit, elaborate filo pastry croustade de Gascogne, and some of the wines. Note the deliberate absence of anything remotely trendy here (dismissed by the Ligniers for 'lacking depth and soul') and enjoy instead more classical red mullet soup, or squab pigeon wrapped in pastry.

Some of the technically demanding dishes work well, as in a light soufflé-like warm terrine of scallops, or nuggets of pink, tasty, fine-grained lamb served with sweetbreads. Saucing at an inspection meal veered between a rather heavy-handed buttery one and an excellent shellfish one to accompany crayfish tails and lobster with tagliatelle. Some undistinguished dishes have disappointed, while some of the incidentals have impressed, particularly the 'outstandingly good' home-made breads flavoured with tomatoes or black olives. A few wines from south west France including Madiran and Jurançon, plus a handful of Rhônes and Loires, add interest to the two dozen clarets and attractive Burgundies. A few prices are on the high side, but house wine is £11.
CELLARMAN'S CHOICE: Pouilly Fumé 'En Chaillaux' 1994, D. Dageneau, £25; Madiran, Ch. Montus Cuvée Prestige 1989, £32.

CHEF: Bernard Lignier   PROPRIETORS: Bernard and Jane Lignier   OPEN: Tue to Fri L (bookings only) 12 to 1.15, Tue to Sat D 7 to 9.30   CLOSED: 1 week Christmas, 3 weeks Aug   MEALS: alc (main courses £14.50 to £15). Set L £21, Set D Tue to Fri £21. BYO £5   SERVICE: not inc   CARDS: Access, Amex, Delta, Switch, Visa   DETAILS: 26 seats. Private parties: 30 main room. Vegetarian meals. Children's helpings. Smart dress preferred. Wheelchair access (no WC). No music

---

The Guide *relies on feedback from its readers. Especially welcome are reports on new restaurants appearing in the book for the first time. All letters to the* Guide *are acknowledged.*

Simpson's 🍴✕

101–103 Warwick Road, Kenilworth CV8 1HL	COOKING 1*
TEL/FAX: (01926) 864567	COST £24–£42

Walls decorated with menus from 'more illustrious restaurants' and stencilled images of chefs are reminders that Andreas Antona's lively venue is firmly in the serious food business. The décor is all bare brick and cane chairs, while the kitchen delivers modern interpretations of the classics with Mediterranean touches and a healthy disregard for convention. Menus are fixed-price for two or three courses: marinated salmon with deep-fried scallops, kleftiko with buttered cabbage and garlic potatoes, then iced tiramisù parfait with coffee-bean sauce, for example. Variety is the key. One lunchtime visitor worked his way through goats' cheese with roast aubergine, then an 'absolutely perfectly cooked' piece of cod with lentils (which reduced his 'aversion to fashionable pulses') and finished with a fruit gratin coupled with a clean-tasting lemon sorbet. Service is young and hyper-attentive. The wine list provides reasonably priced drinking from cosmopolitan sources. House French is £9.95.

CHEFS: Andrew Waters and Luke Tipping PROPRIETORS: Andreas and Alison Antona OPEN: Mon to Sat (exc Sat L) 12.30 to 2, 7 to 10 CLOSED: Christmas to New Year, bank hols MEALS: Set L £14.95 to £21.95, Set D £18.95 (2 courses) to £21.95 SERVICE: not inc CARDS: Access, Amex, Delta, Diners, Switch, Visa DETAILS: 80 seats. Private parties: 70 main room, 10 private room. Car park. Vegetarian meals. Children's helpings. Smart dress preferred. No smoking in 1 dining-room. Music. Air-conditioned

---

KESWICK Cumbria   map 10

▲ Swinside Lodge 🍴✕

Newlands, Keswick CA12 5UE
TEL/FAX: (01768) 772948

off A66 Penrith to Cockermouth road, turn left at	COOKING 2*
Portinscale and follow Grange road for 2m	COST £28–£37

'From the back of the hotel you look out to Cat Bells and Grisedale Pike, and to the front Skiddaw and even Helvellyn were visible,' noted a reporter, intent on getting her bearings before another day's fell-walking. Remember to stop at the off-licence while you're out, as Swinside is unlicensed.

This is the Cumbrian deal writ large: majestic scenery, lots of sheep, a Victorian lodge and a five-course set menu served at a single sitting, with choice only at dessert stage. Evenings begin with a complimentary sherry, after which proceedings get into their stride quite often with a pasta dish, such as tagliolini with salmon and watercress. A vegetable-based soup comes next: carrot and coriander, perhaps, or cauliflower and mustard. Main courses keep to simple but sound ideas, as in braised salmon on a bed of shredded leeks with a herbed sauce, or Lakeland lamb cooked pink in a sauce infused with rosemary. The care in cooking, the excellence of the materials and – not least – the profusion of vegetables help to spread contentment. Dessert is a good moment to introduce the element of choice, because only then do people know how full they feel. A poached peach with ice-cream may be quite enough for some, while others find room for hot chocolate soufflé pudding with chocolate sauce. Not-to-be-missed cheeses come last; around ten, mostly from the north of England, served with fine home-made savoury biscuits.

CHEFS: Chris Astley and Graham Taylor   PROPRIETOR: Graham Taylor   OPEN: all week D only 7.30 (1 sitting)   CLOSED: mid-Dec (but open Christmas) to mid-Feb   MEALS: Set D £25 to £28. Unlicensed, BYO (no corkage)   SERVICE: not inc   CARDS: none   DETAILS: 18 seats. Private parties: 6 main room. Car park. No children under 12. Smart dress preferred. No smoking in dining-room. No music   ACCOMMODATION: 7 rooms, all with bath/shower. TV. D,B&B £69 to £145. Deposit: £20. No children under 12. Afternoon teas. Garden (*The Which? Hotel Guide*)

KEYSTON Cambridgeshire   map 6

Pheasant Inn ▮ 🛋 ⅍

Keyston PE18 0RE
TEL: (01832) 710241   FAX: (01832) 710340   COOKING 1
on B663, 1m S of junction with A14   COST £22–£43

The Pheasant is a thatched village pub, part of the Huntsbridge group (see entries for the Three Horseshoes, Madingley, and the White Hart, Great Yeldham). It subscribes to the estimable philosophy of an informal open house, with the same wide-ranging menu available throughout the building: eat what you like wherever you like. It can be treated as anything from a casual drop-by pub to a bookable restaurant. Martin Lee serves fashionably British food with strong Mediterranean leanings, assembling a long menu that takes in wild boar sausages and mashed potato alongside seared scallops with a ravioli of provençale vegetables.

For pub food it is very good, though there is a sense that the menu came first, and the kitchen then had to work out how best to get things like the timing (of risotto, for instance, or twice-baked goats'-cheese soufflé) just right. Fish and vegetable dishes account for a good portion of the menu and are well reported. Wines are first-rate, with much to enjoy at under £12 a bottle as well as plenty of classics. They are grouped according to style and prefaced by a large, intelligent bunch of house wines which include non-vintage Pommery champagne at a sympathetic £22 a bottle and £3.95 a glass. House Italian is £8.95. CELLARMAN'S CHOICE: Stormy Cape Chenin Blanc 1995, South Africa, £9.75; Salice Salentino 1990, Candido, £10.50.

CHEF: Martin Lee   PROPRIETOR: Huntsbridge Ltd   OPEN: all week 12 to 2, 6 (7 Sun) to 10 CLOSED: D 25 and 26 Dec   MEALS: alc (main courses £7 to £15). BYO £4.50   SERVICE: not inc, card slips closed   CARDS: Access, Amex, Delta, Diners, Switch, Visa   DETAILS: 120 seats. 38 seats outside. Private parties: 40 main room. Car park. Vegetarian meals. Children's helpings. Smart dress preferred. No smoking in 1 dining-room. No music

---

🛋 *indicates a change of chef since last year's* Guide.

Restaurateurs justifiably resent no-shows. If you quote a credit card number when booking, you may be liable for the restaurant's lost profit margin if you don't turn up. Always phone to cancel.

KINGSBRIDGE Devon   map 1

▲ Buckland-Tout-Saints Hotel, Queen Anne ▼

Goveton, Kingsbridge TQ7 2DS
TEL: (01548) 853055   FAX: (01548) 856261   COOKING 2
1½m off A381, 2m NE of Kingsbridge   COST £23–£43

The square grey-stone house wears its 300 years well, and the Taylors have
worked hard to create an unostentatious ambience of grand living in hopes of
luring people to Devon's southern fringe. In spring 1996 Richard Cranfield
(trained at the Carved Angel, Dartmouth; see entry) took up the reins as head
chef, and seems to have given new focus to the cooking. Duck liver pâté on
brioche with Madeira jelly and a shallot and bacon vinaigrette is a supremely
confident rendition of a country-house dish, the textures nicely balanced, the
vinaigrette adding the right note of astringency. 'Tranche viennoise' is a
crumbed slice of firm white fish, seemingly cod, in a grain-mustard sabayon, its
counterpointing of flavours judged to a nicety, while 'unelaborately delicious'
carved lamb fillet on baby turnips in a winey reduction is eminently satisfying
too.

The balancing act continues in desserts, the piquancy of rhubarb giving edge
to a wedge of lemon tart served with a crème brûlée quenelle. The wide-ranging
wine list contains much of interest and is thoughtfully annotated. France is the
main focus, but there are some attractive New World additions and plenty of
half-bottles to choose from. Eight house wines start at £9.75.

CHEF: Richard Cranfield   PROPRIETORS: John and Tove Taylor   OPEN: all week 12.30 to 1.45,
7.30 to 9.30   MEALS: Set L £14.50, Set D £27.50. BYO £5. Bar food available   SERVICE: not inc,
card slips closed   CARDS: Access, Amex, Delta, Diners, Switch, Visa   DETAILS: 36 seats. 40
seats outside. Private parties: 40 main room, 16 private room. Car park. Vegetarian meals.
Children's helpings. Smart dress preferred. No smoking in dining-room. Music
ACCOMMODATION: 13 rooms, all with bath/shower. TV. Phone. D,B&B £60 to £120. Children
welcome. Dogs welcome. Afternoon teas. Garden (*The Which? Hotel Guide*)

KING'S CLIFFE Northamptonshire   map 6

King's Cliffe House ✸ | NEW ENTRY |

31 West Street, King's Cliffe PE8 6XB   COOKING 2
TEL: (01780) 470172   COST £22–£38

The grey-white local stone in this quiet village off the A43 improves as it darkens
with age, adding to the appeal of the three-storeyed old house. It is a family
home – only two small rooms are used for the restaurant – and operates on a
distinctly domestic scale: Emma Jessop cooks, Andrew Wilshaw does front-
of-house. The dining-room overlooks the garden, a source of herbs, fruit,
vegetables, and even St George mushrooms which accompanied breast of
guinea-fowl at one May meal. Lamb is local, and some produce is organic. It all
adds up to an impression of 'simple, honest country cooking, as if a keen amateur
cook is behind it'.

There are no flashy gestures, clichés are largely avoided, and a spectrum of
gentle flavours is explored. Loin of lamb has been served with an olive-flecked

325

herb and crumb crust, in a stock sauce lightly sweetened with crab-apple jelly. Meals might begin with grilled asparagus in season, shellfish bisque, or a plate of smoked meats, and one dinner ended with duck egg crème brûlée 'of perfect consistency' helped along with an intriguing splash of Marsala. A short, well-chosen wine list stays mostly under £20, with four house wines around £10.

CHEFS/PROPRIETORS: Emma Jessop and Andrew Wilshaw OPEN: Wed to Sat D only 7 to 9 CLOSED: 25 and 26 Dec, 1 Jan, 1 week spring, 1 week autumn MEALS: alc (main courses £9 to £14) SERVICE: net prices CARDS: none DETAILS: 20 seats. Private parties: 20 main room. Car park. Vegetarian meals. Children's helpings. Smart dress preferred. No smoking in dining-room. No music

---

KING'S LYNN Norfolk map 6

Riverside

27 King Street, King's Lynn PE30 1HA	COOKING 1
TEL: (01553) 773134	COST £18–£44

King's Lynn has two market-places, and the Riverside is just off the big 'Tuesday' version. Go through the courtyard, past the craft shops and galleries, and up the stairs to the 500-year-old listed building made of ships' timbers and conserved by the National Trust. The setting is a big scoring point, with views from the picture windows, and tables on the terrace in clement weather. If the menu changes, nobody seems to notice. One-dish lunches of fisherman's pie or lasagne turn more substantial at dinner, when dressed crab might be followed by salmon en croûte, or roast leg steak of lamb. 'Ingredients are fresh, there's no flash, just sound honest cooking,' reckoned one seasoned reporter. Desserts might make more use of the market, service is friendly and helpful, and the list of around 50 varied wines offers fair choice at under £20, plus a decent number of half-bottles.

CHEFS: Dennis Taylor and Pat Isbill PROPRIETORS: Michael and Sylvia Savage OPEN: Mon to Sat 12 to 2, 7 to 10 MEALS: alc (main courses £6 to £17.50). Set D Nov to Apr £16.95 SERVICE: not inc, card slips closed CARDS: Access, Delta, Switch, Visa DETAILS: 70 seats. 50 seats outside. Private parties: 70 main room. Car park. Vegetarian meals. Children's helpings. Smart dress preferred. Music

---

Rococo ▼

11 Saturday Market Place, King's Lynn PE30 5DQ	COOKING 2
TEL/FAX: (01553) 771483	COST £24–£51

The listed building in the old part of town is welcoming and cheerfully decorated. Its pluses, according to one reporter, include attractive, warm, comfortable and colourful surroundings, unusual pictures, imaginative flavour contrasts, and charming and professional service. Although the kitchen may operate within a relatively small compass, the menu bristles with bright-sounding flavours – tempura of anchovies with coriander salsa, steamed monkfish with ginger and lemon grass – and the general effect is one of lightness, not least because fish and vegetable dishes are given prominence.

The most popular starter, the Andersons tell us, is sauté wild mushrooms on toasted brioche with a poached local duck egg. Otherwise, fish has come in for special commendation, from sweet scallops with saffron noodles to sea bass with aubergine crisps. Meat dishes range from confit of locally reared duck on a bed of smoked vegetables to saddle of venison, or fillet of pork with prunes and garlic, while puddings might take in almond parfait with caramel sauce, or a walnut and sultana steamed sponge with syrup. The set lunch is 'amazing value', according to one grateful reporter. The wine list has flair, opening with a lively 'personal choice' and including Canada among its sources. Wines are high-quality in general and the short Australian section is exemplary. House wines start at £11.95.

CHEFS: Nick Anderson and Timothy Sandford   PROPRIETORS: Nick and Anne Anderson   OPEN: Tue to Sat L 12 to 2, Mon to Sat D 7 to 10   CLOSED: 25 to 30 Dec   MEALS: Set L £9.95 (2 courses) to £13.50, Set D £22.50 (2 courses) to £32.50. BYO £5   SERVICE: not inc, card slips closed   CARDS: Access, Amex, Delta, Switch, Visa   DETAILS: 40 seats. Private parties: 40 main room. Vegetarian meals. Children's helpings. Smart dress preferred. Wheelchair access (also WC). Music

---

KINGSTON UPON THAMES Surrey　　　　　　　　　　　　　　　map 3

Ayudhya ✱

14 Kingston Hill, Kingston upon Thames KT2 7NH　　　　COOKING 2
TEL: (0181) 549 5984　　　　　　　　　　　　　　　　　　COST £29–£55

'In summary, this is some of the best Thai food I've had in this country,' reckoned one seasoned reporter, noting that quality of ingredients, preparation and cooking all show the imprint of an accomplished Thai kitchen. A feeling of 'quality and substance' pervades the three floors, with pictures of Thai royalty adding gravitas, and fairy lights preventing it from getting too heavy. Somjai Thanpho has been here for over two decades and has the measure of her customers. On the one hand, Ayudhya is very Western-friendly. The menu gives advice on how to order and eat Thai food, and dishes are succinctly and accurately described. On the other hand, it doesn't take short cuts or compromise for the sake of Western tastes.

There is plenty of variety in all departments, from kai bai toey (chicken wrapped in pandanus leaf), or yam mamuang (green mango salad), to gaeng pa (spicy jungle curry), or kung sawoy (a dish of stir-fried prawns with green beans and red curry paste). The 90-something items manage to include one or two unusual ideas, from paht pak boong (stir-fried water spinach – aka aquatic morning glory – with black-bean sauce and chilli) to their own version of fried rice which includes smoked frankfurters alongside the more usual shrimp, squid, spring onion, peas and egg. Three dozen wines are arranged by style, and the list is as helpful as the menu, full of interest, and good value. House wine starts at £8.55.

CHEF/PROPRIETOR: Somjai Thanpo   OPEN: Tue to Sun 12 to 2.30, 6.30 to 11 (11.30 Fri and Sat) CLOSED: 25 to 27 Dec, 1 and 2 Jan, bank hols   MEALS: alc (main courses £5 to £9)   SERVICE: not inc, card slips closed   CARDS: Access, Amex, Delta, Diners, Switch, Visa   DETAILS: 85 seats. Private parties: 36 main room, 36 private rooms. Vegetarian meals. Children welcome. Smart dress preferred. No smoking in 1 dining-room. Wheelchair access (no WC). Music

▲ *Penrhos Court* ⁵✳

Kington HR5 3LH
TEL: (01544) 230720   FAX: (01544) 230754   COOKING 1*
on A44, 1m E of Kington   COST £33–£40

Penrhos – a painstakingly resuscitated house and farm, seven centuries old – is
forever growing, forever seductive. Martin Griffiths lets us into a secret: 'For the
21 years that Daphne Lambert has been owner/chef at Penrhos, she has only once
handed over her kitchen to someone else – Marco Pierre White, on her 35th
birthday.' Daphne is not only chef but nutritionist, presenter of cookery courses
and green-fingered nurturer of herbs and vegetables. Healthy virtues count for a
great deal here: bread is baked each day, almost everything is organic, and salt is
rarely called into action. Four-course dinner menus give equal billing to meat,
fish and vegetarian options, as in intensely green asparagus soup, colourful
avocado, papaya and mango salad with orange dressing, and chargrilled chicken
with polenta and red pepper sauce. Cheeses are often Welsh, and desserts might
include oranges in Grand Marnier with vanilla ice-cream. The fairly priced wine
list is moving steadily into organic territory. House wine is £10.50.

CHEF: Daphne Lambert   PROPRIETORS: Daphne Lambert and Martin Griffiths   OPEN: all week D
only 7.30 to 9.30 (10 Sat)   MEALS: Set D £25   SERVICE: not inc, card slips closed   CARDS:
Access, Amex, Delta, Visa   DETAILS: 70 seats. 120 seats outside. Private parties: 100 main
room, 20 and 100 private rooms. Car park. Vegetarian meals. Children's helpings. No smoking in
dining-room. Wheelchair access (also WC). Music   ACCOMMODATION: 19 rooms, all with
bath/shower. TV. Phone. B&B £50 to £92.50. Deposit: 50%. Rooms for disabled. Children
welcome. Baby facilities. Garden

▲ *Dundas Arms* ♥ ⁵✳

53 Station Road, Kintbury RG15 9UT
TEL: (01488) 658263 and 658559
FAX: (01488) 658568   COOKING 1
1m S of A4, between Newbury and Hungerford   COST £27–£46

David Dalzell-Piper is about to celebrate 30 years at the tiller of this highly
appealing Berkshire pub/restaurant. The setting counts for a great deal: the Arms
stands at the junction of the River Kennet and the Kennet and Avon Canal, an
area overflowing with wildlife. No wonder that tables on the jetty and towpath
are snapped up at a rate of knots on sunny days. The short restaurant menu steers
a steady course between traditionalism and fashion, taking in home-cured
gravlax, moules marinière, and calf's liver with bacon and onion gravy, in
addition to warm spiced aubergine salad, grilled fillets of red mullet with tomato
and soy, and roast duck breast with lemon-grass sauce. Lighter meals and real
ales are served in the bar.
   The wine list offers an imaginative selection at very fair prices. Connoisseurs
will enjoy browsing the lengthy claret section, while those in search of a bargain
will find plenty of characterful drinking under £15. House wines kick off at £10.

CELLARMAN'S CHOICE: Matua Valley Sauvignon Blanc 1995, Auckland, New Zealand, £11.50; Devil's Lair Pinot Noir 1992, Margaret River, W. Australia, £21.

CHEFS: David Dalzell-Piper, Sue Bright and Stuart Hall   PROPRIETORS: D.A. and W.E. Dalzell-Piper   OPEN: Mon to Sat L 12 to 1.30, Tue to Sat D 7.30 to 9   CLOSED: 25 Dec to 1 Jan   MEALS: alc D (main courses £12.50 to £15). Set L £19.50. Bar food available   SERVICE: not inc   CARDS: Access, Amex, Delta, Switch, Visa   DETAILS: 40 seats. 40 seats outside. Private parties: 22 main room. Car park. Children's helpings. Smart dress preferred. No smoking in 1 dining-room. Wheelchair access (no WC). No music   ACCOMMODATION: 5 rooms, all with bath/shower. TV. Phone. B&B £55 to £65. Rooms for disabled. Children welcome. Dogs welcome (*The Which? Hotel Guide*)

KIRKHAM Lancashire   map 8

Cromwellian ▼

16 Poulton Street, Kirkham PR4 2AB   COOKING 3
TEL/FAX: (01772) 685680   COST £23–£40

'Wonderful! What a find,' enthused a reporter impressed by both the food and friendly service. The Fawcetts are now into their second decade in this small low-beamed restaurant, happy to cook in a style to which reporters have become accustomed. The menu stoops to tweeness by naming dishes Pot Luck (a mystery starter for anybody willing to take a chance), or else calling a main course (sorry, a Main Event) Winter Craving when in fact it is a spicy lamb casserole with apricots. But the food itself is not subject to such flights of fancy; rather it is broadly traditional and deceptively simple. Guinea-fowl with lentils, and pork with prunes in a sauce of cream and armagnac are as straightforward as they sound.

The Lancashire theme is apparent, but does not follow in the tripe and cow-heel pie tradition; instead it takes in black pudding (The Local Hero is a warm potato and black pudding salad) and potted Morecambe Bay shrimps. Soup comes with 'splendid bread', and good vegetables include 'the famous potatoes' baked with cream and onions. Richness builds to the very end, but nobody seems to mind finishing with upside-down apple sponge pudding with butterscotch sauce, or a mixture of dried fruit and amaretti biscuits encased in chocolate with a hot chocolate sauce. Wines are carefully chosen, with the strongest range from Burgundy, plus a few New World stars. More selection is promised by the glass when the list is 'overhauled' shortly. House wines are £9.50. CELLARMAN'S CHOICE: Namaqua Colombard 1995, Olifants River, South Africa, £12.95; Genus Shiraz 1993, Simonsvlei Winery, South Africa, £11.50.

CHEF: Josie Fawcett   PROPRIETORS: Peter and Josie Fawcett   OPEN: Tue to Sat D only 7 to 9   CLOSED: 1 week Feb, 2 weeks Aug   MEALS: alc (main courses £8.50 to £14.50)   SERVICE: not inc, card slips closed   CARDS: Access, Amex, Delta, Diners, Switch, Visa   DETAILS: 18 seats. Private parties: 10 main room, 8 and 10 private rooms. Vegetarian meals. Children's helpings. Smart dress preferred. Music

---

'"Try this Californian wine," advised the waiter. "It goes well with the monkfish, which is chewy," he explained.' (On eating in Somerset)

KNUTSFORD   Cheshire   map 8

▲ *Belle Epoque Brasserie* 🍴✱ ✓199❷ | NEW ENTRY |

60 King Street, Knutsford WA16 6DT   COOKING 1*
TEL: (01565) 633060   FAX: (01565) 634150   COST £17–£43

La Belle Epoque used to be an ambitious, expensive restaurant with a striking
Edwardian atmosphere. It has now re-invented itself as a good-value brasserie
with lower prices and simpler food, and toned down much of the décor in the old
dining-room, though some original art nouveau remains. It is encouraging to see
such a sensible change greeted with enthusiasm by reporters, and the place now
thrives.

The menu offers a long list of British brasserie staples which don't place the
kitchen under too much stress, including baked tripe, Bury black pudding,
sausage and mash, fish and chips, and lamb hotpot. A few exotic spices are
brought in to perk up, say, a timbale of duck, and although there may be some
erratic seasoning, dull vegetables and occasional neglect of detail, much more
importantly there is sound buying of materials, fair pricing and personal
attention from the owners. Wines are good value too, with some interesting
bottles from around the world. Prices start at £9.95.

CHEF: David Mooney   PROPRIETORS: Nerys and Keith Mooney   OPEN: Mon to Fri L 12 to 2, Mon
to Sat D 7 to 10.30   CLOSED: bank hols   MEALS: alc (main courses £8 to £14). Set L £10.50
SERVICE: not inc, card slips closed   CARDS: Access, Amex, Delta, Diners, Switch, Visa
DETAILS: 100 seats. 30 seats outside. Private parties: 20 to 80 private rooms. Vegetarian meals.
Children's helpings. No children under 10. Smart dress preferred. No smoking in 1 dining-room.
Music   ACCOMMODATION: 7 rooms, all with bath/shower. TV. B&B £40 to £50. No children under
10. Garden (*The Which? Hotel Guide*)

LANGAR   Nottinghamshire   map 5

▲ *Langar Hall* 🍴✱

Langar NG13 9HG
TEL: (01949) 860559   FAX: (01949) 861045   COOKING 1*
between A46 and A52, 4m S of Bingham   COST £22–£53

Approach Langar Hall down its own long drive. Here is a country house in rural
Nottinghamshire where time appears if not to have stood still then at least to be
dragging its feet. The appeal to reporters derives equally from Imogen Skirving's
practised bonhomie out front and the unostentatious flair of the kitchen team.
New Lincolnshire asparagus in May came anointed with balsamic vinegar and
adorned with shavings of Parmesan, a simple treat. Smoked fish terrine has been
applauded, as has melt-in-the-mouth venison served on a peppery port sauce. At
inspection, a main course of properly matured duck was cooked medium-rare
and offered in nicely judged quantity, bedded on leeks and plums with a plum
sauce. Praline mousse is the real thing, while local cheeses – including Colston
Bassett Stilton – are 'very special' and are accompanied by Bath Olivers. The
wine list continues to improve, and offers well-selected bottles from around the
world at canny enough prices. House French is from £9.75.

CHEFS: Toby Garratt and Chris Ansell   PROPRIETOR: Imogen Skirving   OPEN: all week L 12.30 to 2.30, Mon to Sat D 7 to 9.30 (10 Fri and Sat; Sun D residents only)   CLOSED: 3 days Christmas   MEALS: alc (main courses £9.50 to £17.50) Set L Mon to Sat £12.50 (2 courses) to £15, Set L Sun £17.50, Set D Mon to Thurs £15   SERVICE: not inc, card slips closed   CARDS: Access, Amex, Delta, Diners, Visa   DETAILS: 50 seats. Private parties: 40 main room, 8 and 22 private rooms. Car park. Vegetarian meals. Children's helpings. No smoking in 1 dining-room. Wheelchair access (also women's WC). Music   ACCOMMODATION: 11 rooms, all with bath/shower. TV. Phone. B&B £60 to £135. Children welcome. Baby facilities. Dogs by arrangement. Afternoon teas. Garden. Fishing

---

LANGHO Lancashire   map 8

▲ *Northcote Manor* 🏃✸

Northcote Road, Langho BB6 8BE
TEL: (01254) 240555   FAX: (01254) 246568   COOKING 3
on A59, 8½m E of M6 exit 31   COST £22–£70

The red-brick manor sits in two acres of wooded gardens in this most picturesque corner of the Ribble Valley. It affords stark but lovely views across to Pendle Hill, where they once hanged witches and where they now hang-glide. Refurbishment was continuing apace in the opening months of 1996, and there is a deep-piled sense of comfort about it now, enhanced by the jovially booming tones of Craig Bancroft.

Chef and co-owner is Nigel Haworth, an industrious and conscientious presence concerned to offer something for everyone in the form of both fixed-price and à la carte menus at lunch-time and dinner. Top billing goes to the grandiose five-course gourmet menu, whose only choice is at dessert stage. The kind of line-up to expect might include 'scalded' Orkney scallops on tomatoes and tapénade, then truffle and celeriac risotto, a melon and muscat sorbet, followed by smoked duckling breast with tempura-fried apricots and sage stuffing, and chocolate tart to finish. One man wrote of a splendid main course that comprised a saddle and thigh of hare, 'the one roasted pink, the other braised to moist stickiness', accompanied by a mille-feuille of artichokes and salsify on a grape *jus*. Jam roly-poly and rhubarb crumble will make everybody feel at home, while culinary explorers may follow the trail of banana clafoutis with prune ice-cream. Breakfasts, too, are highly commended.

The encyclopedic wine list deals well by nearly all the regions it covers, but the cost of mark-ups can be high: six-year-old pink Sancerre at £32 will take a lot of selling. Halves abound, though, and the tasty house wines from Pays d'Oc are worth a flutter at £12.50 a bottle.

CHEF: Nigel Haworth   PROPRIETORS: Craig Bancroft and Nigel Haworth   OPEN: all week 12 to 1.30 (2 Sun), 7 to 9.30 (10 Sat)   CLOSED: 2 and 3 Jan   MEALS: alc (main courses £12 to £25). Set L £15, Set D £35   SERVICE: 10% (optional), card slips closed   CARDS: Access, Amex, Delta, Diners, Switch, Visa   DETAILS: 80 seats. Private parties: 100 main room, 40 private room. Car park. Vegetarian meals. Children's helpings. Smart dress preferred. No smoking in dining-room. Wheelchair access (also WC). Music   ACCOMMODATION: 14 rooms, all with bath/shower. TV. Phone. B&B £75 to £105. Rooms for disabled. Children welcome. Afternoon teas. Garden (*The Which? Hotel Guide*)

LANGLEY MARSH Somerset   map 2

▲ *Langley House Hotel* ▼ ✻

Langley Marsh, Wiveliscombe TA4 2UF
TEL: (01984) 623318   FAX: (01984) 624573   COOKING 3
½m N of Wiveliscombe   COST £36–£49

Two farm cottages on the edge of Exmoor were joined in 1720, and the house
retains a Georgian feel. It is a peaceful setting in immaculate gardens, with a
graceful mix of antiques and pretty fabrics. The scale is small (just six tables),
enabling Peter and Anne Wilson to make use of their own kitchen garden. They
buy fish from Brixham and stock West Country cheeses. Dishes may appear
relatively plain in a modern context, but are by no means lacklustre. The
repertoire does not change dramatically, and techniques have been honed over
the years, so the food achieves an impressive consistency. One brief report
summed it up as follows: 'Food really good, varied, with strong flavours.'
Escalope of salmon might be served with tomato butter and sorrel, monkfish
with a herb crust and red pepper coulis. There is no choice in any of the first three
courses, and then, all of a sudden, there are six puddings: terrine of dark and
white chocolates, sticky toffee pudding, or a spiced apple, raisin and cinnamon
shortcake, for example. The wine list covers Bordeaux thoroughly, in terms of
châteaux, age and price. Burgundy is well represented too, and several wines
from both regions are available in magnums or by the half-bottle. Elsewhere,
Australian reds, sparkling wines and champagnes, and ports dating back to 1955
provide most interest. House wines are from £10.50. CELLARMAN'S CHOICE:
Auxey-Duresses 1990, Louis Latour, £21.50; Smith-Dartmoor Merlot 1989,
Matua Valley, New Zealand, £18.50.

CHEF: Peter Wilson   PROPRIETORS: Peter and Anne Wilson   OPEN: all week D only 7.30 to 8.30
MEALS: Set D £25.50 to £29.65. BYO £7.50.   SERVICE: not inc, card slips closed   CARDS:
Access, Amex, Visa   DETAILS: 20 seats. Private parties: 18 main room, 18 private room. Car
park. Children's helpings. No children under 7. Smart dress preferred. No smoking in
dining-room. Wheelchair access (also unisex WC). No music   ACCOMMODATION: 9 rooms, all
with bath/shower. TV. Phone. B&B £64.50 to £114.50. Children welcome. Baby facilities. Dogs
welcome in bedrooms only. Garden (*The Which? Hotel Guide*)

LAVENHAM Suffolk   map 6

▲ *Great House*

Market Place, Lavenham CO10 9QZ   COOKING 2
TEL: (01787) 247431   FAX: (01787) 248007   COST £23–£50

One couple summed up the appeal of the Crepys' much-loved restaurant-
with-rooms: 'Here you can eat in a medieval house looking out over the Market
Square – virtually unchanged for 800 years – enjoying French cuisine.' Lunches
are tailored to the tourist trade, and visitors to the town can call in for a two- or
three-course lunch or just a snack. Evening menus strike a more formal note.
Although the bedrock of the cooking is France, the kitchen also brings its talents
to bear on such things as carpaccio of beef, a 'beautifully tender' Tuscan lamb and
tomato stew, and monkfish and salmon with pesto. Elsewhere, the choice

extends to mussels cooked with garlic and parsley butter, sauté veal kidneys with grain-mustard sauce, and pavé of beef with green peppercorns. Desserts have featured a fine rendition of lemon tart with whipped cream. Great coffee and home-made chocolates are served in the restful atmosphere of the lounge. The wine list is a good one, with plenty of quality bins from France and a broad choice for under £20. House wines start at £11.50, although they are not the cheapest on the list.

CHEF: Regis Crepy   PROPRIETORS: Mr and Mrs Regis Crepy   OPEN: Tue to Sun L 12 to 2.30, Tue to Sat D 7 to 9.30 (open some Mons – phone to check)   CLOSED: 3 weeks Jan   MEALS: alc D (main courses £10 to £17). Set L Tue to Sat £9.95 (2 courses) to £12.95, Set L Sun £16.95 (children £9), Set D Tue to Fri £16.95. Bar L available   SERVICE: not inc   CARDS: Access, Amex, Delta, Visa   DETAILS: 45 seats. 30 seats outside. Private parties: 50 main room. Vegetarian meals. Children's helpings. Smart dress preferred. Music   ACCOMMODATION: 4 rooms, all with bath/shower. TV. Phone. B&B £50 to £88. Deposit: £25. Children welcome. Baby facilities. Dogs welcome. Afternoon teas. Garden (*The Which? Hotel Guide*)

LEAMINGTON SPA Warwickshire   map 5

▲ *Lansdowne* ⁵⨀ | NEW ENTRY |

87 Clarendon Street, Leamington Spa CV32 4PF   COOKING 1
TEL: (01926) 450505   FAX: (01926) 421313   COST £25–£34

'This is a traditional restaurant in a traditional setting,' summed up one report. The white-stuccoed Regency corner house has some genuine antiques, an informal feel, and staff with a positive 'can do' attitude. It is a place for a quiet dinner of two or three courses in which griddled Aberdeen Angus steak (at a small supplement) is the recurring centrepiece: 'a wonderful, tender piece of meat, cooked exactly as requested'. The appeal is 'old-fashioned cuisine of a high standard' which has included chicken with Stilton in a port wine sauce, and whole lemon sole with herb butter. The choice is around only four items per course, but one meal that began with creamy green pea and pesto soup, and a variation on prawn cocktail (with juicy prawns, and tarragon in the mayonnaise) was prepared and served with 'unimpeachable craftsmanship'. Ice-creams taste of what they should, meringues are light, and the short, almost entirely French wine list is sensibly priced, starting at £8.65.

CHEFS: Lucinda Robinson and Carol Bosdorff   PROPRIETORS: David and Gillian Allen   OPEN: Mon to Sat D only 6.30 to 9.30 (residents only Sun D)   CLOSED: 24, 25 and 31 Dec   MEALS: Set D £14.95 (2 courses) to £17.95   SERVICE: not inc, card slips closed   CARDS: Access, Delta, Visa   DETAILS: 24 seats. Private parties: 24 main room. Car park. Children's helpings. No children under 5. Smart dress preferred. No smoking in dining-room. Wheelchair access (no WC). No music   ACCOMMODATION: 14 rooms, all with bath/shower. TV. Phone. B&B £49.95 to £61.90. Deposit: £20. No children under 5 (*The Which? Hotel Guide*)

Les Plantagenêts ⁵⨀

15 Dormer Place, Leamington Spa CV32 5AA   COOKING 2
TEL: (01926) 451792   FAX: (01926) 435171   COST £15–£32

Rémy Loth's restaurant in the basement of a Regency terraced house is 'just the sort of place one hopes to encounter in rural France'. It deals in simple French classics from mushroom-stuffed chicken breast cooked in white wine and cream, to a large bowl of 'perfectly cooked mussels, no cream', and wins points for consistency. Service is 'tempered with Gallic idiosyncrasy', a reference to the proclamation of daily specials. Rémy Loth might well announce the extra dishes himself, his recitation 'well tailored to his assessment of the client'. Show interest and you will get the full works, including a wide range of seafood from sea bass and monkfish to scallops and oysters. As a reporter observed of a neighbouring table, a party of four Leamington worthies 'who had heard so much about you we simply had to come', and who eventually ordered sirloin steaks 'with no garlic, please', received 'a very abbreviated performance'. You might wish to check the price of extra dishes. Meat is served 'pink and moist', and vegetables are 'slightly undercooked'. Floating islands have been described as 'correct', and the cheeseboard as 'truly handsome, the condition impeccable, and the service generous'. House wines, from France, are £9.25.

CHEF/PROPRIETOR: Rémy Loth   OPEN: Mon to Fri L 12 to 2.15, Mon to Sat D 7.15 to 10   MEALS: Set L £6.95 (2 courses) to £8.25, Set D £18.50   SERVICE: not inc   CARDS: Access, Amex, Visa DETAILS: 40 seats. Private parties: 42 main room. Children's helpings. Smart dress preferred. No smoking in 1 dining-room. Music

---

LECK Lancashire   map 8

▲ *Cobwebs* 🍷 ⁵⁄✳

Leck, Cowan Bridge LA6 2HZ
TEL/FAX: (01524) 272141
2m SE of Kirkby Lonsdale on A65, turn left at Cowan   COOKING 3
Bridge   COST £39–£46

The open country on the edge of Kirkby Lonsdale is well off the tourist track; to survive in these parts, any establishment has to be good. Paul Kelly and Yvonne Thompson know what it takes to succeed. Their lovely Victorian residence is decked out with plush, velvet-covered furniture, period pictures and bold wallpaper, and they run it as house and home: 'Occasionally we have an "en famille" on Sundays and Mondays if the guests agree. Tall tales abound!'

Yvonne manages the kitchen single-handedly, which seems little short of a minor miracle. Her daily four-course dinner menus offer no choice apart from the starters, which always feature two different soups side by side in one bowl (carrot and orange with 'luscious' courgette and rosemary delighted one reporter). As an alternative there is fish: king prawns and fleshy wild salmon with 'slippery' stir-fried noodles, for example. The centrepiece is generally a thumping roast with 'lightly cooked' vegetables: perhaps loin of lamb with mushroom dumplings, or fillet of beef with champ and a spring onion and grain-mustard sauce. For dessert there might be strong-tasting chocolate cheesecake surrounded by an uncompromisingly sharp berry coulis, while meals finish with a splendid North Country cheeseboard that includes such names as Shepherd's Purse ('the original farmhouse Wensleydale'), and Cumberland Farmhouse from Carolyne Fairburn's dairy near Wigton. Supporting the whole enterprise is vigorous domestic industry: four kinds of bread, vinegars, jams, marmalades and much more. It's well worth staying the night to sample some of these delights at breakfast, which some say is among the best of its kind.

The wine list is a gem, sparsely annotated but with many old vintages from top producers and a particularly impressive New World section, especially from Australia. High points are Mountadam from Australia, Zind-Humbrecht from Alsace and a clutch of vintage Krugs. Even the house wines show imagination: Bonny Doon's Bloody Good Red and White from California at £14. CEL-LARMAN'S CHOICE: Wairau River Sauvignon Blanc 1993, New Zealand, £16; Coteaux Varois, Dom. des Alysses 1990, £16.

CHEF: Yvonne Thompson   PROPRIETORS: Paul Kelly and Yvonne Thompson   OPEN: Tue to Sat D only 7.30 for 8 (1 sitting)   CLOSED: end Dec to mid-Mar   MEALS: Set D £28   SERVICE: not inc, card slips closed   CARDS: Access, Visa   DETAILS: 30 seats. Private parties: 30 main room. Car park. Vegetarian meals. No children under 12. Smart dress preferred. No smoking in dining-room. Music   ACCOMMODATION: 5 rooms, all with bath/shower. TV. Phone. B&B £45 to £60. Deposit: 10%. No children under 12. Afternoon teas. Garden (The Which? Hotel Guide)

LEDBURY Hereford & Worcester   map 5

▲ Hope End ♥ ⁵✱

Hope End, Ledbury HR8 1JQ
TEL: (01531) 633613   FAX: (01531) 636366   COOKING 3
2m N of Ledbury, just beyond Wellington Heath   COST £34–£41

Edward Moulton Barrett, erstwhile owner of this Georgian red-brick house, added a Turkish folly to its charms in the early nineteenth century. Perhaps it seemed like a good idea at the time, but at any rate it was later demolished, leaving behind only a minaret. Little Greek temples, however, still pop up in the grounds, which are pleasingly unkempt, so that there is an impression of 'nature running riot'.

Patricia Hegarty's cooking ploughs as singular a furrow as the surroundings would imply, the provender of a well-tended kitchen garden its mainstay. Running through it is an English pastoral vein that brings in a hotpot of wild rabbit with smoked bacon and cider (a starter, that), pork loin with crackling and a perry sauce, and puddings such as grilled apple rings with quince sorbet. Three choices at each stage is the drill, each dish having earned its place, and partnerships tend to be classical and well considered. Scallops (with their corals) are timed to a nicety, accompanied by crisp lardons and thrown into relief with some sharply dressed sorrel. An intense sauce of red pepper and tomato makes a 'happy combination' with baked monkfish, while a morello cherry relish has accompanied 'moist and flavour-packed' duck breast. Herbs can crop up unexpectedly, producing for example an unusual and intriguing dessert of green tansy custard, served on a compote of orange segments, which provides a light and refreshing note on which to finish. The cheese option is self-service from three good specimens, typically Lancashire, Worcester and Shropshire Blue. 'Impeccable' breakfasts await those who stay.

Traditional English choices – sherry, Madeira, port and cider – all play their part on a classic wine list. The list of clarets, including plenty of half-bottles, is superb, while those venturing outside Bordeaux will particularly enjoy Burgundy, Australia and the Rhône. House wine is £8.

CHEF: Patricia Hegarty   PROPRIETORS: John and Patricia Hegarty   OPEN: all week D only 7.30 to 8.30   CLOSED: mid-Dec to early Feb   MEALS: Set D £30   SERVICE: none, card slips closed   CARDS: Access, Delta, Switch, Visa   DETAILS: 24 seats. Private parties: 8 main room. Car park. Vegetarian meals. No children under 12. Smart dress preferred. No smoking in dining-room. No music   ACCOMMODATION: 8 rooms, all with bath/shower. Phone. B&B £85 to £140. Deposit: £60. No children under 12. Garden (*The Which? Hotel Guide*)

LEEDS West Yorkshire   map 8

Brasserie Forty Four

42–44 The Calls, Leeds LS2 7EW	COOKING 2*
TEL: (0113) 234 3232 FAX: (0113) 234 3332	COST £20–£43

This is the informal part of Michael Gill's operation, down by the riverside next door to Pool Court (see entry, below) and The Calls Hotel. The success of northern brasseries (see also Heathcote's in Preston) may be bound up with urban rejuvenation, but they are nothing without their on-the-ball owners. Here, converted warehousing with modern art and close-set tables provides the backdrop for smart cosmopolitan eating: grilled black pudding and zampone (a sticky Italian version of stuffed pig's trotter) with a lentil casserole, and deep-fried shredded duck pancakes with sweet plum sauce.

The evening early-bird deal is well worth considering, and there is a one-course light lunch (with coffee) for a fiver. Vegetarian first courses offer some choice, fish might include roast Whitby cod cooked on sea salt, and there are side orders of olive oil mash, and couscous with coriander. This is one of the few places at which you can eat both potted duck and spotted dick, along with rice pudding, and baked chocolate tart. Service has varied from 'pleasant and efficient' to 'lacking the human touch'. Fifty-odd wines from around the world stay mostly under £20.

CHEF: Jeff Baker   PROPRIETOR: Michael Gill   OPEN: Mon to Fri L 12 to 2, Mon to Sat D 6.30 to 10.30 (11 Fri and Sat)   CLOSED: bank hols   MEALS: alc D (main courses £7 to £12). Set L and early-bird D £8.75 (2 courses) to £11.95. Light lunch available.   SERVICE: not inc; 10% for parties of 10 or more   CARDS: Access, Amex, Delta, Diners, Switch, Visa   DETAILS: 110 seats. Private parties: 52 main room, 52 private room. Vegetarian meals. Children's helpings. No cigars/pipes in dining-room. Wheelchair access (also WC). Music. Air-conditioned

▲ *Haley's*

Shire Oak Road, Headingley, Leeds LS6 2DE	COOKING 2
TEL: (0113) 278 4446 FAX: (0113) 275 3342	COST £22–£46

Country meets city in this welcoming Victorian mansion two miles from the centre of Leeds. After joining in 1995, chef Jon Vennell seems to have found his feet and most reports confirm that his cooking is up to scratch. Lunch is a homespun affair of the 'Waldorf salad, chicken cordon bleu and apple crumble' variety, while the monthly-changing evening *carte* aims to impress with some deliberately showy gestures. Prices are for main course and starter, with desserts and coffee extra.

Home-cured duck breast is served with a sweet potato relish, chargrilled chicken comes with scallops and a saffron sabayon, and roast fillet of beef is accompanied by two sauces and a Yorkshire pudding filled with foie gras. Among sweets you might find lemon mousse with stewed black cherries, and warm bread-and-butter pudding with kirsch cream. Cheeses are English and French; coffee includes petits fours. Staff are young, well trained and eager to please. Wines are keenly chosen from the world cellar – there is even a representative from the Leventhorpe Vineyard in Yorkshire. Eight house wines start at £10.15, and most are served by the glass.

CHEF: Jon Vennell PROPRIETOR: John J. Appleyard OPEN: Tue to Fri and Sun L 12.15 to 1.45 (12.30 to 2 Sun), Mon to Sat D 7.15 to 9.45 CLOSED: 26 Dec to 30 Dec, and Sun in summer MEALS: alc (main courses L £8 to £9.50, main courses D inc starter £16 to £20). Set L Sun £14.50 SERVICE: not inc, card slips closed CARDS: Access, Amex, Diners, Switch, Visa DETAILS: 45 seats. Private parties: 45 main room, 14 and 25 private rooms. Car park. Vegetarian meals. Children welcome before 8pm (children's helpings). Smart dress preferred. No cigars/pipes in dining-room. Music. Air-conditioned ACCOMMODATION: 22 rooms, all with bath/shower. TV. Phone. B&B £55 to £112. Children welcome. Baby facilities. Afternoon teas

Leodis 🍷

Victoria Mill, Sovereign Street, Leeds LS1 4BJ	COOKING 2
TEL: (0113) 242 1010 FAX: (0113) 243 0432	COST £19–£46

Only cities and large towns can support brasseries, and Leeds has taken to them with relish, indicating something of the vitality of the place. The converted mill beside the canal is in the redeveloped commercial heart of the city. Original cast-iron columns, a wooden floor and glass screens, dividing the space into manageable sections, combine to produce a distinctive setting that, despite the industial overtones, is 'warm and comfortable'. Service chips in with relaxed, friendly and knowledgeable support.

Despite some French and Italian input along the lines of duck confit or osso buco, the long menu is a very British interpretation of the brasserie idea, bringing steak and kidney pudding and bangers and mash to the fore. Prepared starters of potted salmon, or ham and mustard terrine allow the kitchen to concentrate on grilling and roasting main courses of calf's liver or duck breast. This is hearty food on a crowd-pleasing scale. Bread-and-butter pudding appears as a savoury starter, while desserts might include lemon tart or chocolate marquise. The wine list is lengthy and considerably priced; many bottles are under £12, and those that aren't are grouped into a section bluntly headed 'expensive'. The choice is international, with Australia particularly impressive. House wines start at £7.95. CELLARMAN'S CHOICE: Enate Chardonnay 1993, Somontano, Spain, £16.25; Carlyle Estate Cabernet Sauvignon 1992, Victoria, Australia, £12.50.

CHEF: Steven Kendell PROPRIETORS: Martin Spalding and Steven Kendell OPEN: Mon to Fri L 12 to 2, Mon to Sat D 6 to 10 (11 Fri and Sat) CLOSED: 25 and 26 Dec, 1 Jan MEALS: alc (main courses £6.50 to £14.50). Set L and D (exc Sat after 7.30pm) £11.95 SERVICE: not inc CARDS: Access, Amex, Delta, Diners, Switch, Visa DETAILS: 180 seats. 60 seats outside. Private parties: 200 main room. Car park. Vegetarian meals. Children's helpings. Smart dress preferred. Wheelchair access (also WC). Music

Pool Court at 42

42–44 The Calls, Leeds LS2 7EW COOKING 3*
TEL: (0113) 244 4242   FAX: (0113) 234 3332 COST £27–£56

'The room, the food and the service are in harmony. Meals are uncluttered, elegant and technically proficient, and prices are reasonable,' summed up an inspector. The small, stylish dining-room overlooking the river has 'an air of tranquillity, even in the centre of Leeds', and achieves a cool, modern feel with chrome and blond wood. Blue and grey colours, and sensitive lighting, give it the air of a serious restaurant, a fact confirmed by the classical cast of the largely French menu. Dishes are arranged into different set-price options with two choices on the less-expensive lunchtime menus, and five on the others.

The repertoire is a skilful assembly of reassuring dishes and luxury items, and adopts a balanced approach that is bright and interesting without being worryingly experimental. It deals in creamed eggs with caviare, grilled boudin blanc, and fillet of beef served with a miniature oxtail pie. Tarte Tatin of foie gras is a speciality. Fish ranges from 'accurately timed' baked turbot, to 'juicy and fresh' cold poached lobster on a rocket salad with a pungent pesto sauce. Other accompaniments might include risotto or 'unctuous olive mash', and saucing is well tuned, as in a braised pigeon, cooked pink, served with small mounds of earthy Puy lentils and a rich red wine sauce scattered with lardons of smoked bacon.

Among desserts, an 'intensely fruity' summer pudding with a blob of clotted cream has appealed, and pithiviers is a favoured format, perhaps filled with chocolate and almond, or apples and sultanas. Staff are efficient and know-ledgeable, and 'left us to enjoy the meal in peace', according to one couple. Around 60 well-chosen wines are arranged by colour in price order. If in doubt, advice is worth taking.

CHEF: Jeff Baker   PROPRIETORS: Michael and Hanni Gill   OPEN: Mon to Fri L 12 to 2, Mon to Sat D 7 to 10 (10.30 Fri and Sat)   CLOSED: bank hols   MEALS: Set L £12.50 (2 courses) to £17, Set D £23.50 (2 courses) to £37.50   SERVICE: 10%, card slips closed   CARDS: Access, Amex, Delta, Diners, Switch, Visa   DETAILS: 37 seats. 20 seats outside. Private parties: 38 main room. Vegetarian meals. Children's helpings. Smart dress preferred. No cigars/pipes in dining-room. Wheelchair access (also WC). Music. Air-conditioned

Rascasse

W. YORKSHIRE 1997 NEWCOMER

NEW ENTRY

Canal Wharf, Water Lane, Leeds LS11 5BB COOKING 3*
TEL: (0113) 244 6611   FAX: (0113) 244 0736 COST £21–£50

A lot has happened in Simon Gueller's 15-mile trip from Harrogate to Leeds. He has exchanged a small bistro for a thumping big warehouse conversion, and moved the cooking up a whole couple of notches. The building that Rascasse occupies, at the terminus of the Leeds–Liverpool Canal, was originally a grain store, and refurbishment has produced a stylishly modern space; the combination of glass, wood, stainless steel and smartly turned-out customers gives it a distinctly prosperous feel. It is worth going up to the bar for the staircase alone, and views of the canal add to the character.

The bright contemporary food is Anglo-French, with a bias towards fish and the Mediterranean, as the name (an essential ingredient of bouillabaisse) implies. Seared tuna with aubergine caviare and an intensely flavoured basil oil was a 'stunning starter' at one meal, while an 'utterly fresh' fillet of turbot stole the show at another. A return to old-fashioned (but perfectly good) saucing includes gribiche with a terrine of duck and foie gras, and an excellent ravigote with asparagus, while others consist of minimal slicks and splashes, acting like condiments or seasonings. Vegetables are part of the dish, not a separate entity, and the impression is of a kitchen that thinks carefully about how components should hang together.

Its assurance is evident in creamy herb risotto, pink grilled calf's liver, and fat squab pigeon breasts wrapped up Wellington-style in Savoy cabbage, with a stuffing of wild mushrooms. Especially pleasing is that the cooking is all done without recourse to fussy or decorative bits, and that goes for plain but classic lemon tart, for smooth, rich dark chocolate tart, and first-rate sorbets. The room is patrolled by 'great numbers of well-meaning and pleasant staff' who seemed to two reporters wanting in expertise, while others have found service 'friendly' and 'attentive'. Wines are as modern as everything else, with a good range of styles and prices from £9.50.

CHEF: Simon Gueller   PROPRIETORS: Simon Gueller and Nigel Jolliffe   OPEN: Mon to Fri L 12 to 2.15, Mon to Sat D 7 to 10.30   CLOSED: 25 Dec to 4 Jan   MEALS: alc (main courses £9.50 to £15.50). Set L £11.50 (2 courses) to £14. Bar L available   SERVICE: not inc   CARDS: Access, Amex, Delta, Diners, Switch, Visa   DETAILS: 100 seats. Private parties: 25 main room. Car park. Vegetarian meals. No children under 8. Smart dress preferred. No cigars/pipes in dining-room. Wheelchair access (also WC). Music. Air-conditioned

Sous le Nez en Ville ▮ £

The Basement, Quebec House, Quebec Street,
Leeds LS1 2HA   COOKING 2
TEL: (0113) 244 0108   FAX: (0113) 245 0240   COST £16–£42

A reviving meal in this lively modern venue is just the ticket after a shopping trip in the city, and a couple who partake regularly reckon that Sous le Nez gets better, thanks to 'greater confidence and consistency'. The place divides into two: one half is a bar where you can drink and nibble tapas; the other is for more formal meals. The style is unashamed brasserie. There is an early-evening 'menu du soir' which remains 'irresistibly good value' for big bowls of pasta with smoked salmon, confit of duck with couscous, rare ribeye steak with a pair of sauces, and a 'robust combo' of calf's liver, bacon and red cabbage. The full *carte* is supplemented by a board of fish specials which, according to the owners, now constitute up to 50 per cent of their orders. No wonder, when there is the option of chargrilled tuna with black olives and balsamic vinegar, and red mullet stuffed with smoked salmon mousse, as well as grilled haddock with mash and cheese sauce.

Desserts range from classic creamy rice pudding to scoops of white chocolate ice-cream rolled in crunchy pistachio praline. Service is 'efficient and affable, neither snooty nor familiar'. The well-annotated wine list offers many appealing bottles at £20 and under, plus top-quality bottles from across the globe. France and Australia are the highlights, followed closely by Italy and New Zealand. Thirteen wines come by the glass, and two decent house wines are £8.50.

CELLARMAN'S CHOICE: Mâcon-Igé, Dom. des Roches 1994, Carpi-Gobet, £12.95; Rioja Reserva 1982, Viña Real, CVNE, £21.50.

CHEF: Andrew Carter   PROPRIETOR: C.R.C.R. Partnership   OPEN: Mon to Sat 12 to 2.30, 6 to 10 (11 Fri and Sat)   CLOSED: 3 days Christmas, bank hols   MEALS: alc (main courses £7 to £14). Set L Sat £13.95 (inc wine), Set D 6 to 7.30 £13.95 (inc wine). BYO £10. Bar food available   SERVICE: not inc   CARDS: Access, Amex, Delta, Switch, Visa   DETAILS: 85 seats. Private parties: 45 main room, 16 private room. Vegetarian meals. No children under 10. Smart dress preferred. Music

---

LEICESTER Leicestershire   map 5

Welford Place

9 Welford Place, Leicester LE1 6ZH	COOKING 2
TEL: (0116) 247 0758 FAX: (0116) 247 1843	COST £18–£43

This distinguished Victorian building in the town centre, with high ceilings and chandeliers, could easily serve as a backdrop for a period costume drama. It feels 'conservative and elegant, comfortable in the grand manner', and not only opens every day of the year from 8am until midnight, but (as the owners tell us) also serves all menus except breakfast 'throughout the day without restrictions'. If that isn't flexibility, we don't know what is.

Given the all-day nature of the food, its kaleidoscopic mix should be no surprise. The breakfast menu (which also operates in the afternoon) serves up the full cooked English works for £5.75. The daily menu might offer chunky leek and potato soup, and spinach and ricotta pithiviers with pesto cream sauce. The generous *carte* sustains with jellied terrine of lamb and vegetables, baked cheese soufflé, and steamed jam pudding with custard. There is a set-price option, too, not to mention a supplementary menu that deals in chilli con carne, a fillet steak and tarragon mustard sandwich, toasted teacakes and the like. The food may not be wildly original, but it could not do more to oblige. The wine list offers some reliable names at reasonable prices. House wines are usefully listed by the bottle (£9.90), large glassful (£4.50) and small glassful (£2.50).

CHEF: Lino Poli   PROPRIETORS: Michael and Valerie Hope, and Sarah Hope   OPEN: all week 8am to midnight   MEALS: alc (main courses £8.50 to £14.50). Set L and D £10.50. BYO, corkage by arrangement   SERVICE: not inc, card slips closed   CARDS: Access, Amex, Delta, Diners, Switch, Visa   DETAILS: 216 seats. Private parties: 60 main room, 16 to 60 private rooms. Vegetarian meals. Children's helpings. No music

---

LIDGATE Suffolk   map 6

Star Inn

The Street, Lidgate CB8 9PP	
TEL: (01638) 500275	COOKING 1
on B1036, 6m SE of Newmarket	COST £20–£37

There cannot be much Catalan cooking in East Anglia, but Maria-Teresa Axon's 500-year-old inn at Lidgate has brought in enough of a postbag since last year's *Guide* to suggest that the market was ready and waiting. The show-stopping Mediterranean fish soup receives predominantly good notices once again, as do the prawns malagueña, which come with a sauce of 'lovely strong garlicky flavour' and a finger-bowl. Succulent navarin of lamb cooked in red wine was, for one couple, 'a brilliant example of how to make use of the poorer cuts of meat'. Otherwise, there are lambs' kidneys cooked in sherry, real paella with both chicken and seafood, and a handful of French dishes. Puddings are the usual pub fare. House French wine is £9.

CHEF/PROPRIETOR: Maria-Teresa Axon   OPEN: all week L 12.30 to 2, Mon to Sat D 7.30 to 10   MEALS: alc (main courses £7.50 to £12.50). Set L Sun £12.50   SERVICE: not inc, card slips closed   CARDS: Access, Amex, Delta, Switch, Visa   DETAILS: 35 seats. 25 seats outside. Private parties: 25 main room. Car park. Vegetarian meals. Children's helpings. Smart dress preferred. Music

LIFTON Devon   map 1

▲ *Arundell Arms* ⑂✴

Lifton PL16 0AA
TEL: (01566) 784666   FAX: (01566) 784494   COOKING 2*
just off A30, 3m E of Launceston   COST £26–£47

One reporter heading west found this sporting-inn 'by far the best place to break a journey'. The original building is getting on for 300 years old, and there was an inn on the site before that, so it has seen some travellers in its time. The fabric has grown gradually to accommodate fisherfolk and the conference trade, two of the principal users, but they don't impose on the casual visitor. Adaptability, along with amiable service, is part of the genuine desire to please, producing a good-value menu of soup, salmon fish-cakes and croque-monsieur in the bar, and two- or three-course lunches and dinners in the smartly set dining-room.

Dishes are carefully considered, and occasionally given a fresh spin. Braised oxtail, for example, might come with prunes as well as root vegetables. Even the simplest items impress. A chicken breast salad, 'tasting of real chicken, succulent and juicy, the dressing redolent of lime juice and quite wonderful', is testament to that. Nor is the food considered expensive. 'The bill seemed ridiculously small for the quality', and one of the modestly priced wines, perhaps from the New World, will help to keep it within reason. House wine starts at £9.75

CHEFS: Philip Burgess and Nick Shopland   PROPRIETOR: Anne Voss-Bark   OPEN: all week 12.30 to 2.30, 7.30 to 9.30   CLOSED: D 3 nights Christmas   MEALS: Set L £13.50 (2 courses) to £17, Set D £24.50 to £28.50. Bar food available   SERVICE: not inc   CARDS: Access, Amex, Diners, Switch, Visa   DETAILS: 70 seats. Private parties: 80 main room, 30 private room. Car park. Vegetarian meals. Children's helpings. Smart dress preferred. No smoking in dining-room. Wheelchair access (no WC). Music   ACCOMMODATION: 29 rooms, all with bath/shower. TV. Phone. B&B £61 to £97. Children welcome. Baby facilities. Dogs welcome. Afternoon teas. Garden. Fishing (*The Which? Hotel Guide*)

Not inc *in the details at the end of an entry indicates that no service charge is made and any tipping is at the discretion of the customer.*

LINCOLN Lincolnshire

map 9

Jew's House ⅝✳

15 The Strait, Lincoln LN2 1JD	COOKING 1*
TEL: (01522) 524851	COST £19–£49

The Strait is a short alley off Steep Hill; the best plan is to approach the restaurant from the top of the hill, and then carry on down after eating. 'A mixture of rustic and cottagey' is how one reporter described the interior: beams and exposed stone are, not surprisingly, something of a feature in a building that went up around 1180. The result is an unpretentious restaurant that welcomes all, regardless of age or smartness of dress.

A Gallic influence pervades the cooking, taking in roast partridge with apples and calvados, or a Grand Marnier soufflé, but Richard Gibbs is not doctrinaire about this. Local ingredients get a look-in, perhaps in the form of steamed Lincolnshire samphire with lemon butter, while marinated duck breast with tabbouleh, or a simple spaghetti carbonara bring added variety. Puddings are on the rich side (chocolate cheesecake, for example), and even a plate of summer berries comes with clotted cream. The deal is a good one: three courses for a modest set price at lunch, and four courses at dinner, with tea or coffee included, and the flexibility of a *carte* thrown in for good measure. The wine list is sensibly constructed and well priced, with some real treats popping up here and there. House wines from Australia are £9.50.

CHEF: Richard Gibbs   PROPRIETORS: Richard and Sally Gibbs   OPEN: Tue to Sat 12 to 1.30, 7 to 9   CLOSED: 25 and 26 Dec   MEALS: alc (main courses £12.50 to £16). Set L £12.95, Set D £23 to £25   SERVICE: not inc   CARDS: Access, Amex, Delta, Diners, Switch, Visa   DETAILS: 26 seats. Private parties: 30 main room. Vegetarian meals. Children's helpings. No smoking in dining-room. Music

Wig & Mitre £

29 Steep Hill, Lincoln LN2 1LU	
TEL: (01522) 535190 and 523705	COOKING 2
FAX: (01522) 532402	COST £20–£43

Many of the original features of this fourteenth-century inn – in the oldest quarter of Lincoln – were retained when it was restored, and a 'homely, friendly and noisy' sense of cheer is dispensed throughout. Take what you want from any of the menus on offer – there are no rules to adhere to.

In like spirit, the kitchen turns out what, for an old pub, are relatively unusual dishes of curried mussel soup with saffron, salmon with spinach and a chive and lemon butter, and guinea-fowl baked in filo with black pudding and cabbage. One luncher's rack of lamb on puréed root vegetables was much enjoyed: it was 'perfectly pink and came with a thin, tasty gravy'. Plentiful vegetables accompany the main dishes, and puddings tend to be indulgent, as in treacle tart, banoffi pie and chocolate amaretti pots. 'The staff respond at a pace that suits you best,' is the promise. The wine list is ambitious by pub standards, and helpfully groups wines by style. There are 13 half-bottles and house wines start at £9.90.

LISKEARD

CHEFS: Paul Vidic and Peter Dodd   PROPRIETORS: Valerie and Michael Hope   OPEN: all week 8am to 11pm (10.30pm Sun)   CLOSED: 25 Dec   MEALS: alc (main courses £6 to £16).   SERVICE: not inc, card slips closed   CARDS: Access, Amex, Delta, Diners, Switch, Visa   DETAILS: 120 seats. 24 seats outside. Private parties: 60 main room, 45 private room. Vegetarian meals. Children's helpings. Wheelchair access (also WC). No music

---

LINTON   West Yorkshire
map 8

▲ *Wood Hall* ⁵⚹

Trip Lane, Linton LS22 4JA
TEL: (01937) 587271   FAX: (01937) 584353
from Wetherby take A661 N for ½m, turn left to
Sicklinghall and Linton, then left to Linton and Wood
Hall, and turn right in Linton opposite Windmill pub

COOKING 1
COST £25–£61

The Georgian house is set in magnificent surrounds, overlooking rolling hills and fields in Wharfedale. Displays of flowers keep the atmosphere light, and Stephanie Moon dreams up some attractive ideas, as in a terrine of langoustine and leek with saffron jelly and truffle dressing. She serves game in the form of wild boar, and includes some traditionally based dishes such as pan-fried skate wing with beurre noir, and lemon parfait. She also has a welcome openness to materials: deep-fried blue-tip shark, for instance. An oriental influence might appear in a consommé of Peking duck under a choux pastry cage, although some gestures are perhaps more elaborate than necessary. Service has varied from 'impeccable, very professional yet friendly' to 'surly and unhelpful'. Wines on the extensive list make an effort to supply decent bottles under £20, but there is plenty of headroom for big spenders, and some mark-ups are high. House wines start at £11.95.

CHEF: Stephanie Moon   PROPRIETOR: Arcadian International plc   OPEN: Sun to Fri L 12.30 to 2, all week D 7 to 9.30   MEALS: alc (main courses £20.50 to £24). Set L £16.95, Set D £27.95. Bar L available   SERVICE: not inc   CARDS: Access, Amex, Delta, Diners, Switch, Visa   DETAILS: 50 seats. 30 seats outside. Private parties: 20 main room, 20 private room. Car park. Vegetarian meals. Children's helpings. Smart dress preferred. No smoking in dining-room. Wheelchair access (also WC). Music   ACCOMMODATION: 42 rooms, all with bath/shower. TV. Phone. B&B £90 to £145. Rooms for disabled. Children welcome. Dogs welcome. Afternoon teas. Garden. Swimming-pool. Fishing

---

LISKEARD   Cornwall
map 1

Bacchus Bistro £
NEW ENTRY

18 Pike Street, Liskeard PL14 3JE
TEL: (01579) 347031

COOKING 2
COST £16–£34

Michael and Raquel de Oliveira Green deserve 'a civic award' for raising Liskeard's gastronomic pulse – so concludes an inspector. What they have created is a stylish, high-ceilinged venue embellished with lots of delightful touches. Vases of flowers decorate the tables, jazz plays in the background.

Menus are written on blackboards, and the repertoire is an eye-opener: it takes real nerve to kick off proceedings with whole roast garlic with mint and parsley vinaigrette, before crostini of lambs' brains, or home-smoked field mushrooms. One dish regularly steals the show, namely sliced pigeon breast arranged around a pile of couscous over which is poured a chocolate game sauce. Elsewhere, reporters have commented on 'truly wonderful' seafood chowder, home-cured gravlax, medallions of pork with a pudding of wild berries, and John Dory with candied aubergines and a 'vibrant' provençale sauce. This is not the run-of-the-mill stuff you might expect in a Cornish backwater. As for desserts, there might be banoffi pie, or 'simply the best chocolate mocha marquise I've ever tasted'. Raquel is a polite and charming hostess who knows her way around the adventurous, keenly priced wine list. Eight house wines start at £7.95.

CHEFS: Michael de Oliveira Green and Glenn Gatland PROPRIETOR: Michael de Oliveira Green OPEN: Tue to Sat L 12 to 2.30, Mon to Sat D 7 to 10.30 MEALS: alc (main courses £9 to £13). Set L and D £9.95 SERVICE: not inc, card slips closed CARDS: Access, Delta, Switch, Visa DETAILS: 54 seats. Private parties: 60 main room. Vegetarian meals. Children's helpings. Wheelchair access (also WC). Music

---

LITTLE SHELFORD Cambridgeshire

map 6

Sycamore House ♦ ⁵⚹

1 Church Street, Little Shelford CB2 5HG	COOKING 2*
TEL: (01223) 843396	COST £29–£35

Reflecting on the smartly turned-out tables, the chintzy curtains and the well-wrought English domestic cooking at Sycamore House, one reporter mused that 'if Delia Smith set up a restaurant, it might be like this'. The business is dinner, five nights a week, the format a four-course menu with a leafy salad between starter and main ('an infinitely better palate-refresher than sorbet,' according to one). Four choices are offered to start, led by a soup such as carrot and caraway, or Stilton and bacon, and taking in hot chicken livers in a curry sauce, perhaps, or an onion tart with olive pastry. One or two more modish turns are tried with fish – such as griddled scallops on pea purée with mint vinaigrette – while meats are given assertive accompaniments, as in 'very gamey' pigeon breasts with a sauce of armagnac, orange and blackcurrant that an inspector rated highly for its 'balance of tartness and sweetness'.

Bread-and-butter pudding with a zesty marmalade sauce has been judged a winner, too, while home-made ice-creams that come in brandy-snap baskets are always creamy and full-flavoured. Enthusiasm for wine shines through on the list of 60-odd varied bottles. Mark-ups are refreshingly low. 'Where else would you find Guigal's Côtes du Rhône at £9.75?' asked one delighted reporter. Sparkling wines and champagnes are at bargain prices; house wines start at £8.50. CELLARMAN'S CHOICE: Green Point sparkling 1992, Dom. Chandon, Victoria, Australia, £16.50; Frog's Leap Zinfandel 1993, Napa Valley, California, £16.50.

CHEF: Michael Sharpe PROPRIETORS: Michael and Susan Sharpe OPEN: Tue to Sat D only 7.30 to 9.30 CLOSED: Christmas MEALS: Set D £21.50. BYO £5 SERVICE: not inc, card slips closed CARDS: Access, Visa DETAILS: 24 seats. Private parties: 24 main room. Car park. Vegetarian meals. No children under 12. Smart dress preferred. No smoking in dining-room. No music

▲ Old Bakehouse 🍴✱

33 High Street, Little Walsingham NR22 6BZ
TEL/FAX: (01328) 820454
on B1105, 4½m N of Fakenham

COOKING 1
COST £30–£41

The pilgrims' village of Little Walsingham has claimed miracles since the Middle Ages and, according to one ecstatic reporter, another is brewing within the confines of this likable culinary sanctuary. Upstairs is all pink and pine, with plants everywhere and brass rubbings of medieval knights gazing from the walls. Some think the repertoire (which includes a full vegetarian menu) too long for a modest establishment way out in the country, but the cooking generally sounds a reassuring note. Recent hits have included curried parsnip soup, smoked herring roulade, smoked goose breast with a spicy cranberry chutney and fillet of beef in puff pastry with button mushrooms. The garlic bread is heartily endorsed, as are the imaginatively handled vegetables. Puddings range from banoffi pie to home-made ice creams. The wine list is a sound collection of fairly priced bottles, with house French at £9.75.

CHEF: Christopher Padley   PROPRIETORS: Christopher and Helen Padley   OPEN: Sun L (every 4–6 weeks) 12.30 to 1.30, Tue to Sat D 7 to 8.30   CLOSED: Tue Nov to Easter, 1 week Nov, 2 weeks Jan – Mar, 1 week Jun   MEALS: alc (main courses £14 to £15.50). Set L Sun £12.50, Set D £12.50. BYO £3   SERVICE: not inc, card slips closed   CARDS: Access, Delta, Switch, Visa
DETAILS: 40 seats. Private parties: 40 main room. Vegetarian meals. No children under 10. Smart dress preferred. No smoking in dining-room. Wheelchair access (no WC). Music
ACCOMMODATION: 3 rooms, 1 with shower. TV. B&B £22.50 to £40. Deposit: £5. Children welcome. Dogs welcome exc in restaurant during meal times (*The Which? Hotel Guide*)

Far East 🍴✱ | NEW ENTRY |

27–35 Berry Street, Liverpool, L1 9DF
TEL: (0151) 709 3141

COOKING 1
COST £11–£38

Liverpool is home to Britain's oldest Chinese community, and many of its inhabitants are descendants of nineteenth-century seamen. What remains of 'Chinatown' is centred around Berry Street and Nelson Street, and the Far East is one of its best known venues. The setting is a sprawling, ultilitarian dining-room above the Shun On supermarket; views of desolation and crumbling brickwork are not part of the draw, but the food makes amends. The menu is old-school Cantonese with bountiful seafood, casseroles, roast meats and no stinting on esoteric ingredients. Dim-sum (served noon to 6pm) are a high point. Deep-fried prawn dumplings, wrinkly steamed beef dumplings with ginger and spring onion, and spare ribs with chilli and black bean sauce have been recommended. Hefty portions and big, bold flavours also typify wun-tun soup, crispy aromatic duck and an intriguing dish of 'three kinds of vegetables' stuffed with prawn meat. One-dish specials are available at lunch-time and a buffet is laid out three nights a week. Service is on the ball. House wine is £8.

CHEF: C.K. Cheung   PROPRIETOR: T.Y. Cheung   OPEN: all week noon to 11 (12.50am Fri and Sat)   CLOSED: Good Fri, 25 and 26 Dec   MEALS: alc (main courses £6 to £10). Set L £5.80 to £6.50, Set D £13.50 (minimum 2 people) to £15.80 (minimum 6 people)   SERVICE: not inc, card slips closed   CARDS: Access, Amex, Delta, Diners, Switch, Visa   DETAILS: 200 seats. Private parties: 250 main room. Car park. Vegetarian meals. Children's helpings. Smart dress preferred. No smoking in 1 dining-room. Wheelchair access (also WC). Music. Air-conditioned

Lyceum Library   NEW ENTRY

1A Bold Street, Liverpool L1 4DD   COOKING 1
TEL: (0151) 709 7097   FAX: (0151) 708 8751   COST £26–£49

As far as restaurants are concerned, Liverpool's city centre is 'the least well endowed of any in Great Britain' according to one reporter who welcomed another new addition. Bold Street may have lost some of its lustre, but the restoration of this handsome late-eighteenth-century building is entirely praiseworthy. The restaurant occupies the old business library, once used by every shipping merchant in the city: a magnificent circular space with a huge cupola and Regency columns. The kitchen is an eager follower of fashion, and although it occasionally trips up over some basic techniques and saucing, and tries to incorporate rather too many flavours within a single dish, the menu does balance fillets of sea bass or brill against confit of duck and roast loin of venison, and has produced a successful terrine of moist and meaty smoked chicken and duck served with a good chutney and slices of brioche. Iced orange parfait, and hot apple and praline strudel are among desserts. Service might be a little inexperienced, but tries hard and is friendly 'in a chirpy Liverpudlian way'. The short wine list stays mostly under £20, with house wines at £9.95.

CHEF: Simon Collard   PROPRIETORS: Robert and Michael Gutmann   OPEN: Mon to Fri L 12 to 3, all week D 7 to 10   MEALS: alc (main courses £10 to £17). Set L £12.95 (2 courses), Set D £16.95 (2 courses)   SERVICE: not inc, card slips closed   CARDS: Access, Amex, Delta, Switch, Visa   DETAILS: 90 seats. Private parties: 75 main room. Vegetarian meals. Children welcome. Wheelchair access (also WC). Music

---

LIVERSEDGE West Yorkshire   map 9

▲ Healds Hall Hotel ⁵✳

Liversedge WF15 6JA   COOKING 1
TEL: (01924) 409112   FAX: (01924) 401895   COST £14–£39

The eighteenth-century stone-built house in the Spen Valley has an air of calm, a modern pink-hued dining-room and attentive service. Things are getting busier, too, with the kitchen now baking its own bread and selling jams and chutneys. Plentiful game appears in season, and summer brings fruit from a local allotment. Dinner is the main meal, offering a generous and mainstream *carte*, plus a weekly-changing set-price menu with a number of bright ideas, among them a first course of breast of lamb – braised, pressed and then grilled, and served with an aubergine pickle – and home-made guinea-fowl sausage. Other unusual ideas have included mackerel served with a casserole of bacon, potato and wild mushrooms, and a prune and calvados version of Bakewell tart. A good cheese selection might include unpasteurised Ashdale and Cotherstone. The personal and 'special' selections at the front of the wine list are well worth exploring. House wines are £8.25.

CHEF: Philip McVeagh   PROPRIETORS: Thomas and Nora Harrington   OPEN: Sun to Fri L 12 to 2, Mon to Sat D 6.30 to 9.30   CLOSED: 26 Dec, 1 Jan, bank hol Mons   MEALS: alc (main courses L £3 to £12, D £7 to £14.50). Set L Mon to Fri £9.50, Set L Sun £9.75, Set D £16.95   SERVICE: not inc, card slips closed   CARDS: Access, Amex, Delta, Diners, Switch, Visa   DETAILS: 50 seats. Private parties: 18 main room, 12 and 30 private rooms. Car park. Vegetarian meals. Children's helpings. Smart dress preferred. No smoking in dining-room. Wheelchair access (also WC). Music   ACCOMMODATION: 25 rooms, all with bath/shower. TV. Phone. B&B £35 to £70. Rooms for disabled. Children welcome. Baby facilities. Dogs welcome in bedrooms only. Afternoon teas. Garden

---

LOCKINGTON   East Riding of Yorkshire   map 9

Rockingham Arms

52 Front Street, Lockington YO25 9SH   COOKING 1
TEL: (01430) 810607   FAX: (01430) 810734   COST £33–£40

A relaxed atmosphere pervades the dining-room of this converted pub between Beverley and Great Driffield. David Barker, who has ceded his place in the kitchen to Philip Leech, comes around to help with service and have a chat, and, although prices have increased since last year, the set-price format remains. Attractive ideas might include black pudding and chicken liver dumplings on a sauce containing smoked bacon, and a fish sausage – a mousse really, with a filling of chunky fish pieces – on a bed of leeks with a cream sauce. Strongly flavoured capsicum and tomato consommé with black olives has turned up trumps, and one couple finished with a pancake filled with ice-cream and syrup, and a rather 'chewy' orange and pecan sponge. Around 50 wines are carefully chosen and generally fair on the pocket. House wines are £9.95.

CHEFS: Philip Leech and Susan Barker   PROPRIETORS: David and Susan Barker   OPEN: Tue to Sat D only 7 to 10   CLOSED: 25 Dec, 2 weeks in summer, bank hols   MEALS: Set D £20.95 (2 courses) to £24.95   SERVICE: not inc   CARDS: Access, Delta, Switch, Visa   DETAILS: 60 seats. Private parties: 24 main room. Car park. Vegetarian meals. No children under 6. Smart dress preferred. Music

---

LONG CRENDON   Buckinghamshire   map 2

▲ Angel Inn ▼ ⚡✳

Bicester Road, Long Crendon HP18 9EE
TEL: (01844) 208268   FAX: (01844) 238737   COOKING 1
on B4011, 2m NW of Thame   COST £24–£40

Reporters who keep up with the Joneses write in fulsome praise of the fresh fish cookery, which is the main event at this inviting country pub. The building shows its age in the glassed-over section of exposed wattle-and-daub wall in one of the dining-rooms; the conservatory is of more recent vintage. On offer here is a mixture of traditional pub fare with some modern brasserie touches. An inspector was impressed by 'pleasantly sweet' parsnip and apple soup 'almost thick enough for the spoon to stand up in', and a main course of salmon with a shrimp sauce showing 'skill and confidence' in the timing. Classic fish dishes sit alongside attention-grabbing things like halibut with spring onions and lime cream, and there are textbook meat dishes too. Finish with the likes of blackberry fool with cassis. Wines, grouped by style, 'continue to improve', as one reporter put it. The list has certainly been upgraded of late, and now includes an imaginative choice from quality growers. The vast majority of bottles are under £20, although there is a fine-wine section for those who want to push the boat out. House wines start at around £8.50.

CHEFS: Mark Jones and Wendy Rowley   PROPRIETORS: Mark and Ruth Jones   OPEN: all week L 12 to 2.30 (3 Sun), Mon to Sat D 6 to 10   CLOSED: 25 and 26 Dec, 1 Jan   MEALS: alc (main courses £7.50 to £13). BYO £1   SERVICE: not inc, card slips closed   CARDS: Access, Switch, Visa   DETAILS: 80 seats. 20 seats outside. Private parties: 40 main room, 10 and 20 private rooms. Car park. Vegetarian meals. Children's helpings. No smoking in 1 dining-room. Music ACCOMMODATION: 4 rooms, all with bath/shower. TV. Phone. B&B £35 to £50. Children welcome (*The Which? Hotel Guide*)

LONG MELFORD   Suffolk   map 6

Scutcher's Bistro ♥

| Westgate Street, Long Melford CO10 9DP | COOKING 1* |
| TEL: (01787) 310200 and 310620 | COST £21–£37 |

Long Melford is an Aladdin's cave of antique shops, and Nicholas Barrett's homely bistro offers an oak-beamed retreat after a day's browsing. The menu is in the what-you-see-is-what-you-get tradition of such places, so that 'a simple plate of our own smoked salmon with lemon' is just that, and plenty of it. More robust appetites have approved of duck confit served on leek and potato mash with a balsamic *jus* as a starter. Meat and game are confidently handled, as in sympathetically cooked pork loin chop on buttered spinach with a green peppercorn sauce, or pheasant cooked in cider and served with glazed apples. Simple fruit salads and sticky sponge puddings are the favoured desserts, but lemon and thyme sorbet may give pause for thought as well. The food represents undoubted value, and service is 'impeccable' throughout.

Nearly 100 wines are grouped by grape variety, so that under Sauvignon you will find bottles from New Zealand, California and South Africa as well as France. The brief tasting notes are helpful. Eight house wines start at £8.50 a bottle, £1.70 a glass. CELLARMAN'S CHOICE: Uiterwyk Chardonnay 1995, Stellenbosch, South Africa, £13.20; Uiterwyk Cabernet Sauvignon 1991, Stellenbosch, South Africa, £17.50.

CHEF/PROPRIETOR: Nicholas Barrett   OPEN: Tue to Sat 12 to 2, 7 to 9.30   CLOSED: 25 and 26 Dec, bank hols   MEALS: alc (main courses £7 to £13.50)   SERVICE: not inc   CARDS: Access, Amex, Delta, Switch, Visa   DETAILS: 75 seats. 40 seats outside. Private parties: 75 main room. Car park. Vegetarian meals. Children's helpings. Smart dress preferred. No cigars/pipes in dining-room. Wheelchair access (also WC). Music

---

▮ *denotes an outstanding wine cellar;* ♥ *denotes a good wine list, worth travelling for.*

Paul Heathcote's 🛏✱

104–106 Higher Road, Longridge PR3 3SY
TEL: (01772) 784969 FAX: (01772) 785713
from Preston, follow Town Centre signs, drive uphill
through centre of Longridge, then turn left, following
signs for Jeffery Hill

COOKING 4
COST £32–£82

'An impeccably fine restaurant by any standards' was an inspector's view of Lancashire's premier eating-spot. The clutch of immaculately white-fronted stone cottages conceals a split-level lounge, a succession of small dining-rooms, and lots of flounce and comfort. Visitors on the Lancashire heritage food trail will not be disappointed to find black pudding, Goosnargh duckling, and pig's trotter (although there is no tripe), while the contrast with luxury items – a feature of 1990s cooking – is pointedly made with a salad of foie gras served with a truffle dressing.

The black pudding starter comes as a 'doorstop-thick slice' of gently peppery intensity, on a bed of half-way-to-mashed potato ('crushed' is the technical term) and baked white haricot beans, 'all awash in a thick, beefy gravyish broth of warming comfort'. This is superb wintertime food, full of 'earthy, nursery tastes', at which the kitchen excels. Such chargrilling as there is errs on the gentle side, resulting in impeccable halibut at inspection (excellent fish and faultless timing), in a rich tarragon and chervil beurre blanc. Meat is treated equally sensitively, producing roast spring lamb 'of dreamlike tenderness and sweetness'. Vegetables are integral to the dish, and potatoes – from new Jersey Royals to a wedge of 'hotpot' potatoes – add greatly to the enjoyment.

The admirable down-to-earth batting for Lancashire by a chef who is 'at or very near the peak of his powers' is perhaps at odds with the 'metropolitan faffing' of out-of-season asparagus, and summer berries in spring. Nevertheless, a hot strawberry soufflé at Easter, with its accompanying roasted almond ice-cream, worked extremely well. Pudding ditherers are consoled by a plate of seven desserts, considered good value at £11.50 for two people. Excellent 'heavenly fresh' bread includes a pungent sage and onion, and canapés and petits fours are 'exceptional in variety and quality', including a mini-cottage pie to start and tiny fruit tartlets to finish. Lunch is four courses (a lot for some), while dinner, in addition to the *carte*, offers a ten-course option of specialities. Although prices are 'wincingly high for these parts', common sense prevails in the maximum service charge of £15. Service is one-hand-behind-the-back formal, but has also been 'cosseting, relaxed and friendly'. Burgundy plays a major role on the wine list, supported by an international cast. Half-bottles and dessert wines are strong, but prices are high in general and there isn't a great deal of choice under £20 a bottle.

CHEFS: Paul Heathcote and Andrew Barnes PROPRIETOR: Paul Heathcote OPEN: Fri and Sun L 12 to 2.15, Tue to Sun D 7 to 9.30 MEALS: alc D (main courses £17 to £20). Set L £22.50, Set D £35 to £55 SERVICE: 10% (optional; max £15), card slips closed CARDS: Access, Amex, Delta, Diners, Switch, Visa DETAILS: 60 seats. Private parties: 60 main room, 18 private room. Car park. Vegetarian meals. Children welcome. Smart dress preferred. No smoking in dining-room. Wheelchair access (no WC). Music

LOWER BEEDING   West Sussex   map 3

Jeremy's at the Crabtree ✦✦

Brighton Road, Lower Beeding RH13 6PT
TEL: (01403) 891257   FAX: (01403) 891606   COOKING 2*
on A281, just S of village   COST £21–£40

The Crabtree looks like a straightforward pub, but the ambience and the
intentions are a little more serious than that. Jeremy Ashpool is a critical
self-appraiser, 'slotting comfortably into middle age' (as he himself writes); but
don't let such modesty mislead. There is plenty to attract attention.

An inspection meal took in nicely mature grilled goats' cheese on rösti dressed
with basil oil, a generous bowl of mixed fish and leek soup, and poached lemon
sole fillets with asparagus on a frothy chive butter sauce, all of which were
enjoyed. Fashionable European influences help to lift many of the dishes, as in
monkfish baked with fennel, peppers and tapénade, or grilled lamb chump with
roasted onions, tomatoes and bulgar wheat. Fruit crumbles and toffee pudding
are pub-style crowd-pleasers, although the latter is a hazelnutty variant of the
usual sticky version and may well come with a kumquat if you're lucky.
Friendliness and enthusiasm are hallmarks of the service, and there is a
stimulating list of fairly priced wines, opening with some tasty southern
hemisphere stuff. House French is £9.95.

CHEFS: Jeremy Ashpool, Pia Waters and Tammy Charleston   PROPRIETOR: Jeremy's
Restaurants Ltd   OPEN: all week L 12.30 to 2, Mon to Sat D 7.30 to 9.45   CLOSED: 25 Dec, D
bank hols   MEALS: alc L (main courses £7 to £10), Set L Mon to Sat £9.50 (2 courses), Set L Sun
£14.95, Set D Tue to Thur £12.50, Set D Tue to Sat £23.50   SERVICE: not inc L, 10% D, card slips
closed   CARDS: Access, Amex, Delta, Switch, Visa   DETAILS: 40 seats. 12 seats outside.
Private parties: 26 main room, 26 private room. Car park. Vegetarian meals. No smoking in 1
dining-room. Wheelchair access (no WC). No music

▲ South Lodge ✦✦

Brighton Road, Lower Beeding RH13 6PS
TEL: (01403) 891711   FAX: (01403) 891766   COOKING 2
on A281, 6m SE of Horsham   COST £28–£72

The fact that this Victorian country house is only a short hop from Gatwick
Airport helps to explain its reliance on the business and conference trade.
Display cases full of objects for sale seem designed 'to extract the last penny from
conferences', but friendly and attentive service counters the huge scale of the
house and grounds, and pleasant views across meadows contribute to the
tranquil feel. Lunch appears good value, offering perhaps red mullet with
spinach and tomato sauce, home-smoked belly of pork, and steamed jam sponge
pudding. It also comes with a very decent choice of wines by the glass.

The kitchen adopts an attractive modern stance, with ideas from Italy and the
Mediterranean – such as open ravioli with fish and shellfish – balancing more
traditional and weightier veal kidneys with mustard sauce. The variety afforded
by wild mushroom and truffle sauce (for pan-fried fillet of beef) on the one hand,
and a bright lemon and coriander *jus* (for loin of lamb) on the other, makes this an
appealing style of cooking. The lively tone continues in lavender-flavoured

crème brûlée, and a charlotte of blackberries and apples with a bay-leaf-infused custard. Wines are classy but pricey, with house wines £14.50.

CHEF: Timothy Neai   PROPRIETOR: Laura Hotels Ltd   OPEN: all week 12.30 to 2.30 (3 Sun), 7.30 to 10 (10.30 Fri and Sat)   MEALS: alc D (main courses £20 to £24). Set L £16, Set D £25 to £32 SERVICE: not inc, card slips closed   CARDS: Access, Amex, Delta, Diners, Switch, Visa DETAILS: 40 seats. Private parties: 80 main room, 8 to 80 private rooms. Car park. Vegetarian meals. Children's helpings. Jacket and tie. No smoking in dining-room. Wheelchair access (also WC). No music   ACCOMMODATION: 39 rooms, all with bath/shower. TV. Phone. Room only £90 to £255. Rooms for disabled. Children welcome. Afternoon teas. Garden. Fishing. (*The Which? Hotel Guide*)

LOWER SLAUGHTER Gloucestershire   map 5

▲ *Lower Slaughter Manor* 🛏 ✺

Lower Slaughter GL54 2HP
TEL: (01451) 820456   FAX: (01451) 822150   COOKING 3
off A429, at sign 'The Slaughters'   COST £27–£63

As we went to press, Audrey and Peter marks announced their retirement from the seventeenth-century manor house of soft Cotswold stone that they have run since 1991. The new owners are Roy and Daphne Vaughan, who already own Buckland Manor (see entry, Buckland), and their intentions are to remain at Buckland, leaving Lower Slaughter in the hands of a manager, and of chef Alan Dann, who himself only arrived at Easter 1996.

Attention has been lavished on the house's interior, and the atmosphere is one of unimpeachable formality, while country-house riches have always been the kitchen's mode, typically elevated by the thoughtful use of unexpected flavours. Sweetcorn soup is lifted with Indian spices, crab ravioli with Chinese, while a risotto contains all the Mediterranean touchstones of saffron, dried tomatoes and Reggiano Parmesan. A main-course inspection dish that consisted of a piece of tuna studded with chopped black olives in a sweet pepper sauce with 'very sensuous' herbed mashed potato demonstrates the kitchen's understanding of both timing and balance. More ordinary is loin of new season's lamb with aubergine caviare in a heavily reduced stock sauce.

Desserts have included a warm and very loose-textured caramel sponge, bravely – and just about successfully – accompanied by rosemary ice-cream, and pear soufflé. Pre-prandial nibbles, appetisers and plated canapés appear in sufficient number to take the edge off most appetites. Service by a largely French team is scrupulously polite, although one report indicates that they may be more keen to insist on the jacket and tie rule than to get the order right. The predominantly French wine list is enormously impressive in its way, but prices take some digesting. Australia and New Zealand provide relative relief. House Burgundy is £16.

'There seems to be some lack of attention to detail about the place. "Welcome to our weekly-changing menu," it said, but it was dated for the previous week!' (On eating in Essex)

CHEF: Alan Dann   PROPRIETORS: Roy and Daphne Vaughan   OPEN: all week 12.30 to 2 (2.30 Sun), 7 to 9.30 (10 Fri and Sat)   CLOSED: 2 to 9 Jan   MEALS: Set L £12.95 to £18.95, Set D £32.50   SERVICE: not inc   CARDS: Access, Amex, Delta, Switch, Visa   DETAILS: 36 seats. Private parties: 30 main room, 16 and 30 private rooms. Car park. Vegetarian meals. No children under 10. Jacket and tie D. No smoking in dining-room. No music   ACCOMMODATION: 14 rooms, all with bath/shower. TV. Phone. D,B&B £145 to £320. No children under 10. Afternoon teas. Garden. Swimming-pool (*The Which? Hotel Guide*)

LOW LAITHE North Yorkshire   map 9

Dusty Miller

Low Laithe, Summerbridge HG3 4BU
TEL: (01423) 780837 FAX: (01423) 780065   COOKING 3
on B6165, 2m SE of Pateley Bridge   COST £34–£74

The old stone house on the main road is dark and restful inside, decorated with lots of drink-related items, from old lead-lined boxes to an interesting collection of spirits. The demure and sedate feel is just right for the careful, restrained but skilled cooking that comes out of Brian Dennison's kitchen. He takes note of the seasons, makes the effort to acquire wild salmon, and gets his lamb and herbs locally. But he adds another dimension with beluga caviare and foie gras, so it is not all simple country cooking. The serious Anglo-French approach is not deflected by current fads, but prefers to concentrate mostly on fish and game. The appeal of these materials is their variety and versatility, and their responsiveness to simple treatments. Grilled Dover sole or baked halibut make fine centrepieces, after shellfish bisque, or perhaps game terrine with onion confit.

Interest is maintained with a sauté of kidneys and mushrooms, and a few vegetable first courses along the lines of asparagus hollandaise or carrot and coriander soup. The unadorned style may seem stark in modern cosmopolitan terms, but is entirely appropriate to the quality of ingredients, and in any case the food generally turns out to be more exciting than the descriptions, thanks to assured techniques: pastry-work is good, timing is accurate, and combinations are balanced. Desserts include vanilla ice-cream, or fresh fruit sorbet, at one end of the scale, and tarte Tatin, or a 'de luxe' bread-and-butter pudding, at the other. Service from Elizabeth Dennison is 'first-class, with genuine customer care'. The short French wine list 'looks a bit scrappy' but has some good bottles. House French is £12.50.

CHEF: Brian Dennison   PROPRIETORS: Brian and Elizabeth Dennison   OPEN: Tue to Sat D only 6.30 to 11   CLOSED: 25 and 26 Dec, 1 Jan, 2 weeks Aug   MEALS: alc (main courses £17 to £18). Set D £24   SERVICE: not inc, card slips closed   CARDS: Access, Amex, Visa   DETAILS: 44 seats. Private parties: 30 main room, 14 private room. Car park. Vegetarian meals. Children's helpings. No children under 9. Smart dress preferred. Wheelchair access (no WC). No music

---

The Guide *office can quickly spot when a restaurateur is encouraging customers to write recommending inclusion – and sadly, several restaurants have been doing this in 1996. Such reports do not further a restaurant's cause. Please tell us if a restaurateur invites you to write to the* Guide.

LUDLOW Shropshire map 5

Merchant House ⅝✳

Lower Corve Street, Ludlow SY8 1DU
TEL/FAX: (01584) 875438

COOKING 3*
COST £33–£40

'We went with high hopes and were more than satisfied,' began one report typical of the postbag. The Jacobean terraced house, down the hill from the town centre, operates on a small scale – just a couple of simply furnished rooms – and is relaxed and comfortable. 'There are no frills to the restaurant and no superfluous details on the plates.' Shaun Hill has an assured professionalism – and nothing to prove to anybody – so he concentrates on what matters, producing 'outstandingly good food with vibrant flavours'.

The three-course meal is considered extremely good value, with a choice of four items at each stage, preceded by nibbles. A first course of 'perfectly cooked' calves' kidneys and sweetbreads in a caper and chive sauce, served with olive potato cake, has received ringing endorsement. Main courses on the well-balanced menu might include fish, a braise, an offal dish and a roast: rack of very young lamb has been exceptionally good. Saucing might vary from one day to the next, but the essentials remain: fine ingredients are treated intelligently, as in a piece of brill surrounded by an apparently casual arrangement of vegetables, with a vermouth and watercress sauce. 'This is top-class cooking,' concluded an inspector, who also enjoyed a 'deeply chocolatey, yet light and fluffy' fudge cake, and rated a plum and almond tart served with Amaretto ice-cream 'a knockout pud'. Flavours are clear and distinct throughout, though not necessarily forthright: 'understated and subtle' is how one reporter saw them.

Bread is crisp granary and excellent white milk rolls, not to be missed. Anja Hill is warmly welcoming and keeps things running smoothly in a quietly unobtrusive way, which is much appreciated, and there is no extra charge for service. Californian and French wines stand out on the list, and there are plenty of half-bottles. House Italian is £11.50.

CHEF: Shaun Hill PROPRIETORS: Shaun and Anja Hill OPEN: Fri and Sat L 12.30 to 2, Tue to Sat D 7 to 9.30 MEALS: Set L and D £25 SERVICE: net prices, card slips closed CARDS: Access, Amex, Delta, Switch, Visa DETAILS: 24 seats. Private parties: 10 main room. No smoking in dining-room. No music

LYDGATE Greater Manchester map 8

White Hart ♥ ⅝✳ NEW ENTRY

51 Stockport Road, Lydgate, nr Oldham OL4 4JJ
TEL: (01457) 872566 FAX: (01457) 875190
on A6050, 3m E of Oldham

COOKING 2
COST £21–£37

Charles Brierley and John Rudden bought and renovated this 200-year-old inn, high on a hillside opposite Lydgate church, during 1994, opening it as a ground-floor brasserie and first-floor restaurant. The idea of a revived 'hostelry' is strong (it still functions as a pub), though the renovation has yet to acquire its own character. The restaurant's short and carefully balanced set menu is an up-to-date mix of plain and posh, offering a terrine of leek and potato topped with black pudding, and a salad of crab fritters and lambs' sweetbreads. Endeavours to do the right things include serving good canapés and fresh bread, and buying locally shot game, English squab pigeon, free-range Berkshire pork and Aberdeen Angus beef.

Confit of duck with creamed parsnips and flageolet beans cooked in red wine impressed an inspector, although the dish was felt to be slightly out of place as a starter. Fillet of beef came decorated with batons of warm tongue coated in crushed black pepper (which might have made a main course in themselves). Desserts incorporate fruits and chocolate. Service is prompt and friendly. As we went to press there was no accommodation, but 12 rooms are planned for winter 1996. The lengthy restaurant wine list shows imagination, with spicy Malbec from Argentina, lesser-known southern French grape varieties, and even a pair of Canadians. Pricing is generous throughout. CELLARMAN'S CHOICE: Pinot Grigio 1994, Ronco Calaj, Russolo, £14.75; Rioja Gran Reserva, Campo Viejo 1985, Spain, £15.75.

CHEF: John Rudden   PROPRIETORS: Charles Brierley and John Rudden   OPEN: restaurant Sun L 12 to 2.30, Tue to Sat D 7 (6.30 Sat) to 10; brasserie Tue to Sun 12 to 2.30, 6 to 9 (Sat D bookings only)   MEALS: brasserie alc (main courses £5.50 to £11); restaurant Set L Sun £12.95, Set D £22. BYO £5   SERVICE: not inc, card slips closed   CARDS: Access, Delta, Switch, Visa DETAILS: restaurant 56 seats, brasserie 44 seats. 20 seats outside. Private parties: 70 main room. Car park. Vegetarian meals. Children's helpings. Smart dress preferred. No smoking in restaurant dining-room. Wheelchair access to brasserie only (also WC). Music

---

LYMINGTON Hampshire   map 2

▲ *Gordleton Mill Hotel, Provence* ♥ ※

Silver Street, Hordle, Lymington SO41 6DJ   COOKING 4
TEL: (01590) 682219   FAX: (01590) 683073   COST £25–£67

'To start at the end,' began one report, 'we all four concluded that there would be no contest hereafter as to where to spend anniversaries and lottery winnings.' Oohs and aahs generally start with the approach via trickling streams, ducks, flowers and white-painted bridges. The dining-room is 'hard to describe, not obviously Mediterranean, or contemporary, or rustic', but with 'loads of lovely space between tables'.

Toby Hill seems to be on a roll. 'The degree of proficiency combined with the carefully considered balance of flavours and textures marks Hill out as a star,' summed up an inspector. It is taken for granted that he uses only the finest and freshest ingredients, 'but then he seems to extract something extra from them'. Daily deliveries help, and seafood positively sings: at one meal king scallops were roasted 'to that instant when the outside is slightly crisp and the inside is distinctly moist', and served with scoops of tomato sorbet of 'powerful flavour'.

Various strands contribute to the style, from earthy stews and casseroles to the sunny south, as in a colourful charlotte of provençale vegetables that combines purple aubergine, red pepper and green courgette with pink lamb fillet. Cream and butter add to the richness, and luxuries crop up but are not overdone. Turbot, for example, is served with a 'titillating accessory' of foie gras enclosed in pasta, as well as crunchy shredded celery and a creamy mustard sauce that all 'melded into one succulent taste thrill whose different elements it was difficult – and unnecessary – to distinguish'.

As for desserts, 'we didn't know whether to faint with pleasure or shriek with laughter at their outrageousness'. A trio of chocolate, for instance, consists of three chimneys of white, milk and dark chocolate, one tall, one short and one medium, while café minute is in the form of a coffee-cup (made out of chocolate) enclosing a coffee mousse; in the saucer is a spoon made from biscuit, and three 'sugar lumps' which turn out to be chocolate truffles. 'We were all gobsmacked at the technical achievement.'

Service has been described as 'Jeeves-like in its unobtrusive, all-seeing, self-effacing efficiency', and both the maîtresse d' and the wine waiter have come in for praise. The gargantuan wine list is dominated by classic French regions. The names are great, but some mark-ups are on the high side. French country wines are convincing, too, particularly from Provence. Otherwise, vintage champagnes and the grander wines of the New World – Penfolds Grange, Opus One and the like – impress. CELLARMAN'S CHOICE: Henschke Mount Edelstone Shiraz 1992, Adelaide Hills, Australia, £35; Dom. de Trévallon Rouge 1991, Eloi Dürrbach, £29.50.

CHEF: Toby Hill   PROPRIETOR: William Stone   OPEN: Wed to Mon L 12 to 2, Mon and Wed to Sat D 7 to 10   CLOSED: 2 weeks Nov   MEALS: alc (main courses L £12, D £17). Set L and D £20 (inc wine), Set D Sat £40. BYO £10   SERVICE: not inc   CARDS: Access, Amex, Delta, Diners, Switch, Visa   DETAILS: 55 seats. 30 seats outside. Private parties: 60 main room, 16 private room. Car park. Children's helpings. Children under 7 by arrangement. Smart dress preferred. No smoking in dining-room. Wheelchair access (also WC). Music. Air-conditioned   ACCOMMODATION: 7 rooms, all with bath/shower. TV. Phone. B&B £97 to £136. Deposit: 25%. No children under 7. Dogs welcome. Afternoon teas. Garden. Fishing (The Which? Hotel Guide)

LYMPSTONE Devon   map 1

▲ River House ⁵✳

The Strand, Lympstone EX8 5EY   COOKING 1
TEL: (01395) 265147   COST £42–£55

The view through the dining-room windows is attractive, though curtains would be nice for when it disappears after dark. The Wilkeses run an outside catering business and a freezer-filling service as well as residential courses in painting and cookery. They grow herbs, some vegetables and soft fruits, and Shirley Wilkes cooks 'up-market dinner-party dishes' along the lines of roast duck with cherry sauce, or plaice stuffed with prawns, with Catalan chicken or lamb rogan josh for variety.

At an inspection dinner some dishes worked extremely well, including an 'absolutely divine' onion and red pepper marmalade tart with crisp, light pastry and a topping of melted Somerset Brie. A raviolo impressed for its elasticity, its filling of spinach and crabmeat, and its silky Parmesan-flavoured sauce, while less successful main courses were 'saved by the vegetables'. Puddings may be recited, in which case be prepared for a £3.25 supplement for banana pancakes, which seems a lot. Small bread rolls are a success, and the wine list makes a sincere attempt to supply some good bottles for less than £20; nine are available by the glass.

CHEF: Shirley Wilkes   PROPRIETOR: Michael Wilkes   OPEN: Tue to Sat 12 to 1.30, 7 to 9.30 (10.30 Sat); private parties and residents Sun and Mon   CLOSED: 25 to 27 Dec, 1 and 2 Jan   MEALS: Set L and D £27.95 (2 courses) to £32. Light L available Tue to Sat   SERVICE: not inc   CARDS: Access, Amex, Delta, Visa   DETAILS: 40 seats. Private parties: 17 main room, 14 private room. Vegetarian meals. No children under 6. Smart dress preferred. No smoking in dining-room. Wheelchair access (no WC). No music   ACCOMMODATION: 3 rooms, all with bath/shower. TV. B&B £55 to £74. No children under 6

MADINGLEY Cambridgeshire   map 6

Three Horseshoes 🍶 | NEW ENTRY |

High Street, Madingley CB3 8AB   COOKING 1
TEL: (01954) 210221   FAX: (01954) 212043   COST £22–£50

The sixteenth-century village pub is thatched and well cared for, with polished wood and gleaming glass. 'Very casual, but stylish with it' is one view. The Huntsbridge philosophy determines the style. As at the Pheasant in Keyston and the White Hart at Great Yeldham (see entries), the same menu is available everywhere on the premises for the same price: bar orders are taken at the counter, while the garden-like conservatory and dining-room are bookable. The style is 'generous, enthusiastic cooking with a fierce Mediterranean edge' helped along by a busy chargrill.

All sorts of aromatics and taste tweakers, from salsas to truffle oil, help to produce some colourful and exciting flavour combinations, while presentation varies from a 'gutsy and nourishing' bowl of chicken and beans to a more layered architectural approach, perhaps of potato pancakes, kidneys and foie gras. Other reporters have enjoyed grilled chicken salad with pesto and couscous, 'a mighty slab of roast monkfish' with rosemary and garlic, and 'stunning' panettone bread-and-butter pudding with Jersey cream. The wine list provides plenty of interest without becoming unwieldy. Italy, Burgundy and the New World are the strongest suits; highlights include California Edna Valley Chardonnay at £21 a bottle and Stanton & Killeen Liqueur Muscat at £25 a bottle and £1.85 a glass. Prices are fair throughout, with decent house wines starting at £8.95 a bottle; 13 of them, including champagne, are sold by the glass. CELLARMAN'S CHOICE: Bergerac Ch. Tour des Gendres 1995, £11.75; Pinot Noir 1994, Dom. De l'Aigle, £13.25.

CHEF: Richard Stokes   PROPRIETOR: Huntsbridge Ltd   OPEN: all week 12 to 2, 6.30 to 10 (7 to 9 Sun)   MEALS: alc (main courses £6.50 to £14.50)   SERVICE: not inc   CARDS: Access, Amex, Diners, Visa   DETAILS: 110 seats. 35 seats outside. Private parties: 60 main room. Car park. Vegetarian meals. Children's helpings. Smart dress preferred. Wheelchair access (no WC). Music

---

Prices quoted in the Guide *are based on information supplied by restaurateurs. The prices quoted at the top of each entry represent a range, from the lowest meal price to the highest; the latter is inflated by 20 per cent to take account of likely price rises during the year of the* Guide.

MAENPORTH Cornwall

map 1

Pennypots

Maenporth TR11 5HN
TEL/FAX: (01326) 250251

COOKING 3
COST £35–£41

The first thing that visitors will notice about Pennypots is that it has moved 13 miles south from Blackwater to a secluded sandy cove just outside Falmouth. The second is that very little has changed apart from the view: a big airy room decorated in pale yellow looks out over the sea, and there are china bears everywhere. It is still relaxed and informal, however, and Kevin Viner's cooking remains much the same. Local produce, especially fish and shellfish, play a big part, though now in a reformatted fixed-price menu. Among the seafood offerings might be roast scallops with cucumber and a Thai butter sauce, or steamed fillet of turbot with a saffron sauce and samphire grass.

Pennypots regulars will also be pleased to see that pan-fried fillet of beef, duo of duck, and Cornish lamb are still in the repertoire, and that the menu continues to offer soup, salad, twice-baked cheese soufflé, and a livery terrine to begin, the latter typically served with a counterbalancing sweet pear chutney. Main courses come with a wide selection of vegetables from shredded swede to a purée of celeriac and sweet potato, while desserts can sound filling: fritters of West Country cheese in a sauce of port and capers, for example, or the long-standing chocolate temptation, with its orange, kirsch and black cherry flavours. In fact, they can also be quite light, as one reporter found with a fluffy lemon mousse accompanied by an Amaretto ice-cream and a blueberry sauce. Service is friendly and efficient. A new wine list is on its way, now there is somewhere to store all the bottles, but in the meantime house French is £8.50.

CHEF: Kevin Viner   PROPRIETORS: Jane and Kevin Viner   OPEN: Tue to Sat D only 7 to 10
CLOSED: 4 weeks winter   MEALS: Set D £21 (2 courses) to £25   SERVICE: not inc, card slips
closed   CARDS: Access, Amex, Diners, Visa   DETAILS: 45 seats. Private parties: 45 main room.
Car park. Vegetarian meals. Children's helpings. No smoking before 10pm. Wheelchair access
(also WC). No music. Air-conditioned

MAIDEN NEWTON Dorset

map 2

Le Petit Canard ♥ ⁵✳

Dorchester Road, Maiden Newton DT2 0BE
TEL: (01300) 320536
off A37, 7m N of Dorchester

COOKING 2*
COST £32–£39

The Chapmans run a small and very personal enterprise, and apply the commitment of true amateurs to just eight tables, on only five nights a week. The dining-room is simple, comfortable and welcoming: 'it is nice to be remembered when you walk into a restaurant you haven't been to for a while.' Geoff Chapman's cooking is bouncy and lively, using black-bean chilli oil, satay sauce or sun-dried tomato vinaigrette to add verve to his fast wok dishes, chargrilling and slow roasting.

Techniques and timing are sound, producing salmon fillet charred on the sea-salted outside and just rare inside, as well as 'sweet and tender' kangaroo.

Chargrilled saddle of rabbit is served on pasta with bacon and thyme, and soups are highly recommended, from roast salmon bisque with mushrooms to a cold one of fresh herbs and potato. Striking puddings include passion fruit tartlet with black pepper ice-cream, and bitter chocolate torte with toffee drizzles. 'At last an espresso machine has been installed, which is another reason for coming back,' concluded one reporter. Wines on the short list are imaginatively chosen, with fashionable labels from California, Italy and Spain, a good clutch of half-bottles and 11 eclectic dessert wines. A small fine wine and bin-end section should please traditionalists. House wine starts at around £11. CELLARMAN'S CHOICE: Franciscan Chardonnay 1993, Pinnacle Vineyards, California, £12.95; Ornellaia 'Le Volte' 1993, Antinori, £15.50.

CHEF: Geoff Chapman   PROPRIETORS: Geoff and Lin Chapman   OPEN: Tue to Sat D only 7 to 9   CLOSED: 1 week Jan, 1 week early summer   MEALS: Set D £22.50. BYO by prior arrangement   SERVICE: not inc   CARDS: Access, Visa   DETAILS: 30 seats. Private parties: 36 main room. Vegetarian meals. No children under 7. No smoking in dining-room. Music

---

MALMESBURY Wiltshire   map 2

▲ *Old Bell Hotel* | NEW ENTRY |

Abbey Row, Malmesbury SN16 0AG   COOKING 1*
TEL: (01666) 822344   FAX: (01666) 825145   COST £21–£36

Originally founded as a guest house for the Norman abbey, the many-gabled, wisteria-draped Old Bell is its junior by roughly half a century, and the team that took over in 1994 is gaining support. Cream teas are served in the afternoon, while the Great Hall (actually a very small room) offers snacks of Welsh rarebit, or bubble and squeak with fried eggs and grilled bacon. The elegant dining-room has an Edwardian feel, with chandeliers, potted palms, well-spaced tables, and a 'much used' silver carving trolley containing the day's roast. 'Unusually good' raw materials and excellent timing characterised an inspection meal that took in bacon-wrapped scallops with chargrilled vegetables, and a dish of duckling cooked two ways (pink breast, well-cooked leg), served with cabbage and lentils. Trios are also popular, from salmon (marinated, tatare and smoked) to begin, to three spiced brûlées: cinnamon, vanilla and nutmeg. Service has been 'unhelpful' for one, and 'bright, perky and smiling' for another, and 50-odd wines arranged by grape variety stay mostly under £20. House wine is £11.75.

CHEF: Darren Barclay   PROPRIETORS: Nigel Chapman and Nicholas Dickinson   OPEN: all week 12.30 to 2, 7.30 to 9.30   MEALS: Set L £15, Set D £18.50 to £24. Light L and D available   SERVICE: none, card slips closed   CARDS: Access, Amex, Delta, Diners, Switch, Visa   DETAILS: 60 seats. 20 seats outside. Private parties: 24 main room, 16 to 24 private rooms. Car park. Children's helpings. Wheelchair access (no WC). Music   ACCOMMODATION: 31 rooms, all with bath/shower. TV. Phone. B&B £60 to £150. Rooms for disabled. Children welcome. Baby facilities. Dogs welcome exc in dining-room. Afternoon teas. Garden (*The Which? Hotel Guide*)

See the inside of the front cover for an explanation of the 1 to 5 rating system for cooking standards.

Croque-en-Bouche ▮ ⁵⁄※

221 Wells Road, Malvern Wells WR14 4HF
TEL: (01684) 565612
on A449, 2m S of Great Malvern

COOKING 4*
COST £31–£53

The Victorian terraced house, and Robin Jones's casual appearance, are testament to the fact that good food does not need a grand setting, flounce or ceremony. The restaurant is open only three nights a week (four in summer), and the five-course format consists of soup; a mostly fish-based second course; a meat course with potato gratin and salad; cheese; and dessert. 'New customers need to know this,' writes Robin Jones. The option of fewer courses and lower prices midweek is designed to tempt in more off-peak customers, but even the more expensive weekend deal is a good one. For one reporter it represents 'the finest value in up-market English cooking in the country today'.

Significantly, it is not just the main items that attract attention, although of course these do. 'Brilliantly fresh fish, brilliantly timed, with brilliant flavour combinations,' ran one tribute to a Cornish cod fillet spiced with ginger and coriander. In addition, 'their salad really is the best in the land', volunteered a seasoned reporter, listing 'strips of Mediterranean chargrilled oily vegetables, aubergines and sweet pepper' among its constituents. The Joneses grow many of their own herbs (around 80), salad leaves and vegetables, and the impact of their freshness is considerable. Vegetables appear in soups and in many second courses, and a single one accompanies the main course – braised cabbage with guinea-fowl for example – along with potato gratin which is sometimes combined with Jerusalem artichokes to good effect.

Vegetables may turn up for dessert too: New England pumpkin pudding was 'an object-lesson in making a fairly mundane vegetable really interesting', and resembled a steamed pudding, served with caramel sauce and a raisin ice-cream. As for service, 'this was quite the most impressive performance of professional waiting that I have ever experienced', reckoned one reporter, impressed by Robin Jones's ability to serve two dozen diners single-handedly 'with no untoward delays' while appearing to have all the time in the world in which to do it. He is, of course, matched in the kitchen by an equally imperturbable and unassisted Marion Jones. The restaurant wine list runs to 140 pages of the fine and rare, as well as the quaffable and inexpensive. It dives into every plausible nook and cranny, coming up with admirable options at every step of the way. The annotations are helpful, and for those who wish to choose quickly there's a short list of suggested wines; several of these are available by the glass, half-bottle and bottle. CELLARMAN'S CHOICE: Dashwood Sauvignon Blanc 1995, New Zealand, £15; Enate Crianza 1993, Somontano, £12.

CHEF: Marion Jones   PROPRIETORS: Robin and Marion Jones   OPEN: Wed to Sat D only 7.30 to 9   CLOSED: Christmas to New Year, 1 week May, 1 week Sept, Wed Oct to May   MEALS: Set D Wed and Thur £22 to £26, Set D Fri and Sat £32 to £35   SERVICE: net prices, card slips closed   CARDS: Access, Delta, Visa   DETAILS: 22 seats. Private parties: 6 main room, 6 private room. Children welcome. No smoking in dining-room. Wheelchair access (no WC). No music

Planters

191–193 Wells Road, Malvern Wells WR14 4HE
TEL: (01684) 575065
on A449, 3m S of Great Malvern

COOKING 1*
COST £26–£46

Originally a row of Victorian cottages in the shadow of the Malvern Hills, this attractive restaurant now deals in South-east Asian home-cooking. Aware of the town's cultural inclinations, the owners open for meals (booking is necessary) before and after the show at the local theatre and concert hall. The short menu spans Indonesia, Thailand, India, Sri Lanka and elsewhere for satays, vaday (lentil rissoles with yoghurt and coconut dip), Singaporean sweet-and-sour duck breast, and stir-fried chicken with lemon grass and cashews. Portions are hefty, flavours are pronounced. The back-up of rice, noodles, pickles and breads is authentic. The 'under a tenner' menu (not served Saturdays) offers one-dish meals with vegetables and rice; if you order a starter from the *carte* with this menu you get a free pudding. Wines on the short list go well with the food, and prices are very fair. House wine starts at £7.50.

CHEF: Chandra de Alwis   PROPRIETOR: Sandra Pegg   OPEN: Tue to Sat (and bank hol Suns and Mons) D only 7 to 9.30 (10 Sat)   CLOSED: Tue in winter   MEALS: alc (main courses £8 to £8.50). Set D Tue to Fri £9.25 (1 course), Set D Tue to Sat £19.95 (min 2)   SERVICE: not inc, card slips closed   CARDS: Access, Visa   DETAILS: 40 seats. Private parties: 40 main room. Vegetarian meals. Children welcome. No cigars/pipes in dining-room. Wheelchair access (no WC). No music

---

MANCHESTER   Greater Manchester   map 8

Chiang Rai

16 Princess Street, Manchester M1 4NB
TEL: (0161) 237 9511

COOKING 1*
COST £25–£37

This large white-painted basement on the periphery of Chinatown is simply but attractively decorated, and this concentrates the appetite wonderfully. Chiang Rai's connection with Thai chef and cookbook writer Vatcharin Bhumichitr has resulted in many unusual northern Thai dishes and a separate, innovative vegetarian menu. Northern dishes include a somtum of grated green papaya with dried prawns and peanuts dressed with searingly hot but mouth-watering juices. Si ooah are little pork sausages, garlicky and herb-flecked, sliced and served with a fiery dip. Chilli heat is mostly toned down for Western tastes, but can be authentically Thai if you request it.

Frying is spot on; the flavours of a prawn tempura are sealed in by a thin, crisp batter. Ingredients are carefully sourced, with bitter Thai aubergines, fresh Thai basil and other signature flavours much in evidence. This place buzzes when busy, though the atmosphere remains pleasant and the service is consistently helpful and informative. The wine list is short but well selected; prices start at £8.90.

Card slips closed *in the details at the end of an entry indicates that the total on the slips of credit cards is closed when handed over for signature.*

CHEF: Suppaporn Klintaworn PROPRIETORS: Mr and Mrs P. Parkhouse OPEN: Mon to Sat L 12 to 2.30, all week D 6 to 11 CLOSED: bank hols MEALS: alc (main courses £5 to £9). Set L £5 to £9 (all 2 courses), Set D £19.50 to £22 SERVICE: 10%, card slips closed CARDS: Access, Amex, Delta, Diners, Switch, Visa DETAILS: 90 seats. Private parties: 90 main room, 60 private room. Vegetarian meals. Children's helpings. Smart dress preferred. Music

Koreana £

Kings House, 40 King Street West,
Manchester M3 2WY
TEL: (0161) 832 4330   FAX: (0161) 832 2293

COOKING 1
COST £11–£32

Manchester's Korean constituency is ably represented by this family-owned restaurant just off Deansgate. Dishes on the main *carte* are not priced: the idea is to build your own three-course menu from an assortment of specialities that covers most accessible aspects of the cuisine. Bulgogi and dak bulgogi – strips of marinated beef or chicken cooked at the table – are best-sellers; the owners also nominate saewoo twighim (deep-fried crispy prawns with a dipping sauce) and dak gang jung (spicy pieces of chicken and potato) as dishes worthy of note. You will also find yook hwae (the Korean version of steak tartare), mandoo soup with dumplings, hotpots, noodles and, of course, fiery kim chee pickle – the defining component of any Korean meal. Drink tea, jung-jong (Korean rice wine) or something from the short list. House French is £7.50.

CHEFS: Mrs H. Kim and Mr H. Shin PROPRIETORS: Mr W. Kim and Mrs H. Kim OPEN: Mon to Fri L 12 to 2.30, Mon to Sat D 6.30 (5.30 Sat) to 10.30 (11 Fri and Sat) CLOSED: 25 to 31 Dec, L bank hols MEALS: Set L £5.50 to £7, Set D £12.50 to £19.50 SERVICE: not inc, card slips closed CARDS: Access, Amex, Delta, Diners, Switch, Visa DETAILS: 60 seats. Vegetarian meals. Children welcome. Smart dress preferred. Music

Kosmos Taverna £

248 Wilmslow Road, Manchester M14 6LD
TEL: (0161) 225 9106   FAX: (0161) 256 4442

COOKING 1
COST £15–£33

As we went to press Loulla Astin was off to Greece to make a television series about the food of her native land. Business in her long-established taverna runs as usual, although an 'early-doors set menu' (also served for Sunday lunch) is new to the set-up. The kitchen deals in all the staples of Greek cuisine – three versions of meze, plus salads, chargrills and casseroles – but Loulla keeps her regulars interested with a handful of weekly specials that are often traditional dishes given an unexpected twist. Peruse the menu and you might encounter such things as pork with leeks in egg and lemon sauce, oven-baked rabbit in red wine, and roasted mixed vegetables with feta cheese. 'No live bouzouki music or plate-smashing' intrude on the atmosphere. The bargain wine list has house Valgardello at £9 a litre.

£ indicates that it is possible to have a three-course meal, including coffee, a half-bottle of house wine and service, at any time the restaurant is open (i.e. at dinner as well as at lunch, unless a place is open only for dinner), for £20 or less per person.

CHEF: Loulla Astin   PROPRIETORS: Stewart and Loulla Astin   OPEN: Sun L 1 to 5, all week D 6 to 11.30 (12.30 Fri and Sat)   CLOSED: 25 and 26 Dec, 1 Jan   MEALS: alc (main courses £5.50 to £11.50). Set L Sun £7.95, Set D Mon to Fri 6 to 7.30 £7.95, Set D (min 2) £11 to £14   SERVICE: not inc   CARDS: Access, Switch, Visa   DETAILS: 90 seats. Private parties: 60 main room. Vegetarian meals. Children's helpings. Smart dress preferred. No pipes in dining-room. Wheelchair access (no WC). Music. Air-conditioned

Lime Tree

8 Lapwing Lane, West Didsbury,	
Manchester M20 8WS	COOKING 1
TEL: (0161) 445 1217	COST £17–£38

Relaxed informality is the overriding theme of this lively restaurant. 'Breasy-going' is one description that captures the mood, although one reporter was unnerved by chain-smoking, and chain-singing of Christmas carols, even if it was December. The kitchen goes in for brisk borrowings of hot Thai beef salad, Moroccan meatballs with couscous, and serves its own game sausages with polenta and gravy. Roasting and chargrilling – of mackerel, monkfish, breast of pheasant – sustain much of the menu, and accompaniments include pesto mashed potato, seasonal chutney, and 'delicious dark mushrooms' that come with tender fillet of beef. Desserts often have a jaunty French air, as in strawberry and Grand Marnier roulade, or Normandy apple tart with lemon curd ice-cream. Note the two-course lunch and early-evening deal. Bin-ends are always worth exploring on the short, unbalanced wine list. House wines are £8.95.

CHEFS: Jem O'Sullivan and Lee Cross   PROPRIETOR: Patrick Hannity   OPEN: Tue to Fri and Sun L 12 to 2.30, all week D 6 to 10.30   CLOSED: 25 and 26 Dec   MEALS: alc (main courses £4.50 to £14). Set L Tue to Fri £8.95 (2 courses), Set L Sun £10.95, Set D 6 to 7 £8.95 (2 courses)   SERVICE: not inc   CARDS: Access, Amex, Switch, Visa   DETAILS: 80 seats. 40 seats outside. Private parties: 30 main room. Vegetarian meals. Children welcome. Children's helpings Sun L only. Music

Little Yang Sing ✓ 1993

17 George Street, Manchester M1 4HE	COOKING 2
TEL: (0161) 228 7722 FAX: (0161) 237 9257	COST £18–£52

The success of this hugely popular Cantonese restaurant has more to do with its food than its surroundings. One reporter thought the basement – hard by Manchester's Metrolink and entertainment venues – could have done with a lick of paint and perhaps new carpets, although the owners tell us that complete refurbishment is planned. Service remains brisk and amiable. Dim-sum platters are some of the highlights, especially coconut-milk balls, fried fun kuo (crabmeat balls) and crispy wun-tun. There's also a fixed-price daytime menu (with cut-price options for children), which centres on appetisers and one-plate meals. Elsewhere, the kitchen has delivered decent aromatic crispy duck plus 'admirable' offerings such as chicken in black-bean sauce, and beef with ginger and spring onions, while vegetarians are well catered for. There are some palatable and suitable wines on the short list; house wine is £9.50.

CHEF: Ting Chung Au   PROPRIETOR: L.Y.S. Ltd   OPEN: all week noon to 11.30pm   CLOSED: 25 Dec   MEALS: alc (main courses £7 to £10). Set L 12 to 6 (5 Sat and Sun) £8.95, Set D £15 to £30 (minimum 2). BYO £4   SERVICE: 10%   CARDS: Access, Amex, Switch, Visa   DETAILS: 90 seats. Private parties: 90 main room. Vegetarian meals. Children's helpings. Smart dress preferred. Music. Air-conditioned

▲ Moss Nook   ✓ 1993

Ringway Road, Manchester M22 5WD
TEL: (0161) 437 4778   FAX: (0161) 498 8089   COOKING 3
on B5166, 1m from Manchester Airport   COST £24–£62

Moss Nook has for so long been the brightest beacon in south Manchester that, as a regular visitor remarks, it is not hard to become repetitive in singing its praises. It does bear reiterating, however, that this is a thoroughly streamlined and impressive operation, run with all the benefit conferred by long experience, both managerially and in the kitchen. The swagged curtains and double layers of table linen, together with the gently vibrant surroundings of deep crimson, make this one of the more conspicuously comfortable dining-rooms. And for those planning a quick getaway, Manchester Airport is a mile off.

Kevin Lofthouse cooks Anglo-French haute cuisine with a keen eye to presentation and an even surer understanding of flavour. A straightforward salad of lobster comes on well-dressed leaves with little pools of carefully made marie-rose sauce. Chicken and leek soup served as a complimentary second course 'seems to capture the very essence of chicken'. Pinkly roasted spring lamb is arranged in medallions around a turret of truffled chicken mousse, only a slightly strident note of fruit acidulation in the sauce threatening to disrupt the balance. Vegetables are accorded the same care and attention as the central elements, a kind of spring roll of bean sprouts, shredded cabbage and chillies appearing among them one night. Menus occasionally essay a more speculative turn, such as chicken stuffed with Emmental on a red pepper and tomato coulis, but never stray into the ridiculous.

Pastry-work is a strong suit among desserts, supported by temptations such as chocolate mousse with caramelised chestnuts and a mint cream. Clever canapés and excellent freshly ground coffee fill in the details. 'The professionalism,' commented an inspector, 'is such that it all seems so easy.' The wine list is very classical, too, in its way, majoring in France, with short, sharp selections from elsewhere, the prices fairly high but reflecting farily accurately the quality and venerability of what's on offer. House wines open at £9.50.

CHEF: Kevin Lofthouse   PROPRIETORS: Pauline and Derek Harrison   OPEN: Tue to Fri L 12 to 1.30, Tue to Sat D 7 to 9.30   CLOSED: 2 weeks Christmas   MEALS: alc (main courses £18 to £19.50). Set L (by table only) £16.75, Set D (by table only) £29.50   SERVICE: not inc, card slips closed   CARDS: Access, Amex, Diners, Visa   DETAILS: 65 seats. 16 seats outside. Private parties: 50 main room. Car park. No children under 12. Smart dress preferred. No pipes in dining-room. No music   ACCOMMODATION: 1 room in cottage, with bath/shower. TV. Phone. D,B&B £90 to £140

▲ *This symbol means accommodation is available.*

Pearl City

33 George Street, Manchester M1 4PH
TEL: (0161) 228 7683 and 236 2574
FAX: (0161) 237 9173

COOKING 1
COST £11–£46

Pearl City is a cut above the usual run of Chinese restaurants in the heart of Manchester's Chinatown. It serves consistent Cantonese food to a mostly Western clientele (who are provided with cutlery while oriental diners are given chopsticks). An extensive dim-sum list is served all day. Law mai kai ('assorted meats' lurking inside glutinous rice wrapped in lotus leaf) uses good-quality meat fragments, while prawn dumplings are 'small, but quite tender'. There's a bewildering array of set menus to choose from, but from the *carte* steamed sea bass with ginger and spring onion is a whole fish competently cooked then expertly filleted at table. A dish of fried vermicelli Singapore-style – a generous portion of good texture – has a pleasant peppery taste. Service is 'adequate'. House wines are £7.90.

CHEF: Tony Cheung   PROPRIETORS: Tony Cheung, Peter Lee and Patrick Keung   OPEN: all week noon to 1.30am (3.30am Sat, 11.30pm Sun)   MEALS: alc (main courses £6 to £25). Set L £4.90 to £9, Set D (min 2) £15.50 to £19.50. Minimum £8 D   SERVICE: 10%   CARDS: Access, Amex, Delta, Switch, Visa   DETAILS: 430 seats. Private parties: 230 main room. Vegetarian meals. Children welcome. Smart dress preferred. Music. Air-conditioned

Tai Pan

| NEW ENTRY |

Brunswick House, 81–97 Upper Brook Street,
Manchester M13 7TD
TEL: (0161) 273 2798   FAX: (0161) 273 1578

COOKING 1
COST £24–£48

'This is the best example I know in Manchester these days of the Chinatown eating house,' reckons one reporter. The Cantonese restaurant shares the warehouse-style building with a Chinese cash-and-carry and the pink, hangar-like dining-room, decorated with dragon panels, attracts a greater-than-average share of Chinese customers. The menu is a 171-dish trot through the repertoire, with some crossover dishes such as prawn balls in almond flakes, a good choice of dim-sum, plus various banquets and set-price options. Some of the raw materials and saucing ingredients are in need of help – a 'brown Windsor-type sauce' is applied to steak rolls, for instance – but cooking techniques are skilful enough to turn out 'accurately cooked' roast duck in a sweet plum sauce, and deep-fried dishes are ungreasy and crisp: prawn balls, and juicy prawns wrapped in rice-paper impressed an inspector. Service is 'pleasant', and the package is fair value for money.

CHEF: Gary Wan   PROPRIETORS: Sandy Wong, V. Yeung, K.C. Liang and C. Chan   OPEN: all week noon to 11.30 (9.30 Sun)   MEALS: alc (main courses £6.50 to £30). Set L £4.45 to £5.45 (2 courses, minimum 2), Set D £14 to £22 (minimum 2). BYO £4   SERVICE: 10%   CARDS: Access, Amex, Diners, Switch, Visa   DETAILS: 250 seats. Private parties: 250 main room. Car park. Vegetarian meals. Children welcome. Smart dress preferred. Wheelchair access (also WC). Music. Air-conditioned

The Good Food Guide *is a registered trade mark of Which? Ltd.*

That Café

1031–1033 Stockport Road, Levenshulme,
Manchester M19 2TB
TEL: (0161) 432 4672

COOKING 1
COST £20–£38

There may be a touch of 'Mabel Lucy Atwell cutery' about the bric-à-brac in this converted antique shop, but the overall effect is entirely pleasing. Joe Quinn's cooking hits the target pretty accurately, largely because he doesn't overstretch his talents. His good-value *carte* and set menus also change often enough to keep customers on their toes. Proceedings might begin with celeriac soufflé on a bed of spinach, or warm duck salad with pungently earthy wild mushrooms. Main courses range from lamb en croûte with Madeira sauce to a delicate piece of salmon with watercress sauce. Puddings are mostly old-stagers from the fruit crumble/chocolate roulade school of cookery: baked crêpes filled with brandy butter and nuts have also been pleasantly satisfying. Service bubbles with friendly interest. The wine list is an ever-improving slate: more half-bottles and a specials blackboard are promised. House wine is £8.50.

CHEF: Joseph Quinn PROPRIETORS: Joseph Quinn and Stephen King OPEN: Sun L 12 to 5, Tue to Sat D 6 to 11 CLOSED: 1 week Aug MEALS: alc D (main courses £9 to £14.50). Set L Sun £12.95, Set D Tue to Fri £14.95. BYO £3 SERVICE: not inc, card slips closed; 10% for parties of 8 or more CARDS: Access, Amex, Delta, Switch, Visa DETAILS: 80 seats. Private parties: 55 main room, 35 private room. Vegetarian meals. Children's helpings. Wheelchair access (no WC). Music

Yang Sing £

34 Princess Street, Manchester M1 4JY
TEL: (0161) 236 2200 FAX: (0161) 236 5934

COOKING 2
COST £20–£50

Crowds are ever present in the lively, packed basement, where slickness rules and service varies from helpful to, for one reporter, uninterested. The kitchen works best at the extremes of the gastronomic scale. Daytime dim-sum draw regular – but not unqualified – choruses of approval: prawn pancakes with chilli, fried turnip cakes, and scallops with soy, ginger and spring onions have all been well received. At the other end of the scale are the banquets – financially flexible feasts which draw on an extended repertoire for exotica such as ducks' tongues, and chickens' feet with a scallop and mango roll. In between the two is a long menu of Cantonese stalwarts, from pork with pineapple, and 'fat, juicy' fried king prawns to casseroles and one-plate dishes. Despite protestations, the practice of leaving credit card slips open while levying an obligatory ten per cent service charge continues unabated. The wine list is fairly priced and promises dependable drinking. House wine is £9.50. The Steamboat Room on the ground floor is a new venture offering a Chinese version of fondue, and has been tentatively approved. More reports please.

CHEF: Harry Yeung PROPRIETORS: Yang Sing Restaurant Ltd OPEN: all week noon to 11 CLOSED: 25 Dec MEALS: alc (main courses £5 to £14). Set L and D (min 2) £14, Banquets from £17.50 SERVICE: 10% CARDS: Access, Amex, Switch, Visa DETAILS: 140 seats. Private parties: 20 to 220 private rooms. Vegetarian meals. Children welcome. Smart dress preferred. No music

MARSDEN West Yorkshire   map 8

Olive Branch

Manchester Road, Marsden HD7 6LU
TEL: (01484) 844487   COOKING 1
on A62, between Slaithwaite and Marsden   COST £22–£41

The informality and fair pricing of the Olive Branch are typical of the new wave
of pub restaurants. Stone built, with good Pennine views, it totes a blackboard
menu with generous choice, and (despite the name) the food is not particularly
Mediterranean in style. True, it might offer tomato soup with pesto, but it also
takes in braised lamb shank, confit of duck with onion and sultana marmalade,
and braised beef bourguignonne. What strikes most forcibly is that the cooking
is 'full flavoured, rich and satisfying'. 'Sauces are my speciality,' writes John
Lister, who bravely adds 'a touch of chocolate' to enrich a red wine *jus* that
accompanies roast wood pigeon. The dessert repertoire ranges from sticky toffee
pudding to a more unusual treacle, oat and lime tart, or there is a cheese of the
month. The 80-strong list includes wine from Oregon and Israel, and is fairly
priced. House French is £9.90.

CHEF: John Lister   PROPRIETORS: John and Ann Lister   OPEN: Tue to Sun 12 to 1.45, 7 to 9.30
(10 Sat, 8.45 Sun)   CLOSED: first 2 weeks Jan, 12 to 22 Aug   MEALS: alc (main courses £7 to
£14). Set D £13.95 to £16.95. BYO £5   SERVICE: not inc, card slips closed   CARDS: Access,
Delta, Switch, Visa   DETAILS: 68 seats. 20 seats outside. Private parties: 36 main room, 36
private room. Car park. Vegetarian meals. Children welcome. Smart dress preferred. Wheelchair
access. Music

MASHAM North Yorkshire   map 9

Floodlite

7 Silver Street, Masham HG4 4DX
TEL: (01765) 689000   COOKING 3
off A6108, 9m NW of Ripon   COST £16–£43

The setting is a small market town 'with no other attractions', according to one
visitor who appears to have missed Theakston's brewery and the delights of Old
Peculier. The converted shop with artificial flowers and glass cabinets is not
designed expressly to lift the spirits, but all the Floods' efforts go into the food.
They started in 1986, and the operation is all the more impressive for its low-key
approach. Menus read deceptively simply – mussels marinière, or roast loin of
English lamb with provençale herbs – but behind them lies a high degree of
skill. Honest and direct flavours are to the fore, and textures are not lost, whether
in simple roast asparagus or watercress soup.

Charles Flood loves to cook game – hare, deer, boar and grouse are all likely to
appear – and when they are not in season he might well transfer his affections to
fish, serving grey mullet with chillies, perhaps, or Dover sole with lemon butter
sauce. The absence of brash accompanying flavours concentrates attention on the
main item, making reporters aware of the 'first-class beef' and accurate timing.
One of the more inventive desserts is an unusual hybrid – blackberry and apple
bread-and-butter pudding – which one reporter considered 'featherlight and

ambrosial'. Dinner is by no means expensive, but lunch is considered exceptionally good value, while the 90-strong wine list is very fairly priced and well off for half-bottles. House French is £7.50.

CHEF: Charles Flood PROPRIETORS: Charles and Christine Flood OPEN: Fri to Sun L 12 to 2, Tue to Sat D 7 to 9.30 CLOSED: 2 weeks Jan, 1 week Oct MEALS: alc (main courses £9 to £16.50). Set L £10.95. BYO £5 SERVICE: not inc CARDS: Access, Amex, Switch, Visa DETAILS: 36 seats. Private parties: 28 main room. Vegetarian meals. Children's helpings. Smart dress preferred. Music

MATLOCK Derbyshire   map 5

▲ *Riber Hall* 🗌 ⁑

Matlock DE4 5JU
TEL: (01629) 582795 FAX: (01629) 580475
1m off A615 at Tansley

COOKING 1*
COST £27–£50

Riber Hall is a beautiful Elizabethan building of Derbyshire stone, with carved Jacobean furniture, 'lavish' silk curtains and drapes, and just slightly less room to lounge about in than reporters would like. Christopher Billingsley, who arrived in February 1996, divides the menus roughly into traditional British lunches and provincial French dinners. His interpretation of provençale fish soup is a clear saffron-scented garlicky broth with mussels, salmon, white fish and a king prawn. The food makes an effort to be modern and sophisticated, as in a boudin blanc with a sauce of truffle, foie gras and calvados, and the inspector who ate that sausage confessed that the best thing about it was undisclosed on the menu: an onion tart of 'excellent pastry with sweet, succulent onions and a creamy custard on top'.

Among the kitchen's strengths are a commendable commitment to lightness – portions don't overface – and good bread and pastrywork, although at inspection underseasoning and inattentive timing took the shine off things. Desserts, such as prune and armagnac ice-cream, or floating islands, can be very sweet. Service aims for pleasant friendliness, and the largely French wine list makes few concessions on price. House wine is £12.75

CHEF: Christopher Billingsley PROPRIETOR: Alex Biggin OPEN: all week 12 to 1.30, 7 to 9.30 MEALS: alc D (main courses £13 to £17). Set L £11.25 (2 courses) to £14.75 SERVICE: not inc, card slips closed CARDS: Access, Amex, Delta, Diners, Switch, Visa DETAILS: 75 seats. Private parties: 40 main room, 14 to 40 private rooms. Car park. Vegetarian meals. Children's helpings. Smart dress preferred. No smoking in 1 dining-room. No music ACCOMMODATION: 11 rooms, all with bath/shower. TV. Phone. B&B £85 to £150. Deposit: £35. No children under 10. Dogs by arrangement. Afternoon teas. Garden (*The Which? Hotel Guide*)

'It was the mankiest, driest, lousiest-kept cheeseboard ever to have outlived its sell-by date. Mercifully the oddly spoken head waiter was so obscure of tongue that none of us managed to gather the names of these offerings, apart from the Dorset Blue Vinny which, one assumed, had completed a course at the Warminster School of Infantry and been returned black and lifeless in an inert heap.' (On eating in Dorset)

MAWGAN Cornwall   map 1

Yard Bistro

Trelowarren, Mawgan TR12 6AF
TEL: (01326) 221595
off B3293, 3m SE of Helston

COOKING 1
COST £13–£37

Follow the signs for Trelowarren, and the bistro is at the end of a mile-long drive. It overlooks a sheltered courtyard, puts on occasional live jazz and cream teas, and feels relaxed and informal. The blackboard menu is 'mostly improvised on the day', according to Trevor Bayfield. Hitting them on the right day might produce steamed sea bass on a lime and coriander balsamic dressing, or mushrooms such as honey fungus or ceps in season served with scrambled eggs and chives. Flavours are generally upbeat: for example, a warm tomato and sherry dressing with an asparagus soufflé, or a mixture of garlic, lemon and sage to accompany roast monkfish. Pigeon on toast to begin, a tofu main course (perhaps with spinach and a red pepper coulis), and a terrine combining dark and white chocolate with honey, all add to the interest. The wine list is short, sensibly priced and more interesting outside France than within. House wines start at £9.30.

CHEF/PROPRIETOR: Trevor Bayfield OPEN: Tue to Sun and bank hol Mon L 12 to 2, Wed to Sat and bank hol Mon D 7 to 9 CLOSED: Christmas MEALS: alc (main courses L £5 to £6.60, D £11 to £13.50). Set L Sun £7.75 SERVICE: not inc, card slips closed CARDS: Access, Switch, Visa DETAILS: 45 seats. 12 seats outside. Private parties: 60 main room. Car park. Vegetarian meals. Children's helpings. Wheelchair access (also WC). Music

MAWNAN SMITH Cornwall   map 1

▲ Nansidwell

Mawnan Smith TR11 5HU
TEL: (01326) 250340 FAX: (01326) 250440
off A494 Helston road, take left fork at Red Lion in village

COOKING 2
COST £23–£56

A narrow drive leads to the large Victorian granite house overlooking the River Fal, and a homely feel pervades. Family snapshots cover the walls, and Jamie Robertson, 'wearing green tartan trousers and a multi-coloured waistcoat with matching bow tie', is manifestly in charge of the operation. Supplements to the basic set-price dinner mean that it can cost up to £35.50 for three courses. What the food may lack in zingy excitement, it makes up for in sound and serviceable ideas using good ingredients.

Their own smoking of fish and shellfish produces 'a lovely oaky flavour', and might be applied to salmon and king prawns, or to scallops (wrapped in bacon and served with sea bass), which emerge with a good moist texture. A lot tends to happen on the plate, although the menu states that dishes may be prepared more simply on request. Puddings have included half a peach on a meringue, with chestnut praline and a honey sauce, and well-kept cheeses might run to Stilton, Somerset Cheddar, Cornish Yarg and goats'. Spain is a relatively strong

suit on the short and rather uneven wine list. Half a dozen house wines begin at
£10.

CHEF: Anthony Allcott PROPRIETORS: Jamie and Felicity Robertson OPEN: all week 12.30 to
1.45, 7 to 9 CLOSED: Jan MEALS: Set L £15.75, Set D £25 SERVICE: not inc, card slips
closed CARDS: Access, Delta, Switch, Visa DETAILS: 40 seats. 10 seats outside. Private
parties: 40 main room. Car park. Children's helpings. Smart dress preferred. No cigars/pipes in
dining-room. Wheelchair access (no WC). No music. Air-conditioned ACCOMMODATION: 12
rooms, all with bath/shower. TV. Phone. £55 (B&B) to £210 (D,B&B). Deposit: £100. Rooms for
disabled. Children welcome. Baby facilities. Dogs welcome in bedrooms only. Garden

---

MELBOURN Cambridgeshire   map 6

Pink Geranium 🍴✳

Station Road, Melbourn SG8 6DX
TEL: (01763) 260215 FAX: (01763) 262110   COOKING 3
just off A10, 2m N of Royston   COST £22–£72

Since Steven Saunders started appearing on TV's 'Ready, Steady Cook',
business has apparently doubled in this pretty-as-a-picture thatched cottage
restaurant. Walk through the garden to reach the entrance, listen to the birds
singing and soak up the subdued background music. It hardly needs
emphasising that the colour pink dominates. The cooking is of a high order:
elaborate, carefully considered, stylish and bold. Those looking for complexity
of classical cuisine should focus on the *carte*, which promises such things as
mille-feuille of scallops and samphire with tomato and basil beurre blanc,
saddle of wild venison with celeriac purée and truffle *jus*, and hot raspberry
soufflé with framboise sorbet.

More contemporary ideas find their way on to the regularly-changing
fixed-price menu. One couple lunched in the most pleasurable fashion by
ordering warm smoked haddock served on a bed of spinach with a nicely
balanced cream and tarragon sauce, followed by roast breast of pheasant with a
fricassee of couscous and wild mushrooms. As a finale, they chose chocolate tart
served with butterscotch sauce and a refreshing fruit coulis with blueberries.
The Saunders' wine list is strong on value for money, there is a useful section of
bottles for '£15 and under' – all of which are available by the glass – and others
are marked out as personal favourites (a 1989 Ch. Plince from Pomerol, for
example). House wines start at £10.

CHEFS: Steven Saunders and Paul Murfitt PROPRIETOR: Steven and Sally Saunders OPEN:
Tue to Fri and Sun L 12 to 2, Tue to Sat D 7 to 10 MEALS: alc (main courses £21 to £29). Set L
Tue to Fri £10 (2 courses) to £14, Set L Sun £19.95, Set D £20 (2 courses) to £25 SERVICE: not
inc CARDS: Access, Amex, Diners, Switch, Visa DETAILS: 65 seats. Private parties: 40 main
room, 16 private room. Car park. Vegetarian meals. Children welcome. Smart dress preferred.
No smoking in dining-room. Wheelchair access (also WC). Music

---

*The Guide is totally independent, accepts no free hospitality, and survives on the number
of copies sold each year.*

MELKSHAM Wiltshire   map 2

▲ *Toxique* ¾✳

187 Woodrow Road, Melksham SN12 7AY   COOKING 2*
TEL: (01225) 702129   COST £26–£53

While time may dim the impact of Toxique's interiors for faithful regulars, it is
worth repeating that first-timers may be surprised at what goes on behind the
red-brick garden wall and wrought-iron gate. Nocturnal blueberry hues are the
theme in the lounge, the armchairs aglow with gold lamé bolsters, while auroral
yellow dominates one of the dining-rooms, where the sun pours in through a
large window on to Peter Jewkes's huge Cézannesque study of provençale hills.
Thus dazzled, you may be just about ready for a roast quail on dandelion leaves
with truffled soy sauce.

That was how an inspection dinner opened, and jolly good it was too, the fatty
skin and juicy meat of the bird oddly reminiscent of good duck. John Dory
followed, 'perfectly cooked to a still gelatinous flakiness', accompanied by a
'confit' of leeks, mushrooms and potato in a broth powerfully infused with
tarragon. Helen Bartlett's two new French chefs have a bold way with fish,
cooking snapper in red wine and star anise, for example. Wild boar is accorded
full honours: the fillet is served with mushrooms, smoked bacon and sauté
potatoes as well as caramelised silverskin onions with shredded radicchio.
Nougat glacé with red fruit coulis, and tangerine parfait are ways to finish. The
infectious buzz about the place, and the fact that it seems to be 'never knowingly
closed', indicates the confidence that experience has brought. The wine list deals
methodically with the main French regions before branching out into southern
Europe and points south. Selections are mostly very assured, but prices can be
high. House French starts at £9.75.

CHEFS: Helen Bartlett, Eric Lepine and Laurent Dohollo PROPRIETORS: Helen Bartlett and Peter
Jewkes OPEN: all week 12.30 to 2, 7.30 to 10 MEALS: Set L £16 (2 courses) to £19, Set D
£29.50 SERVICE: not inc, card slips closed CARDS: Access, Amex, Delta, Diners, Switch,
Visa DETAILS: 40 seats. 12 seats outside. Private parties: 26 main room. Car park. Vegetarian
meals. Children's helpings. Smart dress preferred. No smoking in dining-room. Music
ACCOMMODATION: 4 rooms, all with bath/shower. D,B&B £90 to £135. Deposit: £50. Children
welcome. Baby facilities. Garden (*The Which? Hotel Guide*)

MELMERBY Cumbria   map 10

Village Bakery ¾✳ £

Melmerby CA10 1HE
TEL: (01768) 881515 FAX: (01768) 881848   COOKING 1
on A686, between Penrith and Alston   COST £16–£27

Behind the busy little shop selling craft souvenirs, home-baked cakes, bread and
jam lies perhaps the country's foremost small bakery. It is too much to hope that
every village might have one, since it takes a man of Andrew Whitley's
commitment and dedication to run it. He has been making organic bread since
1976 in a converted stone barn in this attractive Pennine village, using a brick,
wood-fired oven. Renewable fuel and sustainable agriculture are integral to the

operation, as is recycling: free-range pigs fed on waste bread find their way on to the menu, along with produce from the bakery's own five-acre smallholding, plus Lakeland char, and Bar Woodall's Waberthwaite ham and sausages. The flavour of the enterprise is best given by the Baker's Lunch – a selection of breads and North Country cheeses – perhaps followed by Cumberland rum Nicky or damson tansy. Organic drinks include tea, wines and beers. Breakfast is served until 11.

CHEF: Diane Richter   PROPRIETOR: Andrew Whitley   OPEN: all week L only 12 to 2. Snacks available all day to 5   CLOSED: 25 and 26 Dec, 1 Jan   MEALS: alc (main courses £5.50 to £8). BYO (no corkage)   SERVICE: not inc, card slips closed   CARDS: Access, Delta, Diners, Switch, Visa   DETAILS: 45 seats. Private parties: 25 main room. Car park. Vegetarian meals. Children's helpings. No smoking in dining-room. Wheelchair access. Music

---

MIDDLESBROUGH Middlesbrough   map 10

Purple Onion | NEW ENTRY |

80 Corporation Road, Middlesbrough TS1 2RF   COOKING 1
TEL: (01642) 222250   COST £25–£45

Back in the late 1960s the original Purple Onion was the hottest venue in the north-east and a breeding ground for aspiring rock stars. Its revival by a relative of the renowned McCoy brothers (see entry, Staddlebridge) is funkier than ever, a hodgepodge Aladdin's cave of a place, with bags of panache and a menu that makes all the right modern noises. It also functions as a 'café sportique', and there may be dancing on the tables at weekends. The kitchen knows all about good buying, and the results are commendable: tagliatelle comes with crab, smoked salmon, coriander and sun-dried tomatoes, while grilled wild salmon is served on warm potato and red pepper salad with salsa verde. You might find risotto of smoked Whitby haddock, Szechuan duck breast with honey-glazed vegetables, and crème brûlée with poached raspberries. The wine list is fairly up-market with prices to match. House wine is £10.95.

CHEFS: Graeme Benn and Massimo Cecere   PROPRIETORS: John and Bruno McCoy   OPEN: Mon to Sat 12 to 2.30, 6 to 10.30   CLOSED: 25 and 26 Dec, 1 Jan   MEALS: alc (main courses £10 to £14.50). Bar snacks available   SERVICE: not inc, card slips closed   CARDS: Access, Switch, Visa   DETAILS: 100 seats. 20 seats outside. Car park. Vegetarian meals. Children's helpings. Wheelchair access (also WC). Music. Air-conditioned

---

MIDDLE WALLOP Hampshire   map 2

▲ Fifehead Manor

Middle Wallop SO20 8EG   COOKING 2
TEL: (01264) 781565   FAX: (01264) 781400   COST £20–£48

Fifehead is way ahead of the pack in the antiquity stakes, the manor itself being pre-Domesday. Rooms are on an intimate scale, full of healthy-looking plants and attractive flower arrangements that are echoed in the fabrics. King Harold's mother once ruled the roost here, but Lesley Bishop-Milnes is probably a more sympathetic hostess, and the warm, welcoming and quite individual house owes much to 'personable, observant and intelligent' service. New chef Wayne

Leadon arrived in February 1996, and puts himself to a lot of trouble with a long menu and some intricate dishes.

'The starter bespoke an enormous amount of effort, rather good raw materials and a very good sauce indeed,' commented an inspector of a crab and scallop ravioli with poached asparagus. Other items varied from 'fussy nouvelle garnishes' served with Scotch beef fillet, to an appetiser of lobster thermidor tartlet with Cajun-spiced leek tagliatelle – 'not as terrifying as it sounds' – indicating the potential for interesting textures and flavour combinations. Home-made bread is excellent too, while 'pretty presentation' gave a lift to a meringue nest of assorted alcoholic sorbets on a passion-fruit and orange coulis. Wines are mainly French, with good value among the token bottles from Mexico, Chile and elsewhere. House French is £9.

CHEF: Wayne Leadon   PROPRIETORS: Lesley Bishop-Milnes and Roy Bishop-Milnes   OPEN: all week 12 to 2, 7 to 9.30   MEALS: alc D (main courses £14.50 to £17). Set L £10.50 (2 courses) to £13.50   SERVICE: not inc, card slips closed   CARDS: Access, Amex, Delta, Switch, Visa   DETAILS: 30 seats. 20 seats outside. Private parties: 43 main room, 16 private room. Car park. Vegetarian meals. Children's helpings. Smart dress preferred. No smoking in dining-room. Wheelchair access (also WC). Music   ACCOMMODATION: 15 rooms, all with bath/shower. TV. Phone. B&B £55 to £110. Rooms for disabled. Children welcome. Baby facilities. Dogs welcome. Afternoon teas. Garden. Fishing

---

MIDHURST West Sussex   map 3

▲ *Angel Hotel* ❢

North Street, Midhurst GU29 9DN   COOKING 2
TEL: (01730) 812421   FAX: (01730) 815928   COST £25–£52

The Angel's Elizabethan rose garden overlooks the parkland and ruins of Cowdray Castle in this attractive market town. The hotel itself started life in the sixteenth century as a coaching-inn, though the conference centre and car park are of more recent provenance. Andrew Stephenson does the cooking now, as Peter Crawford-Rolt seems to have his hands full. So do the waitresses, who toil gamely with enormous trays, serving the three eating-areas with 'commendable cheerfulness'. Starters may include 'excellent' game terrine, accompanied by home-made pickles of cucumber and grape. Pickling is clearly enjoyed, but can be taken to extremes, as in a main course where red cabbage and apple somewhat overwhelmed the flavour of its partner, roe-deer. Devon brill with 'perfect' corpulent seared scallops and a 'dreamy' wine sabayon has worked much better.

A slice of 'delicious and very light' Sauternes and olive oil cake with 'sensational' marmalade ice-cream has been adjudged a winning dessert, and chocolate bread-and-butter pudding is served with an orange sabayon and chocolate sorbet. In spite of the hurry and flurry going on all around, 'the atmosphere is entirely conducive to relaxation'. The wine selection is intelligently annotated, even down to the tips for matching food and wine. It's a long list, with much of interest, including fine New World producers and great fizz, but some fairly hefty mark-ups. House wines from Bordeaux are £9.95 a bottle and £1.95 a glass. CELLARMAN'S CHOICE: Cloudy Bay, Pelorus Brut 1990,

Marlborough, New Zealand, £30; Valdepeñas, Senorio de Los Llanos 1984, Cosecheros Abastacedore, £15.95.

CHEF: Andrew Stephenson PROPRIETORS: Peter Crawford-Rolt and Nicholas Davies OPEN: all week 12 to 2.30, 7 to 9.30 (10 Sat) MEALS: alc (main courses £14 to £18). Set L Mon to Sat £9.95 (2 courses) to £17.95, Set L Sun £17.95. BYO £10. Bar food available SERVICE: 12.5% (optional), card slips closed CARDS: Access, Amex, Diners, Switch, Visa DETAILS: 60 seats. 20 seats outside. Private parties: 100 main room, 30 and 70 private rooms. Car park. Vegetarian meals. Children's helpings. Smart dress preferred. No cigars/pipes in dining-room. Wheelchair access (also WC). Music ACCOMMODATION: 25 rooms, all with bath/shower. TV. Phone. B&B £75 to £140. Rooms for disabled. Children welcome. Baby facilities. Afternoon teas. Garden (*The Which? Hotel Guide*)

Maxine's 🍴✶

Elizabeth House, Red Lion Street, Midhurst GU29 9PB
TEL: (01730) 816271

COOKING 2*
COST £21–£38

'We have been eating at Maxine's for the past 13 years, and they are still the best value for money in Sussex,' maintains one supporter of this half-timbered restaurant. Good food at a fair price in an informal atmosphere is exactly what turns locals into appreciative regulars. Simple honesty and straightforwardness pervade the 15-year-old enterprise, from the lack of hidden extras (vegetables and service charge are included, for example) to Robert de Jager's style of cooking. Mussels in garlic butter, and breast of chicken with tarragon sauce are the kinds of things he deals in, plus an occasional offal dish such as lambs' kidneys and sweetbreads in a white wine sauce.

Fish soup with rouille and croûtons, and gravlax with a mustard and dill sauce are standards of a repertoire that rarely gets more exotic than crab-cakes with a tomato and coriander sauce, or risotto of wild mushrooms. It all goes to prove that plain and unpretentious cooking, when done well, still has enormous appeal. 'Marti de Jager is unfailingly welcoming, charming and efficient.' Most of the four dozen wines stay comfortably below £20. House French is £8.50.

CHEF: Robert de Jager PROPRIETORS: Robert and Marti de Jager OPEN: Wed to Sun L 12 to 1.30, Wed to Sat D 7 to 9.30 MEALS: alc (main courses £9 to £16). Set L £14.95, Set D Wed to Fri £14.95 SERVICE: net prices, card slips closed CARDS: Access, Visa DETAILS: 26 seats. Private parties: 30 main room. Vegetarian meals. Children's helpings. Smart dress preferred. No smoking in dining-room. No music

---

MILFORD ON SEA Hampshire   map 2

Rocher's

69–71 High Street, Milford on Sea SO41 0QG
TEL: (01590) 642340
on B3058, 3m SW of Lymington

COOKING 2*
COST £22–£36

Despite appearances, Rocher's has never been a gift shop. It is a detached house in the centre of the village, with a strong local following and an equally warm welcome for all. 'We were charmingly received and chatted to,' noted one, while another appreciated Alain Rocher's tour of the tables at the end of the evening. His cooking is French, unshowy and well executed. 'It may at times lack a little adventure,' suggested one reporter, but cooking doesn't have to surprise to be good. Even a simple fan of avocado with bacon bits and a salad impressed a summer visitor with its excellent balsamic dressing.

But the workmanship also takes in poached egg florentine, twice-baked cheese soufflé, and venison terrine. Fish might appear as local sand sole cooked in butter with lemon juice and parsley, or River Itchen salmon with watercress sauce, while winter can bring a main course trio of pork, beef and lamb in a rich red wine sauce. Finish perhaps with crème brûlée, or a hot chocolate gateau served with coffee ice-cream. Wine mark-ups are industry standard on a well-chosen and predominantly French list, with bags to drink under £20. A short New World selection adds interest, half-bottles are fair, and a dozen house wines cost around £10.

CHEF: Alain Rocher   PROPRIETORS: Alain and Rebecca Rocher   OPEN: Sun L 12.15 to 1.30, Wed to Sat D 7.15 to 9.30 (and Sun D bank hols)   CLOSED: 2 weeks June   MEALS: Set L £14.50, Set D £12.95 (2 courses, week nights only) to £21.90   SERVICE: not inc   CARDS: Access, Amex, Delta, Diners, Switch, Visa   DETAILS: 24 seats. Private parties: 34 main room. No children under 7. Smart dress preferred. No cigars/pipes in dining-room. Wheelchair access (no WC). Music

---

MINSTER LOVELL Oxfordshire   map 2

▲ *Lovells at Windrush Farm* ♸ ╳

Old Minster Lovell OX8 5RN
TEL: (01993) 779802   FAX: (01993) 776212
off B4047, 3m NW of Witney, on S bank of River   COOKING 3
Windrush   COST £29–£51

Here is one of Oxfordshire's superior dining experiences, in a county hardly deficient in that department. 'Forget the image that the word "farm" summons, of produce-shops and well-meaning cafés – this is serious,' a reporter assures us. A baronial feel sets in as you ascend to the gallery for pre-dinner business, and fades again as you proceed to a 'light, uplifting dining-room' for the main show.

The menu is seven courses with no choice, flanked by amuse-gueules and coffee with petits fours. If that sounds like a blow-out, rest assured that Marcus Ashenford is a chef with an uncommonly fine sense of judgement. A meal in May began with sound gravad lax, followed by a cup of deeply flavoured asparagus soup topped with a slick of hazelnuts and cream, and went on to John Dory on grapes, leeks and fennel scattered with tempura-battered haricot beans. Vertical constructions are favoured, and another tower arrived at meat stage – a small piece of beef fillet sitting on a 'sublime' cylinder of layered potato with cream and bacon – the reduction sauce strewn with Jerusalem artichoke and 'intense caramelised shallots that collapsed in the mouth'. Cheeses from Jeroboam's are truly excellent, and include some astonishingly mature French specimens.

At the same meal a lightly cheesy-textured lemon parfait made a clever transition to the main desserts: a tiny serving each of bread-and-butter pudding, caramelised pear with honey and almond ice-cream, and chocolate parfait piled with raspberries. 'We sailed home in a warm glow.' Service throughout was exemplary. After an unassuming start three years ago, Lovells appears to be flying. Wines are taken seriously, with a comprehensive trawl through France and a meticulously chosen handful from other major countries. There's plenty to splash out on, but head for French country wines to spend under £20. CELLARMAN'S CHOICE: Brut Champagne NV, Alain Thiénot, £26.50; Rioja Crianza 1989, Viña Amézola, £17.50.

CHEF: Marcus Ashenford   PROPRIETOR: Lovells Windrush Farm Ltd   OPEN: Fri and Sun L 1 (1 sitting), Tue to Sat D 7.45 (1 sitting)   CLOSED: Jan   MEALS: Set L £19.50, Set D £32   SERVICE: not inc   CARDS: Access, Amex, Delta, Diners, Visa   DETAILS: 18 seats. Private parties: 18 main room. Car park. Vegetarian meals. Children's helpings. No children under 10. Smart dress preferred. No smoking in dining-room. Wheelchair access (no WC). No music ACCOMMODATION: 2 rooms, both with bath/shower. TV. D,B&B £85 to £160. Children welcome. Baby facilities. Dogs by arrangement. Garden. Fishing

---

MOLLINGTON Cheshire   map 7

▲ *Crabwall Manor* ♟

Parkgate Road, Mollington CH1 6NE
TEL: (01244) 851666   FAX: (01244) 851400   COOKING 3
off A540, 3m N of Chester   COST £35–£60

The crenellated battlements and clock-tower present an exotically eccentric introduction to this Victorian folly, though the add-on luxury accommodation creates a more mundane 1990s feel. The manor specialises in functions and the conference trade, but also produces technically impressive modern food for large numbers of people, among them a solid local following. There is plenty of movement in the repertoire, so regulars never need be bored. Menus read excitingly, and fish and vegetable dishes feature prominently.

Presentation is not left to chance: a first-course salad combines three triangular slices of seared tuna, pink in the middle, with a sculpted artichoke heart filled with chopped onions, cucumbers and green peppers dressed in a salty anchovy vinaigrette. At inspection the food sometimes failed to deliver the zip that distinguishes the really first-rate places – stock reductions are not as well defined or concentrated as they might be, for instance – but the kitchen does turn out some fine dishes, including a creamy lobster bisque with succulent pieces of flesh, and a gamey-tasting dodine of duck, with slices of breast on top, and a scattering of morel mushrooms and other vegetables.

Desserts also rely on fine workmanship, and include tarts, parfaits, terrines and a layered gâteau marjolaine with hazelnut cream and chocolate mousse. One reporter who asked for cheese (it was not on the menu) was presented with three good-quality unpasteurised British ones. An inspector found that some of the details – bread, butter, vegetables – were not quite up to the rest of the operation, but the meal began and ended with accomplished canapés and petits fours. Staff are amiable and competent, and the whole experience is 'very pleasant and cosseting'. The vast wine list roams the world but is strongest in France; country wines, Alsace and Champagne stand out alongside Bordeaux and Burgundy. House Burgundy is £13. CELLARMAN'S CHOICE: Mâcon-Viré, Dom. André Bonhomme 1992, £23; St-Aubin premier cru, Les Castets 1992, Dom. Lamy-Pillot, £26.50.

The Guide *always appreciates hearing about changes of chef or owner.*

CHEF: Michael Truelove PROPRIETORS: Carl Lewis, Julian Hook and Michael Truelove OPEN: all week 12 to 2, 7 to 9.30 MEALS: alc (main courses £16 to £22.50). BYO by arrangement SERVICE: not inc, card slips closed CARDS: Access, Amex, Delta, Diners, Switch, Visa DETAILS: 80 seats. Private parties: 80 main room, 20 and 80 private rooms. Car park. Vegetarian meals. Children's helpings. Jacket and tie. No cigars/pipes in dining-room. Wheelchair access (also WC). Music. Air-conditioned ACCOMMODATION: 48 rooms, all with bath/shower. TV. Phone. B&B £78 to £130. Children welcome. Afternoon teas. Garden (*The Which? Hotel Guide*)

MONTACUTE Somerset   map 2

▲ Milk House ✳

The Borough, Montacute TA15 6XB   COOKING 1
TEL: (01935) 823823   COST £31–£40

For hundreds of years this honeyed-stone building actually sold milk from its stable block, before becoming a small hotel/restaurant during the 1970s. The setting, opposite one of England's most enchanting Elizabethan mansions, remains part of its attraction. Lee Dufton's cooking is defined by wholefood principles, self-sufficient enterprise and a serious commitment to organic production. Her fixed-price menus tell their own story. The style is French provincial, with detours into the world larder. Warm goats'-cheese salad, wild boar with red wine and juniper sauce, and monkfish with grain mustard sauce line up alongside mushrooms in pesto marinade, or feizinjan (a Persian dish of duck collops with walnuts, lemon and pomegranates). Vegetarians might be offered pine-nut cromesquis with spinach sauce, while desserts range from spiced plum pudding to vacherin glacé. Reputable organics feature strongly on the affordable wine list, and house wine is £9.80.

CHEF: Lee Dufton PROPRIETORS: Lee and Bill Dufton OPEN: Wed to Sat D 7.30 to 9 (L by arrangement for 6 or more) CLOSED: 23 Dec to 2 Jan, 1 month late summer MEALS: alc (main courses £14). Set L £14.50, Set D £22.90. Minimum £15.90 D. BYO £5 SERVICE: not inc CARDS: Access, Visa DETAILS: 40 seats. 12 seats outside. Private parties: 40 main room, 20 to 20 private room. Vegetarian meals. Children's helpings. Smart dress preferred. No smoking in 1 dining-room. Wheelchair access (no WC). No music ACCOMMODATION: 3 rooms, all with bath/shower. B&B £40 to £58. Deposit: £20. No children under 8. Garden (*The Which? Hotel Guide*)

MORETON-IN-MARSH Gloucestershire   map 5

Annie's   [NEW ENTRY]

3 Oxford Street, Moreton-in-Marsh GL56 0LA   COOKING 1
TEL/FAX: (01608) 651981   COST £25–£49

Down a side-street near the centre, this small, cottage-like restaurant makes a welcome return to the *Guide*. It looks inviting, with a flagstoned floor, three fireplaces, family photographs, dried flowers and 'Burgundy chintz'. Candles are lit for dinner, an appetiser appears, a basket of bread is left on the table, and the daily fish offerings are announced: at one meal a tail piece of steamed Cornish turbot, served with a tomato and red pepper sauce. Proceedings might begin with soup, duck leg confit, or tiger prawns wrapped in filo pastry, pan-fried and spiked with garlic, spring onions and chilli. Other dishes have a more traditional English slant, from a home-made pie of chicken, smoked bacon and mushrooms in a light velouté sauce, with a well-browned puff pastry lid lying jauntily on top, to fruit crumble or treacle tart. Service is 'nicely informal'. Wines are mostly French, including four house wines at £12.50.

CHEF: David Ellis PROPRIETORS: David and Anne Ellis OPEN: Sun L 12 to 2, Mon to Sat D 7 to 9.30 (10 Sat) CLOSED: end Jan to early Feb MEALS: alc D (main courses £15 to £19.50). Set L Sun £18.50 SERVICE: net prices, card slips closed CARDS: Access, Amex, Diners, Visa DETAILS: 30 seats. Private parties: 32 main room, 8 private room. Children's helpings. Smart dress preferred. Music

Marsh Goose ✦✱

High Street, Moreton-in-Marsh GL56 0AX	COOKING 3
TEL: (01608) 652111 FAX: (01608) 652403	COST £20–£55

This attractive Cotswold-stone building is divided up into small eating-areas that produce a 'charming, unpretentious and yet "special" atmosphere'. The operation is distinguished by a high level of staff involvement that keeps ideas bubbling. 'Since having her first child, Sonya Kidney now restricts herself to a 40- to 50-hour week,' and Rupert Staniforth ably oversees the rest. The constantly changing set menus are flexible, and in addition (partly to avoid the necessity of price supplements) a *carte* has been introduced on Saturday evenings to see how it goes. All menus have one thing in common, however: they sparkle with interesting and innovative dishes.

Reporters are impressed by straight, honest flavours, whether in a simple array of 'splendid' seasonal vegetables, or cauliflower soup with rosemary and grain mustard. This is an intelligent kitchen that doesn't just turn out modish copies of new classic ideas, but has 'an excellent understanding of how flavours work together', producing combinations of ingredients and tastes that are 'unusual, imaginative and delicious'. For one reporter the red wine risotto served with loin of lamb was 'a revelation of what can be done with rice'. Other successes have included 'three slices of glorious ox-tongue with three deep-fried nuggets of foie gras', and a 'really scrumptious' apricot and elderflower terrine.

Timing is precise and portions are well judged. 'The meal left me feeling I had eaten exactly the right amount for lunch.' Service is 'friendly, attentive and unobtrusive'. A shop next door sells some 'delectable items' from the kitchen. Wines are taken seriously, with a wide range of quality bottles grouped into sections according to style ('light reds', 'aromatic dry whites' and so on). There's plenty to choose from among the half-bottles and dessert wines. Mark-ups throughout are on the steep side, although house wines are £9 for Spanish red and white.

CHEFS: Sonya Kidney and Rupert Staniforth PROPRIETORS: Sonya Kidney, Leo Brooke-Little and Gordon Campbell Gray OPEN: Tue to Sun L 12.30 to 2.30, Tue to Sat D 7.30 to 9.45 CLOSED: 26 and 27 Dec, 1 and 2 Jan MEALS: alc L Tue to Sat (main courses £11 to £14), alc D Sat (main courses £15 to £18). Set L Tue to Sat £13.50, Set L Sun £18, Set D £24. BYO by arrangement SERVICE: not inc CARDS: Access, Amex, Delta, Diners, Switch, Visa DETAILS: 60 seats. Private parties: 22 main room, 14 private room. Vegetarian meals. Children's helpings. Smart dress preferred. No smoking in dining-room. Wheelchair access (also WC). No music

MORSTON Norfolk   map 6

▲ *Morston Hall* ♀ ⅙✳

Morston NR25 7AA
TEL: (01263) 741041   FAX: (01263) 740419   COOKING 2*
on A149, 2m W of Blakeney   COST £22–£41

This is an Area of Outstanding Natural Beauty and a conservation area, and the
village bustles with visitors to the local seal sanctuary. The brick and flint house
dates from Jacobean times, but the décor and furnishings are modern; it is a
delightful small country hotel with everything in apple-pie order. Evenings are
anchored by a single sitting, at 7.30 for 8, and there is no choice until pudding.

Fish usually features in one of the two first courses (skate wing with
deep-fried leeks, for example), and main courses vary from a roast (best end of
lamb in a herb crust, perhaps) through pot-roasting to pan-frying of, say, rump
of beef. Stocks and herbs provide much of the saucing material, and four
vegetables are the standard accompaniment. When local vegetables are used in
preference to baby sweetcorn and unseasonal asparagus, the results are more
impressive: turnips, sliced, slow-baked, and served with garlic cream, are 'a
revelation'. Puddings have 'a touch of splendour' to them, and one reporter was
smitten by a 'brilliantly executed' poached pear on pan-fried brioche with a
butterscotch sauce and iced coffee granola.

Service is very correct, rather 'tense' for one reporter, but with 'just the right
measure of detached friendliness' for another, and Galton Blackiston's lap of
honour around the dining-room is universally welcomed. Wines are listed in
groups by grape variety on the well-annotated list. Two wines of the month (at
especially keen prices) are highlighted on the menu, and a separate 'Director's
Selection' features fine examples from Corney & Barrow. Nine lively wines are
available by the glass, starting at £2, and French house wines are £9.90. CC:
Mitchelton Reserve Marsanne 1993, Victoria, Australia, £17; Foppiano
Zinfandel 1993, Sonoma County, California, £14.50.

CHEFS: Galton Blackiston and Daniel Smith   PROPRIETORS: Tracy and Galton Blackiston, and
Justin Fraser   OPEN: Sun L 12.30 for 1, all week D 7.30 for 8   CLOSED: 1 Jan to end Feb
MEALS: Set L Sun £15, Set D £26   SERVICE: not inc, card slips closed   CARDS: Access, Amex,
Delta, Switch, Visa   DETAILS: 40 seats. 26 seats outside (drinks only). Private parties: 40 main
room, 18 private room. Car park. Children's helpings. Smart dress preferred. No smoking in
dining-room. Wheelchair access (also WC). No music   ACCOMMODATION: 6 rooms, all with
bath/shower. TV. Phone. D,B&B £80 to £150. Children welcome. Baby facilities. Dogs welcome.
Afternoon teas. Garden (*The Which? Hotel Guide*)

MOULSFORD Oxfordshire   map 2

▲ *Beetle & Wedge* ♀ ⅙✳

Ferry Lane, Moulsford OX10 9JF
TEL: (01491) 651381   FAX: (01491) 651376   COOKING 3
off A329, down Ferry Lane to river   COST £31–£54

The stunning setting beside the wide reaches of the Thames makes for relaxed
eating, though it can also be very busy, with boats of all shapes and sizes coming
and going. 'Several craft moored up and their occupants immediately jumped

ashore for a meal.' The red-brick inn dating from 1904 looks quite grand, and Richard Smith cooks in a rich, generous and hearty style, pairing calves' kidneys and black pudding with lyonnaise onions and truffle sauce, or combining pigeon breast and rabbit fillet with noodles and red peppers, both of these merely for openers. High protein and cholesterol seem to be part of the deal, if fillet steak with snails and foie gras butter is anything to go by, but there is plenty of high-quality fish, from brill to sea bass, to even things out. Fruit and alcohol appear among desserts in the form of sloe-gin pancakes with black-currants, or plum and apricot in brandy syrup. Lunch offers a choice of three items per course, dinner seven, and lunch on Sunday, unusually, is more expensive than it is during the week.

Quality is high throughout the mostly French wine list, Burgundy fans are particularly well looked after, and mark-ups – surprisingly, given such an otherwise encouraging approach – are standard. Nevertheless there is good drinking under £20, and the dipstick idea applies to most wines under £25: order a full bottle, drink as much as you like, and pay pro rata, plus a £1.25 supplement. Five house wines are £12.75. CELLARMAN'S CHOICE: Eden Crest Chardonnay 1994, Eden Valley, S. Australia, £15.50; Vino da Tavola Toscana, Col di Sasso 1994, £18.50.

The Boathouse has a separate chef and kitchen (to which the cooking rating of 3 does not apply), and its own distinctly informal style and atmosphere. It runs mostly on chargrilling of Dover sole, calves' kidneys or Barnsley chop, but also offers the likes of asparagus with hollandaise or moules marinière, with ice-cream, meringue and fruit combinations to finish.

CHEF: Richard Smith   PROPRIETORS: Kate and Richard Smith   OPEN: Tue to Sun L 12.15 to 2, Tue to Sat D 7.15 to 10   CLOSED: 25 Dec   MEALS: Set L Tue to Sat £17.50 (2 courses) to £21.50, Set L Sun £27.50, Set D £30 (2 courses) to £35. Boathouse alc (main courses £10 to £15) all week L & D   SERVICE: not inc   CARDS: Access, Amex, Delta, Diners, Switch, Visa   DETAILS: 35 seats (Boathouse 60 seats). 60 seats outside. Private parties: 60 main room, 12 and 60 private rooms. Car park. Vegetarian meals. Children's helpings. Smart dress preferred. No smoking in dining-room. Wheelchair access (also WC). No music   ACCOMMODATION: 10 rooms, all with bath/shower. TV. Phone. B&B £80 to £125. Rooms for disabled. Children welcome. Baby facilities. Garden. Fishing (*The Which? Hotel Guide*)

MOULTON North Yorkshire   map 9

Black Bull Inn

30 YEARS · 1997 · IN THE GUIDE

Moulton DL10 6QJ
TEL: (01325) 377289   FAX: (01325) 377422
1m SE of Scotch Corner, 1m from A1

NEW CHEF

COST £21–£55

One of the attractions of a pub is informality, which includes just being able to drop in when you feel like it. The fish bar of this whitewashed old inn is for exactly that, typically offering anything from light dishes of smoked salmon, shellfish salads, smoked haddock soup, or moules marinière to the full restaurant menu. You might have to wait your turn, because it is popular, but the freshness of the seafood makes it worth while. Other rooms include the Brighton Belle (a beached 1932 Pullman carriage) and a conservatory dining-room with a vine and pots of flowers, both of which are bookable.

Paul Grundy arrived in the kitchen too late for us to confirm the cooking mark, but it would take a brave man to deflect this old stalwart from its course. Seafood has long dominated proceedings, the bigger fish being sold by weight, and beef has been Aberdeen Angus. Fair prices characterise the wine list – with good choice under £20 – and France is the strong suit. House wines are £7.75.

CHEF: Paul Grundy   PROPRIETORS: G.H. and A.M.C. Pagendam   OPEN: Mon to Fri L 12 to 2, Mon to Sat D 6.45 to 10.15   CLOSED: 24 to 27 Dec   MEALS: alc (main courses £13.50 to £19.50). Set L £13.95. BYO £5. Bar L available   SERVICE: not inc   CARDS: Access, Amex, Delta, Switch, Visa   DETAILS: 100 seats. 16 seats outside. Private parties: 30 main room, 10 and 30 private rooms. Car park. No children under 7. No music

---

NAILSWORTH Gloucestershire

map 2

William's Bistro 🥄

3 Fountain Street, Nailsworth GL6 0BL
TEL: (01453) 835507   FAX: (01453) 835950

COOKING 3
COST £23–£51

William Beeston leaves nobody in doubt about his intentions, and describes his bistro as 'a place to relax in and eat well rather than a poseur's paradise'. It forms a rear extension of his rather good deli and is a simply decorated place with roller blinds at the windows, French memorabilia on the walls, plastic sheets on the tables and no music clogging the airways. Craig Schofield and the owners' daughter Katie have now taken over the kitchen and brought a new air of excitement to the proceedings.

An inspection meal in June turned up some expertly timed cooking based on superb raw materials. It began with 'a chunk of monkfish' accompanied by octopus and mussels in a fine shellfish stock. Next was a nicely judged presentation of lamb loin fillets with roasted plum tomatoes and field mushrooms and a ramekin of 'light and acid' lemon mayonnaise. More classical combinations of skate with capers, and Dover sole with watercress cream, alongside scallops with spiced red onion salsa show that fish cookery – still the bistro's principal concern – is marked by great versatility. Desserts are today's favourites, a chocolate and mascarpone cheesecake, for example, or lemon tart garnished with a cornucopia of red fruits and a juglet of cream. William's has set itself new standards. The wine list offers a bright array of flavours, the provenance overwhelmingly French in keeping with the décor. Prices are restrained, starting at £8 for house wines.

CHEFS: Craig Schofield and Katie Beeston   PROPRIETORS: William and Rae Beeston   OPEN: Tue to Sat D only 7 to 9.30   CLOSED: 2 weeks Christmas, Good Friday, Tue after bank hols MEALS: alc (main courses £8.50 to £16)   SERVICE: not inc, card slips closed   CARDS: Access, Switch, Visa   DETAILS: 40 seats. Private parties: 40 main room. Children's helpings. No music

---

The 1998 Guide *will be published before Christmas 1997. Reports on meals are most welcome at any time of the year, but are particularly valuable in the spring (no later than June). Send them to* The Good Food Guide, *FREEPOST, 2 Marylebone Road, London NW1 1YN. Or e-mail your report to guidereports@which. co. uk.*

NANTWICH Cheshire   map 5

Churche's Mansion ♐ ⁵⁄✳

150 Hospital Street, Nantwich CW5 5RY   COOKING 2*
TEL: (01270) 625933   FAX: (01270) 627831   COST £27–£44

Built for Richard and Margery Churche in 1577, this atmospheric mansion has
also done duty as a corn store and ladies' boarding-school. True to form, it claims
a ghost. Graham Tucker heads the kitchen, and monthly fixed-price menus (with
supplements for fish and cheese) bristle with interesting ideas. At lunch you
might find wild mushroom risotto on a bed of spinach and Parmesan, or
succulent braised lamb shank with butter-beans. Dinner heralds greater
elaboration in the shape of game-stuffed cabbage served on gingered pears with
a Puy lentil game *jus,* or pan-fried monkfish on a saffron potato purée with
chorizo, roasted peppers and tomato sauce. The lengthy pudding list might
include apple and blackberry strudel ('Where do they get that cream?' enquired
one reporter), while British farmhouse cheeses are kept in 'wonderful condition'. Service remains as pleasing as ever.

The carefully annotated wine list has something for everyone, happily mixing
classical and modern producers at a wide range of prices. French wines are
strongest, but look out for a few gems listed under Australia and California.
House wine is £9.95. CELLARMAN'S CHOICE: Katnook Estate botrytised
Chardonnay 1992, Coonawarra, S. Australia, £13.50 (half); St-Emilion, Ch.
Fleur de Lisse 1990, £16.90.

CHEF: Graham Tucker   PROPRIETORS: Robin Latham and Amanda Latham   OPEN: Tue to Sun L
12 to 2.30, Tue to Sat D 7 to 9.30   CLOSED: Jan   MEALS: Set L £13.95 (2 courses) to £17.25, Set
D £26.75. BYO £8 (£10 champagne)   SERVICE: not inc, card slips closed   CARDS: Access,
Delta, Diners, Switch, Visa   DETAILS: 55 seats. 20 seats outside. Private parties: 48 main room,
24 private room. Car park. Vegetarian meals. Children's helpings. No children under 10 D. Smart
dress preferred. No smoking in dining-room. Music

NAYLAND Suffolk   map 6

Martha's Vineyard ♐ ⁵⁄✳

SUFFOLK
1997
RAVE

18 High Street, Nayland CO6 4JF
TEL: (01206) 262888   COOKING 3
off A134, 5m N of Colchester   COST £28–£34

An inspector sums up as follows: 'The style of Martha's Vineyard is as integral to
its success as is the quality of the cooking. That is not to belittle the many gentle
and the more occasional spectacular surprises that Larkin Rogers pulls out of her
gastronomic repertoire.' The setting is an informal but vibrantly colourful
dining-room with green wooden panels, Matisse-like curtains and 'utilitarian'
crockery. Christopher Warren retains an amicable presence out front. The short
menu is fixed price for two or three courses, and encourages flexibility. The style
is American with Mediterranean and British interventions, and the owners have
a crusading approach to local produce: inspiring vegetables and outstanding
meat from rare breeds are just two of their assets.

One who eats here regularly cites many high points: wonderful freshly baked bread (a different type each day), the use of an obscure local spring green as a vegetable, and the perfect combination of 'old and new' in a passion-fruit syllabub, although 'it is the solid quality of the effort that stands out'. Fish stews are one of Larkin's trademarks: intensely smoky Hatteras 'fish muddle' conjured up the 'rugged country ambience of the southern US' for one reporter. Other star turns have included an appropriately named 'spring tonic soup' bursting with the clarity of fresh herbs and dramatically finished with a pesto punch, lamb osso buco, and a revelatory and inspirational dish of pan-fried turkey breast smeared with tapénade and Provolone cheese. Pasta might appear as tagliatelle with spring onions and crabmeat, or wide, lasagne-like sheets topped with a mushroom ragoût and brilliant green asparagus spears. Desserts could range from rhubarb cobbler to citrus poundcake enhanced by a potent orange and clove compote.

The wine list is not long, but it packs a punch. Forty wines span a wide range of styles and flavours; most are youthful, lively and reasonably priced. The California and Oregon section offers some serious reds. House French is £10.95. CELLARMAN'S CHOICE: Mulderbosch barrel-fermented Sauvignon Blanc 1994, Stellenbosch, South Africa, £16.50; Chinon, Varennes du Grand Clos 1993, £19.95.

CHEFS: Larkin Rogers and Melissa Deckers   PROPRIETORS: Christopher Warren and Larkin Rogers   OPEN: Sun L 12.30 to 2, Thur to Sat D 7.30 to 9.30   CLOSED: 2 weeks winter, 2 weeks summer   MEALS: Set L and D £16.50 (2 courses) to £20. BYO £5   SERVICE: not inc; 10% for parties of 6 or more   CARDS: Access, Visa   DETAILS: 41 seats. Private parties: 30 main room, 14 private room. Vegetarian meals. Children's helpings. No smoking in dining-room. Wheelchair access (no WC). No music

White Hart ⁵✳

NEW ENTRY

11 High Street, Nayland CO6 4JF
TEL: (01206) 263382   FAX: (01206) 263638

COOKING 1*
COST £21–£43

Roux protégé Mark Prescott acquired this Suffolk pub in late 1995, with a little help from his friend at the Waterside Inn (see entry, Bray). The intention is to maintain the pub atmosphere, serving simple hearty food in unpretentious surroundings at prices that won't affront. The repertoire takes in spiced tiger prawns on wafer-thin Japanese noodles, Tuscan-style white bean soup with pesto, and spinach and ricotta pancake with tomato sauce. Breast of woodpigeon was a little 'high' for one inspector though well cooked with chunks of field mushrooms and bacon in a good gamey reduction sauce. Fish may include breaded Dover sole with parsley butter. Chicken and chips are available, but only if you are under ten and only at lunch-times in summer, when the Patio Menu also operates. Jam pudding, hugely buttery apple tart, and chocolate pudding may be supplemented by specials such as impressively delicate red fruit sablé with appropriate coulis. The imaginative wine list shows New Worlders first in the modern way. Flavours are stimulating and prices mostly quite sane. House Duboeuf is £8.40 for the white and £8.90 for the red.

CHEF/PROPRIETOR: Mark Prescott OPEN: Tue to Sat 12 to 2, 6 to 9.30 MEALS: alc D (main courses £6.50 to £13.50). Set L £13.50 (2 courses) to £19 SERVICE: not inc CARDS: Access, Amex, Delta, Diners, Switch, Visa DETAILS: 70 seats. 50 seats outside. Private parties: 70 main room, 40 private room. Car park. Vegetarian meals. Children's helpings. No smoking in 1 dining-room. Music

NEAR SAWREY Cumbria map 8

▲ *Ees Wyke*

Near Sawrey LA22 0JZ
TEL/FAX: (01539) 436393 COOKING **2**
on B5286 from Hawkshead COST £25–£30

'A likeable place, run with humour and a lovely relaxed attitude' is a fair summary of the ambience, and the views above Esthwaite are enough to put anybody in a good mood. Margaret Williams is 'everywhere, greeting guests, waiting at table, taking orders, welcoming new arrivals, you name it, and makes everyone feel at home'. The dining-room is a spacious add-on behind the house, with distant hills for a backdrop. Dinner is good value for non-residents, but exceptional for those who stay – 'you would have to be mad not to'.

John Williams works hard on his soups, reckoned one couple, who particularly enjoyed both watercress and asparagus during their stay: 'full of flavour and body'. Alternative first and second courses might include asparagus with hollandaise sauce, smoked haddock rarebit, pasta, savoury tartlets or something salady. Main courses tend to be robust and filling, such as pork fillet in a Dijon mustard marinade, or paupiette of beef in a rich Burgundy sauce, while vegetables are varied and plentiful. Timing is good. What impressed one reporter is that 'John W. gets the difficult things – those that spoil in a few minutes – to the table in such good condition', citing precisely cooked oeufs en cocotte and poached salmon. Sweets – rhubarb fool or chocolate roulade, perhaps – are followed by cheese, and coffee is help-yourself in the lounge. Thirty-eight wines appear on the list at modest prices. House Vin de Pays d'Oc is £9.

CHEF: John Williams PROPRIETORS: John and Margaret Williams OPEN: all week D only 7 for 7.30 (1 sitting) MEALS: Set D £12 residents, £18.50 non-residents. BYO by arrangement SERVICE: not inc, card slips closed CARD: Amex DETAILS: 20 seats. Private parties: 30 main room. Car park. Vegetarian meals. No children under 10. Smart dress preferred. No smoking in dining-room. No music ACCOMMODATION: 8 rooms, all with bath/shower. TV. B&B £40 to £80. Children welcome. Dogs welcome. Garden (*The Which? Hotel Guide*)

NEW ALRESFORD Hampshire map 2

▲ *Hunters*

32 Broad Street, New Alresford SO24 9AQ COOKING **2**
TEL/FAX: (01962) 732468 COST £21–£40

The neat and comely village of New Alresford boasts a steam railway called the Watercress Line that runs alongside the Farnham road. Disembark and look for the red canopy that announces Hunters, a bow-windowed house in a row of others which has a trio of guest rooms as well as a restaurant. In the summer of 1995 Jake Watkins assumed responsibility in the kitchen.

The short, modern menus (three choices at each course) are supplemented by daily blackboard specials, and the cooking enthuses reporters. A salad of Cornish crab arrives as a round mound of white meat bound with mayonnaise and garnished with asparagus tips, the freshness and care in presentation elevating it well above the simple-but-honest category. Local lamb with pommes Anna and morels delivers winningly pink and tasty meat and a well-rendered wine and stock reduction. Chargrilled tuna with mussels and saffron risotto, and charred salmon with ratatouille are examples of the kitchen's ways with fish. Puddings may include rhubarb tart served cold with rice pudding. The audible squeal of the grinder announces quality coffee that comes with good truffles. Wines are from Eldridge Pope and represent a somewhat conservative but fairly priced selection. House wines are from £8.95.

CHEF: Jake Watkins   PROPRIETOR: Martin Birmingham   OPEN: Mon to Sat 12 to 2, 7 to 10 CLOSED: Christmas   MEALS: alc (main courses £6.50 to £14.50)   SERVICE: not inc   CARDS: Access, Amex, Delta, Diners, Switch, Visa   DETAILS: 30 seats. 10 seats outside. Private parties: 75 main room. Vegetarian meals. Children's helpings. No smoking before 2 L and 10 D. Wheelchair access (also WC). Music   ACCOMMODATION: 3 rooms, all with bath/shower. TV. B&B £32.50 to £47.50. Deposit: £10. Children welcome. Baby facilities. Garden

---

NEWCASTLE UPON TYNE   Tyne & Wear   map 10

Courtney's

| 5–7 Side, Newcastle upon Tyne NE1 3JE | COOKING 2 |
| TEL: (0191) 232 5537   FAX: (0191) 221 1745 | COST £22–£43 |

In the shadow of the Tyne Bridge, on the redeveloped quayside, Courtney's has its finger on the pulse of a knowledgeable metropolitan crowd. Inside may be a touch cramped, but Michael Carr's menus – fixed-price at lunch and a *carte* at dinner – offer contemporary cooking of distinctive ability: goose and apple filo with a sage sauce, perhaps, or blackened tuna with mango and basil relish. In between the more *outré* dishes, Courtney's is careful to attract another kind of customer by offering the likes of Caesar salad, chicken with a curry sauce, and caramelised banana with ice-cream and butterscotch. Any kitchen that partners potted lobster with a Gewürztraminer jelly and truffle oil demonstrates at the least an intrepid approach to flavour. 'Quietly professional' service helps to make Courtney's a winner. The up-to-date wine list is pleasingly concise, even if the Australian and Californian wines shine a little more brightly than the staider French choices. House Australian is £10.

'When we asked who the pianist was on the record of the Goldberg Variations, the waitress returned from her mission of inquiry to announce "Bach".' (On eating in East Sussex)

Several sharp operators have tried to extort money from restaurateurs on the promise of an entry in a guidebook that has never appeared. The Good Food Guide *makes no charge for inclusion.*

CHEF: Michael Carr PROPRIETORS: Michael and Kerensa Carr OPEN: Mon to Fri L 12 to 2, Mon to Sat D 7 to 10.30 CLOSED: 1 week Christmas, 2 weeks May, bank hols MEALS: alc D (main courses £12 to £15.50). Set L £13 (2 courses) to £15 SERVICE: not inc, card slips closed CARDS: Access, Amex, Delta, Switch, Visa DETAILS: 30 seats. Private parties: 26 main room. Children's helpings. Smart dress preferred. No cigars/pipes in dining-room. Music. Air-conditioned

Fisherman's Lodge ⁝✳

Jesmond Dene, Jesmond,
Newcastle upon Tyne, NE7 7BQ   COOKING 3
TEL: (0191) 281 3281   FAX: (0191) 281 6410   COST £26–£76

The Lodge enjoys one of those sublimely paradoxical urban locations: it sits, a substantial nineteenth-century residence, in the middle of a large expanse of parkland a couple of miles from the centre of Newcastle. Within, 'a gallimaufry of colours and patterns' meets the eyes, the waiters' waistcoats contributing to the dazzle.

Steven Jobson's cooking is designed to appeal to both traditionalists and modernists. The former should peruse the 'Chef's Classics', offering avocado with prawns, smoked salmon, and Surf n' Turf. Even the more adventurous dishes, however, have a homely feel about them, reflecting the acknowledged inspiration of Gary Rhodes's style of cooking. Among the showpiece seafood specialities are grilled scallops with crisped aubergine, black olives and tomato relish, and lemon sole with lobster in a cheese and mushroom sauce. Sauces and dressings are subtle and presentation stylish. So much is fish the orientation that main-course meats may be limited to just a couple: lamb shank with leek pudding, perhaps, or breast of duck with confit of duck leg and orange sauce. Most desserts seem to arrive in the company of an ice-cream of one sort or another, say raspberry yoghurt ice with strawberry cheesecake. The cheese selection is always generous and good, coffee and petits fours likewise, and it is all borne along by 'fleet-of-foot' staff. Wines are mainly French, with shorter outings to Italy, Spain and Australia, but the choices are somewhat on the staid side for the cooking. House wines are £11.

CHEF: Steven Jobson PROPRIETORS: Franco and Pamela Cetoloni OPEN: Mon to Fri L 12 to 2, Mon to Sat D 7 to 11 CLOSED: bank hols MEALS: alc (main courses £16 to £27). Set L £17.80, Set D Mon to Fri £26.50 SERVICE: not inc CARDS: Access, Amex, Delta, Diners, Switch, Visa DETAILS: 65 seats. 40 seats outside. Private parties: 16 main room, 14 and 43 private rooms. Car park. Children's helpings. No children under 9 D. Smart dress preferred. No smoking in dining-room. Wheelchair access (also WC). Music

Leela's

20 Dean Street, Newcastle upon Tyne NE1 1PG   COOKING 2
TEL: (0191) 230 1261   FAX: (01661) 823916   COST £17–£48

The spirit of South Indian home cooking is alive and well in Leela Paul's tasteful restaurant on one of Newcastle's main thoroughfares. Inside, the mood is a refreshing change from the 'twilight' of many provincial curry-houses, and Leela's personal presence dominates proceedings. According to one reporter, the food is 'rather special – subtle yet strong, and eminently well balanced'. All tastes and persuasions are catered for, and the menus are a mixture of the familiar and the tantalisingly esoteric. Packavadas (better known as pakoras) continue to please, and you will also find paper dosas (thin rice and lentil pancakes), dhai vada and uthappam among the appetisers. Even more interesting are chicken pappas (marinated and cooked with cream and mild spices), fillet of lamb in a sauce of almonds and coconut milk, and pork chuttathu baked in foil and served with spiced apple salad. Accompaniments are generally excellent. To finish, East meets West in the shape of death by chocolate, and payasamu (roasted vermicelli with coconut milk, cashew-nuts and sultanas). Leela pays more than lip service to the idea of wine with Indian food, and her short list includes some promising offerings. House wine is £8.95.

CHEF: Kuriakose Paul PROPRIETORS: Kuriakose and Leela Paul OPEN: Mon to Sat 12 to 2.30, 5.30 to 11.30 CLOSED: 2 weeks Jan MEALS: alc (main courses £8 to £13). Set L £9.95, Set D £13.95 to £16.95 (2 courses) SERVICE: not inc CARDS: Access, Amex, Delta, Diners, Visa DETAILS: 45 seats. Private parties: 35 main room. Vegetarian meals. Children's helpings. Smart dress preferred. No smoking D. Music

21 Queen Street 🍷

19–21 Queen Street, Princes Wharf, Quayside,
Newcastle upon Tyne NE1 3UG   COOKING 3*
TEL: (0191) 222 0755 FAX: (0191) 221 0761   COST £26–£63

Terence Laybourne continues to move and shake, having overseen the opening of a third outlet during the past year (see Bistro 21, Durham, and Café 21, Ponteland). His achievement is to make good food available to all, or to as many as can afford the quite reasonable prices, in cheerful surroundings. The light, bright, Scandinavian-style décor of the flagship original may strike a minimalist chord, but it is 'sympathetic and gives a warm feel'. 'Since switching from a formal place to a more bistro-like atmosphere, the place buzzes,' reckoned one regular visitor who, after some 40 meals here, found very little to quibble about.

Both the style and the cooking carry conviction. Modern European fare of tomato tart with pistou, or salmon and asparagus with chervil butter sauce may be the foundation, but the kitchen is also perfectly at home with a dash of Eastern flavouring in a Shanghai shellfish risotto with crispy ginger, the cultural clash causing barely a stir. Luxuries such as foie gras are used intelligently, to add extra richness in a classic partnership with roast squab pigeon, or to intrigue when served in a prince and pauper terrine with ham knuckle and pease pudding.

Soufflés both sweet and savoury have come in for praise, including spinach and cheese to begin, and 'light and airy' rhubarb to finish, while the range of high-calorie desserts might include sticky toffee pudding, or a warm chocolate and banana bread pudding with Horlicks ice-cream and crème fraîche. Some dishes on the *carte* carry a supplement ('which is not a trend to encourage' in one reporter's view), but the value is still considered fair overall. Service is 'Geordie friendliness tempered by professionalism'. Much thought has gone into constructing a fairly priced, compact wine list that spans a wide range of styles. Fine names abound, but Trimbach and Hugel from Alsace, Jaboulet and Guigal from the Rhône, Frog's Leap, Hunter's and Coldstream Hills from the New World stand out. House wines start at £11.80. CELLARMAN'S CHOICE: Auxey-Duresses 1992, Jean Pascal et fils, £27; Pomerol, Ch. Beauregard 1989, £42.50.

CHEF/PROPRIETOR: Terence Laybourne   OPEN: Mon to Fri L 12 to 2, Mon to Sat D 7 to 10.45
MEALS: alc (main courses £15.50 to £20.50). Set L £14 (2 courses) to £16   SERVICE: not inc
CARDS: Access, Amex, Diners, Visa   DETAILS: 70 seats. Private parties: 65 main room.
Vegetarian meals. Children's helpings. Smart dress preferred. No pipes in dining-room.
Wheelchair access (no WC). Music

NEW MILTON Hampshire   map 2

▲ *Chewton Glen, Marryat Restaurant*

Christchurch Road, New Milton BH25 6QS
TEL: (01425) 275341   FAX: (01425) 272310
from A35 follow signs to Walkford and Highcliffe,
take second turning on left after Walkford down   COOKING 3
Chewton Farm road   COST £33–£78

Although the literary connection may be modest – until Emma Thompson turns *Children of the New Forest* into a film, Captain Marryat is destined to remain a minor celeb – the old red-brick house retains something of the calm it must have had in his day. It is helped by 70 acres of garden and parkland on the edge of the New Forest, and has survived additions and extensions with some grace. Leisure facilities are big, and the hotel is one of the few top ones in private hands: Martin and Brigitte Skan have been here for 30 years. The restaurant, like everything else, benefits from their combination of close personal involvement and ability to delegate to well-trained staff who 'remember guests' names and say "good morning"'.

The cheaper lunch offers two simple courses – smoked haddock with poached egg, perhaps, followed by dessert from the main lunch menu – while the price of dinner reflects the wide choice available. The scale (a dozen starters, for instance) begins to make the place feel like a brasserie, but the style is varied and the dishes attractive. Light meals might take in grilled vegetable salad, or braised fillet of sea bass with shiitake mushrooms and bean sprouts, but that still leaves room for more indulgent options such as onion and cream-cheese tart, or fillet of beef with bone-marrow. Braised Hampshire hog with truffle potatoes keeps the local flag flying, while desserts have included hot pistachio soufflé with chocolate ice-cream, and a baby pineapple filled with exotic sorbets and baked in meringue.

Venerable bottles from Bordeaux and Burgundy form the backbone of an impressive wine list, but the lesser regions of France, including Jura, Cahors and Madiran, make an appearance too, while Languedoc-Roussillon offers good-value drinking. Italy, New Zealand and Australia are strongly represented. This is not a pompous list, for all its myriad clarets, champagnes and Alsace grands crus, and there are plenty of wines under £20. House wines from New Zealand and France start at £13. CELLARMAN'S CHOICE: Alsace Riesling 1992, Marcel Deiss, £28.15; St-Julien, Ch. St-Pierre 1989, £33.

CHEF: Pierre Chevillard PROPRIETORS: Martin and Brigitte Skan OPEN: all week 12.30 to 1.45, 7.30 to 9.30 MEALS: Set L Mon to Fri £12.50 (2 courses), Set L Mon to Sat £23.50, Set L Sun £27, Set D £42.50. BYO £10 SERVICE: not inc, card slips closed CARDS: Access, Amex, Delta, Diners, Switch, Visa DETAILS: 120 seats. 30 seats outside. Private parties: 120 main room, 6 to 120 private rooms. Car park. Vegetarian meals. No children under 7. Jacket and tie. No smoking in dining-room. Wheelchair access (also WC). Music ACCOMMODATION: 53 rooms, all with bath/shower. TV. Phone. D,B&B £248.50 to £510. Rooms for disabled. No children under 7. Afternoon teas. Garden. Swimming-pool (*The Which? Hotel Guide*)

NEW POLZEATH Cornwall   map 1

▲ *Cornish Cottage Hotel* ✸✱ | NEW ENTRY |

New Polzeath PL27 6US
TEL: (01208) 862213 FAX: (01208) 862259
signposted off B3314 between Wadebridge   COOKING 3
and Port Isaac   COST £22–£46

The owners renamed this hotel (formerly called Pentire Rocks) on the north Cornish coast to give it a homelier feel, but the ruggedness of the surrounding landscape is still an attraction in itself. It stands just off the coastal footpath, handy for committed walkers as well as the surfers on Polzeath beach. A huge conservatory extension has been added, but the dining-room is within the original house.

Tim Rogers came to cook in late 1995 after stints with Marco Pierre White and Raymond Blanc, indicating something of the owners' ambitions for this place. Dishes look very busy in the Marco vein, with much complicated (but never inapposite) garnishing, and without sacrificing impact on the palate. Bodmin boar and goose terrine with apple and tomato chutney was 'almost unbelievably good' at inspection, studded with pistachios and full of pungency and fragrance. Robust fish treatments are a trade mark of Marco-trained chefs, and here a dish of roasted hake fillets is presented on roasted aubergine and peppers, topped with caviare in two colours and given a 'divinely silky' sauce chock-full of salmon roe. Meat typically receives simpler treatment, as in roast lamb with redcurrant and mint *jus*, or beef fillet in rich red wine gravy. Vegetarian dishes are as carefully constructed as everything else, and might include lasagne of wild mushrooms in truffle cream sauce topped with apple crisps and served with saffron potatoes.

No let-up in kitchen labours is permitted at dessert stage, whether it be for honey-roasted strawberries with white wine sabayon and amaretto ice-cream, or majestically risen and airily light raspberry soufflé with liqueur-soaked raspberries at the bottom 'like buried treasure'. Wines are a sound enough international bunch, but the cooking undoubtedly deserves more exciting choices. House wines start at £9.50 and include a pair from Chile's Concha y Toro at £10 that are worth trying.

✸✱ *indicates that smoking is either banned altogether or that a dining-room is maintained for non-smokers. The symbol does not apply to restaurants that simply have no-smoking areas.*

CHEF: Tim Rogers   PROPRIETORS: Clive and Christine Mason   OPEN: Sun L 12 to 1.30, all week
D 7 to 9   CLOSED: last 2 weeks Nov, last 2 weeks Jan   MEALS: alc D (main courses £8.50 to
£16.50). Set L Sun £14.95, Set D £25   SERVICE: not inc, card slips closed   CARDS: Access,
Amex, Delta, Diners, Switch, Visa   DETAILS: 32 seats. 16 seats outside. Private parties: 50 main
room. Car park. Vegetarian meals. No children under 12. Smart dress preferred. No smoking in
dining-room. Wheelchair access (no WC). Music   ACCOMMODATION: 12 rooms, all with
bath/shower. TV. Phone. B&B £47 to £94. Deposit: £30. No children under 12. Small dogs
welcome (ground floor only). Afternoon teas. Garden. Swimming-pool

---

NORTHAMPTON Northamptonshire   map 5

Le Sous-Sol ⚡✕ | NEW ENTRY |

32B Gold Street, Northampton NN1 1RS   COOKING 2*
TEL: (01604) 20829   COST £17–£38

It is a while since Northampton had a main entry in the *Guide*, but Darren Kerley
is a local lad who has passed through Raymond Blanc's kitchens and emerged
with enough skill and ambition to make a mark. He operates from a bright
yellow basement in the town centre, tailoring output to suit casual lunchers and
serious diners alike. In both cases a smart appetiser arrives, followed by a basket
of good bread. Materials are very fine, including a rabbit 'probably shot this
morning' that impressed for its 'wonderful flavour'; the saddle was cooked pink,
and expertly paired with strong tarragon and delicate mustard.

The style is as modern as white-bean soup with truffle oil, and Kerley is keen
on haystacks of deep-fried angel-hair vegetables. A first-rate tranche of salmon
arrives with its tasty skin separate, 'crisply cooked and stiff as a board'. Lunch,
meanwhile, has produced a thick slice of boned, rolled and braised shoulder of
lamb with 'really lamby' flavour. Tarte Tatin, often a much-abused cliché, is
executed here with 'wonderful' classic simplicity. A basic 30-bottle wine list is
carefully put together and fairly priced. House wine is £8.

CHEF/PROPRIETOR: Darren Kerley   OPEN: Tue to Sat L 12 to 2.30, Mon to Sat D 7 to 10.30
CLOSED: 2 weeks Jan to Feb   MEALS: alc (main courses £5.50 to £15)   SERVICE: not inc, card
slips closed   CARDS: Access, Delta, Switch, Visa   DETAILS: 30 seats. Private parties: 20 main
room. Vegetarian meals. Children's helpings. No children under 10. No smoking in dining-room.
Music

NORTH CHEAM Surrey   map 3

Partners Brasserie £

23 Stonecot Hill, North Cheam SM3 9HB
TEL: (0181) 644 7743   COOKING 2
on A24, 1m S of Morden, nr Woodstock pub   COST £19–£35

Tim McEntire is back cooking full-time, and standards have markedly improved. He is co-owner of Partners West Street (see entry, Dorking), but will
remain at the stoves here 'for the foreseeable future'. Decorated in primary
colours with dozens of 'arty' prints, the brasserie offers a wide-ranging menu
with a good balance of meat and fish. Chargrilling is applied to rump steak, liver

and bacon, and tiger prawns, but there are also casseroles, poached salmon, and perhaps roasted Cornish skate wing.

'One of the best had for a long time' was one reporter's judgement of a warm salad of pink and tender chicken livers with a first-rate vinaigrette, followed by two fillets of correctly cooked red mullet on a bed of cold 'niçoise' containing beans, anchovies, potatoes and tomato. There are Haagen Dazs ice-creams, but also treacle tart, a rich chocolate pot, and 'superb' plum crumble with lemon crème fraîche. 'Service continues to be friendly, attentive and informed,' and a 20-bottle wine list stays mostly under £15. House Vin de Pays d'Oc is £7.95.

CHEF: Tim McEntire   PROPRIETOR: Partners Restaurants plc   OPEN: Tue to Fri L 12 to 2, Tue to Sat D 7 to 9.30   MEALS: alc (main courses £7 to £11). Set L and D Tue to Fri £8.95 (2 courses) to £11.95   SERVICE: 10%, card slips closed   CARDS: Access, Amex, Delta, Diners, Switch, Visa DETAILS: 30 seats. Private parties: 34 main room. Children's helpings. No pipes in dining-room. Wheelchair access (no WC). Music. Air-conditioned

---

NORTHLEACH Gloucestershire   map 2

Old Woolhouse

Market Place, Northleach GL54 3EE   COOKING 3
TEL: (01451) 860366   COST £52–£63

'Having read previous *Good Food Guide* reviews of this restaurant,' began one report, 'I was prepared for a different dining experience, and different it certainly is.' Northleach is one of the most attractive Cotswold villages, and the Old Woolhouse, which shows no visible signs of being a restaurant, fits in unobtrusively. The red carpet, standard lamps and 'pre-Habitat armchairs' can be disconcerting, as can the 'uncompromising rigidity' of having no written menu. No prices are posted, but the set meal costs £37.50 and includes coffee. Typically, the choice might be between two first and four main courses. If there is fish, it will generally start the meal, and has included sea bass in an intensely flavoured and creamy crab sauce, and crab and scallops in a spicy sauce.

Main courses revolve around 'memorable' noisettes of lamb, pheasant (for two), chicken, or veal kidneys, accompanied by dauphinois potatoes. Dishes are well executed, but reporters are divided over the sauces: 'too much salt, too much vinegar, too much sugar' for one, and simply 'outstanding' for a couple who began with scallops and wild mushrooms in a white wine sauce, and then went on to fillet of sea bass in a red wine sauce. In French fashion, a salad follows the main course, then an 'excellent' cheese such as St-Marcellin, and 'first-class' desserts that have included raspberry torte, and peach shortcake. The handwritten wine list consists of nothing other than champagne, Burgundy and claret, and prices are steep: the cheapest bottle is £20.

CHEF: Jacques Astic   PROPRIETORS: Mr and Mrs Jacques Astic   OPEN: Tue to Sat D only from 8; other times by arrangement   CLOSED: 1 week Christmas   MEALS: Set D £37.50   SERVICE: not inc   CARDS: none   DETAILS: 18 seats. Private parties: 18 main room. Children welcome. Smart dress preferred. No music

---

'We have fought off all inducements to install a tank of tropical fish for diners to look at, as we prefer them to look at what is on their plates.' (Co Durham restaurateur)

Wickens 🍴✦

Market Place, Northleach GL54 3EJ	COOKING 3
TEL: (01451) 860421	COST £19–£37

'To hear this quiet restaurant filled with orgasmic cries of "delicious" from every table tells its own story,' commented one happy soul. Christopher and Joanna Wickens' stone-walled dining-room remains 'mercifully unchanged' and they continue to enthral visitors with their dedication to English cooking. No short cuts are taken: a salad of mixed leaves is moistened with green herb vinaigrette and topped with shavings of Old Worcester White cheese, rather than the ubiquitous Parmesan, and cassoulet is prepared using wild boar and Gloucester Old Spot pork ('an excellently done dish with the usual generous array of vegetables,' noted a regular). Elsewhere, local lamb is braised with apricots, winter vegetables and Three Choirs wine, while hare from nearby Hampnett is casseroled with stout and button onions. The kitchen strays further afield for chargrilled salmon with soy and ginger, and isn't afraid to borrow from other cooks' books (Nigel Slater's onion tart served with crabapple relish, or Madhur Jaffrey's 'pungent' okra with rice and ginger, for example). Fixed-price three-course dinners kick off with an abundance of nibbles and finish with fascinating farmhouse cheeses – Stinking Bishop and Waterloo, to name but two – or a dessert such as Trinity College crème brûlée, Williams pear with Kirsch sorbet, or date and toffee pudding. Vegetarians are well cared for and the menu highlights dishes that are low in fat.

Those who have called in for lunch have been equally taken by the sheer quality of the cooking, singling out a soup of green pea with white bean and apple, a 'superb' salad of black pudding and red onion with a zesty orange dressing, an earthy stew of lamb with lentil and apricot, and a bittersweet chocolate marquise. Service is generally low-key and well informed, although it can seem a touch 'frosty' at times. Wines have previously been a strong point, but, as the *Guide* went to press, the list was due to be overhauled after the Wickens's supplier went into liquidation. Expect a lively New World selection on the new list, as this is where their interest largely lies.

CHEFS/PROPRIETORS: Christopher and Joanna Wickens   OPEN: Tue to Sat 12.30 to 1.30, 7.20 to 9   CLOSED: Nov to April   MEALS: Set L £9.95, Set D £21. BYO £5   SERVICE: not inc, card slips closed   CARDS: Access, Amex, Delta, Switch, Visa   DETAILS: 36 seats. Private parties: 22 main room. Vegetarian meals. Children's helpings. No smoking in dining-room. No music

---

NORWICH Norfolk	map 6

Adlard's 🍷

79 Upper St Giles, Norwich NR2 1AB	COOKING 4
TEL: (01603) 633522	COST £26–£56

The small, unassuming, green restaurant is covered in so many paintings it could double as an artist's studio, and is barely more formal. 'Sit anywhere,' suggests the waitress, in a refreshing change from the norm. Life has changed for David Adlard over the course of the past year, and includes a new pair of hands in the kitchen and new faces out front. The fixed price remains, and the menu's versatility makes it 'the sort you want to eat through from top to tail'. Among the offerings might be an accomplished asparagus risotto with red pepper dressing, pigeon sausage with lentils and 'a tinglingly intense sauce', and a wonderfully English pudding of elderflower fritters in a thick batter with gooseberry coulis.

'We were stunned by the herbs,' recorded an inspector of a heady, oil-laden sauce that surrounded small nuggets of monkfish wrapped in basil and home-made pancetta; young capers, shallot, parsley, coriander and halved black olives brought the liquid vividly to life. A sense of vitality pervades even apparently simple dishes, such as a vegetable main course whose components included a thin pastry tart of long-sweated dark brown onions, a chunk of roasted aubergine, and a thin slice of polenta with chargrilled red and yellow peppers. It came with 'an unctuous, rich, thick, yellow river of pesto sauce with a brilliantly herby taste, and we asked how it was made'. David Adlard was summoned, but confessed, 'I don't know, I've never made that sauce, I'll go and ask my chef.' This struck the reporters as odd, considering he lists himself as a chef, but no matter. Sam Clifford is doing a wonderful job.

David Adlard, meanwhile, spends time running in and out of the dining-room, waiting at table, doing odd jobs. 'I am sure we lost some of our customers in the past because they went to sleep waiting for the main course,' he admits in one of his newsletters, resolving to do better in future. Perhaps that is why he wants to keep an eye on things. This is a unique and engagingly personal restaurant that owes its style and character to the man who runs it. For that reason alone it is to be cherished. Add food of this quality and it is to be celebrated.

The wine list is serious in content and lacking in pretension. Classical France is strong (with Rhône getting a good look in), and there are rich pickings to be had from the New World, especially New Zealand and Australia. Brief tasting notes are useful, and there are half-bottles galore. French house wines are £9.50. CELLARMAN'S CHOICE: Viña Casablanca Sauvignon Blanc 1994, Lontué Valley, Chile, £15; Rothbury Estate Shiraz 1993, Hunter Valley, Australia, £18.

CHEFS: David Adlard and Sam Clifford   PROPRIETORS: David and Mary Adlard   OPEN: Tue to Sat L 12.30 to 1.45, Mon to Sat D 7.30 to 10.30   CLOSED: 25 and 26 Dec   MEALS: Set L £11 (1 course) to £16.50, Set D £32 to £35   SERVICE: not inc, card slips closed   CARDS: Access, Amex, Delta, Diners, Switch, Visa   DETAILS: 40 seats. Private parties: 40 main room. Vegetarian meals. Children welcome. No smoking until after main course. No music

Brasted's

| 8–10 St Andrews Hill, Norwich NR2 1AD | COQKING 1 |
| TEL: (01603) 625949   FAX: (01603) 766445 | COST £21–£47 |

On the corner of a cobbled lane in the heart of Norwich, the building dates from the sixteenth century and has a 'reassuringly comfortable' air. John Brasted oversees a handsome if slightly eccentric dining-room with great swaths of boldly striped fabric on the walls, a few mirrors, ancient pine Welsh dressers, and empty Methuselahs of champagne. 'The menu obviously isn't trying to take Norfolk by storm,' reckoned one visitor, eyeing the beef Stroganov and fillet of pork en croûte, but it explores other corners of the repertoire with a first course of tomato tart with pesto and cheese, a plate of home-made noodles with pancetta, peas and cream, and a coarse Breton terrine of pork, liver and bacon. Local resources include samphire, sole, crab and lobster, while rabbit casserole with carrots, celery and artichokes adds variety. The extensive wine list indulges both traditional and contemporary tastes. Prices start at £9.75.

CHEF: Adrian Clarke   PROPRIETOR: John Brasted   OPEN: Mon to Fri L 12 to 2, Mon to Sat D 7 to 10   MEALS: alc (main courses £10 to £17.50). Set L £9.50 (2 courses) to £15   SERVICE: not inc CARDS: Access, Amex, Delta, Diners, Switch, Visa   DETAILS: 24 seats. Private parties: 24 main room. Vegetarian meals. Children's helpings. Smart dress preferred. Music

▲ By Appointment 🐸✖

27–29 St Georges Street, Norwich NR3 1AB	COOKING 1
TEL: (01603) 630730	COST £28–£43

Go through the kitchen to reach the dining-room in this cluster of fifteenth-century merchants' houses. Robert Culyer tours the tables incanting the blackboard menu in profuse detail, while Timothy Brown and Toby Skipper hold sway at the stoves. This is an industrious set-up that bakes breads, churns ice-creams and smokes meat, poultry and fish. Most dishes continue to rely heavily on elaborate composition, as in red sea bream, scallops and Medi-terranean prawns wrapped in puff pastry with spinach, and served with a lobster sauce. Marinated salmon comes with pickled samphire and dill vinaigrette, loin of lamb is stuffed with apricots and pistachio nuts, while roast Aylesbury duckling receives a sweet-and-sour sauce of spring onion, lime and ginger. Desserts range from a compote of fresh fruits to Jamaican banana and pecan nut crumble. The wine list is well spread and varied in price, with house wine £9.95.

CHEFS: Timothy Brown and Toby Skipper   PROPRIETORS: Timothy Brown and Robert Culyer OPEN: Tue to Sat D only 7.30 to 9.30   MEALS: alc (main courses £12 to £15)   SERVICE: not inc, card slips closed   CARDS: Access, Delta, Switch, Visa   DETAILS: 40 seats. Private parties: 36 main room, 5 to 36 private rooms. Car park. Vegetarian meals. No children under 12. Smart dress preferred. No smoking in dining-room. Wheelchair access (also WC). Music ACCOMMODATION: 3 rooms, all with bath/shower. TV. B&B £65 to £85. Deposit: 10%. No children under 12 (The Which? Hotel Guide)

Marco's 🐸✖

17 Pottergate, Norwich NR2 1DS	COOKING 1*
TEL: (01603) 624044	COST £23–£46

And still the years clock up. Marco Vessalio sailed serenely through his quarter-century in 1995 at his small Italian restaurant near the centre of Norwich. Traditional fare such as seafood linguine and sauté king prawns with garlic butter make the most of Norfolk's catch, and are supplemented by racier items such as wild boar bresaola with buffalo mozzarella with extra-virgin dressing. Salmon is partnered with capers, apple and green pepper in a light sauce of white wine and cream, while local lamb is given the fruity treatment with orange and redcurrants. Ice-creams are made in-house, and there is of course zabaglione. The speciality dessert is an assemblage of prune ice-cream, pear poached in red wine, with chocolate sauce and almonds. Wines are an Italian treasure-chest, plundering the country from the Veneto to Calabria, with a few champagnes thrown in to show there are no hard feelings. House Sicilian is £9.50.

CHEF/PROPRIETOR: Marco Vessalio   OPEN: Tue to Sat 12 to 2, 7 to 10   CLOSED: bank hols
MEALS: alc (main courses £9.50 to £17). Set L £14   SERVICE: not inc, card slips closed   CARDS:
Access, Amex, Diners, Visa   DETAILS: 22 seats. Private parties: 12 main room. Vegetarian
meals. Children's helpings. Smart dress preferred. No smoking in dining-room. Wheelchair
access (no WC). Music

St Benedicts

9 St Benedicts Street, Norwich NR2 4PE   COOKING 1
TEL/FAX: (01603) 765377   COST £19–£32

Call it a grill, bistro, brasserie or even a restaurant (and it does get called all
those): the style is simple food in the functional surroundings of pitch-pine
panelling, bare tables and Victorian pews. The utilitarian menu, helped along by
blackboard specials, revolves around a few tasty ideas such as home-made
lamb-burger, or smoked chicken and sweet potato pancakes, while proximity to
the coast produces lobster, crabs and samphire. A Mediterranean twist might be
applied to seared prawns, or a fish stew with rouille, although grilled sea bass
has been served enterprisingly with oriental prawn and ginger dumplings.
Finish with brown bread and marmalade ice-cream, or apple and cinnamon
beignets, and drink a modestly priced bottle of wine from the short but sharply
chosen list. House wine starts at £7.25.

CHEFS: Nigel Raffles and Edward Hipkiss   PROPRIETORS: Jayne and Nigel Raffles   OPEN: Tue
to Sat 12 to 2, 7 to 10 (10.30 Fri and Sat)   CLOSED: 25 Dec to L 31 Jan   MEALS: alc (main courses
£7 to £12)   SERVICE: not inc   CARDS: Access, Amex, Delta, Diners, Switch, Visa   DETAILS: 42
seats. Private parties: 42 main room, 25 private room. Vegetarian meals. Children welcome.
Smart dress preferred. No cigars/pipes in dining-room. Wheelchair access (no WC). No music

---

NOTTINGHAM Nottinghamshire   map 5

Café de Paris ⁵✕ £   NEW ENTRY

2 Kings Walk, Nottingham NG1 2AE   COOKING 2
TEL: (0115) 947 3767   FAX: (0115) 947 3800   COST £17–£32

Jean-Louis David cooked in Nottingham several years ago and returns to the city
after a stint in Leicestershire. As the name suggests, this is a dead straight French
bistro-style operation, which is what he does best. Blackboard menu listings
and an 'arts-and-crafts' feel to the dining-room are the mood, and the menu
matches it with pâté du chef (garlicky pork liver with peppercorns), baked
avocado with Stilton, substantially filled baguettes and granary bread
sandwiches, and a selection of pasta dishes, including a generous plateful of
spaghetti with leeks and mussels in cream. Twice-baked Roquefort soufflé (with
walnut-dressed celeriac salad) is a triumph of 'great flavour with a lovely creamy
middle'. Daily specials have included asparagus with oyster mushrooms and
balsamic, and sea bream with an acidulated tomato and basil sauce. Trad
desserts take in îles flottantes, crème caramel with orange zest, and cheesecake of
the day. Service is 'friendly and eager to please'. An unpretentious, but by no

means exclusively French, wine list keeps prices within a respectable compass. House French is £6.50.

CHEF: Jean-Louis David   PROPRIETORS: Jean-Louis David and Sergio Capobasso   OPEN: Mon to Sat 10.30 to 3, 5 to 10.30   MEALS: alc (main courses £8 to £12)   SERVICE: not inc, card slips closed   CARDS: Access, Amex, Delta, Diners, Switch, Visa   DETAILS: 100 seats. Private parties: 22 main room. Vegetarian meals. Children welcome. No smoking in 1 dining-room. Music

Sonny's

3 Carlton Street, Hockley, Nottingham NG1 1NL
TEL: (0115) 947 3041   FAX: (0115) 950 7776

COOKING 1
COST £18–£40

The fashionably regenerated lace-market area aspires to be Nottingham's Covent Garden, and Sonny's fits in perfectly. Action takes place in an airy white room that hums with atmosphere at peak times, and Graeme Watson's cooking is in tune. Like the parent branch in London (see entry) it relies on heavy doses of pasta, polenta and olives, spiked with influences from the New World and the Orient. Peppered duck breast comes with mango, sesame and lemon grass dressing, chargrilled chicken is accompanied by black-bean salsa. Timing is generally spot on: witness rib of beef 'served very rare', baked salmon in a hazelnut crust with lime chutney, and pink rack of lamb with rosemary and Parmesan polenta. To conclude, there might be crème brûlée or sticky toffee pudding. The wine list is knowledgeably described and affordable; house wines are £8.95.

CHEF: Graeme Watson   PROPRIETOR: Rebecca Mascarenhas   OPEN: all week 12 to 3 (2 Sun), 7 to 10.30 (11 Fri and Sat)   CLOSED: bank hols exc Good Fri   MEALS: alc (main courses £8 to £12). Set L Mon to Fri £7.50 (2 courses) to £10, Set L Sun £10.50   SERVICE: not inc, 10% for parties of 6 or more   CARDS: Access, Amex, Switch, Visa   DETAILS: 75 seats. 20 seats outside. Private parties: 75 main room. Vegetarian meals. Children welcome. No cigars/pipes in dining-room. Wheelchair access (no WC). Music. Air-conditioned

OLD BURGHCLERE Hampshire   map 2

Dew Pond 🍴✳

Old Burghclere RG20 9LH
TEL: (01635) 278408
off old A34, 3m W of Kingsclere

COOKING 3
COST £36–£49

Once upon a time a pair of drovers' cottages, and more than 400 years old, Dew Pond doesn't seem anything like its age. Over the past seven years the Marshalls have built the place up as an evening venue with a fondly loyal following. Reporters are impressed by the unflustered efficiency with which it is run, and the measurable sense of refinement that has taken place in the cooking. Here is the virtuous circle that restaurateurs dream of: a bedrock of support that allows a kitchen to hone its skills and carry on improving as time passes.

The fixed-price menus may not be cutting-edge, but that can come as a relief in today's climate of endless experimentation. That said, a chunky guinea-fowl sausage makes an enterprising first course, sliced and fanned on a calvados sauce with a judicious dash of cream and a pile of caramelised apple balls. Spring rolls filled with duckmeat on a sweet-and-sour sauce, or generous seafood salad with balsamic dressing are other ways of starting. A couple of reports mention saddle of roe-deer cooked pink and served on a peppercorned red wine reduction, the strength and intensity of the sauce complementing the tender meat to a T. Sea bass is given a familiar oriental treatment with spring onion, ginger and Thai-spiced juices, while vegetarians might be offered a wild mushroom mille-feuille layered with purée vegetables on a Stilton and chive cream sauce. Fruit flavours turn up in desserts – lemon tart with a well-made strawberry coulis and blackcurrant sorbet, for example – while the miniature assortment brings chocolate mousse, sorbets and crème brûlée in Lilliputian form.

Wines offer a dependable rather than thrilling selection from France and the New World, with the rest of Europe, barring the odd German, being discreetly passed over. Prices are fairly brisk, but there is enough under £20 to furnish adequate choice. House selections start at £11.

CHEFS/PROPRIETORS: Keith and Julie Marshall   OPEN: Tue to Sat D only 7 to 10   CLOSED: Jan and 2 weeks Aug   MEALS: Set D £25   SERVICE: not inc   CARDS: Access, Switch, Visa DETAILS: 44 seats. 12 seats outside. Private parties: 40 main room, 20 private room. Car park. Vegetarian meals. No children under 10. Smart dress preferred. No smoking in dining-room. Wheelchair access (also WC). No music

---

OSWESTRY Shropshire   map 7

▲ *Sebastian*

45 Willow Street, Oswestry SY11 1AQ	COOKING 2
TEL: (01691) 655444 FAX: (01691) 653452	COST £23–£48

So many French restaurants have modernised and remade themselves in recent years that the comfy old bistro has all but disappeared from our high streets. It is a genre of restaurant regarded with considerable affection by many, and happily here is a delightful example, set in a sixteenth-century town house bedecked with flowers. Three bedrooms have been added since last year, but otherwise the deal is pretty much as it was: bare tables, promotional champagne posters, French Muzak and a good variety of menu options to choose from.

A short monthly-changing set menu supplements the *carte*, and lunches are light snacks unless agreed otherwise when booking. The range is wide, and typically takes in seafood soup, sirloin steak, whole Dover sole, and breast of duck, with cheese soufflé or a filled pancake for vegetarians. Prime-quality materials are treated with skill and respect. In good old-fashioned style there is a fair bit of cream in sauces, and desserts have included a French version of bread-and-butter pudding served with an apricot brandy custard. Some less-well-known producers feature on the largely French wine list, and prices are eminently fair, starting at £8.95.

CHEF: Mark Sebastian Fisher   PROPRIETORS: Mark Sebastian and Michelle Fisher   OPEN: Wed to Fri L 12 to 2, Tue to Sat D 6.30 to 10   MEALS: alc (main courses £3.50 to £19). Set L and D £15.95. Light lunches also available   SERVICE: not inc, card slips closed   CARDS: Access, Amex, Delta, Switch, Visa   DETAILS: 45 seats. Private parties: 20 main room. Vegetarian meals. Children welcome. Smart dress preferred. Wheelchair access (no WC). Music ACCOMMODATION: 3 rooms, all with bath/shower. TV. B&B £32 to £40. Children welcome. Baby facilities. Afternoon teas. Garden

Walls

NEW ENTRY

Welsh Walls, Oswestry SY11 1AW
TEL: (01691) 670970   FAX: (01691) 653820

COOKING 1
COST £20–£54

There are English Walls as well as Welsh Walls in Oswestry, reflecting its border-town status. Walls is to be found in the latter – a quiet lane just outside the town centre – in a vast, unlovely early-Victorian school building facing a large public park. Three years ago, Geoffrey Hughes turned it into a 200-seater modern brasserie, and the transformation has been successful. The cooking sticks to tried and tested ideas rather than trying to set the world on fire, though there is still room for a robust partnering of fillet steak and ostrich with a wild mushroom and Madeira sauce, and for wild boar steak in scrumpy cider sauce. A dish of huge, tasty mussels in garlic and herb butter might start the ball rolling, while chocolate terrine, and an inventive strudel of rhubarb and apricot are the kinds of puddings to expect. A thoughtfully selected wine list draws inspiration from both hemispheres at broadly reasonable prices. House French is £8.

CHEF: Geoffrey Hughes   PROPRIETORS: Geoffrey Hughes, Katherine Bottons and Ruth Williams   OPEN: all week L 12 to 3, Mon to Sat D 6 to 10   CLOSED: 26 and 27 Dec   MEALS: alc (main courses £10 to £25). BYO £5. Bar meals available   SERVICE: not inc   CARDS: Access, Visa   DETAILS: 200 seats. 30 seats outside. Private parties: 110 main room, 30 and 60 private rooms. Car park. Vegetarian meals. Children's helpings. Wheelchair access (also WC). Music

---

OXFORD Oxfordshire

map 2

▲ *Al-Shami* £

25 Walton Crescent, Oxford OX1 2JG
TEL: (01865) 310066   FAX: (01865) 311241

COOKING 1
COST £18–£39

Tucked away down a residential crescent, a short walk from the city centre, Al-Shami continues to be a useful address for the neighbourhood. All-day opening is one of its assets. The menu is billed as authentic Lebanese, and its real strength lies in the range of hot and cold meze which can be ordered to make up a full meal. Offal addicts should appreciate the fried chicken livers and a salad of lambs' brains, while those with vegetarian inclinations could plump for mohammara bil-jawz (mixed crushed nuts with red capsicum, olive oil and spices), or zahra maqlia (fried cauliflower topped with sesame oil, parsley, garlic and lemon juice). The chargrill comes into its own for most of the high-protein main courses, but there are alternatives such as baked cod fillet in hot tomato sauce, and mujadara (rice and lentils with fried onions). To finish, try the Arabic ice-cream. House Lebanese wines are £9.99.

CHEF/PROPRIETOR: Mimo Mahfouz   OPEN: all week midday to midnight   MEALS: alc (main courses £6.50 to £12). Cover £1   SERVICE: not inc, card slips closed   CARDS: Access, Delta, Switch, Visa   DETAILS: 70 seats. Private parties: 60 main room, 30 private room. Vegetarian meals. Children welcome. Smart dress preferred. Wheelchair access (also WC). Music   ACCOMMODATION: 12 rooms, all with bath/shower. TV. Phone. B&B £35 to £45. Children welcome

▲ Bath Place ▼ ⁺✳

4–5 Bath Place, Holywell Street, Oxford OX1 3SU	COOKING 1*
TEL: (01865) 791812 FAX: (01865) 791834	COST £31–£85

The cluster of seventeenth-century cottages down an alley that make up Bath Place has been part of Oxford's life blood for as long as anyone can remember: parts of the original city wall are exposed within the restaurant. There's little doubt that Jeremy Blake O'Connor is capable of cooking very well, but recent reports suggest that flaws are starting to surface. On the plus side have been high-quality canapés, deeply flavoured provençale fish soup, and onglet of beef which was beautifully timed and served with a potent green peppercorn sauce and caramelised onions. Against these must be set 'quite unpleasant' woodpigeon with blackcurrants and cassis sauce, and 'undercooked' roast chicken on a 'greasy' cream sauce.

Puddings generally save the day, as in ultra-modern warm apple tart, and a wildly chocoholic 'soupe au chocolat'. Lunch on Sunday has been appreciated, while at other times there's a great-value two-course deal for £10, which needs to be booked in advance. The wine list is well organised: a legion of good bottles carefully marshalled into groups according to style with brief but accurate notes to describe each. French and Australian offerings make the strongest impression. House wines are £11.95. CELLARMAN'S CHOICE: Stafford Ridge Chardonnay 1991, Lenswood, South Adelaide Hills, S. Australia, £22.50; Cahors Ch. de Cèdre Le Prestige, 1992, £19.50.

CHEFS: Jeremy Blake O'Connor and Eric Pages   PROPRIETORS: Kathleen and Yolanda Fawsitt   OPEN: all week 12 to 2.30, 7 to 10 (10.30 Sat, 9 Sun)   MEALS: alc (main courses £13.50 to £30). Set L £10 (2 courses; must be pre-booked) to £18.75, Set D £19 (2 courses) to £25   SERVICE: not inc, card slips closed; 10% for parties of 5 or more   CARDS: Access, Amex, Delta, Switch, Visa   DETAILS: 32 seats. 12 seats outside. Private parties: 38 main room. Car park. Vegetarian meals. Children's helpings. Smart dress preferred. No smoking in dining-room. Wheelchair access (no WC). Music. Air-conditioned   ACCOMMODATION: 10 rooms, all with bath/shower. TV. Phone. B&B £75 to £120. Deposit: £25. Children welcome. Baby facilities. Dogs by arrangement

Cherwell Boathouse 🍾

Bardwell Road, Oxford OX2 6SR	COOKING 2
TEL/FAX: (01865) 52746	COST £22–£35

The Boathouse is as much an Oxford institution as the Radcliffe Camera. When drizzle gloomed the river view one March lunch-time, the tabletop candles were lit and a flicker of cheer transformed the scene. Gerard Crowley's food moves gracefully with the times, introducing classical Oxford palates to pork salad with dates and cranberries, fricassee of monkfish with yellow-bean salsa, and mackerel fillets with rhubarb sauce. Imam bayaldi is a stayer; vegetarians are thoughtfully catered for. Desserts may be more stalwart than the preceding two courses, bringing on gingerbread pudding, lemon tart, and chocolate and hazelnut brownies. 'Unobtrusive and yet attentive' service is much appreciated. Themed dinners with pre-selected wines are especially well supported, and it isn't hard to see why.

This is a restaurant that knows its wines. Merchants Morris & Verdin have put together a first-rate list from around the world, with plenty of affordable bottles and frequent forays into the fine and rare. The well-priced house selection provides a suitable introduction to the range (from £7.50), and don't forget the venerable dessert wines. CELLARMAN'S CHOICE: Pinot Gris 'Barriques' 1992, Ostertag, Alsace, £17; Bonny Doon, Ca' del Solo Big House Red 1994, California, £12.

CHEF: Gerard Crowley   PROPRIETOR: Anthony Verdin   OPEN: Tue to Sun L 12 to 2, Tue to Sat D 6 to 10.30   CLOSED: 24 to 30 Dec   MEALS: alc L (main courses £8 to £12). Set L £10 (2 courses) to £16.50, Set D £17.50   SERVICE: not inc; 10% for parties of 6 or more   CARDS: Access, Amex, Diners, Visa   DETAILS: 60 seats. 24 seats outside. Private parties: 50 main room, 120 private room. Car park. Vegetarian meals. Children's helpings. No smoking L before 2.15 and D before 10.30. Wheelchair access (also WC). No music

15 North Parade ✱

15 North Parade, Oxford OX2 6LX	COOKING 1*
TEL: (01865) 513773	COST £21–£45

The gradual metamorphosis of 15 North Parade in recent years into a bustling, modern brasserie-style operation, complete with open-plan kitchen, paper table-covers and unusual menus, has been received with mixed feelings in North Oxford. When Sean Wood is in full flow, his ideas are powerfully impressive, vegetarian dishes in particular demonstrating both cogency and skill. Avocado and papaya salad followed by rice and oyster mushrooms wrapped in nori was a springtime treat for one non-meat-eater. The striving for uniqueness brings on items such as venison and chocolate sausage, cod baked with serrano ham and Spanish cheese, or pumpkin and parsnip curry with lentils and cabbage. Desserts keep up the pace with lychee pannacotta, and banana mille-feuille with rum and lime sorbet. Reports of maladroit organis-ation, even panic, when the place is full – as it often is – are too numerous for comfort. A slate of classic cocktails bolsters a good but rather pricey wine list, opening with house wines at £9.75.

CHEF: Sean Wood   PROPRIETOR: Georgina Wood   OPEN: Tue to Sun L 12 to 2, Tue to Sat D 7 to 10   MEALS: alc (main courses £9.50 to £16). Set L £10 (2 courses) to £12.50, Set D £15   SERVICE: not inc   CARDS: Access, Delta, Switch, Visa   DETAILS: 80 seats. 25 seats outside. Private parties: 50 main room, 30 private room. Vegetarian meals. Children's helpings. Smart dress preferred. No smoking in 1 dining-room. Wheelchair access (also WC). Music

Gee's

61A Banbury Road, Oxford OX2 6PE	COOKING 1
TEL: (01865) 53540 FAX: (01865) 310308	COST £25–£38

In the evening this Oxford landmark – a large Victorian greenhouse – makes a truly magical backdrop for Graham Corbett's lively cooking, which inhabits the realms of carpaccio of tuna, angel-hair pasta with king prawns and lemon grass, chargrilled chicken, and roasted vegetables with couscous. Customers also pack the place for excellent weekday set lunches of avocado and feta cheese salad, or bratwurst with onion gravy and parsnips. Desserts are a high point: poached pear with fresh figs and mascarpone gratin, or baked peach on shortbread, for example. There's no denying the value for money or the friendliness of the service, either. The wine list is modern, keenly priced and peppered with good names. House wine is £10. Gee's is under the same ownership as the Old Parsonage Hotel (see entry below).

CHEF: Graham Corbett   PROPRIETOR: Jeremy Mogford   OPEN: all week 12 to 2.30, 6 to 11 (all day Sun)   CLOSED: 25 and 26 Dec   MEALS: alc (main courses £9 to £12). Set L Mon to Fri £11.50 (2 courses)   SERVICE: not inc; 10% for parties of 7 or more   CARDS: Access, Switch, Visa DETAILS: 75 seats. Vegetarian meals. Children welcome. Smart dress preferred. No pipes in dining-room. Music. Air-conditioned

▲ Old Parsonage Hotel, Parsonage Bar

1 Banbury Road, Oxford OX2 6NN	COOKING 1
TEL: (01865) 310210 FAX: (01865) 311262	COST £28–£53

The Old Parsonage performs the 'excellent trick of bringing Oxford fantasies alive', notes a keen-eyed reporter. She was referring to the initial impression of English country living created by the creeper-clad frontage, and the stylishness of the interior, a mixture of 'Conran modern', oil-paintings and club armchairs. The short menu is equally suited to a light lunch, or the full works in the evening, and portions are on the large side. Warm salads, such as bacon and goats' cheese with croûtons, are abundant with greenery, and the kitchen also courts brasserie fashion with toasted bagels and smoked salmon, roasted plum tomatoes with asparagus, and steak with frites. Desserts feature some carefully made ice-creams, baked Alaska, and a finely executed pear tarte Tatin. The wine list is brisk, eclectic and youthful, with a dozen served by the glass from £2.95.

CHEF: Alison Watkins   PROPRIETOR: Jeremy Mogford   OPEN: all week 12 to 3, 6 to 11   CLOSED: 1 week Christmas   MEALS: alc (main courses £9.50 to £17)   SERVICE: not inc, card slips closed   CARDS: Access, Amex, Diners, Switch, Visa   DETAILS: 37 seats. 8 seats outside. Car park. Vegetarian meals. Children welcome. Smart dress preferred. No pipes in dining-room. Wheelchair access (no WC). Music. Air-conditioned   ACCOMMODATION: 30 rooms, all with bath/shower. TV. Phone. B&B £115 to £195. Children welcome. Dogs by arrangement. Afternoon teas. Garden (The Which? Hotel Guide)

Le Petit Blanc

NEW ENTRY

71–72 Walton Street, Oxford OX2 6AG	COOKING 2*
TEL: (01865) 510999 FAX: (01865) 510700	COST £18–£42

Raymond Blanc has come full circle, back to Oxford with another Petit Blanc, the previous one having disappeared in the early 1980s. He is older and wiser now, and certainly seems to have got the measure of the market. Here is an all-day brasserie with a page of flexible offerings, slots for breakfast, lunch and afternoon tea, and only a short van drive from the well-supplied mother ship at Great Milton (see entry). If anybody can make a go of a brasserie, surely it is Raymond Blanc on his own territory, and, despite a couple of early chef changes, indications are that Oxford has taken to it wholeheartedly.

The Conran design team has turned a humble end-of-terrace property into a very smart address, from the glass front and blue awning, through the small bar and casual front room to the rather more sophisticated dining-room with its view into the kitchen. The food stays simple and bright, using some excellent materials (chump of lamb to equal any, for example), and a feeling of assurance runs through expertly made crab ravioli, morel risotto with crisp Parmesan wafers, and a range of tip-top puddings from raspberry soufflé to a selection of Manoir sorbets and ice-creams, plus a first-rate feuillantine of Valrhona chocolate. Prices are keen, and the children's menu is very fair. On the downside, bookings tend to be a bit inflexible (rather against the grain of an informal brasserie), but service has been willing and friendly. Wines are decently priced, though some essential details are missing. House wines are £8.95.

CHEF: Stuart Busby   PROPRIETOR: Blanc Restaurants Ltd   OPEN: L 12 to 3.30, D 6.30 to 11. Snacks available all day   CLOSED: 25 Dec   MEALS: alc (main courses £7 to £14). Set L £14 SERVICE: not inc; 10% for parties of 8 or more   CARDS: Access, Amex, Delta, Diners, Switch, Visa   DETAILS: 120 seats. Private parties: 10 main room. Vegetarian meals. Children's helpings. Wheelchair access (also WC). Music. Air-conditioned

Restaurant Elizabeth ▼

| 82 St Aldate's, Oxford OX1 1RA | COOKING 1 |
| TEL: (01865) 242230 | COST £23–£47 |

While the world changes around it, Elizabeth sails serenely on. The building is seventeenth-century, although Antonio Lopez has only been here since 1966, doing more or less the same thing now as when he arrived: serving salmon quenelles with sauce Nantua followed by duck breast with orange sauce, then candied chestnuts in kirsch. There is a view that if you adopt the culinary equivalent of flared trousers, sooner or later the fashion for them will come round again. There may be some truth in this, given a menu that embraces pipérade, taramasalata, prawns with aïoli, and mussels baked in butter, any of which might appear on a typical bistro table. Chicken, salmon, beef and lamb are main-course staples, wine and cream do their share of saucing, while chocolate mousse and crème brûlée are standard ways to finish. Good Rioja backs up a fine showing of claret (much of it venerable, some as old as the restaurant), decent Burgundy and classic Sauternes. Unlike Columbus, they have not discovered the New World. House wine is £9. CELLARMAN'S CHOICE: Chardonnay Latour 1993, Louis Latour, £14.15; Pauillac, Ch. Haut Pauillac 1988, £22.55.

CHEF: Salvador Rodriguez   PROPRIETOR: Antonio Lopez   OPEN: Tue to Sun 12.30 to 2.30, 6.30 to 11   CLOSED: 24 to 30 Dec, Good Fri   MEALS: alc (main courses £13.50 to £17.50). Set L £15. Cover £1. Minimum £12.50   SERVICE: net prices   CARDS: Access, Amex, Diners, Switch, Visa DETAILS: 40 seats. Private parties: 40 main room, 20 and 40 private rooms. Vegetarian meals. Children's helpings. Smart dress preferred. No music. Air-conditioned

Whites ▼ ⁵✳

| 16 Turl Street, Oxford OX1 3DH | COOKING 2 |
| TEL: (01865) 793396   FAX: (01865) 200303 | COST £24–£58 |

This informal but smart city-centre restaurant is a 'rag-rolled, pink-washed delight' as well as being 'comfortable, suitable for taking out parents, or meeting friends'. It is also up for sale, so circumstances may change during the currency of the *Guide*, but for the time being the practice continues of serving 'sensible-sized portions' (as the generous platefuls are described) and of offering a glass of wine with each course of the more expensive menus. 'A place that tries hard, and if you like having your wines chosen for you it's ideal.'

Good-quality protein underpins the cooking, resulting in braised lamb shank, venison steak or, perhaps on Sunday, sirloin of beef with wild mushrooms. A rack of lamb for one reporter proved to be 'an orthodox roast elevated by its arty presentation'. Indeed, good presentation typifies the approach and 'adds to the overall sense of theatre'. Accompaniments range from a hoisin dressing for marinated duck to a yellow pepper sauce for fillet of salmon, while desserts tread the familiar path of tarte Tatin or baked vanilla cheesecake. Wines are a meticulously chosen and concise set, with France well to the fore. A few wines from Chile and Italy add extra interest, as do 24 half-bottles. House wines are £9.50. CELLARMAN'S CHOICE: Chablis 1994, La Chablisienne, £20; Médoc, Ch. Loudenne 1990, £17.50.

CHEFS: Christopher Lennox-Bland and Bertrand Faucheux   PROPRIETOR: Whites Restaurant (Oxford) Ltd   OPEN: all week L 12.30 to 2, Mon to Sat D 6.30 to 9.45   CLOSED: 1 week Christmas, Sun L summer   MEALS: alc (main courses £10 to £18). Set L Mon to Fri £14.95 (2 courses) to £38.50 (inc wine), Set L Sun £17.50, Set D Mon to Fri £14.95 (2 courses) to £38.50 (inc wine), Set D Sat £29.50 to £38.50 (each inc wine)   SERVICE: not inc   CARDS: Access, Amex, Delta, Diners, Switch, Visa   DETAILS: 45 seats. Private parties: 30 main room. Vegetarian meals. Children's helpings. No smoking in 1 dining-room. Wheelchair access (no WC). Music

---

PADSTOW Cornwall   map 1

Bistro Margot Thomas ⅝✳

11 Duke Street, Padstow PL28 8AB	COOKING 1*
TEL: (01841) 533441	COST £25–£30

Even at the height of the season, when tourists cram the souvenir shops, Padstow has an unimpaired and tranquil grace that is quintessentially Cornish-fishing-village. This cosy bistro a little way around the harbour exerts its own, quieter influence and has earned solid local support as a reliable evening venue. Elaine Meredith's fixed-price menus are bolstered by a daily-changing list of blackboard specials, so there looks to be plenty of choice.

Mix-and-match culinary styles take in two present-day favourites: the Mediterranean (onion bruschetta with Parmesan), and the East Asian (tiger prawns stir-fried in ginger and coriander). Hake is roasted and served with a ham dauphinois – a robust fish dish if ever there was. Pork with Puy lentils, and duck confit with 'crushed' potatoes add to the impression of earthiness in the cooking. Zesty caramelised lemon tart, and crème brûlée with fruits of one sort or another make frequent dessert appearances while one diner reported the bread-and-butter pudding to be 'outstanding'. Generous cafetières of coffee enhance the feeling of well-being. The short international wine list is ser-viceable. Trebbiano and Sangiovese house wines from Romagna are £7.95.

CHEFS: Elaine Meredith and Adrian Oliver   PROPRIETORS: Mike and Elaine Meredith   OPEN: Tue to Sat D only 7 to 9.30 (open D Mon to Sat in high season)   CLOSED: Jan and Feb   MEALS: Set D £17.95   SERVICE: not inc, card slips closed   CARDS: Access, Delta, Switch, Visa   DETAILS: 32 seats. Private parties: 24 main room. Children welcome. Smart dress preferred. No smoking in dining-room. Music. Air-conditioned

▲ *Seafood Restaurant* 🍷

Riverside, Padstow PL28 8BY	COOKING 4
TEL: (01841) 532485 FAX: (01841) 533344	COST £30–£84

'A seafood restaurant of exceptional quality, with attentive service, delightful ambience and marvellous food,' enthused one reporter. On form, this is undoubtedly one of the best fish restaurants in Britain. A conservatory bolted on to the front faces out across the breakwater, and the bright dining-room is enlivened with colourful modern paintings, feeling more cosmopolitan than its fishing-village location might suggest. Cooking is often simple and straight-forward: the best way with fish.

Three courses on the set-price menu are considered good value, and might begin with fish and shellfish soup with rouille and croûtons, followed by grilled haddock with spring onion mash and morels, and pannacotta with stewed rhubarb. The *carte* is more ambitious, offering perhaps a large plate of shellfish in French fashion, with mayonnaise and a small toolkit, or grilled local lobster from the tank, with a herb-flecked shellfish fumet. At inspection a whole and 'utterly fresh' Dover sole was sprinkled with sea salt, grilled, and served with fresh lime. 'One of the great joys of Dover sole is the texture, and this was brilliant...bouncy and firm.' Even unlikely sounding partnerships work well, as in a filleted mackerel stuffed with ginger and chilli: 'I could not imagine it working as well with any other fish.' One or two niggles about timing have surfaced, but it is generally spot on. There are meat dishes for variety, such as duck breast or a steak, and among desserts that have pleased are a light apple tart with cinnamon ice-cream, and sticky toffee pudding.

The restaurant's casualness – find where to sit in the conservatory, pour your own wine – is not to everybody's taste. The Seafood does not have the gestures of a grand restaurant; it has something more important: an atmosphere in which people can enjoy themselves without fuss. To take delight in such a naturally informal environment, and to eat such honest food, is something the *Guide* supports wholeheartedly. Popularity has meant that two sittings operate at busy times. Wines are shrewdly chosen and seafood-friendly, from white Burgundy to less obvious partners of Manzanilla sherry, white Cassis and Alsace Gewurztraminer. Reds get a decent look in too. It is a pleasant surprise to see so many appealing wines under £20 alongside the great and glorious. House French Sauvignon Blanc is £10.50. CELLARMAN'S CHOICE: Muscadet, Clos de Beauregard 1994, Leroux, £13.50; Madiran, Dom. Meinjarre 1992, Alain Brumont, £12.50.

As we went to press, Jason Fretwell took over as chef at the Seafood's kid brother St Petroc's, a short walk up the hill at 4 New Street. It too majors in fish, and has always received support for its unassuming and informal good value.

CHEF/PROPRIETOR: Rick Stein OPEN: Mon to Sat 12 to 2, 7 to 10 CLOSED: 22 Dec to 5 Feb MEALS: alc (main courses £13.50 to £36). Set L £20.25, Set D £29.30 SERVICE: not inc CARDS: Access, Delta, Switch, Visa DETAILS: 70 seats. Children's helpings. No children under 5. Smart dress preferred. Music. Air-conditioned ACCOMMODATION: 18 rooms, all with bath/shower. TV. Phone. B&B £30 to £120. Deposit: 25%. Children welcome. Baby facilities. Dogs welcome (*The Which? Hotel Guide*)

PAINSWICK Gloucestershire map 2

Country Elephant ⚑✴

New Street, Painswick GL6 6XH COOKING **2**
TEL: **(01452) 813564** COST **£23–£50**

This informal country restaurant of Cotswold stone has an open fireplace in the lounge, a comfortable dining-room and an attractive garden for summer meals. The food appeals both for its heartiness (a hot soup of onions and Cheddar cheese, or braised oxtail stew, for instance) as well as for its sensitivity to varied appetites in offering two-course set lunches and dinners. 'Many of the dishes packed quite a punch, looked attractive, and featured some very good combinations of flavours and textures,' reported a visitor.

A show of luxury may be achieved by dribbling truffle oil on to smoked salmon or chicken livers, but Robert Rees makes dishes interesting without relying too heavily on the customary line-up of extravagant materials. Terrine of poached duck leg, for example, is seasoned with aniseed and jasmine, while roast scallops might come with a coriander tuile. Cooking techniques are versatile, sauces often combine stock and alcohol of various kinds, and herbs are used judiciously. Finish with British cheeses or desserts such as crème brûlée or steamed ginger pudding. Service is 'pleasant and friendly', while 30-odd well-chosen wines combine interest with value; seven are available by the glass for around £2 to £3.

CHEFS: Robert Rees and Tom Kerridge PROPRIETOR: John Rees OPEN: Wed to Sun 12 to 2, 7 to 10 CLOSED: first 2 weeks Jan MEALS: alc (main courses L £5 to £10, D £12 to £17). Set L Wed to Sat £10 (2 courses), Set L Sun £12 (2 courses) to £15, Set D Wed to Fri and Sun £13 (2 courses) to £18 SERVICE: not inc CARDS: Access, Amex, Delta, Diners, Switch, Visa
DETAILS: 34 seats. 25 seats outside. Private parties: 34 main room. Vegetarian meals. Children's helpings. No smoking in dining-room. Music

---

PAULERSPURY Northamptonshire map 5

▲ *Vine House* ⚑✴

100 High Street, Paulerspury NN12 7NA
TEL: **(01327) 811267** FAX: **(01327) 811309** COOKING **2**
off A5, 2m SE of Towcester COST **£23–£40**

'I hadn't noticed the garden before,' commented one reporter, who paused to admire the herbs on his way from the car park to the small bar lounge for a glass of refreshing house ginger beer. Julie Springett pours the enterprising brew and takes the orders, helped by a handful of young students, while Marcus Springett appears to have discovered tall towers and builds up his food as high as he dares, setting the staff a tricky balancing task. A country air pervades his menu in the form of woodpigeon pâté, perhaps, or the fruit crumbles and flavoured jellies that figure among desserts.

Some of the workmanship can produce impressive results, among them a home-made wild rabbit sausage tasting lightly and attractively gamey, and a wobbly rhubarb jelly (a small tower in itself) with a pleasantly tart tang to it. The 'super-smooth' and typically sweet saucing looks attractive, but doesn't always have the depth of flavour and savoury richness that a proper stock reduction might achieve. Many of the central items, though, are good. At inspection, three seared scallops on a 'compote' of tomatoes confirmed the freshness of supplies, and a large breast of tasty chicken was cooked just the right length of time. The rather uneven wine list features a reasonable selection of Bordeaux. House wines are £9.95.

CHEF: Marcus Springett   PROPRIETORS: Julie and Marcus Springett   OPEN: Thur and Fri L 12.30 to 1.45, Mon to Sat D 7 to 9.15   CLOSED: 25 Dec to 7 Jan   MEALS: Set L £13.95, Set D Mon to Thur £19.95, Set D Fri and Sat £23.50   SERVICE: not inc   CARDS: Access, Visa   DETAILS: 45 seats. Private parties: 35 main room, 12 private room. Car park. Children's helpings. Smart dress preferred. No smoking in dining-room. No music   ACCOMMODATION: 6 rooms, all with bath/shower. TV. Phone. B&B £39 to £61. Children welcome. Garden (*The Which? Hotel Guide*)

PENZANCE Cornwall   map 1

Harris's

46 New Street, Penzance TR18 2LZ
TEL: (01736) 64408; changes in early 1997 to   COOKING 2
(01736) 364408   COST £30–£59

It is not surprising that neighbouring Newlyn harbour is the motor that drives the menu in this whitewashed restaurant with its lobster-coloured interior. The Harrises have been in the driving seat for 25 years, following a commendably simple route that takes in king prawns in garlic butter, grilled Dover sole, and smoked salmon salad. Meat is not neglected: Cornish lamb and beef appear alongside guinea-fowl with lemon and basil, or locally shot game such as venison served in a red wine sauce with mushrooms. The repertoire may not vary much, but the combination of fresh supplies and a light hand with the cooking makes the nightly fish options well worth exploring. Poached lobster with lemon butter sauce, grilled scallops with fresh herbs, or John Dory with saffron sauce are all likely candidates. Lunch is a relatively light affair of perhaps goats' cheese and bacon salad, salmon pancakes, or a sweet onion and thyme tart. The charge for service surprised one reporter, since it was all done by the patrons, but he nevertheless declared the place 'my favourite restaurant in Cornwall'. France dominates the wine list, with a few bottles from Spain, Germany and the New World. House wines are £12.50.

CHEF: Roger Harris   PROPRIETORS: Roger and Anne Harris   OPEN: Tue to Sat L 12 to 2, Mon to Sat D 7 to 10   CLOSED: 2 weeks Nov, 1 week Feb, D Mon Nov to May   MEALS: alc (main courses £11.50 to £25). Light L available   SERVICE: 10%, card slips closed   CARDS: Access, Amex, Visa   DETAILS: 40 seats. Private parties: 20 main room, 20 private room. Vegetarian meals. Children welcome. Smart dress preferred. No cigars/pipes in dining-room. Music

---

All details are as accurate as possible at the time of going to press, but chefs and owners often change, and it is wise to check by telephone before making a special journey. Many readers have been disappointed when set-price bargain meals are no longer available. Ask when booking.

PITTON Wiltshire   map 2

Silver Plough ♀

Pitton SP5 1DZ
TEL: (01722) 712266 | NEW CHEF |
off A30, 5m E of Salisbury   COST £22–£40

This is the best kind of unspoiled rural pub, full of genuinely cheery atmosphere. A pair of inspectors who ate here in the spring heard 'shrieks of laughter and bursts of applause' coming from a back room somewhere, while a former Prime Minister was absorbing the bonhomie out front. David Scott arrived just as we went to press, sadly too late for us to award a cooking mark, but the wine list remains a commendable selection of lively bottles, many at generous prices. It is also, refreshingly, a tight ship: there's the sense that each wine has thoroughly earned its place. House wines change regularly and start at £9.50. CELLARMAN'S CHOICE: Aotea Sauvignon Blanc 1995, Gisborne, New Zealand, £11.95; Te Mata Cabernet/Merlot 1994, Hawkes Bay, New Zealand, £13.95.

CHEF: David Scott   PROPRIETOR: Michael Beckett   OPEN: all week 12 to 2, 7 to 9.30 (10 Sat)
MEALS: alc (main courses £8.50 to £15). Bar food available   SERVICE: not inc, card slips closed
CARDS: Access, Amex, Diners, Visa   DETAILS: 90 seats. 35 seats outside. Private parties: 45
main room. Car park. Vegetarian meals. Children's helpings. Smart dress preferred. Music

PLUMTREE Nottinghamshire   map 5

Perkins ⁵⋇ £

Old Railway Station, Plumtree NG12 5NA
TEL: (0115) 937 3695   FAX: (0115) 937 6405   COOKING 2
off A606, 2m S of Nottingham   COST £20–£35

In 1997 Tony and Wendy Perkins celebrate 15 years in this conversion beside Plumtree's old railway line. Why is it only when stations close that the food improves? Welcoming staff, a relaxed feel, fresh flowers, and 'jolly, clattery sounds from the kitchen' are all part of the atmosphere. 'Bar Bistro' has been dropped from the title, but the informal style continues, and a regular confirms that the standard is maintained. The easy-going nature of the place accommodates drinkers, snackers, lone diners, large parties, family groups, and anyone in search of good value.

A regular menu is suplemented by a blackboard of daily specials, and it seems there is very little that Tony Perkins doesn't cook. He is happy with starters of cold fish terrine with a spiced spring onion dressing, or a hot mille-feuille of goats' cheese and tapénade, and main courses of roast Lincolnshire partridge, or a grilled brochette of pork fillet. Reporters, meanwhile, have been happy with smoked salmon with scrambled eggs, 'excellent' Dover sole, lamb in a pastry case, and treacle tart and cream. The short, well-chosen wine list includes a sympathetically priced selection of French country wines, a dozen half-bottles, and four house wines at £8.30, available in two glass sizes.

🍾 denotes an outstanding wine cellar; ♀ denotes a good wine list, worth travelling for.

CHEF: Tony Perkins   PROPRIETORS: Tony and Wendy Perkins   OPEN: Tue to Sat 12 to 2, 6.45 to 9.45   CLOSED: 1 week Christmas, 1 week Aug, bank hols   MEALS: alc (main courses £7.50 to £10.50)   SERVICE: not inc   CARDS: Access, Amex, Delta, Diners, Switch, Visa   DETAILS: 73 seats. 24 seats outside. Private parties: 30 main room, 30 private room. Car park. Vegetarian meals. Children welcome. Smart dress preferred. No smoking in 1 dining-room. Wheelchair access (no WC). No music. Air-conditioned

---

PLYMOUTH Devon   map 1

Chez Nous ♟

13 Frankfort Gate, Plymouth PL1 1QA   COOKING 3*
TEL/FAX: (01752) 266793   COST £39–£48

This may look like a small and very modest French bistro, even down to the blackboard menu, but Jacques Marchal's cooking lifts it into the realms of a seriously good restaurant. There is no doubting the French credentials though. It would surprise no one if Jacques emerged wearing a string of onions and a striped jersey, given that the décor has already used up most other clichés, from the red, white and blue colour scheme via ads for Pernod and Gauloises, to menus from the chefs who have inspired him. Roger Verge's cuisine spontanée may account for the blackboard menu, which enables Marchal to incorporate whatever the market brings his way.

It may also account for the Mediterranean element of grilled red mullet with fennel and tomato coulis, or a bouillabaisse du Barbican, a local version of the provençale classic that might contain scallops, salmon, John Dory and gurnard, served with the customary rouille and garlic croûtons. Generous portions of fresh cod and turbot pleased one lunching reporter, testimony to the high quality of fish and shellfish that Plymouth can provide. Meat dishes maintain the essential element of balance, perhaps using a traditional stock and alcohol reduction as in beef fillet with bone marrow and a port sauce, or going all out for the hearty effect of oxtail braised in red wine.

The set-price menu operates at both lunch and dinner and might include such old French favourites as le treacle pudding et clotted cream, or tiramisù ice-cream with strawberries in red wine. Alternatively St Maure, Livarot, Roquefort or Epoisses might be among the cheeses. The wine list naturally continues the Gallic theme, with a wide range of fine French bottles, including mature clarets. A selection from the rest of the world fills a single page at the back of the list. House wines are £10.50. CELLARMAN'S CHOICE: Montagny premier cru, Caves des Producteurs de Buxy 1993, £19; Pinotage 1993, Saxenburg Estate, Stellenbosch, South Africa, £11.50.

CHEF: Jacques Marchal   PROPRIETORS: Suzanne and Jacques Marchal   OPEN: Tue to Sat 12.30 to 2, 7 to 10.30   CLOSED: first 3 weeks Feb and first 3 weeks Sept   MEALS: Set L and D £28.50   SERVICE: not inc   CARDS: Access, Amex, Diners, Switch, Visa   DETAILS: 28 seats. Private parties: 32 main room. Children welcome. Smart dress preferred. Music. Air-conditioned

---

Not inc in the details at the end of an entry indicates that no service charge is made and any tipping is at the discretion of the customer.

PONTELAND Northumberland   map 10

Café 21

35 The Broadway, Darras Hall, Ponteland NE20 9PW   COOKING 1*
TEL/FAX: (01661) 820357   COST £21–£38

So successful has Café 21 been that Terence and Susan Laybourne have given birth to Bistro 21 (see entry, Durham). We await Brasserie 21 with bated breath. In the meantime the bright European style of the café continues with Andrew Moore at the helm. In a row of modern shops in an affluent part of Newcastle, it has the feel of a French café, with paper table-covers and a serious attitude to food, yet a relaxed informal style; just what any city needs.

Variety is achieved by offering braised oxtail or slow-cooked venison alongside omelette or chargrills of chicken or fish: salmon with warm potato salad, for instance. Modern bistro standards include Caesar salad, spinach and Cheddar soufflé, or roasted tomato soup with pesto, while desserts run to nougat glacé with raspberries, or chocolate marquise with pistachio ice-cream. A well-chosen, lively, modern wine list completes the fair-priced deal, beginning with house French at £9.50.

CHEF: Andrew Moore PROPRIETORS: Terence and Susan Laybourne OPEN: Tue to Sat 11.30 to 2.30, 6 to 10.30 (11 Sat) CLOSED: bank hols MEALS: alc (main courses £6.50 to £12.50). Set L £11.50 (2 courses) to £13.50 SERVICE: not inc CARDS: Access, Amex, Delta, Diners, Visa DETAILS: 40 seats. Private parties: 40 main room. Vegetarian meals. Children's helpings. Smart dress preferred. No pipes in dining-room. Wheelchair access (also WC). Music

---

POOLE Dorset   map 2

▲ Mansion House ⅝✳

Thames Street, Poole BH15 1JN   COOKING 1*
TEL: (01202) 685666   FAX: (01202) 665709   COST £19–£42

The listed Georgian building, in a cul-de-sac a hundred yards from the quayside, operates as a private dining club as well as a restaurant. Members get a 15 per cent discount on normal prices, as do hotel residents. Menus offer generous choice and adopt a broadly British stance, taking in Bury black pudding, home-cured salmon, and calf's liver with onion gravy. Game from local shoots features in season, while a Mediterranean tendency comes to the fore in monkfish osso buco, and Chinese-style duck rings other bells. An hors d'oeuvre table and a roast of the day swing into operation for Saturday dinner and Sunday lunch, and weekday lunch can be completed in 50 minutes for those in a hurry. Finish, perhaps, with the British and Irish cheeseboard. The managerial style is 'hands-on with unremitting enthusiasm', and staff are young, helpful and uniformed. The wine list is divided into a classic no-expense-spared French section, and a good-value jaunt around the rest of the world that stays commendably under £22.

▲ *This symbol means accommodation is available.*

CHEF: Gerry Godden PROPRIETOR: Robert Leonard OPEN: Mon to Fri and Sun L 12 to 2, Mon to Sat D 7 to 9.30 CLOSED: L bank hol Mons MEALS: Set L £11.25, Set D £16 (2 courses) to £21.50. Bistro food available SERVICE: not inc CARDS: Access, Amex, Delta, Diners, Switch, Visa DETAILS: 85 seats. Private parties: 100 main room, 14 to 40 private rooms. Car park. Vegetarian meals. Children's helpings. No children under 5. Smart dress preferred. No smoking in 1 dining-room. Music. Air-conditioned ACCOMMODATION: 28 rooms, all with bath/shower. TV. Phone. B&B £52 to £122. Children welcome. Baby facilities. Dogs by arrangement. Afternoon teas (*The Which? Hotel Guide*)

PORTHLEVEN Cornwall　　　　　　　　　　　　　　　　map 1

▲ *Critchards* ⁵✳

The Harbourside, Porthleven TR13 9JA　　　　　　　COOKING 1
TEL: (01326) 562407　　　　　　　　　　　　　　　COST £24–£60

Given the harbourside setting of this 300-year-old mill, it should be no surprise that seafood is the main business; but the cooking is no mere variant on the fish-and-chip theme. Jo Critchard cooks, Steve runs front-of-house, and good supplies are assured from Newlyn across the bay. Mackerel and gurnard are welcome alternatives to the more usual monkfish and sole, while razor shells and soft-shell crab make enterprising additions to the repertoire. Dishes trawl far and wide for ideas, producing a Cantonese version of scallops, and a mildly spicy Caribbean sauce for grilled John Dory, which is served with banana, fragrant rice, and arame seaweed. These are in addition to more mainstream European items of wine-poached Helford mussels, Dover sole with lemon and parsley butter, and grilled Cornish lobster. A 50p charge is made for bread. Around 40 wines lack the excitement of the food. House wine is £9.50.

CHEF: Jo Critchard PROPRIETORS: Steve and Jo Critchard OPEN: Mon to Sat plus occasional Sun in season, D only 6.30 to 9.30 CLOSED: 2 weeks Nov, 3 to 4 weeks Jan MEALS: alc (main courses £9 to £28) SERVICE: not inc, card slips closed CARDS: Access, Switch, Visa DETAILS: 44 seats. Private parties: 10 main room. Vegetarian meals. Children's helpings. No children under 6. Smart dress preferred. No smoking in dining-room. Music ACCOMMODATION: 1 room, with bath/shower. TV. B&B £42 (double room). Deposit: 25%. No children under 6

PORTHOUSTOCK Cornwall　　　　　　　　　　　　map 1

Volnay ⁵✳

Porthoustock, St Keverne TR12 6QW
TEL: (01326) 280183　　　　　　　　　　　　　　COOKING 2
off B3293, 1m E of St Keverne　　　　　　　　　COST £25–£38

Once a fishing village on the 'undiscovered' east side of the Lizard Peninsula, Porthoustock is now a holiday retreat boasting an excellent local restaurant. Steven Chapman and Colin Rye converted a fisherman's cottage close to the beach into a low-ceilinged dining-room with white walls, red-tiled floors and a smattering of bare wooden tables. There is no printed menu: instead, blackboards advertise the day's offerings and Steven verbally describes each dish in 'lip-licking' detail.

The name 'Volnay' may suggest Burgundy, but the cooking is emphatically Mediterranean: pan-fried chicken livers are spiked with Marsala and served on a sunflower pattern of young spinach leaves; crab tart with ricotta, spring onion and ginger is made with beautifully thin pastry; and a vegetarian risotto uses three kinds of rice. Main courses range from a confit of duck (leg and breast) with sun-dried tomatoes to tournedos of beef with braised onions and celeriac mash, or roast monkfish with garlic and fennel. Desserts are equally Italianate: chocolate torrone with vanilla custard, and torte di dolcelatte, not to mention vin santo with biscotti. The wine list is short, keenly priced and, for the most part, youthful. House Italian is £9 a litre.

CHEF: Colin Rye   PROPRIETORS: Steven Chapman and Colin Rye   OPEN: Tue to Sat and bank hol Mon D only 7.30 to 9   MEALS: alc (main courses £9 to £14)   SERVICE: not inc   CARDS: none   DETAILS: 18 seats. Private parties: 18 main room. Vegetarian meals. Children welcome. No smoking in 1 dining-room. Music

---

POULTON-LE-FYLDE Lancashire   map 8

▲ River House

Skippool Creek, Thornton-le-Fylde,
Poulton-le-Fylde FY5 5LF
TEL: (01253) 883497 and 883307
FAX: (01253) 892083
at roundabout junction of A585 and B5412 take third   COOKING 1*
exit; after 50yds turn right, signposted Skippool Creek   COST £29–£56

Bill Scott is now in sole charge of the River House, which his family has been running for nigh on 40 years, and it is fair to say the place has a pretty well-worn feel these days. Fashions roll in and out with the tides outside the door, but certain things remain. Bulky pea and ham soup, goujons of salmon in white wine and cream, and chateaubriand with béarnaise hark back fondly to yesteryear. An inspector found the meat cookery less than beguiling, although the out-of-season pheasant was as gamey as could be. Crème brûlée comes with a separate pot of stewed rhubarb, and ticky tacky pudding will please those with memories of the school dinner-hall. Despite the *Guide*'s entreaties, the wine list is still inadequately written. Would you risk £19.30 on Pouilly-Fumé when you know neither the grower nor the vintage? House wines are £12.50.

CHEF/PROPRIETOR: Bill Scott   OPEN: Mon to Sat D only 7.30 to 9.30; L by appointment   MEALS: alc (main courses £16 to £20). Set L and D £18.50   SERVICE: not inc   CARDS: Access, Delta, Switch, Visa   DETAILS: 40 seats. 8 seats outside. Private parties: 40 main room, 14 private room. Car park. Children welcome. Smart dress preferred. Music   ACCOMMODATION: 5 rooms, all with bath/shower. TV. Phone. B&B £50 to £80. Children welcome. Baby facilities. Dogs welcome. Garden (*The Which? Hotel Guide*)

'The menu is brought. We tilt it towards the light and try to decipher it. "What's that – stormed?" "Sautéd, I think." "Smeared?" "Oh skewered. Skewered Scottish scallops." "And the main course?" "Er, that is the main course."' (On eating in London)

POWBURN Northumberland   map 10

▲ Breamish House ⑤✳

Powburn NE66 4LL	COOKING 1
TEL: (01665) 578266 FAX: (01665) 578500	COST £22–£39

The Johnsons' elegantly furnished Georgian hotel stands in five well-tended acres, with an inspiring view of the Cheviot hills. A 'warm welcome' helps people feel properly looked after, and some care has gone into the thoughtfully conceived fixed-price menus. At dinner, four courses plus coffee comes at an eminently fair price, the second always an 'interesting' cream soup such as lettuce, pea and sorrel. Game terrines with fruity jelly to start are appreciated, or there may be watercress mousse garnished with prawns and tomato concasse. Main-course meats are more straightforward offerings. Desserts from the trolley might include choux buns with imported fruits and cream. Coffee comes with fine home-made truffles. The reliable wine list ranges far and wide, leading with Gascon house wines at £12.50 for a litre carafe.

CHEFS/PROPRIETORS: Doreen and Alan Johnson   OPEN: Sun L 12.30 for 1, all week D 7.30 for 8   CLOSED: Jan to 13 Feb   MEALS: Set L Sun £13.50, Set D £23.50   SERVICE: not inc, card slips closed   CARDS: Access, Delta, Switch, Visa   DETAILS: 28 seats. Private parties: 28 main room, 15 private room. Car park. No children under 12 except by prior arrangement. Children's helpings Sun L only. Smart dress preferred. No smoking in dining-room. Wheelchair access (also WC). No music   ACCOMMODATION: 11 rooms, all with bath/shower. TV. Phone. D,B&B £69.50 to £152. Deposit: £25 per person. No children under 12 except by prior arrangement. Dogs welcome in bedrooms only. Afternoon teas. Garden (*The Which? Hotel Guide*)

PRESTBURY Cheshire   map 8

▲ White House

New Road, Prestbury SK10 4DG	
TEL: (01625) 829376 FAX: (01625) 828627	COOKING 1*
on A538, 2m N of Macclesfield	COST £21–£56

A smartly converted eighteenth-century farmhouse is home to the Wakehams' popular village restaurant. Fixed-price menus at lunch and dinner back up the firmly contemporary *carte*, culinary breezes from the Orient and the Mediterranean wafting over the more traditional British foundations. Smoked salmon finds itself in the company of arugula and a tropical fruit salsa, while monkfish receives the tandoori treatment, complete with raita and a little nan. Pasta dishes are offered as in-betweens or main courses, while caramelised fruit pancakes, or rhubarb and apple crumble with custard set the parameters for puddings.

A couple who ventured here again after six years found the cooking much better than they remembered it, enjoying seared Cornish mackerel with salade niçoise, roast lamb with tapénade, and treacle and walnut tart. They immediately rebooked. Europe is made to wait until the rest of the world has had its more inspiring say on the wine list. A fair range of half-bottles and wines by the glass is available. House French is £12 a litre.

CHEFS: Mark Cunniffe and Ryland Wakeham   PROPRIETORS: Ryland and Judith Wakeham
OPEN: Tue to Sun L 12 to 2, Mon to Sat D 7 to 10   CLOSED: 25 Dec   MEALS: alc (main courses
£8.50 to £14). Set L Tue to Sat £12.50, Set D Mon to Fri £13.95 (2 courses) to £16.95   SERVICE:
not inc   CARDS: Access, Amex, Delta, Diners, Switch, Visa   DETAILS: 75 seats. 12 seats
outside. Private parties: 60 main room, 5 to 40 private rooms. Car park. Vegetarian meals.
Children's helpings. Smart dress preferred. No cigars/pipes in dining-room. Wheelchair access
(no WC). Music   ACCOMMODATION: 9 rooms, all with bath/shower. TV. Phone. B&B £65 to £110.
Children welcome. Baby facilities. Dogs welcome. Garden (*The Which? Hotel Guide*)

PRESTON Lancashire   map 8

Heathcote's Brasserie

23 Winckley Square, Preston PR1 3JJ   COOKING 2
TEL: (01772) 252732   FAX: (01772) 203433   COST £18–£50

'We've had more good meals here than anywhere else,' report one local couple,
obviously pleased at the way Paul Heathcote's first venture outside Longridge
(see entry) has gone. Winckley Square is Georgian, quite a contrast to the chic,
modern interior, with its glossy wood, colourful mural and comfortable Philippe
Starck chairs. Both the downstairs seafood and rôtisserie bar, and the cosmopolitan brasserie are relaxing and informal.

The menu changes every three months and packs in a good variety of solidly
British dishes along the lines of home-made black pudding, lamb shank, oxtail
with horseradish mash, bread-and-butter pudding, and sherry trifle. Then there
is the Mediterranean input – roasted yellow pepper soup with polenta croûtons,
for example – and the more free-ranging ideas, as when tuna gets a vivid version
of the gravad lax treatment, with coriander, ginger and lime. 'This is careful
cooking with excellent ingredients,' notes a supporter, while another found an
ordinary-sounding vanilla cream with a compote of fruits to be worthy of the
Longridge flagship. Remember, when ordering soup, that bread is charged for
separately. Service has ranged from professional to unco-ordinated. A short
wine list changes along with the menu, stays between £10 and £20, and includes
a good variety of flavours.

CHEF: Max Gnoyke   PROPRIETOR: Paul Heathcote   OPEN: all week 11.45 to 2.15, 6 to 10.30;
seafood bar Mon to Sat noon to 9   CLOSED: 25 and 26 Dec, 1 Jan   MEALS: alc (main courses
£8.50 to £20). Set L £8.50 (2 courses) to £10.50   SERVICE: not inc   CARDS: Access, Amex,
Delta, Switch, Visa   DETAILS: 90 seats. Private parties: 70 main room. Vegetarian meals.
Children's helpings. No cigars/pipes in dining-room. Music

PULBOROUGH West Sussex   map 3

Stane Street Hollow 🍷 ⁵✹

Codmore Hill, Pulborough RH20 1BG
TEL: (01798) 872819   COOKING 2
on A29, 1½m NE of Pulborough   COST £25–£47

In the absence of mountains and snow, René Kaiser has to rely on cowbells to
remind him of home. This is a long-standing family business in which good
supplies and a strong French bias determine the style of the cooking, from

bouchées à la reine to quenelles de poisson. The more Germanic face of Switzerland is represented by gamier dishes, such as a casserole of venison, pheasant and rabbit marinated in red wine, while a few more exotic flavours appear from time to time, including banana and mango chutney with plaice, which sounded an odd mixture for one reporter, 'but it came off'.

The set-price lunch offers a minuscule choice, except on Sunday when it expands to half a dozen items per course, about the same as the monthly-changing dinner *carte*. Herbs, soft fruits and vegetables come from the garden, though what used to be the 'outstanding feature' of the food for one reporter has been replaced by 'a small plate of mixed vegetables in a style wearisomely familiar elsewhere'. Home-smoking – mostly of salmon – is a feature, and cream is often used in sauces as well as in some of the puddings. Pancakes usually put in an appearance, too, often filled with a fruit compote. France dominates the wine list, and there are lively touches elsewhere, plus a bunch of dessert wines and a quartet from Switzerland. CELLARMAN'S CHOICE: Pinot d'Alsace, Vieilles Vignes 1992, Zind-Humbrecht, £15.50; Palliser Estate Pinot Noir 1993, North Island, New Zealand, £16.50.

CHEF: René Kaiser   PROPRIETORS: René and Ann Kaiser   OPEN: Wed to Fri and Sun L 12.30 to 1.30, Wed to Sat D 7.15 to 9   CLOSED: 2 weeks May, 2 weeks Oct   MEALS: alc (main courses £10 to £13). Set L Wed to Fri £11.50 (2 courses) to £14.50, Set L Sun £14.50 (2 courses) to £17.50   SERVICE: not inc, card slips closed   CARDS: Access, Delta, Switch, Visa   DETAILS: 30 seats. Private parties: 20 main room, 14 private room. Car park. Vegetarian meals. Children's helpings. Smart dress preferred. No smoking in dining-room. Wheelchair access (no WC). No music

RAMSBOTTOM Greater Manchester   map 8

Village Restaurant ▮ ⁵✳

16–18 Market Place, Ramsbottom BL0 9HT
TEL: (0170) 6825070 FAX: (0170) 6822005   COOKING 2*
off A56/M66, 4m N of Bury   COST £14–£31

'Now performing much better in its new guise' was one assessment of this highly personal and individual operation. 'The party atmosphere is back!' enthused another, 'and the evening is as long as it used to be.' Chris Johnson and Ros Hunter combine a first-class food shop with a restaurant in two terraced stone cottages in this former mill town, and deliver some of the best-sourced ingredients in and around Manchester. They have a mission to seek out free-range and organic materials from artisan producers, and if the encouragement and promotion of small-scale sustainable agriculture ever did seem cranky, it certainly appears more sane and reasonable with every year that passes.

Beef is reared 'to organic or conservation-grade standards', mostly on grass on the West Pennine Moors and Cumbrian hills, and is then 'hung for weeks'. Chicken does not feature because of antibiotic problems, while strict seasonality means that strawberries appear for only a few weeks in summer. The deliberately slow pace of dinner, and the lack of choice, may not suit everyone, although special requirements are discussed when booking. Lunches tend to be light.

413

Church pew seating and polished tables are the setting, and a typical dinner might begin with appetisers from the delicatessen, then a 'simple but enjoyable' first course of pickled herring, salmon and lightly baked scallops, followed by winter vegetable soup. Beef might be served two ways, a slice of pink sirloin and a casserole on the same plate. Finally, sticky toffee pudding and a trio of sorbets have been 'exemplary'. Chris Johnson is less of a waiter, more of an enthusiastic dinner-party host.

Trips to the cellar for wine provide diversion. There is a list of about 20 for those who don't wish to rummage, but another 600 are available downstairs at shop prices plus a specified mark-up: from £5 for the cheaper wines to £9 for anything that sells in the shop at £15 and over. Thus, a Chambolle-Musigny 1989 from Georges Lignier that might sell in the region of £50 on a standard list will set you back £30.25 here, a sum that would seem to benefit everybody. There's a good selection of beers too. CELLARMAN'S CHOICE: Alsace, Edelzwicker 1991, Rolly-Gassman, £14.50; Bordeaux, Ch. Puygueraud 1989, £18.50.

CHEF: Ros Hunter   PROPRIETORS: Ros Hunter and Chris Johnson   OPEN: Wed to Sat L 12 to 2.30, Sun L 1 for 1.30 (1 sitting), Wed to Sat D 7.30 for 8 (1 sitting)   MEALS: alc L (main courses £4.50 to £8.50). Set L Wed to Sat £5 (2 courses) to £8.50 (inc wine), Set L Sun £18.50, Set D £18.50   SERVICE: not inc, card slips closed   CARDS: Access, Amex, Delta, Diners, Switch, Visa   DETAILS: 40 seats. Private parties: 30 main room, 10 private room. Vegetarian meals. Children's helpings. Smart dress preferred. No smoking in dining-room. Music

---

REIGATE Surrey   map 3

Dining Room £✻

59A High Street, Reigate RH2 9AE	COOKING 2*
TEL: (01737) 226650	COST £18–£54

The first-floor room – like a relaxed private dining-room – is sited above another restaurant, but once you have found out where you need to be, the waiters, in 'long, white, crisply laundered pinnies', are very good at making you feel at home.

Anthony Tobin takes a full-blooded approach to flavour and borrows freely in today's way from other cuisines, so seared scallops on pipérade sit next to crispy crab spring rolls with a ginger dipping sauce. Sheer technique wins converts and establishes confidence among diners, so that when the kitchen tries one of its more offbeat-sounding constructions – such as cod baked with Thai spices, served with curried artichokes and a Sauternes sauce – it can be trusted to bring it off. The three-course lunch menu for £10 looks a very tempting bargain, and even if it does offer breadcrumbed plaice and chips, you know it won't be *that* sort of plaice and chips. Vegetables are charged for separately. The lightness and depth of a dark treacle sponge with ginger sauce demonstrates skill with desserts. The brief wine list picks up around two dozen bottles from all over the globe, not one a makeweight. Even the Vin de Pays d'Oc house wines, at £8.50, have plenty to say for themselves.

CHEF: Anthony Tobin   PROPRIETOR: Paul Montalto   OPEN: Mon to Fri L 12 to 2, Mon to Sat D 7 to 10   CLOSED: 2 weeks Christmas, 1 week Easter, 1 week Aug   MEALS: alc (main courses £13.50 to £20). Set L £7.50 (2 courses) to £10, Set D £13.95 (2 courses)   SERVICE: not inc   CARDS: Access, Amex, Switch, Visa   DETAILS: 50 seats. Private parties: 40 main room. Vegetarian meals. Children's helpings. Smart dress preferred. No smoking in dining-room. Music

---

RICHMOND Surrey   map 3

Burnt Chair ♥   ☐ NEW ENTRY

5 Duke Street, Richmond TW9 1HP   COOKING 1
TEL: (0181) 940 9488   COST £27–£41

The unremarkable shop-front is in a one-way street between the Green and the main thoroughfare. Every chair in the place is different, and the burnt one is in use all the time. Despite the slightly cramped surroundings there is a sense of calm, partly thanks to Mr Oo – a 'beatific presence' – who works the tables and takes a genuine interest in his customers, offering good advice on request. Simple Anglo-French dishes are the mainstay, ranging from black pudding, via asparagus and leek soufflé, to skate wing with capers and beurre noisette. Among dishes that have impressed are a coarse terrine of woodpigeon and pulses encased in cabbage, a dark, soupy risotto of ceps with truffle oil, and a large piece of beef in a good winey sauce with 'an excellent leek pithiviers sitting on top', with moist chocolate brownie, perhaps, to finish.

Wine is taken seriously. Mature vintages, plenty of half-bottles and some good New World bins add depth and interest to a long, mainly Gallic list. Consult the useful notes under each wine, or turn to the knowledgeable Mr Oo for extra help. CELLARMAN'S CHOICE: Pouilly-Fumé 1995, Dom. des Berthiers, J-C Dagueneau, £18.50; Concannon Vineyard, Petite Sirah 1993, Alameda, California, £17.

CHEFS: Gordon Gellatly and Weenson Oo   PROPRIETOR: Weenson Oo   OPEN: Mon to Sat D only 6 to 11   CLOSED: 1 week Christmas, 10 days Aug   MEALS: alc (main courses £9 to £12.50). Set D £12.50 (2 courses). Cover £1   SERVICE: not inc   CARDS: Access, Amex, Visa   DETAILS: 31 seats. Private parties: 36 main room. Vegetarian meals. Children's helpings. Music

---

Chez Lindsay £   ☐ NEW ENTRY

11 Hill Rise, Richmond TW10 6UQ   COOKING 1*
TEL: (0181) 948 7473   COST £16–£42

Lindsay Wotton's cosy bistro in the lower reaches of Richmond Hill has outstripped the local opposition with its bare-boarded informality and highly biddable Breton cooking. Crêpes and galettes are the specialities, the latter made with coarse buckwheat flour and variously filled with anything from a simple but 'very tasty' egg and cheese mixture to onions, lardons and walnuts with a Roquefort sauce. Main courses, such as grilled tuna with ratatouille, or noisettes of lamb with spinach and hazelnuts, may seem rather prosaic by comparison, although vegetables are prettily presented. The dessert crêpes – banana with chocolate sauce, for example – leave no corner unfilled; lighter appetites may opt for ice-creams or sorbets. A trio of specially imported Breton ciders, served in traditional cups, heads up the drinks list, which then proceeds to a short, sharp round-up of French wines plus one lone Spanish. House wines are £8.90.

CHEFS: Lindsay Wotton and Florence Lipokatics   PROPRIETOR: Lindsay Wotton   OPEN: Mon to Sat 12 to 2.30, 6 to 11   CLOSED: 25 and 26 Dec   MEALS: alc (main courses £5.50 to £10.50). Light snacks available all day   SERVICE: not inc   CARDS: Access, Delta, Switch, Visa   DETAILS: 48 seats. Private parties: 50 main room, 36 private room. Vegetarian meals. Children's helpings. No cigars/pipes while others eat. Wheelchair access (no WC). Music

---

RIDGEWAY Derbyshire   map 9

Old Vicarage 🍷 🍴✺

Ridgeway Moor, Ridgeway S12 3XW
TEL: (0114) 247 5814   FAX: (0114) 247 7079   COOKING 3*
off A616, on B6054 nearly opposite village church   COST £32–£49

The old vicar may have left some while ago, but the house instils a feeling of clerical serenity from the moment you pass through the old arched wooden door, helped by garden views and the gentle hooting of owls as dusk falls. Things have not been quite so serene for the owners in the last couple of years. Tessa Bramley was very poorly for a while at the end of 1994, but happily she is now fully restored and the ship sails on.

Menus are decorated with photographs from the house cookbook; Mrs Bramley is justifiably proud of what she does. A quail is stuffed with potatoes, leeks and olives, roasted, then partnered with sauté chicken livers and more leeks, and that's just for starters. This was beautifully timed in the event, and ingredients likewise proliferate in most dishes. Brill is given a crust of cumin and coriander and presented on mango salsa with deep-fried ginger in sherry vinegar sauce: the culinary equivalent of plate-spinning. Fortunately, the technique can handle all this, as seen in saddle of fallow deer stuffed with apple and cinnamon and served on a red wine reduction; all the elements, down to a sweet compote of blueberries and buttery parsnip purée, performed their task of complementing the 'tender, tasty and slightly pink' meat. The vegetarian option is similarly complex, so no one need feel left out.

A well-risen chocolate and Tia Maria soufflé with coffee ice-cream impressed a diner for balancing lightness and richness. Sponge puddings are often mentioned favourably in reports, and there are excellent artisan cheeses from Britain and Ireland to consider too. The opinion of our inspectors this year is that the Old Vicarage is regaining momentum. The wine list is fascinating, packed with venerable French, German, Italian and Spanish names, many of them dating from the 1970s or before. Top New World producers such as Australia's Peter Lehmann, Jackson Estate from New Zealand, and California's Beringer bring things bang up to date, and service 'couldn't have been better' according to one report. House wines are £14.

CHEFS: Tessa Bramley, Nathan Smith and Andrew Gilbert   PROPRIETORS: Tessa and Andrew Bramley   OPEN: Tue to Fri and Sun L 12.30 to 2.30, Tue to Sat D 7 to 10.45   CLOSED: 1 to 10 Jan   MEALS: Set L Mon to Fri £28, Set L Sun £20 to £24, Set D £35   SERVICE: not inc, card slips closed   CARDS: Access, Amex, Delta, Switch, Visa   DETAILS: 55 seats. Private parties: 48 main room, 12 and 28 private rooms. Car park. Vegetarian meals. Children's helpings. Smart dress preferred. No smoking in dining-room. No music

▲ Boar's Head

Ripley HG3 3AY
TEL: (01423) 771888   FAX: (01423) 771509

COOKING 2*
COST £27–£53

The building is part of Ripley Castle estate, in a little cobbled enclave off the main road, and combines the feel of an old coaching-inn with twentieth-century décor and comforts. The Ingilbys have been at Ripley for 700 years, long enough to get settled in, while Steven Chesnutt moved into the kitchen just before the last edition of the *Guide* was published, and in that relatively short time has inched up the quality. The operation looks 'slightly starchy' and expensive, but the priorities appear to be right: high-quality raw materials, proper attention to tastes and textures, and attractive presentation for good measure.

The choice at dinner is between three menus, perhaps a subconscious reference to Daddy Boar (five courses), Mummy Boar and Baby Boar, the cheapest featuring starters of 'tiny toad-in-the-hole' (with venison sausages) or 'three soups served in one bowl', a junior-sounding dish if ever there was. Lobster, foie gras and a gin and tonic sorbet are reserved for the £35 menu. One pair of winter visitors began with parcels of wild mushroom ravioli in a mild creamy mustard sauce, and 'succulent' monkfish glazed with Stilton, a bit heavy on dairy products, perhaps, but followed by pan-fried loin of lamb, and stuffed breast of guinea-fowl, both with intense stock-based sauces.

Desserts are the same for all three menus, and may include a tipsy version of spotted dick, and a forcefully flavoured syllabub of mascarpone and passion-fruit. Staff are professional and knowledgeable about the food and wine, the latter extending to over 200 fairly priced bins from around the world. House French is £9.95.

CHEF: Steven Chesnutt   PROPRIETORS: Sir Thomas and Lady Ingilby   OPEN: all week 12 to 2, 7 to 9.30   MEALS: Set L £13.50 (2 courses) to £17.50, Set D £25 to £35. BYO £6. Bar food and light lunches available   SERVICE: not inc   CARDS: Access, Amex, Diners, Switch, Visa   DETAILS: 40 seats. Car park. Vegetarian meals. Children's helpings. No children under 10. Smart dress preferred. No smoking in 1 dining-room. No cigars/pipes in dining-room. Wheelchair access (also WC). Music   ACCOMMODATION: 25 rooms, all with bath/shower. TV. Phone. D,B&B £80 to £110. Deposit: £50. Rooms for disabled. Children welcome. Baby facilities. Dogs welcome in bedrooms only. Afternoon teas. Garden. Fishing (*The Which? Hotel Guide*)

Michels'

13 High Street, Ripley GU23 6AQ
TEL: (01483) 224777   FAX: (01483) 222940
off A3, 4m SW of Cobham

COOKING 3
COST £30–£62

The double-fronted red-brick house (Queen Anne with Georgian additions) has a 'very pleasant ambience for a special evening out', helped by the attractive but domestic scale of the dining-room. There is no choice on the set-price menus (dubbed Gourmet and Surprise) and the à la carte has been considered expensive, but dishes such as parsley cream soup with a fricassee of frogs' legs, or a warm mousseline of ceps served with a cooked vegetable salad show a pleasing vein of invention. Not everything may match its description, however. Scallops 'wrapped in celeriac' were encased in pasta for one reporter, and herbs have appeared unannounced, as in a dish of firm and 'beautifully cooked' sea bass 'overpowered by tarragon'.

Reports suggest that the cooking sometimes excels itself and sometimes disappoints, but an inspector was generally pleased with the quality of materials and the taste and timing of, for example, best end of lamb with a powerfully herbed coating. Delicate flavours work well when it comes to dessert: crisply fried apple pieces, for one reporter, served with a delicate apple mousse on a bed of quince jelly-like sauce. A plate of British farm cheeses is included in the à la carte price of pudding at dinner. Service is more or less correct, though it might be more responsive, while wines are an appealing collection from France, Germany and the New World, plus a long list of halves. Eleven varied house wines start at £8.45.

CHEF: Erik Michel   PROPRIETORS: Erik and Karen Michel   OPEN: Tue to Fri and Sun L 12.30 to 1.30, Tue to Sat D 7.30 (7 Sat) to 9 (9.30 Sat)   CLOSED: early Jan, some time during Aug   MEALS: alc (main courses £17 to £22). Set L £21, Set D Tue to Fri £23 to £30 (inc wine)   SERVICE: not inc; 10% for parties of 6 or more   CARDS: Access, Amex, Delta, Switch, Visa   DETAILS: 60 seats. Private parties: 12 private room. Car park (4 cars only). Children welcome. Smart dress preferred. Music

---

ROADE Northamptonshire

map 5

Roadhouse Restaurant

16 High Street, Roade NN7 2NW
TEL: (01604) 863372
off A508, 4m S of Northampton

COOKING 3
COST £22–£39

The Kewleys run a small country restaurant with laudable aims: to provide decent cooking without fireworks at a reasonable price. The appeal is sound, reliable food, perhaps a bit predictable in its format, but generally produced with care and skill, in a comfortable and informal dining-room. Prices have remained commendably stable, and the three or four choices per course on the set-price lunch are extended to half a dozen on the evening *carte*. The style is basically British, but with input from rural France and the Mediterranean, and Chris Kewley reports that general health consciousness has increased sales of fish.

First courses range from refined, smooth-textured, deep-flavoured chicken liver pâté to a plain, thick rustic broth of split pea and ham, although sardines filled with goats' cheese was 'not a happy marriage' for one reporter. By common consent the pastry starter is often the pick, whether of mushroom duxelles with a perfectly poached egg, a dribble of cream and a sprinkling of Parmesan, or made from filo, with onion confit and 'a heap of wonderfully varied mushrooms'. Local game has included (for one November diner) roast breast of pheasant with the minced leg meat wrapped in cabbage leaf, served with a porty gravy.

Timing is good, making a success of such items as liver, kidneys and fish, and saucing might be a simple beurre blanc, or a good stock-based gravy. The same selection of vegetables accompanies all dishes. Puddings range from lemon tart or apple pie to 'super and really wicked' chocolate marquise with Grand Marnier custard. Sue Kewley welcomes in the bar and oversees the whole operation, as well as dispensing wines from the fairly priced 60-strong list. House French is £9.50.

CHEF: Chris Kewley   PROPRIETORS: Chris and Sue Kewley   OPEN: Tue to Fri L 12.30 to 1.45, Tue to Sat D 7 to 9.30 (10 Sat)   CLOSED: 1 week Christmas, 2 weeks in summer   MEALS: alc D (main courses £11 to £16). Set L £12 (2 courses) to £15.50. BYO £7   SERVICE: net prices, card slips closed   CARDS: Access, Amex, Visa   DETAILS: 45 seats. Private parties: 45 main room. Car park. Children's helpings. Smart dress preferred. No music

---

ROMALDKIRK Co Durham   map 10

▲ Rose & Crown ⅙✳

Romaldkirk DL12 9EB
TEL: (01833) 650213   FAX: (01833) 650828   COOKING 1*
on B6277, 6m NW of Barnard Castle   COST £18–£39

Romaldkirk looks every inch the perfectly manicured English village and seems to have everything – apart from a shop. At the centre of things is the Rose & Crown, a handsome stone inn dating from 1733. The Davys have done a grand job in preserving its character, and Christopher's cooking is on the up. A daily four-course dinner menu is served in the panelled restaurant, and seasonal ingredients are admirably deployed across the board. Woodall's Cumbrian air-dried ham comes with two kinds of melon, Cotherstone cheese is made into crisp fritters, and scallops are bravely cooked just beyond rare. Among main courses you might find a 'real flag-waving treat' in the shape of roast loin of pork with rhubarb compote and top-notch gravy from the pan. Steaks are first-rate, and vegetables regularly receive applause. Strawberry shortcake, and iced honey and whisky ice-cream have been recommended among the puddings. Unaffected Englishness sums the place up. The wine list runs encouragingly from the New World to Europe. House French is £8.50.

CHEFS: Christopher Davy and Dawn Stephenson   PROPRIETORS: Christopher and Alison Davy   OPEN: Sun L 12 to 1.30, Mon to Sat D 7.30 to 9   CLOSED: 24 to 26 Dec   MEALS: Set L £11.95, Set D £22.50. Bar food available   SERVICE: not inc, card slips closed   CARDS: Access, Visa   DETAILS: 24 seats. Private parties: 30 main room. Car park. Children's helpings. No children under 6 D. Smart dress preferred. No smoking in dining-room. No music   ACCOMMODATION: 12 rooms, all with bath/shower. TV. Phone. B&B £56 to £78. Deposit: £30. Rooms for disabled. Children welcome. Dogs welcome in bedrooms only. Afternoon teas (*The Which? Hotel Guide*)

ROMSEY Hampshire   map 2

Old Manor House 🍾

21 Palmerston Street, Romsey SO51 8GF   COOKING 3
TEL: (01794) 517353   COST £27–£49

This picture-postcard Tudor restaurant in the centre of Romsey sets the right tone. Venerable beams enclose the dining-room, and a real fire crackles in the grate on chillier nights. The cooking is less Henry VIII, however, and more classical Italian. At its heart is the native experience of Mauro Bregoli, who is, among other things, a skilled butcher. He makes his own sausages from locally reared pigs, and also cures prosciutto and coppa (pork neck); if your taste for the animal is insatiable, a main course of boned pig's head stuffed with morels and served with borlotti beans and red onion marmalade is often available. New Forest mushrooms are enthusiastically used in simple risotti or with gnocchi in a cream sauce, and local fish turns up in dishes such as grilled sea bass with fresh herbs, or scallops served on warm tomato concasse with basil and olive oil.

White chocolate mousse, Bakewell tart with armagnac prunes, and nougat glacé with red fruit coulis shift the desserts in a noticeably French direction. Heavy salting and too much oil spoiled one party's chances of enjoyment, and it has to be said that the youthful staff seem to lack both confidence and English, so perhaps there is room for improvement. Wines are as prestigious as they come, with prices to match, and chosen with an eye for quality first. If this means top-growth claret, so be it, but Italy fares extremely well too. Over a dozen house wines below £20 are a big help, starting with house Italian at £9.95. CELLARMAN'S CHOICE: Perusai 1993, Azienda Barbarossa, £23.50; Carignano del Sulcis 'Rocca Rubia' 1991, Santadi, £19.50.

CHEF/PROPRIETOR: Mauro Bregoli   OPEN: Tue to Sun L 12 to 2, Tue to Sat D 7 to 9.30   CLOSED: 2 weeks Christmas   MEALS: alc (main courses £12.50 to £17.50). Set L and D £17.50   SERVICE: not inc, card slips closed   CARDS: Access, Amex, Switch, Visa   DETAILS: 45 seats. Private parties: 10 main room, 22 private room. Car park. Vegetarian meals. Children welcome. Smart dress preferred. No cigars/pipes in dining-room. No music

---

ROSS-ON-WYE Hereford & Worcester   map 5

▲ *Pheasants* ▮ ❣✳

52 Edde Cross Street, Ross-on-Wye HR9 7BZ   COOKING 1*
TEL: (01989) 565751   COST £34–£41

The rooms in this former cider tavern, dating from the seventeenth century, are small but comfortable and inviting. Victorian-style pictures adorn the dark-red walls, napery shines, and glasses sparkle. Eileen Brunnarius makes much of carefully selected produce, including Trelough duck, Wye pike and local asparagus, from which she fashions a short and interesting menu. Braised lambs' hearts, and mushroom and mascarpone gnocchi with truffles, indicate an unusual but welcome approach within a predominantly Anglo-European framework. The food has been dubbed 'perfectly acceptable' while perhaps lacking some of the promised excitement. Desserts have included a good apple and cinnamon pancake, and poached clementines with a moist slice of Tunisian almond cake to soak up the brandy syrup.

The wine list tries not to be confusing, and the highly personal choice shows flair and a taste for bright, up-to-the-minute excitement. There are lively tasting notes, but in any case Adrian Wells is generally on hand with advice and a dose of infectious enthusiasm. CELLARMAN'S CHOICE: Bonny Doon Ca' del Solo Malvasia Bianca 1994, Santa Cruz, California, £19.20; Blue Pyrenees Cabernet/Shiraz/Merlot 1990, Victoria, Australia, £21.30.

▮ *denotes an outstanding wine cellar;* ❣ *denotes a good wine list, worth travelling for.*

CHEF/PROPRIETOR: Eileen Brunnarius   OPEN: Tue to Sat D only 7 to 10; L Tue to Fri by arrangement   CLOSED: 25 Dec to 2 Jan, 1 week early June   MEALS: Set D £21.50 (2 courses) to £25. BYO £3   SERVICE: net prices   CARDS: Access, Amex, Delta, Diners, Switch, Visa   DETAILS: 22 seats. Private parties: 10 main room. Vegetarian meals. No children under 12. Smart dress preferred. No smoking in dining-room. Wheelchair access (no WC). Music   ACCOMMODATION: 2 rooms. B&B £30 to £60

ROWDE Wiltshire   map 2

George & Dragon ✸ ✓ /96

High Street, Rowde SN10 2PN   COOKING 3
TEL: (01380) 723053   FAX: (01380) 724738   COST £17–£45

The George & Dragon doesn't look much from the outside – a seventeenth-century roadside pub of modest proportions. But Tim and Helen Withers have succeeded in turning it into one of the best pub/restaurants of its kind anywhere in the country. People love the place. They talk about the bare boards and plain pubby furnishings, the 'smiling Wiltshire lasses' who serve in cheerful 'hail-fellow-well-met' style, and the sheer quality of the food – not to mention the value for money. One menu is served throughout the pub and you can eat in the bar, the garden or the modest dining-room. Fish is Tim Withers's healthy obsession: consignments arrive regularly from Cornwall and the specials board is packed with real treasures for piscophiles. The cooking stands or falls on freshness and timing, and there are seldom any serious complaints on either front. Whether it be a plate of 'outstanding' Rossmore oysters, or cod with 'a particularly tasty' parsnip and olive oil mash, or steamed black bream on a bed of chard laced with ginger, the kitchen delivers.

The remainder of the menu is on a par: it ranges far and wide for crostini, lambs' kidneys with bacon and a mustard sauce, mooli rice-cakes with spicy lentil sauce, and confit of duck with Chinese plum sauce. Reporters also commend great helpings of fruit crumble with clotted cream, and delicately poached peaches in a raspberry and champagne sauce. The helpfully annotated wine list should provide more than enough possibilities for the adventurous palate. Sixteen wines are served by the glass; house wines start at £8.25 a bottle.

CHEF: Tim Withers   PROPRIETORS: Tim and Helen Withers   OPEN: Tue to Sat 12 to 2, 7 to 10   CLOSED: 2 weeks Christmas and New Year   MEALS: alc (main courses £6 to £18). Set L £8.50 (2 courses) to £10. BYO £5   SERVICE: not inc, card slips closed   CARDS: Access, Delta, Switch, Visa   DETAILS: 30 seats. 20 seats outside. Private parties: 30 main room. Car park. Vegetarian meals. Children's helpings. No smoking in dining-room. No music

---

RYE East Sussex   map 3

Landgate Bistro £

5–6 Landgate, Rye TN31 7LH   COOKING 2*
TEL: (01797) 222829   COST £19–£32

A couple staying at a B&B in Rye asked their landlady for a recommendation, were pointed in the direction of the Landgate and were grateful for the tip. Both the broad range of choice and the 'interesting and imaginative' flavour combinations induced frissons of delight. The ambience is unpretentious, all 'suburban chintz and lots of magnolia paint', the tables dressed with oilcloth.

Toni Ferguson-Lees is fast becoming one of the country's more noticed women chefs for her style of uncluttered modern cooking, essentially British with gentle Mediterranean overtones. A February dinner began with duck confit that had been grilled to crisp up the skin; sitting on a mound of Puy lentils, it impressed not least because it avoided excess fattiness. Delicate judgment was shown in an orange and vermouth sauce to accompany scallops and brill, while a good piece of cod came with a sauce of grated ginger. Simple meat cookery takes in items such as roast pigeon breast in a red wine reduction, while sharply flavoured sorbets, classical lemon tart and crème caramel won't overload the stomach at meal's end. Service is relaxed, but 'very correct'. The enterprising wine list brings in a good diversity of choice at sane prices, starting with house French at £7.90.

CHEF: Toni Ferguson-Lees   PROPRIETORS: Nick Parkin and Toni Ferguson-Lees   OPEN: Tue to Sat D only 7 to 9.30 (10.30 Sat)   CLOSED: 1 week Christmas, 1 week summer, 1 week autumn   MEALS: alc (main courses £8 to £12). Set D £14.90 (Tue to Thur)   SERVICE: net prices, card slips closed   CARDS: Access, Amex, Delta, Diners, Switch, Visa   DETAILS: 30 seats. Private parties: 30 main room. Children's helpings. No cigars/pipes in dining-room. Music

---

ST IVES Cornwall   map 1

Pig 'n' Fish

Norway Lane, St Ives TR26 1LZ   COOKING 2*
TEL: (01736) 794204   COST £26–£42

The loft of a former pilchard shed, not far from the Tate Gallery, has been simply converted and decorated with interesting paintings. 'High-grade modern seafood cooking in an unpretentious setting' was one reporter's succinct view of the attractions. The preoccupation with fish excludes almost everything else but duck, and local supplies underpin the quality. A Mediterranean breeze wafts through the menu, in the form of cod with a basil crust served with haricot beans in tomato and olive oil, but other flavours make an impact too: mackerel tortilla is served with a tomato salsa, while a plate of sole with ginger, spring onion and soy sauce provided 'superb texture and marvellous flavour' for one reporter.

Sometimes the day's fish might end up simply as a well-timed ragoût, but whatever its destiny it invariably benefits from appropriately light treatment. 'Puddings are worth leaving room for' and generally include something chocolatey and perhaps a lemon surprise pudding, or 'an amazing plum clafoutis'. Prices may seem expensive, but the value is good. Wines are mostly white, well chosen and fairly priced; house wines are around £10. Opening times may vary with the season, so it is best to check first.

CHEF: Paul Sellars   PROPRIETORS: Debby and Paul Sellars   OPEN: Wed to Sun L 12.30 to 1.30, Wed to Sat D 7 to 9.30   CLOSED: Nov to Feb (opening occasional weekends – phone to check)   MEALS: alc (main courses £10.50 to £14.50). Set L and D £17.50   SERVICE: not inc   CARDS: Access, Visa   DETAILS: 30 seats. 30 seats outside. Private parties: 25 main room. Children's helpings. No cigars/pipes in dining-room. Music

ST KEYNE Cornwall   map 1

▲ Well House 🍴✕

St Keyne PL14 4RN
TEL: (01579) 342001   FAX: (01579) 343891
off B3254, 3m S of Liskeard; at end of village near   COOKING 3*
church follow sign to St Keyne Well   COST £32–£45

A single-track lane leads to the old house, which is more cosmopolitan inside
than the quiet countryside round about might suggest. Jazzy fabric in the bar and
bright colours everywhere give the place a positive feel that is echoed in the
welcome from Nick Wainford. He is 'ever present' without getting in the way,
and is observant and full of good advice for those who seek it. The appeal is
first-rate country cooking without fuss, using local lamb, game and line-caught
fish from Looe just three or four miles down the road, and the whole business
shines with sheer professionalism.

A carefully constructed menu (the same format at lunch and dinner) begins
with soup, perhaps a chicken liver parfait with chutney, a fish option, or a salad
incorporating duck confit or maybe pigeon. Balance is characteristic of the
operation, and although Wayne Pearson is at home with contemporary
flourishes of pesto compote and avocado salsa, he is not a flashy cook. The food is
interesting without being too complex, as in a saddle of rabbit stuffed with
rabbit confit, decked out with all kinds of mushrooms, in a properly reduced
sauce.

Sound technique is what provides the impact from pastry dishes to fish
cookery (fish typically accounts for two of the four main-course options) to a
simple but effective iced lemon parfait with raspberry coulis. Meals begin with
herby olives and a pastry or mini-kebab, and finish with excellent candied
orange peel over coffee. Bread is exceptionally good. A sound wine list caters for
a wide range of tastes and pockets, with house wines at £8.75.

CHEF: Wayne Pearson   PROPRIETOR: Nick Wainford   OPEN: all week 12.30 to 1.30, 7 to 9
MEALS: Set L and D £19.95 (2 courses) to £29.70   SERVICE: not inc, card slips closed   CARDS:
Access, Amex, Delta, Switch, Visa   DETAILS: 32 seats. 18 seats outside. Private parties: 32
main room. Car park. Children welcome. No children under 8 D. Smart dress preferred. No
smoking in 1 dining-room. Wheelchair access (also WC). No music   ACCOMMODATION: 7
rooms, all with bath/shower. TV. Phone. B&B £60 to £105. Deposit: £50. Children welcome.
Baby facilities. Dogs welcome. Garden. Swimming-pool (*The Which? Hotel Guide*)

ST MARGARET'S AT CLIFFE Kent   map 3

▲ Wallett's Court 🍴✕

West Cliffe, St Margaret's at Cliffe CT15 6EW
TEL: (01304) 852424   FAX: (01304) 853430
on B2058, off A258 Dover to Deal road, 3m NE of   COOKING 2
Dover   COST £34–£48

Wallett's Court was mentioned in the Domesday Book – and bequeathed to
Robert de Crevecoeur as payment for the design of the tower in Dover Castle that
bears his name – and is now a listed building in which oak beams and Adam

fireplaces abound. 'A view of the sea is just possible on a good day.' Its transformation into a hotel and restaurant 20 years ago owes everything to the dedication of the Oakley family. It has a relaxed atmosphere and everything is done 'with the minimum of fuss'.

A strong British theme runs through the menu, from jugged hare in a damson wine sauce with suet dumplings, and pigeon macerated in local Bishop's Finger ale, to Stilton pancakes, and wild Hebridean salmon served with a Canterbury watercress sauce. Choice is generous on the monthly-changing fixed-price menu, and three courses are increased to five by adding a fish course and a sorbet. Despite the food's richness, flavours tend to be gentle or subtle rather than bold. Puddings have included crème brûlée and a dark chocolate cream with lemon syllabub. 'This was impressive eating,' concluded a couple who stayed two nights. Wines are predominantly French and mostly under £20, beginning with house Burgundy at £14.

CHEF: Chris Oakley   PROPRIETORS: the Oakley family   OPEN: Sun L 12 to 2, all week D 7 to 9 CLOSED: 24 to 28 Dec   MEALS: Set L Sun £15.50. Set D £22.50 to £28. BYO £5   SERVICE: not inc   CARDS: Access, Amex, Delta, Diners, Switch, Visa   DETAILS: 50 seats. Private parties: 30 main room, 20 private room. Car park. Vegetarian meals. Children's helpings. No smoking in dining-room. Wheelchair access (3 steps; also WC). No music   ACCOMMODATION: 12 rooms, all with bath/shower. TV. Phone. B&B £35 to £80. Rooms for disabled. Children welcome. Garden (*The Which? Hotel Guide*)

ST MARY BOURNE   Hampshire   map 2

▲ *George Inn* ⁵⁑ £ | NEW ENTRY |

St Mary Bourne, nr Andover SP11 6BG
TEL: (01264) 738340   COOKING 1*
off B3048, 3m SE of Hurstbourne Tarrant   COST £19–£41

The Bradleys acquired the old inn, a listed building in a pretty village, in 1995 and set about renovating it fairly comprehensively. The result is a set of 'themed' rooms variously dedicated to fishing, military pursuits and cricket. Significantly, the pub side of the business remains intact, while Mark Robertson (formerly at Fifehead Manor; see entry, Middle Wallop) has taken charge of the kitchen. An oyster bar with marble top and high chairs dispenses Helford oysters at £1 each, alongside provençale fish soup and smoked haddock kedgeree, while a bar menu offers ham sandwiches, pork sausages with onion gravy, and steak and kidney pie.

Tables in the beamed, brick-walled, white-plastered dining-room are small and closely packed, but a 'happy ambience' pervades, and the choice might include twice-baked cheese soufflé, dill-marinated herrings, or 'wonderful' thickly cut smoked salmon with buttered brown bread. 'Incredibly good' rump steak impressed an inspector, as did rare duck breast with 'more taste than rare duck usually has'. Suppliers have obviously come up trumps with materials, and Mark Robertson has dealt with them skilfully. Crème brûlée, lemon tart, or bread-and-butter pudding may follow, and well-timed and helpful service is overseen by a friendly head waiter. Good value continues into the short and sensibly priced wine list, which starts at £7 for house wine.

CHEF: Mark Robertson PROPRIETORS: Simon and Fiona Bradley OPEN: all week 12 to 2.15, 7 to 9.30 MEALS: alc (main courses £7.50 to £15). Set L £11.50 (2 courses) to £13.50. Bar food available SERVICE: not inc, card slips closed CARDS: Access, Delta, Switch, Visa DETAILS: 60 seats. 20 seats outside. Private parties: 24 main room, 14 private room. Car park. Vegetarian meals. Children's helpings L. Smart dress preferred. No smoking in 1 dining-room. Wheelchair access (also WC). Music ACCOMMODATION: 2 rooms, both with bath/shower. TV. B&B £45 (double room). Garden

---

ST MICHAEL'S ON WYRE Lancashire   map 8

Mallards

Garstang Road, St Michael's on Wyre PR3 0TE   COOKING 1
TEL: (01995) 679661   COST £17–£33

The building was once the village smithy, though you wouldn't know it now. John and Ann Steel have turned it into a well-supported, modest but reliable restaurant, offering sound cooking, good value and lots of decorative ducks. Bury black pudding remains a stalwart, richly sauced with cheese and leeks on one occasion, with apple and grain mustard on another. Stilton tart with tomato and basil sauce and mildly curried mushroom pilaff are alternatives, while Sunday lunch adds a second-course soup or sorbet choice. An inspector was impressed by a 'very tasty and succulent' fillet of salmon given the Véronique treatment with grapes and a creamy wine sauce, garnished with curls of cucumber. Vegetables are thoughtfully presented, and meals might end with raspberry crème brûlée or orange segments in Cointreau. The wine list takes in a broad spread of international standards at sensible prices. House Burgundy is £8.50.

CHEF: John Steel PROPRIETORS: John and Ann Steel OPEN: Sun L 12 to 2.30, Mon to Sat D 7 to 9 (9.30 Sat) CLOSED: 1 week Jan, 2 weeks July/Aug MEALS: Set L Sun £10.95, Set D £15.50 (2 courses) to £18.95 SERVICE: not inc, card slips closed CARDS: Access, Delta, Switch, Visa DETAILS: 24 seats. Private parties: 36 main room. Car park. Children welcome. Smart dress preferred. No smoking while others eat. Wheelchair access (no WC). Music

---

SALE Greater Manchester   map 8

Hanni's £   NEW ENTRY

---

4 Brooklands Road, Sale M33 3SQ   COOKING 1
TEL/FAX: (0161) 973 6606   COST £20–£35

Hanni Al-Taraboulsy featured in the *Guide* some years ago when he was at Withington. The good news is that he has re-surfaced in larger premises opposite Brooklands Metrolink Station. His extended menu is a broad sweep through Turkey via Lebanon and Israel to Egypt and North Africa. Ingredients are judiciously bought from the Manchester markets, and the results are 'good solid fare'. 'Egg-shaped' kibbeh and crisp falafel garnished with raw red cabbage are approved starters, while hearty main dishes include numerous variations on kebabs and grills as well as roast poussin stuffed with pine-kernels, and kleftiko with okra. Puddings are sticky, and Turkish coffee contains 'enough caffeine to keep you awake for a fortnight'. Service maintains just the right blend of courtesy and family hospitality. The catholic wine list has a promising Middle Eastern contingent. House French is £11.

CHEF: Mr Hooninian   PROPRIETOR: Hanni Al-Taraboulsy   OPEN: Mon to Sat D only 6 to 10.30
(11 Fri and Sat)   CLOSED: last 2 weeks Aug   MEALS: alc (main courses £7 to £11.50)   SERVICE:
not inc   CARDS: Access, Delta, Switch, Visa   DETAILS: 50 seats. Private parties: 50 main room.
Vegetarian meals. Children's helpings. Smart dress preferred. Music. Air-conditioned

---

SANDGATE Kent   map 3

▲ *Sandgate Hotel,*
La Terrasse ▾ ⸸⋇   **NEW ENTRY**

The Esplanade, Sandgate CT20 3DY   COOKING 3
TEL: (01303) 220444   FAX: (01303) 220496   COST £27–£52

Only a main road separates this three-storeyed Victorian terraced house from the pebble beach and the Channel. Tables are placed optimistically outside in anticipation of fine weather, while inside the large mirrors, stained glass, flowers, and picture windows facing out to sea add up to the feel of an 'English country house mixed with French flair'. Indeed, the two strands permeate the entire place. Zara Jackson (English) looks after front-of-house, helped by French staff who have eyes trained to pick up every detail, while Samuel Gicqueau (French) cooks a sophisticated menu that combines classical and modern ideas in a way that would look very much at home across the water.

When the restaurant opened in mid-1995 the owners immediately set themselves very high standards, and 'are thriving on achieving them'. The workmanship is evident in a dish of poached morels stuffed with a powerful poultry mousse, and served with asparagus and a strong meat sauce. For anybody who feels life is too short to stuff a morel, consider half a dozen thick spears of white asparagus in June, partnered by a 'wonderful, thick, smooth' sauce mousseline, or a small fillet of sea bass topped with finely sliced rounds of potato and accompanied by a thin slick of red wine sauce.

Pré-salé lamb has been tender and intensely flavoured, served on potato rösti and finely diced ratatouille vegetables. The cooking is characterised by high-quality ingredients handled with skill and care, and desserts are taken as seriously as everything else, from a combination of mango and clove-scented rhubarb on a crumbly sablé biscuit, to a thin wedge of chocolate 'that turned from sponge to runny mousse as the spoon cut into it'. Valrhona chocolate is at the root of it, and a lemon verbena ice-cream to the side of it. Wine service is friendly and experienced, although accurate tasting notes on the list help answer many questions. A well-balanced range majors on France, naturally, but is not afraid to branch off into the New World, Spain and Germany. French house wines are £11.50. CELLARMAN'S CHOICE: Montagny premier cru, La Grande Roche 1993, Louis Latour, £17.50; Chorey-lès-Beaune 1992, Dom. Maillard, £22.

See the inside of the front cover for an explanation of the 1 to 5 rating system
for cooking standards.

CHEFS: Samuel Gicqueau and Hervé Dodane   PROPRIETORS: Zara Jackson and Samuel Gicqueau   OPEN: Tue to Sun L 12 to 1.30, Tue to Sat D 7 to 9.30   CLOSED: second week Jan to second week Feb   MEALS: alc (main courses £11 to £16). Set L and D £16.50 to £21.50   SERVICE: not inc   CARDS: Access, Amex, Delta, Switch, Visa   DETAILS: 26 seats. 16 seats outside. Private parties: 26 main room. Car park. Children's helpings. Smart dress preferred. No smoking in dining-room. Wheelchair access (no WC). Music   ACCOMMODATION: 15 rooms, all with bath/shower. TV. Phone. B&B £35 to £67. Deposit: £20. Children welcome. Baby facilities. Afternoon teas

---

SANDIWAY Cheshire   map 7

▲ *Nunsmere Hall* 🍴 ⚡

Tarporley Road, Sandiway CW8 2ES
TEL: (01606) 889100   FAX: (01606) 889055   COOKING 2*
off A49, 4m SW of Northwich   COST £29–£61

Nunsmere's history is entwined with ocean-going cruise liners and such, having been built at the beginning of the century for the Brocklebanks of maritime fame. Commandeered as a hospital during the war, it has found its modern vocation, like many such places, as a country-house hotel. It enjoys a splendid site in Cheshire farming country, but has perhaps suffered a little from the blandness that big corporate business inevitably brings.

Stephen Williams arrived in the kitchens in February 1996, and the cooking style – English country-house with gentle Mediterranean inflections – continues as before. A lunch menu that offers both pressed vegetable terrine and crushed potatoes with asparagus suggests that downward pressure is a favoured technique. One reporter began a spring dinner with 'a refreshing pile of tomato flesh' – a timbale, in fact – adorned with aubergine purée and garnished with infant scallops. Fish cookery encompasses brill fillet with crab and gingered cooking juices, and baked cod with the famous shrimps from Morecambe Bay. An inspection dish of assiette of lamb thriftily brought together a herb-coated cutlet, kidneys, slices of liver and tongue and a tartlet of sauced sweetbreads: 'it all looked a little daunting, but restraint in the saucing avoided any feeling of surfeit.' Hot apricot soufflé with almond ice-cream is an agreeably light dessert, while exotic tastes may find nougat glacé with jasmine tea and candied oranges more their sort of thing. The young front-of-house team gives seriously focused service.

Wines major in expensive classical France, but there is a fair proportion under £20 elsewhere. The notes are thoughtfully written, although the evaluation of 1994 Chablis as 'a truly great vintage' might provoke debate among aficionados. House selections start at £13.25.

CHEF: Stephen Williams   PROPRIETORS: Malcolm and Julie McHardy   OPEN: all week 12 to 2, 7 to 10   MEALS: alc D (main courses £13 to £22). Set L £16.95 (2 courses) to £19.50. Bar food available   SERVICE: net prices, card slips closed   CARDS: Access, Amex, Diners, Switch, Visa   DETAILS: 60 seats. 50 seats outside. Private parties: 70 main room, 22 to 70 private rooms. Car park. Vegetarian meals. Children's helpings. No children under 12 D. Smart dress preferred. No smoking in dining-room. Wheelchair access (also WC). Music   ACCOMMODATION: 32 rooms, all with bath/shower. TV. Phone. Room only £98.50 to £275. Rooms for disabled. Children welcome. Afternoon teas. Garden (*The Which? Hotel Guide*)

SAWBRIDGEWORTH Hertfordshire   map 3

Shoes | NEW ENTRY |

52 Bell Street, Sawbridgeworth CM21 9AN   COOKING 1
TEL: (01279) 722554   COST £22–£46

The Shoes have walked all the way from High Ongar in Essex, where they
appeared in the 1995 *Guide*, and the same owners re-opened for business in an
attractive older quarter of Sawbridgeworth in March 1996. The wooden bar of
what was the coaching-inn has been painted white, the dining-room has a
spacious feel, and former sous-chef Allan Stephens is now in the driving seat,
serving up a generous menu of English and French dishes from starters of
bouillabaisse or grilled goats'-cheese salad, to pot-roast lamb shank, braised
oxtail, and chargrilled tuna. At a summer lunch, ravioli of chicken 'looking like a
Cornish pasty' weighed in as 'perhaps the world's biggest single raviolo',
helped by a rich, creamy wild mushroom sauce that was 'classical and delicious'.
Pink Barbary duck breast has impressed more than chocolate mousse. Prices are
reasonable for both food and wine; a sound, 50-strong list includes some
half-bottles, and house French is £9.95.

CHEF: Allan Stephens   PROPRIETORS: Lyndon Wootton, and Peter and Doreen Gowan   OPEN:
Tue to Fri L 12 to 2, Mon to Sat D 7.30 to 9.30 (10 Sat)   CLOSED: 2 weeks after Christmas, first 2
weeks Aug   MEALS: alc D (main courses £10 to £14.50). Set L £9.50 (1 course) to £15, Set D
Mon to Thur £16   SERVICE: not inc   CARDS: Access, Visa   DETAILS: 60 seats. Private parties:
75 main room, 30 to 45 private rooms. Vegetarian meals. Children's helpings. Wheelchair
access (also WC). Music. Air-conditioned

SAXTON North Yorkshire   map 9

Plough Inn ⁵✹

Headwell Lane, Saxton LS24 9PB
TEL: (01937) 557242   COOKING 2
off A162, between Tadcaster and Sherburn in Elmet   COST £18–£39

'I first discovered the Plough after visiting a nearby exhibition, and was
delighted to find a small village pub that obviously has a real passion for food,'
began one report. Built as a farmhouse in the nineteenth century and converted
to a pub in the 1920s, it is a modest and simply decorated inn with a 'cottagey
feel' and a 'bewildering' selection of dishes chalked on blackboards. 'We cover a
wide range of cooking styles and influences,' confirms Simon Treanor, who
appears equally at home with tomato tartlet with pesto, black pudding with red
cabbage, or Chinese-style breast of duck with black-bean sauce.

Lunch can be as simple as hot beef in a toasted baguette, or a ploughman's,
while specials might include venison liver and braised onions, or cod with
curried butter sauce. Pigeons from the local estate have been served with Puy
lentils and wild mushroom sauce. Puddings might be, in one reporter's view,
what 'an averagely skilled cook could knock up', but have included a rich, dense
chocolate marquise and a 'quite scrumptious' almond tart. Staff are 'pleasant and
friendly young people', while a bright and enterprising list of good-value wines

packs in bags of interest below £20, the bulk of it from outside France. House wine is £7.95.

CHEF: Simon Treanor   PROPRIETORS: Simon and Nicola Treanor   OPEN: Tue to Sun L 12 to 2, Tue to Sat D 6.30 to 9.30   CLOSED: 1 to 11 Jan   MEALS: alc (main courses £8.50 to £12.50). Set L Sun £11.95, Set once-a-month 'gourmet' D £29.50 (inc wine)   SERVICE: not inc, card slips closed   CARDS: Access, Delta, Switch, Visa   DETAILS: 65 seats. 16 seats outside. Private parties: 65 main room. Car park. Vegetarian meals. Children's helpings. Smart dress preferred. No smoking in dining-room. Wheelchair access (also WC). Music. Air-conditioned

---

SEAFORD East Sussex   map 3

Quincy's ▼ ⁵✳

42 High Street, Seaford BN25 1PL   COOKING 2*
TEL: (01323) 895490   COST £32–£38

Few would take issue with the reader who called Seaford 'a culinary backwater', but it would look a whole lot bleaker without Quincy's. Fish from the local catch and a fine small butcher are both credited by Ian Dowding as the underpinnings of his success, but his own undoubted flair is what draws the enthusiasm.

Fixed-price dinner menus work within reasonably classical guidelines, with French and Mediterranean influences to the fore. A starter of 'very tasty and unusual' duck sausage with bubble and squeak and onion gravy was 'nearly a meal in itself'. Main courses offer steamed suet pudding of venison with smoked bacon and mushrooms, as well as more provocative twists such as rack of lamb with a filo parcel of more lamb, chopped and spiced, and a mint salsa. Lemon soufflé with caramel ice-cream, and 'intensely flavoured' dark chocolate cake with white chocolate ice-cream, can be show-stopping: 'We found them simply stunning, and sat passing spoonfuls round in disbelief.' Service is pleasant and well informed. Wines hail from far and wide, and many are from good vintages and well-respected producers. The approachable list includes many bottles under £20 and a good handful under £10. Prices are keen throughout and the half-bottle selection is strong. House wines start at £8.25 (£1.75 a glass). CELLARMAN'S CHOICE: Breaky Bottom Müller-Thurgau 1990, England, £11.75; St-Emilion, Ch. Fombrauge 1985, £23.90.

CHEF: Ian Dowding   PROPRIETORS: Ian and Dawn Dowding   OPEN: Sun L 12 to 2, Tue to Sat D 7 to 10   MEALS: Set L and D £18.95 (2 courses) to £22.45. BYO £5   SERVICE: not inc   CARDS: Access, Amex, Visa   DETAILS: 30 seats. Private parties: 20 main room. Vegetarian meals. Children's helpings. No cigars/pipes in dining-room. Music

---

SEATON BURN Tyne & Wear   map 10

▲ *Horton Grange* ⁵✳

Seaton Burn NE13 6BU
TEL: (01661) 860686   FAX: (01661) 860308   COOKING 2*
off A1, at Stannington, 3m N of Newcastle upon Tyne   COST £41–£49

Despite being within the boundaries of Newcastle, Horton Grange affords visitors the experience of being in a 'quintessential small country hotel'. Interiors are done in muted colours, pale green in the lounge and cream in the dining-room, which has a view of the garden. Stephen Martin cooks five-course menus in the grand English country mode, making full use of seasonal garden produce. An inspector felt that there may be some over-reliance on sweetness in sauces and relishes to accompany meat, but the obvious capability of the cooking stills most doubts.

Among starters may be 'smooth and rich' chicken liver parfait with a top layer of grain-mustard mousse, while main courses may include suprême of brill with a dill and Chablis sauce, or rack of lamb ('first-class new season's meat') with a shortcrust tartlet of onions and garlicky breadcrumbs. Desserts are generally made up of many components, as in a brandy-snap basket of poached pear with brown bread ice-cream and a mango and white rum coulis. Hot soufflés are impressively executed, and 'good' cafetière coffee is accompanied by home-made petits fours. The short, serviceable wine list lacks vintage information for many of the white wines. House wines at £10.90 in all three colours are from Ochoa in Navarra.

CHEF: Stephen Martin PROPRIETORS: Andrew and Susan Shilton OPEN: Mon to Sat D only 7 to 8.45 MEALS: Set D £32 SERVICE: not inc, card slips closed CARDS: Access, Amex, Delta, Switch, Visa DETAILS: 32 seats. Private parties: 40 main room, 10 private room. Car park. Children's helpings. Smart dress preferred. No smoking in 1 dining-room. Wheelchair access (also WC). Music ACCOMMODATION: 9 rooms, all with bath/shower. TV. Phone. B&B £59 to £80. Rooms for disabled. Children welcome. Garden. Fishing (The Which? Hotel Guide)

SEMINGTON Wiltshire   map 2

Highfield House, Edward's Dining Room

Semington BA14 6JN
TEL: (01380) 870554   FAX: (01380) 871070   COOKING 1
on A350, 2m S of Melksham   COST £19–£29

The appeal of this symmetrical three-storeyed Georgian building (once a farmhouse, now a town house) derives from a careful approach to food, personal attention to guests, and value for money. Varnished floorboards, muted colours and impressive plasterwork contribute a certain stylishness, and teddies lounge throughout as if at a permanent picnic. Although on offer only three meal-times a week, Eddy Street's menu is a generous one, based around old favourites such as asparagus with hollandaise, or mushrooms simmered in cream and garlic and layered with filo pastry. A few bold ideas surface in the form of mango chutney with deep-fried fillet of sole, or plum and pineapple relish with duckling breast, while puddings tend to be as rich as chocolate marquise, or sticky toffee with pecan sauce. Service 'strikes a happy medium between familiarity and relaxed friendliness', and wines are chalked on a board, with prices starting at £8.95.

CHEF: Eddy Street PROPRIETORS: E.W. and P.L. Street OPEN: Sun L 12 to 2, Fri and Sat D 7 to 9.30 MEALS: Set L £13, Set D £17.50. BYO (no corkage) SERVICE: not inc CARDS: Access, Amex, Visa DETAILS: 40 seats. 12 seats outside. Private parties: 40 main room. Car park. Children's helpings. Music

---

'The proprietor was of unkempt appearance, with grubby, worn-out trousers, and kept helping himself to more beer.' (On eating in Scotland)

SHAFTESBURY Dorset   map 2

La Fleur de Lys ♀

| 25 Salisbury Street, Shaftesbury SP7 8EL | COOKING 2 |
| TEL: (01747) 853717 | COST £28–£49 |

Keep your eyes peeled, or you will miss the sign outside this loyally supported neighbourhood restaurant. A house fronts the street, but the dining-room occupies a converted loft over the stables at the back. The stairs – which start outside the kitchen door – may be steep, but at least 'they keep the enthusiastic young staff fit'. Enthusiasm is the key word here. You cannot fail to notice the meticulous attention to detail, particularly in the pink dining-room, which is as warm and invitingly cosy as an old-fashioned parlour.

The lunchtime *carte* is appreciated, and the kitchen is capable of delivering a succession of skilfully wrought 'works of art' based on top-notch ingredients. The delicacy shows in a pale gold chicken and saffron broth, and a duck liver parfait with raspberry vinaigrette. Good technique and sound judgement are at work in a perfectly timed saddle of lamb in filo pastry, or succulent duck leg with a fragrant herb stuffing on a pool of concentrated *jus*. Among desserts, look for the luscious home-made ice-creams and parfaits. An impressive collection of fine wines has been listed with enthusiastic tasting notes; the list majors on France, but there are exciting South Africans and New Zealanders among the New World wines. The reasonably priced house selection starts with a Spanish white at £9.95. CELLARMAN'S CHOICE: Thelema Mountain Vineyards Sauvignon Blanc 1995, Stellenbosch, South Africa, £15; Corbans Pinot Noir Private Bin 1992, Henderson, New Zealand, £17.50.

CHEFS: David Shepherd and Marc Preston   PROPRIETORS: David Shepherd, Mary Griffin and Marc Preston   OPEN: Tue to Sun L 12 to 2.30, Mon to Sat D 7 to 10   CLOSED: 2 weeks Jan   MEALS: alc (main courses L £12 to £13.50, D £14.50 to £16.50). Set D Mon to Thur £16.95 (2 courses), Set D Mon to Sat £19.95. Minimum £10 L   SERVICE: not inc   CARDS: Access, Amex, Diners, Visa   DETAILS: 46 seats. 10 seats outside. Private parties: 36 main room, 10 private room. Vegetarian meals. Children's helpings. Smart dress preferred. Music

---

SHEFFIELD South Yorkshire   map 9

Greenhead House ⅙✳

| 84 Burncross Road, Chapeltown, Sheffield S30 4SF | COOKING 2 |
| TEL: (0114) 246 9004 | COST £37–£48 |

The format remains unchanging at the Allens' stone house in the northern suburbs of the city: four courses, the second melon or soup, priced according to choice of main course. A domestic cottagey feel derives from the small scale, coal fireplace, and only four openings a week, while the soups they sell locally have a distinctively home-made appeal. Cooking is 'commendably geared to emphasising the flavour of good raw materials, accurately seasoned' and is characterised by fresh herbs and some assertive sauces.

The monthly-changing menu has a predominantly French tilt, and brings with it an understandable predilection for butter and cream, while cheese makes an appearance in a first-course Munster tart, and in a Gruyère sauce to accompany a fillet of poached John Dory stuffed with spinach and mushrooms. Other dishes such as loin of lamb adopt a more Mediterranean outlook in the form of a topping of basil and tomato mousse, the ensemble wrapped in filo pastry and baked. Pastry-work is good, and crème brûlée or tarte Tatin are likely to figure beside English farmhouse cheeses to finish. Most of the 20-odd mainly French wines are sensibly kept below £20. House Australian is £11.

CHEF: Neil Allen   PROPRIETORS: Mr and Mrs Neil Allen   OPEN: Wed to Sat D only 7 to 9 CLOSED: 2 weeks Easter, 2 weeks Aug   MEALS: Set D £28.50 to £30.50. BYO £3.50   SERVICE: not inc, card slips closed   CARDS: Access, Switch, Visa   DETAILS: 34 seats. Private parties: 36 main room. Car park. Children's helpings. Smart dress preferred. No smoking in dining-room. No music

Rafters

NEW ENTRY

220 Oakbrook Road, Nether Green, Sheffield S11 7ED
TEL: (0114) 230 4819

COOKING 1
COST £26–£33

Local boys Wayne and Jamie Bosworth teamed up in 1993 to open this restaurant above a terrace of suburban shops. Rafters support the ceiling, the walls are 'clean-faced' brick and the dining-room is hexagonal. Wayne has an impressive culinary CV and makes good use of his experience in a setting that tries hard to be elegant. The fixed-price dinner menu is sensibly short and full of interest. Seafood fish-cakes are given a shot of Cajun spices and served with mango dressing, while a neat variation on the spring roll theme includes a filling of monkfish wrapped in smoked salmon. Braised leg of lamb is enhanced by rich reduced juices, venison is cooked pink and accompanied by blackcurrant sauce. Puddings are 'posh' offerings such as an up-market bread-and-butter pudding with sticky toffee sauce. The wine list does its job in workmanlike fashion. House wine is £8.90.

CHEFS/PROPRIETORS: Wayne and Jamie Bosworth   OPEN: Mon and Wed to Sat D only 7 to 10 CLOSED: 26 to 28 Dec, 2 weeks Aug   MEALS: Set D £17.95. BYO £1   SERVICE: not inc   CARD: Amex   DETAILS: 40 seats. Private parties: 46 main room. Vegetarian meals. No children under 12. Smart dress preferred. Music

Smith's of Sheffield ⅝✳

NEW ENTRY

34 Sandygate Road, Sheffield S10 5RY
TEL: (0114) 266 6096

COOKING 1*
COST £26–£38

After a spell at Le Neptune and two years cooking for Sir Bernard Ashley in the US, Richard Smith has returned home to open his own restaurant in a former shop. The décor is refreshingly modern, the cooking polished and cosmopolitan with an obvious transatlantic undercurrent. Richard's menu changes weekly and there's a direct simplicity about his output. Meltingly tender confit of duck is perfectly matched with a sauce of oranges, sesame, ginger and soy, while rack of Welsh lamb is served with a rosemary-flavoured sauce spiked with cloves of garlic. Fish is top-quality stuff: a salad of 'superbly undercooked' seared tuna, and grilled red snapper with spicy prawn-cakes and tomato salsa, for example. Crème brûlée, and caramelised banana in puff pastry with rum and raisin ice-cream have made good puddings. The wine list is extensive, although prices, which start at £8.85, may seem a shade high for the area.

CHEFS: Richard Smith and Adrian Cooling   PROPRIETORS: Richard and Victoria Smith, and John and Sallie Tetchner   OPEN: Tue to Sat D only 6.30 to 10; other times by arrangement   CLOSED: last 2 weeks Aug   MEALS: alc (main courses £10 to £14). BYO £1   SERVICE: not inc, card slips closed   CARDS: Access, Delta, Switch, Visa   DETAILS: 45 seats. Private parties: 50 main room, 50 private room. Vegetarian meals. Children's helpings. Smart dress preferred. No smoking in dining-room. Wheelchair access (no WC). Music

---

SHELF   West Yorkshire   map 8

Bentley's £✷

12 Wade House Road, Shelf HX3 7PB   COOKING 1
TEL: (01274) 690992   COST £13–£37

The Bentleys' family business draws its trade from both Halifax and Bradford and succeeds because it provides 'good, solid, down-to-earth food at sensible prices'. The setting is a stone-floored cellar complete with original fireplaces, and the cooking spans the bistro repertoire: here an 'unfashionable cream sauce', there some modish ravioli. Breads, pasta and ice-creams are made on the premises, and the owners are proud of their vegetarian dishes. Fish is delivered from the market twice weekly; otherwise you might find anything from chicken in Dijon mustard sauce to mignons of lamb with mushroom risotto and Marsala. The kitchen saves its best until last, with some well-constructed offerings such as a sablé of fruit (including 'breathtaking' kirsch-soused cherries) with a ginger and butterscotch sauce, and tangy cheesecake dumplings. Prices are held in check on the well-balanced wine list, with house wines starting at £8.95.

CHEFS: Paul Bentley and Anthony Bickers   PROPRIETORS: Paul and Pamela Bentley   OPEN: Tue to Fri and Sun L 12 to 2, Tue to Sat D 6.30 to 9.30   CLOSED: Christmas to New Year, 2 weeks Aug   MEALS: alc (main courses £8.50 to £14). Set L Tue to Fri £4.95 (2 courses) to £6.50. BYO £3.50   SERVICE: not inc, card slips closed   CARDS: Access, Switch, Visa   DETAILS: 44 seats. Private parties: 24 main room. Vegetarian meals. Children's helpings. Smart dress preferred. No smoking in dining-room. Music

---

SHEPTON MALLET   Somerset   map 2

Blostin's

29 Waterloo Road, Shepton Mallet BA4 5HH   COOKING 2
TEL: (01749) 343648   COST £24–£37

In the setting of a plain green terraced house, the warm colours inside come as a pleasant surprise. The theme is a winey one, with red ceilings, wooden case ends and Margaret Loxton pictures, and the place feels 'very bistro'. So do some of the dishes from mix-and-match menus chalked on blackboards, which tend to favour traditional ways of doing things. Soups might be French onion or fish with rouille and croûtons, followed by beef wrapped in pastry, or duck with mushrooms and bacon, with desserts such as treacle and walnut tart or hot chocolate sponge.

Supplies are taken seriously, including fish from Newlyn and boar from a local farm. These above-average raw materials provide a firm foundation, and cooking times are well judged. At one meal a simple warm salad of poached smoked haddock in a vinaigrette proved a highlight. Bright, friendly but relaxed service by Lynn Reed is a plus, and so is the short list of well-priced wines arranged by grape variety. House French is £7.95.

CHEF: Nick Reed   PROPRIETORS: Nick and Lynne Reed   OPEN: Tue to Sat D only 7 to 9.30 CLOSED: 2 weeks Jan, 2 weeks Jun   MEALS: alc (main courses £11.50 to £14). Set D £13.95 (2 courses) to £15.95. BYO £2.50   SERVICE: not inc, card slips closed   CARDS: Access, Delta, Switch, Visa   DETAILS: 32 seats. Private parties: 32 main room, 18 private room. Vegetarian meals. Children welcome. No cigars/pipes in dining-room. Wheelchair access (no WC). Music

---

▲ Bowlish House 🍾

Wells Road, Shepton Mallet BA4 5JD
TEL/FAX: (01749) 342022   COOKING 2*
on A371, on outskirts of town   COST £20–£36

A Georgian house on the edge of a quiet market town within sight of the Mendips became a comfortable restaurant with rooms when Bob and Linda Morley took it over in 1988. They write that, while they try to stay attuned to modern culinary thinking, their art school background prevents them from serving any dish as the 'basic unadorned dollop' seen elsewhere. That said, flavours are clearly accorded their due. Marinated pigeon breast with celeriac purée and bacon makes an assertive enough starter, or there may be a tartlet of fresh and smoked salmon with salad and dill vinaigrette. Red mullet might be given the Moroccan touch with an aromatically spiced sauce and lemon couscous, while vegetarians are imaginatively treated to spinach and pine-nut sausage with tzatziki, followed perhaps by wild mushroom risotto cake with Parmesan shavings and a Madeira sauce. Piquancy is maintained at dessert in coconut ice-cream with lime-zest crème anglaise and passion-fruit, but there is also sticky toffee pudding for the diehards, or a selection of local cheeses.

The wine list is designed to encourage good drinking: variety is impressive, producers are sound and prices are very tempting across the board. Older French vintages intrigue, while Italy, Spain, dessert wines and half-bottles are all taken seriously, and there are six vintages of Ch. Musar. Ten interesting house wines are priced at £9.45. CELLARMAN'S CHOICE: Viognier, Vin de Pays des Comtes Rhodaniens 1993, £11.25; Vino da Tavola Toscana 'Il Latini' 1988, Il Vivaio, £26.50.

CHEF: Linda Morley   PROPRIETORS: Bob and Linda Morley   OPEN: L first Sun of month 1.30 (1 sitting; L other times by appointment), all week D 7 to 9.30   CLOSED: 1 week spring, 1 week autumn   MEALS: Set L Sun £12.95, Set D £22.50. BYO £4   SERVICE: not inc, card slips closed CARDS: Access, Amex, Visa   DETAILS: 24 seats. Private parties: 36 main room. Car park. Vegetarian meals. Children welcome. No smoking while others eat. No music ACCOMMODATION: 3 rooms, all with bath/shower. TV. B&B £48. Children welcome. Baby facilities. Pets welcome. In bedrooms only. Garden (The Which? Hotel Guide)

Dining-rooms where music, either live or recorded, is never played are signalled by No music in the details at the end of an entry.

SHERE Surrey   map 3

Kinghams £※ | NEW ENTRY |

Gomshall Lane, Shere GU5 9HB
TEL: (01483) 202168   COOKING 2
just off A25 Dorking to Guildford road   COST £26–£45

Kinghams is an extravagantly pretty white timbered cottage built in 1620 at a time when Shere made its wealth from wool. Previous owners scraped a living from sheep-stealing and were hanged for their pains, but Paul and Jason Baker have chosen a safer occupation. 'Traditional English food' says the sign outside, which might prepare you for meat and potato pie. In the event, salads of roasted red peppers and shiitakes, moules marinière, and medallions of lamb in filo stuffed with apricots and pine-nuts may be on offer, although to many people these are now traditional English dishes.

This is a much appreciated neighbourhood restaurant of considerable flair. Quality ingredients and conscientious preparation are hallmarks of the cooking. At one meal a trio of scallops served on the half-shell was adorned with julienne of leek, carrot and celery and anointed with a fine garlic and parsley butter. Tuna steak at inspection was 'beyond reproach – singed and charred outside, meltingly tender within', while a honey-coated duck breast with a sauce of pink peppercorns allowed the excellent meat to shine through. Simple desserts, such as orange and pink grapefruit segments marinated in Cointreau with a lime sorbet, may work better than fiddly things like pineapple-chunked crème brûlée served in a tulipe pastry with raspberry compote on the side. An enticingly broad-minded wine list keeps prices comfortably in check, there are some fine wines for those with money to spend, and a good spread of halves. House Australian is £8.95.

CHEF: Paul Baker   PROPRIETORS: Jason and Paul Baker   OPEN: Tue to Sun L 12 to 2, Tue to Sat D 7 to 9   CLOSED: bank hols   MEALS: alc (main courses £9 to £15). Set L and Set D Tue to Thur £10 (2 courses). Minimum £10   SERVICE: not inc   CARDS: Access, Amex, Delta, Switch, Visa   DETAILS: 45 seats. 20 seats outside. Private parties: 26 main room, 26 private room. Car park. Vegetarian meals. Children's helpings. No smoking in 1 dining-room. Music

SHINFIELD Berkshire   map 2

L'Ortolan

The Old Vicarage, Church Lane, Shinfield RG2 9BY
TEL: (01734) 883783   FAX: (01734) 885391   COOKING 4*
off A33, S of M4 junction 11   COST £47–£112

'It is to the credit of L'Ortolan,' wrote a reporter who considers Reading an unlikely location for a high-class French restaurant, 'that they have succeeded on the same site which drove Nico back to London.' That is no reflection on the estimable Mr Ladenis, but a recognition of the tenacity of the Burton-Races – entering their second decade here – and of the fact that enough people are prepared to pay what are generally considered to be high prices. The old red-brick vicarage instils a convincing sense of the countryside considering its proximity to the M4, and the style is 'elegant but simple', with rag-rolled apricot walls, strawberry-pink window-frames and cream tablecloths.

The range of dishes on offer is extremely varied, each one sounding like a minor masterpiece, and the level of technical accomplishment required is daunting. The menu helpfully spells everything out, so you know exactly what to expect of a dish. John Burton-Race is one of the few chefs who manages to bring off really complex ideas with any degree of panache. Dishes are often innovative without being too experimental, resulting in, for example, snails wrapped in a foie gras mousseline, deep-fried, and served with a Madeira and morel sauce. Different components work well together, as in an inspector's first course of scallops wrapped in cured salmon, served with a crisp potato rösti and a delicate celeriac cream sauce. At the same meal the sauce of cooking juices, Madeira and black truffle accompanying a roast breast of guinea-fowl impressed for its 'complex, multi-layered flavour'. The meat came on a bed of pearl barley 'cooked to about as good a consistency as you can cook pearl barley'.

'Vivid flavours, beautiful presentation' and attention to the right kind of detail mark out the kitchen's accomplishment, and desserts are as fine as anything else, from a hot coffee and chocolate soufflé to a 'magnificent, beautifully balanced' array of lemon desserts that include a 'perfect lemon tart'. Front-of-house needs attention: the tussle between the restaurant's role as a training institution for predominantly French waiting staff and reporters' high expectations at these prices is not as happily resolved as it might be. A greater sense of warmth and responsiveness would go some way towards improving things. Fine French wines at staggeringly high prices are tempered by well-chosen alternatives from lesser regions, and half-bottles are in reasonable supply. The house selection starts at £17.50 for Bergerac white and red.

CHEF: John Burton-Race PROPRIETOR: Burton-Race Restaurants plc OPEN: Tue to Sun L 12 to 2.15, Tue to Sat D 7 to 10 CLOSED: last 2 weeks Feb, last 2 weeks Aug MEALS: alc (main courses £28 to £33). Set L £29.50 to £85, Set D Tue to Fri £39.50 to £85, Set D Sat £85 (higher-priced set meals are for a minimum of 2 people and inc wine) SERVICE: not inc CARDS: Access, Amex, Diners, Switch, Visa DETAILS: 65 seats. Private parties: 40 main room, 10 and 25 private rooms. Car park. Vegetarian meals. Children's helpings. Smart dress preferred. No pipes in dining-room. Wheelchair access (also WC). Music

---

SHOTLEY Suffolk   map 6

Old Boot House ♥ ⁵✳

Main Road, Shotley IP9 1EY
TEL: (01473) 787755   COOKING 2
10m SE of Ipswich on B1456   COST £20–£39

The Boot stands on the end of a little peninsula, alone among rising corn-fields. Almost everyone has to travel to it, but invariably it seems worth the journey. In the dim and distant past it was a pub, but now the pastel-hued dining-room adorned with botanical prints provides a gentle setting for Ian Chamberlain's increasingly accomplished cooking. Ideas flow freely. 'Rashers' of smoked salmon are chargrilled and served on balsamic-dressed spinach leaves, while another starter of an individual rabbit pie contains pieces of tender and flavourful meat packed with mushrooms in a crust of exemplary pastry. Roasted walnuts and horseradish have made a happy marriage in a sauce with beef fillet, and black pudding comes with lamb tenderloin.

That talented hand with pastry can be seen at work again in a tartlet of peaches and Greek yoghurt under a strawberry glaze. There is much evidence of the right sort of creativity going on here, and most things succeed. Pamela Chamberlain runs 'an efficient, tight, friendly operation out front'. Adnams now supplies the wines, around 50 in all, a shrewdly chosen bunch at very competitive prices. French house wines are £7.50.

CHEF: Ian Chamberlain   PROPRIETORS: Ian and Pamela Chamberlain   OPEN: Tue to Sun L 12 to 1.30, Tue to Sat D 7 to 9   MEALS: alc (main courses £7 to £15)   SERVICE: not inc, card slips closed   CARDS: Access, Visa   DETAILS: 45 seats. Private parties: 45 main room. Car park. Children welcome. Smart dress preferred. No smoking in dining-room. No music

---

SHURDINGTON Gloucestershire   map 2

▲ The Greenway ❢ 🍷

Shurdington GL51 5UG
TEL: (01242) 862352   FAX: (01242) 862780   COOKING 2
on A46, 2½m S of Cheltenham   COST £29–£51

The Greenway (named after an old drovers' track that runs along the nearby Cotswold ridge) takes full advantage of its spellbinding location to weave an inescapably English kind of magic. The setting is the flagstoned magnificence of the great hall of a sixteenth-century manor-house, with log fires in every lounge. Dinner is served in a conservatory extension. Peter Fairclough took charge of the kitchen in February 1996, and seems determined to raise the Greenway's profile. The format is fixed price for lunch and dinner, and the style is enlivened with Mediterranean flourishes such as crab risotto with saffron sauce or goats'-cheese ravioli with tomato and basil salsa. Even the Welsh rarebit has sun-dried tomatoes on it.

At inspection, main courses were served in gargantuan portions, mobilising some fine raw materials, as in the crumbed sauté calf's liver with a lot of red onion compote in a port reduction. Very light cooking of vegetable garnishes seems a trademark, perhaps a bit old hat these days and certainly not acceptable in the case of potatoes. Bravado and an eye for presentation combine to produce puddings such as a slice of lemon tart next to a brandy-snap turret of lime parfait in which a pair of zigzag-shaped almond biscuits had been stuck. Prices reflect fair value for the context. Service moves at a stately pace and is fittingly formal. Wines are traditional and up-market, with an emphasis on claret, Burgundy and champagne, at some very lofty prices. Strong sections of vintage port and fine wines by the glass add interest. CELLARMAN'S CHOICE: Lussac-St-Emilion, Ch. Lyonnat 1990, £24.25; Montagny premier cru, La Grande Roche 1993, Louis Latour, £24.25.

'A surprising number of young ladies were serving. Whenever we reckoned we'd counted them all, another would materialise.' (On eating in Yorkshire)

CHEF: Peter Fairclough   PROPRIETORS: David and Valerie White   OPEN: Sun to Fri L 12.30 to 2, all week D 7.30 to 9.30 (8 Sun)   MEALS: Set L £17, Set D £29.50   SERVICE: not inc, card slips closed   CARDS: Access, Amex, Diners, Switch, Visa   DETAILS: 50 seats. 20 seats outside. Private parties: 64 main room, 14 and 24 private rooms. Car park. Vegetarian meals. Children's helpings. No children under 7. Smart dress preferred. No cigars/pipes in dining-room. Wheelchair access (also WC). Music   ACCOMMODATION: 19 rooms, all with bath/shower. TV. Phone. B&B £87.50 to £180. No children under 7. Afternoon teas. Garden (*The Which? Hotel Guide*)

SISSINGHURST Kent

map 3

Rankins' Restaurant

The Street, Sissinghurst TN17 2JH   COOKING 1
TEL: (01580) 713964   COST £31–£41

The Rankins have occupied this small, timber-framed, weatherboarded shop in the main street for over a decade. Reasonably spacious, with medieval 'hunting scene' curtains and everlasting flowers, it opens just four evenings a week, plus Sunday lunch-times. Baked gnocchi, ceviche of cod, and hot smoked salmon are among the varied dishes that Hugh Rankin turns out, alongside commendably light first courses such as caramelised onion and Cheddar cheese tart made from filo pastry. 'Simple yet enjoyable' is how an inspector described grilled salmon and cod interleaved together and served with a caper sauce, a sentiment that goes for much of the rest. Flavour combinations are sensible, including duck breast with mushrooms and green olives. Vegetables come in a help-yourself dish, and puddings have met with a mixed response, from 'hard' profiteroles to a 'wonderful' chocolate and almond cake with a lychee sorbet. Service from Leonora Rankin is 'relaxed and nicely paced', and the short, well-balanced, under-£20 wine list is strong on half-bottles too. House wine is £8.50.

CHEF: Hugh Rankin   PROPRIETORS: Hugh and Leonora Rankin   OPEN: Sun L 12.30 to 1.30, Wed to Sat D 7.30 to 9   CLOSED: 25 and 26 Dec, bank hols   MEALS: Set L Sun £18.95 (2 courses) to £21.95, Set D £19.95 (2 courses) to £24.95   SERVICE: not inc   CARDS: Access, Delta, Visa   DETAILS: 30 seats. Private parties: 25 main room. Vegetarian meals. Children's helpings. Smart dress preferred. Wheelchair access (no WC). No music

---

SOUTHALL Greater London

map 3

Brilliant £

72–74 Western Road, Southall UB2 5DZ   COOKING 2
TEL: (0181) 574 1928   FAX: (0181) 574 0276   COST £19–£31

'Indian food at its very best,' proclaimed one reporter. Since 1975 this restaurant has lived up to its name by concentrating on a short menu and putting flavour, freshness and subtlety above all else. There is barely a dish that has not drawn unqualified praise, and reports abound with mouthwatering superlatives. 'Divine' fish pakora is a slab of pomfret suffused with a marinade of spices and cooked to perfection in a casing of batter. Prawns are as delicate as can be, and butter chicken is a benchmark dish. Vegetables remain outstanding: okra are dry-cooked in a wok to retain their texture, aubergines have a revelatory firmness, and stupendous dhal recipes evolve over time. New this year is a dish called vegetable keema, which makes use of soya 'mince'. Service is casual, happy-go-lucky and entirely appropriate. Prices are low, portions are mighty: you may often get 'leftovers enough for a two further meals', observed a regular. Imported Tusker beer suits the food, lassi is 'excellent', and there are a few wines for good measure. House French is £7.50.

CHEF: D.K. Anand   PROPRIETORS: K.K. and D.K. Anand   OPEN: Tue to Fri L 12 to 2.30, Tue to Sun D 6 to 11.15 (midnight Fri and Sat; booking essential Fri, Sat and Sun)   CLOSED: Aug MEALS: alc (main courses £5 to £8)   SERVICE: 10%, card slips closed   CARDS: Access, Delta, Diners, Switch, Visa   DETAILS: 200 seats. Private parties: 80 main room, 70 private room. Vegetarian meals. Children's helpings. Smart dress preferred. No smoking in 1 dining-room. Wheelchair access (also WC). Music. Air-conditioned

Madhu's Brilliant £

39 South Road, Southall UB1 1SW   COOKING 1*
TEL: (0181) 574 1897   FAX: (0181) 813 8639   COST £19–£38

'All credit to Madhu's for trying to stand out from the crowd,' observes a reporter. The intentions of the place are clear as soon as you glance at the menu: here is Indian home cooking without compromise. Among the list of starters you might find the renowned butter chicken as well as chilli corn, fried mogo (cassava root) and something called 'pilli pilli bogha'. Moving on, there are tandooris (unlike at the Brilliant – see entry above – with its oven-free kitchen), masala chicken, keema peas, karahi specialities and a reliable supporting cast of vegetables, breads and rice. Some observers of the scene feel that standards have slipped of late, perhaps because Sanjay Anand and his head-chef brother are now putting most of their energies into catering functions. Lassi and lager are the preferred tipples; house wine is £8.

CHEFS: Sanjeev Anand and Satpal Gill   PROPRIETORS: Jagdish Kumar Anand, Krishna Kumari Anand, Sanjay Anand and Sanjeev Anand   OPEN: Mon and Wed to Fri L 12.30 to 2.30, Mon and Wed to Sun D 6 to 11.30 (midnight Fri and Sat)   MEALS: alc (main courses £3.50 to £10). Set L £12.50 (minimum 8), Set D £15 (minimum 8)   SERVICE: not inc, card slips closed   CARDS: Access, Amex, Delta, Diners, Switch, Visa   DETAILS: 104 seats. Private parties: 60 main room, 60 private room. Vegetarian meals. Children welcome. Smart dress preferred. Wheelchair access (no WC). Music. Air-conditioned

SOUTHSEA Hampshire   map 2

Bistro Montparnasse

103 Palmerston Road, Southsea PO5 3PS   COOKING 1*
TEL/FAX: (01705) 816754   COST £24–£42

This agreeable bistro continues to cater for locals and cross-Channel travellers. Gillian Scott runs an industrious kitchen, and the results are there for all to taste: home-made game sausages are served on a white vegetable purée, pickled silverside comes with gherkins and sour-dough bread. More speciality breads and focaccia head the billing, although they are priced as a mini-course with olives and olive oil. The thrust of the cooking is Anglo-French, and menus change with the seasons. Typical offerings range from 'excellent' crispy duck with a compote of cherries and onions, to pan-fried fillet of beef with mushroom goulash. Fish varies daily, there is always something for vegetarians, and traditionalists will feel comforted by the pudding list. Around 40 wines make up a thoughtful, realistically priced slate. House wine is £10.50.

CHEF: Gillian Scott   PROPRIETORS: Gillian Scott and Peter Moore   OPEN: Mon to Sat D only 7 to 9.30 (10 Sat)   CLOSED: bank hols   MEALS: alc (main courses £11 to £15.50). Set D Tue to Fri £14.50   SERVICE: not inc   CARDS: Access, Amex, Delta, Visa   DETAILS: 60 seats. Private parties: 30 main room, 30 private room. Vegetarian meals. Children's helpings. Smart dress preferred. No cigars/pipes in dining-room. Wheelchair access (no WC). Music

---

SOUTHWATER West Sussex   map 3

Cole's 🍷✱

Worthing Road, Southwater RH13 7BS   COOKING 2
TEL: (01403) 730456   COST £22–£46

'A delightful place – even on a wet Sunday!' noted correspondents who ventured out to this impressive but appealing barn conversion in an out-of-the-way Sussex backwater. Their lunch was traditional to a fault: piping hot spinach soup, roast beef with Yorkshire pudding, fillet of salmon with watercress sauce, plentiful vegetables, then apple and blackberry crumble and lemon tart. The presence of the charming and endearing Cole family proved to be the icing on the cake. Elizabeth Cole also makes the best of South Coast fish for more elaborate dishes such as pan-fried scallops with saffron sauce, and steamed fillet of turbot with chanterelles and leeks accompanied by a chive sauce. Roast duck with orange and ginger sauce is a favourite, and she is quite happy to serve a plainly grilled Scotch fillet steak. A fair spread of desserts takes in such things as armagnac parfait with prunes and Earl Grey syrup, and mango crème brûlée as well as pancakes and profiteroles. The accessible wine list continues to grow, and more New World bins have been added over the last year. House French is £9.95.

CHEF: Elizabeth Cole   PROPRIETORS: the Cole family   OPEN: Tue to Fri and Sun L 12 to 2, Tue to Sat D 7 to 9   MEALS: alc (main courses £11.50 to £18). Set L £12.95 (2 courses) to £15   SERVICE: not inc   CARDS: Access, Amex, Delta, Diners, Visa   DETAILS: 36 seats. Private parties: 36 main room, 10 private room. Car park. Vegetarian meals. No children under 12. Smart dress preferred. No smoking in dining-room. Wheelchair access (also WC). Music

---

SOUTHWOLD Suffolk   map 6

▲ The Crown 🍷 ✱

High Street, Southwold IP18 6DP   [NEW CHEF]
TEL: (01502) 722275 FAX: (01502) 727263   COST £21–£31

Lest it be forgotten, Southwold is Adnams the wine merchant's nerve-centre, the Crown its flagship. Not only does the company sell wine, but it also brews beer, so the chances are that if you slake your thirst one way or the other in this endearing seaside town, you will have bought into the Adnams experience. One of the best ways of doing that is to eat at the Crown, where the superior bar food is supplemented by an ambitious restaurant menu served at tables clothed in damask.

Chefs do seem to come and go with dizzying speed, however (the present incumbent arrived just as we went to press, hence no cooking mark), and yet standards don't seem to waver much. The superb wine list lives up to expectations in its range, its imaginative selection and its candid notes on French vintages. Mark-ups are heart-warmingly low throughout; indeed, there's plenty to choose from at under £10 a bottle. House wines start at £7.50 for Spanish red. CELLARMAN'S CHOICE: Pouilly-Fumé 1993, Ch. de Tracy, £14.75; Charles Melton Nine Popes 1994, Barossa Valley, S. Australia, £14.95.

CHEF: Gary Marsland PROPRIETOR: Adnams Hotels OPEN: all week 12.30 to 1.30, 7.30 to 9.30 CLOSED: second week Jan MEALS: Set L £12.95 (2 courses) to £15.50, Set D £17.95 (2 courses) to £19.95. BYO £5. Bar food available SERVICE: not inc, card slips closed CARDS: Access, Amex, Delta, Diners, Switch, Visa DETAILS: restaurant 22 seats, bar 58 seats. 12 seats outside. Private parties: 22 main room, 22 private rooms. Car park. Vegetarian meals. Children's helpings. Smart dress preferred. No smoking in dining-room. No music. Air-conditioned ACCOMMODATION: 12 rooms, all with bath/shower. TV. Phone. B&B £40 to £63. Children welcome. Baby facilities (*The Which? Hotel Guide*)

STADDLEBRIDGE North Yorkshire   map 9

▲ *McCoy's* ♥

The Tontine, Staddlebridge DL6 3JB
TEL: (01609) 882671   FAX: (01609) 882660   COOKING 3
6m NE of Northallerton, at junction of A19 and A172   COST £30–£55

'This is my ideal haven' writes a reporter of this roadside halt beside the A19. It is idiosyncratic, which is why people love it. The décor does a good impression of being higgledy-piggledy and exotic, various lamps give precious little illumination, although mirrors and open fires help, and 'it is one of the few restaurants worth going to for the Muzak'. One who had not visited for some time found it 'considerably more kempt' than before and was worried that 'if they smarten it up any more, it will begin to look respectable'. Another was attracted to it partly because of the laid-back attitude of the McCoy brothers, partly because 'even pets are made welcome' and partly because 'the food is wonderful'.

The ground-floor restaurant now opens only three evenings a week, but this hardly matters since the basement bistro is open all week and both serve the same menu anyway. The food is as cosmopolitan as anything in London. Warm mushroom tart with Muscadet sauce, or fresh tuna with a tomato and coriander dressing are among the attractions. Modern flavourings rub shoulders with more traditional preparations such as roast rump of lamb with a cassoulet of flageolet beans, or honey-roast Bresse pigeon with mixed pulses and foie gras sauce. This is sensible, accurate cooking, making good use of materials and putting taste before appearance. There is no more pretence in the cooking than in the décor.

Puddings in particular tend to be an assembly of old favourites, from a thin pastry with crème pâtissière and strawberries, to chock-o-block Stanley, a chocolate fondant with sponge, Tia Maria and a coffee-bean sauce. The wine list doesn't let the side down; a concise range treads as carefully in the New World as in the Old, and there are plenty of half-bottles. French house wines are £12.95.

CHEF: Tom McCoy   PROPRIETORS: the McCoy brothers   OPEN: bistro all week 12 to 2, 7 to 9.30, restaurant Thur to Sat D only 7 to 9.30   CLOSED: 25 and 26 Dec, 1 Jan   MEALS: alc (main courses £11 to £19). BYO £5   SERVICE: not inc   CARDS: Access, Amex, Diners, Switch, Visa   DETAILS: 70 seats. Private parties: 12 main room, 30 private room. Car park. Vegetarian meals. Children welcome. Music. Air-conditioned   ACCOMMODATION: 6 rooms, all with bath/shower. TV. Phone. Air-conditioned. B&B £79 to £99. Children welcome. Dogs welcome. Garden

---

STAITHES North Yorkshire   map 9

▲ Endeavour ✦

1 High Street, Staithes TS13 5BH	COOKING 1
TEL: (01947) 840825	COST £23–£44

'We had a good meal in pleasant surroundings,' summed up one visitor to this quaint old seaside village where Captain James Cook once worked (at the village shop) among the narrow streets and jumble of cottages. Lisa Chapman's restaurant, a few yards from the quay, commemorates Captain Cook's ship. Fish from local boats features prominently on the blackboard menu, alongside sirloin steak, or well-trimmed lamb cutlets, 'tender and sweet', in an 'excellent' port and redcurrant sauce. Dishes are simple, and first courses (apart from soup) are often cold, presumably so that the kitchen can concentrate on the main business of grilling tuna fillet, roasting Whitby cod or serving firm-fleshed and perfectly timed fillet of turbot in a creamy, herby sauce. Hot vegetable strudel or courgette pancakes introduce another dimension, and puddings have included a sharp, tangy lemon cheesecake. Homely service and 40 well-priced wines add to the appeal.

CHEF/PROPRIETOR: Lisa Chapman   OPEN: Mon to Sat 12 to 2, 6.45 to 9, Sun bank hols, and Sun throughout summer   CLOSED: weekdays Feb   MEALS: alc (main courses £8 to £17)   SERVICE: not inc   CARDS: none   DETAILS: 45 seats. Private parties: 30 main room, 12 and 18 private rooms. Vegetarian meals. Children welcome. Smart dress preferred. No smoking in 1 dining-room. Music   ACCOMMODATION: 3 rooms, 1 with bath/shower. TV. B&B £19 to £48. Children welcome. Dogs welcome

---

STAMFORD Lincolnshire   map 6

▲ George of Stamford ▮

St Martins, Stamford PE9 2LB	
TEL: (01780) 55171 (755171 from 1 Jan 1997)	COOKING 2
FAX: (01780) 57070 (757070 from 1 Jan 1997)	COST £27–£61

Few reporters can resist the charm of the setting: a sixteenth-century coaching-inn by the River Welland, with oak panelling, log fires and a cobbled courtyard with hanging baskets that doubles as a dining-room in summer. A conference centre attracts business customers, and a range of dining-rooms and menus means that most people can find something to suit their circumstances. Light lunches might go in for warm goats'-cheese salad, or roast beef and Yorkshire pudding from the carving trolley, while the *carte* offers spicy crab-cake, or perhaps duck with Savoy cabbage and roast garlic. And you can't say the kitchen doesn't try to keep up with the field. Why else would it serve breast of woodpigeon on a bed of black pudding polenta with a wild mushroom sauce? Food in the Garden Room is a more informal mix of pasta, fish and chips, sausage, and a cold buffet.

Technique, however, is not always up to the exacting demands of proper pasta, perfect risotto and so on. Desserts are from a trolley, and cheeses may be limited. 'The food is on the expensive side for its quality' is a view shared by more than one correspondent. Service is generally friendly, courteous, relaxed and efficient. It is hard to fault the wine list, which touches on much that is exciting, encourages experimentation, and homes in on France, Italy, Australia and California in particular. The classics are here too; indeed, in 12 pages they've managed to stuff in a bit of nearly everything, including a dozen wines by the glass, plenty of half-bottles and a page called 'big bottles' which speaks for itself. Tasting notes are spot on and prices are agreeable. House wines start at £8.95. CELLARMAN'S CHOICE: Mount Langi Ghiran Riesling 1994, Victoria, Australia, £13.50; Nuits-St-Georges 1992, Dom. de l'Arlot, £19.95.

CHEF: Chris Pitman   PROPRIETOR: Poste Hotels Ltd   OPEN: all week 12.30 to 2.30, 7.30 to 10.30   MEALS: alc (main courses £9 to £18.50). Set L £13.50 to £16.50 (2 courses). Light lunches available   SERVICE: not inc   CARDS: Access, Amex, Delta, Diners, Switch, Visa   DETAILS: 90 seats. 140 seats outside. Private parties: 90 main room, 14 to 34 private rooms. Car park. Vegetarian meals. Children's helpings. Jacket and tie. Wheelchair access (also WC). No music   ACCOMMODATION: 47 rooms, all with bath/shower. TV. Phone. B&B £72 to £160. Children welcome. Baby facilities. Dogs welcome. Afternoon teas. Garden (*The Which? Hotel Guide*)

STANTON Suffolk   map 6

Leaping Hare Café   🍽

Wyken Vineyards, Stanton IP31 2DW   COOKING 1
TEL: (01359) 250287   FAX: (01359) 252256   COST £22–£33

Follow the signs to Wyken Vineyard and park your car in the farmyard. Depending on the time of year, the sheds you tramp past may well contain men shearing sheep, but don't mind them. Set a course for the two farm shops and there, bisecting them, is the Leaping Hare. Lucy Crabb (formerly of London's Blue Print Café – see entry) arrived in early '96, but the menus continue as before with an evocative mixture of English, Tuscan and Napa Valley modes. Presentations may puzzle, as in the houmous that arrived as a garnished slab rather than a dip, but flavours are usually readily appreciable. For one reporter, 'the combinations were a delight', and included smoked haddock with Puy lentils and a mustard sauce. The signature dish is 'our great big salmon fish-cake' with sorrel sauce. An inspection dish of sauté rump steak came with an acceptable red wine and shallot reduction, though more tender meat would have suited better. Among desserts, 'Chocolate Silk' turns out to be a nut-crusted mousse, and the cheeses are usually worth investigating. The vineyard's own wines form the bulk of the list, and are all available by the glass from £2 for the cautious.

🍳 *indicates a change of chef since last year's* Guide.

CHEF: Lucy Crabb PROPRIETOR: Kenneth and Carla Carlisle OPEN: Thu, Fri, Sun and bank hol Mon L 12 to 3 (and Sat L Nov and Dec), Fri D 7 to 9.30 CLOSED: 24 Dec to 9 Feb MEALS: alc (main courses £8 to £10). Set L £12.50 (2 courses inc wine), Set D £18.50 SERVICE: not inc, card slips closed CARDS: Access, Switch, Visa DETAILS: 45 seats. 16 seats outside. Private parties: 50 main room. Car park. Vegetarian meals. Children's helpings. No smoking in dining-room. Wheelchair access (also WC). No music

---

STOKE-BY-NAYLAND Suffolk   map 6

▲ *Angel Inn* ⁊✳ £

Stoke-by-Nayland CO6 4SA
TEL: (01206) 263245 FAX: (01206) 263373   COOKING 2
on B1068, 5m SW of Hadleigh   COST £20–£33

The format is a good one. Take an old pub – in this case a sixteenth-century inn in one of John Constable's favourite villages – and divide it into an informal bar, and a not much posher restaurant in which tables are bookable (cover charge here is £1.50). Serve the same food throughout, and everybody is happy. The eating is casual but the buying and preparation are serious, and flexible enough to respond to the markets. Fish from Billingsgate and meat from a local butcher arrive daily, and both ostrich and kangaroo have found their way on to the chalkboard menu from time to time.

Treatments are as simple as can be, from dressed crab with mayonnaise through griddled fish (sardines, plaice or wing of skate) to roast meats such as duck or honey-glazed rack of lamb, or liver sauté with bacon. A few herbs or a simple sauce are mostly all that is added. Brown bread ice-cream or raspberry bavarois are the kind of thing to expect for pudding. Beer is well kept and wines are reasonably priced, with a sensible range from around the world, mostly at under £20. House French is £7.75 (£1.55 a glass).

CHEFS: Mark Johnson, Terry Walker and Chris Boddice PROPRIETORS: Richard Wright and Peter Smith OPEN: all week 12 to 2, 6.30 (7 Sun) to 9 CLOSED: 25 and 26 Dec, 1 Jan MEALS: alc (main courses £6 to £10.50). Cover £1.50 SERVICE: not inc CARDS: Access, Amex, Delta, Diners, Switch, Visa DETAILS: 80 seats, 16 outside. Private parties: 28 main room. Car park. Vegetarian meals. No children under 8. Smart dress preferred. No smoking in 1 dining-room. Wheelchair access (no WC). No music ACCOMMODATION: 6 rooms, all with bath/shower. TV. Phone. B&B £49 to £59. No children under 8 (*The Which? Hotel Guide*)

STOKE HOLY CROSS Norfolk   map 6

Wildebeest Arms ⁊✳   [NEW ENTRY]

Norwich Road, Stoke Holy Cross NR14 8QJ
TEL: (01508) 492497 FAX: (01603) 766403
from Norwich take A140 Ipswich road; directly
after roundabout take the left turn signposted Stoke   COOKING 1
Holy Cross   COST £19–£41

The drift from restaurant kitchens to country pubs continues. One of the latest to defect is Eden Derrick, who gave up cooking at Adlard's (see entry, Norwich) to make his name at this curiously named one-roomed inn. Reporters have described it as a 'fun, trendy spot', with a few touches of old colonial in the African spears suspended over the fireplace. Big-city influences are obvious in dishes such as Simon Hopkinson's grilled aubergine with pesto, and smoked haddock rarebit with tomato and chive salad (à la Gary Rhodes). Elsewhere, the kitchen has a confident stab at smoked chicken sausage with onion marmalade, chargrilled medallions of beef with oyster mushrooms, and smoked cheese, apple and prune tart with a skilfully made spinach and leek sauce. Desserts could range from chocolate marquise with mint custard to glazed lemon tart. The wine list is eminently attractive and affordable. House wine is £9.50.

CHEF: Eden Derrick   PROPRIETORS: Henry Watt and Andrew Wilkins   OPEN: all week 12 to 2 (3 Sun), 7 to 10   CLOSED: 25 Dec   MEALS: alc (main courses £7 to £14.50). Set L Mon to Sat £12   SERVICE: not inc, card slips closed   CARDS: Access, Amex, Delta, Diners, Switch, Visa   DETAILS: 70 seats. 100 seats outside. Private parties: 60 main room. Car park. Vegetarian meals. Children's helpings. No smoking in 1 dining-room. Music. Air-conditioned

STOKESLEY North Yorkshire   map 10

▲ Chapters

27 High Street, Stokesley TS9 5AD   COOKING 2
TEL: (01642) 711888   FAX: (01642) 713387   COST £18–£43

Chapters is now far removed from a traditional coaching-inn: 'not a copper kettle in sight,' admits owner Alan Thompson. The River Leven meanders through the garden; inside, the style is pure bistro, with solid wooden tables, red slate floors and pleasing colour schemes. A restaurant continues to operate for those who want a touch more comfort.

The menu 'changes like the weather', and it's hard to fault the quality of raw materials or how they are handled. A filo 'pizza' is topped with basil, spinach, pancetta, tomatoes and dolcelatte, while smoked haddock fish-cakes receive a lemony beurre blanc, and grilled halibut is served with ginger, spring onions and lemon grass. Meat dishes are in similar vein: tender noisettes of new season's lamb with a mini-ratatouille, and loin of local roe-deer with gin and juniper, for example. Sauces can 'lack finesse', according to an inspector, and vegetables may disappoint, but puddings such as banana, kiwi and apple strudel, or luscious crème brûlée are 'a delight'. Service is efficient and professional. The wine list is workmanlike and prices are very reasonable. House wine is £9.20. The Thompsons have recently opened a second establishment at the Lodge, Middleton Road, Pickering: reports, please.

CHEFS: Richard West and Alan Thompson   PROPRIETORS: Alan and Catherine Thompson   OPEN: Mon to Sat 12 to 2, 7 to 9.30   CLOSED: 25 Dec   MEALS: alc (main courses L £6 to £11, D £9.50 to £15). BYO £3.50   SERVICE: not inc   CARDS: Access, Amex, Delta, Diners, Switch, Visa   DETAILS: 60 seats. 40 seats outside. Private parties: 70 main room. Children's helpings. No smoking in 1 dining-room. Music   ACCOMMODATION: 13 rooms, all with bath/shower. TV. Phone. B&B £38 to £62. Children welcome. Dogs welcome. Afternoon teas. Garden (*The Which? Hotel Guide*)

All entries in the Guide *are rewritten every year, not least because restaurant standards fluctuate. Don't rely on an out-of-date* Guide.

STON EASTON   Somerset   map 2

▲ *Ston Easton Park* ♀ ✦

Ston Easton BA3 4DF
TEL: (01761) 241631   FAX: (01761) 241377   COOKING 3*
on A37, 12m S of Bristol   COST £33–£73

'Exceptional food in exceptional surroundings; a wonderful combination,'
enthuses a typical report. The aristocratic Palladian mansion in Bath stone –
formidably elegant and slightly austere – is immaculately run by the Smedleys
and has 'the best of atmospheres'. The dining-room forsakes the traditionalism
of the rest of the hotel in favour of a summery feel with bamboo-style chairs. Fine
weather brings patio tables into action, and the view over eighteenth-century
landscaped gardens is more inspiring than that over the car park.

'During our visit we ate four complete meals, and every course of each meal
was top rate.' The food suits the international mix of well-heeled guests: it is
well sourced, elegantly presented (birds are jointed, fish filleted) and sophisticated rather than challenging. Complex and sometimes earthy flavours might
emerge in a tian of honey-roast aubergine and plum tomatoes with Parma ham
and balsamic dressing, or in a dish of duck confit with potato terrine, couscous
salad and garlicky vinaigrette. The norm, however, is generally a clear, simple,
well-considered partnering of, for example, coriander cream with braised saddle
of rabbit, or roast rack of lamb with a lavender crust.

Materials are notably fresh, and timing makes the most of them, so that
chargrilled duck breast emerges pink and juicy, and whole Dover sole retains its
texture. 'They have a great pastry cook', and desserts are as accomplished as a
glazed blackcurrant mousse accompanied by a passion-fruit sorbet and coulis.
Well-kept British and Irish cheeses might include Milleens. Staff are well
trained and responsive, if slightly formal, and the customer-oriented approach
continues to impress: eagle-eyed waitresses bring cushions the moment they
spot an unsupported back. 'London prices' are generally forgiven in view of the
quality, and the fact that meals include good canapés and appetisers, and there is
strictly no additional service charge.

A deeply serious wine list includes much that is venerable and grand but
keeps prices in check. France is elegantly represented, both within and without
Burgundy and Bordeaux, but for those who do not want to flick through page
after page of classic fine wines, the whole list is prefaced by a short house
selection of less-expensive, but high-quality, bottles. CELLARMAN'S CHOICE:
Riesling, Clos Ste-Hune 1986, Trimbach, £36 (half); Côtes du Rhône 1991,
Guigal, £19.50.

CHEF: Mark Harrington   PROPRIETORS: Peter and Christine Smedley   OPEN: all week 12.30 to 2,
7.30 to 9.30 (10 Fri and Sat)   MEALS: alc D (main courses £19 to £28). Set L £26, Set D £38.50
SERVICE: none, card slips closed   CARDS: Access, Amex, Diners, Switch, Visa   DETAILS: 40
seats. Private parties: 8 main room, 24 private room. Car park. Vegetarian meals. Children's
helpings. No children under 7. Jacket and tie D. No smoking in dining-room. Wheelchair access
(2 steps). No music   ACCOMMODATION: 21 rooms, all with bath/shower. TV. Phone. B&B £93.50
to £337. No children under 7. Dogs kennelled by arrangement. Afternoon teas. Garden (*The
Which? Hotel Guide*)

STONHAM

STONHAM

STONHAM Suffolk	map 6

Mr Underhill's ♟ ⁵⁄✶

Stonham IP14 5DW	
TEL: (01449) 711206	COOKING 4
on A140, 300 yards S of junction with A1120	COST £35–£46

In March 1996 the Bradleys and their Aga notched up 15 years of serving meals, the latter celebrating with two new lids and a major overhaul. It is long enough for young customers who came with their parents in 1981 to be bringing children of their own, surely a testament to the integrity and timeless values that Mr Underhill's represents. The Bradleys' own assessment is that the secret of longevity is 'no short cuts, no second best', and reporters are inclined to agree: 'definitely one of the best restaurants in East Anglia,' reckoned one of them. The deal is simple: a set meal at a set price, with no choice before dessert except whether or not to have cheese.

Do not expect fireworks or gimmicks. The emphasis is on food cooked with skill and sensitivity. 'We never set out to be revolutionary, more evolutionary,' write the Bradleys, as a reading of their menus confirms. There may be the odd exotic flavouring – coriander and ginger with hot smoked salmon, for instance – but the basics are as plain as can be. One meal began with terrine of lobster, and progressed to fillet of beef with red wine and mushrooms. Preferences are discussed when ordering, and it may be that different menus are being served to different tables at the same time.

For one party, Barbary duck with lemon grass and Stonham honey came with a 'truly superb' vegetable tart containing carrot, swede, turnip and potato, while for another the highlight was dessert: a creamy bread-and-butter pudding, and 'lemon tart with all the flavour'. Half a dozen desserts are usually offered, and might include hot chocolate tart, or poached pear served with a sorbet flavoured with pear juices 'and a cream sauce punctuated by blackcurrants'. Lunches are by arrangement, and the same format and pricing apply, except for an occasional special deal on Sundays. Service has been described as 'very poor, the waitresses never spoke to us', and 'very good, the husband-and-wife team made us feel very much at home', and the no-smoking policy is applauded.

The Bradleys have extended a strong list of classic wines with plenty of exciting, lesser-known bottles. Many of the gems are from the New World, including a handful from Argentina and Arizona. A fair pricing policy encourages experimentation. French house wines are £9. CELLARMAN'S CHOICE: Chablis Vieilles Vignes 1994, Hamelin, £25.50; Wirra Wirra Church Block 1994, McLaren Vale, S. Australia, £16.50.

CHEF: Christopher Bradley   PROPRIETORS: Christopher and Judy Bradley   OPEN: Tue to Sat D only 7.30 to 8.45; L Tue to Fri and Sun by arrangement   MEALS: Set D £25 (2 courses) to £28   SERVICE: not inc   CARDS: Access, Visa   DETAILS: 24 seats. 6 seats outside. Private parties: 24 main room. Car park. Children's helpings. Smart dress preferred. No smoking in dining-room. Wheelchair access (no WC). No music

Report forms are at the back of the book; write a letter if you prefer; or if you are on the Internet, e-mail us at guidereports@which. co. uk.

STONOR   Oxfordshire   map 2

▲ *Stonor Arms* 🍞

Stonor RG9 6HE
TEL: (01491) 638345   FAX: (01491) 638863   COOKING 1
on B480, 5m N of Henley on Thames   COST £28–£41

A change of management and chef in 1996 produced an altered format. Two
dining areas still exist, but there is now only one menu, with no minimum
charge, and with the option to eat as little or as much as you wish, thus bringing
Stonor into line with general relaxed '90s practice. Eat in either the conservatory,
overlooking the neat, well-tended garden, or in the well-appointed
dining-room, and contemplate smoked eel with potato, or a Stonor salad: a
constellation of mixed leaves, avocado, quail eggs, bacon and croutons with a
garlic dressing. Main courses run to pigeon breast with lentils, or salmon with a
herb crust. An inspector, who felt the cooking had yet to achieve a steady and
reliable standard, considered poached pear in a saffron sauce with coconut
ice-cream to be the highlight of the meal. Service is friendly, and a new wine list
was under construction as we went to press.

CHEF: Toby Bult   PROPRIETOR: Stonor Hotels Ltd   OPEN: all week 12 to 2, 7 to 9.30   MEALS: alc
(main courses £8 to £16). Bar L available   SERVICE: not inc   CARDS: Access, Amex, Delta,
Switch, Visa   DETAILS: 60 seats. 20 seats outside. Private parties: 24 main room, 12 private
rooms. Car park. Vegetarian meals. Children welcome. Smart dress preferred. No cigars/pipes
in dining-room. Wheelchair access (also WC). Music   ACCOMMODATION: 10 rooms, all with
bath/shower. TV. Phone. B&B £85 to £95. Rooms for disabled. Children welcome. Baby
facilities. Afternoon teas. Garden (*The Which? Hotel Guide*)

STORRINGTON   West Sussex   map 3

▲ *Manleys* 🍷

Manleys Hill, Storrington RH20 4BT   COOKING 3*
TEL: (01903) 742331   FAX: (01903) 740649   COST £32–£64

'An elegant professional restaurant with pretty décor, outstanding food, and
immaculate service,' summed up one visitor to this small country restaurant
below the South Downs, just up from the South Coast. The focus is on
high-quality cooking in the classical French tradition, but with unmistakable
mid-European flourishes reflecting Karl Löderer's Austrian background – a
pan-fried chicken breast with spätzli here, a Salzburger Nockerln there – and all
done with quiet expertise. The foundation is superb-quality ingredients, not
least wonderful fish and shellfish, from briefly seared nutty scallops to lemon
sole stuffed with fresh crab and surrounded by a langoustine sauce.

You don't have to go hunting to find out what makes the food special; it comes
out to meet you. 'We were not very hungry, but the food was so good,' wrote one
reporter who polished off three courses without any trouble. The skill that goes
into the cooking is properly directed: it makes people sit up and take notice of the
flavours and balance. Even fish-cakes are not merely the common assembly
bound with potato, but a combination of salmon, turbot and cod mixed with a

panade flavoured with a fish reduction and served with beurre blanc. Butter sauces are a forte.

Pastry work is top-notch, applied winningly to a first course with mushrooms, asparagus tips and a chive-cream sauce, while a lemon tart was 'drooled over'. Meals begin in fine style with nibbles in the bar and amuse-gueules at table, and finish with a silver cake-stand of petits fours, details that confirm the striving for perfection. A certain formality reigns, service is courteous and graceful, and 'Mrs Löderer keeps a strict eye on things'. Wines come from Austria (naturally), France and Germany, with three Australians tucked away at the back of the list. The standard is high throughout, particularly from Burgundy, and prices reflect this. House wine is £14.80. CELLARMAN'S CHOICE: Chablis premier cru 1992, Montmain, £26.75; Margaux, Ch. Prieuré-Lichine 1981, £29.

CHEF/PROPRIETOR: Karl Löderer OPEN: Tue to Sun L 12.15 to 1.45, Wed to Sat D 7.15 to 8.45 (9.30 Sat) CLOSED: first 10 days Jan. MEALS: alc (main courses inc starter £31.50). Set L Tue to Sat £19.60, Set L Sun £23.50, Set D £30. BYO by arrangement SERVICE: not inc, card slips closed CARDS: Access, Amex, Delta, Switch, Visa DETAILS: 48 seats. Private parties: 34 main room, 14 and 22 private rooms. Car park. Children's helpings. Smart dress preferred. No cigars/pipes in dining-room. Wheelchair access (also WC). Music. Air-conditioned ACCOMMODATION: 1 apartment, with bath/shower. TV. Phone. B&B £55 to £95

Old Forge

6 Church Street, Storrington RH20 4LA	COOKING 1*
TEL: (01903) 743402 FAX: (01903) 742540	COST £21–£42

This country restaurant is a rambling assembly of centuries-old cottages, complete with the expected showing of 'old beams and nookery'. An air of 'undemanding contentment' fills the dining-room. Clive and Cathy Roberts offer a *carte* as well as fixed-price options at all sessions, and their cooking shows noticeable touches of skill, even if descriptions can sometimes sound complicated (tenderloin of pork with prune and haggis stuffing wrapped in cabbage with a port sauce, for example).

Ingredients are fresh and seasonal: witness steamed game pudding or 'nicely moist' fillets of salmon and brill with mushroom sauce. Puddings are a high point, and here the elaboration pays off: an apple and frangipane soufflé, surrounded by calvados custard and slices of fried apple, was judged outstanding by one veteran. 'Cheerful' sums up the service. The manageable wine list is dominated by some interesting non-Europeans; don't miss the dessert wines. House wine is £9.75.

CHEFS/PROPRIETORS: Cathy and Clive Roberts OPEN: Wed to Fri and Sun L 12.15 to 1.30, Tue to Sat D 7.15 to 9 CLOSED: 1 week late spring, 3 weeks Oct MEALS: alc (main courses £11 to £14.50). Set L £12 (2 courses) to £14.50, Set D £16.50 (2 courses) to £21 SERVICE: not inc, card slips closed CARDS: Access, Amex, Delta, Diners, Switch, Visa DETAILS: 36 seats. Private parties: 16 main room, 12 private room. Vegetarian meals. Children's helpings. Smart dress preferred. No smoking while others eat. Music

CELLARMAN'S CHOICE: *Wines recommended by the restaurateur, normally more expensive than house wine.*

STOW-ON-THE-WOLD Gloucestershire   map 5

▲ *Wyck Hill House* ✝✸

Burford Road, Stow-on-the-Wold GL54 1HY
TEL: (01451) 831936   FAX: (01451) 832243   COOKING ?
on A424, 2m SE of Stow-on-the-Wold   COST 1*£21–£67

Towering gateposts and flagpoles are outward signs of the opulence within this
Cotswold-stone hall in the middle of nowhere. Sombre oils on deep red walls in
the dining-room set the tone, which is one of great formality. Ian Smith's
cooking is modern British, much given to complexity. Palpable hits have been
scored with a substantial first course of king prawns with a sole mousse and two
fine sauces (one shellfish, one a buttery emulsion), and a main dish of venison
medallions with a tasty rabbit sausage and a redcurrant sauce. Vegetarians are
given their own menu, while the sweet-toothed will favour crisp-fried bananas
with caramel sauce. Service has been variously described as 'spotty', 'quite good'
and 'anonymous'. The huge wine list majors in French classics at stiffish prices.
House wines are £11.95.

CHEF: Ian Smith   PROPRIETOR: Lyric Hotels   OPEN: all week 12 to 2, 7.30 to 9.30 (10 Sat); light L
available Mon to Sat   MEALS: alc D (main courses £12 to £25). Set L £10.95 (2 courses) to
£13.50   SERVICE: not inc   CARDS: Access, Amex, Delta, Diners, Switch, Visa   DETAILS: 70
seats. Private parties: 70 main room, 40 private room. Car park. Vegetarian meals. Children
welcome. Smart dress preferred. No smoking in dining-room. Wheelchair access (also WC).
Music. Air-conditioned   ACCOMMODATION: 30 rooms, all with bath/shower. TV. Phone. B&B £70
to £180. Rooms for disabled. Children welcome. Dogs welcome in bedrooms only. Afternoon
teas. Garden

STRATFORD-UPON-AVON Warwickshire   map 5

Liaison   [NEW ENTRY]

1 Shakespeare Street, Stratford-upon-Avon CV37 6RN   COOKING 1*
TEL: (01789) 293400   FAX: (01789) 297863   COST £23–£54

This is a converted Methodist chapel that, for all its lingering overtones of
'fire-and-brimstone sermons and hardy 1930s temperance', brings considerable
uplift. A short trot from The Birthplace, its 'tremendous space and airiness' are a
great asset. Patricia Plunkett cooks in recognisably modern idiom, but with a
more painstaking approach to presentation than is generally fashionable at the
moment, producing a sculptural rendition of bouillabaisse on a champagne
sabayon and an artfully designed chocolate mousse with fruit salad that could
have hung in the Louvre. Assertively salty rillettes of ham come on a cloud of
garlic and olive oil mash topped with a soft poached egg and rings of caramelised
onion, while a 'pot-au-feu' of mussels with fresh linguine is generous to a fault.
As long as flavours remain focused and are not sacrificed to the straining for
visual impact, the indications are that this could be one to watch. France is the
fulcrum of the wine list, with shorter shrift given to the trendier regions. Prices
are mostly comfortable, with house French £11.50.

CHEF: Patricia Plunkett   PROPRIETORS: Ank van der Tuin and Patricia Plunkett   OPEN: Mon to Fri L 12 to 2.30, Mon to Sat D 6 to 10.30   CLOSED: 2 weeks Jan   MEALS: alc (main courses £14 to £17). Set L £11.50 (2 courses) to £13.95, Set D £21.95   SERVICE: not inc   CARDS: Access, Amex, Delta, Diners, Switch, Visa   DETAILS: 55 seats. Private parties: 80 main room, 25 private room. Vegetarian meals. Children welcome. Smart dress preferred. Wheelchair access (also WC). Music

---

STRETE Devon   map 1

Laughing Monk ✸✶

Strete TQ6 0RN
TEL: (01803) 770639   COOKING 1
5m from Dartmouth on coast road to Kingsbridge   COST £17–£35

The Rothwells inherited the somewhat unusual name from the previous ownership, and have learned to live with it. All is in best West Country homely mode, although the dining-room has been re-done with new curtains described as 'jazzy but not garish'. Inventive domestic cooking lives on, as in pork flambé with sloe gin, pan-fried veal with cream and marsala, or rack of lamb with a herb crust. Brochettes of monkfish and fat prawns on rice with a drizzle of garlic butter were much enjoyed one night, as was crisp-skinned, ginger-glazed duck with black cherry sauce. Puddings are worth leaving room for, whether it be a 'very slightly astringent' apricot roulade or apples in calvados topped with nutty meringue. Wines are a lively selection, grouped according to style and offering plenty of choice under £15. House Burgundy is £8.25.

CHEF: David Rothwell   PROPRIETORS: Trudy and David Rothwell   OPEN: Sun L (last Sun in month only) 12 to 1.30, Tue to Sat D (and Sun bank hols) 7 to 9.30   MEALS: alc (main courses £11 to £13.50). Set L Sun £11.50   SERVICE: not inc, card slips closed   CARDS: Access, Visa   DETAILS: 50 seats. Private parties: 50 main room. Car park. Vegetarian meals. Children welcome. Smart dress preferred. No smoking in 1 dining-room. Wheelchair access (also women's WC). Music

---

STUCKTON Hampshire   map 2

Three Lions ♟

Stuckton Road, Stuckton SP6 2HF
TEL: (01425) 652489   FAX: (01425) 656144
½m SE of Fordingbridge, off A338 but not signposted
from it: take the turn just S of Fordingbridge and   COOKING 3*
follow a sign down a narrow country lane   COST £29–£48

The modernised pub has an open-plan layout and enough pine to feel 'slightly Norwegian'. It is on the edge of the New Forest, half an hour's drive from good fish supplies. Dishes vary frequently – hence the blackboard menu, which is hefted around the small bar so that everybody, eventually, gets a good look: a piece of paper might do the job better. Dinner may be meatier than lunch and work out slightly more expensive, but the overall style is of serious restaurant cooking at reasonable prices in an informal setting.

The signal freshness of fish, and a sense of timing that maximises taste and retains texture, marks the cooking. Another overriding characteristic of the food is, quite simply, flavour. There is lots of it, deriving directly from the main ingredients and from 'intense' accompaniments, such as a shellfish sauce with brill fillet, or a 'gutsy' bouillabaisse with a fillet of sea bass. Flavour contrasts also bring some dishes into sharp focus, such as a foie gras terrine with a tangy onion confit, or breast of mallard served with blueberries (balanced for sweetness and tartness) and a port sauce.

Michael Womersley also turns with the seasons, scattering wild mushrooms as he goes, for example, perhaps in puff pastry or with tagliatelle. Vegetables on a side-plate look like so many common or garden versions, but he makes a better job of them than most. Praise has been heaped on a zingy lime parfait with a passion-fruit coulis and confit of lime zest, and an 'outstanding' warm chocolate pudding, cakey outside and oozing liquid inside. Bread deserves special mention: wonderfully chewy, crisp of crust and 'absolutely gorgeous'. The whole operation is ably supervised by 'welcoming, attentive, on-the-ball' Jayne Womersley. The wine list explores some unusual corners, yet shows a tidy mind, with a sound collection of bottles from all over, mostly under £20. The choice of 15 house wines starts at £11.75. CELLARMAN'S CHOICE: Rothbury Estate Sauvignon Blanc 1995, Marlborough, New Zealand, £16.50; Parrots Hill Shiraz 1992, Barossa Valley, S. Australia, £18.25.

CHEF: Michael Womersley   PROPRIETORS: Michael and Jayne Wormersley   OPEN: Tue to Sun L 12 to 2, Tue to Sat D 7 to 9.45 (10 Sat)   CLOSED: 3 weeks end Jan/early Feb   MEALS: alc (main courses £8.50 to £15)   SERVICE: not inc   CARDS: Access, Switch, Visa   DETAILS: 60 seats. 20 seats outside. Private parties: 30 main room. Car park. Vegetarian meals. Children welcome. Wheelchair access (no WC). Music

---

STURMINSTER NEWTON Dorset   map 2

▲ Plumber Manor

Sturminster Newton DT10 2AF
TEL: (01258) 472507   FAX: (01258) 473370
from A357 to Sturminster Newton take first left to   COOKING 2
Hazelbury Bryan; on left-hand side after 2m   COST £23–£39

In spring a host of golden daffodils amid the great old chestnut trees makes a beguiling setting for Plumber Manor, although this is not Wordsworth country, of course, but Hardy's Wessex. The Manor is an informally run but trimly maintained country hotel that has been in the Prideaux-Brune family for centuries. Everything, down to Bertie the labrador snoozing in front of the fire, plays its part in creating an atmosphere of restful contentment.

Brian Prideaux-Brune's cooking is more assured of late. Even if the word 'unsubtle' cropped up in an inspection report, the strong, forthright flavours were appreciated. A light hand produced a well-timed stir-fry of scallops and prawns, while loin of venison with a rosemary and redcurrant sauce delivered 'exceptionally good meat' in a boldly fruity sauce with a heap of chestnut purée. The kitchen's commitment to good beef in the form of chateaubriand with béarnaise has survived on the menu through difficult times. Traditional British desserts such as sticky ginger pudding score highly, the little pot of butterscotch

SUDBURY

sauce served with it 'positively fragrant with beautiful local cream'. Service is 'uppercrust in a homely sort of way'. Bordeaux and Burgundy are the principal business of the wine list, but there are some thoughtfully chosen Australian bottles as well. House French is £10.

CHEF: Brian Prideaux-Brune PROPRIETOR: Richard Prideaux-Brune OPEN: Sun L 12.30 to 1.30, all week D 7.30 to 9.30 CLOSED: Feb MEALS: Set L Sun £17.50, Set D £15 (2 courses) to £27.50 SERVICE: net prices, card slips closed CARDS: Access, Amex, Diners, Switch, Visa DETAILS: 60 seats. Private parties: 45 main room, 15 and 21 private rooms. Car park. Vegetarian meals. Children's helpings. Smart dress preferred. Wheelchair access (also WC). No music ACCOMMODATION: 16 rooms, all with bath/shower. TV. Phone. B&B £65 to £120. Rooms for disabled. Children welcome. Baby facilities. Dogs welcome. Garden (*The Which? Hotel Guide*)

SUDBURY Suffolk   map 6

Mabey's Brasserie ⁵✳

47 Gainsborough Street, Sudbury CO10 7SS   COOKING 1
TEL/FAX: (01787) 374298   COST £21–£34

Since appointing a new chef at Regatta (see entry, Aldeburgh), Robert Mabey is spending more time at the stoves of his Sudbury brasserie. It may not be as gigantic as other places bearing that designation, but the jaunty décor of nautical blue and the small pine tables evoke a fresh, modern feel. The cooking has had its ups and downs of late, so perhaps the owner's return was overdue. Salmon and smoked salmon terrine was well-made but a reporter found the accompanying lemon sauce lacked taste, while the smoked duck salad incorporated pungently aromatic meat with chopped bacon and excellent croûtons. Chargrilled lamb leg steak with minted couscous and a red wine sauce was the high point of one meal: top-quality meat sensitively cooked on accompaniments that were 'both pretty and delicious'. Decent crème brûlée is joined on the dessert list by other favourites such as sticky toffee pudding, and hot chocolate tart. Wines, from £8.50, are a reasonable international mixture.

CHEF: Robert Mabey PROPRIETORS: Robert and Johanna Mabey OPEN: Tue to Sat 12 to 2, 7 to 10 MEALS: alc (main courses £8 to £12) SERVICE: not inc, card slips closed CARDS: Access, Amex, Visa DETAILS: 60 seats. Private parties: 60 main room, 40 private room. Vegetarian meals. Children welcome. No smoking in 1 dining-room. No music. Air-conditioned

Red Onion Bistro £

57 Ballingdon Street, Sudbury CO10 6DA   COOKING 1*
TEL: (01787) 376777   COST £14–£26

Opinions differ as to the cultural orientation of the Onion: it's 'like having France down the road' or it's 'more 1990s British brasserie than 1920s French bistro', depending on which side of the fence you are standing on. Most reporters appreciate the vibrant daily-changing menus and the atmosphere of happy bustle. The crab-cakes are 'better than in Maryland', while smoked chicken and broccoli pancakes with boulangère potatoes are 'pleasingly distinctive'. Chargrilled salmon kebab with chermoula salsa, and lamb à la grecque with tomatoes and olives in a red wine sauce suggest that both British and French labels may be

453

wide of the mark. Apricot fritters with vanilla ice-cream, and lemon syrup pudding are mentioned favourably in reports, while crème brûlée has been 'outstanding'. Wines by the 75-centilitre jug are available from £6.50, with a display of bottles to choose from in a storeroom, but no actual list.

CHEFS: Darren Boyles and Gerard Ford   PROPRIETORS: Gerard, Jane and Henry Ford   OPEN: Mon to Sat 12 to 2, 6.30 to 9.30   CLOSED: 1 week after Christmas, bank hols   MEALS: alc (main courses £4 to £9). Set D Mon to Thur £9.75   SERVICE: not inc, card slips closed   CARDS: Access, Delta, Switch, Visa   DETAILS: 70 seats. 25 seats outside. Private parties: 30 main room. Car park. Vegetarian meals. Children's helpings. No cigars/pipes in dining-room. Wheelchair access (no WC). No music

---

SWAFFHAM Norfolk   map 6

▲ *Strattons*

Stratton House, 4 Ash Close,
Swaffham PE37 7NH   COOKING 2
TEL: (01760) 723845   FAX: (01760) 720458   COST £28–£34

A correspondent sets the scene: 'As you drive into an oval grassy courtyard, the details of the place instantly make themselves known. A rabbit grazes loose on the lawn. A swing [hangs] from a large tree; a cat lounges on a stone step... Ducks, hens. Quiet!' Les and Vanessa Scott's eighteenth-century Palladian villa is a hotel, although the mood is that of a beguiling family home. Sitting-rooms overflow with the appealing clutter of a domestic residence, the modest dining-room is bedecked with dried hops and china animals.

Vanessa's cooking shows all the attributes of 'enthusiastic amateurism', and is based resolutely on home-grown and East Anglian produce. Herbs and flowers are from the garden, vegetables are organic, flour comes from Letheringsett Mill, while the coast provides everything from Stewkey Blue cockles to marsh samphire. The four-course dinner menu has yielded some real treasures: 'brilliant' wild mushroom pâté with oriental spices and a sauce laced with sherry vinegar, outstanding mushroom risotto, collops of monkfish with a vibrant tomato and dill sauce, wild apricot fool, and ice-creams. Emphatically British farmhouse cheeses come with home-made biscuits. The illustrated, hand-written wine list offers plenty of wines by the glass. House Chianti is £8.60.

CHEF: Vanessa Scott   PROPRIETORS: Les and Vanessa Scott   OPEN: all week D only 6.50 to 9.30; L by arrangement   CLOSED: 25 and 26 Dec   MEALS: Set D £24   SERVICE: net prices, card slips closed   CARDS: Access, Switch, Visa   DETAILS: 23 seats. 8 seats outside. Private parties: 14 main room, 15 private room. Car park. Vegetarian meals. Children's helpings. Smart dress preferred. No smoking in dining-room. Music   ACCOMMODATION: 7 rooms, all with bath/shower. TV. Phone. B&B £50 to £80. Deposit: 25%. Children welcome. Baby facilities. Dogs welcome. Afternoon teas. Garden (*The Which? Hotel Guide*)

Prices quoted in the Guide *are based on information supplied by restaurateurs. The prices quoted at the top of each entry represent a range, from the lowest meal price to the highest; the latter is inflated by 20 per cent to take account of likely price rises during the year of the* Guide.

SWANAGE Dorset   map 2

Galley

9 High Street, Swanage BH19 2LN   COOKING 1
TEL: (01929) 427299   COST £24–£32

'The £2 each way on the Sandbanks Ferry does not deter us,' write a couple who travel regularly from nearby Poole to the Storers' converted shop. Once over the threshold, there's no doubt that you are in a seaside fish restaurant: the deep sea-blue ceiling is covered with nets, and decorative tiles are much in evidence. The kitchen wins points for good produce and a wide-ranging menu that appeals to all comers. Simply wrought successes from recent meals have included 'a jug' of rich red fish soup, baked local scallops with herb butter, codling with bacon, and fillet of trout and sea bass in a sausage of puff pastry with chive and dill sauce. Roast duck breast with apples and calvados has been a good carnivorous alternative, while puddings might include steamed pudding dowsed with tart damson sauce. Service is prompt. The wine list is sensibly priced, starting with house wine at £8.50.

CHEF: Nick Storer   PROPRIETORS: N.D. and M.G. Storer   OPEN: all week D only 6.45 to 9.30 (10 Sat)   CLOSED: 3 weeks Nov, 1 Jan to 14 Feb   MEALS: Set D £16.50. BYO £5   SERVICE: not inc, card slips closed   CARDS: Access, Amex, Delta, Diners, Visa   DETAILS: 36 seats. Private parties: 36 main room. Vegetarian meals. Children welcome. Wheelchair access (no WC). Music. Air-conditioned

---

TADCASTER North Yorkshire   map 9

Singers   `NEW ENTRY`

16 Westgate, Tadcaster LS24 9AB   COOKING 1
TEL: (01937) 835121   COST £22–£27

There are no prizes for guessing the main theme running through this modest, recently opened venue. Sheet music adorns the white walls, and even the closely packed tables are identified not with numbers but with names such as 'Armstrong' and 'Cole'. Piped music harks back to the old days. The short, attractive menu is bolstered by a few specials including some fresh fish, and the kitchen clearly knows what it is doing. Mushrooms and asparagus are served in crisp puff pastry, 'excellent' warm salad of roasted peppers with bacon and avocado is a decorative treat, while quick-roasted spring chicken comes with its skin crisped up and heavy hints of garlic. Turbot is a fine specimen, filleted, just cooked, full of flavour, firm and 'unspoiled'. Desserts feature some straight-forward ideas such as glazed pear with honey and almond tart. Service is smiling and helpful. House Duboeuf is £7.95.

CHEFS: David Lockwood and Steven Ardern   PROPRIETORS: Philip Taylor and Guy Vicari   OPEN: Tue to Sat D only 6 to 9.30   CLOSED: 1 week Feb, 1 week Aug   MEALS: Set D Tue to Thur £11.95 (2 courses) to £14.95, Set D Fri and Sat £14.95   SERVICE: not inc, card slips closed   CARDS: Access, Delta, Switch, Visa   DETAILS: 38 seats. Private parties: 40 main room. Children welcome. Smart dress preferred. Music

TADWORTH Surrey

map 3

Gemini

28 Station Approach, Tadworth KT20 5AH
TEL: (01737) 812179

COOKING 1*
COST £20–£41

Framed Moulin Rouge prints may grace the walls, but nothing can disguise the fact that this was once a 1930s Tudor tea-room, enjoyably cosy for couples, a bit of a squash for larger parties. The cookery grows less French as time passes, the pork noisettes with apples and calvados now hedged about with Thai-spiced mussels, and prawns in puff pastry with tandoori seasonings and coriander. Crab and salmon rissoles with a salsa of roasted vegetables works well, although at inspection a main-course best end of lamb might have been more accurately timed and sensitively sauced. Roquefort served with dried fruits steeped in calvados is an interesting dessert/cheese crossover dish, and other puddings may include crème brûlée with raisins, or apple charlotte. A compact international wine list comes at eminently reasonable prices. House French starts at £8.85.

CHEF/PROPRIETOR: Robert Foster   OPEN: Tue to Fri and Sun L 12 to 2, Tue to Sat D 7 to 9.30
CLOSED: 2 weeks New Year, 2 weeks in summer   MEALS: Set L Tue to Fri £11.50 (2 courses) to
£13.50, Set L Sun £14.50, Set D Tue to Fri £18.50 (2 courses) to £22.50, Set D Sat £22.50. BYO
£4   SERVICE: not inc, card slips closed   CARDS: Access, Delta, Switch, Visa   DETAILS: 40
seats. Private parties: 40 main room. Vegetarian meals. Children's helpings Sun L. No children
under 12 D. Smart dress preferred. No cigars/pipes in dining-room. Wheelchair access (no WC).
Music

TAPLOW Berkshire

map 3

▲ Cliveden, Terrace ♥ ※

NEW ENTRY

Taplow SL6 0JF
TEL: (01628) 668561   FAX: (01628) 661837
off A4, 2m N of Taplow on Cliveden Rd

COOKING 3
COST £47–£101

Although both the Terrace and Waldo's (see entry below) are supervised by Ron Maxfield, it appears from reports and inspections that the two are not operating at quite the same level; hence the separate entries. They share, of course, the splendour of the setting. Cliveden is one of the truly grand houses of England, with portraits and suits of armour in the entrance hall, and magnificent flower displays. At lunch, views from the Terrace impress, and sympathetic lighting gives the room itself a boost in the evening. There are fireplaces at either end, *trompe-l'oeil* bookshelves, and tables set with matching gold monogrammed china and elegant candleholders.

Nobody, we trust, would come here in search of bargain-basement prices, but an inspector felt that the food was not overpriced given the nature of ingredients, the quality of the cooking and the obvious costs of upkeep and high staffing levels. If you want luxuries, they got 'em: moist duck foie gras and fig terrine with truffle salad is the sort of thing to look forward to. The modern European approach takes in salmon with a pesto and marrow crust, and breast of duck on an 'enjoyably chewy' pearl barley risotto, with a light but intensely flavoured Madeira sauce.

The pudding department is as strong as any, serving rhubarb crumble with a mascarpone ice-cream, and a dish of perfectly poached and thinly sliced pear interleaved with sesame and caraway-seed tuiles. Bread is varied and flavourful, and dome-lifting service is attentive. One reporter felt that 'it seemed faintly ridiculous that on one of the hottest days of the year jacket and tie were still required'. Wines are the same in both the Terrace and Waldo's: classically French, with some excellent bottles in every section. But the appeal is diminished by some very high mark-ups; only a handful make it under the £20 barrier, three of them from England. House wine is £19. CELLARMAN'S CHOICE: Roero Arneis 'Cru San Michele' 1994, Deltetto Carlo, £26; Mercurey Chateau de Chamirey 1991, A. Rodet, £31.

CHEF: Ron Maxfield   PROPRIETOR: Cliveden plc   OPEN: all week 12.30 to 2, 7 to 9.30   MEALS: alc (main courses £14 to £29). Set L £26, Set D £38.50 (set meals for residents only)   SERVICE: net prices, card slips closed   CARDS: Access, Delta, Diners, Switch, Visa   DETAILS: 54 seats. Private parties: 54 main room, 12 to 54 private rooms. Car park. Vegetarian meals. Children's helpings. Jacket and tie D. No smoking in dining-room. Wheelchair access (also WC). No music   ACCOMMODATION: 37 rooms, all with bath/shower. TV. Phone. Room only £220 to £398. Rooms for disabled. Children welcome. Baby facilities. Dogs welcome. Garden. Swimming-pool. Fishing

---

▲ *Cliveden, Waldo's* ♈ ⁙✳

Taplow SL6 0JF	COOKING 4
TEL: (01628) 668561 FAX: (01628) 661837	COST £57–£104

The approach to the house is very grand, past the Fountain of Love commissioned by William Waldorf Astor, and up a sweeping drive to the palatial entrance hall. Debate continues as to whether Waldo's is in the 'basement', as a reporter maintains, or on the 'lower ground floor', as the management would have it. Whichever it is, the wood panelling and club-like atmosphere make it one of the best appointed of its kind. The bar has been visibly 'antiqued' with mock books and paintings, and the dining-room is spacious.

Of the two restaurants (see entry above), this is where the creative energy is concentrated, and – if it is possible – even more luxuries are used. Perhaps one of the most indulgent menus in the country is the six-course 'truffle' menu. In fact only four courses contain truffles – the sorbet doesn't (although the ice-cream does) and cheeses have to manage without – but as a fantasy menu for truffle-holics it takes some beating. Begin with a cappuccino of white beans and truffle with foie gras before a dish, sorry a 'symphony', of white and black truffles with quail's eggs. The main course is a pot-au-feu of guinea-fowl, helped along by more black Périgord truffles.

In general the food is modern and often complex. Roasted sea bass (cooked with bone-marrow) is served with a ravioli of lobster and lentils, breast of chicken is given a pithivier of livers, and lamb comes five ways. There is an inevitability about some of the dishes: like most menus that call themselves modern, this one has to include a risotto, and what else would you expect it to be made from here except foie gras and langoustine? Despite all the riches, there doesn't appear to be a feeling of having eaten too much. 'The cheeseboard was first-class, every cheese was whole', and the selection is mainly French. The liquorice ice-cream that comes with prune and almond tart is top-notch, while hot vanilla soufflé partnered with gooseberry crumble has been 'well executed and enjoyable'.

Incidentals are up to scratch. In addition to olives and crisps, nibbles include a generous helping of caviare on a potato blini, while an amuse-bouche of foie gras ravioli on a smear of truffle oil and balsamic vinegar is brought to table. First-class petits fours – a mini pecan and pistachio tartlet, for instance – are served with coffee. Service is young and attentive. Wines are the same as in the Terrace.

CHEF: Ron Maxfield   PROPRIETOR: Cliveden plc   OPEN: Tue to Sat D only 7 to 10.30   MEALS: Set D £45 to £75   SERVICE: net prices, card slips closed   CARDS: Access, Delta, Diners, Switch, Visa   DETAILS: 28 seats. Private parties: 12, 18 and 54 private rooms. Car park. Vegetarian meals. Children welcome. Jacket and tie. No smoking in dining-room. Wheelchair access (also WC). Music. Air-conditioned   ACCOMMODATION: 37 rooms, all with bath/shower. TV. Phone. Room only £220 to £398. Rooms for disabled. Children welcome. Baby facilities. Dogs welcome. Garden. Swimming-pool. Fishing

---

TAUNTON Somerset   map 2

▲ *Castle Hotel* ❢ ⭐

Castle Green, Taunton TA1 1NF   COOKING 4
TEL: (01823) 272671   FAX: (01823) 336066   COST £32–£66

At the right time of year purple wistaria completely covers the sizeable walls of this imposing building, while inside are high ceilings, pale muted colours and expensively draped tables. Kit Chapman is a significant mover and shaker in the restaurant business, and the partnership with Phil Vickery, now into its seventh year, runs on smoothly oiled rails. There are two set-price menus, with little to separate them in terms of skills and ingredients; the less expensive option is slightly more conservative. What the Castle has always championed is a savvy interpretation of English food, a streak exemplified perhaps by 'quite amazing' deep-fried wing of skate in a light batter served with beetroot and a saffron-flavoured tartare sauce, or a vanilla blanc-mange with coriander syrup and shortbread.

One reporter felt it was 'classic, safe cooking' that lacked the 'adventure of British provincial cooking'. This is probably truer of the repertoire as a whole – which seems not to evolve significantly – than it is of individual dishes. Some ideas (at least on the more expensive menu) are exciting, and execution is very professional, from the pastry in a crab tart, to careful timing of main-course fish and meats, to well-judged stock-based sauces. Presentation is strikingly simple and stylish, and there is gratifyingly little inclination to try to impress with expense-account ingredients. The quality of materials shows in, for example, tournedos of beef with a sliver of truffle on top, or roast best end of lamb, both served with dauphinois potatoes. Only greater intensity of flavour would have improved an inspector's meal.

'Phil Vickery's most sublime moments are provided by his puddings' was one reporter's view: baked egg custard with either nutmeg or lemon curd ice-cream is popular, and a lot of effort goes into producing the intricate selection of chocolate desserts. Appetisers, bread and sweetmeats support the general impression of a kitchen with a high degree of skill. Service from a succession of Continental youngsters, though willing enough, may lack the control and direction which the food deserves. But there is lots of it. The wine list opens promisingly with nine sherries by the glass, pauses at a 'short' house selection of three dozen wines and then launches into the full list. Here the French classics hold sway, but the spread from other countries is more than adequate, and the ports and whiskies are tempting. House wines are £11.25. CELLARMAN'S CHOICE: Simon Hackett Chardonnay 1994, Barossa Valley, S. Australia, £13.90; Minervois 1992, Ch. de Gourgazaud, £12.80.

CHEF: Phil Vickery   PROPRIETORS: the Chapman family   OPEN: all week 12.30 to 2, 7.30 to 9 MEALS: Set L £31 to £35, Set D £20.90 to £35   SERVICE: not inc, card slips closed   CARDS: Access, Amex, Diners, Visa   DETAILS: 65 seats. Private parties: 110 main room, 16 and 25 private rooms. Car park. Children's helpings. Smart dress preferred. No smoking in dining-room. Wheelchair access (also WC). Music   ACCOMMODATION: 36 rooms, all with bath/shower. TV. Phone. B&B £75 to £185. Rooms for disabled. Children welcome. Baby facilities. Dogs welcome in bedrooms only. Afternoon teas. Garden (*The Which? Hotel Guide*)

TAVISTOCK Devon map 1

▲ *Horn of Plenty* 🍴✱

Gulworthy, Tavistock PL19 8JD
TEL/FAX: (01822) 832528
3m W of Tavistock on A390, turn right   COOKING 3
at Gulworthy Cross   COST £25–£62

Views across the woods and fields of the Tamar Valley from this self-styled 'restaurant-with-rooms' instil in the visitor a sense of calm. Accommodation is in a converted stable block, and dining takes place in a couple of comfortable rooms in the Georgian house. 'Confidence is evident both in the style of management and in the products of the kitchen,' observed an inspector, and people generally appreciate the 'close to impeccable' service and the combination of charm and command from Elaine Gatehouse. Reporters find it difficult to choose between dishes: crab bisque, or ravioli of lamb sweetbreads to begin, and then duck with a black pepper and cider sauce, or sea bass with scallops and a calamari sauce, for instance.

Chef Peter Gorton gets around – to Thailand, Japan and Australia – and his experience turns up in, for example, outstandingly good poached salmon in a cupful of broth with chilli, coconut and ginger. High-quality raw materials are a distinguishing feature, including 'two magnificent pigeon breasts' at one meal that were 'pink, with a gorgeous smooth texture, rested after roasting, with a wonderful flavour'. They were helped by a nugget of foie gras on top, and a shallot and potato cake underneath. Here is a chef who knows how to buy well and time things perfectly.

One reporter for whom 'any gelatine is too much gelatine' was disappointed by an orange and caramel 'cream' (that also contained fresh raspberries in February), but pastry work is good, and meals can end on the bright flavours of a passion-fruit bavarois, or a lemon and mint tart. The largely French wine list makes a sincere effort to include good bottles for less than £20, including half a dozen house wines from £10.75 that are also available by the glass.

CHEF: Peter Gorton   PROPRIETORS: Ian and Elaine Gatehouse   OPEN: Tue to Sun L 12 to 2, all week D 7 to 9   CLOSED: 25 and 26 Dec   MEALS: Set L £10.50 (2 courses) to £17.50, Set D £18.50 (Mon only) to £28.50   SERVICE: not inc   CARDS: Access, Amex, Switch, Visa   DETAILS: 50 seats. 20 seats outside. Private parties: 50 main room, 12 private room. Car park. Vegetarian meals. No children under 13 (exc Sun L). Smart dress preferred. No smoking in dining-room. Wheelchair access (also WC). No music   ACCOMMODATION: 7 rooms, all with bath/shower. TV. Phone. B&B £58 to £98. Deposit: 20%. Rooms for disabled. Children under 13 by arrangement only. Dogs welcome in bedrooms only. Garden (*The Which? Hotel Guide*)

Neil's ✹✶

27 King Street, Tavistock PL19 0DT	COOKING 1*
TEL: (01822) 615550	COST £25–£39

Janet Neil's single-handed operation occupies a 400-year-old farmhouse where two streets meet. Tightly packed tables and a tiny bar area make the place feel suitably cosy. The kitchen repertoire is based around a nucleus of favoured dishes, with top-quality meats the outstanding feature. Tamworth pork, Aberdeen Angus beef and rare-breed Shropshire lamb lend class to any menu. That last came as a rack roasted with a herb and brioche crumb crust and impressed for both flavour and texture, only being slightly let down by a 'bland' garlic and thyme cream sauce. Potted pheasant with a port jelly and cranberry relish, seafood chowder, and smoked haddock and watercress pancakes crop up among starters. Meals might end with brown-sugar meringues and ice-cream. An imaginative list of wines from all over is bulked with a good range of halves. House French is £8.95.

CHEF/PROPRIETOR: Janet Neil   OPEN: Tue to Sat D only 7 to 9   MEALS: alc (main courses £12 to £14). Set D £17   SERVICE: not inc   CARDS: Access, Amex, Visa   DETAILS: 20 seats. Private parties: 22 main room. Vegetarian meals. Children welcome. Smart dress preferred. No smoking in dining-room. No music

---

TEFFONT EVIAS   Wiltshire   map 2

▲ Howard's House ✹✶

Teffont Evias SP3 5RJ	
TEL: (01722) 716392 and 716821	
FAX: (01722) 716820	
off B3089, W of Dinton and 9½m W of Salisbury,	COOKING 2*
signposted Chicksgrove	COST £27–£44

Make your way through the unruffled serenity of the Nadder Valley west of Salisbury, turn left at the Black Horse pub and a delightful hodge-podge of architectural styles comes into view, in the form of this seventeenth-century manor house, roofed in the Swiss manner 200 years later. The dining-room's shades of green seem designed to blend in with the rural setting, but anybody who expects the cooking to be equally bucolic will be surprised by Paul Firmin's imaginative modern menus.

Duck rillettes with mango and chilli salsa, marinated rabbit with polenta and red-pepper sauce (a first course), and lamb in puff pastry with pistachios and pickled walnuts are representative of world-wide influences ranging from the Far East to the West Indies. One experienced reporter commented that 'the food is exciting enough to make meals memorable'. Others approved of 'melt-in-the-mouth medallions' of chicken sauced with tarragon and lemon, and the excellent accompanying vegetables. Desserts take in 'clear and fruity' mixed sorbets, as well as 'extremely rich' chocolate pecan pie with maple ice-cream. 'Unobtrusively efficient' service and top-drawer breakfasts also contribute to a sense of fine style. The predominantly French wines are good rather than great, with prices on the high side. House wines start at £12.95.

CHEFS: Paul Firmin and Stephen Bredemear PROPRIETORS: Paul Firmin and Jonathan Ford
OPEN: Sun L 12.30 to 2, all week D 7.30 to 9.30; L other days by arrangement MEALS: Set L Sun
£18.50, Set D £23 (2 courses) to £26.50. BYO £6–£8 SERVICE: not inc, card slips closed
CARDS: Access, Amex, Delta, Diners, Switch, Visa DETAILS: 32 seats. 12 seats outside. Private
parties: 40 main room. Car park. Children's helpings. No smoking in dining-room. Wheelchair
access (also men's WC). Music ACCOMMODATION: 9 rooms, all with bath/shower. TV. Phone.
B&B £75 to £115. Children welcome; baby-listening. Dogs welcome. Afternoon teas. Garden
(*The Which? Hotel Guide*)

TETBURY Gloucestershire   map 2

▲ *Calcot Manor* ♥ ⌂ ✻

Tetbury GL8 8YJ
TEL: (01666) 890391 FAX: (01666) 890394   COOKING 2*
on A4135, 4m W of Tetbury   COST £24–£51

Calcot is a Cotswold farmhouse, the land around once the preserve of Cistercian monks. The surrounding barns and stables are now reinvented as guest rooms, while the rose-coloured dining-room is adorned with zoological prints. Michael Croft took over the kitchen at the end of 1995, putting more of a contemporary spin on things, and his 'modern English' approach suits Calcot's gradual conversion to a brasserie format. Minestrone risotto might sound like an original contribution to the culinary lexicon, but turns out to be a fine rendition of classic risotto with a pair of delicious toasty scallops, plenty of shaved Parmesan and diced tomato. Or there may be textbook cheese soufflé with spinach and walnuts.

Main courses span the range from whole fried lemon sole to chargrilled beef fillet with wild mushroom pâté and a red wine sauce, though pot-roast guinea-fowl with lime and redcurrants may make a sharper alternative. The execution of tarte Tatin with a scoop of vanilla ice-cream in the middle and a two-tone feathered sauce of caramel and crème anglaise could not be faulted, although service at inspection could have been better informed.

Wines have been sourced with care and inspire fine drinking as well as offering plenty of choice under £20. Outside France, Australia and the US look the most tempting sections. Half-bottles are plentiful and varied. French house wines are £11.50. CELLARMAN'S CHOICE: Jurançon Sec 1992, Dom. Lapeyre, £20; Barolo 1990, Josetta Saffirio, £32.50.

CHEF: Michael Croft   PROPRIETORS: Michael and Louisa Stone   OPEN: all week 12.30 to 2, 7.30 to 9.30   MEALS: alc (main courses L £8 to £11, D £10 to £16.50). Set L £17, Set D £22   SERVICE: not inc, card slips closed   CARDS: Access, Amex, Delta, Diners, Switch, Visa   DETAILS: 64 seats. 20 seats outside. Private parties: 65 main room, 15 to 65 private rooms. Car park. Children's helpings. Smart dress preferred. No smoking in dining-room. Wheelchair access (also WC). Music   ACCOMMODATION: 20 rooms, all with bath/shower. TV. Phone. B&B £75 to £135. Rooms for disabled. Children welcome. Baby facilities. Afternoon teas. Garden. Swimming-pool (The Which? Hotel Guide)

THORNBURY   South Gloucestershire   map 2

▲ *Thornbury Castle* ⚡✻

Castle Street, Thornbury BS12 1HH
TEL: (01454) 281182   FAX: (01454) 416188   COOKING 2
off B4061, at N end of town   COST £29–£65

'This is a theatrical experience, but with food,' summed up one reporter impressed by the set: a Tudor castle covered in ivy, housing a nineteenth-century Gothic interior, with Holbein prints and a convincing suit of armour from the props department. 'Dignified,' thought one; 'unduly pretentious,' reckoned another. However the place strikes you, there is a view that the food has to work hard to match the surroundings.

Choice is generous, and Steven Black's repertoire stays largely with familiar ideas such as roast rack of lamb with a rosemary crust, or treacle tart with clotted cream. The emphasis is on quick roasting, poaching, grilling or pan frying, and a specific vegetable usually accompanies the main course: 'The pigeon deserves particular mention; it was tender and went well with the Swiss chard and rosemary-scented *jus*.' One reporter found the kitchen willing and able to produce a vegan meal (even down to the appetisers) with advance notice, and the whole thing was backed up by 'friendly and helpful' service. 'Poor' and 'good' are contrasting views of the value for money. Venerable bottles and three-figure prices pepper the wine list, but there is just enough under £20 for those with tickets in the stalls.

CHEF: Steven Black   PROPRIETORS: Baron and Baroness of Portlethen   OPEN: all week 12 to 2, 7 to 9.30 (10 Fri and Sat, 9 Sun)   CLOSED: 2 days Jan   MEALS: Set L £13.50 (2 courses) to £20.50, Set D £31 to £43. BYO £10   SERVICE: none, card slips closed   CARDS: Access, Amex, Diners, Switch, Visa   DETAILS: 60 seats. Private parties: 26 main room, 12 and 26 private rooms. Car park. Vegetarian meals. No children under 12. Jacket and tie. No smoking in dining-rooms. Music   ACCOMMODATION: 18 rooms, all with bath/shower. TV. Phone. B&B £75 to £220. No children under 12. Afternoon teas. Garden (The Which? Hotel Guide)

All details are as accurate as possible at the time of going to press, but chefs and owners often change, and it is wise to check by telephone before making a special journey. Many readers have been disappointed when set-price bargain meals are no longer available. Ask when booking.

Card slips closed *in the details at the end of an entry indicates that the total on the slips of credit cards is closed when handed over for signature.*

THORNTON-CLEVELEYS Lancashire map 8

▲ *Victorian House*

Trunnah Road, Thornton-Cleveleys FY5 4HF
TEL: (01253) 860619   FAX: (01253) 865350
off A585, 3m N of Blackpool

COOKING 1
COST £16–£36

'Here is the best, unfussy, simple restaurant that I have visited in the last year,' wrote one satisfied customer, impressed by both the food and the value. Lunch is taken in the conservatory wine bar and bistro (rechristened Didier's) and runs to soups, salads, pâtés, roast or grilled fish, or perhaps a beef casserole or sauté lamb kidneys. The cooking has taken a more modern turn since last year, adopting fast roasting and charcoal grilling, and seems to have brightened considerably. Dinner is still a weightier four courses, with an intermediate soup or sorbet, but the new style means it is not daunting. A typical menu might produce steamed mussels, leek and potato soup with sweetcorn, grilled noisette of lamb with mustard sauce, and a blackcurrant and lime charlotte. Ice-creams are from Häagen-Dazs. Reliable French producers dominate the wine list, and house wine is £9.50.

CHEF: Didier Guérin   PROPRIETORS: Louise and Didier Guérin   OPEN: all week L 12 to 2, Tue to Sat D 7 to 9.30   CLOSED: first week Feb, 2 weeks Nov   MEALS: alc L (main courses £5 to £10.50). Set L £5 (2 courses), Set D £21. BYO £5   SERVICE: not inc, card slips closed   CARDS: Access, Amex, Switch, Visa   DETAILS: 60 seats. Private parties: 40 main room. Car park. Children's helpings. No children under 6. Smart dress preferred. Music   ACCOMMODATION: 2 rooms, both with bath/shower. TV. Phone. B&B £35 to £40. No children under 6. Dogs welcome in bedrooms only. Garden

TORQUAY Devon map 1

Table ♥

135 Babbacombe Road, Torquay TQ1 3SR
TEL/FAX: (01803) 324292

COOKING 1*
COST £31–£38

The previous owners sold the Table to Julie Tuckett (ex-Peat Spade Inn, Longstock) in May 1996. Since both décor and name remained unaltered, some confusion was engendered in the early days of the new régime, but a change of culinary style is certainly in evidence. In a less than prepossessing location, an expanding suburb up the road from Torquay, there is a homelier feel to it all than hitherto. Pork rillettes is a chef's special from Longstock days: coarse, tasty and cleverly partnered with pickled cucumber and a cherry and ginger chutney to cut the fat. Sweetly sauced meats (Madeira for tournedos, blackcurrants and cassis with Barbary duck) are generally successful, or there may be salmon with a butter sauce perfumed with white truffle and balsamic. Puddings such as apricot brioche soufflé with a rich egg-custard texture, or chocolate mousse served with nut-studded cream have won early converts. Service in the first days of the new regime was a little hesitant, but things should settle. Some of the wines remain from the Table's previous list, though the arrangement is now different: by country instead of style. An upper limit of around £25 keeps the whole thing sensibly affordable, there are some 20 half-bottles, and a house selection starts at £10.15, with around a dozen available by the glass.

CHEF/PROPRIETOR: Julie T. Tuckett   OPEN: Tue to Fri L 12.15 to 1.45, Tue to Sat D 7.30 to 9.30
CLOSED: 2 weeks early Feb, 2 weeks end Mar, bank hols   MEALS: Set L £11.85, Set D £23.50
SERVICE: not inc, card slips closed   CARDS: Access, Amex, Delta, Diners, Switch, Visa
DETAILS: 20 seats. Private parties: 20 main room. No children under 12. Smart dress preferred.
No smoking until after D. No cigars/pipes in dining-room. Wheelchair access (no WC). No music

---

TRUSHAM Devon   map 1

▲ Cridford Inn ⁵⁺✷ £

Trusham TQ13 0NR
TEL: (01626) 853694
3m N of Chudleigh; from A38 take Teign Valley exit
on to B3193, follow signs for Trusham; inn is   COOKING 1
signposted after 3m, at lower part of village   COST £19–£42

'A most comfortable and welcoming inn of the true variety,' noted one traveller who drove down rain-soaked country lanes seeking shelter from the storm. David and Sally Hesmondhalgh have lovingly restored 'the oldest domestic dwelling in Devon', and run the place in tandem: she serves, he cooks. A bistro menu is available lunch and evening, while the main restaurant is open for dinner Tuesday to Saturday. What you are offered is traditional English food with a few foreign touches, but based emphatically on local produce. Seafood is regularly applauded, whether it be home-smoked salmon, crab or fish lasagne. Also good are wild mushrooms in garlic and cheese sauce with home-baked bread, roast duckling, and chocolate roulade. Ploughman's comes with a quartet of Devon cheeses. Local Trusham ale is a pleasing tipple and the short wine list from Christopher Piper has a fine choice by the glass. House wine is £10.75.

CHEF: David Hesmondhalgh   PROPRIETORS: David and Sally Hesmondhalgh   OPEN: restaurant
Tue to Sat (all week in summer) D only 7 to 9, bistro all week 12 to 2, 7 to 9   CLOSED: 25 Dec
MEALS: alc restaurant and bistro (main courses £5 to £16)   SERVICE: not inc, card slips closed
CARDS: Access, Visa   DETAILS: 65 seats. 25 seats outside. Private parties: 18 main room. Car
park. Vegetarian meals. Children's helpings. Smart dress preferred. No smoking in 1
dining-room. Music   ACCOMMODATION: 4 rooms, all with bath/shower. TV. B&B £40 to £60.
Deposit: 20%. Dogs welcome (£2.50 per day)

TUNBRIDGE WELLS Kent   map 3

Sankey's ⁵⁺✷

39 Mount Ephraim, Tunbridge Wells TN4 8AA   COOKING 1
TEL: (01892) 511422   FAX: (01892) 536097   COST £18–£57

Fish is the main preoccupation of this Dutch-gabled villa built in 1895, as the piscatorial pictures and memorabilia make plain. The York-paved cellar wine bar is perhaps the liveliest spot, but other rooms are full of character too. Guy Sankey has been in the business long enough to be sure of good supplies: oysters come from Ireland and potted shrimps from Morecambe, Cornish crabs and lobsters are kept in a sea-water tank, while scallops, langoustines and smoked salmon are from Loch Fyne. Simple preparation and treatment are the order of the day, from langoustines with mayonnaise, or wing of skate with beurre noir, to cock crab with black-bean sauce. Staples of the repertoire include fish soup, a cold seafood platter, and grilled Dover sole, while puddings run to French apple tart and banoffi pie. While one reporter found the service 'poor', another thought it 'friendly and efficient'. White wines have been chosen carefully to partner fish dishes, but there is no shortage of reds or sparklers, all at very acceptable prices. House wine from France starts at £9.50 a bottle.

CHEF: Eleuterio Lizzi   PROPRIETOR: Guy Sankey   OPEN: restaurant Mon to Fri L 12 to 2, Mon to Sat D 7 to 10; wine bar Mon to Sat 12 to 2, 7 to 10   CLOSED: 25 and 26 Dec   MEALS: alc (main courses £10 to £25). Set L £7.50 (2 courses). BYO by arrangement   SERVICE: not inc   CARDS: Access, Amex, Delta, Diners, Switch, Visa   DETAILS: 70 seats. Private parties: 20 main room. Vegetarian meals. Children's helpings. Smart dress preferred. No smoking in 2 dining-rooms. Music. Air-conditioned

Thackeray's House ▼

85 London Road, Tunbridge Wells TN1 1EA
TEL/FAX: (01892) 511921

COOKING 3
COST £34–£66

The lounge of this small house, once the home of the novelist, has now been pressed into service as an extra dining area, and drinks are taken in a comfortable drawing-room upstairs. Apart from that, Bruce Wass 'is cooking as well as we ever remember'. He offers a good-value set lunch, the flexibility of a set-price menu and a *carte* at dinner, and elicits lots of enthusiasm. He claims not to cook in any particular style, but simply changes the menu daily 'depending on what is available'. If there is a common thread, it is probably that he produces the best sort of French provincial or English country cooking.

A number of things stand out: the 'absolute accuracy' of timing in, for example, a fillet of cod with tapénade crust; the 'perfect marriage of flavours' in a simple leek and almond soup; the lightness of a venison and pigeon parfait; or the dressing, using particularly good olive oil, for a salad of rare and tender pigeon breast with soft halved quail's eggs and crisp bacon dice. Flavours, as in a mousseline of lemon sole, can be 'delicate but not bland', but also explore other dimensions, as in a breast of pheasant with diced black pudding, ceps and hedgehog mushrooms that was judged 'rich, winey, smoky, with lots of depth'.

'The toffee pudding has developed,' according to one visitor, 'adding walnuts and apricots to its original ginger, but the amazing toffee sauce is the same.' Another was bowled over by the 'inspired assembly of flavour and texture' of îles flottantes scented with rose-water. Coffee and bread are 'of the best', although service is not always up to the standard of the kitchen; 'slow and unsmiling' is one view. A bistro in the basement serves lighter food. Wines are a classy, international bunch. The French selection impresses, as does the solid range from Italy and the vast number of half-bottles. House wines are £11.75. CELLARMAN'S CHOICE: Pinot Bianco 1994, Druis, Friuli, £19.40; Coteaux du Languedoc, Mas Bruguière 'Pic St Loup' 1994, Coteaux du Languedoc, £21.25

▮ denotes an outstanding wine cellar; ▼ denotes a good wine list, worth travelling for.

CHEF/PROPRIETOR: Bruce Wass   OPEN: Tue to Sun L 12.30 to 2, Tue to Sat D 7 to 10   CLOSED: 5 days Christmas   MEALS: alc D (main courses £12 to £18). Set L Tue to Sat £12 to £19.50 (2 courses), Set L Sun £15.50 (2 courses) to £19.50, Set D Tue to Thur £23.50 to £44, Set D Fri and Sat £44   SERVICE: not inc   CARDS: Access, Delta, Switch, Visa   DETAILS: 50 seats. 30 seats outside. Private parties: 50 main room, 8 to 25 private rooms. Vegetarian meals. Children's helpings. No cigars/pipes in dining-room. Wheelchair access (no WC). No music

---

TWICKENHAM   Greater London   map 3

McClements

2 Whitton Road, Twickenham TW1 1BJ   COOKING 3
TEL: (0181) 744 9610   FAX: (01784) 240593   COST £25–£43

The adjacent bistro that looked likely to open last year has not materialised, which may be all to the good, since John McClements's cooking is once more on an upswing, as reports from his followers attest. It is a long, thin room with tables to either side, decorated in restrained up-market style with smart wooden panelling, an array of pleasing paintings, and strains of Edith and Ella reprising through to dinner's end.

Crisp sea bass with lobster and caviare beurre blanc has been pronounced a 'smash hit'. Delicacy marks another first course of sea scallops in a salad garnished with asparagus and black truffle shavings. Medallions of venison on (salty) shredded cabbage with roast chestnuts and shallots has been described as both 'well cooked and attractively presented', using first-class meat. Complex dessert constructions might include rum babas that come with crème Chantilly and a biscuit cup of 'delightful' lime sorbet, the plate further decorated with circlets of white chocolate and fresh raspberries. Give or take a bit of inaccurate seasoning, this is a solidly confident performance. House wines are £10.

CHEF/PROPRIETOR: John McClements   OPEN: Mon to Sat 12 to 2.30, 7 to 11   MEALS: Set L £15, Set D £21 (2 courses) to £25   SERVICE: 10%   CARDS: Access, Visa   DETAILS: 45 seats. Private parties: 50 main room. Children welcome. Wheelchair access (also WC). Music. Air-conditioned

---

UCKFIELD   East Sussex   map 3

▲ Horsted Place 🍴✳

Little Horsted, Uckfield TN22 5TS
TEL: (01825) 750581   FAX: (01825) 750459   COOKING 2*
on A26, 2m S of Uckfield   COST £27–£61

It calls itself, with considerable justification, a luxury country-house hotel, and has a modest sporting estate of 1,100 acres. The building was designed by Pugin, after whom the dining-room is now named, and the whole lot remains in its original state. Open fires, a pianist, linen, silver and crystal all contribute to the feeling of extravagance, and staff are attentive and professional without being too stiff. Despite the hauteur – menu French, and pricing conveyed as, for instance, 'five pounds and eighty pence' – the food does not rely on luxury ingredients for effect. Instead there is potted rabbit with quince jelly, twice-baked goats'-cheese soufflé, and chump of lamb with rosemary sauce. This is sensible cooking, well executed and attractively presented.

The *carte* may be more ambitious than the set-price menus, but commendably avoids piling on extras for gaudy effect. Hence grey-legged partridge is served with an apple and potato rösti with calvados sauce, and entrecôte of beef comes with a simple bone marrow and herb crust. The kitchen smokes its own salmon and venison, and makes preserves. Vegetarians are given serious attention; one began a meal with a tian of provençale vegetables ('the mould must be like a giant thimble') in a swirl of delicate basil sauce, and finished with an individual chocolate sponge with butterscotch sauce. The wine list majors on grandiose wines, and mark-ups are high, but there are just enough bottles under £20 for ordinary mortals to enjoy themselves. House wine is £12.50.

CHEF: Allan Garth   PROPRIETOR: Granfel Holdings   OPEN: all week 12 to 2, 7.30 to 9.30   MEALS: alc (main courses £13.50 to £22). Set L £14.95, Set D £28.50. BYO £12.50   SERVICE: not inc, card slips closed   CARDS: Access, Amex, Delta, Diners, Switch, Visa   DETAILS: 40 seats. 30 seats outside. Private parties: 40 main room, 6 to 30 private rooms. Car park. Vegetarian meals. Children welcome. Jacket and tie. No smoking in dining-room. Wheelchair access (also women's and men's WC). No music   ACCOMMODATION: 20 rooms, all with bath/shower. TV. Phone. Room only £70 to £285. Deposit: 50%. Rooms for disabled. Children welcome. Dogs welcome by arrangement. Afternoon teas. Garden. Swimming-pool (*The Which? Hotel Guide*)

ULLSWATER Cumbria   map 10

▲ *Sharrow Bay* ▼ ⁵⁺✳

Ullswater CA10 2LZ
TEL: (01768) 486301   FAX: (01768) 486349
2m from Pooley Bridge on E side of lake, signposted   COOKING 3*
Howtown and Martindale   COST £38–£58

This is a place for a special occasion, an indulgence. Even those who have looked forward to eating here for years are not disappointed. 'It fully lived up to my expectations,' wrote one half of a twentieth wedding anniversary party. 'Sharrow is not cheap, but we did not begrudge the price of dinner,' confirmed another. It divides reporters – a 'bench-mark hotel' for one, a 'fossilised legend' for another – but as a national institution is generally viewed with the same affection as the Royal Albert Hall, and still overseen by Francis Coulson and Brian Sack, 'two nice men who are quite unaffected by the affluence of those they cater for'.

'We sat in the bay of the picture window and watched the sun set behind the mountains,' wrote one couple, conveying the romance that many feel. A sense of ritual is also integral: filing past the array of puddings on the way into dinner, for instance. It is one of the few places, outside busy brasseries, where a long menu is just about sustainable. A certain fussiness is apparent in some dishes, and the number of courses and portion sizes – including large helpings of meaty fish, such as brill or halibut, that arrive with a creamy soufflé suissesse after the first course – all add up to a substantial meal.

Ingredients and cooking are first-rate, though some of the combinations – mango and cassis sauce with calf's liver, for one reporter – may not work as well as others. While some kitchens shed ingredients to give dishes more direct impact, Sharrow Bay pursues its rather more involved traditional English style, using chutneys, dumplings, fruity sauces, locally cured ham, borrowing foie

467

gras or peperonata, and ending with British cheeses. Staff, who 'now seem to be getting older', are 'remarkably friendly' and strike a balanced and informative tone. Quality is reassuringly high on a wide-ranging wine list. It opens with nearly three dozen by the glass, keeps standards high through the classic regions of France, and has plenty of good entries from Germany, Australia and California. House wines are £12.95.

CHEFS: Johnnie Martin and Colin Akrigg PROPRIETORS: Francis Coulson and Brian Sack OPEN: all week 1 to 1.30, 8 to 8.45 CLOSED: early Dec to late Feb MEALS: Set L £31.75, Set D £41.75 SERVICE: net prices CARDS: none DETAILS: 64 seats. Private parties: 10 main room. Car park. No children under 13. Smart dress preferred. No smoking in dining-room. Wheelchair access (also WC). No music. Air-conditioned ACCOMMODATION: 28 rooms, 24 with bath/shower. TV. Phone. D,B&B £100 to £320. Rooms for disabled. No children under 13. Afternoon teas. Garden. Fishing (The Which? Hotel Guide)

ULVERSTON Cumbria   map 8

▲ Bay Horse Inn ♀ ⅚✕

Canal Foot, Ulverston LA12 9EL
TEL: (01229) 583972   FAX: (01229) 580502
off A590; just before centre of Ulverston, follow signs   COOKING 2*
to Canal Foot   COST £25–£43

Past the industrial bulk of the Glaxo factory, the inn overlooks the tranquil Leven Estuary. It consists of a comfortable bar (snacks are available) with exposed beams and brasses, and a conservatory dining-room out front to make the most of views across Morecambe Bay. The *carte* offers around five options per course (the set-price lunch is either/or until a wider choice at dessert), and the kitchen is very busy wrapping and filling things: stuffing mushroom and onion pâté into a breast of guinea-fowl, and then enclosing that in puff pastry, for instance.

Main courses tend to favour alcoholic, creamy or roux-based sauces, although there are plain alternatives of Aberdeen Angus steak. One reporter enjoyed a relatively simple meal of gazpacho followed by scallops with smoked bacon, ending with cheese and home-made soda bread. Another thought that more might be done to preserve essential flavours – of a fillet of turbot stuffed with avocado, prawns and mushrooms, for instance. Vegetables come in profusion, the same for all dishes. Meringues, sponges and clotted cream may well feature among rich puddings. One reporter commented on the 'unfailing professionalism' of the staff led by Peter McKinnon. A short selection of Old World wines is eclipsed by the lively New World list – 50 bottles from Australia and New Zealand, plus a handful from South Africa and California, the vast majority of them excellent. Prices are reasonable and kick off at £11.95.

'My husband had another pudding, about which he had asked that the bill be adjusted, but it was not charged and when he queried he was told, "[The proprietor] admires anyone who has more than one pudding".' (On eating in Shropshire)

CHEFS: Robert Lyons and Esther Jarvis PROPRIETORS: John Tovey and Robert Lyons OPEN: Tue to Sat L 12 to 1.30, all week D 7.30 for 8 (1 sitting) MEALS: alc (main courses £14 to £16). Set L £16.50. Minimum £8.50. Bar L available SERVICE: 10%, card slips closed CARDS: Access, Visa DETAILS: 50 seats. Private parties: 50 main room, 20 and 30 private rooms. Car park. Vegetarian meals. No children under 12. Smart dress preferred. No smoking in dining-room. Wheelchair access (also WC). Music. Air-conditioned ACCOMMODATION: 7 rooms, all with bath/shower. TV. Phone. D,B&B £80 to £150. No children under 12. Dogs welcome in bedrooms only. Afternoon teas (*The Which? Hotel Guide*)

UPPER SLAUGHTER Gloucestershire   map 5

▲ *Lords of the Manor* ⅚✹

Upper Slaughter, nr Bourton-on-the-Water GL54 2JD	
TEL: (01451) 820243 FAX: (01451) 820696	COOKING 3
turn W off A429, 3m S of Stow-on-the-Wold	COST £34–£68

If this seventeenth-century former rectory is anything to go by, it can't have been a bad life in the Church, what with eight acres of garden and twenty-eight bedrooms. Deep in honey-coloured Cotswold country, the Manor is now equipped with deep sofas, Old Master prints, and variable service that has been described as 'over-flunkied', 'indifferent' and 'attentive'. Clive Dixon cooks attractive modern dishes with upbeat flavours, applying a crushed bacon and chilli dressing to beef tartare, for instance, or underpinning a first course of tuna with a salad of chorizo, potato, lime and coriander.

He is keen on the contrast between humble items and more luxurious ones, putting himself in the running for a foie gras promotional prize, pairing it variously with pork knuckle in a terrine, with ox-tongue, with mushy peas, and even more unusually with home-salted cod. Pig's trotter, meanwhile, is stuffed with sweetbreads and served with trompettes-de-mort mushrooms and a dribble of truffle oil. Desserts favour lightness over the general down-to-earth character of main courses, although they are not without an element of indulgence. Hot coconut soufflé is served with chocolate and banana sorbet, while a chocolate and rose-water mousse comes with an orange blossom brûlée. The wine list is 'extensive, expensive and strictly for special occasions', thought one reporter, and, although there are 16 wines by the glass, they are as highly priced as the rest. House wines are £14.95.

CHEF: Clive Dixon PROPRIETORS: James Gulliver, Andrew Gulliver, James Gulliver Jnr. and Philip Good OPEN: all week 12.30 to 2 (2.30 Sun), 7 to 9.30 MEALS: Set L £16.95 (2 courses) to £39.50, Set D £32.50 to £39.50. Bar L available SERVICE: not inc L, 12.5% D, card slips closed D CARDS: Access, Amex, Delta, Diners, Switch, Visa DETAILS: 60 seats. 56 seats outside. Private parties: 60 main room, 30 private room. Car park. Children's helpings. Smart dress preferred. No smoking in dining-room. Wheelchair access (also WC). Music ACCOMMODATION: 28 rooms, all with bath/shower. TV. Phone. B&B £90 to £225. Deposit: £50. Rooms for disabled. Children welcome. Baby facilities. Afternoon teas. Garden. Fishing (*The Which? Hotel Guide*)

'It is easy to forget, eating in GFG-listed restaurants, that the United Kingdom enjoys such an evil reputation for poor food. Here was proof indeed that basic standards in this country are lamentable.' (On eating in Cheshire)

VIRGINSTOW Devon   map 1

▲ *Percy's at Coombeshead* ❉

NEW ENTRY

Virginstow, nr Launceston EX21 5EA
TEL: (01409) 211236   FAX: (01409) 211275
follow signs to Percy's at Coombeshead from
Gridley Corner on A388, or from B3218 at   COOKING 2*
Metherell Cross junction   COST £26–£39

The Bricknell-Webbs already use their Devon farmstead to supply Percy's in
Harrow (see entry). At Easter 1996 they opened a restaurant-with-rooms down
on the farm. You eat in the 'sensitively decorated' 400-year-old longhouse and
sleep in the barn. Ben Reeve has been tempted away from a Cornish hotel, and
the fixed-price menus bear a resemblance to their Harrow counterparts, the
modern eclecticism somehow gaining an extra *frisson* beyond Dartmoor.

Among the starters may be chargrilled cuttlefish strips on exotic salad leaves
with a chilli pepper dressing and marigold petals, a visually stunning dish that
delivers a medley of poignant flavours too. 'Meltingly tender' Aberdeen Angus
fillet is cooked rare and comes with a 'slightly sweet but piquant' sauce of thyme
and peppercorns. Fish options have included roasted monkfish with fennel,
peppers and leeks. Ingredients are clearly tip-top, including excellent vegetables grown a stone's throw from the dining-room. Flavours are cleverly
marshalled at dessert stage as well, as in a 'properly light and slightly gooey'
meringue nest containing rosemary ice-cream, a mango coulis and toasted
hazelnuts. The wine list is full of sound modern selections from all over, and
does an efficient job of reining most prices in below £20. House South Africans
are £8.50.

CHEF: Tina Bricknell-Webb   PROPRIETORS: Tony and Tina Bricknell-Webb   OPEN: all week 12
to 2.30, 6.30 to 10   MEALS: Set L £14.50 (2 courses), Set D £18   SERVICE: not inc   CARDS:
Access, Amex, Delta, Diners, Switch, Visa   DETAILS: 50 seats. 20 seats outside. Private parties:
34 main room, 16 private room. Car park. Vegetarian meals. Children's helpings. No children
under 10. Smart dress preferred. No smoking in dining-room. Wheelchair access (no WC).
Music   ACCOMMODATION: 8 rooms, all with bath/shower. TV. B&B £34 to £78. Deposit: 20%.
Rooms for disabled. Children welcome. Baby facilities. Garden

WALKINGTON Humberside   map 9

▲ *Manor House*

Northlands, Walkington HU17 8RT
TEL: (01482) 881645   FAX: (01482) 866501   COOKING 1*
off B1230 towards Beverley from Walkington   COST £25–£44

The Baughs have clocked up a decade at this peaceful, rural Victorian country
house. Their dining-room is 'classy and formal', and service is polite and
courteous. The choice of menus depends on whether you opt for three or four
courses. The former (not available Saturdays) is short but balanced, and changes
weekly, while the four-course version offers a more generous choice and throws
in a soup or sorbet after, perhaps, smoked haddock fish-cake, or tempura of
mussels, sprats and squid.

With the exception of such things as braised oxtail, main courses tend towards fast searing and wok cooking. 'No dish takes more than six minutes to cook, start to finish,' claims Derek Baugh. Woodcock and partridge are among the game birds that come from the hotel's own shoot, and good ingredients generally provide a firm foundation. Rich bread-and-butter pudding is considered 'a signature dish, and it would be difficult to see how they could improve it much'. Vintage clarets and carefully chosen Burgundies are the pearls of the wine list, while under-£20 drinking is to be found in Beaujolais, Spain and the New World. House French is £8.95.

CHEF: Derek Baugh   PROPRIETORS: Lee and Derek Baugh   OPEN: Mon to Sat D only 7.15 to 9.15 (9.45 Sat)   CLOSED: Christmas   MEALS: Set D £16.50 to £28.50 (£16.50 not available Sat)   SERVICE: not inc, card slips closed   CARDS: Access, Delta, Switch, Visa   DETAILS: 50 seats. Private parties: 70 main room, 24 to 45 private rooms. Car park. Vegetarian meals. Children's helpings. Smart dress preferred. No cigars/pipes in dining-room. Music   ACCOMMODATION: 7 rooms, all with bath/shower. TV. Phone. B&B £70 to £110. Children welcome. Well-behaved dogs welcome. Garden

---

WAREHAM Dorset   map 2

▲ *Priory Hotel*

Church Green, Wareham BH20 4ND   COOKING 3
TEL: (01929) 551666   FAX: (01929) 554519   COST £24–£63

A low, rambling, sixteenth-century building, this creeper-clad hotel was once the priory of Lady St Mary. Only a gravel drive separates it from the church itself, while the gardens – a horticultural delight in the right weather – slope down to the River Frome. There are two dining-rooms, one for lunch and one for dinner, the latter a rather sepulchrally lit space called the Abbots Cellar.

Stephen Astley, who started out here as a mere strip of a lad some years ago, returned as head chef at the end of 1995. Suddenly, an upswing is in the air, as Wareham girds its loins for Moroccan lamb soup with braised cannellini beans, and baked monkfish wrapped in air-dried ham with basil and balsamic dressing. A first-course salad of queen scallops and lobster, 'irreproachable as regards freshness and quality', comes on an impressively apposite curried cream sauce. Sauces are an undoubted strong suit, as evidenced by the stock reduction with redcurrant jelly and juniper berries that accompanies loin of venison: 'subtle, yet clear and silky'. Vegetables are thoughtfully prepared. More than a hint of the Priory's traditionalism survives in beef Wellington for two carved at the table, and – more dispiritingly – in the presentation of desserts on a trolley. The 'superb' pastry of a lemon tart has been let down by its filling – 'not at all tangy' – and a spring visit to the Priory found service 'gawky' and 'not really in keeping with the food'.

Wine gets serious treatment, particularly the older clarets (there are still several from the 1970s) and red Burgundies. France forms the backbone of the list, but Italy and Germany are handled with care, as is a clutch of fine reds from Australia. House wines from Dom. Laroche are £10.50. CELLARMAN'S CHOICE: Wairau River Sauvignon Blanc 1994, Marlborough, New Zealand, £19.50; Nebbiolo d'Alba Vignaveja 1991, Gaja, £30.50.

CHEF: Stephen Astley   PROPRIETORS: John and Stuart Turner   OPEN: all week 12.30 to 2, 7.30
to 10   MEALS: alc (main courses £19 to £22). Set L £12.95 (2 courses) to £14.95, Set D Mon to Fri
£24.50, Set D Sat £28.50   SERVICE: not inc, card slips closed   CARDS: Access, Amex, Delta,
Diners, Switch, Visa   DETAILS: 68 seats. 10 seats outside. Private parties: 44 main room, 24 and
44 private rooms. Car park. Vegetarian meals. Children's helpings. Smart dress preferred.
Wheelchair access (also WC). Music   ACCOMMODATION: 19 rooms, all with bath/shower. TV.
Phone. B&B £70 to £195. Rooms for disabled. Children welcome. Afternoon teas. Garden.
Fishing (*The Which? Hotel Guide*)

WARMINSTER Wiltshire   map 2

▲ *Bishopstrow House* ⁵✖

Warminster BA12 9HH
TEL: (01985) 212312 FAX: (01985) 216769   COOKING 1*
on B3414, SW of Warminster   COST £24–£53

'A Georgian manor-house with no dress codes' sounds almost a contradiction in
terms, but that is how the owners describe it, a luscious-looking ivy-clad house
heavy on the soft furnishings within. Chef Chris Suter has moved towards a
more recognisably British stance of late. Potted rabbit and duck with spiced
pears has an 'olde English' ring to it. Fish-cakes rolled into balls and coated with
polenta is a novel – if not entirely home-grown – idea that works well, the
cornmeal adding an effective crunchy coating. Braised lamb shank comes with
good mashed potato and a strongly reduced *jus*, and a chocolate sponge pudding
with chocolate pecan sauce has also impressed. Service is normally the height of
solicitude but 'left much to be desired' on one occasion. The wine list tries to be
exhaustive, but prices ascend steeply. The bidding opens at around £11.

CHEF: Chris Suter   PROPRIETORS: Simon Lowe, Andrew Leeman and Howard Malin   OPEN: all
week 12 to 2, 7.30 to 9.30   MEALS: alc (main courses £6.50 to £16). Set L £12.50 (2 courses) to
£14.50, Set D Fri and Sat £26.50. Bar food available   SERVICE: 15% (optional), card slips
closed   CARDS: Access, Amex, Delta, Diners, Switch, Visa   DETAILS: 65 seats. 50 seats
outside. Private parties: 65 main room, 25 private room. Car park. Vegetarian meals. Children's
helpings. Smart dress preferred. No smoking in dining-room. Wheelchair access (also WC).
Music   ACCOMMODATION: 30 rooms, all with bath/shower. TV. Phone. B&B £95 to £165.
Deposit: £100. Rooms for disabled. Children welcome. Baby facilities. Dogs welcome.
Afternoon teas. Garden. Swimming-pool. Fishing (*The Which? Hotel Guide*)

WATERHOUSES Staffordshire   map 5

▲ *Old Beams* 🍷 🍽 ⁵✖

Waterhouses ST10 3HW
TEL: (01538) 308254 FAX: (01538) 308157   COOKING 3*
on A523, 7m SE of Leek   COST £28–£53

'For consistency the Beams cannot be faulted,' writes a regular visitor to this
restaurant-with-rooms. After more than a decade and a half at the stoves, Nigel
Wallis is happy to take a bit of time off now and then, leaving the kitchen in the
capable hands of his former sous-chef Michael Wignall, and there seems barely a
ripple in the standard. A conservatory opens on to a garden at the back, while

inside are low ceilings and the regulation beams, though it is such a convivial family affair that one might imagine the name refers to their facial expressions.

The cooking has a classic French foundation, which accounts for the techniques and format of some dishes (a feuilleté of chicken in a cream sauce with asparagus, perhaps), but it is brought up to date with contemporary flourishes along the lines of a salad of scallops marinated in lime and coriander, or black pudding served on a bacon rösti with a purée of sweet turnips and deep-fried leek. An inspector was impressed by the 'assertive fresh flavours' of a vegetable and venison terrine, and by the impact of a crisp tartlet of lambs' sweetbreads and gamey pigeon breasts, surrounded by a sticky stock reduction.

Among puddings, plum soufflé has won praise for being light and refreshingly unsweet. 'The waiter pierced it and inserted a quenelle of vanilla ice-cream and a warm plum sauce. Wonderful!' First-class bread rolls are 'heavy but springy', and 'superb' home-made biscuits arrive with the well-kept unpasteurised cheeses. Champagne comes in at a hefty £8.60 a glass, though choices are many on the inspiring and well-annotated wine list: Ch. Pétrus 1981 at £365, perhaps. Giddy heights aside, there are plenty of wines around £20 a bottle from all over the world. France dominates in terms of numbers, but New World producers, particularly the Australians, are almost all good names. House wines start at £13.90 for French rosé. CELLARMAN'S CHOICE: Côtes de Bourg, Ch. Roc de Cambres 1992, £21; Wairau River Sauvignon Blanc 1994, Marlborough, New Zealand, £17.10.

CHEF: Michael Wignall   PROPRIETORS: Nigel and Ann Wallis   OPEN: Wed to Fri and Sun L 12 to 1.45, Tue to Sat D 7 to 9.30   MEALS: Set L £13.75 (2 courses) to £20, Set D £23 to £36.50   SERVICE: none, card slips closed   CARDS: Access, Amex, Delta, Diners, Switch, Visa   DETAILS: 40 seats. 8 seats outside. Private parties: 40 main room. Car park. Children welcome. No smoking in dining-room. Wheelchair access (also WC). Music   ACCOMMODATION: 5 rooms, all with bath/shower. TV. Phone. B&B £55 to £89.95. Rooms for disabled. Children welcome. Baby facilities. Garden (*The Which? Hotel Guide*)

WATERMILLOCK Cumbria   map 10

▲ *Rampsbeck Country House Hotel* ♥ ⁵⁄✷

Watermillock, Ullswater CA11 0LP
TEL: (01768) 486442   FAX: (01768) 486688   COOKING 3
on A592 Penrith to Windermere road   COST £27–£54

The pretty white house is set in 18 acres of formal gardens and meadow stretching down to Ullswater, with the kind of views one would hope for. Furnishings are in keeping with the age of the house – it is eighteenth-century – and although the bar is out of character, lounges and dining-room are large and elegant, the latter endowed with a marble fireplace, well-spaced tables, with heavy drapes and swags framing the view. Dining-room lunches need to be booked 24 hours in advance. Three different menus are in operation for dinner – one of them vegetarian.

The more expensive option offers wider choice and rather more elaborate dishes, as in a first course of pressed terrine of oxtail and foie gras served with a mushroom brioche. A sorbet follows. Sometimes unusual ingredients such as roast teal might appear, served imaginatively with chanterelles, foie gras, chickpeas and a thyme-flavoured *jus*. A third item may be added to the main meat or fish and its sauce, such as a baked feuilleté of stir-fried lamb offal to accompany roast best end of Cumbrian lamb with a tangerine-scented *jus*.

Fish has been singled out for praise: moist and flavoursome sea bass, for example, and 'big, fat juicy scallops, seared on the outside, and the centre almost like mother-of-pearl', served with courgettes and crunchy water-chestnuts. Puddings are well considered and generally well received, including a hot mirabelle plum soufflé with an iced parfait of the same fruit, and a baked Alaska with blackberry ripple ice-cream. Service is friendly. Short, accurate notes on every wine make for an easy-to-use list. Wines are grouped carefully by acidity, oak and tannin levels; thus, stylistically, Lebanon is next to Australia, and Canada to New Zealand. House Chilean is £9.95. CELLARMAN'S CHOICE: Coteaux de Tricastin, Dom. le Vieux Micocoulier 1990, £13.50.

CHEF: Andrew McGeorge PROPRIETORS: Mr and Mrs T.I. Gibb, and Mrs M.J. MacDowall OPEN: all week 12 to 1.15, 7 to 8.30 CLOSED: early Jan to mid-Feb MEALS: Set L Mon to Sat £22, Set L Sun £19.95, Set D £26 to £36. BYO £4. Light lunches available SERVICE: not inc, card slips closed CARDS: Access, Visa DETAILS: 40 seats. 15 seats outside. Private parties: 60 main room, 15 private room. Car park. Vegetarian meals. Smart dress preferred. No smoking in dining-room. No music ACCOMMODATION: 21 rooms, all with bath/shower. TV. Phone. B&B £50 to £160. Deposit: £15. Children welcome (high tea served at 6). Dogs welcome by arrangement. Afternoon teas. Garden (*The Which? Hotel Guide*)

WATH-IN-NIDDERDALE North Yorkshire　　　　　　　　　　map 8

▲ *The Sportsman's Arms* ♥ ⁵⁄✕

Wath-in-Nidderdale HG3 5PP
TEL: (01423) 711306 FAX: (01423) 712524
take B6156 or B6265 to Pateley Bridge, follow signs by 　　　COOKING 2*
village, 2m NW of Pateley Bridge 　　　　　　　　　　COST £22–£46

The River Nidd meanders through Wath, while nearby Gouthwaite Reservoir is an ornithologist's paradise. The Carters' hotel and restaurant, an austere-looking stone building with a weeping willow in front, makes the most of its serene Dales setting. A portrait of Basil Fawlty in the bar may strike trepidation into the hearts of new visitors, but relax. Courtesy and charm are the bywords. Ray Carter's cooking capitalises on top-quality regional supplies, including locally reared meats. Starters might essay seafood feuilleté in a white wine and orange sauce, or tomato-crusted baked avocado with Chaumes and Stilton, while classic preparations such as pork loin with mustard sauce are the bulwark of main courses. Populist puddings include coffee crème brûlée, and lemon tart, as well as showy banana and rum pancakes with almonds and coconut, or there may be an old-fashioned savoury. The cheeseboard runs a cosmopolitan gamut from unpasteurised Swaledale to Bleu d'Auvergne.

A real effort has been made to come up with a wide range of good wines under £15. Even the pricier bottles offer excellent value. The emphasis is firmly on France and house wines start at £9.50. CELLARMAN'S CHOICE: Sancerre Cuvée Prestige, Dom. Lucien Crochet 1990, £27.50; Morton Estate Black Label Cabernet/Merlot 1992, Hawkes Bay, New Zealand, £21.15.

CHEF: Ray Carter   PROPRIETORS: Ray and Jane Carter   OPEN: Sun L 12 to 2.15, Mon to Sat D 7 to 9.30   CLOSED: 25 Dec, D 26 Dec, 1 Jan   MEALS: alc (main courses £10.50 to £17). Set L £15, Set D £19.75 (inc wine). Bar food available   SERVICE: not inc, card slips closed   CARDS: Access, Visa   DETAILS: 60 seats. 30 seats outside. Private parties: 60 main room. Car park. Vegetarian meals. Children's helpings. Smart dress preferred. No smoking in dining-room. Wheelchair access (also women's WC). No music   ACCOMMODATION: 7 rooms, 2 with bath/shower. TV. B&B £39 to £58. Children welcome. Dogs welcome. Afternoon teas. Garden. Fishing (*The Which? Hotel Guide*)

WELLS Somerset	map 2

Ritcher's

5 Sadler Street, Wells BA5 2RR	COOKING 2
TEL/FAX: (01749) 679085	COST £16–£30

Ritcher's is down a narrow alley near the market-place and the cathedral, managing to feel a little off the beaten track while being plumb in the middle of Wells. On the first floor, reached by a wrought-iron spiral staircase, is the restaurant proper; the ground floor is more bistro-like, and there is also a tiny courtyard for summer dining. This is a kitchen that likes to accord star billing to the mango, in a first course salad with avocado and Parma ham, or with gravad lax, a surprisingly apposite combination of flavours. A catholic collection of fish is assembled for a seafood 'rendezvous' – shark, coley, smoked cod, halibut and salmon – while three animals keep a regular tryst in the main course of beef, lamb and pork fillets with button mushrooms and a smear of melted Stilton. More cheese is used in chicken breast baked with spinach and Brie served with sauce béarnaise. Dark chocolate terrine is made with cream cheese. Cafetière coffee has been very weak. The wine list does a quick trip through Western Europe and Australasia at highly agreeable prices. House French is £7.95.

CHEFS: Nicholas Hart and Sarah Walklett   PROPRIETORS: Nicholas Hart and Kate Ritcher   OPEN: all week 12 to 2, 7 to 9   CLOSED: 26 Dec, 1 Jan   MEALS: Set L £5.50 (2 courses) to £7.50, Set D £12.95 (2 courses) to £14.95   SERVICE: not inc, card slips closed   CARDS: Access, Delta, Switch, Visa   DETAILS: 36 seats. 12 seats outside. Private parties: 24 main room. Vegetarian meals. No children under 10 D. Smart dress preferred. No cigars/pipes in dining-room. Wheelchair access (no WC). Music

---

WELLS-NEXT-THE-SEA Norfolk	map 6

Moorings ♥ ⅝✷

6 Freeman Street, Wells-next-the-Sea NR23 1BA	COOKING 2*
TEL: (01328) 710949	COST £29–£47

'Who would have thought, when we started in 1986, that a man would be making a living gathering mushrooms from Norfolk fields and woodlands?' write the Phillipses. During that time they have devoted themselves to presenting local and seasonal materials 'in the best possible way', and have based the menu on good suppliers, some of whom, like the mushroom man, they have helped to establish and encourage.

Herring, sea trout, pike and eel, native oysters, cockles, mussels, whelks and crabs all make a change from the more typical restaurant fare of halibut and monkfish; likewise samphire, sea spinach, local asparagus, and a great variety of herbs and salad leaves, not to mention pigeon, hare and rabbit. Fishy offerings have included 'hedgerow herring' marinated in home-made blackberry vinegar, and grilled fillet of huss marinated in lime and coriander. Among the half dozen or more vegetables might be courgettes with lime, or gratin of potatoes with rosemary and garlic, and salad is 'always gloriously fresh', according to one reporter: 'I grow my own and know what fresh means.'

The atmosphere is relaxed, the surroundings simple, the service friendly and professional. Desserts might not always measure up, although one couple enjoyed trifle and a 'perfectly nice' ice-cream. The wine list caters for all tastes, from its highly respectable French classic sections to a wide-ranging choice of sparkling wines and some top-notch additions from the New World, especially New Zealand whites. There are 11 half-bottles and the same number of mixed house wines, starting at £8.50. CELLARMAN'S CHOICE: Thelema Sauvignon Blanc 1994, Stellenbosch, South Africa, £13.50.

CHEF: Carla Phillips   PROPRIETORS: Bernard and Carla Phillips   OPEN: Fri to Mon L 12.30 to 1.30, Thur to Mon D 7.30 to 8.30   CLOSED: 2 weeks early Dec, 2 weeks early June, 25 Dec, 1 Jan   MEALS: Set L and D £11.50 (1 course) to £24. BYO £3.75   SERVICE: not inc   CARDS: none   DETAILS: 32 seats. Private parties: 32 main room. Vegetarian meals. Children's helpings. No smoking in dining-room. Wheelchair access (also WC). No music

---

WEST BAY Dorset   map 2

Riverside

West Bay DT6 4EZ
TEL: (01308) 422011   COOKING 1
off A35, m S of Bridport   COST £21–£58

All-round windows guarantee fine views of the water, gulls, boats and weather. For over 30 years the Watsons have been serving a daunting array of fish and shellfish, ranging from seafood platters through simple lobster with garlic butter, to fried haddock, brandade of salt cod with truffles, and Thai king prawn curry with coconut rice. 'You name it, and it is there,' summed up one. Lapses in performance occur, but this is essentially 'a simple caff', its strongest suit one of fresh fish, simply grilled and priced according to weight and the market. Worthy of mention might be seared scallops on a thin bed of lentils, or a fiercely garlicky bourride. The nursery puddings are quite rich, and wines are chosen for interest and value: around 50 of them (the majority) cost £15 or less. House wine is £11.50 a litre. A new oyster and seafood snack bar was about to open as the *Guide* went to press.

CHEFS: Neil Fanous and Nic Larcombe   PROPRIETORS: Arthur and Janet Watson   OPEN: Tue to Sun L 12 to 2.30, Tue to Sat D 6.30 to 9, and bank hol Mon   CLOSED: early Dec to early Mar, some evenings Mar to Apr and Oct to Nov   MEALS: alc (main courses £6 to £28)   SERVICE: not inc, card slips closed   CARDS: Access, Delta, Switch, Visa   DETAILS: 75 seats. 30 seats outside. Private parties: 80 main room. Vegetarian meals. Children's helpings. Wheelchair access (no WC). Music

WETHERSFIELD Essex   map 6

Dicken's ▼

| The Green, Wethersfield CM7 4BS | COOKING 3 |
| TEL/FAX: (01371) 850723 | COST £23–£40 |

The pinky-orange house beside the village green dates from the seventeenth century, and its half-timbered dining-room and minstrels' gallery add to the character. John Dicken is an astute borrower, and his menus pack in all kinds of interesting dishes: as traditionally French as Toulouse cassoulet, as rural as country pâté with bramble jelly, as Mediterranean as fish soup with rouille and croûtons, and as nursery as crispy banana fritters with vanilla ice-cream. Set meals are considered extremely good value, and some of the seasonal specials are a knockout. One couple took advantage of a 'January sale lunch' at £8.75 for three courses, 'and we have to say that, in all our years of reporting to the *Guide* – 34 of them – this was almost certainly the best value'.

Sometimes the search for value means that a dish may not quite fulfil its promise, though there is no doubting the skill that is brought to bear on everything from simple olive bread (charged extra, but worth it) to a braised lamb and onion pudding that combines the idea of English suet with Mediterranean spicing. Black-bean sauce with roasted sea bass, or a red pepper and lentil salsa with monkfish, also adds zest. Fruity puddings are the norm, from warm apple pancake to passion-fruit and mango parfait. The wine list kicks off with a full page of Argentinian wines, then moves on to a wide range from around the world, grouped by style. The focus throughout is on high quality: all bottles are helpfully annotated and reasonably priced, with ten house wines from £7.95. CELLARMAN'S CHOICE: Menetou-Salon 1995, Dom. de Chatenoy, £15.50; Pinot Noir 1988, Luigi Bosca, Argentina, £14.25.

CHEF/PROPRIETOR: John Dicken   OPEN: Wed to Sun L 12.30 to 2, Wed to Sat D 7.30 to 9.30   MEALS: alc D (main courses £11 to £15). Set L and Wed to Fri D £15.   SERVICE: not inc   CARDS: Access, Delta, Switch, Visa   DETAILS: 60 seats. 6 seats outside. Private parties: 36 main room, 10 and 18 private rooms. Car park. Vegetarian meals. Children's helpings. Smart dress preferred. Wheelchair access (also WC). Music

---

WHIMPLE Devon   map 1

▲ Woodhayes ⅝✗

Whimple EX5 2TD	
TEL: (01404) 822237 FAX: (01404) 822337	COOKING 2
off A30, 9m E of Exeter	COST £31–£37

A short way off the Honiton to Exeter road, deep in the heart of cider-apple territory, the village of Whimple is home to the Rendle family's white-fronted Georgian country house. The interiors are done in muted pastoral tones and filled with flowers to provide splashes of seasonal colour. Michael and Katherine Rendle share the cooking, and keep proceedings on a sensibly domestic scale, offering a six-course no-choice dinner menu, with options only for dessert. Portions are impressively judged so the cumulative effect is not one of being force-fed.

At an autumn meal, Stilton pâté with pear, chicory leaves and walnuts was not as heavy as it sounds, and a 'creamy classic' bowl of carrot and fennel soup was followed by the night's fish course: fillets of sea bass simply grilled and served on mixed leaves. 'Meltingly succulent' beef fillet came next, accompanied by an excellent béarnaise and good vegetables. Chocolate, toffee and banana are mainstays of the pudding course, but reports suggest that the sorbets, too, are spot on, nicely balanced between sweet fruit flavour and tartness. Service is solicitous and efficient. An inspired international choice of house wines, all at £11.50, leads off a mainly French list. Prices are keen throughout.

CHEFS: Michael and Katherine Rendle   PROPRIETORS: Frank, Katherine and Michael Rendle   OPEN: all week D only 7.30 for 8 (1 sitting); L residents only   CLOSED: 4 days Christmas   MEALS: Set D £25   SERVICE: net prices, card slips closed   CARDS: Access, Amex, Delta, Diners, Switch, Visa   DETAILS: 14 seats. Car park. Vegetarian meals. No children under 12. Smart dress preferred. No smoking in dining-room. Music   ACCOMMODATION: 6 rooms, all with bath/shower. TV. Phone. B&B £65 to £90. No children under 12. Afternoon teas. Garden (The Which? Hotel Guide)

WHITBY North Yorkshire   map 9

Magpie Café �✖ £

14 Pier Road, Whitby YO21 3PU   COOKING 1*
TEL/FAX: (01947) 602058   COST £14–£38

In a nutshell, the Magpie is 'a typical seaside café but with untypical food'. The queues get longer – and so does the wait – yet crowds still drive for miles to this old merchant's house by the quay for the best fresh fish in town. As well as top-drawer chippy classics, you might find gutsy seafood chowder, grilled salmon with garlicky new potatoes, and expertly cooked whole sea bass. If you still have room and are prepared to wait even longer, there is a daunting array of home-made cakes and puddings to round things off. Afternoon tea is a slap-up affair, and the Magpie provides every amenity for couples with children. It's refreshing to see a wine list on offer, as well as pots of tea; and more surprising to discover that you can also sip champagne by the glass. House wine is £6.95.

CHEF: Ian Robson   PROPRIETORS: Ian Robson and Alison McKenzie Robson, Sheila and Ian McKenzie   OPEN: Sun to Thur 11.30 to 6.30, Fri and Sat (all week May to Sept) 11.30 to 9   CLOSED: Jan to mid-Feb   MEALS: alc (main courses £4.50 to £12). Set L and D £8.95 to £13.45   SERVICE: not inc, card slips closed   CARDS: Access, Delta, Switch, Visa   DETAILS: 100 seats. Private parties: 50 main room. Vegetarian meals. Children's helpings. No smoking in dining-room. Music. Air-conditioned

---

WHITSTABLE Kent   map 3

▲ Whitstable Oyster Fishery Co

Royal Native Oyster Stores, The Horsebridge,
Whitstable CT5 1BU   COOKING 1*
TEL: (01227) 276856   FAX: (01227) 770666   COST £26–£53

'Surroundings and other diners a great hoot, and, with stormy brown sea outside, quite atmospheric,' wrote one visitor in epigrammatic style. This converted warehouse is a 'lesson in how to open a restaurant without spending too much money'. It stands hard by the long flinty beach (the North Sea laps against the door when gales are blowing), and there is a cinema upstairs to attract custom out of season. All comers descend on the place, not simply for the fun of it, but to tuck into great plates of Whitstable's finest oysters and other fruits of the sea. The simplicity speaks for itself. Wonderful fresh crabs are cooked, dissected and brought to the table, a pair of splendid hake steaks are served with home-made mayonnaise, and a whole sea bass (head dangling off the plate) is cooked perfectly with lots of onion and garlic. Also worth noting are the home-smoked kippers, potted shrimps, and archetypal cod and chips. The short wine list has some drinkable whites. House wine is £9.95.

CHEF: Nikki Billington   PROPRIETOR: Whitstable Oyster Fishery Co   OPEN: Tue to Fri 12 to 2, 7 to 9, Sat 12 to 2.30, 6.30 to 9.30, Sun 11.30 to 3.30, 6.30 to 8.30   CLOSED: 25 Dec   MEALS: alc (main courses £8.50 to £20)   SERVICE: not inc   CARDS: Access, Amex, Delta, Diners, Switch, Visa   DETAILS: 150 seats. 50 seats outside. Private parties: 100 main room, 100 private room. Car park. Vegetarian meals. Children's helpings. Wheelchair access (also WC). Music ACCOMMODATION: 5 rooms, all with bath/shower. TV. Room only £45. Children welcome. Baby facilities

WICKHAM Hampshire   map 2

▲ *Old House*

The Square, Wickham PO17 5JG
TEL: (01329) 833049   FAX: (01329) 833672   COOKING 2
2½m N of Fareham, at junction of A32 and B2177   COST £36–£48

'We liked it so much we went back for breakfast the next day,' noted a couple from London, who called in for dinner at Richard and Annie Skipwith's modest Georgian house in the country. Despite the Englishness of the setting, the cooking remains firmly in French mode (no doubt influenced by Annie's Gallic roots). Menus – for lunch and dinner – are fixed-price for two or three courses, and the kitchen looks to the regions for inspiration.

Starters might range from twice-baked soufflé of unpasteurised Camembert to poached fillets of trout served cold with julienne of orange and lemon zest, while main courses could include grilled fillets of salmon and brill with chives, or noisettes of lamb given a Mediterranean vibrancy with tapénade, anchovies and capers. Sauces are 'lovely'. Home-made ice-creams continue to earn praise; otherwise, you might choose pink grapefruit and Sauternes granita, or pears poached in red wine with apricots, prunes, sun-dried cranberries and blueberries. The list of 40 wines naturally favours France, although Spain, Italy and the New World are not neglected. Chilean house wine is £12.75.

CHEF: Nicholas Harman   PROPRIETORS: Annie and Richard Skipwith   OPEN: Tue to Fri L 12.30 to 1.45, Mon to Sat D 7.30 to 9.30   CLOSED: 2 weeks Christmas, 1 week Easter, 2 weeks Aug MEALS: Set L and D £21 (2 courses) to £27. BYO £6   SERVICE: net prices, card slips closed CARDS: Access, Amex, Diners, Visa   DETAILS: 40 seats. Private parties: 40 main room, 14 private room. Car park. Children's helpings. Smart dress preferred. No cigars/pipes in dining-room. Wheelchair access (no WC). No music   ACCOMMODATION: 12 rooms, all with bath/shower. TV. Phone. Room only £57 to £80. Children welcome. Baby facilities. Garden (*The Which? Hotel Guide*)

ENGLAND

WILLINGTON Co Durham map 10

Stile ⁵⨉

97 High Street, Willington DL15 0PE
TEL: (01388) 746615 FAX: (01388) 747400   COOKING 1
on A690, 4m N of Bishop Auckland   COST £22–£38

'As a rural restaurant we tend to feel a member of an endangered life form, but
we survive,' write Mike Boustred and Jenny James. Their jolly place – with a
particularly fine conservatory – adds a spark of life to a somewhat 'dreary village'
away from the city lights of Durham and Bishop Auckland. The cooking is in
keeping: forthright, strong on flavour and unhampered by formal training.
France continues to loom large as an inspiration, but the kitchen also takes on
board English stalwarts such as smoked haddock with rarebit topping, steak
pie, and ginger and syrup sponge. The fixed-price menu is now a two-course
deal featuring grilled goats'-cheese and walnut salad, perhaps, or pork tenderloin with orange. Vegetables are treated with proper respect. The fondness
for all things French shows in the well-reported theme nights and in the tilt of
Mike's keenly chosen, informative wine list. House wines are £8.20.

CHEFS: Jenny James and Helen Pryce PROPRIETORS: Mike Boustred and Jenny James OPEN:
Tue to Sat D only 7 to 9.30 MEALS: alc (main courses £10 to £13). Set D £12.50 (2 courses, not
available theme nights) to £17.50 (theme nights only) SERVICE: not inc, card slips closed
CARDS: Access, Visa DETAILS: 45 seats. Private parties: 36 main room, 18 private room. Car
park. Vegetarian meals. Children's helpings. Smart dress preferred. No smoking in dining-room.
No music

WILLITON Somerset map 2

▲ *White House* ▮ ⁵⨉

Williton TA4 4QW   COOKING 3
TEL: (01984) 632306   COST £40–£52

The house is painted white – what else? – with a weeping willow and a palm tree
out front, and its appeal is marked by a blend of individual style and class. The
Smiths (who celebrate 30 years at Williton in 1997) close for a long winter,
recharging themselves for the seven-dinners-a-week summer season, when they
do everything themselves. The deal is three courses, with the option to extend to
four or five with soup or cheese. Despite proximity to the coast, the White House
has traditionally had carnivorous leanings, helped by stocks, meat juices and a
dash of alcohol in the saucing. Positive flavours have characterised grilled breast
of wood pigeon, and saddle of roe deer with a game sauce.

Things are changing, however. 'Due to a wonderful new source of fresh fish
we are slanting our menus in a new direction,' writes Dick Smith. The plan is to
reverse the previous emphasis, and to offer two or three fish main courses to one
meat or poultry. Dover sole will be served simply with a slice of lemon, while a
whole range of others might include grilled red mullet with rosemary and
anchovy sauce, or tuna, stewed with red peppers, onions, garlic, tomatoes and
waxy potatoes. Puddings might include a simple fruit salad or a brandied
chocolate sponge.

480

A host of excellent suppliers help Dick Smith keep the wine list well up to scratch. He casts his net wide, astutely pulling in fine champagnes from Bruno Paillard, an admirable German range and top New World producers. Mark-ups are very reasonable. Eight wines are available by the glass and house wines start at £14. CELLARMAN'S CHOICE: Sancerre 'Les Grands Genevrières' 1993, £23.50: Bandol, Dom. Tempier 'Cuvée Mijoua' 1985, L. Peyraud, £28.50

CHEFS/PROPRIETORS: Dick and Kay Smith OPEN: all week D only 7.30 to 8.30 CLOSED: early Nov to mid-May MEALS: Set D £27.50 SERVICE: not inc CARDS: none DETAILS: 26 seats. Private parties: 8 main room. Car park. Children's helpings. No smoking in dining-room. Wheelchair access (also WC). No music ACCOMMODATION: 12 rooms, 9 with bath/shower. TV. Phone. B&B £40 to £82. Deposit: £25. Rooms for disabled. Children welcome. Baby facilities. Dogs welcome (The Which? Hotel Guide)

WILMINGTON East Sussex map 3

▲ Crossways ⁵✳

Lewes Road, Wilmington, nr Polegate BN26 5SG | COOKING 1
TEL: (01323) 482455 FAX: (01323) 487811 | COST £32–£39

Despite its French-style green shutters, the small, white-painted country hotel looks and feels very English. It is Georgian, and sits in a couple of acres not far from Glyndebourne. Dinners are four courses (the second a soup) on a seasonally changing menu that declares its individuality in, for example, Camembert ice-cream with spiced plums (that's a first course) or barbecued pork with blackeye bean-cakes. A few old-fashioned dishes appear, and exotic fruit is sometimes paired with fowl, as in duck with peppered pineapple, while the hearty mainstream is represented by braised lamb shank, or beef-in-beer pie. Puddings are recited and have included frozen white chocolate syllabub with a raspberry coulis. The short wine list is serviceable rather than exciting, and includes a few English wines such as the first-rate Breaky Bottom.

CHEFS: David Stott and Juliet Anderson PROPRIETORS: David Stott and Clive James OPEN: Tue to Sat D only CLOSED: 24 Dec to 24 Jan MEALS: Set D £24.95 SERVICE: not inc, card slips closed CARDS: Access, Amex, Delta, Diners, Switch, Visa DETAILS: 24 seats. Car park. No children under 12. Smart dress preferred. No smoking in dining-room. Wheelchair access (no WC). Music ACCOMMODATION: 7 rooms, all with bath/shower. TV. Phone. B&B £42 to £70. No children under 12. Garden

---

WINCHCOMBE Gloucestershire map 5

▲ Wesley House ⁵✳

High Street, Winchcombe GL54 5LJ | COOKING 2*
TEL: (01242) 602366 FAX: (01242) 602405 | COST £23–£45

'What a refreshing change from some of the overpriced and pretentious Cotswold hostelries,' enthused one reporter of this fifteenth-century half-timbered gem in the narrow main street. The compact, heavily beamed former merchant's house, with leaded windows and a view of Sudeley Castle from the dining-room, is a 'haven of hospitality'. Just about everybody who visits resolves to go again. Blackboard specials (some with a price supplement) extend

481

the choice of the modern European menu, which makes judicious use of aïoli, salsas and the like to produce a varied palette of flavours.

The kitchen's confidence is evident in dishes such as a warm tart of 'wonderfully sweet' caramelised shallots, while seafood is typically well handled: 'fabulously light' warm scallop mousse, and 'exquisite' lobster ravioli, both treated to positively flavoured sauces. The kitchen's keen sense of timing produces pinkish slices of rump of lamb (on a prune and thyme sauce), and desserts are 'generous in size and beautifully presented', not least the Wesley House selection of all the desserts on the menu (well worth the supplement). Over 80 sympathetically priced wines include a dozen house recommendations that are available by the glass, starting at £9.95 a bottle.

CHEFS: Jonathan Lewis and James Lovatt   PROPRIETORS: Jonathan Lewis and Matthew Brown   OPEN: all week L 12 to 2, Mon to Sat D, and Sun D preceding bank hol Mons 7 to 9.30 CLOSED: 15 Jan to 12 Feb   MEALS: alc L (main courses £6 to £14.50). Set L £14, Set D £21.50. BYO £8. Light lunches also available   SERVICE: not inc, card slips closed   CARDS: Access, Amex, Delta, Switch, Visa   DETAILS: 55 seats. 12 seats outside. Private parties: 65 main room. Vegetarian meals. Children's helpings. No smoking in dining-room. Wheelchair access (no WC). Music   ACCOMMODATION: 6 rooms, all with bath/shower. TV. Phone. D,B&B £59 to £130. Children welcome. Baby facilities. Afternoon teas (The Which? Hotel Guide)

WINCHESTER Hampshire   map 2

▲ Hotel du Vin & Bistro ▮

14 Southgate Street, Winchester SO23 9EF   COOKING 2*
TEL: (01962) 841414   FAX: (01962) 842458   COST £25–£48

Robin Hutson and Gerard Basset have hit on a format that suits Winchester. The attractively renovated Georgian town house is stylish but informal, the food is bang up to date, and wines are treated in a sensibly matter-of-fact way. Wine-related bits and bobs cover the walls, and the atmosphere is busy and purposeful. Much of the service is Gallic – 'efficient if peremptory', as one diner put it – and seems to improve when the owners are in attendance. The place is open 365 days a year, which is about as helpful as a restaurant can get.

'You have to like Mediterranean cooking,' observed a regular visitor; 'everything comes with olive oil, and sun-dried tomatoes abound.' There is no hard-and-fast division into first and second courses (many dishes function as either), flavours are simple and direct, and combinations are as interesting as honey-roast duck with a mango, coriander and chilli salsa, or half a deep-fried lobster with harissa crème fraîche. Ingredients are fresh and of good quality, vegetables are ordered and charged for separately, and chips are particularly fine. Soup, pasta, roast or grilled fish, steak, and rich puddings make up much of the fare. 'They seem pleased to see guests having a good time,' which is what most guests appear to do.

Diners receive two wine lists, a concise one which changes daily to take in around 12 house wines by the bottle or glass, and a much longer 'cellar list' with lots to pore over. The latter does a round-the-world wine tour, stopping off in Argentina, Austria and Lebanon as well as more obvious spots, and offers a particularly tempting array of dessert wines. What's more, tours of the cellar are offered to guests. CELLARMAN'S CHOICE: Geoff Merrill Semillon-Chardonnay

1989, McLaren Vale, S. Australia, £25; Vino Fino Tinto Cafayate 1990, Arnaldo B. Etchart, Argentina, £16.75.

CHEF: James Martin PROPRIETORS: Robin Hutson and Gerard Basset OPEN: all week 12 to 1.45, 7 to 9.30 MEALS: alc (main courses £8 to £16). BYO £7 SERVICE: not inc, card slips closed CARDS: Access, Amex, Diners, Visa DETAILS: 50 seats. 35 seats outside. Private parties: 48 main room, 48 private room. Car park. Vegetarian meals. Children's helpings. No cigars/pipes in dining-room. Wheelchair access (no WC). No music ACCOMMODATION: 19 rooms, all with bath/shower. TV. Phone. Room only £69 to £99. Rooms for disabled. Children welcome. Garden (*The Which? Hotel Guide*)

Hunters £

5 Jewry Street, Winchester SO23 8RZ
TEL/FAX: (01962) 860006

COOKING 2
COST £19–£41

Antiques and crafts – plus assorted restaurants – seem to be the principal businesses of this well-to-do Winchester thoroughfare, and Hunters settles in among them without making a show of itself. The ambience is cosy, bistro-like, with a touch of Laura Ashley or similar about the décor. The fruity tendency in first courses noted last year seems to have abated, offerings now including salmon and scallop timbale wrapped in spinach with a beurre blanc, or smoked-trout and quail's-egg salad dressed with horseradish.

Complexity is a hallmark of main courses such as rainbow trout roulade filled with saffron mousse on mashed potato with a tomato sauce. Another mousse stuffing, leek this time, goes into a chicken breast, a creamy mustard sauce adding richness. At an autumn meal, a simple fish dish was timed much better than the rather fiddly lamb, which had been stuffed and then baked in pastry. Chocolate terrine with an orange anglaise, or crème brûlée with apricots, ends proceedings on a satisfying note. Wines from Eldridge Pope offer some good names at entirely manageable prices. House wines start at £8.95.

CHEF: Alan Stubbington PROPRIETOR: David Birmingham OPEN: Mon to Sat 12 to 2, 6.30 to 10 CLOSED: bank hols MEALS: alc (main courses £5 to £16). Set L £7.50 (2 courses), Set D £9.95 (2 courses) to £13.50 SERVICE: not inc CARDS: Access, Amex, Delta, Diners, Switch, Visa DETAILS: 42 seats. Private parties: 20 main room, 25 private room. Vegetarian meals. Children's helpings. Wheelchair access (no WC). Music

Old Chesil Rectory 🍴✖

1 Chesil Street, Winchester SO23 8HU
TEL: (01962) 851555 FAX: (01962) 869704

COOKING 2
COST £24–£47

How many of today's buildings, one wonders, will still be standing after five and a half centuries, let alone used to such good effect? At the lower end of the high street, just across the river from King Alfred's statue, the restaurant maintains a restrained and dignified air, with 'stooping doorways and old beams' and immaculately set tables. The Ruthven-Stuarts have now moved entirely to a set-price format, and business, they say, has increased by 20 per cent over the year. The lighter, simpler, lunchtime alternative might include potato, leek and asparagus soup served in a keep-warm pot, followed by chicken with wild mushrooms.

The half-dozen items per course at dinner offer plenty of variety, from a starter of warm fish salad with oriental dressing to a terrine of ham knuckle and foie gras with pease pudding. Nicholas Ruthven-Stuart is an advocate of seam butchery, which isolates individual muscles so as to achieve more even cooking, and sources many of his ingredients locally: Hampshire asparagus, pike from the River Itchen, watercress from the Test valley and so on. Main courses typically combine two or three meats or fish, as in a fricassee of monkfish, cod and salmon in a curried coriander sauce with couscous. Desserts avoid the customary preponderance of chocolate-dominated items in favour of, perhaps, a shortbread sablé with crème brûlée and stewed plums. The wine list includes useful tasting notes on a wide selection from France, supplemented mainly with New World offerings. House wine from Languedoc is £9.50.

CHEFS: Nicholas Ruthven-Stuart and Nicola Saunders PROPRIETORS: Nicholas and Christina Ruthven-Stuart OPEN: Tue to Sat 12 to 2, 7 to 9.30 CLOSED: 2 weeks Christmas, 2 weeks Aug MEALS: Set L £9.95 (2 courses) to £25, Set D (2 courses) £20 to £25 SERVICE: not inc, card slips closed CARDS: Access, Switch, Visa DETAILS: 60 seats. Private parties: 40 main room, 10 and 14 private rooms. Children's helpings. No smoking in 1 dining-room. No cigars/pipes in dining-room. Wheelchair access (no WC). Music

▲ *Wykeham Arms* 🍴✳

75 Kingsgate Street, Winchester SO23 9PE	COOKING 1
TEL: (01962) 853834 FAX: (01962) 854411	COST £18–£36

The Wykeham Arms sounds like every tourist's dream of the perfect English pub. Built in the 1750s, it stands in the back streets of the town, right by the cathedral and the college. Three log fires warm the interior, 1,600 tankards of every description hang from the beams, walking-sticks are arranged in rows, and Eldridge Pope beers are drawn from 36-gallon barrels. The 'Wyke' also has a reputation for good food. Lunch-time brings sandwiches, steaks, Caesar salad, cottage pie and pasta. Evening menus move into the realms of braised pheasant with pearl barley and celeriac risotto, roasted vegetables topped with goats' cheese, and red mullet with basil and garlic mash. Puddings could include 'Eton mess', and kumquat and apple fool. Seventeen wines are offered by the glass, and the list has been chosen with an eye for value as well as quality. House wine is £8.95.

CHEFS: Vanessa Booth, Belinda Watson, Helen Brooks and Jo Brooks PROPRIETORS: Graeme and Anne Jameson OPEN: Mon to Sat 12 to 2.30, 6.30 to 8.45 CLOSED: 25 Dec MEALS: alc (main courses £5.50 to £12.50). Snacks available L SERVICE: not inc, card slips closed CARDS: Access, Amex, Delta, Switch, Visa DETAILS: 65 seats. 20 seats outside. Private parties: 8 main room. Car park. Vegetarian meals. No children under 14. Smart dress preferred. No smoking in 3 dining-rooms. No music ACCOMMODATION: 7 rooms, all with bath/shower. TV. Phone. B&B £67.50 to £77.50. No children under 14. Dogs welcome. Afternoon teas. Garden (*The Which? Hotel Guide*)

Not inc *in the details at the end of an entry indicates that no service charge is made and any tipping is at the discretion of the customer.*

The Good Food Guide *is a registered trade mark of Which? Ltd.*

WINDERMERE Cumbria   map 8

▲ *Gilpin Lodge* ☆ ✳

Crook Road, Windermere LA23 3NE
TEL: (01539) 488818   FAX: (01539) 488058   COOKING 2
on B5284, 2m SE of Windermere   COST £23–£47

Gilpin Lodge must have made a handsome residence in its days as a private
house. In 20 acres of gardens, woodland and moor, it's a mere two-mile jog from
the banks of Windermere. Food, confess the Cunliffes in their brochure, is an
'obsession', with the cheering result that all the incidentals, including breads
and biscuits, are made in-house. 'The welcome,' an inspector noted, 'is warm
and personal, service impeccable without being overbearingly formal.' Although menus look wordy and offer a formidable range of choice, the cooking is
powered by sound logical principles, and flavours generally take wing. Broccoli
and Stilton soup, and braised 'fondant' of lamb with a tarragon, saffron and olive
oil sauce set the tone. A lobster and crab bisque makes an opulent background
for a monkfish fricassee with shallots and button mushrooms. Desserts are as
smartly turned out as everything else, as in meringue glacé with chocolate
ice-cream served on a big black plate with a two-tone sauce and a 'flurry' of icing
sugar.

The wine list is well annotated and as inspiring in Australia, Spain and Italy as
in France. There are two pages of half-bottles and eight wines by the glass,
starting at £2.85. House Vin de Pays d'Oc is £11.50. CELLARMAN'S CHOICE:
Vidal Gewurztraminer 1995, Hawkes Bay, New Zealand, £18.25; Morgon, Dom.
de Souchon 1993, Paul Sapin, £17.95.

CHEF: Christopher Davies   PROPRIETORS: John and Christine Cunliffe   OPEN: all week 12 to
2.30, 7 to 8.45   MEALS: alc L (main courses £6 to £12). Set L Sun £14, Set D £27.50. Snacks
available all day   SERVICE: not inc, card slips closed   CARDS: Access, Amex, Delta, Diners,
Switch, Visa   DETAILS: 65 seats. 14 seats outside. Private parties: 22 main room, 14 and 30
private rooms. Car park. Vegetarian meals. Children's helpings Sun L. No children under 7.
Smart dress preferred. No smoking in dining-room. Wheelchair access. Music
ACCOMMODATION: 11 rooms, all with bath/shower. TV. Phone. B&B £70 to £140. Deposit: £20.
Rooms for disabled. No children under 7. Afternoon teas. Garden (*The Which? Hotel Guide*)

▲ *Miller Howe* ☆ ✳

Rayrigg Road, Windermere LA23 1EY
TEL: (01539) 442536   FAX: (01539) 445664   COOKING 3
on A592, between Windermere and Bowness   COST £22–£50

Despite having spawned other establishments, Miller Howe remains unique,
and this year clocks up a distinguished quarter of a century in the *Guide*. Guests
assemble for dinner, the main meal, at the appointed hour among either
Chesterfield sofas in the 'rather heavy' lounge or in the lighter conservatory.
Lights are dimmed at 8, as the audience makes its way to the two-tier auditorium
with a breathtaking view of Lake Windermere. Happily, 'any theatrical
formality evaporates in the warmth of the smiles of the staff'.

The four-course dinner offers no choice until pudding, but is preceded by
first-rate appetisers. A typical meal began with bobotie, an adaptation of a South

African dish of spiced minced lamb, followed by poached fillet of cod (the second course is invariably fish), and then 'succulent' roast chicken with tarragon inserted under the skin. Good raw materials and accomplished cooking are the norm. The five accompanying vegetables at this meal were mashed swede with cider, diced leeks in wine, mange-tout in walnut oil, glazed carrots with lemon and Pernod, and roast potatoes with coriander. As these are neither run-of-the-mill nor over-the-top fantasies, an inspector concluded that 'the complaint of over-elaboration is not sustainable'. The view of supporters is that people should know by now what kind of menu Miller Howe offers, and they can take it or leave it. The format will not please everyone, but any objective view must applaud its individuality.

Desserts are well made, whether a simple cardamom ice-cream, a hot runny sponge pud, or a sweet pastry with raspberries and crème fraîche. Service is 'attentive and courteous'. A laminated page of classic wines is eclipsed by the longer New World list. It does Australia, New Zealand and South Africa proud, packing in many top producers and a wide range of styles at reasonable prices. House wines are Australian and South African and cost £14.

CHEFS: Chris Blaydes and Susan Elliott PROPRIETOR: John Tovey OPEN: all week 12.30 for 1, 7.30 for 8 (1 sitting) CLOSED: first Sun Dec to last Thur Feb MEALS: Set L £12.50 (inc glass of wine), Set D £30 SERVICE: 12.5% (optional), card slips closed CARDS: Access, Amex, Diners, Visa DETAILS: 70 seats. Private parties: 30 private room. Car park. No children under 8. Smart dress preferred. No smoking in dining-room. Music. Air-conditioned ACCOMMODATION: 12 rooms, all with bath/shower. TV. Phone. D,B&B £90 to £250. No children under 8. Dogs welcome in bedrooms only. Afternoon teas. Garden (*The Which? Hotel Guide*)

Miller Howe Café ⁵✱ £

Lakeland Plastics Ltd, Alexandra Buildings,
Station Precinct, Windermere LA23 1BQ
TEL: (01539) 446732

COOKING 1
COST £15–£26

The café forms part of the Lakeland Plastics shop, with a queuing system for the dozen plain wooden tables. A short menu is supplemented by a long blackboard list of dishes in no particular order that might take in a soup, quiche, and anything from fresh tripe through chilli con carne to rice pudding or rhubarb crumble. Orders are placed at the counter, and dishes brought to the table, but confusion can occur when staff are working under pressure. All the food is available all day until 6pm (earlier on Sundays), helpings are generous, and some of the main courses already come with salad and baked potato. Teas, coffees, and home-made lemonade take their place beside French house wine at £1.50 a glass, or £8.50 a bottle.

CHEF: Ian Dutton PROPRIETORS: Ian and Annette Dutton OPEN: all week, daytime only 9 to 6 (10 to 4 Sun) MEALS: alc (main courses £5 to £6.50) SERVICE: not inc, card slips closed CARDS: Access, Delta, Switch, Visa DETAILS: 60 seats. 16 seats outside. Private parties: 60 main room. Car park. Vegetarian meals. Children's helpings. No smoking in dining-room. Wheelchair access (no WC). No music. Air-conditioned

See inside the front cover for an explanation of the symbols used at the tops of entries.

Roger's ⁺✸

4 High Street, Windermere LA23 1AF	COOKING 2*
TEL: (01539) 444954	COST £24–£44

The green awning opposite the tourist office conceals a small and homely candlelit dining-room. Although the food may be somewhat predictable – 'menus haven't changed for years; we could have eaten the same food here ten years ago' – it is of a consistently good standard. A sound professionalism is applied to everything from a simple tasty cream of celery soup, through a light onion tart with mozzarella or feta cheese, to roast lamb or grouse. Roger Pergl-Wilson is alive to textures and contrasts, and does not adorn his food with unnecessary flourishes: 'no frills, no attempt to wrap it up, just plain and enjoyable,' complimented one reporter.

Sea bream with a well-judged chilli sauce and coriander salsa is one of many fish dishes to impress for both freshness and handling. Puddings might be as traditional as apple and blackberry crumble, or as comforting as chocolate fudge cake with hot fudge sauce. Regular customers are particularly well looked after. The New World is given pride of place on the wine list, and although vintages seem to be all over the place, prices are friendly: two dozen wines can be had for under £12 and house Duboeuf is £9.50 a litre.

CHEF: Roger Pergl-Wilson PROPRIETORS: Roger and Alena Pergl-Wilson OPEN: Mon to Sat D only, 7 to 9.30 (10 Sat) MEALS: alc (main courses £5.50 to £12.50). Set D Mon to Fri £17.50 SERVICE: not inc, card slips closed CARDS: Access, Amex, Diners, Visa DETAILS: 44 seats. Private parties: 28 main room. Vegetarian meals. Children's helpings. No smoking in 1 dining-room. Music

---

WINKLEIGH Devon   map 1

Pophams ⁺✸ £

Castle Street, Winkleigh EX19 8HQ	COOKING 3
TEL: (01837) 83767	COST £16–£37

Painted green inside and out, this tiny ten-seater restaurant is so small 'one can hardly walk between the tables'. The atmosphere is pleasant and friendly, and the chef/owners share in the general conversation. 'A meal here is as much a social occasion as anything else.' Those who take pleasure in watching other people work can easily see what is going on in the kitchen. Film star photographs cover the walls, and a small blackboard carries the menu in all its simplicity: avocado and smoky bacon salad, or leek and potato soup to start, then best end of local lamb in puff pastry, or a warm chicken breast salad with soy sauce and sesame dressing. Pophams serves lunch only, and meals are mostly light.

The repertoire may be limited, but the range of cooking skills and styles is wide, and fresh supplies for the limited menu are used up on a daily basis. 'All the food looked and tasted spruce, fresh and clear,' summed up an inspector who lunched on a chunky terrine of chicken livers served with a fruity Cumberland sauce and a tiny dressed salad, followed by 'a very professionally executed' roast fillet of beef making generous use of excellent material and served in a 'superb' espagnole sauce. Vegetables are interesting and varied and, like everything else, tasty – even red cabbage is expertly done – while bright, distinct flavours extend to home-made ice-creams, particularly blackcurrant. Locally baked granary bread and good coffee add to the appeal. Pophams is unlicensed.

CHEF: Melvyn Popham   PROPRIETORS: Melvyn Popham and Dennis Hawkes   OPEN: Tues to Sat L only 12 to 3   CLOSED: 25 Dec, Feb   MEALS: alc (main courses £7 to £15.50). Unlicensed: BYO (no corkage). Morning coffee available 9 to 11   SERVICE: not inc, card slips closed CARDS: Access, Visa   DETAILS: 10 seats. Private parties: 10 main room. Vegetarian meals. No children under 14. No smoking in dining-room. Music. Air-conditioned

---

WINTERINGHAM   North Lincolnshire   map 9

▲ *Winteringham Fields* ♱ ⁵✳

Winteringham DN15 9PF   COOKING 4*
TEL: (01724) 733096   FAX: (01724) 733898   COST £29–£75

The restaurant is at a crossroads in the centre of the village. Small sitting-rooms have open fires, squishy sofas and little room left for any more ornaments. The Victorian feel stretches from the conservatory at one end, along a narrow corridor to the cool and elegant dark blue dining-room. Germain Schwab's cooking is not particularly concerned with fine renditions of classic dishes, nor does it go in much for exotic flavour combinations. But it is careful about textures, well executed and full of invention. He is an amiable man who loves his craft, always roving, and comfortable with a wide range of ingredients from goat to game birds to offal. There is always something slightly different on the menu, the product of natural enthusiasm and quiet innovation: whoever heard of gravad lax with a pineapple dressing? But it was judged 'excellent'.

Because of the variety it is difficult to single out signature dishes or techniques. Fish is a strength – 'the halibut was superb, so fresh I could believe it had been washed into the kitchen on a wave direct from Grimsby docks' – and timing is spot on, producing 'sweet, firm, just cooked' sea bass for one reporter. Quite a few things are wrapped in pastry, from very rare pigeon breast with a livery farce – 'like a pigeon Wellington' – to scallops in filo. A meat-based sauce with fish is not unusual, as in a 'cobble' of cod with oxtail juices. 'The stunning thing about the food is the sheer intensity of flavour,' writes one reporter, while for another it is the 'contrasting but balanced seasonings and garnishes' that strike home.

New desserts are continually being launched from the kitchen: one minute, paper-thin crystalised apple slices, stuck hedgehog-like into a green apple sorbet; the next, an equally thin cloche of caramel through which you can see the warm soft-fruit pudding. The cheeseboard is one of the best, with a superb collection from across Europe, and comes with fruit, nuts and assorted breads. Appetisers are generous to a fault. The food can be expensive: 'top prices, but worth it', according to one reporter. Lunch, though, is amazing value. Service, overseen by Annie Schwab, is 'formal but not intimidating; everything runs like clockwork'. But then Germain is Swiss. And Swiss wines feature on a list that takes in producers from all corners of the globe. There's plenty under £20 a bottle alongside the famous names, and a good choice of half-bottles. House wines start at £12.50. CELLARMAN'S CHOICE: Boschendal Sauvignon Blanc 'Grande Cuvée' 1994, Paarl, South Africa £20; Médoc, Ch. Cissac 1986, £31.50.

CHEF: Germain Schwab   PROPRIETORS: Germain and Annie Schwab   OPEN: Tue to Fri L 12 to 1.30, Mon to Sat D 7.15 to 9.30   CLOSED: 2 weeks Christmas, first week Aug, bank hols   MEALS: alc (main courses £21 to £24.50). Set L £12.50 (2 courses) to £17.50, Set D £28 to £45   SERVICE: not inc, card slips closed   CARDS: Access, Amex, Delta, Switch, Visa   DETAILS: 45 seats. Private parties: 8 main room, 10 private room. Car park. Children welcome. No smoking in dining-room. Wheelchair access (no WC). Music   ACCOMMODATION: 7 rooms, all with bath/shower. TV. Phone. B&B £60 to £100. Rooms for disabled. No children under 8. Garden (*The Which? Hotel Guide*)

WITHERSLACK   Cumbria   map 8

▲ *Old Vicarage* 🍷 ⅚✳

Church Road, Witherslack LA11 6RS
TEL: (01539) 552381   FAX: (01539) 552373   COOKING 2
off A590, take first left in village to church   COST £25–£44

There is an air of agreeable restraint to the place, quite belied by the 'very hectic' décor of the lounge and the Victorian paintings and watercolours in the dining-room. Stanley Reeve has been running the kitchen since 1980, and it is a tribute to his dedication that standards are maintained from year to year. Starters are kept refreshingly simple, as in gravad lax, pasta flowers with caponata and Parmesan, or sauté chicken livers with lardons, garlic and brandy. A main course of Barbary duckling is half the bird, cooked *à point*, the skin well seasoned and tasty, the texture of the meat 'the same as Chinese crispy duck', served with a clear stock sharpened with rhubarb. A colossal wedge of apricot frangipane tart at inspection – rather like a Bakewell tart in texture – was crammed with chunks of dried apricot. Cheeses are the best of British, and coffee comes with Kendal mint cake. There may be more than a touch of twee in garnishing the butter with forget-me-nots, but there is serious cooking beneath the flounce.

The wine list is a gem: a compact, meticulously organised collection including a fascinating set of Italian rarities. A generous number of half-bottles adds depth, and there's a selection of bottled beers; local Jennings Sneck Lifter sounds fun. CELLARMAN'S CHOICE: Maria Costanza 1994, Milazzo, Agrigento, Sicily, £19.80; Montefalco Rosso 1990, Paolo Bea, Umbria, £21.50.

CHEF: Stanley Reeve   PROPRIETORS: Stanely and Irene Reeve, and Jill and Roger Burrington-Brown   OPEN: Sun L 12.30 for 1 (1 sitting; booking essential), all week D 7.30 for 8 (1 sitting)   MEALS: Set L Sun £13.50, Set D £26.50   SERVICE: not inc, card slips closed   CARDS: Access, Amex, Delta, Switch, Visa   DETAILS: 40 seats. Private parties: 18 main room, 10 private room. Car park. Vegetarian meals. Children's helpings. Smart dress preferred. No smoking in dining-room. Wheelchair access (no WC). Music   ACCOMMODATION: 14 rooms, all with bath/shower. TV. Phone. B&B £59 to £138. Rooms for disabled. Children welcome. Baby facilities. Dogs by arrangement. Afternoon teas. Garden (*The Which? Hotel Guide*)

'Both chefs' wives have the same air of icy competence, with the unspoken message that they could have been brain surgeons or chairpersons of ICI had they so chosen, but while their other halves do this job, they would stand by their man and do their bit as perfectly as possible.' (On eating in the West Country)

WOBURN Bedfordshire   map 6

Paris House

Woburn Park, Woburn MK17 9QP
TEL: (01525) 290692   FAX: (01525) 290471   COOKING 2
on A4012, 1½m E of Woburn in Abbey grounds   COST £34–£68

This imposing timbered white building on the Duke of Bedford's estate really
did once have an address in Paris: it was painstakingly transplanted from the
Great Exhibition there in 1878. It has been owned and run since 1983 by Peter
Chandler, who also cooks, and who might emerge from the kitchen at the end of
dinner 'looking as if he'd just run the London marathon'. For all the pressure
created by offering a five-course menu gastronomique as well as a fixed-price
menu of half a dozen choices at each course, things run admirably smoothly.

Marinated Cajun prawns for one inspector were 'delicately spiced and
delicious', while 'palpably fresh' halibut fillet in champagne sauce proved a
hearteningly substantial portion. Duck breast in a fig and Muscat sauce was a
whole piece of meat, not pre-sliced, the fat cooked to almost Cantonese
crispness, the sauce a forthright but not overpowering amalgam of flavours. The
French accent is strong in desserts such as good tarte Tatin and an accomplished
chocolate soufflé. Service is 'willing' but, in the view of an inspector, 'lacked real
professional confidence'. Quality throughout the wine list is reliable, though a
few more options under £20 would be welcome. House French is £12.

CHEF/PROPRIETOR: Peter Chandler OPEN: Tue to Sun L 12 to 2, Tue to Sat D 7 to 9.30 CLOSED:
Feb MEALS: Set L £25 to £42, Set D £42 to £45 SERVICE: not inc, card slips closed CARDS:
Access, Amex, Diners, Switch, Visa DETAILS: 45 seats. Private parties: 45 main room, 16
private room. Car park. Vegetarian meals. Children's helpings. Smart dress preferred. No music

WOLTERTON Norfolk   map 6

▲ Saracen's Head £

Wolterton NR11 7LX
TEL: (01263) 768909
off A140 Aylsham to Cromer road, through   COOKING 1
Erpingham and Calthorpe   COST £19–£32

The inn, modelled on a Tuscan farmhouse, was built in 1806 as a coaching-house
for Wolterton Hall. Prominent signs advertising food ensure 'the imposing-
looking pub is not accidentally driven past', large parties are catered for
enthusiastically, and Robert Dawson-Smith and his team deal with all comers
'with practised ease and good nature'. Blackboards list the food, starting perhaps
with deep-fried Brie and apricot sauce, or soused mackerel, followed by hearty
lambs' kidneys with bacon, grilled Swaffield trout, or an unusual main-course
'pudding' of layered ratatouille and brown bread. Not surprisingly for a pub, a
few sauces incorporate a slug of sherry or Marsala, the latter also finding its way
into a nutty banana crumble. Special offers include a 'two-choice' lunch at £4.95.
The wine list gets around the world in 16 bottles, all for less than £16, apart from
fizz. House wine is £8.50.

CHEF/PROPRIETOR: Robert Dawson-Smith   OPEN: all week 12.30 to 2.15, 7.30 to 9.30   CLOSED: 25 Dec   MEALS: alc (main courses £6.50 to £10.50). Set L £4.75 (2 courses), Set D Sun £5.95. BYO £4   SERVICE: not inc, card slips closed   CARDS: Access, Amex, Diners, Visa   DETAILS: 50 seats. 50 seats outside. Private parties: 15 main room, 60 private room. Car park. Vegetarian meals. Children's helpings. Wheelchair access (also women's WC). No music ACCOMMODATION: 4 rooms, all with bath/shower. TV. B&B £35 to £50. Deposit: 20%. Children welcome. Dogs welcome in bedrooms only. Garden (*The Which? Hotel Guide*)

WOODSTOCK Oxfordshire	map 2

▲ *Feathers Hotel*

Market Street, Woodstock OX20 1SX	COOKING 2*
TEL: (01993) 812291 FAX: (01993) 813158	COST £36–£56

An enviable location – five minutes' walk from the gates of Blenheim Palace, in a village of pretty Cotswold houses – gives the Feathers an immediate appeal, enhanced by sympathetic restoration. An inherent flexibility about the operation adds to the attraction, taking in informal bar meals, two-course lunches, and full meals from the wide-ranging *carte*. A high level of technical accomplishment is evident in, for example, a cake of wild mushrooms and semolina sitting in a puddle of hollandaise sauce, with slicks of a soy and ginger sauce criss-crossing the hollandaise. There is no shortage of interesting-sounding dishes, from pot-roast guinea-fowl with broccoli and tapénade to twice-baked pistachio soufflé with black cherries. Ambition, however, is probably the downfall of some ideas. As one perceptive reporter put it, 'The kitchen seems to be striving so relentlessly after innovation and sophistication that the importance of whether these dishes actually taste good has somehow slid down the list of priorities.'

Prices are on the high side, an impression not helped by the 15 per cent 'optional' service charge, which every single reporter this year complained about. A Franco-centric wine list offers relatively few bottles under £20, and of course the 'optional' service charge applies to these as well. Half a dozen house wines cost around £12.

CHEF: David Lewis   PROPRIETORS: Simon Lowe, Andrew Leeman and Howard Malin   OPEN: all week 12.30 to 2.15 (2.30 Sun), 7.30 to 9.15   MEALS: alc (main courses £11.50 to £18). Set L £16.50 (2 courses) to £21. BYO £5. Bar L all week, D Mon to Fri   SERVICE: 15% (optional) CARDS: Access, Amex, Delta, Diners, Visa   DETAILS: 60 seats. Private parties: 60 main room, 25 private room. Children's helpings. Smart dress preferred.   ACCOMMODATION: 16 rooms, all with bath/shower. TV. Phone. B&B £78 to £195. Children welcome. Baby facilities. Dogs welcome with own bedding and food. Afternoon teas. Garden (*The Which? Hotel Guide*)

WORCESTER Hereford & Worcester	map 5

Brown's

24 Quay Street, Worcester WR1 2JJ	COOKING 2
TEL: (01905) 26263	COST £23–£45

The appeal of this converted grain mill is its location overlooking the Severn, the ultra-sophisticated atmosphere, and the 'non-British, non-cosy, non-flowery décor'. A new co-chef arrived in 1995, but little else has changed. Menus are fixed price, descriptions are minimal, soup and fish are changed daily.

The kitchen works best with quick, simple dishes, from medallions of monkfish with a translucent Japanese sauce and a salad of sprouting beans, to grilled pears with Roquefort ('a winner all the way'). 'Deliciously chargrilled' fish have also been mentioned. Duck is a favourite of the kitchen: roast with quince purée and cranberries, or presented as a 'beautifully timed' breast with a confit of the leg and orange sauce. Reporters have also singled out whim-wham, a sort of brandy and sherry trifle, and the cheeseboard is a sound bet. 'Service is always good when it's included,' observed one diner, impressed by the hard-working staff. France dominates the wine list, and half-bottles abound. House wine is £10.50.

CHEFS: W.R. Tansley and L. Jones PROPRIETORS: W.R. and P.M. Tansley OPEN: Tue to Fri and Sun L 12.30 to 1.45, Tue to Sat D 7.30 to 9.45 CLOSED: 24 to 31 Dec, bank hols MEALS: Set L Tue to Fri £17, Set L Sun £22, Set D £32 SERVICE: net prices, card slips closed CARDS: Access, Amex, Delta, Switch, Visa DETAILS: 120 seats. Private parties: 90 main room. Vegetarian meals. Smart dress preferred. Wheelchair access (also WC). Music

---

WORFIELD Shropshire   map 5

▲ Old Vicarage Hotel ♥ ⁵✳

Worfield WV15 5JZ
TEL: (01746) 716497   FAX: (01746) 716552   COOKING 2*
1m N of A454, 3m E of Bridgnorth   COST £28–£52

This red-brick Edwardian parsonage, with its elegantly pitched roof, conservatory extension, and lavishly furnished dining-room, sits at the edge of Worfield, one of Shropshire's smaller communities, amid two acres of meadow and farmland. Peter and Christine Iles make full use of regional supply lines for wild Severn salmon, locally bagged game and Welsh lamb, while John Williams, their chef of several years' standing, cures and smokes meat and fish in-house, and makes his own breads and pasta. This is the country-house ethos writ large.

The tone of the cooking is firmly classical British, which means that Galia melon is a possible starter but dressed with jasmine tea, while dill-scented salmon comes with pineapple and capers. A pressed terrine of confit of duck leg, ham hock and duck liver, cemented together with mushy peas, has been described as 'both refreshing and full of down-to-earth flavours'. Vegetable components are well thought out, as in bubble and squeak bristling with spring cabbage to accompany thickly sliced cannon of lamb. Creamy desserts stay within the parameters of banana and mascarpone mousse with toffee ice-cream, and crème brûlée with figs. The impeccable British cheese selection draws on old and new, taking in properly matured Somerset Cheddar as well as Yorkshire Blue ewes'-milk cheese from Thirsk. The wine list is well judged, focusing on France but with serious competition from elsewhere, and with plenty of half-bottles. CELLARMAN'S CHOICE: Bonny Doon, Ca' del Solo Malvasia Bianca 1992, California, £17.50; Ch. Musar 1986, Serge Hochar, Lebanon, £17.50.

CHEF: John Williams   PROPRIETORS: Peter and Christine Iles   OPEN: Sun L 12 to 2, all week D 7 to 9   CLOSED: Christmas and New Year   MEALS: Set L Sun £16.50, Set D Sun to Thur £25, Set D Fri and Sat £30.50   SERVICE: not inc   CARDS: Access, Amex, Diners, Visa   DETAILS: 45 seats. Private parties: 45 main room, 16 private room. Car park. Vegetarian meals. Children welcome. Smart dress preferred. No smoking in dining-room. Wheelchair access (also WC). Music ACCOMMODATION: 14 rooms, all with bath/shower. TV. Phone. B&B £67.50 to £130. Deposit: £50. Rooms for disabled. Children welcome. Baby facilities. Dogs welcome in bedrooms only. Garden (*The Which? Hotel Guide*)

WORLESTON Cheshire   map 5

▲ *Rookery Hall* ⚡ | NEW ENTRY |

Worleston CW6 9DA
TEL: (01270) 610016   FAX: (01270) 626027   COOKING 2
on B5074, 2½m N of Nantwich   COST £25–£56

'Do give this place another try,' wrote a regular reporter, 'it shows how accessible a grand hotel can be.' After a period of flux, Rookery Hall is settling down under an enthusiastic manager and chef, David Alton, who arrived in 1993. A schloss-like tower added by a banking baron contributes to the hall's slightly quirky air, but the mahogany-panelled dining-room provides a 'stunning setting', and young staff are notably keen, informal and friendly. The style is well-presented, modern, country-house cooking, helped by tip-top canapés, petits fours and bread.

At dinner there is no opportunity for eating (or paying for) fewer than the full five courses, but the enterprising menu might include crumbly black pudding ('obviously locally sourced') on risotto, or a dish of pork rillettes with a sweet-sharp chutney, accompanied by medallions of cold, grilled pork loin: 'these were rillettes for the '90s'. Given the high standard of raw materials, however – including duck breast, and loin of lamb with mint and potato dumplings – an inspector felt that greater clarity of flavour would have added greatly to the experience. A hot lemon soufflé pleased one reporter, and cheeses are first-class. Over 20 wines are available by the glass, although mark-ups are high: 'On receiving my bill I was stunned to see that my small glass of champagne had cost £9.50, and a champagne cocktail weighed in at £14. As far as we were concerned this had to be a record.' House wines are £12.50 a bottle.

CHEF: David Alton   PROPRIETOR: Select Hotels   OPEN: all week 12 to 2.30, 7 to 9.30   MEALS: Set L £12.50 (2 courses) to £17.50, Set D £37.50   SERVICE: not inc, card slips closed   CARDS: Access, Amex, Switch, Visa   DETAILS: 36 seats. Private parties: 12 to 66 private rooms. Car park. Vegetarian meals. Children's helpings. Smart dress preferred. No smoking in dining-room. No music   ACCOMMODATION: 45 rooms, all with bath/shower. TV. Phone. B&B £98.50 to £250. Rooms for disabled. Children welcome. Baby facilities. Dogs welcome by arrangement. Afternoon teas. Garden

---

If a restaurant is new to the Guide *this year (did not appear as a main entry in the last edition),* NEW ENTRY *appears opposite its name.*

Not inc *in the details at the end of an entry indicates that no service charge is made and any tipping is at the discretion of the customer.*

WRIGHTINGTON Lancashire

map 8

High Moor

High Moor Lane, Wrightington WN6 9QA
TEL: (01257) 252364 FAX: (01257) 255120
off A5209, between M6 junction 27 and Parbold, take
Robin Hood Lane at crossroads W of Wrightington
Hospital, then next left

COOKING 2
COST £19–£40

The low whitewashed building with mullioned windows 'looks as if it has been modernised to look old', with a few assorted beams for added seventeenth-century effect. Ignore, if you will, the two-foot pepper-mill and concentrate instead on the informality and flexibility, which is achieved via set menus (with reduced prices in the early evening), plus sandwiches, baguettes (filled with cured ham, or smoked salmon perhaps), and a free-ranging *carte* at dinner.

The food is probably best when it deals in unaffected dishes such as beetroot and cabbage soup, deep-fried fish and chips with mushy peas, or a boneless, sticky, braised oxtail stuffed with cabbage leaf, onion and thyme, and served with bubble and squeak. Alcohol might appear as a saucing ingredient, producing a rich-tasting Madeira and mushroom sauce to accompany prime-quality fillet of beef wrapped in bacon, for example. Finish with a wedge of sticky toffee pudding, or chilled but runny rice-pudding served with a dollop of sharp-tasting rhubarb. Service is bright and cheerful, and there is 'intelligent and charming advice' on wines, of which a generous 20 are available by the glass. The list is wide-ranging and tolerably priced.

CHEF: Darren Wynn PROPRIETORS: John Nelson and James Sines OPEN: all week 12 to 2, 5.30 to 10 (8.30 Sun) MEALS: alc D Mon to Sat 7 to 10 (main courses £7 to £14.50). Set L £9.50 (2 courses) to £11.50, Set D all week 5.30 to 7 (8.30 Sun) £9.50 (2 courses) to £11.50. BYO £5. Light lunches available SERVICE: not inc CARDS: Access, Amex, Diners, Switch, Visa DETAILS: 100 seats. 20 seats outside. Private parties: 80 main room. Car park. Vegetarian meals. Children's helpings. Smart dress preferred. Wheelchair access (no WC). Music

WYE Kent

map 3

▲ Wife of Bath

4 Upper Bridge Street, Wye TN25 5AW
TEL: (01233) 812540 and 812232
FAX: (01233) 813630
just off A28, Ashford to Canterbury road

COOKING 2
COST £26–£38

'The restaurant exudes an aura of well-being, even of luxury.' Vinescapes by Sir Hugh Casson adorn the walls, pink linen the tables. Robert Hymers buys fish and seafood on the beach at Hythe, while venison comes from the nearby Brabourne estate. Readers are impressed by the accuracy and generosity of simple dishes such as smoked haddock mousse with black bread and butter, and mushroom tagliatelle with 'almost more mushroom than pasta in the dish'. The crowd-pleasing repertoire extends to soy-dressed filo parcels of crab and coriander as well as black pudding and apple served on rösti with mustard sauce. Among the more assertive accompaniments might be creamed celeriac for local duckling, or prunes and armagnac for saddle of rabbit, while puddings may include a 'fabulous' butterscotch roulade. The wine list does its best to represent a good spread of regions. Although the more expensive French choices are the best, there are also Peter Lehmann wines from Australia and a couple from the excellent Casablanca in Chile. House selections start at £9.95.

CHEF: Robert Hymers   PROPRIETOR: John Morgan   OPEN: Tue to Sat 12 to 2.30, 7.30 to 10   CLOSED: first week Jan, first 2 weeks Sept   MEALS: alc L (main courses £10.50 to £14). Set L £8.75 (2 courses), Set D £21.75. BYO £5   SERVICE: not inc   CARDS: Access, Delta, Switch, Visa   DETAILS: 55 seats. Private parties: 60 main room. Car park. Children's helpings. Smart dress preferred. No pipes in dining-room. Wheelchair access (no WC). No music   ACCOMMODATION: 6 rooms, all with bath/shower. TV. Phone. B&B £40 to £70. Rooms for disabled. Garden (*The Which? Hotel Guide*)

| YARM   Stockton-on-Tees | map 10 |

D.P. Chadwick's ✸ £

| 104 High Street, Yarm TS15 9AU | COOKING 2 |
| TEL: (01642) 788558 | COST £19–£43 |

Yarm is a small market town whose broad main street is flanked by attractive pastel-coloured Georgian buildings, yet with enough vitality to welcome the brisk, cosmopolitan style of Daryl Chadwick's brasserie. There are no reservations, at either lunch or dinner, just a queue that files happily into the large, lively, open, buzzing room 'with music bouncing off the quarry tiles'. Baguettes in a wicker holder, a hunk of Parmesan with a grater, and an espresso machine all bode well. Dishes are picked off a blackboard, and the style is brazenly modern, with a bright Anglo-Franco-Italian orientation, taking in pot-roast chicken with leeks and wild mushrooms, and fish such as bourride, or cod with a horseradish crust.

Every ingredient that should be here *is* here, from roasted peppers, pancetta and ciabatta, to black pudding, Toulouse sausage, and risotto, not to mention Pecorino, Taleggio, and Provolone. Any idea that sounds good is roped in, and you can barely hear the cultures clash above the animated hubbub. Portions can be substantial, puddings are well done, and service is 'young, energetic and rapid'. A couple of dozen humanely priced wines match the upbeat style, taking in South African Shiraz and a Gewurztraminer from Uruguay. House wine is £8.50.

CHEF: David Brownless   PROPRIETOR: D.P. Chadwick   OPEN: Tue to Sat 11.30 to 9.30   CLOSED: second week Oct   MEALS: alc (main courses £4 to £14)   SERVICE: not inc   CARDS: none   DETAILS: 70 seats. Vegetarian meals. Children's helpings. No smoking in 1 dining-room. Music

£ indicates that it is possible to have a three-course meal, including coffee, a half-bottle of house wine and service, at any time the restaurant is open (i.e. at dinner as well as at lunch, unless a place is open only for dinner), for £20 or less per person.

YARMOUNTH Isle of Wight
YARMOUTH Isle of Wight   map 2

▲ *George Hotel*   NEW ENTRY

Quay Street, Yarmouth PO41 0PE   COOKING 2
TEL: (01983) 760331 FAX: (01983) 760425   COST £28–£47

The renovation of this seaside hotel brings new glamour to the western side of
the island. Adjacent to Yarmouth Castle, it was built in the seventeenth century
for an admiral. The current owners have fashioned the interior to make you think
you are deep in the countryside – oil paintings, stags' heads and squashy sofas
adorn the lounge – and if the menu has an air of the Lake District about it, it is
because the kitchen is headed by Kevin Mangeolles, late of Michael's Nook (see
entry, Grasmere).

A discernible opulence is the chosen mode, evident in a terrine of rabbit
dressed with truffles and morels, or a 'tarte Tatin' of turnips with sauté foie gras
in a sauce of red wine and shallots, the latter 'a fabulously smooth and rich'
combination of complementary flavours. Fish cookery is inventive and accomplished, as in sea bass in a delicately cumin-scented sauce with an aubergine
and tomato gâteau, while the treatment of duck – the breast roasted, the leg
presented as a cassoulet, on a sauce with 'a distinct but not overpowering tang of
thyme' – shows great confidence. Puddings to spoil yourself with include richly
gooey chocolate fondant on a coffee sauce, or pear and honey mousse with
nougatine and a red wine sauce. Service is 'unobtrusive but friendly'. An
enterprising wine list adds to the enticement. Selections from outside Europe are
particularly good, and prices are realistic throughout. There is a cosmopolitan
house range, all intelligently priced at £10.95.

CHEF: Kevin Mangeolles PROPRIETORS: Jeremy and Amy Willcock, and John Illsley OPEN:
Sun L 12.30 to 3, Tue to Sat D 7 to 10 MEALS: Set L Sun £22.50, Set D £33.50. BYO £5.
Brasserie food available SERVICE: none, card slips closed CARDS: Access, Amex, Delta,
Switch, Visa DETAILS: 40 seats. 50 seats outside. Private parties: 60 main room, 60 private
room. No children under 10 restaurant; children welcome brasserie. Smart dress preferred. No
music. Air-conditioned ACCOMMODATION: 17 rooms, all with bath/shower. TV. Phone. B&B £70
to £140. Children welcome. Baby facilities. Dogs welcome. Afternoon teas. Garden

YATTENDON Berkshire   map 2

▲ *Royal Oak*

The Square, Yattendon RG18 0UG
TEL: (01635) 201325 FAX: (01635) 201926   COOKING 2
off B4009, 5m W of Pangbourne   COST £29–£53

'I felt instantly welcomed and warmed,' commented one visitor who progressed
from the stone-floored bar to the summery yellow dining-room of this
up-market sixteenth-century inn. Staff, who are well versed in the vocabulary of
'wonderfuls' and 'enjoys', generally keep things moving at a brisk pace. An
appetiser consisting of a single oyster with scrambled eggs and caviare was
reckoned to be 'as sublime and sexy as they come'. Superb chargrilled scallops
are ringed by a purée of potato and a deep star-anise sauce, while quail pâté is
served with a delicate grape and sloe-gin preserve. Main courses are barely less

impressive: assiette of duck brings together a glazed breast stuffed with spinach purée, a seriously oversized piece of pan-fried liver, and a leg sitting on braised cabbage and pine-kernels.

The fondness for variations on a theme also shows in the 'brilliant' trio of prune- and armagnac-based desserts. Bar food aims for a touch more earthiness in the shape of ham hock with casseroled lentils, navarin of lamb, and fish and chips. The wine list exudes quality, and few bottles will disappoint; there is also plenty of good drinking by the glass. House recommendations start at £9.50.

CHEF: Robbie Macrae   PROPRIETOR: Regal Hotel Group   OPEN: Tue to Fri and Sun L 12 to 2 (2.30 Fri and Sun), Mon to Sat D 7.30 to 9.30 (10 Fri and Sat)   MEALS: alc D (main courses £15.50 to £18.50). Set L £15.50 (2 courses) to £19.50. Bar food available   SERVICE: not inc   CARDS: Access, Amex, Delta, Diners, Switch, Visa   DETAILS: 24 seats. 30 seats outside. Private parties: 20 main room, 8 private room. Car park. Children's helpings. Smart dress preferred. No music   ACCOMMODATION: 7 rooms, all with bath/shower. TV. Phone. B&B £90 to £105. Children welcome. Baby facilities. Dogs by arrangement. Afternoon teas. Garden (*The Which? Hotel Guide*)

YORK   North Yorkshire   map 9

19 Grape Lane 🍴 ❋

19 Grape Lane, York YO1 2HU   COOKING 2
TEL: (01904) 636366   FAX: (01904) 702120   COST £19–£43

You may feel a little cheek by jowl with your neighbours at 19 Grape Lane, but that, as a reporter commented, is the true York experience: at one time you could shake hands with the people in the house opposite just by leaning out of the window. This is a 'raftered little building that twinkles in the night', and has long been a haven of good eating in the centre of the old city. David Hind came on board as chef after last year's *Guide* went to press and, while the *carte* may look a shade lengthy for the scale of the place, the kitchen scores many hits.

A fish pancake is generously filled, while medallions of hare with wild mushrooms and Madeira sauce – a winner here under previous chefs – is still good: intensely gamey saddle meat seared to crispness on the outside, red-rare within. Others have praised well-textured broccoli soup and a spinach-wrapped fish terrine with tomato mayonnaise. Puddings offer all that today's restaurant crowds expect, not forgetting Yorkshire treacle tart with custard. A lively bunch of French, Italian and New World wines should suit most tastes, and those after half-bottles are well catered for. House wines from Duboeuf are £8.95.

CHEF: David Hind   PROPRIETORS: Gordon and Carolyn Alexander   OPEN: Tue to Sat 12 to 1.45, 6 to 9 (10 Sat)   CLOSED: 25 to 31 Dec, 21 Jan to 11 Feb, last week Sept, first week Oct   MEALS: alc (main courses £6 to £13.50). Set L £9.95 (2 courses) to £12.50   SERVICE: not inc   CARDS: Access, Delta, Visa   DETAILS: 40 seats. 8 seats outside. Private parties: 22 main room. Vegetarian meals. Children's helpings. No children under 8 D. No smoking in 1 dining-room. No music

---

🍴 *indicates a change of chef since last year's* Guide.

Dining-rooms where music, either live or recorded, is never played are signalled by No music *in the details at the end of an entry.*

Melton's ▼ ⅝✳

7 Scarcroft Road, York YO2 1ND   COOKING 3
TEL: (01904) 634341   FAX: (01904) 629233   COST £19–£37

One of the delights of eating here is that honest, sensible food of high quality is served in totally unassuming surroundings. It is a converted shop with plain wooden tables, solid but comfortable chairs, and paintings for sale. The Hjorts offer flexible eating options and good value, for example knocking £5 off the fixed-price dinner menu for anyone willing to leave by 7.45. 'The food is straightforward in concept and uncluttered in execution, with deft, delicious and clear flavours,' writes an inspector, impressed by garbure (a full-flavoured tureen of 'rib-tickling' broth), and by sauté fillet of cod on a bed of saffron-flecked mash.

Dishes may be as conventional as fish soup with rouille, as interesting as roast fillet of gurnard with bacon and herbs, or as complex as a chartreuse of lightly cooked rabbit and duck topped with pan-fried fillet of rabbit, with wild mushrooms, root vegetables and a trickle of intensely flavoured pan juices. Flavours are carefully considered, timing is good, and vegetables are integral to the dish. As an alternative to rich sticky toffee or bread-and-butter puddings, consider roast pear with a trio of ginger, lime and butterscotch sauces, or the lively contrast afforded by white chocolate parfait with lime syrup.

Menus change regularly, and Tuesdays and Thursdays produce extra vegetarian and fish dishes repectively. Mineral water and tea or coffee are included in the price, 'so the bill came as a very pleasant surprise' for one reporter. Nothing has more than a £10 mark-up on the wine list, which means that the more expensive bottles offer best value. There's also a fine range of single-malt whiskies. CELLARMAN'S CHOICE: Seaview Brut 1991, McLaren Vale, Australia, £13; Côte de Beaune 1993, Joseph Drouhin, £19.90.

CHEFS: Michael Hjort and T.J. Drew   PROPRIETORS: Michael and Lucy Hjort   OPEN: Tue to Sun L 12 to 2, Mon to Sat D 5.30 to 10   CLOSED: 24 Dec to 14 Jan, 1 week Aug   MEALS: alc (main courses £8.50 to £15). Set L £14.50, Set D £14.50 (5.30 to 6.15) to £19.50   SERVICE: net prices, card slips closed   CARDS: Access, Delta, Switch, Visa   DETAILS: 40 seats. Private parties: 30 main room, 14 private room. Vegetarian meals. Children's helpings. No smoking in 1 dining-room. Wheelchair access (no WC). Music

▲ Middlethorpe Hall ▼ ⅝✳

Bishopthorpe Road, York YO2 1QB   COOKING 3
TEL: (01904) 641241   FAX: (01904) 620176   COST £20–£55

The house, built in 1699, stands in 26 acres of gardens and parkland, a mile and a half south of York. Historic House Hotels has worked its customary magic to restore Middlethorpe to a state of grace, producing trimmed lawns, a walled garden, an elegant drawing-room and two dining-rooms. The formal oak-panelled one is open in winter and has two dinner menus, one dubbed 'gourmet'. In summer it offers only the 'gourmet' menu, but a grill room opens downstairs and operates the standard menu. Lunch is three courses and of slightly less complexity.

Andrew Wood turns out gratifyingly rich and accomplished dishes to match the setting, dipping into the luxury bag for an oyster and chive cream sauce to accompany brochette of langoustines, or to make ravioli of chicken and foie gras with Madeira gravy. Fish gets good treatment, from a seared fillet of salmon served on a bed of couscous with ratatouille, to a roast fillet of John Dory that was 'firm, tender, sweet and moist', and generously dressed with olive oil, basil and tomato. 'Three of the puddings required 20 minutes' notice, so we all had the ginger torte' was the dessert compromise of one reporter. Given 20 minutes, consider the vanilla and armagnac soufflé or the baked warm chocolate tart. Tablecloths are starched, but the staff are not, and service is included.

The wine list is long and rather solemn, with few bottles on its eight pages costing less than £15. There is a fine array of classics, mostly from France, and a good clutch of half-bottles. The house selection features six less-expensive wines, starting at £11.50. CELLARMAN'S CHOICE: Bodega Norton Malbec 1991, Argentina, £16; Iron Hill Semillon Chardonnay 1993, S.E. Australia, £15.20.

CHEF: Andrew Wood   PROPRIETOR: Historic House Hotels Ltd   OPEN: all week 12.30 (12 on race days) to 1.45, 7.30 to 9.45   MEALS: Set L Mon to Sat £12.50, Set L Sun £15.50, Set D £25.95 to £36.95. BYO £7.50   SERVICE: net prices, card slips closed   CARDS: Access, Amex, Delta, Switch, Visa   DETAILS: 50 seats. Private parties: 45 private room. Car park. Vegetarian meals. No children under 8. Jacket and tie D. No smoking in dining-room. No music   ACCOMMODATION: 30 rooms, all with bath/shower. TV. Phone. B&B £97 to £220. Deposit: 1 night's stay. Rooms for disabled. No children under 8. Afternoon teas. Garden (*The Which? Hotel Guide*)

Scotland

ABERDEEN Aberdeen   map 11

Courtyard

1 Alford Lane, Aberdeen AB1 1YD	COOKING 1*
TEL: (01224) 213795 FAX: (01224) 212961	COST £21–£34

Tony Heath has gone to Let's Eat (see entry, Perth), but the rest of the team cooks on in this two-tier operation. An informal and lively bistro downstairs (Martha's Vineyard) has a restless blackboard menu. If you like being in the thick of things, this is for you. The upstairs restaurant is more sedate, the pace gentler. Some first courses such as smoked haddock chowder, or risotto with saffron and sun dried tomato, can be upgraded to mains, and the choice throughout is as generous as the style is wide-ranging: from a ramekin of Arbroath smokies and creamed leeks, to a warm array of chargrilled Mediterranean vegetables topped with mozarella cheese. Vegetables are built into the equation – charcoal-grilled lamb cutlets served with salad, new potatoes and a pepper and chilli jelly – and desserts continue the reassuringly simple theme with lemon cheesecake or fresh fruit tart. One short, sharp and sensibly priced wine list services both upstairs and downstairs, starting with house wine at £9.50.

CHEFS: Glen Lawson, Farid Abed-Ghers, Angus McCambley and Bruce Morison PROPRIETOR: Vic Booth OPEN: Tue to Sat 12 to 2.30 (bistro only Sat L), 6.30 to 9.45 CLOSED: 25 Dec, 1 Jan MEALS: alc (main courses £7 to £12.50) SERVICE: not inc, card slips closed CARDS: Access, Amex, Delta, Switch, Visa DETAILS: restaurant 30 seats, bistro 50 seats. Private parties: 50 main room. Vegetarian meals. Children welcome. Smart dress preferred. Music

Faraday's

2 Kirk Brae, Cults, Aberdeen AB1 9SQ	
TEL/FAX: (01224) 869666	COOKING 1
on A93, 2m from city centre	COST £19–£49

'It feels much less like an electricity sub-station than I imagined,' noted a first-time visitor. The building dates from 1904, and the long, thin room is soberly decorated in convincing period colours. The kitchen deals in 'regional country cooking', with an emphasis on native produce and dishes. Plain mince might be served with mealie (oatmeal) and peas, or lamb stew with doughballs (aka dumplings). 'We came away feeling thoroughly uplifted,' announced one couple, which is 'the whole point of having lunch out.' This effect was produced by onion soup and marinated herrings to begin, followed by grilled lamb chops, with caramel ice-cream and crushed meringue to finish. A cheeseboard also featured. 'Simple and homely' is how the food appears. Puddings are read out, and have included slices of marquise-style chocolate with a creamy coffee sauce, and baked lemon cheesecake. Pleasant and helpful service completes the deal, along with 40-odd varied wines; house wine is £12.90.

CHEFS: John Inches, Roger Ross and Dorothy Skene   PROPRIETOR: John Inches   OPEN: Tue to Sat L 12 to 2, Mon to Sat D 7 to 9.45   CLOSED: 26 Dec to 2 Jan   MEALS: alc L (main courses £5 to £12.50). Set D Mon to Thur £15.95, Set D Fri and Sat £21.95. BYO £6.50   SERVICE: 10%, card slips closed   CARDS: Access, Switch, Visa   DETAILS: 40 seats. Private parties: 40 main room. Car park. Vegetarian meals. Children's helpings. Smart dress preferred. No smoking until 2 L, 10 D. Wheelchair access (also WC). Music. Air-conditioned

Silver Darling

Pocra Quay, North Pier, Aberdeen AB2 1DQ   COOKING 2
TEL: (01224) 576229   FAX: (01224) 791275   COST £35–£49

The restaurant has picked a prime spot, in an old Customs House at the mouth of the Dee, where you can watch boats coming in and out of the harbour. It calls itself a 'barbecued seafood restaurant', and a selection of the day's catch is generally cooked over charcoal, but there is more to the operation than just throwing a few prawns on the griddle. Didier Dejean's menu is as French as they come, and he gets through enough butter and cream to prove it, but he also makes dressings of basil and olive oil (applied to a Parmesan tartlet of langoustines and scallops) and serves local salmon on a bed of green cabbage and smoked bacon.

Some spicy flavours surface in Cajun pan-fried oysters, or in the roast garlic, cumin and coriander that accompany roast monkfish, all of which helps to produce a varied and interesting menu. And there might also be a Swiss cheese soufflé with smoked salmon, or perhaps fillet of red deer marinated in whisky and juniper with a blackcurrant sauce. Desserts are thoroughly French, from an iced honey nougat parfait to a crêpe soufflé with Grand Marnier sauce, and the short wine list follows the French route as well, with prices starting at £9.50.

CHEF: Didier Dejean   PROPRIETORS: Didier Dejean, Norman Faulks and Catherine Wood   OPEN: Mon to Fri L 12 to 2, Mon to Sat D 7 to 10   MEALS: alc D (main courses £15.50 to £16.50). Set L £16 (2 courses)   SERVICE: not inc   CARDS: Access, Amex, Diners, Switch, Visa   DETAILS: 30 seats. Private parties: 30 main room. Children welcome. Smart dress preferred. Wheelchair access (also WC). Music

---

ABERFELDY Perthshire & Kinross   map 11

▲ Farleyer House, Menzies Restaurant 🍴✱

by Aberfeldy PH15 2JE
TEL: (01887) 820332   FAX: (01887) 829430
on B846, Aberfeldy to Kinloch Rannoch road,   COOKING 3
1½m W of Weem   COST £21–£48

Menzies Restaurant is open all year, but only for dinner (which took one lunchtime couple by surprise) and the Scottish Bistro is open for both lunch and dinner, but not all year. Drinks and ordering for the restaurant take place in the cluster of upstairs lounges, while synchronised serving in the comfortable antique dining-room, with its green walls and floral curtains, ensures that everybody eats at the same pace throughout the evening.

Charging £32 for four courses – with no choice at all – leads to high expectations. The price does allow for an element of luxury: the beurre blanc for a slice of turbot or sea bass is likely to be made with champagne, and truffles are not uncommon. Judging by an inspection meal, flavours tend to be delicate, and sauces are well-considered dabs that moisten rather than swamp the main item: three contrasting smears to complement the flavours of an unlikely salad of magret of duck and squat lobster, for example. Vegetables are integral to the dish. The famed Scottish larder is a bonus, and Aberfeldy prides itself on its wild Tay salmon.

Puddings, such as trios of chocolate, are sophisticated constructions, and peripherals include tasty appetisers, good breads and constant jugged water. Although the food is fine, the absence of welcome for one visitor, perceived lack of warmth to the place and inexperienced service can take the shine off it. The brightly-coloured and busy bistro, with bare floorboards and tables, mostly runs on cheaper fare of salads and grills. Wines come in all shapes and sizes, from mature claret in magnums (£120 for 1970 Haut Brion) to a Spanish red glugger Torregalan (£8.50 a bottle), by way of two or three bins from most major wine-producing countries.

CHEF: Richard Lyth PROPRIETOR: Janice Reid OPEN: restaurant all week D only 8 (1 sitting); bistro Tue to Sun 12 to 3, 6 to 9.30 MEALS: restaurant Set D £32; bistro alc (main courses £6.50 to £16). BYO £8.95 SERVICE: not inc CARDS: Access, Amex, Delta, Switch, Visa DETAILS: restaurant 30 seats, bistro 45 seats. 15 seats outside. Private parties: 30 main room, 14 private room. Car park. Vegetarian meals. Children's helpings. Jacket and tie restaurant. No smoking in restaurant. Music ACCOMMODATION: 15 rooms, all with bath/shower. TV. Phone. B&B £75 to £170. Deposit: 1 night's charge. Rooms for disabled. Children welcome. Baby facilities. Dogs by arrangement. Afternoon teas. Garden. Fishing (*The Which? Hotel Guide*)

ABERFOYLE Stirling   map 11

Braeval 🍾

Aberfoyle FK8 3UY
TEL: (01877) 382711   FAX: (01877) 382400   COOKING 4
on A81, 1m SE of Aberfoyle   COST £26–£47

'Old Mill' has gone from the name, but the place remains otherwise unchanged. It may look austere from outside, but the small room is attractively decorated, with a wood-burning stove, well-spaced tables and flowers for colour. 'It is probably redundant to write in praise of this establishment,' began one report, going on to detail a fine lunch that included a warm salad of 'perfectly cooked' chicken livers and crisp baby leeks with a pesto dressing, and roast fillet of cod served with 'sensational' mashed potato and spinach. The pattern is three-course set lunches (four on Sunday), and four-course dinners with no choice before dessert, but specific requirements are discussed when booking.

The menu changes daily, and, as often happens under such circumstances, certain devices appear in different guises. Couscous, for example, is used as a base for roast rump of lamb, and equally successfully for very fresh fillet of Dover sole. Chicken livers appear in a salad one day and in risotto (with roasted red peppers and parsley oil) another. The result is a unified style with a pleasing and playful inventiveness; dishes are interesting yet never too exotic. Textures impress, as in a wild mushroom soup 'as smooth as silk', and the combination of richness and delicacy is a characteristic, whether applied to a simple artichoke soup or to desserts. Crème brûlée served with rhubarb is exemplary, and for one reporter a small brandy-snap biscuit filled with chocolate mousse was 'to die for'. It came with a small banana parfait, all splashed with dark and white chocolate sauces. Not bad for 'a self-taught cook who couldn't boil an egg ten years ago', and who now gives lessons.

Bread is 'excellent', and although there is no menu to puzzle over, Parmesan biscuits and little tartlets are provided to begin. Coffee comes with a 'mouth-watering, slightly gritty' tablet (Scottish fudge). Service is 'sweet, charming and smart', and also efficient. The list of around 300 wines spans a wide range of quality and styles and achieves a sensible balance between the traditional and the eclectic. Prices are fair throughout, as much for those who want to splash out as for those on the lookout for bottles under £20. The user-friendly house selection starts at £13.50.

CHEF: Nick Nairn   PROPRIETORS: Nick and Fiona Nairn   OPEN: Wed to Sun L 12.30 to 1.30, Tue to Sat D 7.30 to 9.30   CLOSED: spring and autumn, 1 week June   MEALS: Set L Wed to Sat £16.50, Set L Sun £19.50, Set D £28.95   SERVICE: not inc, card slips closed   CARDS: Access, Delta, Switch, Visa   DETAILS: 34 seats. Private parties: 32 main room. Car park. No children under 10. No cigars/pipes in dining-room. No smoking before coffee. Wheelchair access (also WC). No music

ACHILTIBUIE Highland   map 11

▲ Summer Isles Hotel

Achiltibuie IV26 2YG
TEL: (01854) 622282   FAX: (01854) 622251   COOKING 2
off A835 at Drumrunie, 10m N of Ullapool   COST £38–£46

Summer Isles is at the end of a long road to nowhere else. As a retreat from the daily grind the 'understated' but 'still luxurious' hotel is difficult to beat for peace and remoteness. The menu is posted at the door from around lunch-time, and the only choice is dessert, which, like the cheese, is wheeled around on a trolley. Seafood is a natural component of most meals, perhaps in the form of fish soup, crab-cake with salsa, or large well-cooked scallops on top of spinach and basil leaves inside puff pastry.

The well-balanced meals often involve a vegetable course such as ravioli with wild mushrooms, or blue cheese soufflé, with a centrepiece roast of perhaps rabbit, or saddle of black-faced lamb with lemon and herb dumplings. Cheeses have included some overripe specimens at inspection, as well as good goats' and Bonchester, and come with biscuits and a selection of fruit, while puddings have 'masses of cream on them' and tend to be rich: dark chocolate mousse cake, or steamed syrup pudding with custard, for example.

Wine orders are expected before seven, which allows ample opportunity to browse through the excellent list. France dominates, with classic Bordeaux and

Burgundies notably strong, while shorter collections from Italy, Spain and the New World keep quality buoyed up. Prices span a wide range but are always fair. CELLARMAN'S CHOICE: Pouilly-Fumé Les Berthiers 1994, Serge Dagueneau, £16.50; Penley Estate Cabernet Sauvignon 1991, Coonawarra, South Australia, £26.

CHEF: Chris Firth-Bernard PROPRIETORS: Mark and Gerry Irvine OPEN: all week D only 8 (1 sitting) CLOSED: early Oct to Easter MEALS: Set D £33. BYO £5. Bar food available SERVICE: net prices CARDS: none DETAILS: 26 seats. Private parties: 8 main room. Car park. Children's helpings. Smart dress preferred. No smoking in dining-room. No music ACCOMMODATION: 12 rooms, all with bath/shower. Phone. B&B £46.50 to £98. Deposit: £50. Children welcome. Baby facilities. Dogs welcome in bedrooms only. Fishing (*The Which? Hotel Guide*)

ALEXANDRIA Dumbarton & Clydebank   map 11

▲ *Cameron House Hotel, Georgian Room* ⁵⊁

Loch Lomond, Alexandria G83 8QZ
TEL: (01389) 755565 FAX: (01389) 759522   COOKING 3
off A82, ½m N of Balloch roundabout, 1m S of Arden   COST £26–£70

The hotel offers the peaceful prospect of its own mile-long stretch of the lochside, plus a whole host of invigorating activities – from 'treadmills in the leisure centre' to a round of golf – to hone the appetite. 'Restrained opulence' was one description of the large first-floor dining-room, and cosseting extends to the food, which doesn't stint on luxury ingredients. People who like their food 'smooth, rich and creamy' as well as attractively presented will be well satisfied. The Market Lunch menu is three courses, while dinner slips in an extra fish dish along the lines of a casserole of mussels with glistening root vegetables, or a mousseline of haddock.

The style is in indulgent, modern Euro-classical vein, with walk-on parts for tomato and barley compote, spinach and polenta stuffing, truffle essence and morel *jus*. Fish and shellfish are strong suits – 'lobster bisque was everything I had ever imagined' – and rely on a good supply of scallops, West Coast langoustines and, of course, salmon. Game is also well treated, with venison featuring perhaps in a terrine together with guinea-fowl, or as a main course with woodland mushrooms. 'Flavours danced and sang for us,' wrote one couple, while another found the succession of cream-coloured creamy sauces just too much.

Stars among the puddings have included hot banana soufflé and fig tart. 'The arrival of the bread was quite a pantomime,' involving knife, rubber gloves, tongs and a recitation of the goods on offer, which might include tomato, raisin, cheese, walnut or mustard. The butter label is removed with tweezers. The wine list is full of fine bottles, and lets rip at the top end, with much over £30 a bottle. More down-to-earth prices are found in the South American, Spanish and Beaujolais sections. French house wines are £12.95.

Report forms are at the back of the book; write a letter if you prefer; or if you are on the Internet, e-mail us at guidereports@which. co. uk.

505

CHEF: Jeff Bland   PROPRIETOR: De Vere Hotels   OPEN: Mon to Fri L 12 to 1.45, all week D 7 to 9.45   MEALS: alc (main courses £19 to £20.50). Set L £14.95 (2 courses) to £17.50, Set D £35 to £37.50. BYO £8.50   SERVICE: not inc, card slips closed   CARDS: Access, Amex, Delta, Diners, Switch, Visa   DETAILS: 670 seats. 50 seats outside. Private parties: 275 main room, 40 and 275 private rooms. Car park. Vegetarian meals. Children welcome. Smart dress preferred. No smoking in dining-room. Wheelchair access (also WC). Music. Air-conditioned ACCOMMODATION: 68 rooms, all with bath/shower. TV. Phone. B&B £130 to £350. Deposit: £50. Rooms for disabled. Children welcome. Baby facilities. Afternoon teas. Garden. Swimming-pool. Fishing

---

ALYTH   Perthshire & Kinross   map 11

▲ *Drumnacree House Hotel* 🍴✕

St Ninians Road, Alyth PH11 8AP
TEL/FAX: (01828) 632194
turn off A926 Blairgowrie to Kirriemuir road to Alyth;
take first left after Clydesdale Bank; hotel entrance is   COOKING 2
300 metres on right   COST £26–£34

The Culls call it a country-house hotel, although that seems a rather grand description for a town house with large rooms. The dining-room's baby grand piano, large model of a ship and nice old dresser combine with a Middle Eastern tasselled carpet to produce an exotic air, which appropriately reflects the broad scope of the cooking. Allan Cull enjoys the cut and thrust of Cajun gumbos with dirty rice, plus Chinese-style steaming with ginger and spring onion, as well as the European vein that an inspector sampled, beginning with a ramekin of lambs' kidneys in a 'commercially curried' cream sauce, and ending with a French apple tart.

In between came 'outstandingly good' pink venison served with 'penny bun' boletus mushrooms, and some 'brilliant' pink fir potatoes tasting 'very nutty, slightly earthy'. Aberdeen Angus beef and Scottish lamb and seafood confirm a commitment to native produce, while seasonal surpluses of fruit (including Alpine strawberries from the garden) are preserved in brandy for serving with home-made ice-cream. Aperitifs arrive with a basket of warm game chips 'that taste as if they have just been cooked', and whisky is taken rather more seriously than the three dozen wines. House French is £12.

CHEF: Allan Cull   PROPRIETORS: Allan and Eleanor Cull   OPEN: Tue to Sat D only 7 to 9.30 (all week for residents)   CLOSED: 15 Dec to 31 Mar   MEALS: Set D £19.50   SERVICE: not inc CARDS: Access, Visa   DETAILS: 50 seats. Private parties: 50 main room, 12 and 30 private rooms. Car park. Children's helpings. Smart dress preferred. No smoking in dining-room. Wheelchair access (also WC). Music   ACCOMMODATION: 6 rooms, all with bath/shower. TV. B&B £43.50 to £80. Deposit: £20. Children welcome. Dogs welcome. Garden

---

'We arrived at 8pm. Just before 9 o'clock a plate of amuse-gueules arrived. By this time we were ravenous, and the two offerings hardly touched the sides. The couple beyond us were clearly feeling even hungrier (they had been there longer) as they started to devour each other.' (On eating in Warwickshire)

map 11

Cellar 🍾 ⭐

24 East Green, Anstruther KY10 3AA	COOKING 3*
TEL: (01333) 310378 FAX: (01333) 312544	COST £24–£43

The entrance is under an archway and through a courtyard around the back. Orders are taken in the bar (decorated in various shades of brown), where tiny vol-au-vent appetisers filled with smoked haddock are served, followed at table by thin strands of pickled herring. Stone walls and sewing-machine tables produce a casual air in the dining-room, and there is a matter-of-factness about the food too. Fish is the main business, and apart from a few Mediterranean touches – some oils and dressings, perhaps – doesn't aim to be trendy. 'They make sure the fish is top quality, and cook it simply but properly,' was one reporter's view.

Dressed crab, or smoked haddock omelette is a typical way to begin. Shellfish bisque is dense and concentrated, with fathoms of flavour, while a crumbly pastry quiche of lobster, langoustine and smoked trout was the outstanding dish of one couple's meal: 'full of flavour, yet light and airy in texture.' Pan juices and butters are natural saucing agents, along with a small pot of hollandaise for halibut, the moist fish lightly breadcrumbed and accompanied by shreds of Savoy cabbage and bacon. The cooking has occasionally seemed to lack zip and excitement, resulting in a 'patchy' meal with 'indifferent' chocolate mousse for one pair of seasoned reporters, and there has been some 'inattentive' service, but this is a restaurant full of integrity, which doesn't take itself any more seriously than necessary, a place with a few rough edges, perhaps, but one to be celebrated and enjoyed.

The wine list is excellent, with a fair pricing policy clearly in evidence. Naturally, white wines dominate, with Alsace and white Burgundy taking up a large chunk of the list, but red wines are more than satisfactory. House wines are £12.50. CELLARMAN'S CHOICE: Mâcon Viré 1992, Dom. de Roally, £18.95.

CHEF/PROPRIETOR: Peter Jukes   OPEN: Fri and Sat L 12.30 to 1.30, Tue to Sat D 7 to 9.30   MEALS: alc L (main courses £7 to £12). Set D £26.50. BYO by arrangement   SERVICE: not inc, card slips closed   CARDS: Access, Amex, Delta, Switch, Visa   DETAILS: 30 seats. Private parties: 36 main room. Children's helpings. No children under 8. Smart dress preferred. No smoking in dining-room. Music

---

ARISAIG Highland   map 11

▲ *Arisaig House* 🍴 ⭐

Beasdale, by Arisaig PH39 4NR	
TEL: (01687) 450622 FAX: (01687) 450626	COOKING 2*
on A830, 3m E of Arisaig	COST £27–£49

Arisaig is a large grey-stone house, rebuilt in the 1930s after a fire, and now replete with formal gardens and splendid lochside views. In the dining-room, as the brochure has it, 'the chef's epicurean offerings give promise of the restoration of body and soul'. Since March 1996 Gary Robinson is the man charged with restoring your body. His CV bristles with country-house experience garnered at places that are nearly all *Guide* listings.

In the evenings a fixed-price menu operates, running to four courses and coffee with a choice of soup or salad after the starter. A certain flourish has come with the change of chef, so that codling meunière with a raspberry dressing might set the ball rolling, to be followed by cauliflower and coriander soup, and then maybe marinated venison with hazelnuts and juniper berries. Scallops briefly sauté in soy sauce, and a piece of well-timed salmon in a chive-scented butter sauce make fine, simple but attractively presented dishes for lunch. Citrus flavouring with fish is a favoured combination; orange with halibut, for example. Home-made ice-cream and shortbread are well reported, while those with a passion for elaboration might be tempted by chocolate and orange gâteau with mint crème anglaise. Service is formal but 'pleasant' and attentive. The wine list declines to stray beyond the confines of France, Italy, Spain and Germany, and the main focus is clarets and Burgundies at posh prices, although there is no doubting the quality of the producers. House wines are £14.50.

CHEF: Gary Robinson PROPRIETORS: Ruth, John and Andrew Smither OPEN: all week 12.30 to 2, 7.30 to 8.30 CLOSED: 31 Oct to 1 Apr MEALS: alc L (main courses £10). Set D £33.50. Light L available SERVICE: none, card slips closed CARDS: Access, Amex, Visa DETAILS: 36 seats. 20 seats outside. Private parties: 8 main room. Car park. No children under 10. Smart dress preferred. No smoking in dining-room. Wheelchair access (no WC). No music ACCOMMODATION: 14 rooms, all with bath/shower. TV. Phone. B&B £75 to £240. Deposit: £50. No children under 10. Afternoon teas. Garden (*The Which? Hotel Guide*)

AUCHENCAIRN Dumfries & Galloway   map 11

▲ *Collin House* ⅍

Auchencairn, Castle Douglas DG7 1QN
TEL: (01556) 640292   FAX: (01556) 640276   COOKING 2
off A711, 1m E of Auchencairn   COST £38–£46

The pink house looks particularly striking when rising from a blanket of snow, but the view over Auchencairn Bay is sumptuous at any time. Flowers bedeck the dining-room, its lush red walls and heavy drapes contributing a reassuring feeling of warmth. The drill is a four-course dinner menu, with soup at second, offering alternatives for starter and main and a choice of four desserts. Everyone eats at eight, the striking of an olde worlde dinner-gong signalling the off. Loch Rannoch smoked venison with melon makes a flavourful first course, as does mousse of Arbroath smokies with sauce vierge. Soups can vary from rich lobster bisque to a rather anaemic spinach version. Salmon trout cooked to retain translucence at the centre has been greatly approved, its fish stock sauce with cream and basil providing sensitive support. Good Scottish cheeses make a tempting alternative to puddings such as Drambuie parfait with chocolate sauce, or poached pear with ginger crème anglaise. Service is 'swift and friendly'. House Vin de Pays d'Oc starts the wines off at £8.85.

▲ *This symbol means accommodation is available.*

CHEF: John Wood   PROPRIETORS: Pam Hall and John Wood   OPEN: all week D only 7.30 for 8 (1 sitting)   CLOSED: Jan and Feb   MEALS: Set D £28   SERVICE: not inc, card slips closed   CARDS: Access, Amex, Visa   DETAILS: 16 seats. Private parties: 16 main room. Car park. No children under 11. No smoking in dining-room. No music   ACCOMMODATION: 6 rooms, all with bath/shower. TV. Phone. B&B £40 to £88. Deposit: £30. Children welcome. Dogs by arrangement. Garden (*The Which? Hotel Guide*)

AUCHMITHIE Angus   map 11

But 'n' Ben ✹ £

Auchmithie DD11 5SQ
TEL: (01241) 877223   COOKING 1
on coast, 3m NE of Arbroath, off A92   COST £13–£34

'Satisfaction for the hungry' is what is offered by the But 'n' Ben. With the North Sea a stone's throw away, it isn't surprising that fish is the star. The day's haul could include anything from lobster and crab to king scallops and salmon; the mighty fish platter includes a bit of everything, while renowned Arbroath smokies turn up in a soup and in a delicious griddled pancake. The kitchen also looks inland for Aberdeen Angus steaks, mince and tatties, and game pie. Puddings are displayed on a tiered trolley that reminded one visitor of 'a Women's Institute sale of work: big hearty cakes, tarts and pies' of the wholesome variety. Like everything else here, service is a family affair. Youngest son Ralph has put together a tourist collection of 40 single malts; otherwise there is a workaday list of 20 wines, with house wine £8.

CHEFS: Margaret and Angus Horn   PROPRIETORS: Margaret, Iain and Angus Horn   OPEN: Wed to Mon L 12 to 2.30, and high tea 4 to 5.30, Mon and Wed to Sat D 7 to 9   MEALS: alc (main courses £4.50 to £12.50)   SERVICE: not inc, card slips closed   CARDS: Access, Delta, Switch, Visa   DETAILS: 40 seats. Private parties: 40 main room. Car park. Vegetarian meals. Children's helpings. Smart dress preferred. No smoking in dining-room. Wheelchair access (also WC). No music

---

AUCHTERARDER Perthshire & Kinross   map 11

▲ Auchterarder House ▼ ✹

Auchterarder PH3 1DZ   COOKING 2
TEL: (01764) 663646   FAX: (01764) 662939   COST £24–£58

Grandeur and confidence are not uncommon in Scottish houses, but the combination at Auchterarder is neither intimidating nor remote. The space is pleasantly divided into library, drawing-room, billiard-room and conservatory, and overseen by dedicated owners who 'do not cut corners and do not impose themselves'. Without getting lost or feeling at all touristy, Kiernan Darnell's menu is a clever mixture of classical French, modern British and traditional Scottish.

The classical vein emerges in a Madeira-laced game consommé, or in a sausage made from guinea-fowl and pig's trotter and served with lentils. Home-made chutneys add zest: one of tomato and roasted pepper, for instance, to partner a soufflé of goats' cheese and caramelised onion. The bright, attractive ideas are based on sound cooking principles, and invention is gentle rather than showy, as in a smoked haddock and barley kedgeree served with trout fillet. Scotland contributes many of the ingredients – West Coast fish stew, Shetland salmon fillet with a Cheddar cheese rarebit, and Aberdeen Angus beef on a polenta cake – and it is good to see clootie dumpling making an appearance among desserts, here served with heather honey ice-cream and a warm whisky sauce. Classic French wines from Bordeaux, Burgundy, the Loire and the Rhône dominate a traditional and impressive list. Those in search of mature clarets will enjoy the venerable list of 'limited bottles' dating back to 1959. House wines are £13.50.

CHEF: Kiernan Darnell   PROPRIETORS: Mr and Mrs Ian Brown   OPEN: all week 12 to 2.30, 6 to 9.30   MEALS: Set L £15 to £18.50, Set D £27.50 to £37.50   SERVICE: not inc, card slips closed   CARDS: Access, Amex, Diners, Switch, Visa   DETAILS: 30 seats. Private parties: 50 main room, 30 and 50 private rooms. Car park. Children's helpings. Smart dress preferred L; jacket and tie D. No smoking in dining-room. Wheelchair access (no WC). No music   ACCOMMODATION: 15 rooms, all with bath/shower. TV. Phone. B&B £100 to £225. Rooms for disabled. Children welcome. Dogs welcome in bedrooms only. Afternoon teas. Garden (*The Which? Hotel Guide*)

AYR   South Ayrshire   map 11

Fouter's Bistro ⚡✶ | NEW ENTRY |

2A Academy Street, Ayr KA7 1HS   COOKING 1
TEL: (01292) 261391   FAX: (01292) 619323   COST £17–£46

'The emphasis is on quality produce, not décor,' summed up one reporter of this whitewashed basement with its stone floors, rickety cloth-covered tables, and baskets of cherries cheerily stencilled on the walls. Value for money brings locals back time and again, customers talk to each other, and an 'air of quiet enjoyment prevails'. Scottish produce is given pride of place: smoked salmon from Loch Fyne, local lamb, wild pigeon, and whatever turns up at Ayr's fish market. An inspector was well impressed by a first course fillet of cod – 'the quintessence of codliness, flaking on to the plate, grilled just so' – and a 'splendid slab of rare steak, prime British beef at its best', though saucing and vegetables might have been improved. Full-flavoured mature Cheddar and oozing Camembert in peak condition indicate that cheese is a worthwhile option, although it would be shame to miss the bread-and-butter pudding, chocolate terrine, and a 'farm-sized portion' of steamed ginger pudding, of which 'my domestic science teacher would have approved'. House French wine is from £12.50, and 11 wines are available by the glass.

CHEFS: Robert Brown and Laurie Black   PROPRIETORS: Laurie and Fran Black   OPEN: Tue to Sat L 12 to 2, Tue to Sun D 6.30 to 10 (late post-theatre D by arrangement)   CLOSED: 25 to 27 Dec, 1 to 3 Jan   MEALS: alc (main courses L £4 to £9.50, D £9 to £14.50). Set D £11.95 (2 courses)   SERVICE: not inc   CARDS: Access, Amex, Delta, Diners, Switch, Visa   DETAILS: 38 seats. Private parties: 20 main room. Children's helpings. Smart dress preferred. No smoking in 1 dining-room. Music. Air-conditioned

---

'The wine was decanted upon my asking, but could have done without the sneering and incredulous "DECANTED!" from the head waiter.' (On eating in Surrey)

▲ *Balgonie Country House* 💷✳

Braemar Place, Ballater AB35 5RQ
TEL/FAX: (013397) 55482   COOKING 2
off A93, on outskirts of Ballater   COST £25–£47

'It looks very much the kind of place we would like to stay at, Lottery permitting,' confessed one visitor to this well-kept and secluded Edwardian house with fine lawns, views and well-chosen paintings. Mr Finnie greets guests at the door, introduces himself and obviously takes a close interest in everything. There is a choice of four first and three main courses on a menu that changes daily, and local produce is the foundation, including some herbs and vegetables from the garden. The result might be a homely cream of broccoli soup, or a filo pastry parcel of finnan haddock and halibut on a smoked fish cream. Equally likely, though, is a hint of something from further afield, perhaps a tomato and coriander salsa to accompany a crabmeat strudel, or roast monkfish on a red onion and pepper confit with a warm basil vinaigrette.

Meals finish with a choice of two puddings, on one occasion a spiced apple pie with cinnamon crème anglaise, or white chocolate and rum mousse set on a rich dark chocolate sauce. The set dinner is not cheap, but 'given the style, ambience and situation we feel it represents reasonable value'. The wines are equally reasonable, with a sensible list providing something good from most wine regions. More than a handful are available by the glass, from £2.75.

CHEF: David J. Hindmarch   PROPRIETORS: John and Priscilla Finnie   OPEN: all week 12.30 to 2, 7 to 9 (L Mon to Sat by reservation only)   CLOSED: mid-Jan to mid-Feb   MEALS: Set L £16.50, Set D £28.50   SERVICE: not inc, card slips closed   CARDS: Access, Amex, Delta, Diners, Switch, Visa   DETAILS: 25 seats. Private parties: 32 main room. Car park. No children under 5. Jacket and tie. No smoking in dining-room. Music   ACCOMMODATION: 9 rooms, all with bath/shower. TV. Phone. B&B £55 to £100. Children welcome. Baby facilities. Dogs welcome in bedrooms only and if attended. Afternoon teas. Garden (*The Which? Hotel Guide*)

▲ *Darroch Learg* 🍽 💷✳

Braemar Road, Ballater AB35 5UX   COOKING 1*
TEL: (013397) 55443   FAX: (013397) 55252   COST £19–£41

Commanding a wooded hillside overlooking the Dee Valley, Darroch Learg is a family-run hotel aimed principally at sport-loving holidaymakers. A three-course dinner menu operates alongside a list of specials, and guests can hop between the two. The kitchen revels in abundant local supplies, bakes excellent bread, smokes salmon and rabbit, and stocks its larder with home-made provisions. New chef David Mutter believes in robust flavours and manages to carry them off with some flair. Monkfish might be served as a spicy starter with scallops and squid-ink pasta, or as a centrepiece with saffron sauce. Naturally reared Aberdeen Angus beef has been accompanied by red wine sauce, pigeon is paired with morels and 'two symbolic, marble-sized potatoes'. 'Excellent' puddings have included Williams pear in filo pastry with ginger butterscotch sauce. Service is first-class. The wine list continues to grow as it scours the globe in search of quality. House wines start at £11.50.

CHEF: David Mutter   PROPRIETORS: the Franks family   OPEN: Sun L 12.30 to 2, all week D 7 to 8.30 (9 Fri and Sat)   MEALS: Set L £12.75, Set D £23.75. Light L available   SERVICE: net prices, card slips closed   CARDS: Access, Amex, Delta, Diners, Switch, Visa   DETAILS: 48 seats. Private parties: 48 main room. Car park. Children's helpings. Smart dress preferred. No smoking in dining-room. No music   ACCOMMODATION: 18 rooms, all with bath/shower. TV. Phone. B&B £45 to £110. Deposit: £50. Children welcome. Baby facilities. Dogs welcome in bedrooms only. Afternoon teas. Garden

▲ *Green Inn* £✳

9 Victoria Road, Ballater AB35 5QQ	COOKING 3
TEL/FAX: (01339) 755701	COST £20–£42

The plain, three-storey, granite-fronted terraced house overlooking the kirk and village green is as serious as any restaurant about the Scottish credentials of its cooking, from wild salmon and local game to Cullen skink, Atholl brose, and whipkull, a Shetland equivalent of zabaglione using rum. 'To be honest, our hearts sank a bit when we read the menu,' admitted one couple, who feared the worst from 'over-elaborate preparation and strange combinations'. Fortunately, their qualms were largely groundless. Jeff Purves is quietly inventive, for example taking the Sauternes and foie gras theme a stage further than most by making the wine into a sorbet, the liver into a mousse, and advising customers to eat the two alternately. He also throws in a compote of tomatoes, but makes no recommendation about how to fit this into the sequence.

That the generally complex style of cooking works is due in large part to the combination of good materials and an understanding of how basic flavour combinations interact, as in fillet of salmon marinated in rock salt and Laphroaig whisky, with a delicate smokiness 'like Lapsang Souchong tea'. Even so, an inspector felt that less convoluted cooking might be even more effective, and the menu does offer to serve anything in simpler style on request. Steamed beetroot pudding is something of a rarity, and good chocolate terrine comes with a Drambuie and white chocolate ice-cream as well as a hot confit of Agen prunes in blackberry liqueur. Oatcakes and a small pot of dried fruit accompany a good variety of Scottish cheeses, and a basket of home-baked walnut bread does the rounds to begin. Wines are well chosen and fairly priced, with house wines £9.95.

CHEF: Jeffrey Purves   PROPRIETORS: Jeffrey and Carol Purves   OPEN: Sun L 12.30 to 1.45, all week D 7 to 9   CLOSED: Sun Nov to Mar, 1 week Oct, 2 weeks Nov   MEALS: alc (main courses £12.50 to £14.50). Set L £8.25 (2 courses) to £11.25   SERVICE: not inc   CARDS: Access, Amex, Delta, Visa   DETAILS: 34 seats. Private parties: 36 main room. Vegetarian meals. Children's helpings. Smart dress preferred. No smoking in dining-room. Wheelchair access (no WC). Music. Air-conditioned   ACCOMMODATION: 3 rooms, all with bath/shower. TV. D,B&B £60 to £90. Deposit: 10%. Children welcome. Dogs welcome. Garden

The Guide *office can quickly spot when a restaurateur is encouraging customers to write recommending inclusion – and sadly, several restaurants have been doing this in 1996. Such reports do not further a restaurant's cause. Please tell us if a restaurateur invites you to write to the* Guide.

▲ Tullich Lodge ⅝✳

Ballater AB35 5SB
TEL: (01339) 755406   FAX: (01339) 755397   COOKING 1
off A93, 1½m E of Ballater   COST £32–£38

'I sometimes think we may be a little old-fashioned,' writes Neil Bannister with considerable understatement. He and Hector Macdonald have run this pink-granite baronial-style mansion since 1968, time enough for the conifers outside the beautiful L-shaped mahogany dining-room to grow tall and fill up the windows. It has an air of gentility, and is 'a highly personal enterprise which we enjoyed tremendously'. The format remains much as it has always done: a four-course dinner with no choice (except whether to opt for cheese or dessert), with traditionally cooked beef, lamb or venison typically forming the centrepiece of a well-balanced meal. An inspection dinner began well enough with a dish of ripe avocado on a vivid-tasting tomato sauce, followed by a 'clear, dark, flavoursome' game consommé, but thereafter lost its way with burnt lamb chops, and a hot fruit salad overwhelmed by alcohol. Water comes from their own spring, and wines are predominantly French and up-market. French house wines are £8.

CHEF: Neil Bannister   PROPRIETORS: Hector Macdonald and Neil Bannister   OPEN: all week D only 7.30 to 8.45   CLOSED: end Oct to end Mar   MEALS: Set D £25; bar L available   SERVICE: not inc, card slips closed   CARDS: Access, Amex, Delta, Diners, Switch, Visa   DETAILS: 25 seats. Private parties: 20 main room. Car park. Children's helpings. Jacket and tie. No smoking in dining-room. Wheelchair access (also WC). No music   ACCOMMODATION: 10 rooms, all with bath/shower. TV. Phone. D,B&B £95 to £200. Children welcome. Baby facilities. Pets welcome in bedrooms only. Garden (*The Which? Hotel Guide*)

BALQUHIDDER Stirling   map 11

▲ Monachyle Mhor | NEW ENTRY |

Balquhidder, nr Lochearnhead FK19 8PQ   COOKING 1
TEL: (01877) 384622   FAX: (01877) 384305   COST £21–£33

The restaurant is in a stone farmhouse on a working farm, overlooks two lochs (Voil and Doine) and offers private fishing, deerstalking and grouse shooting. The welcome is the same for hikers and cyclists wanting a sandwich lunch outside as it is for full-scale eaters in the verandah dining-room, and service, from an endless stream of Australians and New Zealanders, 'makes up in friendliness what it lacks in polish'. An inspector summed up the appeal of the place: 'Ingredients are good, the helpings healthy, the food wholesome, sauces unambitious and the values real.'

Menus are well presented, readily understood, and avoid clichés, preferring instead to indulge in first courses of roast kidneys, fried sweetbreads and a cold herb soufflé, all of which appeared on one spring menu. Venison comes from the estate, langoustines are from the West Coast, and the impression is of a committed kitchen that turns out gamey-tasting guinea-fowl, 'unreservedly good' vegetables, and hot bread-and-butter soufflé ('whose only fault was that it was too small'). A serviceable list of fairly priced wines begins with house French at £8.50.

CHEFS: Jean and Tom Lewis   PROPRIETORS: Jean and Rob Lewis   OPEN: all week 12 to 2, 7 to 9   MEALS: Set L £15, Set D £18 to £21   SERVICE: not inc, card slips closed   CARDS: Access, Visa   DETAILS: 32 seats. 20 seats outside. Private parties: 32 main room, 12 private room. Car park. Vegetarian meals. No children under 10. Wheelchair access (also women's WC). No music   ACCOMMODATION: 10 rooms, all with bath/shower. Phone. B&B £37.50 to £70. Deposit: £20. No children under 10. Afternoon teas. Garden. Fishing

BLAIRGOWRIE Perthshire & Kinross	map 11

▲ *Kinloch House* ♥ ⅝✳

by Blairgowrie, PH10 6SG	
TEL: (01250) 884237 FAX: (01250) 884333	COOKING 2
on A923, 3m W of Blairgowrie towards Dunkeld	COST £21–£56

Easily found along the main road, and set in 25 acres of grounds, this looks the part of a country-house hotel: clean and stylish inside with smart new oak panelling, and a man in a kilt to serve drinks and take orders. David (for it is he) and Sarah Shentall supervise the service with that blend of nonchalance and authority that proprietors seem to acquire. Dinner is where the action is: four courses with a generous choice, and supplements for a few items. Dedication to the Highland larder is apparent in salmon – fresh, smoked or marinated in whisky with honey and herbs – and in fillet of Aberdeen Angus beef, one version of which comes with a typically rich sauce of Drambuie, mushrooms and cream.

Relief for travellers who wish to take a break from the Highland trail comes in the form of spinach roulade, pasta, or a baked pork cutlet. Lunch is a lighter affair and did not impress an inspector. Puddings of warm orange clafoutis or chocolate and rose-water mousse are balanced by a savoury alternative such as devilled kidneys on toast. Wines are mostly French, with claret getting the full treatment, grouped by vintage and dating back to 1970. Two pages of half-bottles and a handful of bin-ends fill out the list. House white Burgundy is £11.90.

CHEF: Bill McNicoll   PROPRIETORS: David and Sarah Shentall   OPEN: all week 12.30 to 2, 7 to 9.15   CLOSED: 18 to 30 Dec   MEALS: Set L £14.95, Set D £28.90; bar food available all week   SERVICE: none, card slips closed   CARDS: Access, Amex, Delta, Diners, Switch, Visa   DETAILS: 55 seats. Private parties: 25 private room. Car park. Children's helpings. No children under 7 D. Jacket and tie. No smoking in dining-room. Wheelchair access (also WC). No music   ACCOMMODATION: 21 rooms, all with bath/shower. TV. Phone. D,B&B £79 to £195. Rooms for disabled. Children welcome. Baby facilities. Dogs welcome by arrangement. Afternoon teas. Garden. Fishing (*The Which? Hotel Guide*)

CAIRNDOW Argyll & Bute	map 11

Loch Fyne Oyster Bar ⅝✳

Clachan Farm, Cairndow PA26 8BH	
TEL: (01499) 600236 FAX: (01499) 600234	COOKING 1*
on A83, at head of Loch Fyne	COST £18–£63

The low whitewashed building beside the loch exemplifies the virtues of simplicity and flexibility. Rooms are well laid out, furnished in pine and larch, and service is sharp: no sooner do you sit down than a basket of bread arrives with a pot of butter and a menu. The delight is all-day opening and a completely free-ranging choice, with daily specials of fish and shellfish chalked on boards behind the service counter. This is the largest oyster producer in Scotland, and the bivalves are served plain or fancy: on ice with pork sausages, or baked with spinach and Mornay sauce. Smoked salmon is as good as it comes – in two strengths of cure, as well as hot-kiln smoked – and fresh fish has impressed: breadcrumbed haddock with thin chips and tartare sauce was sweetly fresh, moist and tasty for an inspector, 'as good a piece of haddock as I recall eating'. Two dozen fairly priced wines include eight half-bottles and six by the glass.

CHEF: Morag Keith   PROPRIETOR: Loch Fyne Oysters Ltd   OPEN: all week 9am to 9pm (6pm weekdays 31 Oct to 31 Mar)   CLOSED: 25 and 26 Dec, 1 Jan   MEALS: alc (main courses £5 to £29.50)   SERVICE: not inc   CARDS: Access, Delta, Diners, Switch, Visa   DETAILS: 80 seats. 20 seats outside. Private parties: 45 main room. Car park. Vegetarian meals. Children's helpings. No smoking in 1 dining-room. Wheelchair access (also WC). Music

---

CANONBIE Dumfries & Galloway   map 11

▲ *Riverside Inn* ♟ ⁵⅟✳

Canonbie DG14 0UX
TEL: (01387) 371295 and 371512   COOKING 2
off A7, just over the border   COST £25–£35

'We arrived tired after our journey from Devon, to warmth and welcome,' wrote one grateful couple visiting this black and white seventeenth-century house near the River Esk. It attracts a 'mixed and cheerful' bag of customers – from salmon fishermen to families to visitors from abroad – and still feels like an inn, especially in the informal bar, with sewing-machine tables and a daily-changing blackboard menu of, say, herring fillet in oatmeal, a 'good brown stew' of beef and Guinness, and grilled ham with eggs.

A shorter three-course dinner, in addition to the five-course one, is understandably proving popular. Most of the food is simply cooked: chargrilled steak, poached salmon, late summer pudding, and 'a splendid ice-cream made with oatmeal and whisky'. That down-to-earth approach is appreciated: 'Nothing was pretentious or particularly complicated, but great care had been taken.' Susan Phillips is 'restrained and efficient but friendly,' while Robert Phillips is 'jovial, jaunty and capable'. Wines have been chosen with meticulous care. The 72-strong list packs in many notable producers, and prices are enticingly low. House wines, from Plaimont, are £8.45. CELLARMAN'S CHOICE: Selaks Sauvignon Blanc 1993, Auckland, New Zealand, £13.20; Brouilly 1993, Ch. Thivin, £13.75.

CHEFS/PROPRIETORS: Robert and Susan Phillips   OPEN: Tue to Sat D only 7.30 to 8.30, L by arrangement.   CLOSED: 2 weeks Nov, 25 and 26 Dec, 1 and 2 Jan, 2 weeks Feb   MEALS: Set D £18.50 to £22.50. BYO by arrangement. Bar meals available   SERVICE: not inc, card slips closed   CARDS: Access, Delta, Diners, Switch, Visa   DETAILS: 24 seats. 16 seats outside. Private parties: 24 main room. Car park. Vegetarian meals. Children's helpings. Smart dress preferred. No smoking in dining-room. No music   ACCOMMODATION: 7 rooms, all with bath/shower. TV. B&B £55 to £85. Deposit: £10. Rooms for disabled. Children welcome. Dogs by arrangement. Garden

COLBOST Highland   map 11

Three Chimneys ▼ ⁵✲

Colbost, by Dunvegan IV55 8ZT
TEL: (01470) 511258   COOKING 2
on B884, 4m W of Dunvegan   COST £23–£65

A few scattered dwellings and a jetty for the fishing boats is about all there is to
Colbost, apart from the museum and this pair of white-washed crofters' cottages
with rough stone walls and rustic furniture. Fish naturally constitutes a
significant part of the output, ranging from Parton Bree (crab soup) through
scallops in red pepper cream, or skate wing with lime butter, to a monster
seafood platter (as part of a three course meal for two). The flexible *carte* has
offered a rich, creamy, pink bisque packed full of lobster and prawns, and a salad
of large langoustines, 'fresh that day, firm and sweet'.

What with dinner, a generous spread at lunch, and daytime teas and coffees, 'an
awful lot of cooking goes on here'. At inspection it was felt that the Spears might
be spreading their talents a bit widely, with a tendency to graft on fashionable
ingredients to dishes that didn't need them, such as a blob of pesto added to an
exceptionally good, thick, moist slab of halibut with an already good lemon
sauce. Puddings have included 'homely' blackcurrant torte with a rustic
cinnamon ice-cream. Service has been described as 'sunny' and 'smiling',
though on one occasion it was decidedly slow. The excellent wine list covers
myriad styles and regions, puts high store by quality yet provides enough to
choose from at under £20. Italian house wine is £10.75. CELLARMAN'S CHOICE:
Pinot Blanc Vieilles Vignes 1994, Meyer-Fonne, £14.75; Gabarinza 1991,
Heinrich, Burgenland, Austria, £25.95.

CHEFS: Shirley Spear, Ann Knight, Andrew McInnes and Danny Jackson   PROPRIETORS: Eddie
and Shirley Spear   OPEN: Mon to Sat 12.30 to 2, 7 to 9 (Sun D Easter and Whitsun only)
CLOSED: Nov to Mar   MEALS: alc (main courses L £6 to £27.50. D £13.50 to £27.50). Minimum
3.50 L. Minimum 22.50 D. Light meals and afternoon tea   SERVICE: not inc   CARDS: Access,
Switch, Visa   DETAILS: 30 seats. 8 seats outside. Private parties: 18 main room, 10 and 18
private rooms. Car park. Vegetarian meals. No children under 10D. Smart dress preferred. No
smoking in dining-room. Music

CRINAN Argyll & Bute   map 11

▲ Crinan Hotel, Lock 16 ▼ ⁵✲

Crinan PA31 8SR
TEL/FAX: (01546) 830261   FAX: (01546) 830292   COOKING 1
off A816, 6m NW of Lochgilphead   COST £49–£59

Crinan perches on the coast opposite the Isle of Jura, and this white-painted
family-run hotel has been part of the small fishing village for some two
centuries. It offers snacks at lunch-time, and dinner in the Westward restaurant,
but the star turn is Lock 16, which opens from May to September, for dinner only
on five nights a week, weather permitting. The reason for the weather's
controlling influence is that main courses of lobster from the Sound of Jura, or
jumbo prawns from Corryvrechan, are landed just a couple of hours beforehand.

Or not, as the case may be: it is best to ring ahead and make sure. They are served very simply with melted butter, preceded by a plate of smoked salmon, and perhaps Loch Fyne clams or Loch Craignish mussels before that. Finish with cheese, or perhaps strawberry mille-feuille.

The lengthy wine list contains many bottles that would pair up well with seafood, and much else besides. The annotations on each wine are helpful and precise. French house wines are £9.95. CELLARMAN'S CHOICE: Sancerre, Les Bruyères 1993, L. Thomas, £23; Bonnes-Mares 1992, Georges Roumier, £72.

CHEF: Nick Ryan   PROPRIETORS: Nick and Frances Ryan   OPEN: Tue to Sat D only 8 (1 sitting) CLOSED: 1 Oct to 30 Apr   MEALS: Set D £40. Bar L available, and D in Westward restaurant. SERVICE: not inc, card slips closed   CARDS: Access, Amex, Switch, Visa   DETAILS: 22 seats. Private parties: 22 main room. Car park. Children's helpings. Jacket and tie. No smoking in dining-room. Wheelchair access (also WC). No music   ACCOMMODATION: 22 rooms, all with bath/shower. TV. Phone. D,B&B £75 to £230. Deposit: £50. Children welcome. Dogs welcome. Afternoon teas. Garden (*The Which? Hotel Guide*)

CUPAR Fife   map 11

Ostlers Close ▼

25 Bonnygate, Cupar KY15 4BU	COOKING 3
TEL: (01334) 655574	COST £22–£45

So successful is the Grahams' formula that their small, modestly appointed restaurant changes little from year to year. Simple prints on off-white walls, and serviceable wooden tables and chairs are still in place. Only the menus are different from day to day. They make use of fish and seafood from the Fife coast, ducks from a local free-range supplier, and a cornucopia of wild mushrooms that they glean themselves.

A first course of seafood with pesto delivers three sorts of fish (but not shellfish) including accurately cooked and excellent salmon, and a rustic version of pesto that leaves the garlic, pine-nuts and basil in large chunks. A main course of duck confit with salted pork and Puy lentils is powerfully impressive, with crisp-skinned meat in a good rich stock. Properly cooked halibut has been let down by a watery basil butter sauce, but vegetable accompaniments are hugely imaginative: fried leeks, for example, along with fine ratatouille and a slice of spinach quiche. Apple and calvados sponge with vanilla custard, and honey nougat ice-cream on a coffee caramel sauce are the style of pudding to expect. Amanda Graham's amiably chatty front-of-house approach succeeds in putting everybody at ease. Wines are a lively bunch, with many good bottles from the New World, a wide choice of half-bottles and a quartet of fruity house wines from France and Australia which start at £7.95. CELLARMAN'S CHOICE: C.J. Pask Sauvignon Blanc 1994, Marlborough, New Zealand, £14.25; Rioja Crianza 1990, Bodegas Amezola, £13.25

CHEF: Jimmy Graham   PROPRIETORS: Jimmy and Amanda Graham   OPEN: Tue to Sat 12.15 to 2, 7 to 9.30   CLOSED: 25 and 26 Dec, 1 Jan   MEALS: alc (main courses L £8.50 to £11, D £15 to £17)   SERVICE: not inc, card slips closed   CARDS: Access, Amex, Delta, Switch, Visa   DETAILS: 26 seats. Private parties: 22 main room. Children helpings. No children under 6 D. No smoking while others eat. No music

SCOTLAND

DALRY   North Ayrshire   map 11

Braidwoods ⁵⁺   NEW ENTRY

Drumastle Mill Cottage, by Dalry KA24 4LN
TEL: (01294) 833544   COOKING 2
1m off A737 on Dalry to Saltcoats road   COST £23–£44

Two tiny whitewashed cottages stand side by side in rolling Ayrshire countryside. The Braidwoods live in one, and the other is a two-roomed restaurant,
simply decorated in muted blue. This is a neat, compact operation that has
attracted a loyal following since opening in the summer of 1994. Although the
atmosphere is of family and cottage, the organisation is highly professional.
There is no lounge, so it is straight to table where drinks and canapés are served
and a short menu is produced. Lunch is considered 'a real bargain' and might
offer rillettes of smoked and fresh salmon, baked fillet of brill with ratatouille,
and a chilled lime and lemon cream on a rhubarb compote.

At dinner a second course of Parmesan tart, or sweetcorn soup with smoked
haddock might follow a salad of pigeon breast. 'Everything including the
vegetables looked and tasted freshly cooked,' noted one visitor whose party
enjoyed baked fillet of brill, and honey-glazed breast of Gressingham duck.
Helpings are 'generous' and desserts are 'outstanding', according to a pair of
reporters who finished with rhubarb crème brûlée, and a hot apple pastry with
caramel sauce and cinnamon ice-cream. Service is cheerful, and the well-chosen
wine list is both varied and fairly priced. House wines start at £10.95.

CHEFS/PROPRIETORS: Keith and Nicola Braidwood   OPEN: Wed to Sun L 12 to 1.45, Tue to Sat D
7 to 9   CLOSED: first 3 weeks Jan, last week Sept, first week Oct   MEALS: Set L £13.50 (2
courses) to £15.50, Set D £24.50 (2 courses) to £27.50   SERVICE: not inc, card slips closed
CARDS: Access, Amex, Delta, Switch, Visa   DETAILS: 24 seats. Private parties: 12 main room.
Car park. No children under 12. Smart dress preferred. No smoking in dining-room. No music

DERVAIG   Argyll & Bute   map 11

▲ *Druimard Country House* ⁵⁺

Dervaig PA75 6QW
TEL: (01688) 400345 and 400291   COOKING 1
FAX: (01688) 400345   COST £26–£36

This restored Victorian country house stands on a hillside overlooking Glen
Bellart, close to Mull Little Theatre. Shakespearian posters in the conservatory
hint at the close ties, and the set-up is a simple one of early dinners, though there
is no sense of a quick fix about the menu. A bustling, smiling Wendy Hubbard
makes just about everything on the premises, using local seafood and traditionally reared meat from native breeds. Wild Mull salmon might be served
with a sharp sorrel and lime sauce, local crab has appeared as a salad, and wild
mushrooms have turned up in filo pastry tartlets and as an accompaniment to
fillet of Aberdeen Angus beef. Cheeses are as proudly regional as everything else
– Mull Cheddar, Inverloch and Cairnsmore, for example – while desserts are in
the homely style of apple and redcurrant crumble cake. Around three dozen
simple wines rarely stray above £15. House wines are £8.95.

CHEF: Wendy Hubbard PROPRIETORS: Haydn and Wendy Hubbard OPEN: Mon to Sat D only
6.30 to 8.30 (residents only Sun) CLOSED: Nov to Mar MEALS: Set D £17.50 SERVICE: not
inc CARDS: Access, Visa DETAILS: 30 seats. Private parties: 30 main room. Car park.
Vegetarian meals. Children's helpings. Smart dress preferred. No smoking in dining-room.
Music ACCOMMODATION: 6 rooms, all with bath/shower. TV. Phone. D,B&B £61.50 to £118.
Deposit: £45. Children welcome. Dogs welcome in bedrooms only. Garden (*The Which? Hotel
Guide*)

DRYBRIDGE Moray   map 11

Old Monastery ✻

Drybridge AB56 2JB
TEL: (01542) 832660
2½m S of Buckie, just over 2m S   COOKING 1*
of junction of A98 and A942   COST £23–£49

The Grays will have been here ten years in 1997, sharing their view across the
Moray Firth with visitors who have carried on up the hill from the crossroads,
ignoring the sign for Drybridge, and landed on the doorstep of this small but
sympathetic ecclesiastical conversion. The inner sanctum of what was a retreat
for Benedictine monks is now a convivial eating-place, with a high ceiling that
gives a feeling of space.

The generous *carte* is in simple Franco-Scottish mould, given to honest
cooking using proper ingredients. The kitchen yields Aberdeen Angus beef, fish
and shellfish, and furred and feathered game. While deep-fried Brie, or scampi
and scallop thermidor may not hold many surprises, the rich French onion soup
is made with good stock, venison is served pink – 'rustic but tasting good' – and
vegetables are plentiful and cooked just right. Alcohol trickles through a few
dishes, not least the puddings, and one reporter came away impressed by a
lemon tart, 'its lightness a lesson to many'. The wine list is an astutely assembled
selection of 80 bins from around the world, together with succinct tasting notes
and an impressive array of half-bottles. House wines start at around £10.50.

CHEF: Douglas Gray PROPRIETORS: Douglas and Maureen Gray OPEN: Tue to Sat 12 to 1.30, 7
to 9 (9.45 Sat) CLOSED: 3 weeks Jan, 2 weeks Nov MEALS: alc (main courses £6.50 to £17)
SERVICE: not inc, card slips closed CARDS: Access, Amex, Switch, Visa DETAILS: 45 seats.
Private parties: 45 main room. Car park. Vegetarian meals. Children's helpings. No children
under 8. Smart dress preferred. No smoking in dining-room. Music

---

DUNKELD Perthshire & Kinross   map 11

▲ Kinnaird ✻ 🍾

Kinnaird Estate, by Dunkeld PH8 0LB
TEL: (01796) 482440 FAX: (01796) 482289
from A9 2m N of Dunkeld, take B898, signposted   COOKING 3
Kinnaird, for 4½m   COST £35–£63

'Kinnaird is a fantastic place,' enthused one reporter. Everything is on a grand
scale – from the estate (9,000 acres) to 'massive' bedrooms to a large and
comfortable lounge – and the tastefully decorated Victorian hunting-lodge has a

519

penchant for open fires, even on warm days. Luxurious surroundings have a way of setting up expectations about the food, and sending kitchens in search of lobster and foie gras to meet them. Fortunately John Webber, and not the building, is in charge, so although there may be an occasional indulgence along the lines of a risotto of white truffle and ceps, there may also be humble braised lamb shank.

The 'mainstream modern cooking' relies on seafood from Skye, Tay salmon and local game, with daily dishes supplementing the standard set-price menus according to circumstance. Although a hot mousse of turbot very obviously requires nifty handling, the kitchen does not set out to impress with showy and complicated techniques. With commendable restraint it serves a simple brochette of scallops, or pan-fried fillet of salmon, and has turned out, for example, 'absolutely perfectly cooked quail' on a bed of 'delicious leaves' with a walnut and sherry vinegar dressing. Despite this, dried morels, or raspberries in April, indicate that the kitchen's commitment to seasonal foods can be overridden. And at inspection, ravioli (enclosing rabbit and morel) had little flavour and a poor texture, and halibut was overcooked and suffered an excess of soy. Service 'is able to gauge what degree of informality you require' and supply it, and the manager is 'exceptional'.

The sheer scope of the wine list impresses. Here is an outstanding range of clarets and Burgundies, including many mature vintages, as well as a broad sweep of producers from outside France, and prodigious quantities of half-bottles. House wines are £16. CELLARMAN'S CHOICE: Chablis premier cru Vaillons 1993, Dom. Billaud-Simon, £30; Hollick Pinot Noir 1993, Coonawarra, S. Australia, £28.

CHEF: John Webber PROPRIETOR: Constance Ward OPEN: all week 12.30 to 1.45, 7.30 to 9.30 CLOSED: Mon to Thur from 6 Jan to 16 Mar MEALS: Set L £19.50 (2 courses) to £24, Set D £39.50. BYO by arrangement SERVICE: not inc, card slips closed CARDS: Access, Amex, Switch, Visa DETAILS: 35 seats. Private parties: 25 main room, 25 private room. Car park. No children under 12. Jacket and tie D. No smoking in dining-room. Wheelchair access (also WC). No music ACCOMMODATION: 9 rooms, all with bath/shower. TV. Phone. D,B&B £175 to £355. No children under 12. Dogs welcome. Afternoon teas. Garden. Fishing (*The Which? Hotel Guide*)

DUNVEGAN Highland map 11

▲ *Harlosh House*

Dunvegan IV55 8ZG
TEL/FAX: (01470) 521367 COOKING **2***
off A863, 3m S of Dunvegan COST £35–£42

The attractive eighteenth-century whitewashed house is a bare 50 yards from the shore, with views of the distant Cuillins on a clear day, and small tastefully decorated rooms that make it feel 'homely and friendly'. A set menu is posted by the front door in the afternoon: four courses designed for fish lovers, with no choice before pudding. 'I do venison on a Sunday night,' writes Peter Elford, 'for a reason I don't fully understand.' Flavours may be restrained rather than vivid – the food is 'not exciting or thrilling' – but the style is consistent, with a set dinner to please all tastes, and the absence of distracting elements or superfluous decoration is welcome.

An inspector who began with a timbale of flaked smoked haddock held together by a wobblingly creamy custard felt that Peter Elford 'thought about, and tasted, the food he was serving'. That also went for a soup that combined 'the essence of green peas with an undercurrent of mint', and a main course of poached halibut in a buttery sauce full of threads of dill. If it isn't halibut, the centrepiece is likely to be equally fleshy turbot or monkfish. Triple chocolate terrine with coffee sauce, and ginger pudding with Glendale rhubarb have both impressed, and meticulous attention to detail includes 'outstandingly good, freshly baked bread'. Sixty-plus wines are varied, well chosen and decently priced. House South African is £9.80.

CHEF: Peter Elford   PROPRIETORS: Peter and Lindsey Elford   OPEN: all week D only 6.30 to 8.30   CLOSED: mid-Oct to Easter   MEALS: Set D £24.50   SERVICE: not inc, card slips closed   CARDS: Access, Switch, Visa   DETAILS: 18 seats. Car park. Children's helpings. No smoking in dining-room. Wheelchair access (no WC). Music   ACCOMMODATION: 6 rooms, all with bath/shower. B&B £68 to £90. Deposit: £50. Children welcome. Baby facilities. Afternoon teas. Garden (*The Which? Hotel Guide*)

EDINBURGH Edinburgh   map 11

Atrium ♟

10 Cambridge Street, Edinburgh EH1 2ED   COOKING 3
TEL: (0131) 228 8882   FAX: (0131) 228 8808   COST £25–£45

The Atrium is well placed near the Usher Hall and Traverse Theatre, but its strong and idiosyncratic design statement – 'modern Scottish', they call it – causes a few difficulties. Railway sleepers and wire sculptures may be 'interesting to look at, but not comfortable to live with', and the lighting is generally considered too dim for customers to read the menu: one couple took a torch for that express purpose on their second visit. Fish, game and vegetables take up a large part of the breathlessly modern menu, which counts olive oil, balsamic vinegar, polenta, roasted tomatoes, dill pesto and wild rice among its fashionable accessories.

Timing of meat and fish is precise enough to turn out a piece of cod 'just on the cusp between transparent and translucent', and vegetable accompaniments are generally well matched – celeriac purée with rare pigeon, for example. Some flavour combinations sound better than they taste, but among successes have been 'outstanding' wild mushroom soup, and an impressive salad 'marrying the sweet succulence of plump scallops with the saltiness of Parmesan cheese and slices of salami'. Whatever else, the food has a buzz about it, a certain panache, that has lingered well beyond the initial excitement it caused.

Poached pears and baked bananas, despite their alliteration, were an anticlimax for one couple, though a 'figgy fruit compote was very, very good'. Cheerful and friendly staff are eager to please, and wines are many and varied, with a good selection by the glass, including nine sherries. Half-bottles, fine and rare wines and spirits take up a fair chunk of the list. CELLARMAN'S CHOICE: Entre-Deux-Mers, Ch. de Castelneau 1992, £16.50; Crianza 1989, Valduero, Spain, £15.75.

CHEF: Andrew Radford   PROPRIETORS: Andrew and Lisa Radford   OPEN: Mon to Fri L 12 to 2.30, Mon to Sat D 6 to 10.30 (11 during Festival)   MEALS: alc (main courses £7.50 to £16.50). Snack L available. BYO £3.50   SERVICE: not inc   CARDS: Access, Amex, Switch, Visa   DETAILS: 70 seats. 20 seats outside. Private parties: 100 main room. Vegetarian meals. Children's helpings. Wheelchair access (also WC). No music. Air-conditioned

Café Saint-Honoré ¾※

NEW ENTRY

34 N.W. Thistle Street Lane, Edinburgh EH2 1EA   COOKING 1
TEL: (0131) 226 2211   COST £19–£42

Warm colours beckon passers-by to this French-style city-centre café. 'A welcome addition to the Edinburgh eating scene,' summed up one reporter. Eat at wooden tables, and prepare for a menu where dishes know no culinary boundaries, judging by baked fillet of cod with couscous, chillies and mozarella, or beef bourguignonne with champ potatoes. Warm salads are a feature – chicken livers, bacon, black pudding and wild mushrooms on one occasion, rabbit, lamb kidney and Puy lentils on another – as are soups, terrines, tartlets and fish-cakes. Main courses show an enthusiast's eye for game, fowl, offal and 'moist and flavoursome' fish, including red snapper with lemon, capers and chorizo. Dishes may not always deliver the excitement they promise, and the habit of charging 50p for bread seems designed to get up punters' noses, but the food has some notable successes, the place is unstuffy, and an enthusiastic team works well together. The wine list squeezes a good number of grape varieties into a small compass, and prices are fair. House wines are £9

CHEFS: Christopher Colverson and Stephen Smyth   PROPRIETORS: Christopher Colverson and P.J. Mallet   OPEN: Mon to Fri L 12 to 2.15, Mon to Sat D 7 to 10.30 (open all week during festival)   CLOSED: 25 and 26 Dec, 2 weeks Easter, 1 week Oct   MEALS: alc (main courses L £6 to £10.50, D £14 to £15.50)   SERVICE: not inc   CARDS: Access, Amex, Delta, Diners, Switch, Visa   DETAILS: 45 seats. Private parties: 30 main room, 18 private room. Vegetarian meals. Children's helpings. No smoking in dining-room. Wheelchair access (no WC). Music

Denzler's 121

121 Constitution Street, Leith, Edinburgh EH6 7AE   COOKING 1
TEL: (0131) 554 3268   FAX: (0131) 467 7239   COST £18–£36

A former bank is perhaps an appropriate home for a Swiss chef, although the Denzlers don't play on the cowbell and alp-horn motif, preferring instead the effect of light wood and brass, and opting to hang the walls with contemporary Scottish pictures. Sämi Denzler's repertoire reflects the influences of France, Italy and Germany on his native cooking, and takes in escalope of veal valaisanne (with a mushroom and cream sauce), stecchini alla ticinese (pork with polenta), and Kalbsbratwurst (veal sausage). Air-dried Swiss beef and ham feature, too, and spätzli or pommes berrichonne (cooked with onion, bacon and stock) are the usual main-course accompaniments. There is no hint of revenge in a tourte glacé Montezuma, which is a layered construction of banana mousse, chocolate parfait and biscuit served with a hot rum sauce, but there are the anticipated Apfelstrudel, and coupe nesselrode of meringue, chestnut and whipped cream. A varied selection of wines combines quality, interest and value. House wines are £10.65 a litre.

CHEFS: Sämi Denzler and Ian Gordon   PROPRIETORS: Sämi and Pat Denzler   OPEN: Tue to Fri L 12 to 2, Tue to Sat D 6.30 to 10   CLOSED: 2 weeks end July   MEALS: alc (main courses £7 to £12). Set L £7.95 (2 courses, inc wine), Set D £17.95   SERVICE: net prices, card slips closed CARDS: Access, Amex, Delta, Diners, Switch, Visa   DETAILS: 70 seats. Private parties: 75 main room. Vegetarian meals. Children welcome. Smart dress preferred. Wheelchair access (no WC). No music

Kalpna ⚡✗

2–3 St Patrick Square, Edinburgh EH8 9EZ   COOKING 1*
TEL: (0131) 667 9890   COST £22–£40

Kalpna lays claim to being the best-known Indian vegetarian restaurant in Scotland. With Ajay Bhartdwaj now in sole charge here, cooking remains a fascinating cocktail of meatless dishes drawn from Gujarat, South India and Rajasthan. The menu kicks off with bhel pooris, pakoras, dosais and the like before graduating to specialities such as khoya kaju (with cashew-nuts, sultanas, pistachios and nutmeg) and dam aloo 'Kashmere' (baked stuffed potatoes with two sauces, one of almonds, the other tomato-based). Rice includes brown as well as basmati, and there is a vegan thali. Lunchtime buffets (a more elaborate spread is also served on Wednesday evenings) are an unbeatable deal. The wine list is well thought out and worth considering. House wine is £8.50.

CHEF/PROPRIETOR: Ajay Bhartdwaj   OPEN: Mon to Fri L 12 to 2, all week D 5.30 (6 Sun) to 10.30 (11 Sat, 10.30 Sun)   CLOSED: 25 and 26 Dec   MEALS: alc (main courses £4.50 to £7.50). Set L £4.50, Set D Wed £8.50 (2 courses)   SERVICE: 10%, card slips closed   CARDS: Access, Diners, Visa   DETAILS: 65 seats. Private parties: 30 main room. Vegetarian meals. Children's helpings. Smart dress preferred. No smoking in dining-room. Wheelchair access (no WC). Music

Kelly's

46 West Richmond Street, Edinburgh EH8 9DZ   COOKING 2
TEL: (0131) 668 3847   FAX: (0131) 662 1277   COST £32–£38

Open only four evenings a week, this small-scale restaurant operates in Anglo-French mode, from husband-and-wife teamwork down to the short three-course menu. Light lunches and pre-theatre suppers (the Festival Theatre is nearby) are served in the gallery next door. Among the crossover ideas are a tomato tartlet with smoked Argyll ham, and salmon-cakes served with rouille. There is no desire to broaden the framework with exotic spices, just a gentle use of, for example, sweet pepper chutney to chivvy up a brandied Stilton pâté and its apple and celery salad. Alcohol makes its way into a few sauces, including Noilly Prat and tarragon (for grilled halibut), Madeira with guinea-fowl, and port and rosemary for a quietly inventive dish of roast breast of pigeon which is served on an artichoke and swede rösti, together with a filo parcel of minced lamb, Puy lentils and garlic. Eleven wines are sold by the glass at £2; house wines are £10 a bottle.

SCOTLAND

CHEF: Jacqueline Kelly   PROPRIETORS: Jeffrey and Jacqueline Kelly   OPEN: Wed to Sat D only 7 to 10; L by arrangement   CLOSED: first week Jan, Oct   MEALS: Set D £22   SERVICE: not inc   CARDS: Access, Amex, Delta, Switch, Visa   DETAILS: 30 seats. Private parties: 32 main room, 24 private room. Vegetarian meals. Children's helpings. No children under 6. Smart dress preferred. No smoking in dining-room before 9.30. Wheelchair access (also WC). Music

Martins ▯ ⁵⋇

| 70 Rose Street North Lane, Edinburgh EH2 3DX | COOKING 2 |
| TEL: (0131) 225 3106 | COST £35–£57 |

Martin and Gay Irons are justly proud of their decade-long commitment to wild and organic foods, a philosophy that has stood them in good stead at this comfortable back-alley restaurant in one of Edinburgh's less beguiling quarters. The kitchen is run on prudent lines, offering short menus to minimise waste, using what is seasonally available and changing daily. Saffron tagliatelle with scallops, tomato and capers makes a vivid first course, while soups mix flavours boldly in the likes of apple, celery and blue cheese. Main courses marshal batteries of ingredients in order to make their statements. A tuna steak is chargrilled with shiitake mushrooms, accompanied by an avocado and tomato compote and sauced with basil-scented beurre blanc. Apricots and wild rice go into roasted quail, which comes with broccoli and a sauce of lemon and honey. The desire not to overfeed people carries through to desserts of elderflower and grape sorbet, cardamom ice-cream with prune and apricot compote, and chocolate parfait with nectarines and crème fraîche.

Wines are chosen with care. Highlights are the Alsace whites of Rolly-Gassmann, two Cloudy Bay wines from New Zealand and a handful of intriguing Loire bottles. French and Italian house wines are £9.95. CELLARMAN'S CHOICE: Ashbrook Sauvignon Blanc 1992, Margaret River, Western Australia, £8.25 (half-bottle); Bonny Doon 'Le Sophiste' 1992, California, £35.25.

CHEFS: Forbes Stott, Peter Banks and Andrew Urquhart   PROPRIETORS: Martin and Gay Irons   OPEN: Tue to Fri L 12 to 2, Tue to Sat D 7 to 10   CLOSED: 24 Dec to 23 Jan, 1 week May/June, 1 week Sept/Oct   MEALS: alc (main courses £17 to £19). Set L (2 courses) £12.95   SERVICE: not inc; 10% for parties of 6 or more   CARDS: Access, Amex, Delta, Diners, Switch, Visa   DETAILS: 48 seats. Private parties: 28 main room, 8 and 12 private rooms. No children under 8. Smart dress preferred. No smoking in dining-room. No music

Rendezvous

| 24 Deanhaugh Street, Edinburgh EH4 1LY | COOKING 1 |
| TEL: (0131) 332 4476 | COST £14–£42 |

Action at the Rendezvous takes place in a cellar made of massive stones painted white, with tables huddled together and the lighting dim. The kitchen draws most of its inspiration from the Auld Alliance, which means that pheasant with lemon and honey sauce, and fillet steak stuffed with haggis share the billing with artichoke and grain-mustard soufflé, poached sea bass with fennel and Pernod, and noisettes of lamb stuffed with chicken and rosemary mousse. 'Bountiful' four-course set dinners have included such things as a 'divine' tomato and herb soup, a duo of sole and salmon, decent cheeses, and a 'good flan of peach and pears'. Fixed-price business lunches remain one of the best bargains in the city. Twenty wines offer the prospect of fair drinking at equally fair prices. House wine is £8.50.

CHEF: Richard Easton   PROPRIETOR: Harry Anderson   OPEN: Wed to Sat L 12 to 2.30, Tue to Sun D 6.30 to 10   CLOSED: 25 and 26 Dec, 1 and 2 Jan   MEALS: alc D (main courses £9 to £15.50). Set L £6.75 (2 courses) to £8.20, Set D £18.50   SERVICE: 10%, card slips closed CARDS: Access, Amex, Visa   DETAILS: 24 seats. Private parties: 34 main room. Children's helpings. Smart dress preferred. No smoking while others are eating. Music. Air-conditioned

Shore ⁵✸ £

3–4 Shore, Leith, Edinburgh EH6 6QW
TEL/FAX: (0131) 553 5080   COOKING 1*
off A199 on Firth of Forth, 2m E of city centre   COST £19–£34

The Shore surveys the Water of Leith, where Edinburgh meets the sea. Take your pick between the airy dining-room, where big west-facing windows let the sunshine in, if there is any, and the bar area, where 'real ales, foaming cappuccinos and lively debate' are promised. Fish is the focus, and the treatments it receives are many and varied. Halibut is grilled with garlic, toasted almonds and parsley, sardines with garlic and rosemary, and king scallops are sauté with honey, mustard and coriander. One reporter was delighted with his Dover sole – 'a splendidly large, fine fish' – and finished things off nicely with 'well-textured' pistachio ice-cream. Desserts are otherwise in the crowd-pleasing sticky-toffee-pudding, lemon-tart and chocolate-mousse mould. The predominantly French wine list offers plenty of Sauvignon Blanc and Chardonnay, as well as some good lighter reds. Prices start at £8.80.

CHEFS: Kevin O'Connor and Innes Gibson   PROPRIETOR: Stuart Linsley   OPEN: all week 12 to 2.30 (12.30 to 3 Sun), 6.30 to 10.15   CLOSED: 25 and 26 Dec, 1 and 2 Jan   MEALS: alc (main courses £7 to £12). Set L Mon to Sat £6.95 (2 courses), Set L Sun £9.50 (2 courses) to £11.50 SERVICE: not inc; 10% on parties of 8 or more   CARDS: Access, Amex, Visa   DETAILS: 36 seats. 12 seats outside. Private parties: 36 main room. Vegetarian meals. Children's helpings. No smoking in dining-room. Wheelchair access (no WC). Music

Siam Erawan £

48 Howe Street, Edinburgh EH3 6TH   COOKING 1*
TEL: (0131) 226 3675   COST £14–£32

Simple décor, friendly service and an 'authentic' approach combine to make this Thai restaurant stand out from the crowd. The basement in Edinburgh's New Town is 'pleasantly atmospheric', and rolls along on a tide of informality and enthusiasm. It cooks up typical Thai favourites of aromatic tom kha gai soup with chicken and coconut, satays served with a good peanut dip, a wide range of curries, and gets through its quota of lemon grass, lime leaves and coriander leaf in dishes such as goong nung (steamed prawns). A few other 'specialities' including steamed pomfret add to the variety – the range is impressive – and both wok and chargrill dishes benefit from the abundance and quality of Scottish ingredients. Prices for both wine and food are fair; house wine is £8.50

CHEF/PROPRIETOR: Miss W. Chinnapong OPEN: Mon to Sat L 12 to 2.30, all week D 6 to 11
CLOSED: 25 and 26 Dec, 1 and 2 Jan MEALS: alc (main courses £6 to £8.50). Set L £5.95 (2
courses) to £6.95, Set D £15.95 (2 courses) to £19.95 SERVICE: L not inc, D 10%, card slips
closed CARDS: Access, Switch, Visa DETAILS: 50 seats. Private parties: 30 main room, 13
private room. Vegetarian meals. Children welcome. Music

Silvio's ⚡✶

NEW ENTRY

54 The Shore, Leith, Edinburgh EH6 6RA
TEL/FAX: (0131) 553 3557

COOKING 1
COST £20–£38

This smart addition to Edinburgh's Italian scene stands on a cobbled wharf,
where the Water of Leith runs out into the docks. The whole place is
non-smoking, which is a boon 'given the closeness of the tables'. The menu is a
short, interesting mixture of colourful antipasti, trattoria favourites such as veal
in Marsala sauce, pasta and more modern fish dishes. Spaghetti with garlicky
tomato sauce and chillies has been spot on, and other main-course dishes
include orecchiette with pesto, sirloin steak flavoured with wine and herbs, and
crayfish wrapped in sage and Parma ham. 'Silvio's special' pudding is a thin slice
of frozen cheesecake with a toffee topping that reminded one correspondent of 'a
map of Argentina'. The mood is relaxed, service is 'no problem'. The all-Italian
wine list has a remarkable collection of Barolos dating back to 1935, as well as
numerous vintage brandies. House wine is £8.80.

CHEF: Duncan Leitch PROPRIETOR: Silvio Praino OPEN: Mon to Sat 12 to 2, 6 to 10.30
CLOSED: 25 and 26 Dec, 1 and 2 Jan MEALS: alc (main courses £6.50 to £12.50). Set L £10.50 (2
courses) SERVICE: not inc CARDS: Access, Amex, Delta, Diners, Switch, Visa DETAILS: 35
seats. Private parties: 35 main room. Vegetarian meals. Children's helpings. Smart dress
preferred. No smoking in dining-room. Wheelchair access (also WC). Music

Valvona & Crolla
Caffè Bar 🍷 ⚡✶ £

NEW ENTRY

19 Elm Row, Edinburgh EH7 4AA
TEL/FAX: (0131) 556 6066

COOKING 1
COST £13–£20

'Sheer delight,' enthused an early visitor, happy to see the latest generation of
this long-standing family business making its mark. The address has long been
familiar to wine enthusiasts throughout the UK, and to locals in pursuit of Parma
ham, olive oil and other essential Italian groceries, so the café is a perfectly
natural development, extending back to a see-through kitchen. It is light, bright
and cheerful, with natural wood, dark green furniture and displays of books and
cooking utensils. The simple, rustic Italian food is mostly what is sold in the
shop – sausages, pasta, salads, cheeses, polenta, crostini, risotto, tiramisù,
excellent coffee and 'divine home-made bread' – and the place rolls on all day
from eight in the morning to five o'clock. 'Lunch-time' is distinguished by a
minimum charge of £5, and by a few specials from vegetarian lasagne to a 'crisp
and prefectly thin' seafood pizza. Portions are small but flavours are distinctive,
prices are low, and quality is high.

Wines can be selected from the shop list and served in the café for an additional
£2 corkage charge, so it's possible to drink very well for very little. The vast

Italian range is top-notch and comprehensive, as one might expect from a specialist merchant. A short list of eight recommended wines available by both glass and bottle is helpful, starting at £6.99 a bottle and £1.90 a glass.

CHEFS/PROPRIETORS: the Contini family   OPEN: Mon to Sat 8 to 5   CLOSED: 25 and 26 Dec, 1 to 4 Jan   MEALS: alc (main courses £2.50 to £4.50). Minimum £5 L   SERVICE: not inc   CARDS: Access, Amex, Switch, Visa   DETAILS: 84 seats. 10 seats outside. Private parties: 84 main room. Vegetarian meals. Children's helpings. No smoking in dining-room. Wheelchair access (also WC). Music

Vintners Rooms 🍷 ⅕✳

The Vaults, 87 Giles Street, Leith, Edinburgh EH6 6BZ	COOKING 2*
TEL: (0131) 554 6767 FAX: (0131) 467 7130	COST £20–£48

Step directly off the street into the cheerful, relaxed bar of what is quite possibly Britain's oldest commercial building, dating from the twelfth century. More formal restaurant tables are laid with stiff linen, good glasses and fresh flowers. The cooking has a contemporary thrust, with plenty of room for fish, fowl, game and vegetable dishes, including aubergine fritters, a 'boudin' of wild boar, and guinea-fowl with lentils.

The simpler bar lunch is a bargain, offering al dente fettuccine with a light cream sauce and pieces of smoked salmon added at the end, so preserving colour, texture and taste. Roast chicken with a gently sharp buttery sauce of lemon and lime, and brown bread ice-cream with toffee sauce have also pleased. Occasionally lapses in the cooking occur, however, as when a lunching inspector found that poor timing and 'inept' saucing took the shine off some of the more ambitious (and expensive) à la carte dishes, although a prune, almond and armagnac tart with crisp pastry and 'soft, luscious prunes' was a sure-fire hit.

Wines are carefully chosen. Francophiles will be heartened – not only by the quality names, but also by the agreeable prices. Sound producers represent the New World. Older wines make frequent appearances, and there are nearly 50 half-bottles to browse through. House wines start at £9.50. CELLARMAN'S CHOICE: Chablis, premier cru Fourchaume 1990, G. Duplessis, £28; St-Emilion, Ch. Belair 1986, £35.

CHEFS: Tim Cumming and James Baxter   PROPRIETORS: Sue and Tim Cumming   OPEN: Mon to Sat 12 to 2, 7 to 10.30   CLOSED: 2 weeks Christmas and New year   MEALS: alc (main courses £14 to £17.50). Set L £9 (2 courses) to £12, Set D £25. Bar L available   SERVICE: not inc   CARDS: Access, Amex, Switch, Visa   DETAILS: 60 seats. Private parties: 36 main room. Car park. Children's helpings. Smart dress preferred. No smoking in dining-room. Wheelchair access (no WC). No music

ERISKA Argyll & Bute	map 11

▲ Isle of Eriska 🏆

Ledaig, Eriska PA37 1SD	
TEL: (01631) 720371 FAX: (01631) 720531	COOKING 2
off A828, 12m N of Oban	COST £43–£52

On a remote but accessible island north of Oban, at the entrance to Loch Creran, the Buchanan-Smiths run this imposing but comfortable baronial pile with a house-proud sense of dedication. 'I wouldn't mind having the contract to supply furniture polish,' mused one who marvelled at the gleam. Despite the darkness of the panelling, the atmosphere manages not to be in the least oppressive, although the menus of six courses plus coffee and petits fours might daunt the faint of appetite. Balance is achieved, though, despite the quantities, and the raw materials are generally flawless.

Devilled whitebait is a favoured fish course, an alternative to soup, which may well follow something simple like a warm salad of chicken livers. Roasts, such as rib of beef or free-range turkey, and salmon from Loch Creran are carved on a trolley at the table, after which the drill is pudding, savoury and cheese. Desserts have included good chocolate tart and an item described as 'soup made from fruits of the forest' (which turned out to be a sorbet with fruit), while the cheeses are mostly Scottish, with Stilton the sole English interloper. There is a slight feeling of the formulaic about it all, but the many regulars at least attest to the popularity of such an approach. The lengthy wine list is French-led and fairly classical, but the New World selections are good and bring on names like Hawks Crest in California and Cape Mentelle in Australia. Halves are plentiful. House wines are £8.50.

CHEF: Euan Clark   PROPRIETORS: the Buchanan-Smith family   OPEN: all week D only 8 to 9 CLOSED: Jan to Feb   MEALS: Set D £35. Bar L available   SERVICE: not inc, card slips closed CARDS: Access, Switch, Visa   DETAILS: 40 seats. Private parties: 16 main room. Car park. Vegetarian meals. Children welcome. No children under 10 D. Jacket and tie. No cigars/pipes in dining-room. Wheelchair access (also WC). No music   ACCOMMODATION: 17 rooms, all with bath/shower. TV. Phone. B&B £143 to £205. Deposit: £50. Rooms for disabled. Children welcome. Baby facilities. Dogs welcome in bedrooms only. Garden. Swimming-pool. Fishing (*The Which? Hotel Guide*)

FORT WILLIAM Highland   map 11

Crannog ⅜✴

Town Pier, Fort William PH33 7NG   COOKING 1
TEL/FAX: (01397) 705589   FAX: (01397) 705026   COST £19–£38

Crannog is easily spotted: a white building with a red roof down by the loch. The best views of mountain and water are reserved for non-smokers: 'we are the lucky ones who can see the rain pattering down the windows.' Seafood is the draw, and a blackboard menu of daily specials is trundled round to supplement the printed version. Don't expect refinement – a few corners are cut – and don't expect originality and brilliance, but enjoy the simplest items, such as fresh oysters or smoked salmon, for what they are. Loch Linnhe langoustines might come with a trio of mayonnaises or with garlic butter, although an inspector wished they would 'throw away the dreadful garlic purée'. A first course and a pudding (cranachan, perhaps, or chocolate pot) makes a good-value lunch. Staff are friendly and helpful, and there is a short list of fairly priced wines starting at £8.50.

The Good Food Guide *is a registered trade mark of Which? Ltd.*

CHEFS: Anne Savage, Isobel McDonald and Jonathon Macleod   PROPRIETOR: Crannog Ltd
OPEN: all week 12 to 2.30, 6 to 9.30 (9 in winter)   CLOSED: 25 and 26 Dec, 1 and 2 Jan   MEALS:
alc (main courses £6 to £14.50)   SERVICE: not inc, card slips closed   CARDS: Access, Visa
DETAILS: 70 seats. 24 seats outside. Private parties: 40 main room. Vegetarian meals. Children's
helpings. No smoking in 1 dining-room. Wheelchair access (also WC). Music

▲ *Inverlochy Castle* 🍷 ※

Torlundy, Fort William PH33 6SN
TEL: (01397) 702177   FAX: (01397) 702953   COOKING 3
3m N of Fort William on A82   COST £30–£59

This is a classic country-house hotel doing the right things in some style. The vast and confident Victorian building, set in 500 acres below Ben Nevis, is well looked after and, despite large portraits and intricate chandeliers, is not at all intimidating. The dining-room is well proportioned: quite small considering the size of everything else, yet with ample room in which to spread out. 'It is a delight to see the ambience, service and food all coming together to make a most pleasant evening,' concluded one report. Dinner (the main meal) is four courses (the second a fixed soup) that packs good variety into the comfortable compass of half a dozen choices at each stage.

After five years, Simon Haigh has certainly got the measure of things, combining a rosy Mediterranean outlook with Scottish ingredients of lamb, Loch Linnhe prawns and Aberdeen Angus beef. There is a strong line in terrines to begin, from a warm one of cider-impregnated potatoes with sardines and tomato confit, to looser configurations such as a compressed layer of tomatoes atop an aubergine – the flesh scooped out, mashed and returned – surrounded by just-cooked chanterelles. Little bursts of herbs 'sprang from nowhere' to make the dish taste 'much more exciting than it otherwise might'.

Roast suckling pig, and oven-roast pigeon with foie gras ravioli indicate a hearty streak to the food, and the cooking treads a fine line between earthiness and polish, as in a pot-roast of guinea-fowl, accurately timed to make the most of its texture. 'There is consummate skill here,' reckoned an inspector, who enjoyed the combination of simplicity, directness and delicacy in the food. The cheeseboard is 'small but good', and desserts have included excellent tears of chocolate, and a fine lemon tart served with a creamy cinnamon mousse. The wine list is impressive, with plenty of mature Bordeaux and Burgundy for those who choose to push the boat out. Although the emphasis is firmly on high quality, the lower reaches are not neglected, especially in the New World sections. Half-bottles abound throughout the list. CELLARMAN'S CHOICE: Justerini & Brooks' White Burgundy NV, £13.50; Justerini & Brooks' Claret NV, £12.75.

CHEF: Simon Haigh   PROPRIETOR: Grete Hobbs   OPEN: all week 12.30 to 1.45, 7.15 to 9.15
CLOSED: Dec to Feb   MEALS: Set L £18.50 (2 courses) to £23.50, Set D £42.50   SERVICE: none
CARDS: Access, Amex, Delta, Switch, Visa   DETAILS: 40 seats. Private parties: 30 main room, 8
and 12 private rooms. Car park. Children's helpings. Jacket and tie. No smoking in dining-room.
Wheelchair access (also women's WC). No music   ACCOMMODATION: 17 rooms, all with
bath/shower. TV. Phone. B&B £160 to £330. Children welcome. Baby facilities. Dogs welcome.
Afternoon teas. Garden. Fishing (*The Which? Hotel Guide*)

Buttery

652 Argyle Street, Glasgow G3 8UF	COOKING 1*
TEL: (0141) 221 8188 FAX: (0141) 204 4639	COST £22–£54

'To enter the Buttery is like stepping back into a different era,' reflects a regular of nine years. Encased in crimson plush among a surrealist collection of curios, you may wonder exactly which era; there is a strong hint of 1960s whimsicality, perhaps. Curiosities abound on Stephen Johnson's menus, too, such as rosemary-stuffed guinea-fowl with poached fruits and a tea-flavoured *jus*, or, from the vegetarian menu, cheese and avocado croque-monsieur on banana butter.

If the less adventurous find that sort of thing a little nerve-jangling, there are plenty of more straightforward combinations: salmon and halibut poached in saffron stock, or Highland venison with wild mushrooms and oatmeal in a ginger sauce have a clearer regional ring to them. If you've a mind, this is the place for ported Stilton; then again, chocolate and rum parfait with bees' pollen yoghurt may entice. Service is highly commended, and the petits fours are generosity itself. The wine list has been throroughly overhauled and now names all producers and vintages. It's a worthy range with the focus on France, and there are 17 half-bottles; some mark-ups are highish. House wine starts at £10.95.

CHEF: Stephen Johnson   PROPRIETOR: Alloa Pubs and Restaurants Ltd   OPEN: Mon to Fri L 12 to 2.30, Mon to Sat D 7 to 10.30   CLOSED: 25 and 26 Dec, 1 and 2 Jan   MEALS: alc (main courses £13.50 to £15.50). Set L £14.85   SERVICE: 10%, card slips closed   CARDS: Access, Amex, Delta, Diners, Switch, Visa   DETAILS: 50 seats. Private parties: 12 main room, 10 private room. Car park. Vegetarian meals. Smart dress preferred. No cigars/pipes in dining-room. Music. Air-conditioned

Café Gandolfi £

64 Albion Street, Glasgow G1 1NY	COOKING 1
TEL: (0141) 552 6813	COST £14–£32

In the vanguard of Glasgow's café society revival, Gandolfi has become something of an institution, renowned for its stunning interior design, furniture and stained glass. All-day opening is a bonus, and queues form by the Wait Here sign at lunch-time. The kitchen is loyal to the Scottish larder, making use of everything from Dingwall haggis and Rannoch venison to West Coast seafood and Arbroath smokies for a seasonal menu that is adjusted every two months. Influences are drawn from far and wide: leek and goats'-cheese tartlet is served with tomato salsa, smoked sausage is cooked with haricot beans, and honey-glazed duck comes with grapefruit and ginger sauce. Among the desserts might be meringues with chocolate sauce, and home-made ice-creams. Light meals maintain the momentum during off-peak hours. The wine list is pared down to the bare essentials, but the selection is racily eclectic. House wine is £9.

CHEFS: Maggie Clarence and Alistair Braidwood   PROPRIETOR: Seumas MacInnes   OPEN: all week 9am (noon Sun) to 11.30pm   MEALS: alc (main courses £4 to £11)   SERVICE: not inc; 10% for parties of 6 or more   CARDS: Access, Switch, Visa   DETAILS: 58 seats. Vegetarian meals. Children's helpings. Wheelchair access (also WC). Music

Killermont Polo Club

| 2022 Maryhill Road, nr Bearsden, Glasgow G20 0AB | COOKING 1 |
| TEL: (0141) 946 5412 | COST £15–£41 |

Not exactly in 'pukka Killermont', this converted manse functions as Indian restaurant and polo club (complete with sporting facilities). The main dining-room has a light touch; two other eating areas are Edwardian in style with dark panelling and polo cartoons everywhere. The ambience generally appeals; the Muzak may not. Regional specialities share the menu with a few oddballs from the days of the Raj. Among the starters ('First Chukka') look for the 'samosa duo' with a centrepiece of chickpeas on a pastry base; otherwise try 'wonderful' Goan-style mussels. Sizzling tandoori duck with a faintly citrus edge has won approval, and vegetables include distinctively spiced tarka dhal and 'piquant' koftas. Pilau rice is multi-coloured; kulfi is a 'nouveau' version served with daubs of coulis. Service speeds along swiftly. Alloa Heavy is a suitably named draught beer, and house wine is £8.95.

CHEFS: Jas Sagoo and Balbir Farwaha   PROPRIETORS: Kal Dhaliwal, Parmjit Dhaliwal and Jas Sagoo   OPEN: all week (exc Sun L) 12 to 1.45, 5 to 10   CLOSED: 25 Dec, 1 Jan   MEALS: alc D (main courses £7 to £12). Set L £6.95 (2 courses) to £7.95   SERVICE: not inc, card slips closed   CARDS: Access, Amex, Diners, Switch, Visa   DETAILS: 90 seats. Private parties: 90 main room, 24 to 42 private rooms. Car park. Vegetarian meals. Children's helpings. Smart dress preferred. No cigars/pipes in dining-room. Wheelchair access (also men's WC). Music

Mitchells £   NEW ENTRY

| 157 North Street, Glasgow G3 7DA | COOKING 1 |
| TEL: (0141) 204 4312   FAX: (0141) 204 1818 | COST £17–£34 |

The two Mitchells restaurants (see below) are related. This centrally sited one is a good place at which to savour informal Glaswegian friendliness and patter while listening to an accomplished pianist. Customers range from business people to chatty young couples, and the food is dished up with lots of enthusiasm. Rather sharp dressings of salsa verde or mint and pistachio pesto enliven sound Scottish produce from salmon or halibut to venison and fillet steak. Begin with soup, salad or terrine, and finish with Bakewell tart or an arctic roll rather than uncaramelised tarte Tatin. Around 20 wines are as basic as the prices, starting with house wine at £8.50.

CHEFS: Jim Coakley and Scott Marshall   PROPRIETORS: Angus and Veronica Boyd   OPEN: Mon to Sat 12 to 2.30, 5.30 (5 bank hols) to 10.30   CLOSED: Christmas and New Year, bank hol L   MEALS: alc (main courses L £5 to £9, D £7 to £12). Light meals available. BYO £2.95   SERVICE: not inc   CARDS: Access, Amex, Delta, Diners, Switch, Visa   DETAILS: 60 seats. Private parties: 30 main room. Vegetarian meals. Children's helpings. Music. Air-conditioned

SCOTLAND

Mitchells West End

31–35 Ashton Lane, off Byres Road, Glasgow G12 8SJ	COOKING 1
TEL: (0141) 339 2220 FAX: (0141) 204 4312	COST £21–£36

The West End branch of Mitchells (see also entry above), close to the university, attracts young academic types rather than business clientele, and has made the best of a tight squeeze upstairs with banquette seating, bright pink and green décor and snazzy prints. A sensibly short menu includes good home-made soup (courgette or carrot, perhaps), and simple fresh Scottish staples of roast cod, rib of beef, and Perthshire woodpigeon. Two favourite native ingredients – smoked salmon and cream – work overtime, and plainer dishes are a wiser choice. Chicken liver pâté was 'delicious' at inspection, though vegetables seemed tired. Portions are generous, and sticky toffee shines among the puddings. House wine is £8.50.

CHEFS: Jim Coakley and John Quinn   PROPRIETOR: Angus Boyd   OPEN: Mon to Sat D only 5.30 to 10.30   CLOSED: 25 Dec, 1 and 2 Jan   MEALS: alc (main courses £7 to £12). BYO £1.95 to £2.95   SERVICE: not inc   CARDS: Access, Amex, Delta, Diners, Switch, Visa   DETAILS: 36 seats. Private parties: 30 main room. Vegetarian meals. Children's helpings. Music. Air-conditioned

▲ One Devonshire Gardens 🍷✶

1 Devonshire Gardens, Glasgow G12 0UX	COOKING 3
TEL: (0141) 339 2001 FAX: (0141) 337 1663	COST £39–£67

'I was surprised at the atmospheric impact,' wrote a first-time visitor to Glasgow's star restaurant on the corner of an elegant, Georgian tree-lined road in the West End. Enter a wide hallway carpeted in midnight blue, nibble herby green olives over drinks in a smart, comfortable, sofa-strewn drawing-room, and thence to a heavily decorated dining-room with discreetly spaced tables. It all adds up to a 'meticulously contrived' atmosphere that produces 'a great sense of occasion', and the food rises to it. Andrew Fairlie's style has a firmly French foundation, an easy approach to luxuries, a modern outlook and a welcome clarity of purpose. Scottish supplies run to West Coast fish, local mushrooms, farmhouse cheeses and organic vegetables.

First courses typically include variations on the salad theme, from niçoise with seared tuna, to one of globe artichoke chunks supported (just) by wild mushrooms and a truffle dressing, to a hot foie gras salad, the liver lightly cooked and served with shredded beetroot. A no-choice soup follows, then perhaps Bresse pigeon, braised oxtail, or a well-conceived fishy offering such as two generous rolls of 'juicy' sole fillet encasing a fish mousse, served on a colourful risotto with baby broad beans, and given a slice of crisp, pungent Parmesan.

Careful construction is a characteristic of desserts, among which have been a sharp lemon mousse and granita with a nicely contrasting blackcurrant coulis, and a trio of caramel and banana desserts served with clove and cardamom syrup. All is helped along by the professionalism of friendly and knowledgeable staff who have 'a tasteful sense of humour'. Ask for Johnny Walker here and you will get the wine waiter, who presides over an attractive and lively but rather pricey list, with good selections from California and Australia.

CHEF: Andrew Fairlie   PROPRIETOR: Ken McCulloch   OPEN: Mon to Fri and Sun L 12.15 to 2.15, all week D 7.15 to 10   MEALS: Set L £25, Set D £40   SERVICE: not inc, card slips closed   CARDS: Access, Amex, Diners, Visa   DETAILS: 45 seats. 10 seats outside. Private parties: 42 main room, 12 to 32 private rooms. Vegetarian meals. Children's helpings. Smart dress preferred. No smoking in dining-room. Wheelchair access (also WC). Music   ACCOMMODATION: 27 rooms, all with bath/shower. TV. Phone. B&B £135 to £170. Rooms for disabled. Children welcome. Dogs by arrangement. Afternoon teas. Garden (*The Which? Hotel Guide*)

La Parmigiana

447 Great Western Road, Glasgow G12 8HH   COOKING 1*
TEL: (0141) 334 0686   FAX: (0141) 332 3533   COST £14–£43

The Giovanazzis run a fairly traditional Italian trattoria, but one of sufficient flair for a Berkshire wanderer to wish there were something like it closer to home. The kitchen ties itself to no particular region of Italy, proving equally confident in serving spinach and ricotta ravioli with Parmesan, Tuscan fish stew, or Milanese veal escalope with porcini, asparagus and green beans. Generous helpings of carpaccio and properly presented seafood salad with extra-virgin and garlic receive good notices for starters, while a main-course brace of spatchcocked quail is simply dressed with rosemary and lemon juice and accurately chargrilled. Most of the expected desserts are here, from zabaglione and a sort of tiramisù, via cantuccini biscuits for dunking in Tuscan vin santo. 'Attentive and friendly' service keeps the customer satisfied. Good wines come largely from the northern half of Italy, but there is a smattering of French bottles too. House wines from Friuli are £8.90 a litre.

CHEF: Sandro Giovanazzi   PROPRIETORS: Angelo and Sandro Giovanazzi   OPEN: Mon to Sat 12 to 2.30, 6 to 11   CLOSED: 25 and 26 Dec, New Year, bank hols   MEALS: alc (main courses £6 to £13.50). Set L Mon to Fri £6.90   SERVICE: not inc   CARDS: Access, Amex, Diners, Switch, Visa   DETAILS: 60 seats. Private parties: 60 main room. Vegetarian meals. Children's helpings. Smart dress preferred. No pipes in dining-room. Music. Air-conditioned

Puppet Theatre 🕯✳

11 Ruthven Lane, Glasgow G12 9BG   COOKING 2
TEL: (0141) 339 8444   FAX: (0141) 339 7666   COST £22–£49

'Excellent meal, pleasant staff, quaint surroundings,' summarised one report. Just off Byres Road in Glasgow's West End, the Puppet Theatre is one of the city's more distinctive restaurants, offering a choice of four idiosyncratic dining areas. There is a mirrored room for those who enjoy looking at themselves, one like a Gothic church, one with a grand oak table, and a plant-filled conservatory exploiting the flowing lines of Gaudí. Twenty-five-year-old Ian McMaster comfortably straddles the divide between Scotland and the Mediterranean, and puts a cosmopolitan spin on the food, serving Argyll black pudding with candied sweet potato, and seared cod fillet with ratatouille.

The dinner menu changes monthly, and part of the deal is that vegetables are incorporated into main courses: hence a barley risotto and vegetable casserole with free-range guinea-fowl, or Savoy cabbage and potato pancake, along with Puy lentils, to accompany roast breast of duck. Puddings manage to avoid most of the clichés in favour of, for example, a mango and passion-fruit fool with an orange biscuit, or a hot gratin of pear, milk chocolate and mascarpone with banana sorbet. The short wine list stays mostly under £20 and is generous with half-bottles.

CHEF: Ian McMaster   PROPRIETORS: George Swanson and Ron McCulloch   OPEN: Tue to Fri and Sun L 12 to 2.30, Tue to Sun D 7 to 10.30 (11 Sat)   CLOSED: 25 and 26 Dec, 1 and 2 Jan   MEALS: alc D (main courses £12.50 to £16.50). Set L £9.95 (2 courses) to £12.50   SERVICE: not inc; 10% for parties of 8 or more   CARDS: Access, Amex, Delta, Switch, Visa   DETAILS: 68 seats. Private parties: 26 main room, 12 and 26 private rooms. Car park. Vegetarian meals. No children under 12. Smart dress preferred. No smoking in 1 dining-room. Music. Air-conditioned

Rogano

11 Exchange Place, Glasgow G1 3AN | NEW CHEF
TEL: (0141) 248 4055   FAX: (0141) 248 2608 | COST £26–£67

Glasgow's oldest-surviving restaurant is a monument of unequalled distinction. It is grand yet intimate, with an atmosphere redolent of the 1930s and lavish décor modelled deliberately on the Clyde-built liner *Queen Mary*. Seafood forms the backbone of the menu, and has included fish soup, while Aberdeen Angus beef has pleased carnivores, and there is always something for vegetarians. The old style, we understand, continues under Andrew Cummings, although we learnt of his arrival too late to assess it with confidence. Desserts might range from vanilla sponge pudding to melon and ginger sorbet, and the bill pays for 'a lot of service', with a superfluity of young waiters always in attendance. The sound wine list is tilted towards whites and the quality is good across the range; prices start at around £13. Café Rogano downstairs is open throughout the day for light meals ranging from salmon fish-cakes to grilled lamb cutlets.

CHEF: Andrew Cummings   PROPRIETOR: Alloa Pubs and Restaurants   OPEN: all week 12 to 2.30, 6.30 to 10.30   MEALS: alc (main courses £12.50 to £28.50). Set L Sat and Sun £15, Mon to Fri £16.50   SERVICE: 10%, card slips closed   CARDS: Access, Amex, Delta, Diners, Switch, Visa   DETAILS: 70 seats. Private parties: 70 main room, 16 private room. Vegetarian meals. Children welcome. No-smoking in dining-room until 2 L, 9 D. Wheelchair access (no WC). Music. Air-conditioned

Ubiquitous Chip

12 Ashton Lane, Glasgow G12 8SJ | COOKING 2
TEL: (0141) 334 5007   FAX: (0141) 337 1302 | COST £25–£56

The Chip celebrated its quarter-century in 1996, a tribute to some of the principles of its founder and owner, Ronald Clydesdale. Since he is not a conventionally trained chef, he follows his own intuitive route to devising dishes, resulting in some unusual and refreshing combinations. He is also careful about the provenance of his Scottish materials, and he likes eating to be informal. Brush past the vegetation to a rickety table, and maybe take up the menu's suggestion of a half-bottle of sherry to begin. The à la carte is no more, and the set-price menu might run from haggis (either venison or vegetarian) through lamb's-kidney suet pudding, to a light syrup sponge with dried fruit and custard.

While the cooking may sometimes lack the promised oomph, there is always lots of interest: monkfish with black pudding and parsnip, perhaps, or collops of Renfrewshire mutton with queenies. Service can be 'prompt and pleasant', although one reporter thought it 'an instruction course on the antithesis of good service'. Supplements for some dishes can make the deal seem expensive. Wines, on the other hand, offer superb value. The list is brilliant, crammed with illustrious producers, mature vintages and plenty of halves and magnums. A fine and vast array from France dominates, but wines from other countries, especially Germany, are highly respectable too. House wines from Spain, South Africa and Bordeaux are £9.95.

CHEF/PROPRIETOR: Ronald Clydesdale OPEN: all week 12 to 2.30, 5.30 to 11 CLOSED: 25 and 31 Dec, 1 and 2 Jan MEALS: Set L £18 to £23, Set D £26 SERVICE: not inc, card slips closed CARDS: Access, Amex, Diners, Visa DETAILS: 150 seats. 50 seats outside. Private parties: 80 main room, 25 and 45 private rooms. Vegetarian meals. Children's helpings. No pipes in dining-room. Wheelchair access (also WC). No music

Yes

22 West Nile Street, Glasgow G1 2PW	COOKING 1
TEL: (0141) 221 8044 FAX: (0141) 248 9159	COST £22–£44

The very best sort of modern brasserie design has been brought to bear on Ferrier Richardson's place in the heart of Glasgow: clean hard lines, banquettes in royal-blue plush and generous quantities of space between tables. A fairly restrained style of contemporary cooking is offered in the form of a fixed-price deal of two or more courses including coffee. Seafood minestrone with a Parmesan soufflé, oriental seared chicken with soy vinaigrette, and passion-fruit parfait with coconut sauce is the Esperanto spoken. Three grilled lamb chops timed to retain 'proper succulence' are classically set off with 'tingling mint juices'. Service is 'pleasant and attentive'. A short, up-to-date selection of world wines leads with house vin de pays at £10.95.

CHEF/PROPRIETOR: Ferrier Richardson OPEN: Mon to Sat 12 to 2.30, 7 to 11 CLOSED: 25 and 26 Dec, 1 and 2 Jan MEALS: Set L £11.95 (2 courses) to £14.95, Set D £19.95 (2 courses) to £27.95. Bar L available SERVICE: not inc, card slips closed CARDS: Access, Amex, Delta, Diners, Switch, Visa DETAILS: 100 seats. Private parties: 80 main room, 20 private room. Vegetarian meals. Children welcome. No cigars/pipes in dining-room. Music

GULLANE East Lothian	map 11

▲ Greywalls ♥ ⁵✳

Muirfield, Gullane EH31 2EG	
TEL: (01620) 842144 FAX: (01620) 842241	COOKING 3
on A198, at W end of Gullane	COST £28–£51

The Edwardian house was bought by Giles Weaver's grandfather, Sir James Horlick (of nightcap-drink fame), and turned into a country house hotel in 1948. It is not particularly grand or imposing, though it has wonderful formal gardens and a view of the hallowed Muirfield course. Inside, golfing memorabilia abound, and the feel is 'laid back and helpful'. Though Highland ingredients feature, the menu escapes the 'Scottish tourist' trap, opting instead for more modern Anglo-French fare along the lines of duck rillettes studded with foie gras and ceps, served with a beetroot relish and toasted brioche, or plain grilled Dover sole with chive butter.

Lunch might range from a plate of smoked salmon or cheddar cheese with chutney in the bar, to a short set menu in the dining-room. An inspector enjoyed a light and creamy leek and haddock timbale – 'full marks for presentation and flavour' – a warm goats'-cheese salad, and chicken breast with a creamy wild mushroom sauce. This may sound rather conservative food, but the kitchen meets the challenge of 'getting the familiar right', and offers extremely good value in the process. Dinner is four courses, one of them a soup or sorbet, and although it is more ambitious it retains a sense of realism.

Indulgent desserts might include a chilled malt whisky parfait with an orange caramel syrup, or steamed chocolate and walnut pudding with custard. Wines are well chosen, with the spotlight on classic France, but plenty of support from the rest of Europe and the New World. There is a fine array of mature vintages, especially among the clarets and ports. Six house wines are £12. CELLARMAN'S CHOICE: Rully 1992, Jaffelin, £18.25; Côtes du Rhône 1993, Guigal, £16.50.

CHEF: Paul Baron PROPRIETORS: Giles and Ros Weaver OPEN: all week 12.30 to 1.45, 7.30 to 9.15 CLOSED: Nov to Mar MEALS: alc (L only, main courses £8.50 to £11). Set L £20, Set D £33 SERVICE: not inc, card slips closed CARDS: Access, Amex, Diners, Switch, Visa DETAILS: 50 seats. Private parties: 50 main room (L only), 20 private room. Car park. Children welcome. Jacket and tie. No smoking in dining-room. Wheelchair access (no WC). No music ACCOMMODATION: 22 rooms, all with bath/shower. TV. Phone. B&B £95 to £175. Deposit: £60. Rooms for disabled. Children welcome. Dogs welcome in bedrooms only. Afternoon teas. Garden (The Which? Hotel Guide)

La Potinière

Main Street, Gullane EH31 2AA
TEL/FAX: (01620) 843214
on A198, 4m SW of North Berwick

COOKING 4
COST £25–£42

David and Hilary Brown have been a fixture of the Scottish restaurant scene for over two decades, and do everything themselves. Are they becoming jaded, feeling blasé, winding down or letting standards slip? Not a bit of it. One spring luncher declared the meal 'fantastic, exemplary' and 'a truly great bargain'. It is an 'auld alliance' restaurant, pairing devotedly Scottish ingredients with a seriously French love of gastronomy, and would not look out of place in provincial France: 'understated, tiny, faded round the edges, a bit like someone's living-room', with an atmosphere that is not exactly relaxed but is certainly informal.

It is a very individual restaurant, with quirky opening times and an unwavering commitment to the integrity of materials and techniques. Soups always start things off, and seem to be just right not only for the season but often for the day, too, as if Hilary Brown captures the mood set by the weather: hence a chestnut soup that was 'an appropriate winter dish on a cold night' in December, and an 'exceptional' cream of carrot with potato and haricot beans, fragrant from freshly ground spices, yet delicate and accurately seasoned, that was 'perfectly appropriate on a rainy day in late May'.

The cooking does not mess about. 'It goes straight to the heart of the flavour, and plenty of it', as in a dish of sole combined with pistou, aromatic basil leaves and an excellent sauce vierge; the fish is not overpowered but combines 'superbly' with the other flavours, producing a dish wth balance and textural contrast. Vierge seems to be a favourite Brown sauce, also used successfully with a 'moist and subtle' Arbroath smokie mousse, while an aigre-doux sauce has accompanied breast of guinea-fowl to the sound of echoing superlatives. After the main course comes a 'superb' palate-cleansing salad, then cheese or a dessert such as warm chocolate cake with mascarpone sorbet, or a light café con panna that is 'like a crème caramel but isn't', according to its reporter. Walnut and raisin bread has been 'wonderfully light, crunchy and hugely flavoursome', while coffee is served 'out of a pot that looked as if cowboys had used it out in the desert while driving cattle'.

Wine is a speciality; David Brown has produced a protean list with superb collections from Champagne, Italy and south-west France. One of its main strengths is a plethora of lesser-known gems alongside the classic names. Browsers will find much to enjoy, even among the half-bottle section, but David Brown is happy (and more than able) to advise. House wines are £9.75.

CHEF: Hilary Brown   PROPRIETORS: David and Hilary Brown   OPEN: Mon, Tue, Thur and Sun L 1, Fri and Sat D 8 (1 sitting)   CLOSED: 25 and 26 Dec, 1 and 2 Jan, 1 week June, Oct   MEALS: Set L £20, Set D £30   SERVICE: none   CARDS: none   DETAILS: 30 seats. Car park. Children welcome. Smart dress preferred. No smoking in dining-room. Wheelchair access (no WC). No music

---

INVERNESS Highland   map 11

▲ *Culloden House* ✦✱

Inverness IV1 2NZ
TEL: (01463) 790461   FAX: (01463) 792181
from Inverness take A96 to Nairn, turn right after 1m,   COOKING 1
then left at Culloden House Avenue   COST £25–£57

The ivy-covered house is built on a vast scale. You could re-enact the Battle of Culloden in the garden, the rooms are big enough for a game of tennis, the fireplace is large enough to roast a pig, and you could get a good night's sleep on any of the sofas. As we went to press, Major Gillis bought the house, but Michael Simpson is expected to remain at the stoves. His style is old-fashioned country-house cooking featuring perhaps melon with fresh fruit, poached halibut with smoked trout mousse and a creamed langoustine sauce, and Atholl Brose. Meat eaters get a good deal, with venison tournedos or sirloin of beef, and wild mushrooms in season give some dishes a lift. Brandy-snap baskets and strawberries are a typical pudding accessory, even with an esteemed smooth dark-chocolate parfait with caramel sauce. France is the epicentre of the wine list, and half-bottles are plentiful. House claret is £9.25 and house white Burgundy £12.90.

The Guide *always appreciates hearing about changes of chef or owner.*

CHEF: Michael Simpson   PROPRIETOR: Major Richard Gillis   OPEN: all week 12.30 to 2, 7 to 9
MEALS: alc (main courses £9.50 to £13). Set D £35   SERVICE: not inc, card slips closed   CARDS:
Access, Amex, Diners, Switch, Visa   DETAILS: 40 seats. 16 seats outside. Private parties: 51
main room, 34 private room. Car park. Vegetarian meals. No children under 10. Jacket and tie.
No smoking in dining-room. No music   ACCOMMODATION: 23 rooms, all with bath/shower. TV.
Phone. B&B £69 to £220. Deposit: 1 night's charge. No children under 10. Afternoon teas.
Garden

▲ Dunain Park ⅚✳

Inverness IV3 6JN
TEL: (01463) 230512   FAX: (01463) 224532
on A82, 1m from Inverness town boundary

COOKING 1
COST £27–£43

The attractive country house is set back off the road in half a dozen acres of
woodland, a log fire burns in the lounge, and it is comfortable and homely
enough to be 'the sort of place you can imagine spending a few days when the
weather turns bad, playing Scrabble or just reading'.

Dinner is the main business, with a short, balanced *carte* offering perhaps crab
tart, saddle of rabbit, and a choice of fresh fruit, cheese or 'sweets from the
buffet'. Beef comes from shaggy long-horned Highland cattle, 'difficult to find
but leaner than Aberdeen Angus', according to Ann Nicoll, salmon is from
Shetland, while deer, lamb, pigeon, rabbit and hare are local. Breasts of chicken,
guinea-fowl or quail are usually stuffed with something (haggis, for example)
and served with an alcohol-infused sauce. Lunch is four courses, along the same
lines as dinner but cheaper. A sophisticated, international wine list is matched
by the comprehensive selection of single-malt whiskies (around 200 of them),
including Scotch Malt Whisky Society single-cask bottlings. House French is
£11.50.

CHEF: Ann Nicoll   PROPRIETORS: Ann and Edward Nicoll   OPEN: all week 12 to 1.30, 7 to 9;
booking necessary L   CLOSED: 3 weeks Jan to Feb   MEALS: alc D (main courses £15). Set L
£16.50   SERVICE: not inc, card slips closed   CARDS: Access, Amex, Delta, Diners, Switch,
Visa   DETAILS: 36 seats. Private parties: 12 main room. Car park. Vegetarian meals. Children's
helpings. Smart dress preferred. No smoking in dining-room. Wheelchair access (no WC). No
music   ACCOMMODATION: 14 rooms, all with bath/shower. TV. Phone. B&B £138 to £158 (per
double room). Deposit: £50. Rooms for disabled. Children welcome. Baby facilities. Dogs
welcome. Afternoon teas. Garden. Swimming-pool (*The Which? Hotel Guide*)

Restaurant No 1 ⅚✳

NEW ENTRY

1 Greig Street, Inverness IV3 5PC
TEL: (01463) 716363   FAX: (01463) 234125

COOKING 1
COST £18–£55

With Culloden House and Dunain Park (see entries above) both being out of
town, there is relief that the centre of Inverness 'has finally got itself a restaurant
worthy of the capital of the Highlands'. The part-panelled room looks out over
the River Ness, and the small kitchen is in full view behind glass. Charles
Lockley worked at Clifton House (see entry, Nairn), and his cooking follows a
broadly similar style: Scottish ingredients with a French twist. Reporters have
enjoyed lobster bisque 'with good strong flavour', and fresh-tasting langoustine

salad with a sweet vinaigrette dressing. Around four choices per course keep things manageable for the kitchen, and sauces range from a juniper and port glaze with roast saddle of venison, to a more old-fashioned red wine and blue-cheese sauce with grilled fillet steak. Desserts have included a steamed chocolate and almond pudding, and honey and oatmeal ice-cream (served with fresh raspberries in February). 'Quite expensive, but well worth it,' summed up one supporter. Apart from port, the 40 dependable wines are all from France, with a fair proportion of half-bottles. House French is £9.45.

CHEF: Charles Lockley   PROPRIETORS: Fergus and Avril Euart   OPEN: Mon to Sat 12.30 to 2.30, 6.30 to 10.15   CLOSED: Mon Oct to Mar   MEALS: alc (main courses L £5 to £9, D £14.50 to £22.50)   SERVICE: not inc, card slips closed   CARDS: Access, Switch, Visa   DETAILS: 24 seats. Private parties: 14 main room. Children's helpings. Smart dress preferred. No smoking in dining-room. Wheelchair access (also WC). No music

KENTALLEN Highland

map 11

▲ *Ardsheal House*

Kentallen PA38 4BX
TEL: (01631) 740227   FAX: (01631) 740342
on A828, 5m S of Ballachulish Bridge

COOKING 2
COST £27–£51

The stone-built house dates from around 1760, with subsequent extensions and additions. A splendid location by Loch Linnhe and impressive oak panelling within combine to produce a 'typical' Scottish country-house atmosphere, but Ardsheal goes a step further and marries professional hotelkeeping with relaxed informality. Seafood naturally features, in the form of Loch Linnhe prawns in a filo pastry basket, or grilled fillet of west coast cod, sometimes with a slightly exotic note to the saucing: mild curry and lime on one occasion, champagne and caviare on another.

Lunches consist of three courses, while dinners are extended with a soup before the main course – beetroot consommé with herb dumplings, for instance – and a salad, maybe carrot and poppy seed, afterwards. Choice is sensibly short, and a gentle country feel pervades the repertoire: it maintains interest with combinations such as cardamom and leek sauce, or kümmel and apple sauce for a roast breast of quail, yet takes few risks with twice-baked goats'-cheese soufflé, pavé of lamb with provençale vegetables, and puddings of hot rhubarb crumble or caramelised lemon tart. Over 70 varied wines are well chosen and fairly priced, with house Californian at £13.

CHEF: George Kelso   PROPRIETORS: Mr and Mrs Neil Sutherland   OPEN: all week 12 to 1.30, 8.30 (1 sitting)   CLOSED: 4 weeks from 6 Jan   MEALS: Set L £18, Set D £32.50. Light L available   SERVICE: not inc   CARDS: Access, Amex, Switch, Visa   DETAILS: 40 seats. 10 seats outside. Private parties: 30 main room. Car park. Children's helpings. Smart dress preferred. Wheelchair access (no WC). Music   ACCOMMODATION: 13 rooms, all with bath/shower. Phone. D,B&B £85 to £180. Children welcome. Baby facilities. Dogs welcome. Afternoon teas. Garden (*The Which? Hotel Guide*)

Card slips closed *in the details at the end of an entry indicates that the total on the slips of credit cards is closed when handed over for signature.*

KILCHRENAN   Argyll & Bute   map 11

▲ *Taychreggan* 🍷 ⅝✳

Kilchrenan PA35 1HQ
TEL: (01866) 833211 and 833366   COOKING 1
FAX: (01866) 833244   COST £21–£43

The 300-year-old stone house was originally a drovers' inn, although 'it is
doubtful if the average drover would recognise it today'. A tranquil spot by Loch
Awe, combined with Annie Paul's flair for décor, has produced a stylish and
sophisticated hideaway. One reporter described 'a restaurant of two halves',
referring to the two dining-rooms (one with antique tables) and to the greater
and lesser halves of a meal that included a 'classic' lobster sauce for halibut, and a
wild mushroom risotto overwhelmed by salty duck confit. The fixed-price
dinner consists of five courses, one of them cheese. Plainer dishes are generally
well executed, and any shortcomings in the cooking seem due to Neil Mellis's
quest for the grail of novelty. Roast loin of Argyll venison, seared Loch Etive
scallops, and a well-executed crème brûlée were the highlights of an inspector's
visit. Red Bordeaux is a strength of the well-chosen and fair-value wine list.
House wines are £8.75.

CHEF: Neil Mellis   PROPRIETORS: Euan and Annie C. Paul   OPEN: all week 12.30 to 2, 7 to 8.45
MEALS: alc L (main courses £5 to £11). Set L £12 (2 courses) to £15, Set D £28   SERVICE: not inc,
card slips closed   CARDS: Access, Amex, Switch, Visa   DETAILS: 55 seats. 24 seats outside.
Private parties: 80 main room, 24 and 32 private rooms. Car park. Vegetarian meals. Children
welcome L. Smart dress preferred. No smoking in dining-room. Music   ACCOMMODATION: 20
rooms, all with bath/shower. Phone. D,B&B £75 to £240. Deposit: £50. No children under 12.
Dogs welcome in bedrooms only. Afternoon teas. Garden. Fishing

KILLIECRANKIE   Perthshire & Kinross   map 11

▲ *Killiecrankie Hotel* ⅝✳

Killiecrankie, by Pitlochry PH16 5LG
TEL: (01796) 473220   FAX: (01796) 472451   COOKING 1*
off A9, 3m N of Pitlochry   COST £37–£44

Killiecrankie is a small and attractive town near the tourist honeypot of
Pitlochry, and the stone manse is described as 'clean and modern but with
character'. The bar is furnished in traditional huntin', shootin' and fishin' style,
while the dining-room is more chichi and typically offers four courses (one of
them a varied cheeseboard) with a sensibly limited choice, including a cold
salad option of smoked fish or meat. If a South-east Asian influence is
discernible, as in fillet of turbot with a red Thai curry sauce and sweet sticky rice,
it reflects John Ramsay's first-hand experience; and if there are pickled cherries
with the game, they will be local. Preserving fruit and mushrooms is all in a
day's work for the kitchen. Two desserts are normally offered, and a couple who
stayed reckoned that the hot alternative 'was superior on each occasion'. The
food is not cheap, but an overnight package helps, given the 'excellent and
plentiful' breakfast, while over 50 varied and well-chosen wines are fairly
priced.

CHEF: John Ramsay   PROPRIETORS: Colin and Carole Anderson   OPEN: all week D only 7 to 8.30.   CLOSED: Jan, Feb, 2nd week Dec   MEALS: Set D £28. Bar L and D available all week 12.30 to 2, 6.30 to 9.30   SERVICE: not inc, card slips closed   CARDS: Access, Delta, Switch, Visa   DETAILS: 34 seats. Private parties: 20 main room. Car park. Children's helpings. No children under 5. Smart dress preferred. No smoking in dining-room. No music ACCOMMODATION: 10 rooms, all with bath/shower. TV. Phone. D,B&B £67 to £152. Deposit: £35. Children welcome. Baby facilities. Dogs welcome. Afternoon teas. Garden (*The Which? Hotel Guide*)

KINCLAVEN Perthshire & Kinross

map 11

▲ *Ballathie House* ⁵✳

Kinclaven, by Stanley PH1 4QN
TEL: (01250) 883268   FAX: (01250) 883396
off B9099, take right fork 1m N of Stanley

COOKING 2
COST £21–£43

This is fishing country *par excellence*. The turreted Scottish baronial Victorian mansion stands in a 1,300-acre estate on the peaceful banks of the Tay, and some of the salmon that didn't get away are on display inside. The hotel engenders a feeling of well-being, which the generous menu backs up. At dinner, three courses are extended to four with a choice of soup, sorbet or salad after a starter of perhaps game terrine or steamed West Coast mussels in a creamy garlic sauce. The amount of cream, butter and alcohol in sauces may not be to everybody's taste, but there is no doubting the quality of the seafood, from Skye scallops with braised rice, to steamed salmon with buttered leeks.

Loin of venison or saddle of Perthshire lamb are typical alternatives for main course, with sticky toffee pudding to follow, and lunchtime bar snacks are as varied as a sweet pickled herring salad, or pork and leek sausages. The wide-ranging, well-chosen wine list kicks off with house Australian at £9.75.

CHEF: Kevin MacGillivray   PROPRIETOR: Ballathie House Hotel Ltd   OPEN: all week 12.30 to 2, 7 to 9   MEALS: Set L £11 (2 courses) to £13.95, Set D £25 to £27.50. Bar L available Mon to Sat SERVICE: not inc   CARDS: Access, Amex, Delta, Diners, Switch, Visa   DETAILS: 80 seats. Private parties: 60 main room, 10 to 30 private rooms. Car park. Vegetarian meals. Children's helpings. Smart dress preferred. No smoking in dining-room. Wheelchair access (also WC). No music ACCOMMODATION: 39 rooms, all with bath/shower. TV. Phone. D,B&B £77.50 to £210. Rooms for disabled. Children welcome. Baby facilities. Dogs welcome in bedrooms only. Afternoon teas. Garden. Fishing

KINGUSSIE Highland

map 11

▲ *The Cross* ▮ ⁵✳

Tweed Mill Brae, Ardbroilach Road,
Kingussie PH21 1TC
TEL: (01540) 661166   FAX: (01540) 661080

COOKING 3*
COST £46–£55

The rough-stone tweed mill, a couple of hundred yards uphill from the traffic-lights, was built in the late nineteenth century and converted by the Hadleys in 1993 into a restaurant-with-rooms. It is spacious, but the enterprise is on a small, personal scale. The amiable Tony Hadley welcomes, takes orders and deals intelligently with wine, while Ruth Hadley produces a timeless menu based on Scottish ingredients, from local wild deer (cooked with redcurrants and port) to a trio of salmon: rillettes studded with tiny nuggets of fish, slices in a mild sweetish marinade, and a chunk of hot-smoked salmon.

Her belief that flavours should 'talk to customers, not shout' explains the basic style (of an underplayed smoked haddock fish-cake, for example), though this does not diminish the impact of 'memorable roasted tomato and red pepper soup' that was full-bodied, 'exquisitely flavoured' from ripe tomatoes, and subtly spiked with tarragon, basil and thyme. The simplicity of a tender beef fillet with a sauce made from red wine and stock, and flavoured with ceps, is sensible not only on its own account but also because it opens up so many possibilities on the wine list.

'Mrs Hadley is someone who takes pains over her cooking and can achieve brilliance,' though some combinations have produced less successful results, as when sweet and chewy prunes rather overwhelmed the plums in a tart that also came with a cinnamon ice-cream and blackcurrant coulis. 'Too many competing flavours' was an inspector's verdict. Bread is 'freshly baked baguette with a delicious crust', and the advantages of an overnight stay are not only an excellent breakfast but a chance to recover from the excellent wines that Tony Hadley lists. Over the past 12 months he has ceased stocking up on French wines in protest at France's nuclear testing on Muroroa Atoll, and these wines will eventually be phased out. The list remains as gargantuan as ever (400 bins), thanks to an expanded New World selection. Stylistically, the collection creeps into every vinous nook and cranny, and prices range from around £9 a bottle to £875 for magnums of Ch. Palmer 1949.

CHEF: Ruth Hadley   PROPRIETORS: Tony and Ruth Hadley   OPEN: Wed to Mon D only 7 to 9 CLOSED: 1 to 26 Dec, 6 Jan to 28 Feb   MEALS: Set D £35   SERVICE: not inc, card slips closed CARDS: Access, Delta, Switch, Visa   DETAILS: 28 seats. Private parties: 28 main room. Car park. No children under 12. No smoking in dining-room. Wheelchair access (also WC). No music ACCOMMODATION: 9 rooms, all with bath/shower. Phone. D,B&B £85 to £170. Deposit: £50. No children under 12. Garden

---

KINLOCHMOIDART Highland   map 11

Kinacarra 🍴✷

Kinlochmoidart PH38 4ND
TEL: (01967) 431238   COOKING 2
on A861, at head of Loch Moidart   COST £14–£34

A lochside stone cottage that was once a school, Kinacarra is now a modestly proportioned and unassuming restaurant run by the MacLeans. Chairs and tables are 'plain pine', china and cutlery are 'basic', fresh flowers adorn the tables and antique farm tools and deer antlers hang on the walls: an oddly proportioned mishmash in the eyes of one, a 'little gem of a place' in the view of another.

Frances MacLean's skilled cooking offers plenty of choice while avoiding the pitfalls of vaulting ambition. Scallops and prawns tossed in garlic butter are plump and succulent, served with a green salad containing a plethora of fresh herbs. 'In a top London restaurant it would have cost a fortune.' Robust soups, rich salmon pâté, and pasta dishes with venison à la bolognese or mussels with wine and herbs add to the allure. The odd note of exotica is sounded in the likes of lamb cooked in a ragoût with apricots and cumin, but puddings return to 'most lemony lemon cake', and regional favourites such as Drambuie ice-cream with heather honey. It is all served with chattiness and cheer. The wines are a long way from home in two senses, first in that they are ordered from Lay & Wheeler of Colchester, and second because, with the exception of Italian house red, the list is entirely drawn from outside Europe: an enterprising and perfectly reasonable practice. Prices are from £9.75.

CHEF: Frances MacLean   PROPRIETORS: Angus and Frances MacLean   OPEN: Tue to Sun 12 to 2, 7 to 8.30   CLOSED: L Oct, end Oct to Easter   MEALS: alc (main courses £3.50 to £12.50) SERVICE: not inc   CARDS: none   DETAILS: 24 seats. 4 seats outside. Private parties: 24 main room. Car park. Vegetarian meals. Children's helpings. Smart dress preferred. No smoking in dining-room. Wheelchair access (also WC). No music

KINLOCH RANNOCH   Perthshire & Kinross   map 11

▲ Cuilmore Cottage ⛊✗

Kinloch Rannoch PH16 5QB
TEL/FAX: (01882) 632218
first turning on left of southern loch road   COOKING 2
from Kinloch Rannoch   COST £28–£33

Imagine sitting at an exquisitely laid communal table in the original kitchen of a remote crofter's cottage, sampling the likes of 'boudin of chicken and leek served with a ragoût of mushrooms'. That is the romantic prospect offered by Cuilmore. The Steffens bake superlative breads, tend a luxuriant kitchen garden, raise hens and run 'Scotland's smallest hotel' with a high degree of devotion.

The menu offers no choice (although you can discuss preferences when booking), there is generally one sitting for dinner, but what appears is disarmingly good: witness a stunning avocado mousse decorated with chives, marjoram, a nasturtium flower and herb honey. Visitors have also praised main courses such as Barbary duck with thick tomato sauce, and noisettes of lamb inlaid with rosemary and mint mousse, plus 'a cornucopia of garden-fresh vegetables served, with floral accents, on a huge silver lazy Susan'. As a finale, chocolate mousse with redcurrant coulis has been greatly appreciated. The restaurant is unlicensed, but you can bring your own wine. Stay over, and you can sleep in a lavender-scented bed and dream of fresh raspberries and new-laid eggs for breakfast.

CHEF: Anita Steffen   PROPRIETORS: Jens and Anita Steffen   OPEN: all week D only 7 to 9; non-residents must book at least 24 hours in advance   CLOSED: Nov to Jan   MEALS: Set D £25. Unlicensed. BYO (no corkage)   SERVICE: not inc, card slips closed   CARDS: Access, Visa DETAILS: 10 seats. Private parties: 10 main room. Car park. Smart dress preferred. No smoking in dining-room. Music   ACCOMMODATION: 2 rooms, both with bath/shower. D,B&B £100. No children. Dogs welcome with own bedding. Afternoon teas. Garden. Fishing

'Soup of the day was mushroom, with the emphasis on mush.' (On eating in Wales)

SCOTLAND

KYLESKU Highland   map 11

▲ Kylesku Hotel ⁵✳

Kylesku IV27 4HW
TEL: (01971) 502231   FAX: (01971) 502313
on A894, at S side of old ferry crossing, by new bridge   COOKING 1
linking Ullapool and Kylestrome   COST £21–£41

Stretching away from the dining-room is 'one of the greatest views you are ever likely to encounter,' according to one enraptured reporter. Waves lap against the jetty in this isolated hamlet, and all is informality in the casual restaurant. Among the likely offerings are baked mussels in puff pastry with lobster sauce, smoked salmon salad, pickled herring, and grilled salmon with lobster sauce. 'Is there a theme here?' wondered one reporter: 'it's all lobster sauce and no lobster.' Marcel Klein does in fact get fish and shellfish from boats that land their catch nearby on the pier, and serves them alongside chicken tikka, roast duck breast, and grilled sirloin. Saucing is in need of a re-think, the aforementioned lobster sauce being 'heavily tomato-based' and only 'vaguely shellfishy' at inspection. One man does everything out front, from reception to waiting to breakfast duty. Wines are mostly French, and claret figures prominently. Prices start at £7.95.

CHEF/PROPRIETOR: Marcel Klein   OPEN: all week 12 to 2.15, 7 to 9.30   CLOSED: 1 Nov to 7 Mar
MEALS: alc (main courses £9 to £16.50). Set L and D £12.50 (2 courses) to £16.50. BYO £1.50.
Bar food available   SERVICE: not inc, card slips closed   CARDS: Access, Visa   DETAILS: 28
seats. 16 seats outside. Private parties: 10 main room. Car park. Vegetarian meals. Children's
helpings. Smart dress preferred. No smoking in dining-room. Wheelchair access (also WC).
Music   ACCOMMODATION: 7 rooms, all with bath/shower. TV. B&B £30 to £55. Deposit: 10%.
Children welcome. Baby facilities. Dogs welcome. Afternoon teas. Garden. Fishing

LINLITHGOW West Lothian   map 11

Champany Inn ▮

Champany, Linlithgow EH49 7LU
TEL: (01506) 834532 and 834388
FAX: (01506) 834302   COOKING 3*
2m NE of Linlithgow at junction of A904 and A803   COST £36–£77

There is nowhere else quite like this, where dedication to a single idea is so absolute, uncompromising and convincing. A sea-water pool in the bar contains live lobsters, and hunks of meat are laid out for inspection near the kitchen. The 'very Celtic' circular dining-room, with its mahogany tables and royal blue carpets, looks on to an orchard. Champany applies the idea of untramelled simplicity not just to Loch Gruinart oysters and salmon (both cold-smoked, and hot-smoked over mesquite chips, on the premises) but to beef in particular.

The source is Aberdeen Angus, hung on the bone for three weeks in Champany's own ionised chill-rooms, and then cut into fillet, strip loin, ribeye, T-bone, pope's eye, or to any other specification. The meat is simply grilled and served plain, although fillet may also be presented more flashily with a port and Stilton sauce, or a red wine and oyster version. 'I chose a piece of rib of beef by pointing at it,' remarked one visitor, 'and was asked how I wanted it cooked.' A

544

big basket of fresh vegetables – with ceps, chicken of the wood and chanterelle mushrooms for one autumn luncher – is brought for inspection. The meat is dark-fleshed and charred from the grill, with all the flavour a steak should have. 'Chips are all the better for being cooked in politically incorrect beef dripping.'

Prices may seem high, but they are worth it, and service is first-class. A chop and ale house offers cheaper fare in a family atmosphere. Wines are brilliant and include every possible candidate to match beef, from mature grand cru Burgundy through a long list of South African reds to fine Rioja. Drinkers of white wine should be equally satisfied, especially with the thoughtful list of half-bottles – good for kicking off proceedings. House South African is £10.50. CELLARMAN'S CHOICE: Thelema Mountain Vineyards Sauvignon Blanc 1995, Stellenbosch, South Africa, £24; Tinto Reserva 1987, Bodegas Valduero, Ribera del Duero, £27.50.

CHEF: Clive Davidson   PROPRIETORS: Clive and Anne Davidson   OPEN: Mon to Fri L 12.30 to 2, Mon to Sat D 7 to 10   CLOSED: 25 and 26 Dec, 1 and 2 Jan   MEALS: alc (main courses £12.50 to £25.50). Set L £13.75 (2 courses). Minimum £14.50 D   SERVICE: 10%, card slips closed   CARDS: Access, Amex, Diners, Switch, Visa   DETAILS: 50 seats. Private parties: 50 main room. Car park. No children under 8. Smart dress preferred. Wheelchair access (also men's WC). No music

---

MILNGAVIE East Dumbartonshire   map 11

Gingerhill £

1 Hillhead Street, Milngavie G62 8AF
TEL: (0141) 956 6515   COOKING 1
off A81, 4m N of Glasgow   COST £7–£37

The tiny first-floor restaurant, with paintings by local artist Pam Carter, runs on the enthusiasm and character of Carol Thomson, who 'not only greets and serves but also keeps up several conversations with customers at the same time', and Heather Gorman (formerly Andrew), who cooks a short menu in which seafood and vegetable dishes feature as prominently as meat. Some dishes hardly vary at all – most of the 'appetisers', for instance, which include marinated seafood salad and a choice of soups – and main-course vegetable Stroganov or mushroom thermidor. Meat consists of chargrilled fillet steak or Aberdeen Angus sirloin with a choice of sauces, and seafood depends on the weather, season and catch. Dinner is one sitting only: keep the table all evening, and incidentally note the free mineral water and lack of corkage charge. If that is not falling over backwards, we don't know what is.

CHEF: Heather Gorman   PROPRIETORS: Carol Thomson and Heather Gorman   OPEN: Mon to Sat L 12 to 3, Thur to Sat D 7 (1 sitting)   MEALS: alc (main courses L £2.50 to £9, D £9 to £17). Unlicensed, BYO (no corkage)   SERVICE: not inc, card slips closed   CARD: Visa   DETAILS: 27 seats. 16 seats outside. Private parties: 20 main room, 7 and 20 private rooms. Vegetarian meals. Children's helpings. No smoking while others eat. Music

---

Not inc *in the details at the end of an entry indicates that no service charge is made and any tipping is at the discretion of the customer.*

MOFFAT Dumfries & Galloway	map 11

▲ Well View ▼ ⅀✳

Ballplay Road, Moffat DG10 9JU	COOKING 1*
TEL: (01683) 220184 FAX: (01683) 220088	COST £17–£37

'This is a glorified guesthouse with completely dedicated owners who seem to enjoy the nightly ritual,' wrote one who stayed in this typically solid Borders house in a quiet street half a mile from the town centre. Meals are leisurely, the basic three courses expanded by a mid-meal soup or sorbet, plus a plate of cheese before dessert, and a dinner-party atmosphere surrounds both the evening and the food. Janet Schuckardt's gentle cooking style might produce glazed gammon with Cumberland sauce, or steamed turbot with a mustard and tomato cream sauce. One winter diner who began with an appetiser of haggis rissoles 'palatable enough even for non-haggis-eaters to enjoy' went on to enjoy a minced venison pakora, carrot and apricot soup wth coriander, strips of chicken with oyster mushrooms, and an iced orange parfait, all 'capably handled'. A solid list groups wines by regions, is well priced and includes an intriguing quartet of 'Scottish country wines'. Four house wines start at £8.20/£1.80 a glass.

CHEF: Janet Schuckardt PROPRIETORS: Janet and John Schuckardt OPEN: Mon to Fri and Sun L 12.15 to 1.15, all week D 6.30 to 8.30 MEALS: Set L £13, Set D £26 SERVICE: none, card slips closed CARDS: Access, Amex, Visa DETAILS: 24 seats. Private parties: 8 main room, 6 private room. Car park. Children's helpings. No children under 5 at D. Smart dress preferred. No smoking in dining-room. No music ACCOMMODATION: 6 rooms, all with bath/shower. TV. B&B £36 to £78. Deposit: £20. Children welcome. Baby facilities. Afternoon teas. Garden (*The Which? Hotel Guide*)

MUIR OF ORD Highland	map 11

▲ Dower House ▼ ⅀✳

Highfield, Muir of Ord IV6 7XN	
TEL/FAX: (01463) 870090	COOKING 2*
on A862, 1m N of Muir of Ord	COST £40–£48

A domestic feel is part of the attraction of this small country-house hotel. It is a pink cottage, framed in wrought iron, with family photographs and a warm welcome from the Aitchisons, who serve a four-course no-choice dinner. The problem with such a format is that the food can become ultra-conservative so as not to frighten anybody away, which can make it boring for more adventurous eaters; at the other extreme, madly experimental food might upset others. The Aitchisons manage to straddle these extremes comfortably, dealing in simple Anglo-French provincial fare.

Meals revolve around main courses of, say, breast of guinea-fowl on a bed of cabbage and green lentils, or a slice of herb-crusted halibut in a sorrel butter sauce. Soups have included spiced parsnip, and first courses are normally fish-based: warm scallop salad, perhaps, or a turbot soufflé with cream and mustard sauce. One April meal began with grilled gurnard served with an orange and basil butter sauce, followed by cream of chicory soup, and fillet of lamb with a rosemary sauce. Meals end with a choice of Scottish cheeses or, on this occasion, a gratin of tropical fruit. A straightforward and well-judged wine list spans a fine range of French wines and shorter pickings from Spain and the New World. The lengthy list of halves offers good value. House vins de pays are £13. CELLARMAN'S CHOICE: Allan Scott Sauvignon Blanc 1995, Marlborough, New Zealand, £20; Columbia Winery Pinot Noir 1993, Washington State, £15.

CHEF: Robyn Aitchison   PROPRIETORS: Robyn and Mena Aitchison   OPEN: all week D only 7.30 to 9; L by arrangement   CLOSED: 1 week Mar   MEALS: Set D £30   SERVICE: not inc   CARDS: Access, Amex, Visa   DETAILS: 26 seats. 8 seats outside. Private parties: 26 main room. Car park. Children's helpings. No children under 6 D. Smart dress preferred. No smoking in dining-room. Wheelchair access (also WC). No music   ACCOMMODATION: 5 rooms, all with bath/shower. TV. Phone. B&B £35 to £110. Deposit: 25%. Children welcome. Baby facilities. Dogs by arrangement. Garden

---

NAIRN Highland   map 11

▲ *Clifton House* ▮ ⁵✳

Viewfield Street, Nairn IV12 4HW
TEL: (01667) 453119   FAX: (01667) 452836   COOKING 2
W of town roundabout on A96   COST £24–£40

Nairn may have the air of a faded and genteel seaside resort, but Clifton House is decorated and furnished with the good taste of a true enthusiast: it is a family home, with an impressive personal collection of pictures. 'For J. Gordon Macintyre to have been running this hotel for 45 years and maintain his current degree of enthusiasm is little short of miraculous,' opened one report. The welcome from the man himself – kilted, white-bearded and smiling – is 'gracious, intelligent, amusing and generous', and he appears later with menus (no prices for ladies) and runs through what is on offer.

Mostly the menu will incorporate some fish, a roast, a bird, a grill, and some offal, with a simple French provincial bias (the menu speaks only French) in the form of egg mayonnaise, leg of lamb provençale, or pork kidneys. Grilled queen scallops 'perfectly cooked' with herb butter are a typical first course, and a soup follows: Crécy, perhaps, or fish with pistou. 'Excellent, well-hung beef' and 'a massive plate of shelled langoustines' provided the centrepieces of an inspection meal, although saucing seemed to lack precision. A huge wobbly dish of serve-yourself crème caramel, and an amaretto ice-cream followed.

The wine list is vast. The range of clarets and Burgundies alone is impressive, with claret vintages dating back nearly 40 years. Despite such grand touches, it is a remarkably sensible list that includes a number of highly drinkable wines at under £10 and plenty by the glass. CELLARMAN'S CHOICE: Sancerre 1994, Claude Riffault, £18; Menetou-Salon, Dom. de Chatenoy 1992, £14.50.

CHEF/PROPRIETOR: J. Gordon Macintyre   OPEN: all week 12.30 to 1, 7 to 9.30   CLOSED: mid-Dec to mid-Jan   MEALS: alc (main courses £9.50 to £14)   SERVICE: none   CARDS: Access, Amex, Diners, Visa   DETAILS: 40 seats. Private parties: 60 main room, 12 private room. Car park. Vegetarian meals. Children's helpings. Smart dress preferred. No smoking in 1 dining-room. Music   ACCOMMODATION: 12 rooms, all with bath/shower. B&B £50 to £96. Deposit: 20%. Children welcome. Dogs welcome. Afternoon teas. Garden (*The Which? Hotel Guide*)

SCOTLAND

NEWTON STEWART   Dumfries & Galloway   map 11

▲ *Kirroughtree Hotel* ⁵✗   NEW ENTRY

Newton Stewart DG8 6AN
TEL: (01671) 402141   FAX: (01671) 402425   COOKING 1
off A712, just outside Newton Stewart   COST £18–£40

'The atmosphere is totally conducive to relaxation,' one reporter managed to
summon the energy to write. The eighteenth-century white-painted house
looked 'a bit like a cake decoration' for another, but it is thoroughly steeped in
'old-fashioned values' and takes an opulent line in décor, with a grand staircase,
acres of flock wallpaper, and a semi-circular dining-room done out in attractive
shades of Wedgwood blue. Ian Bennett's food majors on renderings of classic
dishes, from a soup au pistou to locally smoked haddock on sliced Jersey
potatoes with a poached egg and grain mustard beurre blanc. Dishes may sound
complicated but, for a spring visitor, the draw was 'clear and simple flavours',
evident in a tart of tomatoes and anchovies, a crab bisque, and in a fillet of beef
'wonderfully cooked with a deep Madeira sauce and exemplary vegetables'.
Cheese is taken seriously, and crème brûlée with rhubarb compote brought one
reporter out in a rash of superlatives. The wine list needs picking through
carefully: there are some fine wines, but some sky-high prices. House Vin de
Pays d'Oc is £12.

CHEF: Ian Bennett   PROPRIETOR: McMillan Hotels Ltd   OPEN: all week 12 to 1.30, 7 to 9
CLOSED: 3 Jan to mid-Feb   MEALS: alc (main courses £10 to £12.50). Set L Sun £12, Set D
£27.50   SERVICE: none, card slips closed   CARDS: Access, Delta, Switch, Visa   DETAILS: 45
seats. Private parties: 20 main room. Car park. Vegetarian meals. No children under 10. Jacket
and tie. No smoking in dining-room. Music   ACCOMMODATION: 17 rooms, all with bath/shower.
TV. Phone. DB&B £64 to £176. Deposit: £15. No children under 10. Dogs welcome in lower
ground-floor rooms only. Afternoon teas. Garden

OBAN   Argyll & Bute   map 11

▲ *Heatherfield House* ⁵✗

Albert Road, Oban PA34 5EJ   COOKING 2
TEL/FAX: (01631) 562681   COST £19–£54

Refurbishment has continued in this family-run restaurant-with-rooms; the
wooden floor has been stripped and polished, the lounge decorated in cream and
blue, but the overall peace and quiet remain. The Robertsons are industrious
users of local produce. Chanterelles and ceps grow in abundance, as do quince
and blackberries, and eggs are laid by their own hens. A friend has a shoot,
making rabbit, pheasant and grouse easier to come by. Most of all, though, fish of
exceptional freshness and quality is available locally. Lobster, crab and crawfish
come from Corryvrechan, a local diver brings up scallops, mussels are from Loch
Etive, and oysters arrive from Mull. Wisely, these now form the basis of the
menu.

Mussels might be simply and traditionally steamed with white wine, herbs,
shallots and cream, while crab may be spiced, potted and served with a salad.
The oriental flavourings in some dishes owe their inspiration less to current fads

548

and more to Alasdair Robertson's upbringing in Malaya. Scallops and salmon, for instance, are marinated and served with mango on a salad of watercress and spinach. Comforting puddings include sticky toffee, and chocolate rum mousse, while 60-something wide-ranging wines are fairly priced, beginning with house French at £9.25.

CHEF: Alasdair Robertson   PROPRIETORS: Alasdair and Jane Robertson   OPEN: all week 12.30 to 2, 7.30 to 9.30   CLOSED: 4 Jan to end Feb   MEALS: alc (main courses £10.50 to £21). Set D £18.50. Minimum £7.50   SERVICE: not inc, card slips closed   CARDS: Access, Visa   DETAILS: 30 seats. 6 seats outside. Private parties: 35 main room. Car park. Children's helpings. Smart dress preferred. No smoking in dining-room. Music   ACCOMMODATION: 4 rooms, all with bath/shower. TV. D,B&B £40 to £87. Deposit: £30. Children welcome. Small dogs welcome. Garden

▲ *Knipoch Hotel* 🍾 🍴

Knipoch, Oban PA34 4QT
TEL: (01852) 316251   FAX: (01852) 316249
on A816, 6m S of Oban

COOKING 2
COST £39–£60

A long, mustard-coloured house on the shores of Loch Feochan, Knipoch aims for a relaxed version of country-house style. The fixed-price menus are of three or five courses. Salmon is smoked on the premises and served with salads dressed in a good nutty oil. Cock-a-leekie harks back to another era, its 'slight sweetness' derived from the ultra-traditional addition of prunes. Halibut and sole landed off Oban are brought together in a sauce of Pommery champagne and cream, while meats such as parsley-stuffed loin of lamb and impeccable Aberdeen Angus fillets deliver themselves of depths of flavour. Braised red cabbage oozing with sweet red wine liquor could well win converts to that most unloved of vegetables. Spiced dessert wine is the cooking medium for pears served on fudge sauce, while the variation on crêpes suzette that uses a caramel and orange sauce deepened perhaps with a whisky liqueur was judged 'the best course of the whole meal' in one report. Coffee made from green beans may give pause for thought; it means simply that the Craigs roast their own.

The wine list continues to be a major attraction; 'startlingly' long to one reporter, it is a comprehensive trawl through all the major regions of the world, including a whole page of bargain Bulgarians, five English wines, plenty from Beaujolais, Alsace and Germany, and a helpful list of recommendations. Prices will suit all pockets, and house wines start at £11.25. CELLARMAN'S CHOICE: Stoneleigh Vineyards Sauvignon Blanc 1995, Marlborough, New Zealand, £11.40; Côte de Brouilly 1994, Ch. de Thivin, £14.40.

CHEFS: Colin and Jenny Craig   PROPRIETORS: the Craig family   OPEN: all week D only 7.30 to 9; L by arrangement   CLOSED: Nov to mid-Feb   MEALS: Set D £29.50 to £39.50. BYO (no corkage)   SERVICE: not inc, card slips closed   CARDS: Access, Amex, Delta, Diners, Switch, Visa   DETAILS: 38 seats. Private parties: 24 main room, 12 private room. Car park. Children's helpings. Smart dress preferred. No smoking in dining-room. No music   ACCOMMODATION: 16 rooms, all with bath/shower. TV. Phone. B&B £35 to £200. Children welcome. Baby facilities. Afternoon teas. Garden

🍾 *denotes an outstanding wine cellar;* 🍴 *denotes a good wine list, worth travelling for.*

▲ *Peat Inn* 🍾 ✻

Peat Inn KY15 5LH
TEL: (01334) 840206   FAX: (01334) 840530   COOKING 4
at junction of B940 and B941, 6m SW of St Andrews   COST £29–£60

In 1997 David and Patricia Wilson clock up 25 years at this eighteenth-century inn. There is little else at the crossroads in the unassuming hamlet, yet it has drawn visitors from all over for its individual and committed cooking. A smell of wood-smoke in the bright lounge is the first sign that the Wilsons are not given to disguise and have a completely natural approach to everything they do. The food is justifiably proud of its roots, inseparable from its surroundings, and the high input of Scottish produce reflects one of the fundamental principles of a good restaurant. The Wilsons have encouraged, and in some cases helped to establish, cottage industries supplying a number of materials, including herbs, salads, vegetables and honey, and of course they make the most of abundant game and seafood.

Lunch offers no choice, while the à la carte dinner runs to half a dozen or more items per course. Although one visitor found the reliance on pigeon, venison, lobster and salmon (and the absence of white meat or lamb) rather restricting, these are the sorts of things that Scotland does best. The flavours of, say, pan-fried venison liver and kidney, or breast of pigeon with wild mushrooms in a truffle sauce, concentrate on the deep, rich, autumnal end of the spectrum, and are helped along by red wine sauces and piles of spicy lentils. Contrast is provided by light seafood salads, a whole poached lobster in a herb and vegetable broth, or whatever fish the boats bring in, and the two strands are integrated into the set menus to provide a balanced meal. A menu of the day and a tasting menu (evenings only) extend the options.

In all this a distinct lightness of touch is evident, as well as excellent timing, wonderful pastry, accomplished saucing, and a keen sense that, beyond a little careful spicing, dishes should appear relatively straightforward for best effect. Directness and sophistication characterise desserts, too, and although (or perhaps because) the repertoire doesn't change much, the results are mightily impressive, especially the feuilleté of white chocolate ice-cream with dark chocolate sauce. Wines are top-quality, listed without pretension, and particularly impressive from Champagne and Burgundy. Highlights are a large set of Pol Roger champagnes and an exemplary half-bottle range. Prices underline the down-to-earth approach. CELLARMAN'S CHOICE: St-Aubin 'Les Charmois' 1992, Dom. Ramonet, £28; Mercurey 1990, Michel Juillot, £25.

CHEFS: David Wilson and Angus Blacklaws   PROPRIETORS: David and Patricia Wilson   OPEN: Tue to Sat 12.30 for 1 (1 sitting), 7 to 9.30   CLOSED: 25 Dec, 1 Jan   MEALS: alc D (main courses £16 to £19). Set L £18.50, Set D £28 to £42. BYO £6   SERVICE: not inc, card slips closed CARDS: Access, Amex, Diners, Switch, Visa   DETAILS: 48 seats. Private parties: 24 main room, 12 private room. Car park. Vegetarian meals. Children's helpings. Smart dress preferred. No smoking in dining-room. Wheelchair access (also WC). No music   ACCOMMODATION: 8 rooms, all with bath/shower. TV. Phone. B&B £75 to £135. Rooms for disabled. Children welcome. Dogs welcome. Garden (*The Which? Hotel Guide*)

▲ *Cringletie House* ⅝✳

Peebles EH45 8PL
TEL: (01721) 730233   FAX: (01721) 730244   COOKING **2**
on A703, 2½m N of Peebles   COST £18–£38

A tree-lined drive leads to the turreted mansion in 28 acres of well-kept and productive grounds: the conservatory is filled with orchids, while vegetables, herbs and edible flowers emerge from the extensive kitchen garden. The format is very much in traditional country-house mould without much reference to salsas or other contemporary flourishes. Instead, the emphasis remains on the likes of confit of duck with lentils, poached salmon with sorrel sauce, or a vegetarian option such as nut loaf with asparagus cream.

Dinner begins with a no-choice but reliably good soup of perhaps carrot and lovage, or pea and lettuce, and choice thereafter is between three or four items. The kitchen is a busy one, making its own smoked cod's roe pâté, stuffing chicken breast with a Middle Eastern mixture of apricots, currants and sultanas, and providing gratifyingly home-made food along 'dinner-party' lines. Service is efficient and unobtrusive, and the wine list covers a lot of ground at generally sensible prices. House Duboeuf is £6.50 per half-litre.

CHEFS: Aileen Maguire, Sheila McKellar and Paul Maguire   PROPRIETORS: Stanley and Aileen Maguire   OPEN: all week 1 to 1.45, 7.30 to 8.30   CLOSED: 2 Jan to 7 Mar   MEALS: alc L (main courses £6 to £7). Set L Sun £16, Set D £25.50   SERVICE: not inc, card slips closed   CARDS: Access, Amex, Delta, Switch, Visa   DETAILS: 55 seats. Private parties: 27 main room. Car park. Vegetarian meals. Children's helpings. No smoking in dining-room. No music ACCOMMODATION: 13 rooms, all with bath/shower. TV. Phone. B&B £55 to £110. Children welcome. Dogs welcome. Afternoon teas. Garden (*The Which? Hotel Guide*)

PERTH Perthshire & Kinross   map 11

Let's Eat   **NEW ENTRY**

77–79 Kinnoull Street, Perth PH1 5EZ   COOKING **1***
TEL: (01738) 643377   FAX: (01738) 621464   COST £20–£39

'Hooray – Tony Heath is back in town,' exclaimed a Scottish reporter. Having presided over the Coach House in Perth during the 1980s, and more recently the Courtyard in Aberdeen (see entry), the chef in question opened Let's Eat in what was the old Theatre Royal and later an antique shop. The cavernous, high-ceilinged room fairly buzzes with life. Quality and value for money is a difficult equation to get right, but early reports suggest that Heath is on to a winner. His menu is bolstered by daily specials with the emphasis on 'ex-marine life'. Blackened fillet of salmon shares the billing with 'well-hung' ribeye steak, and terrines vary from day to day. Early rave reviews have cited wild mushroom risotto, chicken breasts in ginger and lime sauce, and marinated tuna on a bed of couscous, while 'glorious' puddings might include 'perfect' apple strudel. Service is considerate. The affordable wine list has representatives from most major countries. House wine is £9.25.

CHEFS: Tony Heath, Lewis Pringle and Thomas Burns   PROPRIETORS: Tony Heath and Shona
Drysdale   OPEN: Tue to Sat 12 to 2.15, 6.30 to 9.45   CLOSED: 6 to 23 July   MEALS: alc (main
courses £5.50 to £13)   SERVICE: not inc, card slips closed   CARDS: Access, Amex, Delta,
Switch, Visa   DETAILS: 60 seats. Private parties: 60 main room. Vegetarian meals. Children's
helpings. Wheelchair access (also WC). Music

Number Thirty Three

33 George Street, Perth PH1 5LA   COOKING 1
TEL: (01738) 633771   COST £26–£45

Since 1987 the Billinghursts have worked hard to establish this as a reputable
city-centre seafood restaurant. The décor is a Tardis-trip back to the art deco
world of the 1930s with appropriate musical accompaniment. Visitors can eat
lightly in the Oyster Bar from a menu of starters and sweets ranging from
bouillabaisse, and fettuccine with goats' cheese, sun-dried tomatoes and basil,
to pavlova of Strathmore raspberries. Meals in the restaurant are a touch more
ambitious, with centrepieces such as baked fillet of salmon with cranberry
sauce, grilled turbot with a mild two-pepper sauce, and whole lemon sole with
herb butter. Those wanting red meat might be offered lamb cutlets réforme. The
cooking remains sound, although recent reports suggest that prices may be 'a
wee bit steep'. A new list of more than 100 wines was in the pipeline as we went
to press. House wine is £10.60.

CHEF: Mary Billinghurst   PROPRIETORS: Gavin and Mary Billinghurst   OPEN: Tue to Sat 12.30 to
2.30, 6.30 to 9.30   CLOSED: 25 and 26 Dec, 1 and 2 Jan, last 2 weeks Jan   MEALS: alc (main
courses £11 to £15). Light meals available   SERVICE: not inc   CARDS: Access, Amex, Visa
DETAILS: 24 seats. Private parties: 24 main room. Children's helpings. No children under 5.
Smart dress preferred. No cigars in dining-room. Wheelchair access (no WC). Music

---

PORT APPIN   Argyll & Bute   map 11

▲ Airds Hotel ▐ ⁵✳

Port Appin PA38 4DF
TEL: (01631) 730236   FAX: (01631) 730535   COOKING 4
2m off A828, on E shore of Loch Linnhe   COST £45–£54

The old whitewashed inn looking out across Loch Linnhe 'still retains its
warmth and charm'. The simple garden has been landscaped and provides a
good setting for aperitifs when the weather allows. Otherwise, the ornate rooms
inside, complete with open fire, stag's head and curling prints, offer 'deep
comfort and instant service with exceptional canapés'. The menu (along with the
wine list) is placed in bedrooms beforehand, so that no rushed decisions are
required, and might typically list a choice of four starters, then a fixed soup, three
main courses, and half a dozen desserts.

'The choice is so wide,' one reporter felt, 'that one could only blame oneself if
one did not orchestrate a harmonious dinner from what is on offer.' Another
couple who stayed a few nights, however, were disappointed to find a
significant number of dishes repeated from one evening to the next. Meals are
eaten overlooking the loch, amid fresh flowers, starched linen, polished silver

and gleaming glasses. 'Any thought of smoking or music in the dining-room would be laughable.' One June occasion began with a generous lobster and scallop salad with a 'superb' pesto dressing, the salad topped with onion shredded 'as fine as spun sugar', followed by pea and mint soup.

Graeme Allen's country style of cooking naturally makes the most of local prawns and other seafood in the form of crab tart, or roast monkfish tail, and there is a classical simplicity in his treatment of materials. Breast of woodpigeon, for example, comes with potato galette, foie gras, wild mushrooms and a Madeira sauce, while Aberdeen Angus beef is partnered with leek confit, roasted shallots, morels, and a red wine sauce. Desserts, meanwhile, avoid both cliché and over-elaboration in poached pear shortcake with caramel and lime sauce, or an iced soufflé of coffee and pistachio with a coffee sauce. 'In food, hospitality and service it is supreme,' enthused one supporter, and the dinner and accommodation deal is a good one.

Wines are taken very seriously, and the huge list roams the world. There's plenty to splash out on, but those searching for a good bottle at under £20 won't be disappointed, especially in the south-west-France section. A classy bunch of house wines start at £12.

CHEF: Graeme Allen PROPRIETORS: Eric and Betty Allen, and Graeme and Anne Allen OPEN: all week D only 8 (1 sitting) MEALS: Set D £35. Light L available SERVICE: not inc, card slips closed CARDS: Access, Amex, Switch, Visa DETAILS: 34 seats. Private parties: 40 main room. Car park. Children's helpings. Smart dress preferred. No smoking in dining-room. No music ACCOMMODATION: 12 rooms, all with bath/shower. TV. Phone. D,B&B £98 to £135. Deposit: £100. Rooms for disabled. Children welcome. Baby facilities. Dogs by arrangement. Afternoon teas. Garden (The Which? Hotel Guide)

▲ Pierhouse ⁵✴

Port Appin PA38 4DE
TEL: (01631) 730302   FAX: (01631) 730400
off A828, on E shore of Loch Linnhe,
opposite Lismore ferry

COOKING 2
COST £19–£46

'Some of the most scintillatingly fresh seafood I've ever tasted,' began one enthusiastic reporter, getting straight to the point of this informal lochside diner beside the pier. 'Superlatively good scallops' are collected by a local diver and come with lemon or garlic butter. They impress for the careful timing that sears the outside yet leaves them translucent within. Not a lot of cooking skill may be needed to serve a plate of Dublin Bay prawns in garlic butter, but with such good raw materials straight from the loch, who wants anything more elaborate?

Judicious buying and strict control of freshness play a key part, and it takes a good cook to know when to leave well enough alone. For that reason, some of the simplest dishes appeal: Lismore oysters, Loch Etive mussels, or the big Pierhouse Platter. Vegetables are notably good and freshly prepared, while high-quality dark chocolate is used in the death-by-chocolate pudding. The wide-ranging and up-to-date wine list is fairly priced, with half a dozen bottles under £10, including South African Sauvignon Blanc and Australian Semillon/Chardonnay.

CHEF: Sheila MacLeod   PROPRIETORS: the MacLeod family   OPEN: all week 12 to 3, 6.30 to 9.30   MEALS: alc (main courses £6.50 to £17)   SERVICE: not inc, card slips closed   CARDS: Access, Switch, Visa   DETAILS: 50 seats. 20 seats outside. Private parties: 30 main room, 20 private room. Car park. Vegetarian meals. Children's helpings. Smart dress preferred. No smoking in 1 dining-room. Wheelchair access (also WC). Music   ACCOMMODATION: 11 rooms, all with bath/shower. TV. B&B £35 to £79. Rooms for disabled. Children welcome. Afternoon teas. Garden

---

PORTPATRICK   Dumfries & Galloway   map 11

▲ *Knockinaam Lodge* 🍷 ✸

Portpatrick DG9 9AD
TEL: (01776) 810471   FAX: (01776) 810435   COOKING 1*
off A77, 3m S of Portpatrick   COST £34–£54

The lovely old house is a splendid retreat of unparalleled tranquillity, looking out across a private beach to the Irish Sea. Inside, the décor mixes checks and floral designs, and the French waiter mixes a good cocktail. Tony Pierce has moved up from sous-chef and is a dab hand at pastry, which makes appetisers, desserts and petits fours particularly successful. His food is as classically based as warm globe artichoke with mushroom duxelles topped with poached egg and hollandaise sauce.

In general, though, steaming and fat-free treatments are preferred, and first-class materials have included a stop-watch-timed fillet of cod and tasty guinea-fowl. But the result for our inspector was photogenic food that lacked vitality, interest and zip: a faint, muted and 'polite' tarragon sauce, and more flavour from the chives decorating a celery soup than from the celery itself, for example. The only choice offered on the four-course dinner menu is between cheese and dessert, and if the cheese at inspection was typical, the advice is to take dessert. The wine list is extensive and lists some top properties, but it does include a dozen house wines at under £15.

CHEF: Tony Pierce   PROPRIETORS: Michael Bricker and Pauline Ashworth   OPEN: all week 12 to 2, 7.30 to 9.30   MEALS: Set L £25, Set D £35   SERVICE: not inc   CARDS: Access, Amex, Diners, Switch, Visa   DETAILS: 36 seats. Private parties: 36 main room, 20 private room. Car park. Children's helpings L; no children under 12 D. Smart dress preferred. No smoking in dining-room. Wheelchair access (also WC). Music   ACCOMMODATION: 10 rooms, all with bath/shower. TV. Phone. D,B&B £90 to £186. Deposit: £100. Children welcome; high teas for under-12s. Baby facilities. Dogs by arrangement. Afternoon teas. Garden (*The Which? Hotel Guide*)

'*The dessert was a gratin of summer fruits with a peach parfait. I expected raspberries, strawberries, red and black currants, blackberries, bilberries or loganberries. What I got was sliced apple, pink grapefruit and chopped under-ripe mango all buried beneath a tasteless lurid-pink froth.*' (On eating in Wales)

✸ *indicates that smoking is either banned altogether or that a dining-room is maintained for non-smokers. The symbol does not apply to restaurants that simply have no-smoking areas.*

ST MARGARET'S HOPE   Orkney   map 11

▲ *The Creel* ⁛※

Front Road, St Margaret's Hope KW17 2SL
TEL: (01856) 831311
off A961, 13m S of Kirkwall,   COOKING **3**
on South Ronaldsay island   COST £21–£47

If the journey to Orkney sounds like a hike, you can be sure there are rewards
enough on the way: 'gorgeous scenery in mainland Scotland, a sea crossing with
the majestic island of Hoy towering and glowering to starboard, then over three
sets of barriers linking one island to the next to a small quiet bay.' And there
waits the Creel, Alan and Joyce Craigie's buff-painted three-storey restaurant-
with-rooms. Aquatic themes decorate the dining-room, as well they might, and
the ambience is warmly friendly and informal.

The cooking is a revelation. Bannocks and soda bread 'still steaming from the
oven' are brought to table, the former made from kiln-dried barley to give a
peaty, smoked flavour, the latter golden in the centre from being enriched with
egg. A 'subtle and enjoyable' creamed scallop chowder began one meal, a
gathering of tiny scallops garnishing a smooth, herb-flecked soup. Parton Bree is
another soup, this time a deep-brown crab bisque of astonishing intensity. This
is of course the spot for fish-cakes, too, three crisply deep-fried golfballs bulked
with large salmon flakes on a lemon cream. Orcadian fish stew brings together
firm-fleshed species with a large scallop in a fine fish stock with diced tomato
and carrot. Meats, such as tenderly sauté duck breast on a sauce of roasted red
peppers, may be a touch less impressive, but perhaps only because the fish is of
such exemplary quality that comparison is almost unfair.

A quintet of Orkney cheeses is offered, with Swanney – a pale, Cheddar-like
cows'-milk cheese – getting the vote from one man. Lemon pie is showered with
icing sugar and blowtorched, the filling an unctuous lemon cream of such
richness it appears (deceptively) to be based on cream cheese, while chocolate
mousse rewrites the rulebook for density and power. In a region where good
eating is of necessity not easy to come by, the Creel shines like a beacon. If there
is a downside, it lies in the short and undistinguished wine list that needs an
overhaul. House wines are £7.50.

CHEF: Alan Craigie   PROPRIETORS: Alan and Joyce Craigie   OPEN: all week D only 7 to 9.30 May
to Oct; telephone first to check in Nov and Dec, Mar and Apr   CLOSED: Jan and Feb   MEALS: alc
(main courses £9 to £21.50)   SERVICE: not inc, card slips closed   CARDS: Access, Visa
DETAILS: 34 seats. Private parties: 34 main room. Car park. Children's helpings. Smart dress
preferred. No smoking in dining-room. No music   ACCOMMODATION: 3 rooms, all with
bath/shower. TV. B&B £30 to £65. Deposit: 10%. Children welcome. Baby facilities. Afternoon
teas

---

*Several sharp operators have tried to extort money from restaurateurs on the promise of an
entry in a guidebook that has never appeared. The* Good Food Guide *makes no charge
for inclusion.*

All main entries are fully indexed at the back of the Guide.

STEIN Highland   map 11

▲ *Lochbay* 🍴✳ £

1–2 Macleod Terrace, Stein IV55 8GA   COOKING 1
TEL: (01470) 592235   COST £16–£42

Stein's string of houses ends in a terrace of whitewashed fishermen's cottages, two of which have been converted into the Lochbay restaurant. The Greenhalghs preside over a happy, welcoming atmosphere and serve nothing but fish, much of it local. The 'hearty' fish soup is a good one, full of roughly chopped vegetables and small chunks of fish: 'just what one might hope for in a seaside restaurant.' Alternative openers include 'cephalopods' (squid, octopus and cuttlefish marinated in olive oil), or oysters at £1 each, followed perhaps by grilled lobster. Chips are 'quite the best we have tasted'. The advice is to stay with the simpler dishes. Finish, perhaps, with clootie dumpling, and drink from the short and sympathetically priced list that includes three 'wines' from Scotland. House French is £6.90.

CHEFS/PROPRIETORS: Peter and Margaret Greenhalgh   OPEN: Sun to Fri 12 to 3, 6 to 9   CLOSED: end Oct to Easter   MEALS: alc (main courses £6 to £19)   SERVICE: not inc   CARDS: Access, Visa   DETAILS: 26 seats. 8 seats outside. Car park. Children's helpings. Smart dress preferred. No smoking in dining-room. Wheelchair access (no WC). Music   ACCOMMODATION: 2 rooms, both with bath/shower. TV. B&B £25 to £37. Children welcome. Baby facilities. Afternoon teas. Garden

---

STEWARTON East Ayrshire   map 11

▲ *Chapeltoun House* 🍷 🍴✳

Irvine Road, Stewarton KA3 3ED
TEL: (01560) 482696   FAX: (01560) 485100   COOKING 1
2m from Stewarton on B769 towards Irvine   COST £23–£42

The house was built in 1900 in the Ayrshire countryside as a family home for a Glasgow industrialist. It still conveys all the confidence and comfort that money could buy at the time: oak panelling, teak floors and a sense of space that is rare in such a domestic setting. Dinner offers a generous selection, beginning perhaps with vegetable terrine, or a lamb and tomato broth with tarragon dumplings. Around five main courses are extended with a similar number of 'specialities' for a small supplement, plus a couple of vegetarian options and a dish of the day: fish is taken seriously and varies with the catch. Sauces tend to use sherry, Madeira, port and vermouth to accompany guinea-fowl, rack of lamb, or Aberdeen Angus beef, while desserts might get a slug of an appropriate liqueur: Grand Marnier with an iced bitter chocolate and sultana parfait, for instance.

Around 150 wines have been carefully chosen from all the major regions. Prices range from a generous selection at under £15 to top clarets and 30-year-old Tokai at £180. Half-bottles are plentiful, and French house wines are around £10.60. CELLARMAN'S CHOICE: Bourgogne Blanc Les Sétilles 1993, Leflaive, £15.70; Marienberg Cabernet Sauvignon 1992, McLaren Vale, S. Australia, £14.

CHEF: Tom O'Donnell   PROPRIETORS: Colin and Graeme McKenzie   OPEN: all week 12 to 2, 7 to 9.15   MEALS: Set L £15.90, Set D £19.90 (2 courses) to £23.80   SERVICE: not inc   CARDS: Access, Amex, Delta, Switch, Visa   DETAILS: 50 seats. Private parties: 50 main room, 20 and 50 private rooms. Car park. Vegetarian meals. No children under 12. Smart dress preferred. No smoking in dining-room. Music   ACCOMMODATION: 8 rooms, all with bath/shower. TV. Phone. B&B £70 to £139. No children under 12. Dogs by arrangement. Afternoon teas. Garden. Fishing (*The Which? Hotel Guide*)

STRONTIAN Highland   map 11

▲ *Kilcamb Lodge* ♥ ⅝✳

Strontian PH36 4HY
TEL: (01967) 402257   FAX: (01967) 402041   COOKING 2
on A861, by N shore of Loch Sunart   COST £32–£39

The hotel itself is rather dwarfed by the magnificence of its surroundings; from a distance it is a white dot on the shore of Loch Sunart, a lushly wooded hillside towering behind. Peter Blakeway has recently assumed a greater role in running the place, as well as continuing to cook. The style has been compared by one reader to 'good dinner-party cooking', as opposed to anything more highfalutin. Hence haggis and neeps might be offered as a starter, followed by tomato and mint soup, and then plainly casseroled guinea-fowl served in its cooking juices.

There is, however, a more ambitious bent in open ravioli of squat lobsters with mushrooms both 'wild and tame', quail and spinach pancakes using a nutty batter, and the local salmon, lightly cooked, the flesh 'falling in fat, creamy, pale orange curds', in a sauce of champagne and chives. Whisky tart with heather honey ice-cream is highly praised as a successfully delicious idea and for its impeccable regionality. Service is 'very pleasant and helpful'. Wines are a well-chosen international set, with the New World strongly represented and some genuine bargains dotted about. A sensible set of five house wines starts at £8.50.

CHEF: Peter Blakeway   PROPRIETORS: the Blakeway family   OPEN: all week D only 7.30 (1 sitting)   CLOSED: early Nov to mid-Dec, mid-Jan to early Mar exc some weekends – phone to check   MEALS: Set D £25. Light L available   SERVICE: not inc, card slips closed   CARDS: Access, Delta, Switch, Visa   DETAILS: 28 seats. Private parties: 28 main room. Car park. Children's helpings. Smart dress preferred. No smoking in dining-room. Wheelchair access (also men's WC). No music   ACCOMMODATION: 11 rooms, all with bath/shower. TV. B&B £69.50 to £150. Deposit: £35. Children welcome. Baby facilities. Dogs by arrangement. Afternoon teas. Garden. Fishing (*The Which? Hotel Guide*)

'I didn't know most of the cheeses by sight, and I wasn't told. When I asked, my waiter didn't know either, but offered to find out "if I wanted". I wanted, and he returned to give me five names which he couldn't tie to the slices. He couldn't pronounce the mainly French names, which he recited off a little piece of paper in his hand. When I tried to look at it, he wouldn't let me.' (On eating in London)

See inside the front cover for an explanation of the symbols used at the tops of entries.

SWINTON Borders   map 11

▲ *Wheatsheaf Hotel, Four Seasons* 🍴 £

Main Street, Swinton TD11 3JJ
TEL/FAX: (01890) 860257   COOKING 1
on A6112, Coldstream to Duns road   COST £17–£41

'The Wheatsheaf is a pub that has grown a bit,' writes a reporter of the Reids'
welcoming hostelry within angling distance of the River Tweed. Alan Reid
cooks in a more ambitious vein than found in most pubs, offering a grilled
Teviotdale cheese sauced with redcurrants and port, and pork medallions with
peppers and olives in a tomato and basil sauce. One reader found everything up
to speed at a September dinner, from the marinated herring to the 'very
seductive' desserts, which may include a Scots version of crème brûlée (with
raspberries and Glayva), or prune and apricot tart. Service is friendly. Forage
through the wine list; there are good things among the jumble. House wines start
at £8.45.

CHEFS: Alan Reid and John Keir PROPRIETORS: Alan and Julie Reid OPEN: Tue to Sun 12 to
2.15, 6 to 9.30 CLOSED: 2 weeks end Feb, last week Oct, Sun D Nov to Apr MEALS: alc (main
courses £4.50 to £15) SERVICE: not inc, card slips closed CARDS: Access, Visa DETAILS: 48
seats. 24 seats outside. Private parties: 30 main room, 18 and 30 private rooms. Car park.
Vegetarian meals. Children's helpings. Smart dress preferred. No smoking in dining-room.
Wheelchair access (also WC). No music ACCOMMODATION: 4 rooms, 3 with bath/shower. TV.
B&B £28 to £60. Deposit: £20. Children welcome. Baby facilities. Dogs welcome by
arrangement in bedrooms only. Garden (*The Which? Hotel Guide*)

TROON South Ayrshire   map 11

▲ *Highgrove House*

Old Loans Road, Troon KA10 7HL   COOKING 1
TEL: (01292) 312511 FAX: (01292) 318228   COST £18–£43

Highgrove is a handsome white house with a charming view over the bay. It
offers, according to one reporter, 'bourgeois comfort and solid portions of protein
sourced from reliable local suppliers to satisfy the healthy golfing appetites of
mainly local customers, who love to use it for celebration'. Both the fixed-price
dinner menu and generous *carte* show a leaning towards seafood. Cullen skink at
an inspection meal was a winner – 'thick, creamy, good fish stock base, richly
flavoured with chunks of tasty smoked haddock' – though a rather heavy hand
with the saucing of some dishes proved less successful: cheese glazing is applied
with equal enthusiasm to a gratin of mushrooms and to poached salmon.
Nevertheless, good ingredients feature, and desserts might include a snappy nut
basket with strawberries and iced parfait, or an airy chocolate mousse. A list of
around 60 varied bins includes house wine from north-eastern Spain at £9.95.

CHEF: James Allison PROPRIETORS: William and Catherine Costley OPEN: all week 12 to 2.15,
6.30 to 9.30 MEALS: alc (main courses L £6 to £13, D £12 to £13.50). Set D £22.50 SERVICE:
not inc, card slips closed CARDS: Access, Amex, Switch, Visa DETAILS: 100 seats. Car park.
Vegetarian meals. Children's helpings. Wheelchair access (also WC). Music ACCOMMODATION:
9 rooms, all with bath/shower. TV. Phone. B&B £60 to £120. Children welcome. Baby facilities.
Afternoon teas. Garden

▲ *Lochgreen House* 🍴

Monktonhill Road, Southwood, Troon KA10 7EN	COOKING 2*
TEL: (01292) 313343 FAX: (01292) 318661	COST £26–£43

This may fairly be considered the flagship establishment of the Costleys' chain of two (see entry above), and has seen expansion in the form of seven extra bedrooms and a considerably enlarged kitchen. Tranquillity and space (it has 16 acres of manicured estate) are part of the pull, and these restful themes are echoed in the oak-panelled lounge, and in the comfortable seating and well-spread tables of the dining-room. There is a real commitment to quality in the kitchen's industry. The Scottish larder is called on to supply the customary salmon, venison and smoked fish, and these are dealt with in generally up-to-date fashion. Smoked salmon, for example, is made into a sausage and placed on a mussel casserole with a saffron sauce. Alcohol is a favoured ingredient: a slug of dry sherry is poured into the wild mushroom soup, and a port preserve accompanies a terrine containing chicken, Stilton, red pepper and apple. The speciality of the house is a bread, butter, sherry and sultana pudding with custard. Some interesting bottles pepper the wine list (see white Loires, for instance), and prices cover a wide range, from three-figure pedigree claret to house wine at £12.50.

CHEFS: William Costley and Ian Ferguson   PROPRIETORS: William and Catherine Costley   OPEN: all week 12 to 2, 7 to 9   MEALS: alc L (main courses £8.50). Set L £16.95, Set D £26.50   SERVICE: not inc, card slips closed   CARDS: Access, Amex, Switch, Visa   DETAILS: 85 seats. Private parties: 48 main room, 10 to 40 private rooms. Car park. Vegetarian meals. Children's helpings. Smart dress preferred. No smoking in dining-room. Wheelchair access (also WC). No music   ACCOMMODATION: 15 rooms, all with bath/shower. TV. Phone. B&B £90 to £140. Rooms for disabled. Children welcome. Afternoon teas. Garden (*The Which? Hotel Guide*)

▲ *Turnberry Hotel, Turnberry Restaurant*

Turnberry KA26 9LT	COOKING 3
TEL: (01655) 331000 FAX: (01655) 331706	COST £34–£112

As 1980s advertising might have put it, Turnberry consists of an ace hotel with two quite good championship golf courses attached. Come up the red-paved drive through immaculate expanses of green grass, and find inside a number of eating areas and more menus on offer than you can shake a niblick at. The flagship remains the Turnberry Restaurant, where diners can enjoy the 'marvel-lous' sea views, be soothed by the resident pianist and enjoy Stewart Cameron's assured classical cooking.

The drill is a fixed-price menu of four courses and coffee with soup at second, or an expensive *carte* that kicks off with beluga caviare (at £48 an ounce) and all the trimmings to get you in the mood. Rough-textured prawn- and crab-cakes with tomato and fennel mayonnaise come with plenty of 'gutsy flavour', while chicken consommé (with pieces of good dark meat and superior white wine) shows technique that is confident. Fish may be grilled lemon sole with ratatouille sauce and anchovy butter, meat a pair of 'springy' veal medallions with a sauce of 'crusty pan juices' and Marsala, accompanied by egg vermicelli with a spoonful of truffles folded in. Almond tuile fashioned into a pyramid filled with a feather-light chocolate mousse enriched with treacle makes a show-stopping dessert. Flavours make straight for the flag carefully avoiding the bunkers of fashionability. Service throughout is impeccably painstaking, even putting in overtime to fillet fish at table. The wine list is as expansive as you would anticipate in the context, and of course as expensive. Choices are not uniformly excellent, however, and the £19 for house wine buys either an Entre-Deux-Mers or a red Bordeaux Supérieur, albeit a 1990.

CHEF: Stewart Cameron PROPRIETOR: Nitto World Ltd OPEN: Sun L 1 to 2.30, all week D 7.30 to 10; meals also available in Bay and Clubhouse restaurants MEALS: alc D (main courses £22 to £36.50). Set L Sun £21.50 (inc glass of champagne), Set D £41.50 SERVICE: not inc, card slips closed CARDS: Access, Amex, Diners, Switch, Visa DETAILS: 180 seats. Private parties: 240 main room, 120 private room. Car park. Vegetarian meals. Children's helpings. Jacket and tie. No pipes in dining-room. Wheelchair access (also WC). Music ACCOMMODATION: 132 rooms, all with bath/shower. TV. Phone. B&B £150 to £260. Rooms for disabled. Children welcome. Dogs welcome in bedrooms only. Afternoon teas. Garden. Swimming-pool (*The Which? Hotel Guide*)

UIG   Western Isles   map 11

▲ *Baile-na-Cille* ⁵⭑

Timsgarry, Uig, Isle of Lewis HS2 9JD
TEL: (01851) 672242 FAX: (01851) 672241   COOKING 1*
B8011 to Uig, then right down track on to shore   COST £22–£27

The tiny hotel stands beside a white sandy beach, remote from everything except a number of other white sandy beaches. You can't turn around without seeing a good view of something. The restaurant is somewhat unusual in having neither menu nor wine list. Joanna Gollin simply cooks what is fresh and local, including salmon, mussels, lamb and venison, and uses herbs and fruit from the garden. Preferences are indicated when booking, and the highlight of one reporter's short stay was 'extraordinarily good' mushroom soup, followed by boned and rolled chicken with a pesto stuffing, then individual orange soufflés served with a jug of apricot and orange sauce to pour in. Joanna Gollin's other hobby is flying.

Wines are mostly from Yapp Bros therefore dependably good, and come in at either £8.50, or £12.50 'for the posh ones'. The bottles are laid out in the dining-room 'and you literally took the one you wanted'. All are available by the half-bottle since the Gollins kindly offer to drink the other half. In the Baile-na-Cille newsletter – *An Innkeeper Writes* – Richard Gollin asks himself the question, 'Is it true that you do not include VAT in your prices because you are too thick to work it out?' and answers affirmatively, adding that prices have not changed for four years. The Gollins tell us that they now plan to stay open over winter, although Joanna Gollin won't be doing the cooking then.

The Guide *relies on feedback from its readers. Especially welcome are reports on new restaurants appearing in the book for the first time. All letters to the* Guide *are acknowledged.*

CHEF: Joanna Gollin PROPRIETORS: Joanna and Richard Gollin OPEN: all week D only 7 (1 sitting). Snack L available MEALS: Set D £18. BYO (no corkage) SERVICE: net prices, card slips closed CARDS: Access, Visa DETAILS: 30 seats. Private parties: 30 main room. Car park. Vegetarian meals. Children's helpings. No smoking in dining-room. No music ACCOMMODATION: 12 rooms, 9 with bath/shower. B&B £19 to £60. Deposit: £50. Children welcome. Baby facilities. Dogs welcome. Afternoon teas. Garden. Fishing (*The Which? Hotel Guide*)

ULLAPOOL Highland	map 11

▲ *Altnaharrie Inn* 🍷 ⅝✳

Ullapool IV26 2SS	COOKING 5
TEL: (01854) 633230	COST £72–£86

'The whole Altnaharrie experience is magical.' 'The best meal my wife and I have ever had.' 'Superb setting, unforgettable food, a comprehensive wine list, all delightfully served by Fred Brown.' These are just some of the plaudits for this peaceful lochside retreat. 'How they are able to sustain their level of achievement given this location is truly remarkable.' But sustain it they do, as regulars confirm. 'As with previous visits, Altnaharrie never fails to exceed the high expectations placed on it,' as year in, year out, it ploughs its unique furrow.

The uniqueness stems partly from its 'idyllic setting'. Leave the car behind in Ullapool – there are no roads to Altnaharrie – and journey across the loch. 'Mother Goose' has been replaced by a bigger and sturdier boat, but everyone arrives on an equal footing and the lack of pretension is very much a part of the draw. The house is 'wonderfully decorated and furnished' thanks to Gunn Eriksen's sheer Scandinavian good taste. Don't worry about the noise from the generator, which is switched off at bedtime. After a warm welcome, a sense of eager anticipation sets in, spurred on by appetisers and aperitifs as dinner approaches.

The other reason Altnaharrie is unique is that Gunn Eriksen follows no fads, copies no recipes, joins no school. She is driven by her supply of impeccably fine ingredients, and a chef's good sense of how to get the best out of them. It sounds easy, with fish and shellfish on the doorstep, but all the best materials have to be developed and nurtured, whether they come from lobster creels in the loch, are landed at Lochinver or are bred or shot locally. Their assembly into a meal is significant. Although everybody sits down to eat at 8pm, with no choice before dessert, not all will be eating the same meal, since records are kept and menus arranged so that each visit will be different from the last.

The pattern is five courses, beginning perhaps with a mousseline of scallops and crab in a thin pastry shell, accompanied by two sauces, or salmon in champagne aspic with a warm butter sauce. A soup follows – creamy lobster with cucumber, for example – although reporters seem to find the word 'soup' inadequate for this course. After the lightness of seafood might come the richness of young rabbit, the saddle filled with liver, kidney, mushrooms and foie gras; or else pork, served with a ravioli of pig's trotters and sweetbreads in a red Burgundy sauce. Cheeses from France, England, Scotland, Wales, Ireland, even Gunn Eriksen's native Norway, are followed by dessert, ostensibly a choice, although most reporters seem to eat them all: apple baked on thin pastry with

SCOTLAND

calvados ice-cream and caramel sauce, a soft lemon tart, or perhaps strawberries marinated in champagne. France forms the backbone of an impressive wine list, and receives strong support from top Italian, Spanish and New World producers. The lengthy half-bottle list is commendable, as is the short house selection, although some may find the wines by the glass, including an unnamed champagne at £9, a bit steep. House wines start at at £13.70.

CHEF: Gunn Eriksen   PROPRIETORS: Fred Brown and Gunn Eriksen   OPEN: all week D only 8 (1 sitting).   CLOSED: mid-Nov to Easter   MEALS: Set D £65. Light L in lounge for residents only   SERVICE: none, card slips closed   CARDS: Access, Delta, Switch, Visa   DETAILS: 18 seats. Private parties: 16 main room. Car park. No children under 8. Smart dress preferred. No smoking in dining-room. No music   ACCOMMODATION: 8 rooms, all with bath/shower. DB&B £145 to £350. Deposit: £150. Children by arrangement. Dogs by arrangement. Garden (*The Which? Hotel Guide*)

WALLS Shetland   map 11

▲ *Burrastow House* ⁵⁺

Walls ZE2 9PB
TEL: (01595) 809307   FAX: (01595) 809213
at Walls drive to top of hill, turn left, then follow road   COOKING 1
for 2m to Burrastow   COST £20–£45

This remote eighteenth-century house has its own beach, with seals and otters for entertainment, and plenty of opportunity for walking. In this part of the country, especially after a day out, a peat fire is particularly welcoming, and there is a library to relax in. The isolated location does not mean that Bo Simmons is cut off from the busy culinary world. Lunch might be anything from a bowl of pistou soup to corn fritters with salsa, or farfalle with wild mushrooms and artichokes, while dinner is four courses, one of them cheese. Spinach and coconut soup, half a boiled lobster with mayonnaise, and damson ice-cream were on offer one night, while another produced red pepper and courgette mousse, Greek beef stifado, and chocolate pancakes with a chestnut filling. House wines, from France, are £10.25.

CHEF: Bo Simmons   PROPRIETORS: Bo Simmons and Henry Anderton   OPEN: Tue to Sun L 12.30 to 2.30, Tue to Sat D 7.30 to 9 (residents only Mon L and Sun and Mon D)   CLOSED: 1 Jan to 28 Feb   MEALS: alc L (main courses £6.50 to £8.50). Set D £28.50. BYO 10%   SERVICE: not inc, card slips closed   CARDS: Access, Delta, Switch, Visa   DETAILS: 55 seats. Private parties: 25 main room, 15 and 25 private rooms. Car park. Vegetarian meals. Children's helpings. No smoking in dining-room. Wheelchair access (also WC). Music   ACCOMMODATION: 5 rooms, all with bath/shower. D,B&B £51 to £142. Deposit: 10%. Rooms for disabled. Children welcome. Baby facilities. Dogs welcome. Afternoon teas. Garden. Fishing (*The Which? Hotel Guide*)

562

Wales

ABERDOVEY   Caernarfonshire & Merionethshire   map 7

▲ *Penhelig Arms Hotel* 🍷 ⚒

Aberdovey LL35 0LT
TEL: (01654) 767215   FAX: (01654) 767690
on A493 Tywyn to Machynlleth road, opposite   COOKING 1*
Penhelig station   COST £19–£40

The black and white harbourside inn dating from 1750 is modest, welcoming, informal and unpretentious. The bar has had a face-lift, Robert Hughes is invariably on hand to see that everything runs smoothly, and the appeal is 'straightforward, old-fashioned country cooking' served in generous portions. It all has a homely feel, from thick green pea soup with a swirl of cream to braised lamb, and the no-frills approach also brings fresh-tasting sardines in garlic butter, perhaps followed by pheasant with bread sauce and a deep-flavoured gravy. The simple style continues with blackcurrant crumble, and steamed syrup sponge with custard. Bread could be improved. Sunday lunch is 'an unbelievable £11.50', and an aperitif glass of champagne for £3 is a steal.

Many would agree with the couple who pronounced the wine list 'a joy to browse through and refreshingly lacking in snobbery'. Robert Hughes's enthusiasm for wine jumps off the page – this, the excellent range and generous prices are a formula which inspires. House wines start at £9. CELLARMAN'S CHOICE: Ca' del Solo Malvasia Bianca 1994, Bonny Doon, California, £14.50; Gevrey-Chambertin 1990, Dom. Maume, £19.90.

CHEF: Janie Howkins   PROPRIETORS: Robert and Sally Hughes   OPEN: restaurant Sun L 12 to 2, all week D 7 to 9   CLOSED: 25 and 26 Dec   MEALS: alc bar L (main courses £4 to £9.50). Set L Sun £11.50, Set D £18.50   SERVICE: not inc, card slips closed   CARDS: Access, Delta, Switch, Visa   DETAILS: 34 seats. Private parties: 18 main room. Car park. Children's helpings. Smart dress preferred. No smoking in dining-room. No music   ACCOMMODATION: 10 rooms, all with bath/shower. TV. Phone. B&B £39 to £78. Deposit: £40. Children welcome. Dogs welcome. Afternoon teas. Garden (*The Which? Hotel Guide*)

The text of entries is based on unsolicited reports sent in by readers, backed up by inspections conducted anonymously. The factual details under the text are from questionnaires the Guide *sends to all restaurants that feature in the book.*

The Guide *is totally independent, accepts no free hospitality, and survives on the number of copies sold each year.*

ABERSOCH   Caernarfonshire & Merionethshire   map 7

▲ *Porth Tocyn Hotel*

Abersoch LL53 7BU
TEL: (01758) 713303   FAX: (01758) 713538
on minor road 2m S of Abersoch through hamlets of
Sarn Bach and Bwlchtocyn

COOKING 2
COST £23–£42

This year Porth Tocyn celebrates 40 unbroken years in the *Guide* – the first restaurant outside London to do so – and we offer our congratulations. It has taken three generations of Fletcher-Brewers to do it, and is a tribute to a resilient and committed family. The décor is simple, appointments are sturdy, staff are friendly, children get a fair deal, the owner is a character, and customers are mostly regulars. The wonderful views across Tremadog Bay to Snowdonia remain unchanged, but any successful restaurant must move with the times. 'In a long-established place like this,' writes Nick Fletcher-Brewer, 'change comes about by nuance, not radical shifts.' Perhaps the biggest innovation is that the kitchen is now equipped with a steamer and a charcoal grill, which have expanded the possibilities and the repertoire.

The fare, according to one visitor, is 'hotel food of superior standard' organised around a short menu with four choices per course plus an intermediate soup. Bloody Mary soup sounds a bit electric, but there may also be grilled goats' cheese with a rhubarb and ginger chutney, grilled sea bass, and a steamed sponge for pudding. The tussle between smokers and non-smokers has caused a few problems during the year, although the Fletcher-Brewers are by no means alone in their dilemma, caught between the conflicting demands of equally unsympathetic parties. Wines are carefully selected, cover a lot of ground and, although some mark-ups are on the high side, many attractive bottles sell for well below £20.

CHEF: Louise Fletcher-Brewer   PROPRIETORS: the Fletcher-Brewer family   OPEN: Sun L 12.30 to 2, all week D 7.30 to 9   CLOSED: mid-Nov to week before Easter   MEALS: Set L Sun buffet £16, Set D £20 (2 courses) to £26.75. Light L available Mon to Sat   SERVICE: not inc, card slips closed   CARDS: Access, Delta, Switch, Visa   DETAILS: 50 seats. 30 seats outside. Private parties: 50 main room. Car park. Children's helpings. No children under 7 D. Smart dress preferred. Wheelchair access (no WC). No music   ACCOMMODATION: 17 rooms, all with bath/shower. TV. Phone. B&B £43.50 to £104. Deposit: £40. Rooms for disabled. Children welcome. Baby facilities. Dogs welcome in bedrooms only. Afternoon teas. Garden. Swimming-pool (*The Which? Hotel Guide*)

▲ *Riverside Hotel*

Abersoch LL53 7HW
TEL: (01758) 712419   FAX: (01758) 712671
on A499, 6m SW of Pwllheli

COOKING 1
COST £30–£37

In 1997 John and Wendy Bakewell chalk up 30 years at their 'homely, pristine, warm and comfortable' seaside hotel overlooking the harbour and River Soch. The menu stays as simple as can be, often relying on ingredients alone to do the talking: smoked goose breast on a green leaf salad, toasted goats' cheese with crispy bacon, and a selection of Welsh farmhouse cheeses. Main courses tend to favour white meats and fish, along the lines of tenderloin of pork with a cider brandy sauce, or poached guinea-fowl with celery. While a skinned and poached fillet of brill on parsnip purée may not make much of a splash visually, it was judged by a reporter to be 'in good harmony, with flavours combining well'. Toblerone ice-cream is a house speciality, or there might be an equally rich-tasting toffee pudding. Around 40 mixed wines stay below £20, yet the list includes some exciting names. House wines are from £10.95.

CHEFS/PROPRIETORS: John and Wendy Bakewell   OPEN: all week D only 7.30 to 9   CLOSED: Nov to Mar   MEALS: Set D £22. Bar L available   SERVICE: not inc, card slips closed   CARDS: Access, Amex, Visa   DETAILS: 30 seats. Private parties: 30 main room. Car park. No children under 5 D. Smart dress preferred. Music   ACCOMMODATION: 12 rooms, all with bath/shower. TV. Phone. B&B £32 to £84. Deposit: £30. Children welcome. Baby facilities. Afternoon teas. Garden. Swimming-pool

---

BEAUMARIS Anglesey   map 7

▲ *Ye Olde Bulls Head* ♟ ✻

Castle Street, Beaumaris LL58 8AP	COOKING 2
TEL: (01248) 810329 FAX: (01248) 811294	COST £24–£45

A hundred yards from the castle, and dating from the fifteenth century, the Bulls Head has every excuse for its uneven floors, twisting stairs and small archways. The courtyard claims to have the largest single-hinged gate in the British Isles. The ground floor is a pub, and the route to the upstairs dining-room with its decorative old firearms requires a guide. Few culinary stones are left unturned in a repertoire that takes in Bury black pudding, Arbroath smokies, steamed salmon with laverbread, and a Thai-spiced brochette of monkfish, alongside pasta, pesto, ratatouille and other Mediterranean flourishes.

In true British fashion, relishes and chutneys contribute positive flavours to meats such as duck confit, or to a terrine of chicken and game which, at inspection, needed something to buck it up. The highlight of that meal was a piece of fresh, steamed grey mullet, served unusually with sea kale. Welsh cheeses provide a good alternative to tarts, parfaits and ice-creams, and service is willing and straightforward. Wines have been carefully selected and all essential regions are covered by good producers. Prices are hearteningly low. Five house wines are £13.50. CELLARMAN'S CHOICE: Meursault, Au Vieux Saint Christophe 1993, J.-P. Fichet, £24.75; Underhill Shiraz 1990, Yarra Yering, Victoria, Australia, £23.95.

CHEFS: Soames Whittingham and Keith Rothwell   PROPRIETOR: Rothwell and Robertson Ltd OPEN: Sun L 12 to 1.30, all week D 7.30 to 9.30   CLOSED: 25 and 26 Dec, 1 Jan   MEALS: alc D (main courses £11.50 to £15). Set L Sun £14.75, Set D Mon to Fri £19.95. Bar L available Mon to Sat   SERVICE: not inc   CARDS: Access, Amex, Switch, Visa   DETAILS: 60 seats. Private parties: 60 main room. Car park. Vegetarian meals. Children welcome L. No children under 7 D. Smart dress preferred. No smoking in dining-room. No music   ACCOMMODATION: 15 rooms, all with bath/shower. TV. Phone. B&B £45 to £89. Rooms for disabled. Children welcome. Baby facilities (*The Which? Hotel Guide*)

▲ *This symbol means accommodation is available.*

BRECHFA Carmarthenshire   map 4

▲ Tŷ Mawr ⁵✻

Brechfa SA32 7RA
TEL: (01267) 202332   FAX: (01267) 202437   COOKING 2
on B4310, 6m N of A40 at Nantgaredig   COST £19–£35

Tŷ Mawr is as Welsh as they come. The old stone house stands by the banks of
the Marlais on the edge of Brechfa Forest – some of the most stunning scenery in
Britain. Original Welsh oak furniture is dotted around the heavily timbered
rooms, and the floors are quarry-tiled. Beryl Tudhope is in touch with her roots,
and she uses local ingredients as a focus. Superb home-baked breads are made
with flour from a nearby mill, sewin and salmon are caught on the Towy, beef
and lamb are from a local supplier. Dinner is fixed-price for three courses, and
there is much to recommend: chicken liver and almond pâté gets plenty of votes,
although the speciality is 'Dominicans' – a twice-baked cheese soufflé. Sewin
with sorrel sauce, and hake cutlets topped with lemon and herbs vie for attention
with roast duck breast flavoured with honey, orange and thyme. Puddings may
be 'hit and miss', although pear upside-down pudding has been 'brilliant'. Dick
Tudhope is an extremely charming, quietly efficient host. The wine list offers an
enthralling selection from all parts of the globe and house wine is £9.25.

CHEF: Beryl Tudhope   PROPRIETORS: Beryl and Dick Tudhope   OPEN: Wed to Mon 12 to 2, 7 to
9.30 (bookings only)   MEALS: Set L £12.95, Set D £22   SERVICE: not inc, card slips closed
CARDS: Access, Amex, Visa   DETAILS: 35 seats. Private parties: 35 main room. Car park.
Vegetarian meals. Children's helpings. Smart dress preferred. No smoking in dining-room.
Music   ACCOMMODATION: 5 rooms, all with bath/shower. D,B&B £52 to £116. Deposit: £10.
Children welcome. Baby facilities. Dogs welcome. Afternoon teas. Garden (*The Which? Hotel
Guide*)

BROAD HAVEN Pembrokeshire   map 4

▲ Druidstone £

Druidstone Haven, Broad Haven,
nr Haverfordwest SA62 3NE
TEL: (01437) 781221   FAX: (01437) 781133
from B4341 at Broad Haven turn right at sea; after 1½m   COOKING 1
turn left to Druidstone Haven; hotel ¾m on right   COST £16–£31

'I have never been to a restaurant like this before,' claimed one reporter, adding
that 'it seems to be a mixture of bar, restaurant, arts centre, and holiday home for
children.' The old stone house, on a clifftop overlooking the beach, is littered
with the paraphernalia of painters, actors and holidaymakers, and there are
cheery, chatty children running all over the place. Only in the rather austere
dining-room is there any sense of calm, and although one reporter felt that 'the
restaurant side seemed to be taking second place to arts and philanthropy', it
nevertheless turns out fresh and plentiful crab salad, and good leek soup with
oatmeal, as well as falafel, chicken tikka, stir-fried beef, and strawberry
cheesecake. The food is simple, rustic and homely. Jane cooks by 'instinct',
while Rod takes charge of Indian and West Indian excursions. Service is

cheerful, informal and friendly. Thirty straightforward wines include house French at £7.

CHEFS: Rod and Jane Bell, and Donna Banner   PROPRIETORS: Rod and Jane Bell   OPEN: Sun L 1 to 2, Mon to Sat D 7.30 to 9.30.   CLOSED: Mon to Wed 6 weeks before Christmas and after New Year   MEALS: alc (main courses £6 to £12). Bar food available   SERVICE: not inc, card slips closed   CARDS: Access, Amex, Delta, Switch, Visa   DETAILS: 40 seats. Private parties: 40 main room, 10 private room. Car park. Vegetarian meals. Children's helpings. No smoking while others eat. Wheelchair access (also WC). Music   ACCOMMODATION: 9 rooms. B&B £26.50 to £63. Deposit: £20. Rooms for disabled. Children welcome. Baby facilities. Dogs welcome. Afternoon teas. Garden (The Which? Hotel Guide)

CAPEL GARMON   Aberconwy & Colwyn   map 7

▲ Tan-y-Foel ⚡   **NEW ENTRY**

Capel Garmon, nr Betws-y-coed LL26 0RE
TEL: (01690) 710507   FAX: (01690) 710681
take turning marked Capel Garmon and Nebo from
A470 about halfway between Betws-y-Coed and   COOKING 2
Llanrwst   COST £32–£42

'We were quite bowled over to find such a high standard of cooking in so remote a place,' began one report of this well-run, small and friendly hotel, personably run by the Pitmans. The stone building, once a farm, translates as 'house under the hillside' and overlooks the beautiful Conwy Valley. Although the décor may be a little flamboyant for the setting, it is 'staggeringly outshone' by the cooking. Dine at any time you like – in a conservatory tagged on to the back – so long as it's around 7.45.

The daily-changing menu is not extensive, but Janet Pitman is a confident and accomplished cook who puts an emphasis on local produce and robust flavours, serving up fillet of tuna marinated in Thai spices, grilled and served on a bed of buttered samphire, or a galette of fried aubergine, Carmarthen ham and apple slices with a mustard vinaigrette that was considered 'a triumph'. At inspection, collops of pan-fried monkfish that 'positively tasted of the sea' came with a fresh coriander cream sauce, while a tart apple charlotte with sweet egg custard ended a well-balanced meal. Peter Pitman does front-of-house, and dispenses wine from a varied and fairly priced list with a good selection of half-bottles. Mexican house wine is around £10.

CHEF: Janet Pitman   PROPRIETORS: Peter and Janet Pitman   OPEN: all week D only 7.30 to 8.30   MEALS: Set D £22 to £25   SERVICE: not inc, card slips closed   CARDS: Access, Amex, Delta, Diners, Switch, Visa   DETAILS: 16 seats. Car park. No children under 7. Smart dress preferred. No smoking in dining-room. No music   ACCOMMODATION: 7 rooms, all with bath/shower. TV. Phone. B&B £53 to £136. Deposit: £50. No children under 7. Afternoon teas. Garden (The Which? Hotel Guide)

'"Red sea bream," replied the waiter when I asked after the fish of the day. I wasn't sure if he meant the sea bream was red, or that the bream had come from the Red Sea.'
(On eating in London)

Armless Dragon £

97 Wyeverne Road, Cathays, Cardiff CF2 4BG	COOKING 1*
TEL: (01222) 382357	COST £15–£37

Two knocked-together cottages behind the university are the backdrop for some lively and enterprising cooking. The atmosphere is pleasant, relaxed and friendly, and the dining-room seems to double as a mini art gallery. Daily dishes, chalked on boards and carried around, provide much of the variety and interest. What matters is not where ideas come from, but what the kitchen does with them, and it has a field-day with all sorts of ingredients and treatments. Fish might include gurnard, swordfish, Arctic char, and mahi mahi, while carnivores are kept busy with game pies, lamb and lentil hotpot, and rabbit livers on parsley rice. Meatless dishes are taken very seriously – perhaps laver-balls with mushrooms, or parsnip and artichoke gougère with creamed leeks – and desserts might include a chocolate and brandy ganache. A short list of wines stays mostly under £15, starting with house French at £7.90.

CHEFS: David Richards and Debbie Coleman PROPRIETOR: David Richards OPEN: Tue to Fri L 12 to 2.15, Tue to Sat D 7 to 10.30 (11 Sat) CLOSED: Christmas to New Year MEALS: alc (main courses £8 to £14). Set L £7.50 (2 courses) to £9.50 SERVICE: not inc CARDS: Access, Amex, Delta, Diners, Switch, Visa DETAILS: 45 seats. Private parties: 50 main room. Vegetarian meals. Children's helpings. No smoking while others eat. No cigars/pipes in dining-room. Wheelchair access (no WC). Music

La Brasserie

61 St Mary Street, Cardiff CF1 1FE	COOKING 1
TEL: (01222) 372164 FAX: (01222) 668092	COST £21–£41

One of three Cardiff restaurants under the same ownership (see Champers and Le Monde, below), La Brasserie shares the same zest for informality, with wooden tables, loud pop Muzak, sawdust floors and plain cooking. Order at the counter, choose a salad and wait for the chargrill to work its magic on almost any form of protein you care to name, including king prawns, fillet steak, salmon, spare ribs and brochettes of lamb or fish. Order more, and it's a main course; order less, it's a starter. Extension is planned to accommodate more covers, and opening times are due to increase. Spit roasting will extend from suckling pig to leg of lamb, pigeon, pheasant and rabbit, but the good-value £5 lunch remains. Wines are largely French, with house wine £8.95.

CHEFS: Kurt Fleming and Carmen Laventura PROPRIETOR: Benigno Martinez OPEN: Mon to Sat 12 to 2.30, 7 to 12 CLOSED: 25 and 26 Dec MEALS: alc (main courses £7.50 to £16). Set L £5 (2 courses) SERVICE: not inc, card slips closed CARDS: Access, Amex, Diners, Visa DETAILS: 400 seats. Vegetarian meals. Children's helpings. Smart dress preferred. Music

---

Dining-rooms where music, either live or recorded, is never played are signalled by No music *in the details at the end of an entry.*

Le Cassoulet

5 Romilly Crescent, Canton, Cardiff CF1 9NP   COOKING 2*
TEL/FAX: (01222) 221905   COST £24–£47

The postal address may be Canton, but the Viaders assure us that their restaurant is in the mostly residential area of Pontcanna. Gilbert Viader hails from Toulouse, and cassoulet is a fixture, otherwise the cooking generally plays to a modern beat, and readers have singled out Mark Freeman's technical know-how and his eye for presentation. A poached egg set in smoked salmon and cucumber on a bed of celeriac and olives sounds like a neat construction, as does a pithiviers of marinated goats' cheese with pickled walnuts and a creamed walnut dressing. Stuffing is a favourite device: suprême of chicken is filled with spinach, veal gets an asparagus mousseline, while 'delicious' tenderloin of pork is packed with apricots and accompanied by an intriguing medley of mushrooms. Puddings are impressively handled, as in an 'excellent' cappuccino and Tia Maria mousse served in a cup-and-saucer-shaped tuile. The hard-working owners are ably supported by 'delightful' staff. Wines are drawn exclusively from the French regions, with sound choice across the board. House wine is £9.95.

CHEF: Mark Freeman   PROPRIETORS: Gilbert and Claire Viader   OPEN: Tue to Fri L 12 to 2, Tue to Sat D 7 to 10   CLOSED: 10 days Christmas, Aug   MEALS: alc L (main courses £14 to £16). Set L £11.95 (2 courses) to £14.95, Set D £21 (2 courses) to £26   SERVICE: not inc   CARDS: Access, Amex, Delta, Diners, Switch, Visa   DETAILS: 50 seats. Private parties: 50 main room. Vegetarian meals. Children's helpings. No music

Champers £   ✓   29/1/97

62 St Mary Street, Cardiff CF1 1FE   COOKING 1
TEL: (01222) 373363   FAX: (01222) 668092   COST £18–£36

Where La Brasserie (see entry, opposite) inclines to France, and Le Monde (see entry, below) to fish, this third member of the Martinez group in Cardiff goes in primarily for tapas and meat dishes, with wines to match. It is just as informal as the others, with sawdust on the floor, and a display of meats and fish for chargrilling: rump, sirloin or fillet steaks, kebabs and perhaps monkfish or salmon. Baked potato or French fries usually accompany. Tapas, however, set the place apart, and vary from grilled sardines to diced potatoes with chilli and paprika, from a lima bean stew containing bacon, chorizo and black pudding, to a dish of tripe and chickpeas, all mostly below £3. The food is no less enjoyable for being predictable. Spanish cheeses might include Manchego, and among the wines are some good-quality Riojas. House wines are £8.95.

CHEF: Dinis Louis   PROPRIETOR: Benigno Martinez   OPEN: Mon to Sat L 12 to 2.30, all week D 7 (7.30 Sun) to 12   CLOSED: 25 and 26 Dec   MEALS: alc (main courses £4.50 to £12)   SERVICE: not inc   CARDS: Access, Amex, Diners, Visa   DETAILS: 180 seats. Private parties: 30 main room, 100 private room. Vegetarian meals. Children's helpings. Smart dress preferred. Wheelchair access (also WC). Music

All main entries are fully indexed at the back of the Guide.

Le Monde

60 St Mary Street, Cardiff CF1 1FE   COOKING 1*
TEL: (01222) 387376   FAX: (01222) 668092   COST £23–£45

Wooden floors covered in sawdust typify the informality of this city-centre wine bar, considered the pick of the Martinez trio (see also La Brasserie and Champers, above). There are no bookings, service is 'friendly and swift', and fish is the mainstay, most of it simply charcoal grilled. More to the point, you get to see and choose the fish first. A wide selection is displayed in the chill counter: maybe oysters, shrimps, prawns of various kinds, sea bass, brill, halibut, Dover sole, and a whole host of others depending on season and catch, from local sewin or lobster to grouper and red snapper. 'In my opinion,' ran one report, 'this is the best fish restaurant in South Wales.' It also serves steaks and kebabs, indeed more or less anything that can be charcoal grilled. Desserts are not taken as seriously as the rest of the food – it is either cheese or crêpes suzette – and the wine list specialises in Riojas, clarets and Burgundies. House wine is £9.95.

CHEFS: David Legg, Stephane Harve and Chris Ruck   PROPRIETOR: Benigno Martinez   OPEN: Mon to Sat noon to 2.30, 7 to midnight   CLOSED: 25 and 26 Dec   MEALS: alc (main courses £7.50 to £17)   SERVICE: not inc, card slips closed   CARDS: Access, Amex, Diners, Visa   DETAILS: 180 seats. Private parties: 45 main room, 120 private room. Children welcome. Smart dress preferred. Music. Air-conditioned

---

CLYTHA Monmouthshire   map 2

▲ Clytha Arms ⚑✳

Clytha NP7 9BW
TEL/FAX: (01873) 840206
off old Abergavenny to Raglan road,   COOKING 2
S of A40, 5m E of Abergavenny   COST £16–£36

The whitewashed inn, a dower house to Clytha Manor and the eighteenth-century castle, is on the old route from Abergavenny to Raglan, set back from the road amid lawns and mature trees. The inside is 'pristine', with pitch pine church pew furniture and plenty of room for drinking at the bar. 'We fix a menu for a month, and use the blackboard to try things out,' write the Cannings, whose repertoire displays an increasing maturity and confidence. Quality is apparent at all levels, from one-plate bar lunches of home-made pasties, sausages, or spinach and laverbread rissoles, to a restaurant main course of pink lamb chops served with kidney, liver and sweetbreads.

Roast duck at one meal was 'an old-fashioned, crisp-skinned well-done bird' with moist flesh and a gamey savouriness. 'It is good to see a chef serving duck this way,' wrote an inspector who had obviously had one pink magret too many. Puddings might take in Sauternes cream with prunes, or a firm, creamy pear tart with raspberry sorbet, while cheeses include a roll call of Pencarreg, Llanboidy, Harlech and others in impressively good condition. The fairly traditional wine list is reasonably priced, with drinkable bottles under £10. House wine starts at £7.30.

CHEFS/PROPRIETORS: Andrew Canning and Beverly Canning   OPEN: Tue to Sun and bank hol Mon L 12.30 to 2.15, Tue to Sat and bank hol Mon D 7.30 to 9.30   MEALS: alc (main courses £8 to £13). Set L Sun £9.50. BYO £2.50   SERVICE: not inc, card slips closed   CARDS: Access, Delta, Switch, Visa   DETAILS: 60 seats. 20 seats outside. Private parties: 50 main room, 20 private room. Car park. Vegetarian meals. Children's helpings. No smoking in dining-room. Wheelchair access (no WC). No music   ACCOMMODATION: 3 rooms, all with bath/shower. TV. B&B £40 to £65. Children welcome. Baby facilities. Dogs welcome. Afternoon teas. Garden

---

COLWYN BAY   Aberconwy & Colwyn   map 7

Café Niçoise £

124 Abergele Road, Colwyn Bay LL29 7PS   COOKING 1*
TEL: (01492) 531555   COST £20–£41

The name should leave you in no doubt as to the intentions of this modest bistro. Most approve of the colourfully decorated dining-room, although one reporter felt that a little sprucing up wouldn't go amiss. The menu is chalked on a blackboard which is brought to the table and recited in detail. Warm marinated chicken salad with orange sauce and sesame dressing has been praised, although the ingredients of salade niçoise left much to be desired, particularly the tinned tuna. Main courses have also been uneven: juicy scallops with fillets of red snapper, and 'succulent' medallions of venison with port and juniper sauce have outshone bland 'sausage-like rolls of chicken'. The assiette du chef shows skill in the dessert department, while the cheeseboard is reckoned to be 'one of the best in Wales'. Service gets points for friendliness. The fifty-strong wine list features seven house wines all sold by the glass for £1.65, starting at £7.75 the bottle.

CHEF: Carl Swift   PROPRIETORS: Carl and Lynne Swift   OPEN: Wed to Sat L 12 to 2, Mon to Sat D 7 to 10   CLOSED: 1 week Jan, 1 week June   MEALS: alc (main courses £7 to £14). Set L £10.75 (2 courses) to £12.95, Set D Mon to Fri £10.75 (2 courses) to £12.95. Minimum £5. BYO £3.50   SERVICE: not inc, card slips closed   CARDS: Access, Amex, Delta, Diners, Switch, Visa   DETAILS: 32 seats. Private parties: 30 main room. Vegetarian meals. Children's helpings. Smart dress preferred. Music

---

CREIGIAU   Cardiff   map 4

Caesar's Arms £

Cardiff Road, Creigiau CF4 8NN   COOKING 1
TEL: (01222) 890486   FAX: (01222) 892176   COST £20–£43

The 'massively extended' whitewashed pub set in a vast expanse of car park is not going to win any design awards, but within its many-windowed interior the genuine pub ambience is preserved, and it offers greater comfort than many pubs. Fish and seafood are the principal business, chosen from display cabinets and priced by the pound if whole and cooked to order. The proprietors are proud of their sea bass cooked in rock salt, and rightly so, according to a reporter who judged it 'superb – moist and full of flavour'. Fat crawfish tails, scallops bonne femme, and white fish such as monk and hake are usually on offer, while meat-eaters may settle for Welsh lamb steak or honeyed crispy duck. Rough-cut chips or new potatoes come with everything. Chocolate and orange torte, raspberry pavlova, or apple crumble and custard are the kinds of desserts to expect. It all adds up, thought one patriot, to 'the sort of place that Britain does really well'. House wines from the Languedoc are £7.95.

CHEF: Earl Smikle   PROPRIETOR: Steady Chance Ltd   OPEN: all week L 12 to 2.30 (3.30 Sun), Mon to Sat D 7 to 10.30   CLOSED: 25 Dec   MEALS: alc (main courses £6 to £16)   SERVICE: not inc, card slips closed   CARDS: Access, Amex, Delta, Diners, Switch, Visa   DETAILS: 100 seats. 60 seats outside. Private parties: 30 main room, 60 private room. Car park. Vegetarian meals. Children's helpings Sun L. Smart dress preferred. Wheelchair access (also WC). Music

---

CRICKHOWELL Powys   map 4

▲ Bear Hotel ⁵⁕   NEW ENTRY

Crickhowell NP8 1BW   COOKING 1
TEL: (01873) 810408   FAX: (01873) 811696   COST £25–£40

Like many an old coaching-inn turned country hotel, the Bear retains a palpable feeling of period charm, right down to the bustle in the bar on a busy Saturday night. The dining-room walls bristle with pikes and swords and mounted deer heads, though piped music restores modern banality. The cooking is largely forthright English fare, pleasing for the likes of pumpkin soup with a 'suitably sticky' herb dumpling, or braised lamb hock with 'plump, delicately cooked' kidneys in a rosemary sauce, less so when it tries trendier dishes, as in saffron pasta with warm avocado. Ginger ice-cream is assertively spiced, helped along with a sauce of ginger wine and a brandy-snap. Service remains 'pleasant and competent' even when every seat in the dining-room is taken. Wines offer a well-chosen, enterprising range at fair prices. House French is £7.95.

CHEF: Graham Malia   PROPRIETORS: Judy Hindmarsh and Stephen Hindmarsh   OPEN: Sun L 12 to 2, Mon to Sat D 7 to 9.45 (9.30 Sun)   MEALS: alc (main courses £10 to £15). Bar food available   SERVICE: not inc   CARDS: Access, Amex, Delta, Switch, Visa   DETAILS: 100 seats. 40 seats outside. Private parties: 60 main room, 30 and 60 private rooms. Car park. Vegetarian meals. Children welcome. Smart dress preferred. No smoking in 1 dining-room. Wheelchair access (also WC). Music   ACCOMMODATION: 32 rooms, all with bath/shower. TV. Phone. B&B £42 to £90. Rooms for disabled. Children welcome. Dogs welcome. Garden

---

Nantyffin Cider Mill Inn £

Brecon Road, Crickhowell NP8 1SG
TEL/FAX: (01873) 810775   COOKING 1*
1½m W of Crickhowell at junction of A40 and A479   COST £17–£40

This is a fine location: beside the River Usk, on the edge of the Black Mountains in the Brecon Beacons National Park. The fifteenth-century stone drovers' inn is a pub/restaurant, complete with exposed beams, where meals can be eaten off plain wooden tables in the bar or off linen cloths in the dining-room, which houses an old mill-wheel. The atmosphere is relaxed and service copes well when things get busy. Various menus span a range of dishes, from deep-fried Brie through Indian-spiced lentil fritters to braised oxtail. Local materials figure prominently, including rabbit, pheasant, 'pink and succulent lamb', even suckling pig, and an organic farm supplies vegetables. A contemporary streak runs through the kitchen, too, producing soft, creamy goats' cheese on bruschetta with a dash of pesto, and grey mullet with aubergine salsa and polenta, while puddings can be as 'wonderfully gooey' as hot chocolate fudge brownie. Wines are well chosen, arranged by style and very fairly marked up (with a dozen or so under £10).

CHEFS/PROPRIETORS: Sean Gerrard and Glyn Bridgeman OPEN: Tue to Sun 12 to 2.30, 6.30 to 9.45 (7 to 9 Sun) CLOSED: 2 weeks Jan, 1 week Nov MEALS: alc (main courses £5 to £16). Set L Sun £10.75 SERVICE: not inc, card slips closed CARDS: Access, Amex, Switch, Visa DETAILS: 60 seats. 40 seats outside. Private parties: 65 main room. Car park. Vegetarian meals. Children's helpings. Smart dress preferred. Wheelchair access (also WC). Music

DOLGELLAU Caernarfonshire & Merionethshire map 7

Dylanwad Da 🍷 £

2 Ffôs-y-Felin, Dolgellau LL40 1BS — COOKING 1
TEL: (01341) 422870 — COST £19–£33

'We have a great affection for this charming Dolgellau bistro,' notes a reporter from Wales. The décor adds a splash of inviting colour to a somewhat 'grey street', and the lady of the house ensures that outsiders are as welcome as Welsh-speaking locals. Dylan Rowlands's monthly menus may be bistro by inclination, but the regime is increasingly geared towards full meals – with a heavy cholesterol intake to boot. As one visitor noted, tackling three of Dylan's courses can be daunting 'unless you have just climbed nearby Cader Idris'. Recent successes have included lightly curried kedgeree, pan-fried fillet of sea bass with spiced red cabbage, and sauté breast of chicken with mango, ginger and coriander in a cream sauce. Vegetarians might be offered mushroom and nut goulash, while desserts range from coffee liqueur mousse to almond and sultana sponge.

The choice of wines is trim and well judged: around 30 lively options from reliable producers at bargain prices. Four house wines introduce the list at £8.60 a bottle or £1.60 a glass. CELLARMAN'S CHOICE: Ca'del Solo Malvasia Bianca 1994, Bonny Doon, California, £12.65; Cabernet Sauvignon Grande Réserve 1992, Los Vascos, Chile, £12.05.

CHEF/PROPRIETOR: Dylan Rowlands OPEN: Thur to Sat D only 7 to 9, and all week D Easter, Whitsun and July to Sept; L by arrangement (parties only) CLOSED: Feb MEALS: alc (main courses £7.50 to £12.50). Set D £12.75. BYO £4 SERVICE: not inc CARDS: none DETAILS: 30 seats. Private parties: 30 main room. Vegetarian meals. Children's helpings. No smoking in dining-room. Wheelchair access (also WC). Music

🍾 denotes an outstanding wine cellar; 🍷 denotes a good wine list, worth travelling for.

£ indicates that it is possible to have a three-course meal, including coffee, a half-bottle of house wine and service, at any time the restaurant is open (i.e. at dinner as well as at lunch, unless a place is open only for dinner), for £20 or less per person.

EGLWYSFACH **Powys**   map 7

▲ *Ynyshir Hall* 🌟

Eglwysfach SY20 8TA
TEL: (01654) 781209   FAX: (01654) 781366   COOKING 3
off A487, 6m SW of Machynlleth   COST £29–£48

This small country-house hotel is a riot of colour inside, largely thanks to Rob
Reen's exuberant paintings. The dining-room is welcoming, full of personality,
and the two young lads in the kitchen show no sign of flagging. The idea, the
Reens explain, was that sharing the role of head chef would give them the
confidence that experience had not yet brought. Experience brings other things
too, of course, but the partnership has worked well, and at least one of them is
always on duty, which is a bonus in a seven-day-a-week kitchen.

Their style is indeed confident, grafting Mediterranean shoots on to more
classically French roots, dabbing on some Eastern spicing, and propagating all
sorts of interesting things, from bourride of local seafood with an aubergine tian,
saffron tagliatelle, and a celery and carrot cream (that's all one dish), to breast of
Hereford duck with Thai pancakes filled with duck confit, served with buttered
cabbage and oriental stir-fry (also one dish). These sound very busy, but they
work, even with all the pithiviers, pancakes, pasta and other adornments vying
for attention. An inspector found the aforementioned duck dish 'more bold than
refined, more brash than subtle, but a tasty plateful, well considered and
executed'. Evident workmanship with desserts pays dividends, too, from a
baked dark chocolate and mint soufflé pudding to a perfectly textured raisin
sponge pudding with a moat of thin caramel sauce, as effective as it was simple.
France and Australia are the strongest sections of the imaginative 200-strong
wine list, and 14 'house recommendations' range from £12 to £20.

CHEFS: Christopher Dawson and Ian White   PROPRIETORS: Joan and Rob Reen   OPEN: all week
12.30 to 1.30, 7 to 8.45 (booking essential L)   MEALS: Set L £19.50, Set D £29. Bar meals
available Mon to Sat   SERVICE: not inc, card slips closed   CARDS: Access, Amex, Delta, Diners,
Switch, Visa   DETAILS: 45 seats. Private parties: 30 main room, 18 private room. Car park.
Vegetarian meals. No children under 9. Smart dress preferred. No smoking in dining-room.
Music   ACCOMMODATION: 8 rooms, all with bath/shower. TV. Phone. B&B £80 to £150. Deposit:
20%. No children under 9. Dogs by arrangement. Afternoon teas. Garden (*The Which? Hotel
Guide*)

FISHGUARD **Pembrokeshire**   map 4

▲ *Three Main Street* 🌟

3 Main Street, Fishguard SA65 9HG   COOKING 2
TEL: (01348) 874275   COST £27–£39

'A pleasant, no-nonsense restaurant where one can expect decent food with an
occasional touch of flair,' summed up one report. The setting is a modest
Georgian town house with a cottagey feel, a cheerful atmosphere, a homely
dining-room and a very personal stamp to it. During the day it functions as a
coffee shop, serving light lunches of pasta, salad or savoury pancake, and
afternoon teas. Dinner has more serious intentions. Marion Evans supports the
efforts of local producers who are 'striving to establish and retain regional

specialities', but her repertoire of dishes goes beyond Welsh Black beef, or high-quality Welsh lamb with herbs and garlic, to embrace tarte basquaise, and poached figs with mascarpone cream.

Rich, thick cream of celeriac soup pleased an inspector, as did spicy red pepper mousse with tomato and herb vinaigrette. Guinea-fowl is sensibly served as a roasted breast and casserole of leg, and vegetables might include potatoes with 'real taste', as well as fennel with bacon and cheese. Good bread is baked on the premises using organic flour, cheeses are kept in pristine condition, and wines are carefully chosen and fairly priced.

CHEF: Marion Evans   PROPRIETORS: Marion Evans and Inez Ford   OPEN: Tue to Sat (Wed to Sat winter) D only 7 to 9   CLOSED: Feb   MEALS: alc (main courses £9.50 to £14). Light L available Tue to Sat 12 to 2   SERVICE: not inc   DETAILS: 35 seats. Private parties: 20 main room, 15 to 20 private rooms. Vegetarian meals. Children's helpings. No smoking in dining-room. Wheelchair access (no WC). No music   ACCOMMODATION: 3 rooms, all with bath/shower. B&B £30 to £50. Children welcome (The Which? Hotel Guide)

FORDEN Powys   map 4

▲ Edderton Hall

Forden SY21 8RZ
TEL: (01938) 580339   FAX: (01938) 580452   COOKING 1
off A490, 4m S of Welshpool   COST £21–£35

'There is nothing better than being waited on by a Tory MP,' muses a reader. When the MP is at Westminster, Evelyn Hawksley manages quite well enough on her own in this cluttered but attractive Georgian house, since the appointment of a front-of-house manager this year has allowed her to devote more time to the kitchen. The fixed-price menus are kept within sensible bounds and use many excellent local ingredients. Caerphilly and pine-nut tart comes with Carmarthen ham and roasted leeks, while a game pie crams in wild duck, pheasant, pigeon and rabbit, cider, juniper and herbs. Desserts mix regional stalwarts – Sir Watkin Williams Wynne's pudding turns out to be steamed lemon sponge – with showy items such as banana and rum pancakes with caramel sauce. Service can be a little too sedate. The wine list is well spread without being especially ambitious. House wines are £8.50.

CHEF: Evelyn Hawksley   PROPRIETORS: Warren and Evelyn Hawksley   OPEN: Tue to Sun 12.30 to 3, Tue to Sat D 7.30 to 10   MEALS: Set L £12.95, Set D £22. BYO £5   SERVICE: not inc, card slips closed   CARDS: Access, Amex, Diners, Visa   DETAILS: 40 seats. 40 seats outside. Private parties: 20 main room, 20 private room. Car park. No children under 10. Smart dress preferred. Wheelchair access (no WC). Music   ACCOMMODATION: 8 rooms, all with bath/shower. TV. Phone. B&B £22 to £80. Children welcome. Dogs welcome. Afternoon teas. Garden (The Which? Hotel Guide)

'"We don't do Irish coffee," the waiter told my friend, and then proceeded to bring him a cup of coffee, a small jug of cream and a glass of Irish whiskey: all the ingredients needed to make an Irish coffee!' (On eating in Suffolk)

FREYSTROP Pembrokeshire   map 4

Jemima's ⅋✳

Freystrop SA62 4HB
TEL: (01437) 891109   COOKING 2
on Burton road, 2m SW of Haverfordwest   COST £16–£35

'A slightly eccentric place, but the food makes it all special, and the hostess made us all smile,' summed up one report, adding that 'she knows all there is to know about breads.' The cheerful, friendly atmosphere is as genuine as the food. Ann Owston writes that 'keep it simple' describes her approach. She grows salad items in the garden, makes good pastry and insists that 'nothing is disguised or false'. This directness is appreciated, producing for one couple 'a really memorable meal: fresh ingredients, well balanced, and beautifully cooked fresh fish'.

The simplicity of treatment can be gauged from tomato and basil soup, sauté of sweetbreads with bacon and mushrooms, or a casserole of shoulder of lamb with apricots and lemon. There are no frills or elaborate gestures, and fish is indeed a strong suit, with pickled herring and beetroot salad, salmon and dill quiche, and perhaps lemon sole or brill served with lime butter. Desserts might include Eve's pudding, or bananas with coconut ice-cream. Light lunches are chosen from a blackboard in the bistro. The wine list is short, with house Vin de Pays d'Oc at £8.50.

CHEF: Ann Owston   PROPRIETORS: the Owston family   OPEN: restaurant Tue to Sat D only 7 to 9; bistro Tue to Sun L only 12 to 2   CLOSED: Tue and Wed in winter   MEALS: alc (main courses £4.50 to £11)   SERVICE: not inc, card slips closed   CARDS: Access, Amex, Delta, Visa   DETAILS: 24 seats. Private parties: 16 main room. Car park. Vegetarian meals. Children's helpings. No smoking in dining-room. No music

HARLECH Caernarfonshire & Merionethshire   map 7

▲ *Castle Cottage* ⅋✳

Pen Llech, Harlech LL46 2YL   COOKING 1*
TEL: (01766) 780479   COST £18–£34

A pair of golfers, habitués at St David's, have made Castle Cottage their usual haunt. 'Beautiful' Shropshire pork, 'succulent' salmon and 'excellent' Welsh cheeses may explain why. The Robertses' hotel and restaurant, itself a building of some antiquity, shelters under Harlech Castle's wing. Within the comfortable oak-beamed dining-room, the food strikes a more contemporary chord. Thai noodle soup with chicken, red pepper and Gruyère tart, and a salad of bacon, mango, avocado and quail's egg indicate the range of Glyn Roberts's style. Duck confit on a bed of cassoulet is authentic 'crisp-skinned, melt-in-the-mouth' stuff, according to one reporter, or there may be herb-crusted local lamb with a parcel of leeks in a red wine sauce. Nougat parfait with two sauces – orange and coffee – and chocolate slice with rum cream and strawberries are desserts with a sense of dash. Reports commend the good value and also the 'satisfying' breakfasts. The reasonably priced wine list is especially strong in its New World selections, and the house recommendations, from £8.75, are all thoughtfully chosen.

CHEF: Glyn Roberts   PROPRIETORS: Glyn and Jacqueline Roberts   OPEN: Sun L 12.30 to 2, all week D 7 to 9.30   CLOSED: 3 weeks Feb   MEALS: Set L £12, Set D £17 (2 courses) to £19. BYO £5   SERVICE: not inc   CARDS: Access, Amex, Delta, Switch, Visa   DETAILS: 45 seats. Private parties: 45 main room. Vegetarian meals. Children's helpings. Smart dress preferred. No smoking in dining-room. Wheelchair access (no WC). Music   ACCOMMODATION: 6 rooms, 4 with bath/shower. B&B £24 to £52. Deposit: £10. Children welcome. Baby facilities. Dogs welcome in bedrooms only (*The Which? Hotel Guide*)

LAMPHEY Pembrokeshire   map 4

Dial Inn ✷

The Ridgeway, Lamphey SA71 5NU
TEL/FAX: (01646) 672426   COOKING 1
just off A4139, Tenby to Pembroke road   COST £14–£33

Built in the 1830s, this former dower house to Lamphey Court has been a pub for some 30 years, and does its bit to put Welsh food on the map. Sit outside and you can see across the fields to the ruins of Lamphey Palace, a former residence of the bishops of St David's. Order at the bar, among the diverse items of pottery and china, and wait until summoned. A combination of printed menu and daily blackboard specials together convey a repertoire that rates fish highly and generally includes a number of vegetarian dishes such as falafel, mushroom fritters, and a ploughman's lunch. Among the native offerings might be cawl Cymraeg (a hearty meat and vegetable broth) served with crusty bread and Caerphilly cheese, or else Glamorgan cheese sausages, or poached salmon with laverbread. Around 30 wines, mostly under £15, include house French at £7.25.

CHEFS: Simon Periam and Melanie Fairman   PROPRIETORS: Francis and Jan Parry   OPEN: all week L 12 to 2, Mon to Sat D 7 to 9 (9.30 summer), and Sun D summer   CLOSED: 25 Dec   MEALS: alc (main courses L £5 to £10, D £7 to £14). Set L Sun £7.50. Bar meals available Mon to Sat   SERVICE: not inc, card slips closed   CARDS: Access, Amex, Delta, Visa   DETAILS: 85 seats. 16 seats outside. Private parties: 30 main room, 30 and 25 private rooms. Car park. Vegetarian meals. Children's helpings. Smart dress preferred. No smoking in dining-room. Wheelchair access (no WC). Music

---

LLANBERIS Caernarfonshire & Merionethshire   map 7

Y Bistro ✷

45 High Street, Llanberis LL55 4EU
TEL/FAX: (01286) 871278   COOKING 1
off A4086, at foot of Snowdon   COST £29–£35

It may be slightly off the beaten track, unless you are heading up Snowdon, but the straightforward, generous bistro food is mainstream enough. Nerys Roberts gets through as much local or Welsh produce as possible, including torgoch (Arctic char) from Lake Padarn – she even uses Cariad white wine to poach the Penrhyn mussels – and Welsh lamb and beef are always on the menu. But the larder is stocked with items from further afield, including balsamic vinegar, Camargue rice and much olive oil. Roast rib of beef might share the billing with escalope of pork, or even a 'penny-farthing' dish consisting of half a duckling and a whole quail, roasted to order and served with a Seville orange sauce. Finish with homely apple pie and custard, or suet pudding with a mead sauce, and drink a fairly priced wine from the serviceable list. House wines are £8.50.

CHEFS: Nerys Roberts and Sion Llwyd   PROPRIETORS: Danny and Nerys Roberts   OPEN: Mon to Sat D only 7.30 to 9.30   CLOSED: occasional days in winter   MEALS: Set D £19.50 (2 courses) to £22.50   SERVICE: not inc, card slips closed   CARDS: Access, Delta, Switch, Visa   DETAILS: 50 seats. Private parties: 40 main room, 8 and 20 private rooms. Vegetarian meals. Children's helpings. Smart dress preferred. No smoking in dining-room. Wheelchair access (no WC). Music

---

LLANDDEINIOLEN   Caernarfonshire & Merionethshire   map 7

▲ Ty'n Rhos 🍴

Seion, Llanddeiniolen LL55 3AE
TEL: (01248) 670489   FAX: (01248) 670079
off B4366, 5m NE of Caernarfon on road   COOKING 3
signposted Seion   COST £20–£38

This converted farmhouse was the 'find of the autumn' for one couple, pleased to escape the crowded tourist centres in favour of an 'idyllic rural setting'. It overlooks just about everywhere of significance – Snowdonia, Anglesey and the Menai Strait – and feels comfortable and sophisticated, with soft, relaxing country colours throughout. A strong Welsh commitment is apparent in the sourcing of excellent Black beef and lamb, while the garden yields salad leaves, herbs and soft fruits. First-class chutneys and relishes, and a fine selection of breads, are home-made.

The kitchen is happy in contemporary mode. Meals are priced according to main course (although the variation is small) and descriptions are precise. Some sound positively challenging: collop of venison comes topped with black pudding and a sherry crust and is served with an apple and sage mousseline. Meats, including game and poultry, seem to take precedence over fish. Breast of Trelough duck – cooked pink, crispy on the outside, 'giving off the finest duck flavour imaginable' – has been served with an excellent 'compote' of Puy lentils and pearl barley with onions and mushrooms. Simple breast of chicken has also impressed, though at inspection it was not well served by its laverbread accoutrements.

Timing and seasoning are well handled, and puddings excel themselves, from a gratin of exotic fruits to pwdin Cymraeg, a light bread-and-butter pudding made with curranty bara brith. A wedge of cheese-of-the-day follows, or else Welsh rarebit oddly waiving the opportunity to use home-made bread. A list of 57 round-the-world wines is well chosen and fairly priced, beginning with house French and Australian at £8.50.

CHEFS: Carys Davies, Ian Cashen and Lynda Kettle   PROPRIETORS: Lynda and Nigel Kettle OPEN: Sun L 12 to 1.30, Tue to Sat D 7 to 8.30   CLOSED: 20 to 30 Dec, 1 week Jan   MEALS: Set L Sun £13.95, Set D £19 to £24.50. BYO £5   SERVICE: not inc, card slips closed   CARDS: Access, Amex, Switch, Visa   DETAILS: 35 seats. Private parties: 30 main room, 15 private room. Car park. Vegetarian meals. Children's helpings. No children under 5. Smart dress preferred. No smoking in dining-room. Wheelchair access (also WC). No music   ACCOMMODATION: 11 rooms, all with bath/shower. TV. Phone. B&B £40 to £80. Deposit: 25%. No children under 5. Afternoon teas. Garden (*The Which? Hotel Guide*)

LLANDEGLA Denbighshire   map 7

▲ *Bodidris Hall* `:*` | NEW ENTRY |

Llandegla LL11 3AL
TEL: (01978) 790434   FAX: (01978) 790335   COOKING 1*
on A5104 9m SE of Ruthin   COST £22–£58

The original twelfth-century manor was rebuilt in Tudor times, when it became
the hunting-lodge of Queen Elizabeth's favourite, Robert Dudley, Earl of
Leicester. Partly covered in ivy, it now makes a handsome country hotel, the
dining-room looking out across lawn and ha-ha to a pond with gliding swans.

Philip Weale cooks in modern style, adding dry vermouth and blackcurrants
to a starter of turbot and smoked salmon, and serving a cup of Lapsang Souchong
with fillet steak. At inspection, fillets of sea bass and red mullet failed to impress,
but lamb noisette was beautifully presented, the meat richly mature (this in
April) and served with a glossy mushroom sauce. Desserts keep up the inventive
streak in marzipan and banana liqueur mousse with liquorice sorbet, and cherry
strudel soufflé with whisky ravioli, both adjudged delicious. Fine Welsh
cheeses, good cafetière coffee and home-made chocolates all pull their weight. A
broad-minded wine list offers plenty of choice at acceptable prices; the 'Patron's
Selection' starts at £10.25.

CHEF: Philip Weale   PROPRIETORS: Bill Farden and Tudor Williams   OPEN: Sun to Fri L 12 to 2,
all week D 7 to 9.30   CLOSED: 2 weeks Jan   MEALS: alc (main courses £14 to £23). Set L £10.50
(2 courses) to £14.75, Set D £29.50. Bar L available Mon to Sat   SERVICE: net prices, card slips
closed   CARDS: Access, Amex, Delta, Diners, Visa   DETAILS: 50 seats. 12 seats outside.
Private parties: 50 main room, 20 private room. Car park. Vegetarian meals. Children's helpings.
Jacket and tie D. Smart dress preferred. No smoking in dining-room. Wheelchair access (also
women's WC). Music   ACCOMMODATION: 9 rooms, all with bath/shower. TV. Phone. B&B £55 to
£125. Children welcome. Baby facilities. Dogs welcome. Afternoon teas. Garden. Fishing

---

LLANDEWI SKIRRID Monmouthshire   map 4

Walnut Tree Inn ▮   /12/8/97/

Llandewi Skirrid NP7 8AW
TEL: (01873) 852797   COOKING 4
on B4521, 3m NE of Abergavenny   COST £24–£73

The unassuming white-painted slate-roofed inn looks much like any other pub,
apart from the queues waiting for it to open. 'One is immediately immersed in
sheer warmth, colour, and smells of garlic, tomato and bitter coffee,' which
reflect the sensuous appeal of the Walnut Tree. It is a hybrid that revels in
contradictions. Seated at a cramped table, handed a long (27 puddings) and
'sloppily written' menu, and subjected to bustling and totally unpretentious
service, one may feel as if Franco Taruschio had deliberately set out to break most
of the rules, although it is more likely that he simply couldn't give a toss about
them. 'Who needs tablecloths?' asked one reporter rhetorically. Or, he might
have added, indoor lavatories? The place is totally eccentric, hugely charming
and completely untainted by the ebb and flow of fashion.

Instead, it has its own preoccupations. The same food is served in the bar and
in the bookable dining-room, where there is 'fractionally more elbow room', and

does not put visual attraction or refinement first. It is earthy, rustic, gutsy, powerful, utterly informal in style, and yet with a feeling of generosity: in the range and scope of the menu, and in dishes such as vincisgrassi maceratese, a combination of pasta and porcini mushrooms 'loaded with truffles'. This food is not made to be analysed, but to be enjoyed. Sometimes a slight heavy-handedness might produce overly buttery risotto, or 'village tea-shop' desserts, but these are put in the shade by roast duck breast with an 'old-fashioned gravy', or brodetto: a mixed fish casserole that 'brought the smell and colour of the Mediterranean straight on to the plate', and which an inspector found 'quite outstanding'.

Many dishes have become standards of the repertoire, including Thai pork appetiser (deep-fried with crispy skin and plenty of lemon grass flavour), and 'exquisite' Llanover salt duck accompanied by damsons, gooseberries and ginger. Oysters are as good here as anywhere. A musical analogy occurred to one perceptive couple. 'We would compare Franco Taruschio's cooking to a concert pianist who always makes you think how great the music rather than his playing is.' At inspection, 'a plate of desserts' let the side down, but others have enjoyed raspberry Malakofftorte, whimberry ice-cream, and coffee crème brûlée. House red wine is 'ideally suited to the food and surroundings, and does a great deal to keep the bill down'. Otherwise, delve into the fine Italian section of the list which is packed with exciting wines from renowned producers and includes plenty at under £20. Italy is the highlight, but a sense of liveliness and adventure pervades the entire list, especially in the bright New World sections. Even the house wines surprise, with La Gitana manzanilla sherry at £2.50 a glass alongside Italian white and red at £10.75 a litre.

CHEF: Franco Taruschio   PROPRIETORS: Ann and Franco Taruschio   OPEN: Tue to Sat 12 to 3.30, 7 to 10.15   CLOSED: 5 days Christmas, 2 weeks Feb   MEALS: alc (main courses £7 to £24)   SERVICE: not inc   CARDS: none   DETAILS: 92 seats. 30 seats outside. Private parties: 46 main room. Car park. Vegetarian meals. Children's helpings. Wheelchair access (also WC). No music. Air-conditioned

---

LLANDRILLO Denbighshire

map 7

▲ *Tyddyn Llan* 🍷 ⚡

Llandrillo LL21 0ST
TEL: (01490) 440264   FAX: (01490) 440414
on B4401, 4½ miles S of Corwen

COOKING 3
COST £22–£42

The attractive grey-stone house by the River Dee is set in lovely gardens with ornamental lakes. The Kindreds have been here for 13 years, refurbishing and extending along the way. If the Wedgwood-blue dining-room with cherubs perched above the windows is a little flamboyant, there is no doubting the relaxed feel of the drawing-rooms with their antiques, log fires, and 'the most comfortable of easy chairs'. Chefs have come and gone during the year, and one or two disappointing reports came through, but that was before Jason Hornbuckle arrived from Bistrot Bruno in London in May '96 to galvanise the kitchen. 'This man and Tyddyn Llan are set to be the talk of Wales,' reckoned one with a line to the chattering classes.

Hornbuckle's change of scene is as dramatic as his cooking: robust and full of exciting tastes that are 'quite new to this part of the world'. Dinner is three or four courses, and one evening began with a risotto of mussels, saffron, black olives, tomato and basil that was 'bursting with exciting flavours'. At the same meal, a variation on niçoise salad used grilled skate wing, 'beautifully presented and perfectly cooked', in place of the customary tuna. The second course is a soup – mushroom, chestnut and lovage at one meal – and main courses have included a 'huge portion' of sauté lambs' liver with creamy mashed potatoes and rosemary *jus*, served with deep-fried onion rings, that was judged 'truly superb'.

It is tempting to finish with a 'deliciously mild' Welsh rarebit made with a herb cheese and fresh anchovies, as an alternative to glazed lemon tart with a rich raspberry compote, or chocolate truffle tart with caramel ice-cream. Home-baked bread adds to the delight, as does a youngish list of fairly priced wines.

CHEF: Jason Hornbuckle   PROPRIETORS: Peter and Bridget Kindred   OPEN: all week 12.30 to 2, 7 to 9.30   MEALS: Set L £11 (2 courses) to £13, Set D £23 to £25   SERVICE: not inc, card slips closed   CARDS: Access, Amex, Delta, Diners, Switch, Visa   DETAILS: 60 seats. 10 seats outside. Private parties: 40 main room, 40 private room. Car park. Vegetarian meals. Children welcome. Smart dress preferred. No smoking in dining-room. Wheelchair access (also WC). Music   ACCOMMODATION: 10 rooms, all with bath/shower. TV. Phone. B&B £60 to £102. Deposit: £25. Children welcome. Baby facilities. Dogs by arrangement. Afternoon teas. Garden. Fishing (*The Which? Hotel Guide*)

LLANDUDNO   Aberconwy & Colwyn   map 7

▲ *Bodysgallen Hall* ♆ ⅜✷

Llandudno LL30 1RS
TEL: (01492) 584466   FAX: (01492) 582519   COOKING 2*
off A470, 2m SE of Llandudno   COST £22–£50

The sweep up the drive to this comfortably furnished seventeenth-century house is impressive. The hotel is set in 200 acres, with various walks and a knot garden close to the hall, and has been restored by Historic House Hotels, a group that has also made a success of Middlethorpe Hall, York, and Hartwell House, Aylesbury (see entries). It feels the part, with dark wooden panels, portraits of ancient worthies, and stacks of space for lounging around in, all permeated by a gentle smell of wood-smoke. The choice at dinner is between a set menu of three courses and a more ambitious 'gourmet' version with five. Both menus are well reported.

The country-house style incorporates local produce, which shows to good effect in a realistic but interesting repertoire that has included tomato and basil consommé, and warm crab mousse with marinated scallops and a chilli dressing. The balance of flavours works well, with good judgement showing in, for example, a salad of tuna and olives, and materials are handled simply but effectively, as in well-trimmed pink rack of lamb with lentils, a dish given added depth and interest with tiny black pudding sausages. Perhaps finish with steamed lemon sponge, or warm hazelnut macaroon tart. Wines are a well-chosen, international set with a generous number of half-bottles. Quality is high with the emphasis on the youthful and lively rather than the venerable. A decent set of house wines kicks off at £11.75; there's a further page of wines all at £13. CELLARMAN'S CHOICE: Bordeaux Blanc, Ch. Relais de Cheval Blanc 1994, £13; Gran Legado Tinto 1992, Penedès, £13.

CHEF: Mike Penny   PROPRIETOR: Historic House Hotels   OPEN: all week 12.30 to 2, 7.30 to 9.30   MEALS: Set L £11.50 (2 courses) to £13.50, Set D £27.50 to £36. Bar L available   SERVICE: net prices, card slips closed   CARDS: Access, Amex, Delta, Switch, Visa   DETAILS: 60 seats. Private parties: 40 main room, 40 private room. Car park. Vegetarian meals. No children under 8. Jacket and tie. No smoking in dining-room. Wheelchair access (also WC). Music   ACCOMMODATION: 35 rooms, all with bath/shower. TV. Phone. B&B £85 to £170. Rooms for disabled. No children under 8. Dogs welcome. Afternoon teas. Garden. Swimming-pool (*The Which? Hotel Guide*)

▲ Martin's

11 Mostyn Avenue, Craig-y-Don,
Llandudno LL30 1YS
TEL: (01492) 870070

COOKING 1*
COST £22–£35

Martin James's restaurant in a terrace of shops creates a curious first impression in the minds of some visitors, but there is no denying the serious effort and skill emanating from the kitchen. Meals begin with excellent home-baked rolls. The menu is a lengthy trawl that opens with salads, pâtés and terrines, and progresses to fillet of salmon with sole, prawn and mushroom mousse baked in a lattice of 'excellent' pastry, or pink, juicy lamb chops with a compote of shallots, garlic and rosemary plus a 'lovely glossy gravy'. Furred and feathered game are dressed in the restaurant's own plucking shed: roast, boned partridge comes on a bed of braised lentils, and breast of pheasant is stuffed with liver, pine kernels and herb mousse and served with fresh pasta. The pudding menu might include crème brûlée and white and dark chocolate terrine. Twenty workaday wines are fairly priced. House wine is £7.50.

CHEF/PROPRIETOR: Martin James   OPEN: Tue to Sat D only 7 to 9.30   CLOSED: first 2 weeks Jan   MEALS: alc (main courses £8 to £12.50)   SERVICE: not inc, card slips closed   CARDS: Access, Amex, Delta, Visa   DETAILS: 30 seats. 8 seats outside. Private parties: 30 main room. Vegetarian meals. Children welcome. Smart dress preferred. No-smoking area. Wheelchair access (no WC). No music   ACCOMMODATION: 1 room with bath/shower. TV. B&B £30 to £36. Deposit: £10

Richard's £

7 Church Walks, Llandudno LL30 2HD
TEL: (01492) 877924 and 875315

COOKING 1
COST £20–£34

Richard Hendey clearly relishes everything about being a chef, so much so that he is prepared to work at the stove 365 evenings a year. The décor in his lively basement is all polished tables and church pews 'with cushions to sit on, thank God'. One party who ate during an enormous July thunderstorm, with lights flickering on and off, found the atmosphere 'terrific'. Daily fish specials receive all kinds of accompaniments: fillet of young halibut with a fresh crab sauce was 'bliss' for one correspondent. The printed menu leaps around happily, taking in grilled goats'-cheese salad, sauté black pudding with an 'amazing' plum and port sauce, Thai-style burgers, and stuffed chicken with tomato and basil. Among the 'after-dinner indulgences', you might find pots of Calypso ice-cream and hot banana pudding with butterscotch sauce. The wine list has a great selection under £10, plus some gems from the Alsace. House Spanish is £7.95.

CHEFS: Richard Hendey, Mark Roberts, John Crawford and Sandra Kruger   PROPRIETOR: Richard Hendey   OPEN: all week D only 6 to 11   MEALS: alc (main courses £11 to £13) SERVICE: net prices, card slips closed   CARDS: Access, Amex, Switch, Visa   DETAILS: 48 seats. Private parties: 20 main room, 20 private room. Vegetarian meals. Children welcome. No-smoking area. Music

▲ St Tudno Hotel ♟ ⁵✳

Promenade, Llandudno LL30 2LP
TEL: (01492) 874411   FAX: (01492) 860407

COOKING 2*
COST £22–£56

Those familiar with seaside hotels do not hesitate to pick out St Tudno as a fine example of its kind. Credit is due to the 'dedication and involvement' of the Blands, whose cheerful and well-motivated staff are appreciated. 'We always felt we mattered,' volunteered one couple. Children are welcome, and the well-supported Sunday lunch is considered good value: 'there is an excellent choice and portions are generous.' Dinner is five courses and doesn't always convey a sense of the seasons, but these matters are being addressed as an additional three-course dinner is introduced which promises to be more responsive to the time of year.

In a restaurant that is open seven days a week, the idea of two joint head chefs is a sensible one, helping to ensure consistency. Among the more upbeat dishes might be asparagus and Bresse pigeon risotto with a tomato tart and basil, or Jerusalem artichoke soup with truffle cream. Main courses lean towards red-blooded roasts of Welsh lamb, beef fillet or venison, while puddings provide another bulwark against the bracing sea air in the form of deep-fried banana and strawberry fritters, or dark chocolate fudge with coffee cream. The wine list roams the globe but carries no passengers – a short selection of reliable wines from each major wine country or region has been picked out with care. A sensible house choice at the front of the list adds to a sense of good order and starts at £10.50. CELLARMAN'S CHOICE: Arneis 1994, Damonte, £16; Rockford Dry County Grenache 1994, Barossa Valley, S. Australia, £22.

CHEFS: David Harding and Ian Watson   PROPRIETORS: Martin and Janette Bland   OPEN: all week 12.30 to 1.45, 7 to 9.30 (9 Sun)   MEALS: Set L £16.50, Set D £29.50. Bar food available SERVICE: not inc, card slips closed   CARDS: Access, Amex, Diners, Switch, Visa   DETAILS: 55 seats. Private parties: 30 main room. Car park. Vegetarian meals. Children's helpings. No very young children D. Smart dress preferred. No smoking in dining-room. Wheelchair access (no WC). Music. Air-conditioned   ACCOMMODATION: 21 rooms, all with bath/shower. TV. Phone. D,B&B £85 to £150. Deposit: £50 to £80. Children welcome. Baby facilities. Dogs by arrangement. Afternoon teas. Garden. Swimming-pool (*The Which? Hotel Guide*)

See the inside of the front cover for an explanation of the 1 to 5 rating system for cooking standards.

WALES

LLANFIHANGEL NANT MELAN Powys   map 4

▲ *Red Lion Inn* ✠ £

Llanfihangel nant Melan, nr New Radnor LD8 2TN
TEL: (01544) 350220
on A44 Rhayader to Kington road, 3m W of   COOKING 1
New Radnor   COST £15–£30

The old whitewashed drovers' inn in the Radnor hills is 'emphatically a pub'.
Powered by the enthusiasm of the Johns family, it delivers 'ample portions of
interesting food'. The setting is completely without frills – tables are wood,
napkins are paper – and a menu written on blackboards in the bar takes the
Welsh input seriously: sewin, game, lamb and Black beef, and whimberries in
season. Give your order over the counter and wait to be called to a table.
Simplicity and good value are the draw, from a large plateful of smoked salmon,
or a 'smooth, unctuous' venison and game pâté, to bangers and mash or
monkfish with cockles and bacon. Ginger sponge or chocolate terrine follow,
and the cheeseboard has a good spread. The very short wine list stays
comfortably under £10, and there is draught Hook Norton beer as well as a Welsh
whisky. House wine is £4.95.

CHEF: Gareth Johns PROPRIETORS: Keith, Elizabeth and Gareth Johns OPEN: all week 12 to 2,
6.30 (7 Sun) to 9 (9.30 Sat) CLOSED: Tue Nov to May, 1 week Nov MEALS: alc (main courses £5
to £12) SERVICE: not inc, card slips closed CARDS: Access, Delta, Visa DETAILS: 60 seats. 16
seats outside. Private parties: 20 main room. Car park. Vegetarian meals. Children's helpings.
No smoking in 1 dining-room. Music ACCOMMODATION: 3 rooms, all with bath/shower. B&B
£17.50 to £32. Children welcome. Dogs welcome. Afternoon teas. Garden

---

LLANGAMMARCH WELLS Powys   map 4

▲ *Lake Country House* ♥ ✠

Llangammarch Wells LD4 4BS
TEL: (01591) 620202 FAX: (01591) 620457   COOKING 2
off B483 at Garth, 6m W of Builth Wells   COST £22–£46

A big white house in 50 lush acres of lawns and flower-lined walkways, the
Lake is to many an idyll of the country life-style. The light, many-windowed
dining-room is a relaxing place, and the atmosphere is full of refined civility.
Local organic produce shines forth from Richard Arnold's impeccably seasonal
menus. Vichyssoise 'of precisely the correct consistency', 'softly quivering'
carrot and ginger mousse with 'real hollandaise – thick, buttery and tangy', and a
trio of meats (beef, lamb and venison) accompanied by pickled walnut sauce and
chestnuts have all impressed.

Presentation is afforded great pains, and the flavours back it up. Luxurious
puddings, including 'wonderfully light' bread-and-butter with a cinnamon-
scented custard, get rave reviews, as does the wide range of home-baked breads
taking in rosemary, pistachio and sun-dried tomato varieties. Wines are
numerous and thoughtfully chosen. The lengthy list of clarets is divided into
'growths' and has concise tasting notes. Other strong sections are Spain and
vintage ports dating from 1960. House red and white are £9.75.

CHEF: Richard Arnold   PROPRIETOR: J.P. Mifsud   OPEN: all week 12.15 to 2, 7.30 to 9   MEALS: Set L £15.50, Set D £27.50. Bar food available   SERVICE: not inc, card slips closed   CARDS: Access, Amex, Delta, Diners, Switch, Visa   DETAILS: 60 seats. Private parties: 90 main room. Car park. Vegetarian meals. Children's helpings. No children under 7. Jacket and tie. No smoking in dining-room. Wheelchair access (also WC). No music   ACCOMMODATION: 19 rooms, all with bath/shower. TV. Phone. B&B £75 to £155. Deposit: £80. Children welcome. Baby facilities. Dogs welcome. Afternoon teas. Garden. Fishing

---

LLANSANFFRAID GLAN CONWY   Aberconwy & Colwyn   map 7

▲ *Old Rectory* 🍷 ⁵✳

Llanrwst Road, Llansanffraid Glan Conwy,
nr Conwy LL28 5LF
TEL: (01492) 580611   FAX: (01492) 584555   COOKING 3
on A470, ½m S of junction with A55   COST £42–£50

Michael and Wendy Vaughan's Georgian rectory-turned-hotel sits at the top of a steep little hill, from where it commands breathtaking views of not only the comings and goings of the tideway in the Conwy estuary but also, at night, the floodlit splendour of Conwy Castle. The twin dining-rooms afford a fair amount of visual diversion in themselves, including an oil of Napoleon rebuking his officers. An industrious kitchen, led by Wendy Vaughan, is proud of its real meats, hormone-free Black beef and lamb from the Welsh mountains. Home-made breads nearly stole the show for one couple.

The cooking is in the modern British mould, constantly trying out new ideas and exhibiting real intelligence in the execution. First courses feature fish, maybe silver hake sauté with mustard and tarragon, or red mullet roasted and served with saffron risotto-cakes. If beef or lamb doesn't appear, there could well be something along the lines of pheasant with pear and spinach pastries, or Lunesdale duck breast with braised cabbage. Cheeses come next, either a selection or a simple salad of local goats' cheese. A serving of home-made fruit sorbet is another option before puddings themselves. Service is applauded for friendliness and charm.

The wine list is excellent, with plenty to tempt from France and a small but perfectly formed collection of New World wines. Half-bottles abound, and prices are commendably low. Four French house wines are £12.90. CELLARMAN'S CHOICE: Fumé Blanc 1992, Robert Mondavi, California, £19.90; Gigondas 1988, Delas Frères, £16.90.

CHEF: Wendy Vaughan   PROPRIETORS: Michael and Wendy Vaughan   OPEN: all week D only 7.30 for 8 (1 sitting)   CLOSED: 20 Dec to 1 Feb   MEALS: Set D £29.50   SERVICE: not inc, card slips closed   CARDS: Access, Amex, Diners, Switch, Visa   DETAILS: 16 seats. Private parties: 12 main room. Car park. Children's helpings. No children under 5. Smart dress preferred. No smoking in dining-room. No music   ACCOMMODATION: 6 rooms, all with bath/shower. TV. Phone. B&B £80 to £119. Deposit: £100. No children under 5. Dogs welcome. Garden (*The Which? Hotel Guide*)

CELLARMAN'S CHOICE: *Wines recommended by the restaurateur, normally more expensive than house wine.*

WALES

LLANWDDYN Powys   map 7

▲ *Lake Vyrnwy Hotel* 🍸✕

Lake Vyrnwy, Llanwddyn SY10 0LY
TEL: (01691) 870692   FAX: (01691) 870259   COOKING 1
on B4393, at SE end of Lake Vyrnwy   COST £22–£38

Peeping out over the expanse of Lake Vyrnwy and the hills beyond, with an odd
Gothic tower sticking up out of the water, this 'sporting country house' offers the
full pastoral package of shooting and fishing outdoors and four-posters and
Jacuzzis within. On a clear day or evening the view from the conservatory
dining-room is splendid.

Andrew Wood is an industrious chef and turns his hand to much that others
leave to their suppliers. Home-smoking, chutney-making and the preparation of
charcuterie are enthusiastically practised. Mousses, pâtés and timbales might be
followed by locally shot partridge, or 'amazingly tender' Welsh lamb served
with a 'racy' onion chutney. Apple sponge with fudge sauce or a richly eloquent
dark chocolate mousse with chunky shortbread and a raspberry coulis makes a
comforting dessert. The wine list covers a fair bit of ground, with choices
throughout stolid rather than thrilling. House wines from the Languedoc and
Gascony are £9.85.

CHEF: Andrew Wood   PROPRIETOR: Market Glen Ltd   OPEN: all week 12.30 to 1.45, 7.30 to
9.15   MEALS: Set L £14.95, Set D £23.50. BYO £5 minimum   SERVICE: not inc, card slips
closed   CARDS: Access, Amex, Delta, Diners, Switch, Visa   DETAILS: 70 seats. Private parties:
70 main room, 20 to 120 private rooms. Car park. Vegetarian meals. Children's helpings. Smart
dress preferred. No smoking in dining-room. No music   ACCOMMODATION: 35 rooms, all with
bath/shower. TV. Phone. B&B £64 to £133. Children welcome. Baby facilities. Dogs welcome.
Afternoon teas. Garden. Fishing (*The Which? Hotel Guide*)

LLANWRDA Carmarthenshire   map 4

Seguendo di Stagioni 🍸 £

Harford, Pumpsaint, Llanwrda SA19 8DT
TEL: (01558) 650671 and (01570) 423771
FAX: (01558) 650671
on A482 between Llanwrda and Lampeter, 1½m NW   COOKING 2
of Pumpsaint   COST £15–£40

In the unlikely setting of a higgledy-piggledy but 'country cute' cottage in
remote south-west Wales is an Italian restaurant of rare quality. Aldo Steccanella
bestrides proceedings like a colossus, waxing eloquent about his fine wines,
dispensing copious antipasti, answering the phone and even managing to cook a
bit as well. The food is unrefined hearty country cooking, offering 'firm, richly
eggy and buttery' spaghettini with chicken livers and tomato sauce, swordfish
steak with tomato, capers and garlic, and admirably succulent beef, a whole
piece slowly braised in Barolo. 'There is nothing terribly subtle about the food,
but it is all robustly flavoured,' commented one satisfied customer. Pasta dishes
may well be accompanied by hot ciabatta running with basil-infused olive oil, a
treat in itself. Finish with 'fluffy and delicious' zabaglione or the equally

586

appealing 'grandma's pudding' – almond-studded shortcrust pastry filled with apple purée and crème pâtissière. If there is a 'slightly shambolic' air hovering about the scene, it is comprehensively outweighed by the genuine warmth of the approach.

Wines are wholly Italian and the list a daunting 'minefield' to one reporter. The initiated will disagree: among the great names are Puiatti, Conterno and Mascarello. Piedmont is particularly well represented, and a long selection of grappas ends the list at £2.50 a glass. House wines are £7.95. CELLARMAN'S CHOICE: Vernaccia di San Gimignano 'Terre di Tufi' 1994, Teruzzi e Puthod, £13.95; Nebbiolo delle Langhe 1992, Mascarello, £16.95.

CHEF: Aldo Steccanella   PROPRIETOR: Jennifer Taylor   OPEN: Sun L 12 to 3.30 (bookings only), Wed to Sun D 7 to 10; Tue to Sun in summer (bookings only)   MEALS: alc (main courses £9 to £15). Set L £9.95 to £14.95, Set D £8.95 to £19.75   SERVICE: not inc   CARDS: none   DETAILS: 35 seats. 16 seats outside. Private parties: 45 main room, 15 and 20 private rooms. Car park. Vegetarian meals. Children's helpings. No music

---

LLANWRTYD WELLS Powys   map 4

▲ *Carlton House* ⁵✳

Dolycoed Road, Llanwrtyd Wells LD5 4RA   COOKING 3
TEL: (01591) 610248   FAX: (01591) 610242   COST £28–£44

This genteel restaurant-with-rooms, occupying an Edwardian house, is 'lovingly nurtured by a devoted husband-and-wife team'. Renovations since last year have transformed the former dining-room into a reception area, and a new dining-room has opened at the back. The place is still filled with books, antique furniture and 'fascinating ornaments gathered over generations from all corners of the earth'. Mary Ann Gilchrist is an imaginative and enthusiastic 'amateur cook' who works mostly single-handedly in the kitchen, and offers a basic choice between the four-course set menu and a slightly more expensive 'epicurean menu' with a few more options.

Appetisers – variously filled pastry tartlets – are 'a good omen' for what is to come, and an inspector was impressed by the quality of materials which produces a 'strong, natural and unadulterated taste of the food'. Flavours range from maize-fed chicken accompanied by an exotic sauce of coconut and lime, aromatised with coriander and lemon grass, to 'tender and sweet' trimmed rack of Welsh lamb with pearl barley and leek risotto, served in a sauce of its own natural *jus*. 'Earthy potatoes with an old-fashioned *real* taste' have appeared alongside other first-rate vegetables.

A dessert of tangy iced lime parfait with a lemon cream sauce 'took the top prize' for one reporter, while another found vanilla terrine with an intense blackcurrant coulis 'slightly rubbery but attractively presented'. The wine list globetrots knowledgeably and is kind on the pocket; it is also regularly updated. One reporter who enjoyed a bottle of Gevrey-Chambertin found that it had been removed from the list by the following night; he had drunk the last bottle. House Australian is £9.

CHEF: Mary Ann Gilchrist PROPRIETORS: Alan and Mary Ann Gilchrist OPEN: Mon to Sat D only 7 to 8.30 CLOSED: 2 weeks at Christmas MEALS: Set D £19.50 to £27 SERVICE: not inc, card slips closed CARDS: Access, Visa DETAILS: 12 seats. Private parties: 10 main room. Smart dress preferred. No smoking in dining-room. No music ACCOMMODATION: 6 rooms, all with bath/shower. TV. B&B £35 to £65. Deposit: £15. Children welcome. Baby facilities. Dogs welcome (*The Which? Hotel Guide*)

LLYSWEN Powys   map 4

▲ *Llangoed Hall* ✱

Llyswen LD3 0YP
TEL: (01874) 754525 FAX: (01874) 754545   COOKING 2
on A470, 2m NW of Llyswen   COST £26–£65

The narrow drive decants visitors in front of the imposing façade of this refurbished Jacobean manor house, on which both Clough Williams Ellis and Sir Bernard (Laura Ashley's widower) have made their mark. So many drawings and paintings hang from the walls that a catalogue is needed to keep track of them, and staff appear in sufficient numbers to make reporters feel seriously pampered.

Some of the dishes are treated in similar fashion – a fillet of salmon has an oyster and caviar broth – but the modern approach to country-house cooking is informed by both lightness and depth, as in a breast of Gressingham duck served with a galette of confit duck and a light coriander sauce. Homespun dishes (roast beef with Yorkshire pudding) and provençale motifs (seared tuna with a niçoise salad) co-exist happily beside interesting puddings such as warm lemon sponge with marinated figs. Large sums of money can change hands, but the set-price lunch, one reporter calculated, offers 'tremendously good value' when compared with the *carte*. The wine list is packed with classics, including a page entirely devoted to Ch.Gruaud-Larose, but is better balanced than previously. House French is £8.95.

CHEF: Ben Davies PROPRIETOR: Sir Bernard Ashley OPEN: all week 12.15 to 2, 7.15 to 9.30 MEALS: alc (main courses £13.50 to £19.50). Set L £13 (2 courses) to £16, Set D £29.50 SERVICE: not inc, card slips closed CARDS: Access, Amex, Diners, Switch, Visa DETAILS: 40 seats. Private parties: 50 main room, 14 and 50 private rooms. Car park. Vegetarian meals. No children under 8. Smart dress preferred. No smoking in dining-room. Wheelchair access (also WC). Music ACCOMMODATION: 23 rooms, all with bath/shower. TV. Phone. B&B £110 to £320. Deposit: £50. No children under 8. Dogs welcome in heated kennels. Afternoon teas. Garden. Fishing (*The Which? Hotel Guide*)

MATHRY Pembrokeshire   map 4

Ann FitzGerald's Farmhouse Kitchen ♀

Mabws Fawr, Mathry SA62 5JB
TEL: (01348) 831347   COOKING 1*
off A487, 6m SW of Fishguard   COST £16–£41

Developments at the farmhouse site, including a proper car park, are expected to improve the surroundings. Once inside, since there isn't anywhere for a pre-meal drink, go straight to the table. Ann FitzGerald is a talented cook, whose repertoire has changed little over the years: individual set menus may offer limited choice, but the *carte* is ambitiously extensive for the circumstances. Among its roll call of dishes might be Burgundian snails, fish and chips, and a 'mountain of tempura'. Wine is a common saucing ingredient.

Presentation is rustic, from roughly liquidised soups to a coarse pâté of veal and duck which benefits from a 'rich, beguiling chutney'. And it is bountiful: a bottomless tureen of fish soup, plentiful vegetables, and a wide array of cheeses from Cashel Blue to Pencarreg and Llangloffan. Bread at its best is warm and freshly baked, and apple tart with a dark, sticky, caramel cream sauce pleased an inspector. Standards are well maintained on the wine list. France and Italy are the strong suits, and mark-ups are low. House Italian is £9. CELLARMAN'S CHOICE: Cava Juvé y Camps 1991, Penedès, Spain, £14; Barbera d'Asti 1990, Ceppi Storici, £12.

CHEFS/PROPRIETORS: Ann and Lionel FitzGerald   OPEN: all week 12 to 2.30, 6 to 9.30   CLOSED: L Christmas to Easter exc bookings   MEALS: alc (main courses £5 to £14). Set L £10, Set D £17. BYO £4   SERVICE: not inc, card slips closed   CARDS: Access, Visa   DETAILS: 35 seats. 12 seats outside. Private parties: 45 main room. Car park. Vegetarian meals. Children's helpings. Wheelchair access (also WC). No music

---

NANTGAREDIG   Carmarthenshire   map 4

▲ *Four Seasons*

Cwmtwrch Farm Hotel, Nantgaredig SA32 7NY
TEL: (01267) 290238   FAX: (01267) 290808   COOKING 1
on B4310, 1m N of Nantgaredig   COST £20–£37

The converted farm building, with adjacent leisure club and nine-hole golf course, has a light and airy feel, with a slate floor, whitewashed stone walls, stripped pine and local pottery. The kitchen uses locally smoked salmon, Welsh goats' cheese (served with roasted red pepper as a first course), local lamb and venison, and Towy sewin. It has turned out a 'dreamy' smoked haddock tart with tarragon sauce, commendable rabbit with mustard, and good strawberry pavlova. A missed opportunity, perhaps, is the cheeseboard, which offers Cheddar, Brie and Stilton 'in an area that produces some of the most interesting regional cheeses in the UK'. Service is friendly and informal. 'Townies used to quick service will profit from relaxing,' felt one. Jazz evenings happen once a month, and the advice is to check when booking. An associated wine company supplies around 30 good-value bottles, with house wine starting at £9.

CHEFS/PROPRIETORS: Charlotte Pasetti, and Maryann and Simon Wright   OPEN: Mon to Fri L 12.30 to 2 (bookings only), Mon to Sat D 7.30 to 9.30   MEALS: Set L £12, Set D £18.50 SERVICE: not inc   CARDS: none   DETAILS: 50 seats. Private parties: 50 main room. Car park. Vegetarian meals. Children's helpings. Wheelchair access (no WC). Music   ACCOMMODATION: 6 rooms, all with bath/shower. B&B £36 to £50. Deposit: 10%. Rooms for disabled. Children welcome. Dogs welcome. Garden. Swimming-pool

---

All entries in the Guide *are rewritten every year, not least because restaurant standards fluctuate. Don't rely on an out-of-date* Guide.

NEWPORT Pembrokeshire
map 4

▲ *Cnapan* ¦✳

East Street, Newport SA42 0SY
TEL: (01239) 820575 FAX: (01239) 820878

COOKING 1*
COST £15–£32

Two generations running this charming cottage restaurant in the North Pembrokeshire National Park are joined by a third when the academic year permits. This is an industrious kitchen operating a wide-ranging *carte* at both lunch and dinner. Regional specialities seem to work particularly well: sewin (local sea trout) is poached with laverbread and sauced with mussels, while seaweed may crop up again with gratinated Cardigan Bay crab. Welsh lamb looks to more distant shores when it is marinated with Indian spices, grilled on a skewer with apricots and served with saffron rice. Vegetarians are solicitously looked after, their dishes described in recipe-like detail. Finish with cheesecake and elderflower and gooseberry sauce, or perhaps rich rum and chocolate torte. The inexpensive wine list packs its regions in, not excluding Morocco and Wales. House French is £7.75.

CHEFS: Eluned Lloyd and Judith Cooper   PROPRIETORS: Eluned and John Lloyd, Michael and Judith Cooper   OPEN: Wed to Mon 12 to 2, 7 to 9 from Easter to end Oct; open Fri and Sat D, and Sun L only in winter : CLOSED: Feb   MEALS: alc (main courses L £4.50 to £6, D £9.50 to £12.50)   SERVICE: not inc, card slips closed   CARDS: Access, Visa   DETAILS: 36 seats. 30 seats outside. Private parties: 36 main room. Car park. Vegetarian meals. Children welcome up to early evening. Children's helpings L. Smart dress preferred. No smoking in dining-room. No music   ACCOMMODATION: 5 rooms, all with bath/shower. TV. B&B £24 to £48. Deposit: £30. Children welcome. Baby facilities. Garden (*The Which? Hotel Guide*)

NORTHOP Flintshire
map 7

▲ *Soughton Hall*

Northop CH7 6AB
TEL: (01352) 840811 FAX: (01352) 840382
off A5119, 1m S of Northop

COOKING 1*
COST £34–£63

The former bishop's palace, reached by a half-mile avenue of lime trees, is an opulent and many-splendoured thing, with high painted ceilings, elegant curtains and tapestries, and antique furniture. 'One can see why the Church of England is now ordering humbler dwellings for its bishops.' The owners are due grateful thanks for having restored a lovely old building.

The same à la carte menu is offered at both lunch and dinner, with around eight choices per course, and the kitchen aims high: fillet of beef with potato gnocchi and a ravioli of wild mushrooms with pesto at £21.50, for example. 'I would have felt happier with greater restraint and lower prices,' confessed an inspector, who nevertheless enjoyed a salad of crumbly Welsh goats' cheese on olive bread, and a dish of scallops, sea bass, swordfish and salmon described on the menu as 'catch of the day'. Puddings are ambitious too. Some fine clarets and Burgundies are complemented by decent New World bottles at under £20. As the *Guide* went to press, plans were under way to open a pub/restaurant on the premises called Stables, which will offer lighter food, real ales and wine tastings.

CHEF: Michael Carney PROPRIETORS: John and Rosemary Rodenhurst OPEN: all week 12 to 2, 7 to 9.30 (10 Fri and Sat) MEALS: alc (main courses £13 to £21.50) SERVICE: not inc, card slips closed CARDS: Access, Amex, Visa DETAILS: 50 seats. Private parties: 56 main room, 22 and 120 private rooms. Car park. Vegetarian meals. Children's helpings. Smart dress preferred. Music ACCOMMODATION: 14 rooms, all with bath/shower. TV. Phone. B&B £80 to £150. Deposit: 25%. Room for disabled. Children welcome. Afternoon teas. Garden (*The Which? Hotel Guide*)

PENMAENPOOL Caernarfonshire & Merionethshire   map 7

▲ *Penmaenuchaf Hall* ♈ 🪑 ⁵⋇

Penmaenpool LL40 1YB
TEL/FAX: (01341) 422129   COOKING 2*
off A493, 2m W of Dolgellau   COST £25–£54

The late-Victorian house of dark stone is attractively set in an amphitheatre of hills close to Cader Idris, with views over the Mawddach estuary. An impressive pre-Tudor carved oak fireplace in the hall lends character to an otherwise modernised but extremely pleasant interior. 'I gather that chefs come and go here at a rate of knots,' volunteered one reporter. Standards have varied with the changes, but Hugh Cocker (in the *Guide* last year at Taychreggan in Kilchrenan – see entry, Scotland) seems to have put things on an even keel, pleasing an inspector with the consistently high standard of a May meal.

The up-to-date country-house cooking makes good use of local maritime resources. A lightly pressed terrine of scallops, sea bream, grey mullet and salmon may sound a mixed bag, but 'it is amazing how much contrast there is between different types of fish if they are really fresh and timed nicely'. Wild mushrooms are picked locally, and the taste and texture of new season Bala lamb has impressed. Among desserts, the flavour combinations of a hot banoffi praline soufflé overcame slight technical imperfections for one reporter, while the ensemble is helped by good appetisers and bread, including a foie gras version of brioche. Thanks to 'kind and forbearing' staff, 'one goes away feeling that one has been well cared for in every way'.

The wine list runs the gamut from Eastern European bargains to fine and old vintage port, claret and red Burgundy. Producers are chosen with care throughout. Helpful notes on the list describe claret vintages and point out the best wines for vegetarians. The Mexican house red from L.A. Cetto (£11.95) has been singled out by reporters for praise. CELLARMAN'S CHOICE: Schloss Castell Silvaner Trocken 1994, Franconia, £16.95; Côtes de Castillon, Ch. Roc de Montpezat 1990, £13.50.

CHEFS: Hugh Cocker and Simon Hallas PROPRIETOR: Mark Watson OPEN: all week 12 to 2, 7 to 9.30 (9 Sun) CLOSED: 2nd week Jan MEALS: alc (main courses L £7 to £12, D £14.50 to £18). Set L £12.95 (2 courses) to £14.95, Set D £23. BYO £6. Light lunches available SERVICE: not inc, card slips closed CARDS: Access, Amex, Delta, Diners, Switch, Visa DETAILS: 30 seats. Private parties: 50 main room, 16 private room. Car park. Vegetarian meals. Children's helpings. No children under 8 L and early evening; no children under 10 after 8pm. Smart dress preferred. No smoking in dining-room. Wheelchair access (also WC). Music ACCOMMODATION: 14 rooms, all with bath/shower. TV. Phone. B&B £65 to £150. Deposit: £10. No children under 8 exc babies. Baby facilities. Dogs welcome (to stay in gun room only). Afternoon teas. Garden. Fishing (*The Which? Hotel Guide*)

PONTFAEN Pembrokeshire   map 4

▲ *Tregynon Country Farmhouse Hotel* ⚛✳

Gwaun Valley, Pontfaen SA65 9TU
TEL: (01239) 820531   FAX: (01239) 820808
at junction of B4313 and B4329, take B4313 towards   COOKING 1
Fishguard, then take first right, and first right again   COST £24–£36

The sixteenth-century low-beamed stone farmhouse is set in the Pembrokeshire
Coast National Park, and has an Iron Age fort in the grounds. The style is homely,
with no aspiration to luxury, backed by earnest and healthy ideals. It is a
restaurant with a mission, and an emphasis on meat-free starters (including
vegan soups), lightly cooked vegetables, wholemeal bread, egg-free ice-creams
(the one with whisky and orange marmalade is particularly good), and some
organic foods. The vegetarian leanings, however, still permit home-smoked
bacon and gammon, rack of Pembrokeshire lamb and the like. Main courses
need to be ordered at breakfast (for residents) or the evening before, which takes
away some of the spontaneity. Dishes don't go in for flair and imagination; the
appeal is low-key. An enthusiastic and well-annotated list of 40-odd wines
demands time for study. Gulpable Loire house wines are £9.50.

CHEFS: Peter and Jane Heard, and Siân Davies   PROPRIETORS: Peter and Jane Heard   OPEN:
all week D only 7.30 to 8.45   MEALS: Set D £16.95. BYO £5   SERVICE: not inc   CARDS: Access,
Switch, Visa   DETAILS: 28 seats. Private parties: 16 main room, 12 private room. Car park.
Vegetarian meals. Smart dress preferred. No smoking in dining-room. Music
ACCOMMODATION: 8 rooms, all with bath/shower. TV. Phone. B&B £46 to £67 (double rooms).
Deposit: 25%. Rooms for disabled. Children welcome (high tea served at 6). Baby facilities.
Afternoon teas. Garden (*The Which? Hotel Guide*)

PORTHGAIN Pembrokeshire   map 4

Harbour Lights

Porthgain, nr St David's SA62 5BW
TEL: (01348) 831549   COOKING 2*
off A487 at Croesgoch, 4m W of Mathry   COST £31–£37

The décor of this stone cottage near the Pembrokeshire coastal path is described
by a reporter as 'simple and solid', and there are rough picnic tables outside for
those prepared to brave the elements. Its appeal, according to a regular visitor, is
'fresh food well prepared and served', a 'short but good' wine list, and 'pleasant,
friendly service'. Meals are either two or three courses, and the repertoire reflects
local resources.

Laverbread invariably features, perhaps served with smoked bacon and
Pencarreg cheese, and remains 'a long-term favourite' for one reporter. Fish and
vegetables get a good airing, from a seafood mornay to moist, firm Dover sole.
When beef appears, perhaps in the form of a pan-fried sirloin steak, it will be
organic. Desserts are just as straightforward: from warm apple and rhubarb
pancake to a banana sticky toffee pudding that for one diner was the epitome of
'over-the-top excellence'. Wines are fairly priced, beginning with house French
at £9.50.

CHEF/PROPRIETOR: Anne Marie Davies   OPEN: Tue to Sat D only 7 to 9.30 (phone to check opening times out of season)   MEALS: Set D £19.50 (2 courses) to £22.50   SERVICE: not inc, card slips closed   CARDS: Access, Delta, Switch, Visa   DETAILS: 40 seats. Private parties: 20 main room. Vegetarian meals. Children welcome. Music

---

PORTMEIRION Caernarfonshire & Merionethshire   map 7

▲ *Hotel Portmeirion* ¶ 🥖 ✳

Portmeirion LL48 6ET
TEL: (01766) 770228   FAX: (01766) 771331   COOKING 1*
off A487, signposted from Minffordd   COST £20–£39

'It would be difficult to be disappointed in this very special place,' claimed a visitor in admiration of Sir Clough Williams-Ellis's magnificent Italianate folly on the Traeth Bach estuary. It is dramatic and beautiful whatever the weather, and all the houses making up the village can be let. Since the last edition of the *Guide* Colin Pritchard has moved up to head chef, but the style remains much the same: 'contemporary Welsh with Mediterranean influences', in which Black beef, hill-farmed lamb and local seafood feature.

Lunch in the cream and white semicircular dining-room typically offers three options per course, dinner twice that number. Melon with soft fruits and 'a superb grapefruit sorbet', or a vegetable soup might set the ball rolling, though the highlights for an inspector were 'startlingly good' guinea-fowl in a jasmine sauce, and lemon tart. English and Welsh cheeses offer a viable alternative to dessert, and service is attentive and charming. The wine list gets off to a promising start with two pages of trustworthy bottles at under £13.50. Elsewhere it makes a highlight of Bordeaux and Australia and, naturally, includes a Welsh white wine. Prices are fair throughout, with house wines £9.50. CELLARMAN'S CHOICE: Cyfuniad Sych Pant Teg 1992, Llysfaen, De Morgannwg, £12.50; Graves, Ch. de Seuil 1990, £16.50.

CHEFS: Colin Pritchard and Billy Taylor   PROPRIETOR: Portmeirion Ltd   OPEN: Tue to Sun L 12.30 to 2, all week D 7 to 9.30   CLOSED: 5 Jan to 7 Feb   MEALS: Set L Tue to Sat £10.50 (2 courses) to £13.50, Set L Sun £14, Set D £20.50 (2 courses) to £25   SERVICE: not inc, card slips closed   CARDS: Access, Amex, Delta, Diners, Switch, Visa   DETAILS: 120 seats. 12 seats outside. Private parties: 100 main room, 12 and 30 private rooms. Car park. Vegetarian meals. Children's helpings. Smart dress preferred. No smoking in dining-room. No music ACCOMMODATION: 37 rooms, all with bath/shower. TV. Phone. B&B £55 to £170. Children welcome. Baby facilities. Afternoon teas. Garden. Swimming-pool (*The Which? Hotel Guide*)

PWLLHELI Caernarfonshire & Merionethshire   map 7

▲ *Plas Bodegroes* 🍶 ✳

Nefyn Road, Pwllheli LL53 5TH
TEL: (01758) 612363   FAX: (01758) 701247   COOKING 4
on A497, 1m W of Pwllheli   COST £41–£49

A grand avenue of beech trees leads to the pretty, symmetrical Georgian mansion with a long verandah stretching across the front. It has mature gardens, a heart-shaped lawn, and has been beautifully restored with a touch of minimal modernity. The feel is 'cool and tasteful', helped by paintings and sketches from Kyffin Williams and other local artists, and by a spacious dining-room with pristine table settings.

Although Chris Chown still retains interest in the Hole in the Wall in Bath (see entry), and despite Plas Bodegroes being up for sale, he appears unstinting in the energy he applies to it. Wild innovation is not his bag, although there are some very attractive ideas. The appeal is that quality remains consistent over time and throughout a meal. The menu is skilfully put together, building up from, say, wild mushroom tart, through seared scallops with lime hollandaise and spinach, to traditionally structured main courses such as roast Hereford duck with lentils and bacon in a Madeira sauce.

The five-course dinner has a choice of four or five options per course, and the balance is such that almost any combination would produce a good meal. Richness and depth of flavour are evident in a main course of ribeye of highest-quality beef served with oxtail mash, while accurate timing makes a success of seared tuna and queen scallops with watercress, and of a piece of baked seabass served with smoked prawns in a dark, buttery, fishy sauce.

Balance is a characteristic of the cooking, as in a dish of rich salmon baked in lightly flaky pastry with sappy leeks and laverbread, or a classic ballotine of guinea-fowl enhanced by a sharp and jammy onion marmalade. Contrasts are important too, not least among desserts of warm gratin of pear with a Poire William sorbet, or a creamy parfait of apricot and crunchy praline, sharpened by a smooth raspberry coulis. Despite the five courses (at a stable price) there is 'no feeling of over-fulness from rich sauces or large quantities'. Service is efficient, friendly and relaxed, and France is the focal point of the wine list. The Alsace section is particularly strong, extending far enough to include half-bottles of mature wines. Elsewhere, quality remains high and prices sensible. A house selection of 17 mixed wines starts at £12.

CHEF: Christopher Chown PROPRIETORS: Christopher and Gunna Chown OPEN: Tue to Sun D only 7 to 9 CLOSED: end Oct to mid-Mar MEALS: Set D £30 SERVICE: not inc, card slips closed CARDS: Access, Amex, Switch, Visa DETAILS: 40 seats. Private parties: 50 main room. Car park. Children's helpings. No smoking in dining-room. Wheelchair access (also men's WC). Music ACCOMMODATION: 8 rooms, all with bath/shower. TV. Phone. DB&B £70 to £180. Deposit: £50. Baby facilities. Dogs welcome in bedrooms only. Garden

---

REYNOLDSTON Swansea   map 4

▲ *Fairyhill* ▮

Reynoldston SA3 1BS   COOKING 2*
TEL: (01792) 390139   FAX: (01792) 391358   COST £24–£44

This is an old-fashioned Welsh country house set in acres of garden and parkland, with the welcoming smell of a wood fire, and a friendly escort service from the front door to the comfortable lounge and dining-room. What impresses here is the use of local resources, from game to mushrooms to laverbread. Samphire comes from Loughor marshes, venison from Bwlch, and Penclawdd cockles might be served with scrambled eggs and roast peppers. Herbs and salad leaves grow in the walled garden, and the orchard provides apples, cherries and damsons.

Paul Davies shows that distinctively Welsh cooking need not be confined to lamb and laverbread, though. His output is 'modern' in the sense that flavour and composition come first, even if that means borrowing ideas and ingredients from elsewhere to make a dish work: hence an avocado and lime salsa that accompanies a first course of lambs' liver. The repertoire may not vary much year in, year out, but because local supplies are integral, the food necessarily follows the seasons, producing enough diversity on the monthly-changing menus. There's plenty of variety, too, on the wine list, which spans the vinous globe and even includes a page on Welsh wines. The choice is strong outside France as well as within, and a comprehensive set of half-bottles rounds off the list. House Vin de Pays d'Oc is £9.95. CELLARMAN'S CHOICE: Pouilly-Fumé 1994, Dom. des Fines Caillottes 1994, Jean Pabiot, £19.50; Henschke Mount Edelstone Shiraz 1992, Adelaide Hills, S. Australia, £29.50.

CHEF: Paul Davies   PROPRIETORS: Paul Davies, Andrew Hetherington, and Jane and Peter Camm   OPEN: all week 12.30 to 2, 7.30 to 9.15   CLOSED: bank hol Mon   MEALS: Set L £7.50 (1 course) to £15, Set D £22 (2 courses) to £27   SERVICE: not inc, card slips closed   CARDS: Access, Amex, Delta, Switch, Visa   DETAILS: 60 seats. 16 seats outside. Private parties: 40 main room, 20 and 40 private rooms. Car park. Vegetarian meals. Children's helpings. No children under 8 D. Smart dress preferred. No cigars/pipes in dining-room. Wheelchair access (also WC). Music   ACCOMMODATION: 8 rooms, all with bath/shower. TV. Phone. B&B £65 to £110. Children welcome. No babies under 2. Dogs welcome in bedrooms by arrangement. Afternoon teas. Garden. Fishing (*The Which? Hotel Guide*)

ROSEBUSH Pembrokeshire   map 4

Tate's at Tafarn Newydd ♥ ✳ £

Tafarn Newydd, Rosebush SA66 7RA
TEL: (01437) 532542   COOKING 2
on B4313, 8m SE of Fishguard   COST £15–£39

'An extremely pleasant place to be marooned in in the depths of winter. The hospitality could not be faulted,' concluded a traveller, who added that Tate's seemed to be 'inhabited by deep rustic *Guardian* readers' who were happy to be a part of 'folk-music nights and much rural knick-knackery done in pleasing fashion'. Diana Richards has done a splendid job in revitalising this remote pub at the foot of the pass through the highest part of the Preseli Hills. The public bar and real ales have been preserved, but a cosmopolitan, bistro-style dining-room has been grafted on.

Diana Richards's cooking is wildly multicultural, with local ingredients and specialities from the world larder jostling for the limelight. The menu oozes excitement and enthusiasm. Locally bred Gressingham duck is given a Malaysian twist, wild garlic flavours lamb steak, samphire accompanies sea bass and, of course, there is laverbread (served as an enjoyable gratin with cockles and bacon). Added to that, you might find Thai pork curry, vegetable gumbo, and cod soffritto as well as cawl, oxtail with olives, sticky toffee pudding, and rhubarb crumble. Wines are another passion, to judge from the long and lively list, which opens with an appealing collection of 37 bottles at under £12. France and Australia are the strongest suits. CELLARMAN'S CHOICE: Wakefield White

Clare Chardonnay/Crouchen 1991, Clare Valley, S. Australia, £10.95; Weinert Cabernet Sauvignon 1985, Mendoza, Argentina, £15.50.

CHEF/PROPRIETOR: Diana Richards   OPEN: all week L 12 to 2.30, Tue to Sat D and bank hol Mon D 7 to 9.30   MEALS: alc (main courses £5.50 to £15). Set L Mon to Sat £6.50 (2 courses) to £8.50, Set L Sun £7.50 to £10.50, Set D £12.50 (inc wine). Bar food available Sun D and Mon D   SERVICE: not inc, card slips closed   CARDS: Access, Delta, Visa   DETAILS: 60 seats. 20 seats outside. Private parties: 40 main room. Vegetarian meals. Children's helpings. No smoking in 1 dining-room. Wheelchair access (no WC). Music

---

ROSSETT Wrexham   map 7

Churtons £

Chester Road, Rossett LL12 0HW
TEL: (01244) 570163   FAX: (01244) 570099   COOKING 1
on B5445, off A483, between Chester and Wrexham   COST £17–£36

Not many of the wine bars that sprang up in the early '80s have survived. Those that have – this one opened in 1982 – generally owe their continuing success to the determination of owners who believe steadfastly in the idea, rather than see it merely as a marketing opportunity. The Churtons are from a long-established family of Liverpool wine merchants, and still sell wine to take away by the bottle or case. Many of the wines on offer are excellent value for money and seven are available by the glass to accompany bistro favourites from the blackboard menu: moules marinière, deep-fried blue Brie, moussaka, and peppered rump steak among them. A few exotic notes add interest in the form of Jamaican beef, or Thai-style king prawns in filo pastry with a spicy mango mayonnaise, while puddings might include apple crumble with custard, or the remarkable-sounding chocolate mayonnaise cake.

   Churtons' other wine and food bar can be found at 55 High Street, Tarporley, Cheshire CW6 0DP, (01829) 732483.

CHEFS: Ade Garratt, Jackie Lloyd, Louise MacDougall and Eileen Abbott   PROPRIETORS: Nicholas Churton and James Churton   OPEN: Mon to Fri L 12 to 2.15, Mon to Sat D 7 to 10   CLOSED: 24 Dec to 3 Jan, bank hols   MEALS: alc (main courses £5 to £14)   SERVICE: not inc, card slips closed   CARDS: Access, Amex, Delta, Visa   DETAILS: 55 seats. Private parties: 20 main room, 12 private room. Car park. Vegetarian meals. No children under 12. Smart dress preferred. Wheelchair access. Music. Air-conditioned

---

ST DAVID'S Pembrokeshire   map 4

Morgan's Brasserie

20 Nun Street, St David's SA62 6NT   COOKING 1
TEL: (01437) 720508   COST £17–£35

This small family-run restaurant, in a double-fronted house in Britain's smallest city, is 'a cut above a bistro, but just short of a brasserie'. Mark Strangward (who came from nearby Warpool Court) is new to the stoves since last year, but maintains the tradition of a fish-laden blackboard menu – Dover sole with Penclawdd cockles, or sewin with laverbread sauce – to supplement offerings of goats'-cheese salad or noisettes of lamb. While a few things can let the side down

– over-enthusiastic cooking of some items, a bit less excitement in the Thai spicing than promised – there is an 'honest' quality about the food, from soups, wholemeal rolls and ice-creams made on the premises to good supplies of 'wholesome' local vegetables and cheeses. Red wines are coded for body, whites for sweetness, on the well-priced 40-strong list.

CHEF: Mark Strangward   PROPRIETORS: Ceri and Elaine Morgan   OPEN: Sun L 12 to 2, Mon to Sat D 6.30 to 9, plus Wed to Sat L and Sun D July to Aug; open only Fri and Sat D Nov to Jan (all week D Christmas week plus L 25 Dec)   CLOSED: Feb   MEALS: alc (main courses £5 to £8 L, £9 to £13 D)   SERVICE: not inc   CARDS: Access, Amex, Visa   DETAILS: 38 seats. Private parties: 38 main room. Vegetarian meals. Children's shelpings. Smart dress preferred. Wheelchair access (no WC). Music

---

SWANSEA Swansea   map 4

L'Amuse

2 Woodville Road, Mumbles, Swansea SA3 4AD   COOKING 1*
TEL: (01792) 366006   COST £19–£30

With a name like L'Amuse, it should come as no surprise that filling amuse-gueules are the curtain-raiser in Kate Cole's casually decorated street-corner restaurant. Lunch brings deep-fried local cockles, while evening meals are heralded by a country terrine with baby gherkins and toast. Kate's weekly fixed-price menus are emphatically rustic French, taking in the likes of mussel soup with saffron, warm salad of 'pied de cochon', bourride with ginger, and confit of duck with sauce périgueux. She also caters for stoically British palates with roast sirloin of beef, which comes with red wine gravy and horseradish cream. To finish there might be pineapple croustillant, crème caramel, and chocolate fondant, not to mention a plate of cheese from the Alps served with home-made crackers and walnut bread. Three dozen keenly chosen wines rarely stray beyond the French border. House wine is £8.

CHEF/PROPRIETOR: Kate Cole   OPEN: Tue to Sat 12 to 2.15, 7 to 9   CLOSED: Jan   MEALS: Set L £5.95 (1 course) to £11.95, Set D £17.50   SERVICE: not inc   CARDS: Access, Delta, Visa DETAILS: 35 seats. Private parties: 50 main room. Children welcome. No music

La Braseria £

28 Wind Street, Swansea SA1 1DZ   COOKING 1*
TEL: (01792) 469683   COST £16–£35

Swansea's answer to a Spanish bodega continues to pack them in, thanks to its 'simple no-fuss approach', 'wonderful atmosphere' and excellent-value food. The £6 lunch remains one of the best deals in the city; weekends are a sell-out. Select your own cut of meat or fish ('bought daily'), watch it being chargrilled, then take your pick from eight different salads. Sea bream and bass cooked in rock salt are best sellers, while suckling pig now lines up alongside steaks, pork loin and pheasant. Wines are great value too, particularly if you choose from the racks of Riojas. House Siglo is £8.75.

WALES

CHEF: Miguel Tercero PROPRIETOR: Iceimp Ltd OPEN: Mon to Sat 12 to 2.30, 7 to 11.30
MEALS: alc (main courses £4 to £12). Set L £6 (2 courses) SERVICE: not inc, card slips closed
CARDS: Access, Amex, Delta, Diners, Switch, Visa DETAILS: 170 seats. Private parties: 100
main room. Vegetarian meals. Children welcome. Smart dress preferred. Wheelchair access
(also WC). Music

Number One Wind Street

1 Wind Street, Swansea SA1 1DE
TEL: (01792) 456996

COOKING 2
COST £19–£37

Number One Wind Street – a converted shop a stone's throw from the castle ruins
– generally strikes a happy note. Diners chat to each other between tables, and
staff are helpful. Kate Taylor's cooking is French provincial by inclination,
although she takes a dip in the Mediterranean from time to time for dishes such
as fresh tagliatelle with bacon and pesto. Her loyalty to Welsh produce and
suppliers also means that laverbread with cockles is put on as a starter, and
luscious locally made ice-creams show up at the end of the menu with seasonal
fruit tarts. Otherwise, the Gallic accent is undiluted: provençale fish soup with
aïoli, braised maize-fed chicken in Riesling, fillets of monkfish with Ricard, and
white and dark chocolate mousse. Lunch is a simpler affair, taking in egg
mayonnaise with tapénade, cassoulet, and bread-and-butter pudding. The wine
list naturally includes an affordable French contingent, but also features
representatives from Hungary, Chile and even Wales. House vin de pays is £8.

CHEF: Kate Taylor PROPRIETORS: Peter Gillen and Kate Taylor OPEN: Tue to Sat 12 to 2.30, 7
to 9.30 CLOSED: 25 Dec to New Year, bank hol Mons MEALS: Set L £9.50 (2 courses) to
£11.95, Set D £15.50 (2 courses) to £19 SERVICE: not inc, card slips closed CARDS: Access,
Amex, Visa DETAILS: 40 seats. Private parties: 40 main room. Vegetarian meals. Children's
helpings. No pipes in dining-room. Wheelchair access (no WC). Music

TALSARNAU Caernarfonshire & Merionethshire   map 7

▲ Maes-y-Neuadd 🏶✹

Talsarnau LL47 6YA
TEL: (01766) 780200 FAX: (01766) 780211
off B4573, 1m S of Talsarnau

COOKING 2
COST £19–£45

The manor-house is part fourteenth-century, built of large granite blocks and
reached by a long drive from the main road. Drinks in a comfortable lounge with
views of surrounding Snowdonia begin the process of relaxation that is part of
the draw here. What sets Maes-y-Neuadd apart is an opportunity to unwind,
allied to the industry of a kitchen where all sorts of goodies are fashioned from
surplus fruits and vegetables into jams, pickles, chutneys and oils for sale in the
shop, as well as for use in-house. A kitchen garden and a fisherman in Barmouth
are among the starting-points for Peter Jackson's simple country style of
cooking.

Welsh lamb, or breast of goose with caramelised apples and lentils might form
the centrepiece of a dinner that can vary from three to five courses according to
preference. Soup and/or fish can be interposed after a starter such as terrine of

venison, or a warm seafood salad, and what follows the main course is not called the Grand Finale for nothing: Welsh cheeses followed by no fewer than three puddings, among which might be lemon tart with thick cream, and banana fritter with rum sauce. Lunch is an altogether lighter affair, but shares the excellent choice of breads, and a 150-strong wine list backs it all up. House wines are £9.75.

CHEF: Peter Jackson   PROPRIETORS: Olive and Malcolm Horsfall, and June and Michael Slatter   OPEN: all week 12 to 1.45, 7 to 9   MEALS: Set L Mon to Sat £8 (1 course) to £12.50, Set L Sun £14.95, Set D £23 to £29. BYO £4. Bar L available   SERVICE: not inc, card slips closed CARDS: Access, Amex, Delta, Diners, Switch, Visa   DETAILS: 50 seats. Private parties: 50 main room, 16 private room. Car park. Vegetarian meals. Children's helpings. Smart dress preferred. No smoking in dining-room. Wheelchair access (also WC). Music   ACCOMMODATION: 16 rooms, all with bath/shower. TV. Phone. D,B&B £69 to £193. Deposit: £50. Rooms for disabled. Children welcome. Baby facilities. Dogs by arrangement. Afternoon teas. Garden (*The Which? Hotel Guide*)

TALYLLYN Caernarfonshire & Merionethshire   map 7

▲ *Minffordd Hotel* ⁵✗

Talyllyn LL36 9AJ
TEL: (01654) 761665   FAX: (01654) 761517   COOKING 1
at junction of A487 and B4405, 8m SW of Dolgellau   COST £22–£27

The welcome is friendly at this 300-year-old coaching-inn near the foot of Cader Idris. Polished silver and glass gleam in the low-beamed dining-room, and dinner is at 8 o'clock. Main courses are limited to a choice of two, perhaps loin of Welsh lamb with a port and redcurrant sauce, or lemon sole fillet with a prawn and cream sauce, both sauces indicating the kitchen's traditional approach. Baked sherried grapefruit and chilled melon with port are other old-stagers that few restaurants do these days. Crabmeat profiteroles with hollandaise are more adventurous, while soups incline to vegetable compositions of, say, pea and mint, spiced carrot, or Welsh onion. Game appears in season, while spotted dick, treacle tart, and date and ginger sponge come straight from the nursery. Three dozen wines at commendably friendly prices include the native Monnow Valley Huxelrebe at £10.95.

CHEF: Mark Warner   PROPRIETORS: Mary McQuillan and Mark Warner   OPEN: all week D only 8 (1 sitting)   CLOSED: Jan and Feb   MEALS: Set D £18.50   SERVICE: none, card slips closed CARDS: Access, Delta, Visa   DETAILS: 22 seats. Private parties: 12 main room. Car park. Children's helpings. No children under 5. Smart dress preferred. No smoking in dining-room. No music   ACCOMMODATION: 7 rooms, all with bath/shower. Phone. B&B £31 to £67. Deposit: 20%. No children under 5. Afternoon teas. Garden. Fishing (*The Which? Hotel Guide*)

All details are as accurate as possible at the time of going to press, but chefs and owners often change, and it is wise to check by telephone before making a special journey. Many readers have been disappointed when set-price bargain meals are no longer available. Ask when booking.

THREE COCKS Powys   map 4

▲ *Three Cocks Hotel*

Three Cocks LD3 0SL
TEL/FAX: (01497) 847215   COOKING 2
on A438, between Brecon and Hay-on-Wye   COST £29–£50

The creeper-covered fifteenth-century inn overlooks the beautiful Brecon
Beacons. It has, according to one reporter, a 'nicely antiquated' feel, and 'once
inside, you are transported to a Belgian restaurant-with-rooms'. Mrs Winstone is
a model of old-fashioned courtesy, and the lack of pretension is appreciated. The
set menu (with five options per course, apart from soup) lies at the core and,
despite one or two supplements, 'certainly represents value for money'. Michael
Winstone's repertoire does not alter much, although individual dishes might
range from king prawns with rosemary and harissa to loin of Welsh lamb with
duxelles and blue cheese wrapped in puff pastry.

   Fish is a strength – very fresh and 'cooked to perfection' – and garlic butter is
not in short supply. Meat is well bought too, and the kitchen knows about
accurate timing. Second helpings of soup are offered, and no fewer than seven
'fussy' but organic vegetables are served, all of a high standard. One reporter
found that a rich chocolate truffle cake 'was too much at the end of four good
courses', but there may be sorbets, or perhaps grilled goats' cheese with honey.
Excellent bottled Belgian beers are an alternative to the largely French wines.
Welsh Croffta is £12.50, and house French is £8.

CHEF: Michael Winstone   PROPRIETORS: Mr and Mrs Michael Winstone   OPEN: Mon and Wed
to Sat L 12 to 1, Mon and Wed to Sun D 7 to 9   CLOSED: Dec to 14 Feb   MEALS: alc (main
courses £15.50 to £20). Set L and D £25   SERVICE: net prices, card slips closed   CARDS:
Access, Visa   DETAILS: 30 seats. Private parties: 30 main room. Car park. Vegetarian meals.
Children's helpings. Smart dress preferred. Music   ACCOMMODATION: 7 rooms, all with
bath/shower. B&B £62 (double room). Children welcome. Baby facilities. Afternoon teas.
Garden (*The Which? Hotel Guide*)

TREFRIW Aberconwy & Colwyn   map 7

Chandler's ⅝✳

Trefriw LL27 0JH
TEL: (01492) 640991   COOKING 1*
off B5106, NW of Llanrwst   COST £14–£30

Chandler's, in one of the Conwy Valley's oldest villages, is now entirely a
family-run affair. The school bench seating has gone, and elegant tables and
stylish colourful pictures are part of the new look. Arrive, as one party did, to a
friendly welcome, a drink and appetisers beside an open fire. The brasserie
menu changes every two weeks, takes in many styles of cooking, and typically
embraces Welsh lamb and a few unusual fishy items, such as deep-fried
monkfish in apple batter. One vegetarian reporter was 'surprised and pleased to
be presented with a separate vegetarian menu', and even happier with a
'substantial but interesting' crispy risotto cake. The Rattenburys are not above
modifying a dish to suit individual taste, though bread-and-butter pudding

with marmalade ice-cream, and hot banana and toffee crumble tart have come straight off the short dessert menu. The sharp, modern wine list goes down very well. House wines are £8.25.

CHEFS/PROPRIETORS: Penny and Adam Rattenbury   OPEN: Wed to Fri and Sun L 12 to 2, Thur to Sat D 7 to 9.30   CLOSED: 2 to 3 weeks some time between Jan and Apr   MEALS: alc (main courses L £4 to £6.50, D £8.50 to £11). Set L Wed to Fri £7.50, Set L Sun £12.50, Set D £14.50 to £17   SERVICE: not inc, card slips closed   CARDS: Access, Switch, Visa   DETAILS: 30 seats. Private parties: 30 main room. Car park. Vegetarian meals. Children's helpings. No smoking in dining-room. Music

---

WELSH HOOK Pembrokeshire   map 4

▲ Stone Hall

Welsh Hook, Wolf's Castle SA62 5NS
TEL: (01348) 840212   FAX: (01348) 840815
1½m off A40, between Letterston and Wolf's Castle,   COOKING 1
W of Welsh Hook   COST £24–£38

If age confers dignity on a building, then Stone Hall must be one of the more venerable places at which to eat and stay. Parts of it have been around since the time of Chaucer, the massive beams and slate-flagged floor of the dining-room in particular providing a setting of unrestrained grandeur. Bilingual menus (Martine Watson is French) offer the kinds of rustic dishes that the first British cross-Channel tourists fell in love with: baked mussels filled with garlic and parsley butter, chicken breast in tarragon sauce, magret de canard with a sauce of apples and calvados.

But there are racier things afoot, such as pheasant cooked in tea with sultanas and walnuts. Vegetable accompaniments are good and varied, and the chances are that your favourite French dessert will be there too, whether crème brûlée, nougat glacé or profiteroles with chocolate. Crêpes are well-made and there are some fine local cheeses to supplement the French offerings. The predominantly French wine list is serviceable without being showy, and is headed up by Sauvignon and Gamay varietals from Touraine at £9.80.

CHEFS: Martine Watson and Jean-Yves Poujade   PROPRIETORS: Alan and Martine Watson   OPEN: all week D only 7 to 9.30   MEALS: alc (main courses £11 to £12.50). Set D £16   SERVICE: not inc   CARDS: Access, Amex, Diners, Visa   DETAILS: 34 seats. Private parties: 45 main room, 20 private room. Car park. Children's helpings. Smart dress preferred. No cigars/pipes in dining-room. Wheelchair access (no WC). No music   ACCOMMODATION: 5 rooms, all with bath/shower. TV. B&B £46 to £65. Deposit: £20. Children welcome. Baby facilities. Garden (*The Which? Hotel Guide*)

Prices quoted in the Guide *are based on information supplied by restaurateurs. The prices quoted at the top of each entry represent a range, from the lowest meal price to the highest; the latter is inflated by 20 per cent to take account of likely price rises during the year of the* Guide.

Not inc *in the details at the end of an entry indicates that no service charge is made and any tipping is at the discretion of the customer.*

▲ *The Crown at Whitebrook* ❢ ⚒

Whitebrook NP5 4TX
TEL: (01600) 860254   FAX: (01600) 860607   COOKING 2*
5m S of Monmouth, between A466 and B4293   COST £26–£44

There are echoes of a French auberge in Roger and Sandra Bates's convivial restaurant-with-rooms. The welcome is genuine, they make every effort to please, and the fruits of their gastronomic labours are evident in everything from breads and pastries to ice-creams and sorbets. Sandra cooks to a menu that displays a fondness for things Gallic (dishes are described in French on the dinner menu regardless of their origins). Successes include chicken liver parfait laced with foie gras, crab-cakes on a saffron sauce, and grilled fillet of beef with rösti, pan-fried pleurotte mushrooms and port sauce. Welshness comes to the surface in the shape of smoked sewin with pickled cucumber and a horseradish dressing, and best end of lamb in puff pastry with a laverbread stuffing. Locally made black pudding appears in a trio of offal with caraway mash or on its own with caramelised apples. The Continental net is spread wide for a warm salad of polenta, poached egg, Parmesan and olives, or baked salmon on fennel with ratatouille sauce.

Among desserts there have been votes for boozy flamed pancakes and plates of seasonal fruits. Those looking for something light at lunch-time might choose a single dish, such as venison sausage rolls with potato gratin, or wild mushroom ravioli. An inspiring list of wines reveals a meticulous search for quality producers which stretches into the lesser-known corners of the world, such as Argentina and Lebanon. Prices are sensible, and half-bottles make frequent appearances. House wines are £9.50. CELLARMAN'S CHOICE: Lenton Brae Chardonnay 1994, Margaret River, W. Australia, £16.95; Listrac-Médoc, Chartreuse d' Hosten 1991, £17.50.

CHEFS: Sandra Bates and Dean Selby   PROPRIETORS: Roger and Sandra Bates   OPEN: Tue to Sun L 12 to 1.45, Mon to Sat D 7 to 9 (Sun D residents only)   CLOSED: 25 and 26 Dec, 2 weeks Jan   MEALS: Set L £16.95, Set D £26.95. BYO by arrangement. Bar L available   SERVICE: not inc, card slips closed   CARDS: Access, Amex, Delta, Diners, Switch, Visa   DETAILS: 34 seats. 16 seats outside. Private parties: 24 main room, 12 private room. Car park. Vegetarian meals. Children's helpings. Smart dress preferred. No smoking in dining-room. No music   ACCOMMODATION: 12 rooms, all with bath/shower. TV. Phone. B&B £45 to £80. Children welcome. Baby facilities. Dogs welcome in bedrooms only. Garden (*The Which? Hotel Guide*)

Isle of Man

▲ Boncompte's/La Tasca

Admiral House, Loch Promenade, Douglas IM1 2LX   COOKING 2
TEL: (01624) 629551   FAX: (01624) 675021   COST £20–£47

Jaime Boncompte-Amoros has gone back to his roots and opened an authentic
Spanish restaurant called La Tasca in the basement of Admiral House. Early
reports sound promising. The whitewashed arched cellar tries to evoke España
and there are two bars, 'one for boozing, one for cooking'. Rafael Leon clearly
knows what he is doing. 'Ridiculously good value' set lunches might include
sopa de carne y verduras (vegetables and minced meat in a meat stock), and
moist paella packed with seafood, followed by a sweet such as Cointreau
ice-cream. It is business as usual elsewhere in the hotel: bar lunches (including
home-smoked salmon) have been praised, and Boncompte's restaurant
continues to offer straightforward cooking based on local produce. House wine
is £9.50.

CHEF: Jaime Boncompte (Boncompte's), Rafael Leon (La Tasca)   PROPRIETORS: Jaime and Jill
Boncompte   OPEN: Boncompte's Mon to Fri L 12.30 to 2, Mon to Sat D 7.30 to 10; La Tasca Tue
to Fri L 12 to 2, Mon to Sat D 7 to 10   CLOSED: 25 and 26 Dec, Easter Mon   MEALS: alc (main
courses La Tasca £7 to £9, Boncompte's £11.50 to £16.50). Boncompte's Set L £11.50, Set D
£16.95. La Tasca Set L £7.50. Tapas available La Tasca (12 to 2, 6 to 7). Bar L available
SERVICE: not inc, card slips closed   CARDS: Access, Amex, Diners, Switch, Visa   DETAILS:
Boncompte's 80 seats, La Tasca 85 seats. Private parties: 85 main rooms, 28 private room. Car
park. Vegetarian meals. Children's helpings. Smart dress preferred. No cigars/pipes in
dining-room. Wheelchair access (also WC). Music. Air-conditioned   ACCOMMODATION: 12
rooms, all with bath/shower. TV. Phone. B&B £50 to £110. Rooms for disabled. Children
welcome. Baby facilities

L'Expérience

Summerhill, Douglas IM2 4PL
TEL: (01624) 623103   FAX: (01624) 626214
at the northern end of promenade, at the bottom of   COOKING 1
Summerhill   COST £17–£35

Tony and Jill Quirk tell us that this is the Isle of Man's longest-established
restaurant. The building stands proudly on the promenade overlooking Douglas
Bay, with the tricolour fluttering in the breeze. As if to emphasise the Gallic tone
of the place, the walls are covered with posters, there are candles in bottles and

the waitresses may don Breton jerseys. French onion soup is locally renowned, and the fixed-price menu also deals in provincial classics such as smoked duck breast with onion marmalade, sauté local queenies à la parisienne, navarin of lamb, and grilled fillet steak with Dijon mustard sauce. The mood is thoroughly congenial, but if things start to fall flat Tony may emerge from the kitchen and perform a little table magic for his guests. French regional wines make up the short list, with house wine £8.50 a litre.

CHEF: Tony Quirk   PROPRIETORS: Tony and Jill Quirk   OPEN: Mon and Wed to Sat (all week D in summer) 12 to 2, 7 to 11   CLOSED: 25 and 26 Dec   MEALS: alc L (main courses £5.50 to £6). Set D £14.95 to £21.95   SERVICE: not inc   CARDS: Access, Amex, Diners, Switch, Visa   DETAILS: 65 seats. 8 seats outside. Private parties: 65 main room. Vegetarian meals. Children's helpings. Wheelchair access (also WC). Music. Air-conditioned

Channel Islands

Café du Moulin ✴

Rue du Quanteraine, St Peters GY7 9DP	COOKING 1
TEL: (01481) 65944 FAX: (01481) 65708	COST £14–£39

'On the night we were there,' notes a correspondent, 'the sun shone, birds sang, wildfowl called and all the greenery was that wonderful spring green.' 'Idyllic' really is the word for the Café du Moulin. The arrival of a new second chef in the kitchen has changed the complexion of David and Gina Mann's operation. They now offer snacks and light meals at lunch-time as well as a full menu, and there's an eclectic evening *carte*, plus a three-course set dinner on weekdays. Regular deliveries from France mean that they can serve feuilleté of langoustines with wild asparagus and tiny morels, while supplies from the British mainland yield other inventions. Orkney beef is chargrilled ('wonderfully blue-raw inside') and served with garlicky polenta and tomato salsa, and organic corn-fed chicken finds its way into an eighteenth-century dish called Hindle Wakes. Puddings have been more magical than the cheeseboard. Good names from France and the New World dominate the short wine list. House wine is £7.95.

CHEFS: David Mann and Neil Huyton PROPRIETORS: David and Gina Mann OPEN: Tue to Sun L 12.15 to 1.15, Tue to Sat D 7 to 9 (later in summer) MEALS: alc (main courses £6 to £13.50). Set L £7.50, Set D Tue to Fri £16.95. BYO £5. Light lunch available SERVICE: not inc CARDS: Access, Delta, Switch, Visa DETAILS: 45 seats. 30 seats outside. Private parties: 45 main room. Car park. Vegetarian meals. Children's helpings. No children under 8 D. Smart dress preferred. No smoking in dining-room. Wheelchair access (no WC). Music

---

▲ *Longueville Manor* ✴

St Saviour JE2 7SA	COOKING 2*
TEL: (01534) 25501 FAX: (01534) 31613	COST £25–£69

Devotees of the country-house genre will find Longueville a classic of its kind: in 16 bosky acres, the grounds devoted to tennis and croquet, the interiors to heavy pampering. Andrew Baird has been cooking here since 1991, and has an assured touch. He takes a modern approach, without falling overboard into the Mediterranean, and offers a seven-course tasting menu, some imaginative vegetarian options, and a generous *carte* that might take in poached Jersey lobster on a warm potato salad, or suckling pig with cider cabbage and roast

CHANNEL ISLANDS

apples. One couple had nothing but praise for a Sunday lunch that included twice baked goat's-cheese soufflé, grilled salmon, and bread and butter pudding.

Fruits are used in profusion at dessert stage, whether in blackberry crème brûlée with raspberry ice-cream, or prune and banana tart on brandy cream. Good coffee, waves of petits fours and the impeccable, old-school service will not disappoint. Wines might, though, if expensive claret and Burgundy are not close to your heart. There is a smattering of good southern hemisphere bottles, but mark-ups will weigh heavy on the final bill. House wines, from Burgundy and Chile, start at £12.50.

CHEF: Andrew Baird PROPRIETORS: the Lewis and Dufty families OPEN: all week 12.30 to 2, 7.30 to 9.30 MEALS: alc D (main courses £18 to £22.50). Set L Mon to Sat £18, Set L Sun £17.50, Set D £30 and £50. BYO by arrangement. Light L and snacks available, and afternoon tea SERVICE: net prices, card slips closed CARDS: Access, Amex, Delta, Diners, Switch, Visa DETAILS: 65 seats. 20 seats outside. Private parties: 65 main room, 16 and 22 private rooms. Car park. Vegetarian meals. Children's helpings. Smart dress preferred. No smoking in 1 dining-room. Wheelchair access (no WC). No music. Air-conditioned ACCOMMODATION: 32 rooms, all with bath/shower. TV. Phone. B&B £120 to £230. Deposit: £75. Rooms for disabled. Children welcome. Dogs welcome in bedrooms only. Afternoon teas. Garden. Swimming-pool

Northern Ireland

BALLYCLARE Co Antrim map 16

Ginger Tree

29 Ballyrobert Road, Ballyclare BB9 9RY COOKING 1
TEL: (01232) 848176 COST £13–£42

Japanese food in the setting of a converted farmhouse sounds unlikely, but that is what Ginger Tree offers. Several accessible fixed-price menus are built around chicken teriyaki, sukiyaki and tempura, and a bargain-price 'take' menu is also available Monday to Friday. The full *carte* features appetisers such as kabayaki (grilled eel from Lough Neagh), and butamaki (French beans rolled in thinly sliced pork), as well as yakitori, tori karaage (breast of chicken in Japanese-style batter), and shake shioyaki (fillet of salmon grilled with salt). Sashimi is also served on Friday and Saturday. Drink tea or saké, otherwise choose from the serviceable wine list, starting at £8.95.

CHEFS/PROPRIETORS: Shotaro Obana and Elizabeth English   OPEN: Mon to Fri L 12 to 2.30, Mon to Sat D 7 to 9 (9.30 Sat)   CLOSED: 12 and 13 July, 24 to 26 Dec   MEALS: alc (main courses £8.50 to £14). Set L £6.80 to £10.75, Set D £12.95 to £26.50   SERVICE: not inc   CARDS: Access, Amex, Delta, Diners, Visa   DETAILS: 60 seats. Private parties: 80 main room, 25 private room. Car park. Vegetarian meals. Children's helpings. Smart dress preferred. Wheelchair access (also WC). Music. Air-conditioned

---

BANGOR Co Down map 16

Shanks ▼ NEW ENTRY

The Blackwood, 150 Crawfordsburn Road,
Clandeboye, Bangor BT19 1GB COOKING 3
TEL: (01247) 853313   FAX: (01247) 853785 COST £22–£47

Robbie Millar used to cook at Roscoff (see entry, Belfast), but moved out to the Marchioness of Dufferin's family estate at Clandeboye a couple of years ago. Shanks is the result, a restaurant by a golf course where the chic interior, length of the wine glass stems, and the Marchioness's formidable collection of Hockneys are well matched by the vivacity and confidence of the cooking. Inspiration comes from all over, judging by a tart of duck confit with shiitakes and Chinese five-spice, or chargrilled loin of lamb with grilled vegetables, minted couscous and tsatsiki. But inspiration it certainly is, as one reporter found with a walnut-crusted goats' cheese with 'an odd-sounding but divine' beetroot vinaigrette and a scattering of fresh peas. A tranche of roasted monkfish has been chaperoned by tiger prawns and an 'amazing' risotto of smoked chillies – 'not very fiery but pleasingly pungent' – while chicken breast stuffed with herbed chicken mousse and accompanied by little polenta dumplings in a sauce of truffle oil and balsamic has soared way above expectation. To finish, reporters have enjoyed steamed mango pudding studded with diced fruit and served with fine coconut ice-cream, and hazelnut meringue with Valrhona chocolate mousse and raspberries. Pony-tailed waiters move efficiently amid 'considerable buzz'. Wines are well-chosen, wide-ranging and fairly priced. Big names abound, from Drouhin, Duboeuf and Jaboulet to Mondavi, Penfolds and Cloudy Bay. Fourteen house wines are available by the bottle and glass, starting at £9.50 for Pinot Grigio.

CHEF: Robbie Millar   PROPRIETOR: The Blackwood Golf Centre   OPEN: Tue to Fri L 12.30 to 2, Tue to Sat D 7 to 10   CLOSED: 25 and 26 Dec, 1 Jan, 2 weeks July   MEALS: Set L £10.95 (2 courses) to £14.95, Set D £28.50. BYO £5   SERVICE: not inc; 10% for parties of 6 or more   CARDS: Access, Amex, Visa   DETAILS: 80 seats. Private parties: 10 main room, 24 private room. Car park. Vegetarian meals. Children's helpings. No cigars/pipes in dining-room. Music

---

BELFAST   Co Antrim   map 16

La Belle Epoque

61–63 Dublin Road, Belfast BT2 7RS   COOKING 2
TEL: (01232) 323244   FAX: (01232) 240040   COST £16–£38

A heartily French restaurant in the centre of Belfast, not far from the Opera House, Belle Epoque offers the kind of grand classical French cuisine that others have forsaken in the headlong dash for Mediterranean modernity. Menus are in the lingo, with subtitles for those who aren't sure that sauce Raifort entails horseradish, white wine and cream. A salad of fruits de mer makes the most of what the market can offer – prawns, cockles, queenies, mussels, crab claw and monkfish tail – spiked with a lime-juice dressing. Pastis is used to flavour fish dishes such as roast sea bass, and there's escalope of veal with celeriac purée and red wine sauce. The signature dish is a three-way marriage of beef, pork and chicken on couscous with steamed vegetables. Desserts range from a version of crêpes suzette to chocolate cheesecake with strawberry coulis. Wines are pre-eminently French, but there are too many producers' names and vintages missing to order with confidence. Five house wines start at £7.50.

CHEF: Alain Rousse   PROPRIETORS: A. Rousse, J. Delbart and G. Sanchez   OPEN: Mon to Fri L 12 to 5.30, Mon to Sat D 6 to 11   CLOSED: 25 and 26 Dec, 12 and 13 July   MEALS: alc (main courses £5 to £11.50). Set L £5.95 to £10.95 (both 2 courses), Set D Mon to Thur £15   SERVICE: not inc   CARDS: Access, Amex, Delta, Diners, Switch, Visa   DETAILS: 83 seats. Vegetarian meals. Children welcome. Smart dress preferred. Wheelchair access (also WC). Music

---

Nick's Warehouse

35–39 Hill Street, Belfast BT1 2LB   COOKING 1*
TEL: (01232) 439690   FAX: (01232) 230514   COST £20–£37

Downstairs is the wine bar, and upstairs is the main restaurant with some jazz pictures on the walls and a piano in place. The converted warehouse continues to offer some of the best value in Belfast, from a repertoire that courts fashion without going over the top. Marinated Brie is served with oven-dried tomatoes and a spicy dressing, local black and white pudding comes on a bed of caramelised onions with balsamic *jus*, while fillet of hake receives a dose of pepper, tomato and avocado salsa. Bringing up the rear might be apple and almond flan with crème anglaise, or white chocolate and strawberry trifle; also ask about the Irish cheeses. The short, keenly chosen wine list is fun and affordable: eight house wines are served by the glass, with bottle prices starting at £6.95.

CHEFS: Nick Price and Simon McCance   PROPRIETORS: Nick and Kathy Price   OPEN: restaurant Mon to Fri L 12 to 2.30, Tue to Sat D 6 to 9; wine bar Mon to Fri L 12 to 3, Tue to Sat D 6 to 9   CLOSED: 25 and 26 Dec, Easter Mon, 12 July   MEALS: alc L wine bar (main courses restaurant £4 to £13). Set D restaurant £15.95 (2 courses) to £18.95. Snack menu available in wine bar D. Minimum £7.50 in restaurant L   SERVICE: not inc, card slips closed; 10% for parties of 6 or more   CARDS: Access, Amex, Diners, Switch, Visa   DETAILS: 100 seats. Private parties: 50 main room. Vegetarian meals. Children's helpings in restaurant. Wheelchair access (also WC). Music. Air-conditioned

Roscoff ♟

7 Lesley House, Shaftesbury Square, Belfast BT2 7DB	COOKING 4
TEL: (01232) 331532 FAX: (01232) 312093	COST £24–£51

'Like Kensington Place but in Belfast,' reckoned one Londoner trying to get her bearings, obviously impressed by the breezy sense of space and scale here, as well as the disinclination to stand on ceremony, and the voluble confidence of the food. The comparison is apt, since both Paul Rankin and Rowley Leigh are pioneers of the contemporary mix-and-match cooking style.

Combinations are dramatic and eclectic, but always have an understandable culinary logic, rather than sounding like somebody's idea of a dare. Chargrilling, blackening and barbecuing are generously applied: to squid on black pasta with chilli garlic oil, for example, to monkfish with curried aubergine, or to eel with roast peppers. A bowl of leek and barley soup with salt-cured pheasant sounds like a winter warmer, while those who like piquancy will have a field day with roast venison with hot-and-sour cabbage and sherry vinegar cream. One reporter enjoyed 'excellent' chicken paillard with mushrooms on a nest of noodles; for another, lamb shank on basil mash with baby vegetables was the 'highlight of my day'. Vibrant flavours continue into desserts of bourbon pecan tartlet with banana cream, or coconut crème brûlée with lychee compote. Service is 'friendly'. Some juicy wines pepper the wide-ranging list, which has an unerrring eye for good producers and a sense of fair play with prices. Decent half bottles, and house wines from £12, provide back-up. CELLARMAN'S CHOICE: Bonny Doon Malvasia 1993, California, £22.50; Chorey-lès-Beaune 1994, Tollot-Beaut, £20.50.

CHEFS/PROPRIETORS: Paul and Jeanne Rankin   OPEN: Mon to Fri L 12.30 to 2.30, Mon to Sat D 6.30 to 10.30   CLOSED: 25 and 26 Dec, Easter Mon, 12 July   MEALS: Set L £16.95, Set D £28.95   SERVICE: not inc; 10% on parties of 6 or more   CARDS: Access, Amex, Diners, Switch, Visa   DETAILS: 75 seats. Private parties: 12 main room. Vegetarian meals. Children's helpings. Wheelchair access (also WC). Music. Air-conditioned

Strand £

12 Stranmillis Road, Belfast BT9 5AA	COOKING 1
TEL: (01232) 682266 FAX: (01232) 663189	COST £15–£34

'This has to be what most people imagine a university district bistro to be!' observed a couple of visitors. New owners have moved in since last year, although the mood – and the chef – is unchanged. The colour is now purple, but the atmosphere is still smoky, jazzy music drifts along coolly in the background and the cheerful *bonhomie* seldom flags. This is an 'all ages, all sorts' kind of place, and it's open all day. Think of a flavour, and the chances are that the menu will be able to oblige: it could be an Ulster fry-up for Sunday brunch, spinach roulade at lunch-time, or something more ambitious to occupy the evening. On that front you might choose 'hearty' mushroom and mustard soup, 'really huge' prawns in filo pastry, chicken Wellington, or baked duck breast stuffed with wild rice served on a mound of al dente tagliatelle. Seven-fruit salad makes a refreshing finale. House wine is £7.25.

CHEF: Michael McAuley   PROPRIETORS: Stephen McCombe and Frank Cullen   OPEN: Mon to Sat 12 to 11, Sun 12.30 to 2.30, 7 to 10   CLOSED: 25 and 26 Dec, 12 and 13 July   MEALS: alc (main courses £4.50 to £12). Set L Sun £9.95   SERVICE: not inc   CARDS: Access, Amex, Diners, Switch, Visa   DETAILS: 60 seats. Private parties: 25 main room, 25 private room. Vegetarian meals. Children's helpings. Smart dress preferred. Music. Air-conditioned

---

HELEN'S BAY Co Down map 16

Deanes on the Square

NEW ENTRY

7 Station Square, Helen's Bay BT19 1TN	COOKING 3*
TEL: (01247) 852841	COST £25–£58

The first Marquis of Dufferin and Ava commissioned this bespoke railway station in the style of a Scottish baronial manor in 1863. It sits on the Belfast to Bangor line, and trains still stop here, except that since 1993 it has housed a restaurant rather than a ticket office and waiting-rooms. The caricature portraits of famous chefs on the dining-room walls might give an indication of some of Michael Deane's influences, but the style is unmistakably his own.

There is more than a hint of East meets West to the menus, with Thai seasonings cropping up among first courses and mains, but it is the technical ability and understanding of flavours that impress the most. Look at this first course from a spring menu: a little mound of rabbit rillettes topped with a pair of quail's legs, daintily crossed, a breast of the bird lying to either side, and quail's eggs treated three ways: poached, fried and soft-boiled. A blob of mashed potato and a 'delicate film of truffle oil' provide strong undertones of richness. Thai-style crab consommé with a wun-tun dumpling is equally finely judged, sharp seasonings ringing through the expressive stock. Crab is also fashioned into spiced cakes to garnish a main course of roast salmon fillet. Incidentals are carefully considered, too, as in an amuse-gueule of tantalisingly subtle lobster mousse and a pre-dessert of a tiny bread-and-butter pudding cooked in a dariole mould.

Chocolate and cappuccino tart is a thoroughly 1990s pudding, and the variations-on-a-theme approach expands the range into banana or blackberry, maximising flavour throughout. All of this comes at uncommonly fair prices, for all that vegetables are charged extra (they are not pushed on you, though). Deanes looks set to compete with the best. The wine list is a thoughtful compendium of classical France, southern Europe and the New World. Many of the selections are very fine, and prices are agreeably restrained. House Australian is £9.95.

CHEF: Michael Deane   PROPRIETORS: Michael and Haydn Deane   OPEN: Sun L 12.30 to 2, Tue to Sat D 7 to 9.30 (10 Sat)   CLOSED: Christmas, 1 week Jan, 1 week July   MEALS: Set L £16, Set D £20.95 (2 courses) to £36.95   SERVICE: not inc; 10% for parties of 8 or more   CARDS: Access, Amex, Delta, Visa   DETAILS: 42 seats. Private parties: 15 main room. Vegetarian meals. Children's helpings. Smart dress preferred. Music

---

LONDONDERRY   Co Londonderry   map 16

▲ Beech Hill Country House, Ardmore Restaurant £✳

32 Ardmore Road, Londonderry BT47 3QP
TEL: (01504) 49279   FAX: (01504) 45366
turn off A6 Londonderry to Belfast road at Faughan
Bridge and proceed to Ardmore chapel; hotel is   COOKING 2*
opposite chapel   COST £24–£50

Beech Hill is an elegant, white-fronted eighteenth-century house, once owned by an English judge. The Ardmore affords views of ponds and waterfalls, as well as offering the cooking of Noel McMeel, a much-travelled chef who has done stints in France and the US. Techniques are highly refined and the ideas novel without being silly. A terrine of goose and white peach with blackcurrant and lemon dressing has become something of a signature dish, and there is a sensible approach to complexity, as in fillets of sole sandwiched between layers of potato galette, and accompanied by a raviolo of ratatouille and a saffron sauce.

Beef fillet is cooked spot on, and cod is crumbed, fried and served with 'shoestring fries'. Fruits abound on the dessert menu, perhaps as an apricot steam pudding or kiwi and passion-fruit bavarois. There is a separate vegetarian menu. Unfussy service makes everyone feel at home. The non-European wine selections look somewhat more exciting than the French bottles. House Australian is £8.95.

CHEF: Noel McMeel   PROPRIETOR: Seamus Donnelly   OPEN: all week 12 to 2.30, 6.30 to 9.30 CLOSED: 24 and 25 Dec   MEALS: alc D (main courses £14 to £17). Set L £14.95 to £15.95, Set D £21.95   SERVICE: not inc, card slips closed   CARDS: Access, Amex, Visa   DETAILS: 120 seats. Private parties: 80 main room. Car park. Vegetarian meals. Children's helpings. Smart dress preferred. No smoking in dining-room. Music   ACCOMMODATION: 17 rooms, all with bath/shower. TV. Phone. B&B £52.50 to £100. Children welcome. Baby facilities. Afternoon teas. Garden

---

'My squab pigeon dish was one of those platefuls you wish will never end. The pigeon had flown nowhere. I imagine he spent his young life relaxing on a sofa, resting his drumsticks on a pouffe. I had to know where he came from, and whether he had brothers and sisters who were looking for somewhere to stay in the Bath area.'
(On eating in the West Country)

Ramore

The Harbour, Portrush BT56 8BN   COOKING 2
TEL: (01265) 824313   COST £26–£41

The harbourside is appealing in its own right, but Ramore adds class with its highly distinctive cooking. Reports suggest that 'Mr McAlpin may have raised his standards a notch', and he certainly knows how to pull in the customers. A lively imagination is at work in this kitchen: wild mushroom and asparagus ravioli are served with Jerusalem artichokes and a white truffle broth, while 'absolutely exquisite' fillet of turbot comes with a salsify confit and a wild mushroom sauce. Best all, for one ecstatic visitor, was a warm salad of Lough Neagh eels with potatoes, mushrooms and a pesto and sun-dried tomato mayonnaise. Fillet steaks are tip-top, vegetables are perfectly al dente, and desserts finish proceedings with a flourish. House wine is £8.50.

CHEF: George McAlpin   PROPRIETORS: George and Jane McAlpin   OPEN: Tue to Sat D only 6.30 to 10.30   MEALS: alc (main courses £8.50 to £12)   SERVICE: not inc   CARDS: Access, Switch, Visa   DETAILS: 85 seats. Private parties: 85 main room. Car park. Vegetarian meals. Children welcome. Music. Air-conditioned

Republic of Ireland

We have not given marks for cooking for the Republic of Ireland entries because of a shortage of reports; please do give us feedback should you visit. To telephone the Republic from mainland Britain, dial 00 353 followed by the number listed, but dropping the initial 0. Prices are quoted in Irish punts.

ADARE Co Limerick map 16

▲ Adare Manor

Adare
TEL: (061) 396566 FAX: (061) 396124 COST £35–£57

In one of Ireland's prettiest villages, eighteenth-century Adare Manor has the additional advantage of an 18-hole championship golf course designed by Robert Trent-Jones Snr. Aidan McGrath's food is based on classical French cooking with an Irish slant, using seasonal produce. Dinner might start off with a feuillantine of prawns and sweetbreads, followed by roast saddle of rabbit with girolles in a blanquette sauce, and finish with hot chocolate and vanilla soufflé. The extensive wine list covers the world, has plenty of half-bottles and kicks off with French house wine at £18.

CHEF: Aidan McGrath   PROPRIETOR: Tom and Judy Kane   OPEN: all week 12.30 to 2, 7 to 9.45 MEALS: Set L £21.50, Set D £32.50. BYO £10. Light snacks available L and D   SERVICE: 15%, card slips closed   CARDS: Access, Amex, Diners, Visa   DETAILS: 75 seats. Private parties: 20 main room, 150 private room. Car park. Vegetarian meals. Children's helpings. Jacket and tie. No smoking in dining-room. Wheelchair access (also WC). Music   ACCOMMODATION: 64 rooms, all with bath/shower. TV. Phone. Room only £112 to £315. Rooms for disabled. Children welcome. Dogs welcome in estate kennels only. Afternoon teas. Garden. Swimming-pool. Fishing

---

AHAKISTA Co Cork map 16

Shiro

Ahakista
TEL: (027) 67030 FAX: (027) 67206
on coast road from Durrus towards Sheep's Head COST £50–£60

If Ahakista sounds more Rising Sun than Bantry Bay, then the cultural indicators have worked because this is a sushi and sashimi restaurant in the far south-west of County Cork. Menus change daily, but the formula is essentially zen-zai appetisers and soup followed by a choice of around eight main courses, ranging from tempura-fried fish with tenzuyu dipping sauce to jumbo quail yakitori, and gyoza (minced pork with bamboo shoots and shiitakes in crisp parcels). Home-made ice-cream rounds things off. The wine list starts with plum wine and saké, and includes a 'Chinese Muscadet'.

CHEF: Kei Pilz PROPRIETORS: Kei and Werner Pilz OPEN: all week D only 7 to 9 CLOSED: Christmas and New Year MEALS: Set D £38. BYO £4 SERVICE: 10%, card slips closed CARDS: Access, Amex, Diners, Visa; 5% surcharge on credit card transactions DETAILS: 18 seats. Private parties: 7 main room, 5 private room. Car park. Vegetarian meals. No children under 10. Smart dress preferred. No music. Air-conditioned

---

BALLINA Co Mayo   map 16

▲ *Mount Falcon Castle* ⅚✗

Ballina
TEL: (096) 70811 FAX: (096) 71517
on N57 between Foxford and Ballina   COST £27–£33

Mount Falcon offers one of Ireland's more singular dining experiences. It is a Gothic pile near the River Moy and Mayo's deserted beaches, owned by Constance Aldridge since 1932. Dinner is a no-choice affair, taken at a single large table headed by Mrs Aldridge herself. Expatiating admirably throughout, she pauses only to summon each succeeding course by ringing a small bell. Leave your British reserve at home: it's 'a lovely experience', according to more than one report. Dinner may consist of a hot cheese soufflé, a tureen of vegetable-based soup, stuffed pork loin with apple sauce, Irish cheeses, and a choice of puddings such as crème caramel or rhubarb fool. The conservative wine list offers sound selections at reasonable prices. House French is £9.50.

CHEF: Denise Moyles PROPRIETOR: Constance Aldridge OPEN: all week D only 8 (1 sitting) CLOSED: 1 week Christmas, 1 Feb to 30 Mar MEALS: Set D £20. BYO £5 SERVICE: not inc, card slips closed CARDS: Access, Amex, Diners, Visa DETAILS: 30 seats. Car park. Children's helpings. Smart dress preferred. No smoking in dining-room. Wheelchair access (also men's WC). Music ACCOMMODATION: 10 rooms, all with bath/shower. Phone. B&B £33 to £49. Deposit: £50. Children welcome. Dogs welcome. Afternoon teas. Garden. Fishing

---

BALLYDEHOB Co Cork   map 16

Annie's

Main Street, Ballydehob
TEL: (028) 37292   COST £27–£37

The drill is to call in for the menus, pop across to the pub opposite for a pint where Annie will come and take your order and call you to your table when things are ready. Fresh crab lasagne, smoked salmon roulade or grilled mussels with garlic butter may well then be waiting for you, to be followed up by baked monkfish kebab with lemon sauce, or crisp pork fillet with Cointreau and apple purée. Annie's is a coffee-shop by day for part of the year, and there is a refreshing lack of formality about evening proceedings too. The wine list offers a short but well-chosen selection from each of the regions covered, with house wines from £11.

CHEFS/PROPRIETORS: Dano and Anne Barry OPEN: Tue to Sat D only 6.30 to 9.30 (times may vary in winter). Light meals available June to Sept MEALS: alc (main courses £12 to £14). Set D £22 SERVICE: not inc CARDS: Access, Visa DETAILS: 24 seats. Private parties: 24 main room. Vegetarian meals. Children's helpings. No cigars/pipes in dining-room. Music

BALLYLICKEY Co Cork   map 16

▲ *Ballylickey Manor, Le Rendez-Vous* ⁝✳

Ballylickey, Bantry Bay
TEL: (027) 50071   FAX: (027) 50124   COST £29–£57

The seventeenth-century house offers guests a choice of settings for eating: a cosy dining-room within the main house or a room by the pool that comes into its own in summer. French is the language of the menu, and chef Gilles Eynaud's renditions of simple classic dishes are the mainstays. Summer terrine comes with a tomato coulis, wild salmon with a sauce mousseline, and rack of lamb with a thyme jus. Specials such as aiguillettes of duck breast with fresh ginger are worth investigation, and meals might end with chocolate gâteau, nougat glacé or a cheese selection. The predominantly French wine list majors in Bordeaux, Burgundy and Beaujolais, with prices opening at £13.

CHEF: Gilles Eynaud   PROPRIETORS: Mr and Mrs Graves   OPEN: all week 12.30 to 2, 7 to 9 CLOSED: end Oct to Apr   MEALS: Set L £18, Set D £25 to £35   SERVICE: 10%, card slips closed   CARDS: Access, Amex, Visa   DETAILS: 35 seats. 20 seats outside. Private parties: 25 main room. Car park. Vegetarian meals. No children under 3. Smart dress preferred. No smoking in dining-room. Music   ACCOMMODATION: 11 rooms, all with bath/shower. TV. Phone. B&B £90 to £180. Deposit: 1 night's charge. Children welcome. Dogs welcome. Garden. Swimming-pool. Fishing

---

BALLYVAUGHAN Co Clare   map 16

▲ *Gregans Castle* ⁝✳

Ballyvaughan
TEL: (065) 77005   FAX: (065) 77111
on N67, 3½m S of Ballyvaughan   COST £34–£72

This white-fronted hotel, not looking much like a castle, sits at the foot of Corkscrew Hill in the other-worldly region of the Burren, a limestone landscape south of Galway Bay replete with megalithic tombs and such. If they don't appeal, Paul Gallagher's cooking may be the comforting answer, with its promise of Inagh goats' cheese in a warm salad with croûtons and balsamic dressing, brill with courgettes in tomato and chilli butter, and leg of lamb with ratatouille, braised potatoes and rosemary. Fixed-price dinner menus offer fine choice, with a sharp sorbet preceding the main course. The highly respectable wine list features many good producers, including plenty from the New World. Six house wines start at £12.25.

CHEF: Paul Gallagher   PROPRIETORS: Peter, Moira and Simon Haden   OPEN: all week 12 to 3, 7 to 8.30   CLOSED: 1 Jan to 27 Mar, 20 Oct to 31 Dec   MEALS: alc (main courses £13 to £30). Set D £28. Light L available   SERVICE: 15%, card slips closed   CARDS: Access, Amex, Visa DETAILS: 50 seats. Private parties: 100 main room, 30 private room. Car park. Vegetarian meals. Children's helpings. Smart dress preferred. No smoking in 1 dining-room. Wheelchair access (also WC). Music   ACCOMMODATION: 22 rooms, all with bath/shower. Phone. B&B £66 to £99. Rooms for disabled. Children welcome. Baby facilities. Afternoon teas. Garden

Tree of Idleness

Seafront, Bray
TEL: (01) 2863498   FAX: (01) 2828183   COST £28–£51

This Greek-Cypriot restaurant on the sea-front at Bray has a long-established reputation for both classical and contemporary cooking. The former may be found in grilled halloumi cheese with tahini sauce, filo parcels of feta and mint, or a starter portion of rabbit stifado, all served with hot pitta. Main courses that expand the repertoire take in smoked best end of lamb in a sauce of blackcurrants and wine vinegar, and peppered monkfish with shallots, olives and capers. Desserts may be chosen from the trolley. A huge wine list that would grace a grand hotel is offered, the prices for fully mature clarets in particular looking irresistible. Guigal's Côtes du Rhône in both colours is the house wine at £12.95.

CHEF: Ismail Basaran   PROPRIETOR: Susan Courtellas   OPEN: Tue to Sun D only 7.30 to 11 (10 Sun)   CLOSED: Christmas, last 2 weeks Aug   MEALS: alc (main courses £10 to £16.50). Set D Tue to Fri and Sun £18.95   SERVICE: 10%, card slips closed   CARDS: Access, Amex, Diners, Visa   DETAILS: 50 seats. Private parties: 25 main room. Vegetarian meals. Children's helpings. Smart dress preferred. Wheelchair access (no WC). Music

Chez Hans

Rockside, Cashel
TEL: (062) 61177   COST £33–£45

Hans-Peter Matthiä inhabits an old church at the foot of the Rock of Cashel in the south of Tipperary. An Elizabeth Rivers still life of bottle and citrus fruits adorns the menu cover, while some impeccably contemporary Mediterranean-inspired food offers enticements within. Wild mushroom risotto with smoked duckling, roast tuna à la niçoise, and baked goats' cheese with aubergine caviare and pesto get things going. Meats ply a more classical line in herb-crusted rack of Tipperary lamb with rosemary *jus*, or pheasant with cranberries and a port sauce. The local cheese, Ireland's most famous blue, goes into a chicken breast served on leek sabayon. An expansive wine list kicks off with a red Côtes du Roussillon and the proprietor's own German white, both at £11.

CHEFS: Hans-Peter and Jason Matthiä   PROPRIETOR: Hans-Peter Matthiä   OPEN: Tue to Sat D only 6.30 to 10   CLOSED: 25 and 26 Dec, last 3 weeks Jan, Good Fri   MEALS: alc (main courses £14.50 to £16.50). BYO (no corkage)   SERVICE: not inc   CARDS: Access, Visa   DETAILS: 70 seats. Private parties: 90 main room. Car park. Children's helpings. Smart dress preferred. Wheelchair access (also WC). Music. Air-conditioned

'We arrived with our bikes on our car, and were asked if we were going cycling. We explained that we were on our way home from Dorset. "We won't see you again then," [the proprietor] said grumpily.' (On eating in Dorset)

CASTLEBALDWIN   Co Sligo   map 16

▲ *Cromleach Lodge* ⁵✳

Ballindoon, Castlebaldwin
TEL: (071) 65155   FAX: (071) 65455   COST £40–£48

A small country house overlooking Lough Arrow, Cromleach's repute derives in no small measure from the ambitious cooking of Moira Tighe, among the most accomplished in the north of the Republic. Fixed-price menus are supplemented by a five-course gourmet one for residents only. The ordinary menu may feature tartlet of quail breasts and creamed lentils, goats' cheese soufflé with pineapple and apricot chutney, or chicken sausage with carrot and Sauternes sauce. Views of water and hills enhance the satisfaction. A slate of wines under £20 heads up a largely Western European list, with a smattering from southern climes. House Bordeaux is £12.95.

CHEF: Moira Tighe   PROPRIETORS: Moira and Christy Tighe   OPEN: all week D only 7 to 9 (6.30 to 8 Sun); L by arrangement   CLOSED: 1 Nov to 15 Dec   MEALS: Set D £30   SERVICE: not inc, card slips closed   CARDS: Access, Amex, Diners, Visa   DETAILS: 50 seats. Private parties: 25 main room, 4 and 25 private rooms. Car park. Vegetarian meals. Children's helpings. No children under 7. Smart dress preferred. No smoking in dining-room. Wheelchair access (no WC). Music   ACCOMMODATION: 10 rooms, all with bath/shower. TV. Phone. B&B £50 to £130. Children welcome. Baby facilities. Garden. Fishing

CLONAKILTY   Co Cork   map 16

Dunworley Cottage ⁵✳

Butlerstown, Clonakilty
TEL: (023) 40314
signposted from Timoleague, south of Bandon   COST £20–£46

Proprietor Katherine Norén is whole-heartedly committed to both healthy eating and home produce in her cottage restaurant in the far south of County Cork. Fish is celebrated in first courses that display a Scandinavian influence, such as marinated herrings and cured salmon with crème fraîche. Soups of mussels or nettles are a speciality, and fried fillet steaks form the heart of the main-course business. The house gâteau of vanilla ice-cream with almond biscuits and chocolate sauce is an alternative to fine Irish cheeses. An imaginative wine list begins at £10.25. A new restaurant and shop, Kicki's Cabin, has been opened at 53 Pearse Street, Clonakilty, tel: (023) 33384. The intention is to offer a simpler menu with the emphasis on fish.

CHEF: Mathew Karlsson   PROPRIETOR: Katherine Norén   OPEN: Wed to Sun 12.30 to 3, 7 to 9 (L in summer only; booking essential L and D)   CLOSED: mid-Sept to mid-Mar (phone to check)   MEALS: alc (main courses £6 to £14). Set D £20 to £22   SERVICE: not inc   CARDS: Access, Amex, Diners, Visa   DETAILS: 60 seats. Private parties: 20 private room. Car park. Vegetarian meals. Children welcome. No smoking in 1 dining-room. No music

Not inc *in the details at the end of an entry indicates that no service charge is made and any tipping is at the discretion of the customer.*

CORK   Co Cork   map 16

▲ *Arbutus Lodge*

Montenotte, Cork
TEL: (021) 501237   FAX: (021) 502893   COST £22–£50

If Arbutus Lodge radiates a feeling of accomplishment and confidence in what it does, that is only to be expected. This is one of Cork's more venerable institutions, having been run by the Ryans since the early 1960s. Interior furnishings are sumptuous, and the waiting staff are, in the words of one report, 'such good fun'. The kitchen acquired the services of Kevin Arundel at the beginning of 1996, and he has settled in well if the experience of a party from Sussex was anything to go by. 'Overwhelming generosity' permeated everything from the 'great breakfasts' to the Irish cheeses and the sweet trolley's tempting cargo. Along the way, there had been smoked mussel salad with walnut cream, herb-crusted salmon with a basil beurre blanc, and breast of chicken with wild mushrooms which outshone anything eaten in France. The colour-coded wine list is a masterpiece of discernment, its choices nerveless throughout. Prices open below £10.

CHEFS: Kevin Arundel and Declan Ryan   PROPRIETORS: the Ryan family   OPEN: Mon to Sat 1 to 2, 7 to 9.30   CLOSED: 24 to 28 Dec   MEALS: alc (main courses £14 to £16). Set L £14.50, Set D £22.50. Bar L available   SERVICE: not inc   CARDS: Access, Amex, Diners, Visa   DETAILS: 60 seats. 20 seats outside. Private parties: 12 main room, 20 to 120 private rooms. Car park. Vegetarian meals. Children's helpings. No cigars/pipes in dining-room. No music. Air-conditioned   ACCOMMODATION: 20 rooms, all with bath/shower. TV. Phone. Air-conditioned. B&B £45 to £150. Children welcome. Baby facilities. Garden

Clifford's

18 Dyke Parade, Cork
TEL: (021) 275333   COST £23–£48

Housed in the Georgian splendour of the old Cork library, Michael Clifford's up-market restaurant drew a string of 'excellents' from one couple who treated their son to a break from student fare one evening. Local produce is used enthusiastically, whether it be smoked beef with melon, Milleens cheese in the ravioli that sit in the middle of a chicken consommé, or loin of Cork lamb with courgette and garlic timbale. Fruits for desserts, on the other hand, may come from further afield: banana compote with banana sorbet, or caramelised pineapple in rice pudding. The wine list covers the French regions thoroughly before branching out and taking in Argentina along the way. House wines are from £13. Michael's Bistro next door serves equally enterprising food from an à la carte menu but runs a shorter wine list.

CHEF/PROPRIETOR: Michael Clifford   OPEN: Tue to Fri L 12.30 to 2.30, Tue to Sat D 7.30 to 10.30   MEALS: Set L £13.95, Set D £29.50   SERVICE: not inc   CARDS: Access, Amex, Delta, Diners, Switch, Visa   DETAILS: 45 seats. Private parties: 50 main room, 30 private room. Children's helpings. Smart dress preferred. No smoking in 1 dining-room. No music. Air-conditioned

Crawford Gallery Café £

Emmet Place, Cork
TEL: (021) 274415

COST £19–£28

The café is an offshoot of the Allen empire that owns Ballymaloe House (see entry, Shanagarry). It is part of an eighteenth-century building that was once the Cork Custom House and is a true café in the sense that it caters for shoppers simply wanting a cup of tea as well as those who suddenly discover a craving for bruschetta with flat mushrooms and Parmesan. Fish from the pier at Ballycotton – the previous night's catch – grilled chicken with leek sauce, or lamb stew might tempt you to a main dish. Strawberry meringue roulade, or coffee ice-cream with Irish coffee sauce should fill any remaining gaps. The handful of wines are largely from the southern hemisphere. House wines from Duboeuf are £10, or £2 the glass.

CHEF: Chris O'Brien   PROPRIETORS: the Allen family   OPEN: Mon to Sat L only 12 to 2.30 (3 Sat); D by arrangement   CLOSED: 23 Dec to 4 Jan, bank hols   MEALS: alc (main courses £7 to £8). Light meals available 10 to 5   SERVICE: not inc, card slips closed   CARDS: Access, Amex, Visa   DETAILS: 80 seats. Private parties: 80 main room. Vegetarian meals. Children's helpings. No-smoking area. Music

Ivory Tower

Exchange Buildings, 35 Princes Street, Cork
TEL: (021) 274665

COST £19–£45

'Transethnic fusion' is the stated philosophy of Seamus O'Connell, which is why you will hear 'world music' when you eat in this corniced Georgian dining-room, and why you will see 'flashed' squid San Sebastian, Marseilles mackerel escabèche, and Moroccan lamb sausages on the menu. He has cooked in Japan and Mexico in his time, and clearly absorbs culinary influences like a sponge. Things get pretty weird too: how about Cajun blackened scallops with banana ketchup, or courgette and chocolate chilli-bean chimichanga with mango and lime salsa? Meals end with the likes of 'fabulously nutty tart' or tropical fruit 'aphrodisiac': a description which you may feel inclined to hold the kitchen to later on. Wines are as eclectic as the food and provide some diverting flavours at a mostly reasonable outlay. The starting price is £11.

CHEF/PROPRIETOR: Seamus O'Connell   OPEN: Tue to Sat 12 to 3, 6 to 10.30   CLOSED: 25 Dec, 1 Jan   MEALS: alc (main courses £5 to £16.50). Set D £15. BYO £3   SERVICE: not inc   CARDS: Access, Visa   DETAILS: 40 seats. Private parties: 40 main room. Vegetarian meals. Children's helpings. No cigars/pipes in dining-room. Music

---

DINGLE Co Kerry

map 16

Beginish ⅝✳

NEW ENTRY

Green Street, Dingle
TEL: (066) 51588   FAX: (066) 51591

COST £28–£45

In a Georgian terraced house with an attractive garden, the Moores' restaurant furnishes yet another gastronomic reason to head for Dingle. The dining-room, which extends into a conservatory, is done in summery hues of pink and lime, and Pat Moore's first love is Kerry seafood. It may be presented with tagliatelle in a sauce of Noilly Prat, as mussels from Cromane with garlic cream, or as half a dozen oysters *au naturel*. One reporter enjoyed a main course of turbot fillet on a bed of mash with a white wine sauce; another asked for rack of lamb to be 'pink but not too pink' and got exactly what he wanted: 'the best lamb I have ever tasted'. A rendition of crème brûlée has Grand Marnier added to it. A comprehensive wine list casts its net over Spain, Italy, Chile and New Zealand as well as the traditional French regions, and provides a wide range of half-bottles. Ten house wines are available by the bottle from £9.50, and by the glass from £2.50.

CHEF: Pat Moore   PROPRIETORS: John and Pat Moore   OPEN: Tue to Sun D only 6 to 9.30
CLOSED: end Nov to mid-Mar   MEALS: alc (main courses £11 to £16)   SERVICE: not inc, card slips closed   CARDS: Access, Amex, Visa   DETAILS: 50 seats. Private parties: 18 private room. Vegetarian meals. Children's helpings. No smoking in 1 dining-room. Music

▲ Doyle's ⁵⅄

4 John Street, Dingle
TEL: (066) 51174   FAX: (066) 51816   COST £24–£44

The freshest fish and shellfish prepared in simple, accessible ways is what John and Stella Doyle's restaurant-with-rooms is all about. They smoke their own salmon and sell it by the side to take away as well as by the portion. Herrings in a sweet-and-sour marinade, oysters in Guinness sauce, and shrimp soup are other starters. Fish is the focus of main courses, too, the preparations reckoned to be 'excellent' by a couple who ate grilled turbot and poached lobster, the latter presented live first. Puddings include steamed chocolate sponge and apple tart with cinnamon ice-cream. German vintages from the 1970s add class to a thoughtfully selected wine list. House wines start at £10.80.

CHEF: Stella Doyle   PROPRIETORS: John and Stella Doyle   OPEN: Mon to Sat D only 6 to 9.30
CLOSED: mid-Nov to mid-Mar   MEALS: alc (main courses £11.50 to £16). Set D early evening £15. BYO £5   SERVICE: 10%, card slips closed   CARDS: Access, Diners, Visa   DETAILS: 48 seats. Private parties: 28 main room. Children's helpings. No smoking in 1 dining-room. Wheelchair access (no WC). No music   ACCOMMODATION: 8 rooms, all with bath/shower. TV. Phone. B&B £41 to £65. Deposit: £50. Rooms for disabled. Children welcome

▲ Half Door ⁵⅄

John Street, Dingle
TEL: (066) 51600   FAX: (066) 51297   COST £18–£57

Fish and seafood are the main preoccupations of the O'Connors' restaurant on a windswept peninsula reaching into the Atlantic. Fried oysters on toasted brioche with a chive sauce, baked plaice with a mustard sauce, and salmon in puff pastry with a sauce of Grand Marnier show that not all is unadorned simplicity, either. For meat eaters there's chicken breast stuffed with cream cheese, or grilled entrecôte. Cheesecake made with Bailey's Irish Cream, or fresh fruit pavlova are on hand to round things off. A long slate of house wines starting at £11 opens a wide-ranging list that does its best to keep prices down. Good New World wines complement a strong French selection.

CHEF: Denis O'Connor   PROPRIETORS: Denis and Teresa O'Connor   OPEN: Wed to Mon 12.30 to 2.30, 6 to 10   CLOSED: mid-Jan to 17 Mar   MEALS: alc (main courses £4 to £25). Set D £15.50   SERVICE: not inc   CARDS: Access, Amex, Delta, Visa   DETAILS: 56 seats. Private parties: 20 main room, 20 private room. Children's helpings. No smoking in 1 dining-room. Wheelchair access (no WC). Music. Air-conditioned   ACCOMMODATION: 7 rooms, all with bath/shower. TV. Phone. B&B £20 to £45. Deposit: £20. Children welcome. Baby facilities. Afternoon teas. Garden

Waterside ✸ | **NEW ENTRY**

Strand Street, Dingle
TEL: (066) 51458   FAX: (066) 51222   COST £32–£53

Dingle's handsome range of eating options is enhanced by this cafeteria/bistro/restaurant on the Marina, with John Dillon, ex-Savoy Hotel, London, at the helm. A bowl of mixed fish broth that includes salmon, scallops and mussels for £3 has to be some sort of record. Quiet contentment was the mood of a man who lunched on cauliflower soup, poached salmon salad and a slice of strawberry tart. Roast loin of Kerry lamb on a tomato and olive compôte and 'its own sweet juices' might be a more robust option. Music comes at you from all directions, and it evidently helps to be fond of Bob Marley. The short wine list kicks off with the house selection at £10.

CHEF: John Dillon   PROPRIETORS: John Dillon and Pauline Dillon   OPEN: Sun to Mon 12 to 5.30, 7.30 to 10   MEALS: alc (main courses £15.50 to £23). Set D £23. Snacks available from 10 to 5.30   SERVICE: not inc   CARDS: Access, Visa   DETAILS: 45 seats. Private parties: 18 main room. Car park. Children welcome. No smoking in 1 dining-room. Music

---

DONEGAL Co Donegal   map 16

▲ *Harvey's Point* ✸ | **NEW ENTRY**

Lough Eske, Donegal
TEL: (073) 22208   FAX: (073) 22352   COST £21–£43

Harvey's Point looks as if it thinks it's up in the Alps somewhere, a collection of low-slung Swiss chalets peering through trees towards Lough Eske. That is because the owner himself is Swiss. The menu style is as classical as may be found in smartest Geneva, without the heart-stopping prices. Artichoke with garlic butter is garnished with cubes of salmon, duck terrine with a sweet-and-sour orange preserve. A vegetable terrine using leeks and mushrooms has been particularly praised, and the long list of main courses embraces potato-scaled turbot with red pepper sauce, king scallops with black noodles in a brandy cream sauce, and tournedos Rossini. The house speciality tipple is 'Swiss poteen'; make of that what you will. More conventional tastes will find a well-composed wine list on offer, with a plentiful range of halves. Prices start at around £10.50.

The Good Food Guide *is a registered trade mark of Which? Ltd.*

CHEF: Marc Gysling PROPRIETOR: Jody Gysling OPEN: all week 12 to 2.30, 6.30 to 9.30 CLOSED: midweek Nov to Mar MEALS: alc D (main courses £12.50 to £14.50). Set L £9.50 (2 courses) to £12.50, Set D £22.50 SERVICE: 10%, card slips closed CARDS: Access, Amex, Diners, Visa DETAILS: 70 seats. Private parties: 50 main room, 70 and 200 private rooms. Car park. Vegetarian meals. No children under 10. Jacket and tie. No smoking in 1 dining-room. Wheelchair access (also WC). Music. Air-conditioned ACCOMMODATION: 20 rooms, all with bath/shower. TV. Phone. B&B £55 to £99. Deposit: £35. Rooms for disabled. No children under 10. Dogs welcome. Afternoon teas. Garden. Fishing

---

DOUGLAS Co Cork

map 16

Lovetts

Churchyard Lane, Well Road, Douglas

TEL: (021) 294909 and 293604 FAX: (021) 508568 COST £22–£49

The Lovetts cater for two sorts of clientele – those who want formal eating in the grand manner, and those who find brasserie cooking more in tune with the times. For fish-lovers there is Berehaven squid cooked in olive oil and garlic, poached hake on red onions, and escalopes of salmon with sorrel sauce. Brasserie dishes include moules marinière, crispy duck salad, and pork chop with apple. Seasonal fruit tarts, poached pear with butterscotch sauce, or chocolate truffle meringue round things off. Wines are confidently selected from around the globe, the brasserie providing a scaled-down version of the main restaurant list. Prices start at around £10.

CHEFS: Marie Harding and Margaret Lovett PROPRIETORS: Dermod and Margaret Lovett, and Niamh and Dermod Lovett Jr OPEN: Mon to Fri L 12.30 to 2, Mon to Sat D 7 to 9.30 CLOSED: 1 week Christmas, bank hols MEALS: alc D (main courses £10 to £18). Set L £14.50, Set D £24. BYO £5. Bar food available SERVICE: not inc, card slips closed; 12.5% for parties of 5 or more CARDS: Access, Amex, Diners, Visa DETAILS: 50 seats. Private parties: 50 main room, 20 private room. Car park. Vegetarian meals. Children's helpings. Smart dress preferred. No cigars/pipes in dining-room. Wheelchair access (also WC). Music

---

DUBLIN Co Dublin

map 16

Commons

Newman House, 85–86 St Stephen's Green, Dublin 2

TEL: (01) 4752597 and 4780530 FAX: (01) 4780551 COST £29–£68

Leslie Malone arrived at the end of 1995 to head up the kitchen at what, despite the name, is one of the plushest restaurant addresses in the capital. A commissioned art collection from some of Ireland's best-known painters adds class to the décor. Choice is wide, and takes in monkfish and prawn terrine with caper and gherkin cream, or foie gras and black pudding galantine with herbed Chablis jelly on mango and black pepper caramel sauce. If those starters haven't stopped you in your tracks, aim for a main course of turbot on colcannon with keta caviare and a chive beurre blanc, perhaps, or prune-stuffed rabbit with wild mushrooms on apple and calvados sauce. Irish Mist mousse on a brandy-snap disc with glazed pineapple is a textural study from the dessert list. A very sound, varietally arranged wine list will make for agonising choice. House wines from France, Chile and South Africa are £14.

CHEF: Leslie Malone   PROPRIETOR: Michael Fitzgerald   OPEN: Mon to Fri L 12.30 to 2.15, Mon to Sat D 7 to 10.15   CLOSED: 2 weeks Christmas, bank hols   MEALS: Set L £18, Set D £32 to £42. BYO £5   SERVICE: 15%   CARDS: Access, Amex, Delta, Diners, Switch, Visa   DETAILS: 60 seats. Private parties: 12 main room, 26 and 60 private rooms. Vegetarian meals. Children's helpings. Music. Air-conditioned

Le Coq Hardi ※✱

35 Pembroke Road, Ballsbridge, Dublin 4
TEL: (01) 6689070   FAX: (01) 6689887   COST £29–£76

The Howards are fast approaching 20 years of service at this prestigious address in the Ballsbridge district. As the name would suggest, there is a perceptible Frenchness to the tone of the place which finds its way through to the cooking. A salade tiède of duck breast, roast garlic and pesto is one first course from the *carte*, and may be followed by lobster bisque enlivened with armagnac. The eponymous dish is a breast of corn-fed chicken wrapped in bacon and stuffed with potato, apple and ham, sauced with Irish whiskey. Turbot fillets are given a crust of couscous and bedded on spinach. To finish, there's crème brûlée with berries, or bread-and-butter pudding. The owners are justifiably proud of their wine list, which runs the gamut from Argentinian Chardonnay to Burgundies from Dom. de la Romanée-Conti. Prices start at £16.

CHEFS: John Howard and James O'Sullivan   PROPRIETORS: John and Catherine Howard   OPEN: Mon to Fri L 12.30 to 2.30, Mon to Sat D 7 to 11   CLOSED: 2 weeks Christmas, 2 weeks Aug, bank hols   MEALS: alc (main courses £17.50 to £24). Set L £18, Set D £30   SERVICE: 12.5%, card slips closed   CARDS: Access, Amex, Diners, Visa   DETAILS: 45 seats. Private parties: 50 main room, 10 and 35 private rooms. Car park. Vegetarian meals. Children welcome. Smart dress preferred. No smoking in 1 dining-room. Music. Air-conditioned

Eastern Tandoori

34–35 South William Street, Dublin 2
TEL: (01) 6710428 and 6710506   FAX: (01) 6779232   COST £15–£49

'Don't miss the camel-skin lampshades,' advises a reporter. The striving for authenticity at Dublin's most celebrated Indian restaurant also extends to traditionally dressed staff and a sitar player on some nights. A menu of tandoori favourites is offered, including chicken shashlik, spiced jumbo prawns and quail done in yoghurt, as well as expected classic sauces such as jalfrezi and pasanda. For one customer, vegetable korma was the 'best ever tasted'. Service is snappy and ever ready with the hot towels. The wine list kicks off with house French at £11.50.

CHEFS: Hendry Paul, Olli Ullah and Iqbal Ahmed   PROPRIETOR: Feroze Khan   OPEN: Mon to Sat L 12 to 2.30, all week D 6 to 11.30   MEALS: alc (main courses £8 to £14). Set L £5.95 to £7.95, Set D £17.95 to £19.95   SERVICE: 12.5%, card slips closed   CARDS: Access, Amex, Delta, Diners, Switch, Visa   DETAILS: 64 seats. Private parties: 100 main room. Vegetarian meals. Children's helpings. Smart dress preferred. No-smoking area. Wheelchair access. Music. Air-conditioned

Ernie's

Mulberry Gardens, Dublin 4
TEL: (01) 2693300   FAX: (01) 2693260   COST £23–£63

You won't lack for visual distractions at Ernie's. There is a floodlit garden with
fountain as well as a collection of over 200 oil-paintings to gaze on. A certain
formality marks the approach, but the cooking isn't stuck in any sort of
time-warp. Sandra Earl essays plenty of original ideas and has a high strike-rate.
Smoked salmon comes with tomato salsa and a caper and chive cream, while
strips of woodpigeon are laid on a risotto with wild mushrooms and tarragon.
Main courses include pheasant casseroled with shallots and bacon and sauced
with game stock, and meals might end with chocolate mousse gâteau in two
colours, set off with lemon and lime cream. In traditional Irish fashion, the wine
list begins proudly with mature French classics, followed by a sprinkling from
elsewhere. House wines are from £12.95.

CHEF: Sandra Earl   PROPRIETORS: the Evans family   OPEN: Tue to Fri L 12.30 to 2, Tue to Sat D
7.30 to 10   CLOSED: 1 week Christmas   MEALS: alc D (main courses £13 to £20). Set L £13.95,
Set D £25   SERVICE: 12.5%   CARDS: Access, Amex, Diners, Visa   DETAILS: 70 seats. Private
parties: 80 main room. Vegetarian meals. Children welcome. Children's helpings. Smart dress
preferred. Wheelchair access (no WC). No music. Air-conditioned

Les Frères Jacques ✸✱

74 Dame Street, Dublin 2
TEL: (01) 6794555   FAX: (01) 6794725   COST £23–£53

Plumb in the heart of the renovated Temple Bar district of the capital, this
Franco-Irish restaurant has proved popular with trend-setters. Lobsters displayed live, and slow-roasted côte de boeuf, indicate a kitchen that has not
severed all its culinary moorings, but it is equally at home serving duck breast
with lime, vermouth and ginger, or veal medallions stuffed with spinach and
ricotta and served on a creamy marsala sauce. A coupe of citrus sorbets anointed
with champagne, or sachertorte with coffee-bean sauce are among the sophisticated puddings. Wines are by no means exclusively French, but that is where
the strength lies. Prices are on the high side, but house French in all three colours
comes at £10.50.

CHEF: Nicholas Boutin   PROPRIETORS: Jean-Jacques and Suzy Caillabet   OPEN: Mon to Fri
12.30 to 2.30, Mon to Sat D 7.30 to 10.30 (11 Fri and Sat)   CLOSED: 25 Dec to 2 Jan, bank hols
MEALS: alc D (main courses £14 to £18.50). Set L £13.50, Set D £20   SERVICE: 12.5%
(optional)   CARDS: Access, Amex, Diners, Visa   DETAILS: 65 seats. Private parties: 40 main
room, 16 and 40 private rooms. Car park. Children's helpings. No smoking in 1 dining-room. No
pipes in dining-room. Music

Kapriol ✸✱

45 Lower Camden Street, Dublin 2
TEL: (01) 4751235 and 2985496   COST £26–£55

The Peruzzis' well-established Italian restaurant is close to the heart of the action
in Dublin. All the expected trattoria favourites are offered: cheesy pasta starters,

squid risotto, veal escalopes done in various ways. Wine and cream form the basis for many of the sauces, and there is game in season: for example, pheasant and venison properly hung and marinated for several days. Vegetables are charged extra. Italian wines from the major regions lead the wine list. House Trebbiano and Montepulciano d'Abruzzo are £10.80 for a litre carafe.

CHEF: Egidia Peruzzi   PROPRIETORS: Egidia and Giuseppe Peruzzi   OPEN: Mon to Sat D only 7.30 to 12   CLOSED: 3 weeks Aug, bank hols   MEALS: alc (main courses £8.50 to £17) SERVICE: 12.5%   CARDS: Access, Amex, Diners, Visa   DETAILS: 36 seats. Private parties: 36 main room. Vegetarian meals. Children's helpings. Smart dress preferred. No smoking in 1 dining-room. Wheelchair access (no WC). Music

Locks

1 Windsor Terrace, Portobello, Dublin 8
TEL: (01) 4543391 and 4538352   FAX: (01) 4538352   COST £22–£57

So named because it sits on the banks of the Grand Canal, Locks offers colourful contemporary cooking from the hands of Brian Buckley. Cod crusted with crabmeat and served with prawns might suit the palates of lunchers, while the evening crowd may be regaled with chicken en croûte sauced with blue cheese, or loin of lamb with caramelised onions and a honey and thyme sauce. Gravad lax comes with avocado, and there may be a pasta dish using smoked fish. More elaborate dishes feature on the *carte*. The wine list is heavily French, but choices from elsewhere are equally knowledgeable. House Duboeuf is £10.95.

CHEF: Brian Buckley   PROPRIETOR: Claire Douglas   OPEN: Mon to Fri L 12.30 to 2, Mon to Sat D 7.15 to 11   CLOSED: 1 week Christmas, last week July, first week Aug, bank hols   MEALS: alc (main courses £14.50 to £18). Set L £13.95, Set D £23.50   SERVICE: 12.5%, card slips closed CARDS: Access, Amex, Diners, Visa   DETAILS: 50 seats. Private parties: 40 private room. Children's helpings. Smart dress preferred. Wheelchair access (no WC). No music

Patrick Guilbaud

46 James Place, Dublin 2
TEL: (01) 6764192   FAX: (01) 6610052   COST £30–£76

'The best meal I have ever had anywhere over a long life of eating' was the verdict of a visitor from Wales. 'Two days later, I am still delirious.' The cause was Guillaume Le Brun's deeply distinguished French cuisine at this smart restaurant located behind the head office of the Bank of Ireland. The menu combines both modern and classical strands, so that langoustines in filo with mango rémoulade, and Dover sole with smoked duck and broad beans sit side by side with foie gras en torchon with Sauternes jelly, and beef fillet with bone-marrow and a red wine sauce. 'Faultless' crème brûlée is a popular way to finish. Information on wines was unavailable at the time of going to press.

CHEF: Guillaume Le Brun   PROPRIETOR: Patrick Guilbaud   OPEN: Tue to Sat 12.30 to 2, 7.30 to 10.15   CLOSED: first 2 weeks Jan, bank hols   MEALS: alc (main courses £18 to £23). Set L £22, Set D £35 to £55   SERVICE: net prices   CARDS: Access, Amex, Diners, Visa   DETAILS: 80 seats. Private parties: 80 main room, 28 private room. Car park. Children welcome. Smart dress preferred. No music. Air-conditioned

Roly's Bistro

7 Ballsbridge Terrace, Dublin 4
TEL: (01) 6682611   FAX: (01) 6608535   COST £16–£41

Colin O'Daly is an enthusiastic exponent of cutting-edge modern cooking at this lively restaurant in a smart suburb of Dublin. Eating goes on at two levels, one slightly more formal than the other, but both filled with exuberant buzz. A reporter who has become something of a regular commends the smoked seafood sausage and the deep-fried Brie, and found the prawns Newburg 'exceptionally good' at a December meal. Favourite desserts such as crème brûlée and sticky toffee pudding fulfil all expectations. House wines are £8.95.

CHEF: Colin O'Daly   PROPRIETORS: Roly Saul, John O'Sullivan, John Mulcahy and Colin O'Daly   OPEN: all week 12 to 2.45, 6 to 10   CLOSED: 25 and 26 Dec, Good Fri   MEALS: alc D (main courses £7.50 to £14). Set L £10.50   SERVICE: 10%, card slips closed   CARDS: Access, Amex, Diners, Visa   DETAILS: 150 seats. Private parties: 10 main room. Vegetarian meals. Children welcome. Wheelchair access (also WC). Music. Air-conditioned

La Stampa

35 Dawson Street, Dublin 2
TEL: (01) 6778611   FAX: (01) 6773336   COST £18–£46

'Probably the most beautiful dining-room in the city,' reckons the management, describing this many-mirrored erstwhile ballroom of the Engineers' Institute. Not the least of its charms are the individual painted waistcoats sported by the waiters. Then there is Paul Flynn's cooking, as full of elegant panache as befits a former protégé of Nico Ladenis. Crabmeat pappardelle with ginger and garlic, salmon brochette teriyaki with sesame potatoes, and pork and foie gras pithiviers with a sweet-and-sour sherry sauce suggest a burgeoning oriental influence underpinning the kitchen's production. Lemon tart with chocolate granita, and strawberry mascarpone cheesecake crop up among desserts. House wines are £12.

CHEFS: Paul Flynn and Martin Lynch   PROPRIETOR: Louis Murray   OPEN: Mon to Fri L 12.30 to 2.30, all week D 6.30 to 11.15 (11.30 Fri and Sat)   CLOSED: 25 and 26 Dec, Good Fri   MEALS: alc D (main courses £10 to £16). Set L £10.50   SERVICE: not inc; 10% for parties of 6 or more   CARDS: Access, Amex, Diners, Visa   DETAILS: 200 seats. Private parties: 160 main room, 60 private room. Vegetarian meals. Children welcome. No pipes in dining-room. Music. Air-conditioned

Thornton's ⁑✳

NEW ENTRY

1 Portobello Road, Dublin 8
TEL: (01) 4549067   COST £45–£68

Kevin Thornton opened his canalside restaurant in 1995 and has immediately blazed yet another vivid culinary trail in the Irish capital. A reporter eating in the spring gazed around the dining-room and saw stars (of politics and TV), but the food is where the brightest gleam shines forth. Sauté foie gras with scallops and black truffles, roast guinea-fowl with celeriac mousse and lemon 'confit', and a clafoutis of winter berries with crème anglaise were 'near enough to perfection' for one man, while others have swooned over creations such as marinated wild salmon with cucumber jelly and caviare, and goose magret with chestnuts and a juniper sauce. This is a welcome new addition to Dublin. Wines are a well-chosen bunch, the main thrust being classical France. House Bordeaux from the André Lurton stable is £14.

CHEF: Kevin Thornton   PROPRIETORS: Kevin and Muriel Thornton   OPEN: Tue to Sat D only 7 to 10.30   CLOSED: 10 days Christmas   MEALS: alc (main courses £17.50 to £20.50)   SERVICE: 10%   CARDS: Access, Amex, Diners, Visa   DETAILS: 46 seats. Private parties: 30 main room, 16 private room. Children's helpings. No smoking in 1 dining-room. Music. Air-conditioned

---

DURRUS Co Cork   map 16

Blairs Cove

Durrus, nr Bantry
TEL: (027) 61127
1m out of Durrus on Barleycove to Goleen road   COST £35–£42

The converted outbuildings of a Georgian manor house form the setting for this unusual operation, where you help yourself to starters and desserts from a display. The former generally include gravad lax, marinated herrings, shellfish, grilled vegetables, pâtés and so forth, while the latter offer two-tone chocolate mousse, îles flottantes, Bakewell tart and tiramisù. In between, grilled tuna with spicy tomato sauce, or meats done on a wood-fired grill are the order of the day. The incautious of appetite may visit the buffets as often as they please. Wines work to the Irish formula: a strong French listing supplemented by smatterings from elsewhere. House French is £11.

CHEFS/PROPRIETORS: Philippe and Sabine De Mey   OPEN: Tue to Sat (and Mon July and Aug) D only 7.30 to 9.30   CLOSED: Nov to Mid-Mar   MEALS: Set D £25   SERVICE: 10%, card slips closed   CARDS: Access, Amex, Diners, Visa   DETAILS: 70 seats. Private parties: 30 main room. Car park. Children's helpings. Smart dress preferred. No-smoking area. Music

---

GOREY Co Wexford   map 16

▲ Marlfield House

Courtown Road, Gorey
TEL: (055) 21124   FAX: (055) 21572   COST £26–£48

One of Ireland's most sumptuously appointed country houses, Marlfield is early nineteenth-century, built of sandstone with brick facings. Interiors are lavish, the dining-room painted with ferns and creepers, a vaulted conservatory extension adding to the allure when the weather obliges. New chef Craig Jones has worked at some of the UK's most prestigious country hotels, and brings the requisite touch of flash to Marlfield's kitchen. Roast quail with deep-fried quail's eggs in a walnut-dressed salad is a grand enough way to start, escabèche of red mullet with oyster tempura, bacalhau and caviare an even grander one. Turbot fillet comes with lobster tortellini with truffle cream and a vermouth sauce. Finish, perhaps, with pistachio soufflé and chocolate ice-cream. This is an ambitious operation, as is confirmed by the impressive wine list, which offers Ch. Pétrus 1966 at £675 without batting an eyelid. Seven house wines are £13.

CHEF: Craig Jones PROPRIETORS: Mary and Ray Bowe OPEN: all week 12.45 to 1.45, 7.30 to 9 CLOSED: mid-Dec to late Jan MEALS: Set L £17.50, Set D £30 SERVICE: 10%, card slips closed CARDS: Access, Amex, Visa DETAILS: 60 seats. Private parties: 20 main room, 20 and 30 private rooms. Car park. Vegetarian meals. Children's helpings. No children under 6 D. Smart dress preferred. No smoking in dining-room. Wheelchair access (also WC). No music. Air-conditioned ACCOMMODATION: 19 rooms, all with bath/shower. TV. Phone. B&B £70 to £440 plus 10% service. Deposit: 1 night's stay. Rooms for disabled. Children welcome. Baby facilities. Afternoon teas. Garden

---

HOWTH Co Dublin   map 16

King Sitric 🍴✻

East Pier, Howth
TEL: (01) 8325235 and 8326729   FAX: (01) 8392442   COST £28–£57

The former harbour-master's house overlooking Balscadden Bay celebrated a quarter-century as King Sitric in 1996. Fish is Aidan MacManus's first culinary love, and the menu offers mussels with pesto, baked crab and horseradish gâteau, and seafood paella with saffron and Spanish bomba rice. Specialist tastes may be catered for in snails in a sauce of Chablis, or lambs' tongues in port, while die-hard meat eaters may opt for a sirloin steak in red wine sauce. Crème caramel, banana split and meringues with ice-cream and hot chocolate sauce are among the crowd-pleasing desserts. A splendid wine list majors in whites, but that doesn't preclude a great collection of clarets. There are plenty of half-bottles, and house French in all three colours is £12.

CHEF: Aidan MacManus PROPRIETORS: Aidan and Joan MacManus OPEN: Mon to Sat D only 6.30 to 10.45 CLOSED: first 2½ weeks Jan, bank hols MEALS: alc (main courses £12.50 to £18.50). Set D £24. BYO £4. Light L available in seafood bar in summer SERVICE: not inc, card slips closed CARDS: Access, Amex, Diners, Visa DETAILS: 75 seats. Private parties: 45 main room, 10 and 22 private rooms. Children's helpings. Smart dress preferred. No smoking in 1 dining-room. Wheelchair access (also women's WC). Music

---

KANTURK Co Cork   map 16

▲ Assolas Country House

Kanturk
TEL: (029) 50015   FAX: (029) 50795
signposted from N72, NE of Kanturk, 8m W of Mallow   COST £35–£42

The Bourke family have lived at Assolas for several generations. It is a peacefully sited manor-house built in the seventeenth century, its trim lawns sloping gently down to a trickle of a river alongside. Hazel Bourke has absorbed some of the Mediterranean teachings that have inspired cookery in the 1990s, and so her first courses may take in a roasted pepper and aubergine roulade with goats' cheese, while mains could include venison marinated in olive oil and red wine, or a vegetarian polenta gratin with tomatoes and local Ardrahan cheese. There's even room for Caesar salad. Desserts are served from a trolley, and the cheeses are Ireland's finest. The European wine list offers plenty to go at, including an Irish Reichensteiner. House wines are Guigal's Côtes du Rhône red and white at £14.

CHEF: Hazel Bourke   PROPRIETORS: the Bourke family   OPEN: all week D only 7 to 8.30
CLOSED: 1 Nov to 1 Apr   MEALS: Set D £28   SERVICE: none, card slips closed   CARDS: Access,
Amex, Diners, Visa   DETAILS: 30 seats. Private parties: 18 main room, 18 private room. Car
park. Vegetarian meals. Smart dress preferred. No cigars in dining-room. No music
ACCOMMODATION: 9 rooms, all with bath/shower. Phone. B&B £51 to £154. Deposit: £100.
Children welcome. Baby facilities. Garden. Fishing

KENMARE Co Kerry   map 16

▲ Park Hotel Kenmare 🍴✷

Kenmare
TEL: (064) 41200   FAX: (064) 41402   COST £51–£94

The nineteenth-century grey-stone house looks faintly imposing from without, but any sense of austerity is promptly dispelled on entry by the friendly and solicitous approach of all concerned. Crammed with idiosyncratic antiques, and overlooked by the Caha Mountains, the Park offers a true taste of an Irish yesteryear. Not so the menus of Bruno Schmidt, which introduce a fashionable note of eclecticism. Lobster and green bean terrine with sliced mango and chive mayonnaise might be followed by sauté turbot with spicy cucumber salad and a lemon balm dressing. Accompaniments are always carefully considered, as in poussin braised with cabbage, lardons and cloves and served on a rosemary-infused chicken stock. Verbena lends its scent to the crème anglaise that comes with chocolate and pistachio gâteau. Burgundies from Drouhin, Beaujolais from Duboeuf and a host of premium clarets head up a classical wine list. House wines are £16.50.

CHEF: Bruno Schmidt   PROPRIETOR: Francis Brennan   OPEN: all week D only 7 to 8.45
CLOSED: 2 Jan to mid-Apr, 1 Nov to 23 Dec   MEALS: alc (main courses £18 to £35). Set D £38.
Bar food available   SERVICE: not inc   CARDS: Access, Amex, Diners, Visa   DETAILS: 80 seats.
Private parties: 30 main room, 15 private room. Car park. Vegetarian meals. Children's helpings.
No children under 5 D. Smart dress preferred. No smoking in 1 dining-room. Wheelchair access
(also WC). Music   ACCOMMODATION: 49 rooms, all with bath/shower. TV. Phone. B&B £115 to
£276. Rooms for disabled. Children welcome. Baby facilities. Afternoon teas. Garden

▲ Sheen Falls Lodge, La Cascade

Kenmare
TEL: (064) 41600   FAX: (064) 41386
follow signs for Glengariff from Kenmare; hotel
signposted after about ½m   COST £29–£61

Sheen Falls sits among luxuriant foliage by the side of Kenmare Bay, and its dining-room is named after the waterfalls that can be heard gushing nearby. 'Progressive Irish' is how Fergus Moore styles his cooking, which translates as parsnip and tumeric soup, peppered rabbit loin with tagliolini and tarragon cream, and black sole on leek julienne with a Sauternes butter sauce and grapes. Presentation and creativity are accorded great prominence, and vegetarians are offered their own menu. White chocolate terrine with blueberry purée, or lemon tart with mascarpone are how meals may end. The wine list is an encyclopedic collection of the great and the good, as impressive in regional France and the southern hemisphere as in the auction-catalogue listing of cru classé clarets. House wines are £17.50 for Mâcon white and £18.50 for St-Emilion.

CHEF: Fergus Moore   PROPRIETOR: Bent Hoyer   OPEN: Sun L 1 to 2, all week D 7.15 to 9.30   CLOSED: 10 Nov to 22 Dec, 2 Jan to mid-Feb   MEALS: Set L £17.50, Set D £29.50 (2 courses) to £37.50   SERVICE: not inc, card slips closed   CARDS: Access, Amex, Diners, Visa   DETAILS: 120 seats. 12 seats outside. Private parties: 120 main room, 80 private room. Car park. Vegetarian meals. Children's helpings. Smart dress preferred. No cigars/pipes in dining-room. Wheelchair access (also WC). Music   ACCOMMODATION: 40 rooms, all with bath/shower. TV. Phone. D,B&B £198 to £266. Rooms for disabled. Children welcome. Baby facilities. Dogs welcome. Afternoon teas. Garden. Fishing

---

KILKENNY   Co Kilkenny   map 16

▲ Lacken House ⁵✳

Dublin Road, Kilkenny
TEL: (056) 61085   FAX: (056) 62435   COST £32–£52

Eugene McSweeney's kitchen in this late-Victorian house is stocked almost exclusively from what Kilkenny and Waterford have to offer in the way of local meats, fish from the southern coast and organically grown vegetables. Influences have been gleaned from stints working abroad, but the orientation is unmistakably Irish for all that, producing Clonakilty black pudding with onion marmalade and wholegrain mustard sauce, a sausage of poached sole with lemon butter, and beef fillet on rösti potato with a sauce of Cashel Blue. Pedigree producers are listed from most major wine regions, and mark-ups are steep in places, but house Côtes du Rhône is £12.

CHEF: Eugene McSweeney   PROPRIETORS: Eugene and Breda McSweeney   OPEN: Tue to Sat D only 7 to 10.30   CLOSED: 1 week Christmas   MEALS: alc (main courses £12.50 to £18). Set D £23   SERVICE: not inc, card slips closed   CARDS: Access, Amex, Diners, Visa   DETAILS: 30 seats. Private parties: 35 main room, 16 private room. Car park. Vegetarian meals. Children's helpings. Smart dress preferred. No smoking in 1 dining-room. Music. Air-conditioned   ACCOMMODATION: 8 rooms, all with bath/shower. TV. Phone. B&B £31 to £60. Deposit: 10%. Children welcome. Garden

---

KINSALE   Co Cork   map 16

▲ Blue Haven

3 Pearse Street, Kinsale
TEL: (021) 772209   FAX: (021) 774268   COST £29–£57

Renovations at Blue Haven, a little hotel and pub in the centre of Kinsale just a short trot from the harbour, have continued apace over the last year, and in February 1996 new boy Ross Barrett arrived to head up the kitchen team. The operation is divided between bar food, a special shellfish menu that shows off local lobster to great effect, and a *carte* that deals in elevated poshery. The last may include rabbit confit with cassis-flavoured onion marmalade, sauté scallops with rhubarb sauce, and smoked pork loin with a parsnip and cabbage rösti and orange and cranberry sauce. Seafood Kashmiri and surf 'n' turf combinations extend the versatility. Finish with strawberry meringue or Brazil nut praline laced with Jameson's. An ambitious wine list covers France intelligently and pokes its head round a number of other doors too. Mark-ups are very reasonable, with a wide range under £15 a bottle. House wines start at £10.50.

CHEF: Ross Barrett   PROPRIETORS: Brian and Anne Cronin   OPEN: all week D only 7 to 10.30 CLOSED: 25 Dec   MEALS: alc (main courses £11.50 to £19.50). Set D £25. BYO £5. Bar food available   SERVICE: 10%   CARDS: Access, Amex, Diners, Visa   DETAILS: 90 seats. 35 seats outside. Private parties: 50 main room. Vegetarian meals. Children's helpings. Smart dress preferred. Wheelchair access (also WC). Music. Air-conditioned   ACCOMMODATION: 18 rooms, all with bath/shower. TV. Phone. B&B £45 to £130. Deposit: 1 night's stay. Children welcome. Baby facilities. Afternoon teas. Garden

---

LETTERFRACK   Co Galway   map 16

▲ *Rosleague Manor* ⁵⁺✴

Letterfrack
TEL: (095) 41101   FAX: (095) 41168
on N59 to Westport, 7m NW of Clifden   COST £21–£49

A path through the garden leads to the ocean's edge at the Foyle family's Regency manor on the fringes of Connemara. Nigel Rush works in an assured country-house idiom, cooking food that does not set out to startle, but soothes visitors with such classical offerings as mussels in white wine and garlic, leek and potato soup, venison medallions in red wine, and cold lemon soufflé. A pair of reporters who return every year commend the 'real intensity' of the soups, 'outstandingly fresh' fish and 'simply but carefully treated' vegetables. The compact wine list does an efficient job of covering Western Europe, doffs its cap to Australia, and opens with house French at £11.

CHEF: Nigel Rush   PROPRIETORS: Anne Foyle and Patrick Foyle   OPEN: all week 12.45 to 2.30, 8 to 9.30   CLOSED: 1 Nov to Easter   MEALS: alc (main courses L £6.50 to £12.50, D £10.50 to £15). Set L £14, Set D £25   SERVICE: not inc, card slips closed   CARDS: Access, Amex, Visa DETAILS: 60 seats. Private parties: 50 main room. Car park. Vegetarian meals. Children's helpings. Smart dress preferred. No smoking in dining-room. No music   ACCOMMODATION: 20 rooms, all with bath/shower. TV. Phone. B&B £40 to £140. Rooms for disabled. Children welcome. Dogs welcome in bedrooms only. Afternoon teas. Garden

---

MALLOW   Co Cork   map 16

▲ *Longueville House* ⁵⁺✴

Mallow
TEL: (022) 47156   FAX: (022) 47459
3m W of Mallow on N72 Killarney road   COST £26–£56

The Georgian mansion, built in 1720, sits amid 500 acres of woodland estate overlooking the magnificent Blackwater valley. Interiors are 'of the highest quality without being intimidating', according to one report. That may be because the O'Callaghans run the place as a welcoming family home, their son

William weaving his own kind of magic in the kitchen. The presentation may look painstaking, but flavour is delivered along with every artfully composed dish, as in 'exceptionally good' duck breast with lentils and peppers, or 'absolutely perfect' loin of local lamb baked in a potato crust with tapénade. Prawns and scallops cooked in a nage with baby leeks may start things off well, and crème brûlée with grapefruit granita is 'as good as they come'. Wines offer an alluring array, with 1980s clarets forming the backbone of the list. French, Spanish and Italian house wines are all £13.

CHEF: William O'Callaghan   PROPRIETORS: Michael and Jane O'Callaghan   OPEN: Sun L 12.30 to 2, all week D 7 to 9   CLOSED: mid-Dec to early Mar   MEALS: Set L £17, Set D £28. Bar L available   SERVICE: not inc, card slips closed   CARDS: Access, Amex, Diners, Visa   DETAILS: 50 seats. Private parties: 40 main room, 15 private room. Car park. Vegetarian meals. Children's helpings. Smart dress preferred. No smoking in dining-room. Wheelchair access (also WC). Music   ACCOMMODATION: 21 rooms, all with bath/shower. TV. Phone. B&B £53 to £160. Deposit: 50%. Children welcome. Baby facilities. Afternoon teas. Garden. Fishing

---

MIDLETON   Co Cork   map 16

Farmgate

The Coolbawn, Midleton
TEL/FAX: (021) 632771   COST £15–£38

'Simplicity is the essence of what we do,' says Máróg O'Brien, 'and we do not over-handle good basic ingredients.' That will be music to the ears of many, and this modest but accomplished seaside restaurant on the south coast is not lacking for good ingredients. Mixed seafood is cooked in a tart and served with hollandaise, ditto lambs' kidneys with a mustard sauce. Monkfish and salmon are paired off and given the provençale treatment, while beef fillet is accompanied by a potion based on Jameson's whiskey. Modishness comes to the fore in a warm salad of chicken marinated in soy sauce and ginger with chargrilled red peppers. The wine list is written by hand and ignores vintages, but prices seem eminently fair, opening at £10.

CHEFS: Angela Collins, Máróg O'Brien and David Doran   PROPRIETOR: Máróg O'Brien   OPEN: Mon to Sat L 12 to 3.30, Fri and Sat D 6.30 to 9.30   CLOSED: 5 days Christmas, Easter Sun and Mon   MEALS: alc (main courses £4.50 to £15)   SERVICE: not inc   CARDS: Access, Visa   DETAILS: 60 seats. 20 seats outside. Private parties: 15 main room, 20 private room. Vegetarian meals. Children's helpings. No pipes in dining-room. Wheelchair access (also WC). No music

---

MOYCULLEN   Co Galway   map 16

Drimcong House

Moycullen
TEL: (091) 555115 and 555585   FAX: (091) 555836
on Galway to Clifden road, 1m W of Moycullen   COST £30–£56

Gerry Galvin's declared aim is to give 'interesting new treatments to traditional food' at this family-run restaurant in a 300-year-old country house in the west of Ireland. With that in mind, you must not be surprised to see tabbouleh and pickles with smoked salmon, or capers and mustard with mutton. Flavourings are nothing if not bold: duck confit comes with a sauce of port and pineapple. Fixed-price menus are costed up to five courses, depending on whether you take cheese as well as dessert, and whether you feel like a sorbet or a bowl of soup before the main course. Desserts might feature fresh fruit gratin, or tipsy pudding in mulled wine. The focus of the wine list is France, but Argentina, Greece and Lebanon each get a look in too. The house selection starts at £10.50.

CHEF: Gerry Galvin PROPRIETORS: Gerry and Marie Galvin OPEN: Tue to Sat D only 6.30 to 10.30 CLOSED: Christmas to Mar MEALS: alc (main courses £16.50 to £20). Set D £22 to £24 SERVICE: not inc CARDS: Access, Amex, Diners, Visa DETAILS: 50 seats. Private parties: 50 main room, 10 to 30 private rooms. Car park. Vegetarian meals. Children's helpings. Wheelchair access (also WC). Music

---

NEWPORT Co Mayo   map 16

▲ Newport House ⁵✳

Newport
TEL: (098) 41222 FAX: (098) 41613   COST £38–£56

The 'atmosphere of a private fishing club' that the Thompsons refer to in describing their Georgian house on the north-west coast derives from the salmon-fishing rights that the hotel enjoys. The salmon may end up on the plate with a sauce of basil or lemon and chive cream, or may be smoked in-house. Six-course dinners also take in venison and duck terrine with Cumberland sauce, chargrilled veal with tarragon and mustard, and steamed turbot fillet with saffron sauce. Irish cheeses precede desserts such as poached pears with honey and walnut ice-cream, and there is an option to add half a dozen oysters in season after the first course. Claret and champagne are the pride and joy of an impressive wine list which includes plenty of mature vintages. Prices are sensible and French house wines start at £10.

CHEF: John Gavin PROPRIETORS: Kieran and Thelma Thompson OPEN: all week D only 7 to 9.30 CLOSED: 3 Oct to 18 Mar MEALS: Set D £29. Light L available 12 to 2 SERVICE: not inc, card slips closed CARDS: Access, Amex, Diners, Visa DETAILS: 38 seats. Private parties: 12 main room. Car park. Children's helpings. Smart dress preferred. No smoking in dining-room. Wheelchair access (also WC). No music ACCOMMODATION: 18 rooms, all with bath/shower. Phone. B&B £50 to £132. Rooms for disabled. Children welcome. Baby facilities. Dogs welcome in courtyard rooms only. Afternoon teas. Garden. Fishing

---

OUGHTERARD Co Galway   map 16

▲ Currarevagh House ⁵✳

Oughterard, Connemara
TEL: (091) 552312 and 552313 FAX: (091) 552731
4m NW of Oughterard on Hill of Doon Lakeshore road   COST £26–£32

The Hodgsons' ancestors built Currarevagh in the middle of the nineteenth century. Connemara is all around, so the walking and views are reassuringly majestic, and the house generates a feeling of comfort. Formality and luxuries are forgone in favour of a relaxed, domestic feel, buttressed by the no-choice dinner menus served at eight. A first-course mussel and chowder soup, or chicken and asparagus mousse, might be followed by spiced salmon steak, then haunch of venison with Cumberland sauce. A rich pudding such as chocolate cheesecake or baked Alaska is then followed by Irish cheeses. 'Excellent' was the verdict of one reporter, who added: 'First-class breakfasts too.' The well-annotated wine list has something for most tastes and purses. House Mommessin is £8.80.

CHEF: June Hodgson PROPRIETORS: Harry and June Hodgson OPEN: all week D only 8 (1 sitting) CLOSED: 25 Oct to 1 Apr MEALS: Set D £19.50 SERVICE: 10%, card slips closed CARDS: Access, Visa DETAILS: 32 seats. Private parties: 10 main room. Car park. Smart dress preferred. No smoking in dining-room. No music ACCOMMODATION: 15 rooms, all with bath/shower. B&B £45 to £90. Children by arrangement. Dogs welcome. Garden. Fishing

---

RATHMULLAN Co Donegal map 16

▲ Rathmullan House ⅖✳ | NEW ENTRY |

Rathmullan
TEL: (074) 58188 FAX: (074) 58200 COST £21–£37

This sprawling white country house in the far north-west brings culinary relief to an under-represented area. It peeps over lush green countryside to the rippling waters of Lough Swilly, which can be glimpsed from the conservatory where you eat beneath a tented ceiling. A 'fairly restrained' touch is evident in starters such as squid-ink pasta with smoked salmon in a cream sauce. Halibut may be served with an 'accomplished' gâteau of polenta and spinach, while meats might take in duckling confit with a sauce of pickled ginger, or loin of lamb stuffed with bacon and herbs on a rosemary *jus*. Finish with rhubarb pie or coconut parfait. A serviceable international wine selection is offered, opening at around £9, plus a treasure trove called Connoisseurs Corner.

CHEF: Kevin Murphy PROPRIETORS: the Wheeler family OPEN: Sun L 1 to 2, all week D 7.30 to 8.45 MEALS: Set L £13.50, Set D £22.50. Bar food available in summer SERVICE: 10%, card slips closed CARDS: Access, Amex, Diners, Visa DETAILS: 70 seats. Private parties: 30 main room. Car park. Vegetarian meals. Children's helpings. Smart dress preferred. No smoking in dining-room. No music ACCOMMODATION: 20 rooms, all with bath/shower. TV. Phone. DB&B £37.50 to £120 plus 10% service. Deposit: £25. Children welcome; high teas provided. Baby facilities. Afternoon teas. Garden. Swimming-pool

---

SHANAGARRY Co Cork map 16

▲ Ballymaloe House ⅖✳

Shanagarry, nr Midleton
TEL: (021) 652531 FAX: (021) 652021
2m outside Cloyne on Ballycotton road COST £25–£48

Ivan and Myrtle Allen's south Cork country hotel is one of Ireland's gastronomic institutions. So unruffled is it by the winds of change that one reporter described eating here as 'a wonderful experience of yesteryear'. However dated the cooking may seem to a metropolitan clientele, Ballymaloe does what it does with great aplomb, and anyway it isn't a metropolitan restaurant. Praise has come in for poached salmon in hollandaise sauce, and for desserts such as blackcurrant mousse, meringue with oranges, and caramel ice-cream. Quail véronique, or roast rack of lamb with redcurrant sauce, turnip purée and caramelised onions, demonstrates a willingness to give the odd twist to more familiar offerings. The handwritten wine list delves into the southern hemisphere and the major French regions with equal confidence. House wines are £13.

CHEF: Rory O'Connell   PROPRIETORS: Ivan and Myrtle Allen   OPEN: all week 1 to 1.45, 7 to 9   CLOSED: 24 to 26 Dec   MEALS: Set L £16, Set D £30. BYO £5   SERVICE: not inc, card slips closed   CARDS: Access, Amex, Diners, Visa   DETAILS: 100 seats. Private parties: 30 main room, 10 to 30 private rooms. Car park. Vegetarian meals. Children's helpings. Smart dress preferred. No smoking in 1 dining-room. Wheelchair access (no WC). Music   ACCOMMODATION: 32 rooms, all with bath/shower. Phone. B&B £75 to £130. Deposit: £30. Rooms for disabled. Children welcome. Baby facilities. Garden. Swimming-pool

---

SCHULL   Co Cork   map 16

Restaurant in Blue   NEW ENTRY

Gubbeen, Schull
TEL: (028) 28305
2m out of Schull on main Crookhaven road   COST £30–£36

Guess what colour this place is. It is a converted barn beside a stream, conscientiously restored and decorated with old photographs and paintings. An Irish pair were bemused to be offered a choice of books or a jigsaw puzzle to mull over after ordering. Who in Ireland, they wondered, doesn't want to talk? To start, cumin-spiced lamb might be served en croûte with honey and mint sabayon, or prawns from Dunmanus fashioned into a sort of pudding with garlic and parsley. An 'honestly impeccable' main course of sliced duck breast with an apricot and ginger sauce was the high point of one evening. Uniformly excellent Irish cheeses and a no-choice platter of desserts, including banana mousse and crème caramel, round things off nicely. The 50-odd bottle wine list spans most of the globe, with house wine starting at £10.

CHEF: Burvill Evans   PROPRIETORS: Christine Crabtree and Burvill Evans   OPEN: Tue to Sun D only 7 to 9.30   CLOSED: mid-Nov to late Dec, early Jan to mid-Feb   MEALS: Set D £22.50   SERVICE: not inc   CARDS: Access, Amex, Diners, Visa   DETAILS: 50 seats. Private parties: 36 main room. Car park. Children's helpings. No children under 9. Smart dress preferred. Music

---

WATERFORD   Co Waterford   map 16

Dwyers ✦

8 Mary Street, Waterford
TEL: (051) 877478   FAX: (051) 871183   COST £21–£39

The Dwyers' comfortable little restaurant in the far south-east is a must for an English couple who regularly use the car ferry to and from Rosslare. Value for money and hospitality are the keys to its success. Clonakilty white pudding dressed with apples and honey is the sort of thing to expect, alongside rösti nests of garlic prawns, monkfish in gazpacho sauce, or pork fillet with bacon and juniper berries. Tricoloured chocolate terrine is a show-off dessert that wins praise, or there may be homelier rhubarb and orange crumble. A short wine list furnishes reasonable drinking at friendly prices, starting at £10.20.

CHEF: Martin Dwyer   PROPRIETORS: Martin and Sile Dwyer   OPEN: Mon to Sat D only 6 to 10
CLOSED: 1 week Christmas   MEALS: alc (main courses £13 to £14). Set D 6 to 7.30 £14
SERVICE: not inc   CARDS: Access, Amex, Diners, Visa   DETAILS: 32 seats. Private parties: 20
main room, 8 private room. Children's helpings. No smoking in 1 dining-room. Wheelchair
access (also WC). Music

WICKLOW   Co Wicklow   map 16

▲ Old Rectory ✾

Wicklow
TEL: (0404) 67048   FAX: (0404) 69181   COST £33–£47

A tranquil country house on the edge of the harbour town of Wicklow, the Old
Rectory enhances the sense of pastoral in its surroundings by means of Linda
Saunders's fondness for edible flowers. Salads are strewn with them, crêpes
festooned with them, but they are not *de rigueur*, and a meal may as easily consist
of chicken and pheasant sausage on a bed of cabbage, hot grapefruit with Irish
whiskey, wild salmon in filo with sauce véronique, and summer pudding. That
was what a pair of English travellers enjoyed here on an autumn jaunt around
Ireland. Spain gets a fairer crack of the whip than it does on most wine lists, but
the choices from elsewhere are sound too. Prices open at £12.

CHEF: Linda Saunders   PROPRIETORS: Paul and Linda Saunders   OPEN: all week D only 8 (1
sitting)   CLOSED: Jan and Feb   MEALS: alc (main courses £15.50 to £18). Set D £27   SERVICE:
net prices, card slips closed   CARDS: Access, Amex, Diners, Visa   DETAILS: 16 seats. Private
parties: 20 main room, 12 private room. Car park. Vegetarian meals. Children's helpings. Smart
dress preferred. No smoking in dining-room. Wheelchair access (no WC). Music
ACCOMMODATION: 5 rooms, all with bath/shower. TV. Phone. B&B £69 to £92. Deposit: £30.
Children welcome. Baby facilities. Garden

YOUGHAL   Co Cork   map 16

▲ Aherne's

163 North Main Street, Youghal
TEL: (024) 92424   FAX: (024) 93633   COST £22–£41

A converted pub where seafood is the theme, Aherne's offers both restaurant and
bar eating as well as accommodation, and impressed one reporter with mussels
in onion and garlic cream, lemon sole with crisply sauté potatoes and ratatouille,
and a considerate selection of vegetarian dishes. Another enjoyed the seafood
platter (though not the garnishes) and found some good things among the
selection of desserts, such as mousse-like lemon cheesecake and 'first-class'
raspberry and blackberry ice-cream. Wines are priced from £11.50.

CHEF: David Fitzgibbon   PROPRIETORS: the Fitzgibbon family   OPEN: all week 12.30 to 2.15,
6.30 to 9.30   CLOSED: 6 days Christmas   MEALS: Set L £14.50, Set D £25. Bar food all week 11
to 10.30   SERVICE: 10%, card slips closed   CARDS: Access, Amex, Diners, Visa   DETAILS: 60
seats. Private parties: 60 main room, 20 private room. Car park. Vegetarian meals. Children's
helpings. Smart dress preferred. Wheelchair access (no WC). Music   ACCOMMODATION: 12
rooms, all with bath/shower. TV. Phone. B&B £55 to £70. Deposit: 30%. Rooms for disabled.
Children welcome. Afternoon teas

Round-ups

Looking for a suitable place to eat at can be a lottery, especially if you are travelling around the country with no set plans in mind. The Round-up section is intended to provide some interesting gastronomic possibilities, whether you find yourself in the West Country or the northern outposts of Scotland. Pubs are becoming increasingly valuable as sources of high-quality food, but the listings also include modest family-run enterprises in country towns, racy café/bars and ethnic restaurants in big cities, and a sprinkling of hotel dining-rooms in all parts of the land. Dip into this section and you are almost bound to find somewhere that suits your needs and your pocket. Entries are based on readers' recommendations supported by inspectors' reports. Sometimes a restaurant appears in the Round-up section instead of the main entries because seasonal closures or weekly openings limit their usefulness, or because there are changes in the air, or because positive feedback has been thin on the ground. Reports on these places are especially welcome, as they help to broaden our coverage of good eating places in Britain. Round-up entries (outside London) are arranged alphabetically by location within England, Scotland, Wales, the Channel Islands and Northern Ireland.

England

● **ALDEBURGH** (Suffolk)
Cafe 152 152 High Street, (01728) 454152. The North Sea meets the Mediterranean in this up-and-coming venue (formerly the Festival Wine Bar). Expect roasted tomato soup, tortellini with wild mushrooms, cod with pesto mash, and grilled squid salad, as well as rabbit terrine and salmon fish-cakes. Sit outside when the sun shines and peruse the Adnams wine list.

● **ALTRINCHAM** (Greater Manchester)
Franc's 2 Goose Green, (0161) 941 3954. Straightforward, French-style cooking is the draw at this popular bistro. The menu offers a salad of melon, avocado, walnuts and St-Augur cheese, and sole Florentine with Noilly Prat cream sauce. Service is good. There is a second branch in Chester (see Round-up entry).

● **AMERSHAM** (Buckinghamshire)
Gilbey's 1 Market Square, (01494) 727242. Happy-go-lucky bistro where wines are sold at shop prices and cooking is in the modern vein: goats' cheese on baked aubergine, or calf's liver with pesto mash, for example. Puddings include

creations such as lemon tart, and lime mousse.

● **ASHFORD** (Derbyshire)
Riverside Country House Hotel Fennel Street, (01629) 814275. Quaint little stone manor house, enticingly situated in the heart of the Peak District. The River Wye meanders through the garden, and the mood is almost domestic. The restaurant menu offers fixed-price meals of pork and sweetbread terrine, and pan-fried turbot with saffron mash, for example, while lighter dishes, salads, and sandwiches are available all day in the 'terrace buttery' bar.

● **BAKEWELL** (Derbyshire)
Renaissance Bath Street, (01629) 812687. Comfortable restaurant that is fast gaining a reputation for worthwhile French cooking. Skill and care are evident in scallop mousse, carrot and cheese gateau, boeuf bourguignon, and orange crème with Grand Marnier sauce. The fixed-price menus are excellent-value.

● **BARHAM** (Kent)
Old Coach House Dover Road, (01227) 831218. France comes to Kent in the shape of this small hotel handy for the

Channel Tunnel. Jean-Claude Rozard uses local fish and game as well as home-grown herbs and salads for a menu that ranges from crab mayonnaise, and sole meunière, to lamb steak in garlic sauce, and chicken with tarragon.

● **BARNARD CASTLE** (Co Durham)
Market Place Teashop 29 Market Place, (01833) 690110. 'Clean, warm and uncluttered' teashop offering wholesome daytime sustenance to local shoppers and famished moorland hikers. 'Very pleasant' service, 'excellent' food and 'delicious' coffee.

● **BASLOW** (Derbyshire)
Cavendish Hotel, Garden Room Baslow, (01246) 582311. Conservatory extension to the aristocratic Cavendish Hotel overlooking Chatsworth Estate. Prices are not bargain-basement, but the food is creditable. Throughout the day you can enjoy anything from plates of smoked salmon, to chargrilled steaks, fish and chips, and chocolate mousse. Good choice of teas and coffees.

● **BATH** (Avon)
New Moon Seven Dials, (01225) 444407. Cosmopolitan venue in a snazzy courtyard development close to the Theatre Royal. All-day brasserie menus (until 7pm) and pre-theatre deals scour the globe for Thai fish-cakes, Moroccan lamb with cardamom couscous, and Japanese simmered salmon with wasabi mayonnaise. The evening *carte* offers more elaborate dishes such as Tuscan pot-roasted quail with sage and tomato coulis.

Priory Hotel Weston Road, (01225) 331922. Grand Georgian hotel with 'lovely gardens' on the outskirts of Bath. The mood is friendly and relaxed, service endeavours to cater for unusual requests, and the kitchen moves confidently between roast beef, rabbit with prunes, and confit of duck. Cheeses and ice-creams are praised. Much in demand for special occasions.

● **BEESTON** (Nottinghamshire)
Brasserie 69 69 Chilwell Road, (0115) 925 9994. Tiny brasserie in a converted shop, offering lively cosmopolitan food.

Fixed-price menus and a *carte* promise such things as celeriac soup with truffle oil, rump of lamb with flageolet beans, and grilled sea bass with rock salt and roast tomato dressing. Open evenings only, Tuesday to Saturday. More reports, please.

● **BEVERLEY** (East Riding of Yorkshire)
Cerutti 2 Beverley Station, (01482) 866700. Bright, cheerful place that is an ideal pit-stop for rail travellers and others. East coast fish is the strong suit on a menu that includes stir-fried scallops, baked avocado with prawns and the like. Coffee is good and strong, the wine list is 'adequate'. The original Cerutti is in Hull.

● **BIRMINGHAM** (West Midlands)
Prego on the Water Waterlinks, Aston Cross, Rocky Lane, (0121) 333 5255. Enterprising Mediterranean venue that brings bruschetta to Brum in a big way. Other pleasing dishes might include chargrilled squid with rocket, linguine with jumbo prawns, chilli and salsa, and roast monkfish with sauté broccoli and roasted garlic. Well-chosen wines. Sit by the canal on fine days. More reports, please.

San Carlo 4 Temple Street, (0121) 633 0251. Modern city-centre ristorante/ pizzeria, a few minutes' walk from New Street Station. Home-made pasta dishes are well-timed and the blackboard of fish specials adds an extra dimension to the cooking. 'Wonderful' sea bass and 'beautiful' Dover sole have been greatly enjoyed. 'Smashing atmosphere' and excellent service.

● **BLACKMORE END** (Essex)
Bull Blackmore End, (01371) 851037. Christopher Bruce cooks, his wife and family lend a hand in this spruced-up Essex country pub. Potato skins with garlic mayonnaise, sweet-cured herrings with beetroot, and tender, juicy venison casserole have been enjoyed of late. Up to five real ales are available on draught and the wine list continues to improve.

● **BLEWBURY** (Oxfordshire)
Blewbury Inn London Road, (01235) 850496. Home-baked bread, home-grown fruit and dependable supplies of

local game set the tone in the kitchen of this refurbished Oxfordshire country pub. Paul Lane produces such dishes as pork terrine with pickled plums, brochette of gurnard with chilli, and warm strawberry pancakes. Wines from Christopher Piper, good real ales.

● **BOTTESFORD** (Leicestershire)
La Petite Maison 1 Market Street, (01949) 842375. Howard Brown was promoted to head chef in November 1995 and early reports suggest that he is still finding his feet. The kitchen has served good renditions of pigeon breast with haricot beans, roast fillet of lamb with aubergine and onions, and grey mullet with red pepper sauce. The mood is genteel 'country bistro'.

● **BRADFORD** (West Yorkshire)
Bharat 502 Great Horton Road, (01274) 521200. Long-serving and 'above average' Indian restaurant in an area of predominantly Pakistani cafés. The décor is muted, service is 'gravely courteous', but the standard range of curries and tandooris has a distinctive edge. Thalis are worth ordering. Good value, especially the early-bird menu (served 6 to 7pm).
Mumtaz Paan House 390 Great Horton Road, (01274) 571861. Bright, modern and alcohol-free, this Muslim restaurant offers great-value Indian food. Look for excellent bus-stop snacks such as dhal tikki, channa roll and garlic pakoras, as well as karahi dishes, vegetable curries, and reliable rice and breads. Finish with barfi or stuffed paan leaves. Cook-it-yourself take-aways are also available.
Symposium 7 Albion Street, (01274) 616587. The early-bird set menu is the best deal in this locally popular wine and food bar three miles from the city centre. Bistro cooking is the order of the day, with dishes ranging from chicken livers in filo pastry to rack of lamb with rosemary and ratatouille. Sweets are capably handled.

● **BRAUNSTON** (Leicestershire)
Blue Ball Inn Cedar Street, (01572) 722135. Rejuvenated seventeenth-century inn offering a taste of France in rural Rutland. The regularly changing menu promises beef bourguignon, guinea-fowl in raspberry sauce and 'super' apples caramelised in calvados. Five real ales are on draught.

● **BRIDGNORTH** (Shropshire)
Six Ashes Six Ashes, (01384) 221216. Part teashop, part country restaurant in a converted sub-post office between Stourbridge and Bridgnorth. David Ostle offers an appetising menu of leek, potato and apple soup, duck breast with caramelised oranges, and baked halibut with prawns in herb sauce. Desserts and coffee are deemed 'excellent'.

● **BRIGHTWELL BALDWIN** (Oxfordshire)
Lord Nelson Inn Brightwell Baldwin, (01491) 612497. Wonderfully inviting village pub with a showpiece garden and patio overflowing with exotic gladioli, petunias and begonias. Eat in the neat and tidy bar or dining area from a bistro-style menu that takes in, for example, pan-fried tiger prawns with garlic, chilli and coriander, or lighter snacks such as Welsh rarebit.

● **BRISTOL** (Bristol)
Michael's 129 Hotwell Road, (0117) 927 6190. For more than two decades this has been a fixture of the Bristol restaurant scene. The value for money remains excellent, and set menus are full of good ideas. Seared scallop and mange-tout salad, medallions of pork with sweet-and-sour fig sauce, and glazed pear with Poire William sorbet are typical examples.
Red Snapper 1 Chandos Road, (0117) 973 7999. Promising neighbourhood restaurant serving food with plenty of positive flavours. Fresh fish might include anything from chargrilled tuna and red mullet with olives, to gurnard, and John Dory. Warm goats'-cheese salad, and 'velvety' venison have also been praised. Interesting wines. More reports, please.

● **BROADSTAIRS** (Kent)
Marchesi Bros 18 Albion Street, (01843) 862481. Opened in 1886 and now into its fourth generation, Marchesi's is clearly no nine-day wonder. The kitchen woos Kentish holiday-makers with monthly menus in the good old tradition of asparagus with melted butter, calf's liver

with bacon and onion rings, and duck with black cherry sauce. Set lunches are great value.

● **BROMLEY** (Kent)
Chapter One Farnborough Common, Locksbottom, (01689) 854848. Very polished and professional restaurant/ brasserie with menus planned and overseen by David Cavalier (although he no longer cooks here). Open ravioli of duck livers with sage and Parmesan, fillet of pork wrapped in prosciutto, and peach crème brûlée are typical dishes. Good service by mainly Italian staff.

● **BROUGHTON IN FURNESS** (Cumbria)
Beswicks The Square, (01229) 716285. Home cooking, a warm welcome and a relaxed atmosphere bring the crowds to this family-run restaurant overlooking Broughton Square. Soups, sweets and cheeseboard 'deserve a special mention', as does the reasonably priced wine list.

● **BROXTON** (Cheshire)
Frogg Manor Nantwich Road, (01829) 782629. Eccentrically run, plush Georgian house with fake frogs everywhere and old-time Muzak from the likes of Al Bowley. Expect unfussy dishes along the lines of sauté vegetable salad, roast rack of lamb with port and red wine sauce, whole Dover sole, and strawberry mousse with Cassis. Great fun, great value.

● **BURFORD** (Oxfordshire)
Lamb Inn Sheep Street, (01993) 823155. Picture-postcard Cotswold inn oozing history and photo-opportunities with its trailing creepers, stone walls and country garden. The kitchen tries hard and succeeds with dishes of warm chicken liver salad, sea bass on a purée of green vegetables, and summer pudding. Service is beyond reproach.

● **BURGH LE MARSH** (Lincolnshire)
Windmill 46 High Street, (01754) 810281. Pleasant village restaurant adjoining a restored mill that provides the kitchen with flour. Local produce and 'exciting' seasonal vegetables define a menu that might include poached mushrooms with garlic croustades,

monkfish kebabs provençale, fillet of beef with brandy sauce, and crème brulée.

● **BURNHAM MARKET** (Norfolk)
Hoste Arms The Green, (01328) 738777. Lively seventeenth-century inn that is invariably packed with 'happy folk' eating, drinking and making merry. Local fish dominates the ambitious bar and restaurant menus: marinated salmon with citrus dressing, seafood fricasee with saffron rice, and chargrilled chicken have been recommended. First-rate real ales and a wide range of wines. More reports, please.

● **BURPHAM** (West Sussex)
Burpham Country Hotel Burpham, (01903) 882160. Converted vicarage in a beautiful corner of the South Downs serving dependable food to a gentrified crowd decked out in 'tweed and pearls'. Cream and wine are used with a free hand in dishes such as filo parcels of smoked chicken, rolled fillet of pork stuffed with spinach, and baked cod with lobster sauce.

● **BURY ST EDMUNDS** (Suffolk)
Ravenwood Hall Rougham Green, (01359) 270345. Much liked for its 'delightful country house ambience' and lovely rural setting, Ravenwood Hall pleases visitors with crispy fried whitebait, and chicken with mustard sauce. Good beers and wines, including some interesting fruity tipples.

● **BYTHORN** (Cambridgeshire)
White Hart Bythorn, (01832) 710226. Bill Bennett continues to shine in this pub-cum-restaurant a stone's throw from his old home patch, The Pheasant at Keyston (see main entry). A typically 'seductive' menu might take in smoked duck breast with fresh pineapple, monkfish kebabs with lime and coriander sauce, and some good-looking puddings.

● **CAMBRIDGE** (Cambridgeshire)
Midsummer House Midsummer Common, (01223) 369299. This walled Victorian house has much to commend it: lovely views of Midsummer Common and a sun-drenched conservatory to name but two features. Yet another new chef has arrived. Carpaccio of salmon,

poached guinea-fowl with orange and garlic confit, and mille-feuille with hot apple and cinnamon have been acceptable; some other dishes less so.

● CHEAM (Surrey)
Bistro des Amis 22 Ewell Road, (0181) 643 8838. A great little bistro in a converted shop, offering unbeatable value and sound French cooking with echoes of *grand-mère*. Set menus might offer salmon and monkfish roulade, casseroled leg of duck with vegetables, and apricot tart with crème anglaise. Good cheap wines, pleasant French staff.

● CHELTENHAM (Gloucestershire)
Beaujolais 15 Rotunda Terrace, (01242) 525230. 'Quite austere surroundings', but a creditable venue for decent French food. The excellent-value two-course table d'hôte may offer goats' cheese in filo pastry, roast salmon with chive sauce and 'impeccably cooked vegetables', and duck leg with honey and soy.

● CHESTER (Cheshire)
Franc's 14A Cuppin Street, (01244) 317952. Related to Franc's in Altrincham (see Round-up entry) and run along similar lines. Expect French bistro cooking in a vibrant atmosphere with posters on the walls and a menu listing such things as grilled leg of lamb with ratatouille, whole baked Camembert, or salmon cooked in white wine and lemon with tomato sauce. Good for families. Open all day.

● CHETTLE (Dorset)
Castleman Hotel Chettle, (01258) 830096. Once the Dower House belonging to the Estate village of Chettle, now a rather gracious hotel and restaurant. New owners (ex-Moonacre, Alderholt) are settling in and their short menu takes few risks. Pigeon terrine with pickled cherries, sea bass with sorrel sauce, and strawberry cream pot are typical. More reports, please.

● CHITTLEHAMHOLT (Devon)
Highbullen Chittlehamholt, (01769) 540561. Splendid Victorian Gothic mansion on high wooded ground between the Mole and Taw Valleys. The Neils are amiable hosts and their daughter

cooks. Buffet lunches attract a full house, while dinner menus include crab salad, roast lamb, and Spanish-style cod. Good wine list, excellent value.

● COGGESHALL (Essex)
White Hart Market End, (01376) 561654. Immaculately maintained coaching-inn with an 'outstanding' fifteenth-century lounge and a stylish restaurant offering mostly old-school Italian cooking. Pasta is home-made and french fries come 'splendidly cooked' in vast portions. Wines are worth noting.

● COLCHESTER (Essex)
North Hill Exchange Brasserie 19 North Hill, (01206) 769988. Cavernous, low-ceilinged brasserie in one of Colchester's best-known Georgian-fronted buildings. Expect dishes such as marinated seafood salad, chicken roasted with satay sauce, and nougat parfait with apricot coulis. Short, eclectic wine list. A useful lunch spot for students, tourists and shoppers.

● CORBRIDGE (Northumberland)
Valley Old Station House, (01434) 633434. Special 'Passage to India' deals bring visitors from Newcastle by train to this Indian restaurant housed in an old station building by the railway line. The menu has a few noticeable up-market twists.

● CRICK (Northamptonshire)
Edwards Of Crick The Wharf, (01788) 822517. Admirable eating-house in a converted wharf by the Grand Union Canal. Downstairs is an all-day coffee-house serving robust soups, pizzas and snacks. Upstairs in the restaurant, expect English home cooking along the lines of potted cheese with oatcakes, faggots with mustard gravy, and treacle tart.

● CRONDALL (Hampshire)
Chesa Bowling Alley, (01252) 850328. The dining-room of this small modern restaurant might seem like 'the large front room of a comfortable suburban house', but the mood is cheerful and staff are keen to please. Fresh asparagus with mushroom sauce, quails stuffed with garlic and spinach, and bread and butter pudding have been endorsed.

● **CROYDE** (Devon)
Whiteleaf at Croyde Croyde, (01271) 890266. This may well be the Wallingtons' last year in the business – they are in their 60s – although they said that last year and are still here. Openings remain restricted, but there is no let-up in the scope of the menu, which ranges from smoked salmon chowder to oxtail with polenta, and simple old favourites such as fish-cakes with rustic chips.

● **CUMNOR** (Oxfordshire)
Vine Inn 11 Abingdon Road, (01865) 862567. The eponymous vine is trained across the whitewashed front of this eighteenth-century country inn, handily placed 15 minutes' drive from Oxford. The kitchen aims high and the menu is long: salmon fish-cakes, duck breast with plum sauce, fruit tart, and bread-and-butter pudding have been recommended. Wines are better than average for a pub. Service is cheerful and efficient.

● **DARTMOUTH** (Devon)
The Exchange 5 Higher Street, (01803) 832022. Imaginative bistro cooking with transatlantic overtones in a centuries-old Dartmouth dwelling. Sit upstairs and enjoy crab-cakes with a throat-tingling salsa, wild mushrooms with pine kernels, and grilled bananas with crème fraîche. 'Simple, uncomplicated, good-value' food, backed up by some decent wines.

● **DENT** (Cumbria)
Stone Close Main Street, (01539) 625231. 'We spent a most happy two hours with good food, wine and company': one reporter's verdict which sums up the enduring appeal of this Dales tea-shop-cum-B&B. Sound home cooking, an atmosphere of 'relaxed efficiency' and exceptional value are bonus points. Open only during the day.

● **DERBY** (Derbyshire)
Le Dijon 115 London Road, (01332) 205050. 'A unique training and education concept' allowing students at Derby Tertiary College to test their culinary skills in the market-place. All-comers are welcome for 'theme' lunches and impressive dinners with a French accent. Service is 'erratic! which is to be expected, but eager to please' and guided sensitively by tutors. 'Wonderful' value for money.

● **DODDISCOMBSLEIGH** (Devon)
Nobody Inn Doddiscombsleigh, (01647) 252394. Archetypal and slightly off-beat West Country inn famed for its breathtaking selection of local cheeses and a mammoth wine list running to 750 bins. The food is robust, country-style stuff ranging from home-made sausages and mash to bread pudding with clotted cream. Well-kept beers and ciders.

● **DULVERTON** (Somerset)
Ashwick House Dulverton, (01398) 323868. Visiting this little Edwardian house by the breathtaking Barle Valley is 'like being a guest in someone's home'. Richard Sherwood is a diligent cook for whom 'nothing is too much trouble'. Sunday lunch of crab fricassee, quail with grapes and pommes dauphinoises, plus desserts or cheese, has been recommended.

● **EDENBRIDGE** (Kent)
Haxted Mill Haxted Road, (01732) 862914. Oak-beamed brasserie in a wonderful location next to the mill pond overlooking the Eden River. Piedmont roasted peppers, blackened redfish with lime, Thai-style chargrilled chicken, and kidneys flamed with cognac and grain mustard in puff pastry are examples from the highly eclectic menu. 'Exciting' wines, too.

● **ELTON** (Cambridgeshire)
Loch Fyne Oyster Bar The Old Dairy, (01832) 280298. East Anglian sibling of the highly rated oyster bar founded in Cairndow (see main entry, Scotland). Stay with the molluscs, and fresh and smoked fish for the most pleasing results. Snacks and full meals can be eaten in the courtyard and there's a shop counter on the premises for take-aways.

● **EPPING** (Essex)
Neil's 142 High Street, (01992) 576767. A valuable alternative to the plethora of fast food outlets dominating the scene in south Essex. Fish is particularly recommended: baked sea bass, skate with Mediterranean prawns, and home-made

fish-cakes, for example. Locally picked ceps are a seasonal speciality, and puddings get rave reviews.

● **EYTON** (Hereford & Worcester) *Marsh Country Hotel* Eyton, (01568) 613952. Lovingly restored medieval house complete with a stream and lily pond in the enchanting garden. Martin and Jacqueline Gilleland offer seasonal fixed-price menus that might take in warm chicken-liver mousse with peppers, salmon with fish mousseline and Puy lentils, and calvados parfait with caramelised apples.

● **FAWLEY** (Buckinghamshire) *Walnut Tree* Fawley, (01491) 638360/ 638617. Tranquil country inn tucked away in the Chiltern backwoods. Eat in the bar, restaurant or glazed conservatory from a range of menus offering, for example, spinach and ricotta ravioli, fillet steak with parsley butter, and home-made ginger and honey ice-cream. Meals may be accompanied by real ales or good-value wines.

● **FLETCHING** (East Sussex) *Griffin Inn* Fletching, (01825) 722890. Archetypal village inn opposite the church, with gardens overlooking the Ouse Valley. The setting is pure England but menus range far and wide for paella, and chicken breast with mascarpone and ceps, as well as bread-and-butter pudding. Outstanding family hospitality, good real ales, sound wines.

● **FORTON** (Lancashire) *El Nido* Whinney Brow Lane, (01524) 791254 Sound Continental cooking with a Spanish slant. The setting is an old stone building in the Bowland foothills, and customers are particularly attracted by the value for money. Light, brasserie-style dishes such as chorizo and salami pasta support the *carte*, and an early-bird menu is served most evenings from 6 to 7pm.

● **FOULSHAM** (Norfolk) *The Gamp* Claypit Lane, (01362) 684114. 'Simple home cooking' in an East Anglian oasis. Daphne and Andy Bush's menu is likely to include such dishes as Cromer crab and cheese pots,

roast Norfolk duckling with gooseberry relish, chargrilled salmon steak with hollandaise, and strawberry Romanoff. Special events are a feature.

● **FRISTON** (Suffolk) *Old Chequers* Aldeburgh Road, (01728) 688270. Comfortable, warm and welcoming village pub-cum-restaurant hidden away down a winding country lane. Lunch revolves around a buffet carvery, while evening menus move into the realms of stuffed quail, and lamb provençale. Real ales and good wines by the glass.

● **GEDNEY DYKE** (Lincolnshire) *Chequers* Main Street, (01406) 362666. Highly popular Fenland free house largely given over to food. Fresh fish, such as Cromer crab, dabs with chips, and halibut with green peppercorn sauce are well thought of. Otherwise go for pub staples such as 'brilliant' steak and kidney pudding. Special events are a feature. Good real ales, sound wines.

● **GOATHLAND** (North Yorkshire) *Mallyan Spout Hotel* Goathland, (01947) 896486. Victorian Gothic hotel, popular with tourists and train buffs travelling the nearby Pickering steam route. Local produce figures in dishes such as grilled goats' cheese, or home-cooked ham with chips. Desserts could include bread and butter pudding; coffee comes with home-made fudge.

● **GOSFIELD** (Essex) *Green Man* The Street, (01787) 472746. 'Consistently good English country cooking' in a bustling, beamed pub not far from the Essex conurbations. Buffet lunches and more elaborate dinners range from lamb chops, and tournedos Rossini, to garlicky mussels, and plum tart. Smiling service, well-kept Greene King ales, some interesting wines.

● **GOUDHURST** (Kent) *Hughenden* The Plain, (01580) 212065. Charming little restaurant overlooking the village pond. Nick and Sue Martin offer a good-value set menu that might take in wild mushrooms in pastry with Madeira sauce, baked goats' cheese, salmon and monkfish in lobster sauce, and 'wicked' chocolate terrine. Wines are reasonably priced, service is 'great'.

● **GRAMPOUND** (Cornwall)
Eastern Promise 1 Moor View, (01726) 883033. China comes to Cornwall in the shape of this popular family-run restaurant. The menu promises an accessible mix of Peking and Szechuan dishes along the lines of crispy aromatic duck, sizzling chicken and stir-fried pork with mange-tout. Service is charming and wines interesting.

● **GRANGE IN BORROWDALE** (Cumbria)
Borrowdale Gates Hotel Grange-in-Borrowdale, (01768) 777204. Family-run Victorian country house set among some of the most spectacular scenery in the Lake District. Four-course dinners offer dishes such as Finnan haddock tartlet, cream of fennel soup, stuffed breast of free-range Goosnargh chicken with pasta, and Cumberland rum Nicky. Friendly, attentive staff.

● **GREAT YARMOUTH** (Norfolk)
Seafood Restaurant 85 North Quay, (01493) 856009. Cosy converted pub that now delivers splendid fish cooking of the old school with charming service to match. Fresh fish from the cold slab might appear in the guise of seafood platter, turbot in herb butter, and lobster mornay. Chips are spot on, puddings are calorific and there is champagne by the glass.

● **GRIMSBY** (Humberside)
Granary Haven Mill, (01472) 346338. A down-to-earth restaurant, full of 'old knick-knacks', in a converted waterfront grain mill close to the National Fishing Heritage Centre. Its attributes include Bateman's ales on draught and a blackboard menu with simply cooked, local fish as the star: grilled halibut, and haddock with red-pepper sauce have been recommended.

Leon's Family Fish Restaurant
Alexandra Road, (01472) 356282. One of the best fish and chip shops in the Kingdom of Cod, and tailor-made for families wanting a sit-down meal rather than a take-away. Wonderfully fresh fish, especially haddock and skate, in light batter is served with piles of crisp hot

chips. Home-made fish-cakes are also worth noting. Licensed.

● **GUISELEY** (West Yorkshire)
Harry Ramsden's White Cross, (01943) 874641. 'The world's most famous fish & chips,' says the brochure. It began with a wooden hut in 1928, but the empire has now spread beyond Britain to Hong Kong and Melbourne. Go for the experience of eating humble food in a glamorous setting of cut-glass chandeliers, oak panelling and stained-glass windows.

● **HARROGATE** (North Yorkshire)
Bettys 1 Parliament Street, (01423) 502746. The first-born of a famous mini-chain of North Country tea-rooms with branches in Ilkey, Northallerton and York. Opened in 1919, it continues to shine with outstanding patisserie, breads, cakes and all kinds of savoury dishes, some with a strong Yorkshire accent. Long queues, but tailor-made for families.

Garden Room Harlow Carr Botanical Gardens, (01423) 505604. Modern purpose-built restaurant feeding visitors to Harlow Carr Botanical Gardens. It makes a delightful setting in which to enjoy snacks and light lunches or more elaborate evening meals (Thursday to Saturday only). Dishes range from casseroled oxtail to baked halibut fillets on braised celeriac and green grapes.

● **HATCH BEAUCHAMP** (Somerset)
Nightingales Bath House Farm, (01823) 480806. Cosy, personally run restaurant in converted farm buildings outside Taunton. The cooking has Mediterranean and oriental overtones, as in warm salad of beef with Japanese seasoning, baked aubergines, and chargrilled chicken. Open Friday and Saturday evenings and Sunday lunch-time, plus occasional group bookings.

● **HAWKSHEAD** (Cumbria)
Room With A View Laburnum House, (015394) 36751. Popular vegetarian venue catering principally for the tourists that descend annually on Beatrix Potter's home patch. Starters are 'excellent', main courses are served in generous helpings and puddings vary from good to 'rather stodgy'. Totally non-smoking.

● **HEMEL HEMPSTEAD** (Hertfordshire)
Gallery Restaurant Old Town Hall Arts
Centre, (01442) 232416. Good news for
Hemel Hempstead: the café/restaurant
above the local arts centre offers no-
nonsense food at fair prices. Blackboard
specials range from spinach, bacon and
avocado salad, to spiced almond risotto.
Snacks and baguettes are also available.
● **HEYBRIDGE** (Essex)
Chigborough Lodge 1 Chigborough
Road, (01621) 853590. Pint-sized barn
conversion run by a 'harmonious'
husband and wife team. The kitchen
delivers variety and high quality in the
shape of moules marinière, halibut with
tomato vinaigrette, and crêpes with pecan
ice-cream. 'Impeccable' service, 'fantastic'
value for money. Wines are also praised.
● **HONLEY** (West Yorkshire)
Balooshai Brown Sugar Cafe The Old
Silk Mill, Meltham Road, (01484)
660360. Open-plan mill floor on the edge
of Honley village serving creditable
Indian food in cheery, colourful
surroundings. Bhel pooris, potato cutlets
perked up with kidney beans and
sweetcorn, and three-bean curry have
been mentioned favourably in reports.
Rice and breads are up-to-scratch.
● **HOVE** (East Sussex)
Quentin's 42 Western Road, (01273)
822734. 'Goes from strength to strength',
notes a local reporter. The setting is all
stripped pine, the welcome is
'enchanting', and the cooking shows an
increasing lightness of touch. Fillet of
pork stuffed with black pudding has been
recommended, along with 'glorious'
desserts such as lemon tart.
● **ILKLEY** (West Yorkshire)
Bettys 34 The Grove, (01943) 608029.
One of a quartet of tea-rooms-cum-
restaurants spread across West and North
Yorkshire. Bread and cakes have a near-
legendary reputation, while more
substantial savoury dishes often have
bistro/brasserie overtones. Tip-top
facilities for families with children.
● **IPSWICH** (Suffolk)
Il Punto Neptune Quay, (01473)
289748. Floating restaurant situated on a
boat moored in Ipswich docks. Despite
the name, the food is decidedly French:
mixed seafood in filo pastry, sea bass with
endives, venison pie with calvados, and
chicken with lemon and tarragon. Service
is willing and youthful.
● **KEIGHLEY** (West Yorkshire)
Headley's 396–398 Skipton Road,
(01535) 607375. 'Seems to go from
strength to strength' is one verdict on this
splendidly refurbished restaurant, where
dishes such as herb and Guinness
Yorkshire pudding with black pudding
and onion gravy, or duck breast with
jasmine and sultana sauce are typical.
Dining-club menus and early-bird
dinners are worth noting, as is the wine
list.
● **KNOWSTONE** (Devon)
Masons Arms Inn Knowstone, (01398)
341231/582. City-dwellers seeking
sanctuary can expect 'all-round star
treatment' in this gem of a fourteenth-
century thatched inn. Great character,
charm, good country food without frills,
excellent wine and genial hosts are just
some of its many attributes. Top-drawer
West Country real ales, too.
● **LANGTOFT** (East Riding of Yorkshire)
The Old Mill Mill Lane, (01377) 87284.
Useful hotel/restaurant away from it all
on the Wolds road to Driffield. Portions
are geared to big Yorkshire appetites and
the cooking is hearty with it. Sunday
lunch is a popular occasion, and specials
such as a 'melody' of salmon, sole and
halibut are worth noting. Friendly, 'non-
intrusive' service.
● **LECHLADE** (Gloucestershire)
Rieunier's 6 Oak Street, (01367) 52587.
Old menus line the walls of this pleasant
little restaurant, where the kitchen serves
some ambitious dishes, including salad of
foie gras, and chicken and mushroom
ravioli. Bread, vegetables and service all
come in for praise, and there are one or
two interesting wines on the short list.
● **LEEDS** (West Yorkshire)
La Grillade 31–33 East Parade, (0113)
245 9707. Breakfasts and all-day snacks
support the main menu in this dyed-in-
the wool French brasserie. Grills are the

mainstay, fish is fresh each day and there are also *plats du jour* such as pieds de cochon pannés. Set menus are good value and the *formule express* (not available Saturday evening) is unbeatable.
Olive Tree 55 Rodley Lane, Rodley, (0113) 256 9283. George and Vasoulla Psarias continue to champion the cause of Greek cooking in their high-profile restaurant a few miles from the centre of Leeds. The food is described as 'delicious', the ambience is exceedingly pleasant and staff are welcoming.
● LEICESTER (Leicestershire)
Heath's 169 Evington Road, (0116) 273 3343. Enterprising seafood restaurant owned by John Heath of Leicester fish-market fame. The lively menu offers specialities such as grilled sardines with garlic sauce, baked swordfish with samphire and basil sauce, and red bream with tomato and orange coulis. Dishes score for their freshness and generosity.
● LEWDOWN (Devon)
Lewtrenchard Manor Lewdown, (01566) 783256. 'Still the same lovely place', with its air of Old World tranquility and charm, and the owners, décor and pleasant ambience remain unaltered. New chef Jason Buck arrived in April '96, bringing dishes such as terrine of leeks and langoustine, pan-fried pigeon with creamed potatoes and lentils in a port sauce, and salmon cooked three ways. More reports, please.
● LEWES (East Sussex)
Bistro Twenty 20 Fisher Street, (01273) 487568. Greatly favoured neighbourhood bistro with laudable aspirations. Local produce, including fish from Newhaven, is the foundation of a menu that includes tomato and Mozzarella salad, roast silverside of free-range beef, John Dory with orange, ginger and spring onions, and rhubarb and mango compote.
● LITTLE BEDWYN (Wiltshire)
Harrow Inn Little Bedwyn, (01672) 870871. New licensees, but it's business as usual at this Victorian village inn that was bought by the locals in 1991. Modern pub cooking is the order of the day, the menu typified by dishes such as smoked

salmon with scrambled eggs, chicken with lentils, and lemon tart. Good real ales.
● LIVERPOOL (Merseyside)
Armadillo 31 Mathew Street, (0151) 236 4123. Tidy, affluent reincarnation of the original Armadillo in the heart of the Cavern quarter. Menus are seasonal, fish shows up well, and dishes range from steamed rockfish on Chinese greens with ginger and chilli, to guinea-fowl with Puy lentils and lime salsa. Lunch and early-evening menus are particularly good value.
Becher's Brook 29A Hope Street, (0151) 707 0005. An 'excellent location' close to the Philharmonic Hall and Everyman Theatre is one of the attractions here, and early-evening menus are good value. The bare-walled dining-room is full of ethnic arts and crafts and the overtly ambitious cooking has oriental overtones.
Number Seven Cafe 7 Falkner Street, (0151) 709 9633. A locally popular asset convenient for Liverpool's revitalised cultural attractions, much favoured by students and families. Martin Cooper (formerly of Armadillo, see entry, above) offers unfussy food at rock-bottom prices, from cashew-nut curry to meatballs with tomatoes and aubergines. Number Seven is part of a complex that includes an art gallery and an excellent deli.
● LONG MELFORD (Suffolk)
Chimneys Hall Street, (01787) 379806. Half-timbered sixteenth-century residence that will be familiar to fans of TV's 'Lovejoy'. Regulars speak highly of salmon and prawn brochette, spring lamb with 'wonderful' vegetables, and ginger ice-cream in a ginger snap basket. Decent wines by the glass, good value for money.
● LOWER ODDINGTON (Gloucestershire)
Fox Inn Lower Oddington, (01451) 870555. Sympathetically extended Cotswold pub with several eating areas and a walled garden. Weekly-changing menus feature such things as twice-baked goats'-cheese soufflé, salmon koulibiac, and ragoût of wild rabbit. Pasta and salads

also loom large. Well-kept real ales and a good choice of keenly chosen wines.

● **LUDLOW** (Shropshire)

Dinham Hall (01584) 876464. Luxury cooking and a relaxed country house atmosphere go together well in this Georgian hotel by Ludlow castle. Expect dishes such as pan-fried foie gras with toasted brioche, partridge with truffles on a bed of greens, and warm chocolate tart with 'superb' ice-cream.

Oaks 17 Corve Street, (01584) 972325. Ken Adams cooks, his wife assists in this 'charmingly relaxed' little restaurant. Organic produce is favoured and fixed-price menus hit the target. Goats' cheese in pastry with beetroot confit, 'subtly herbed' sea bass, and duck breast with caramelised onions and figs have impressed. Service comes with a big smile. More reports, please.

● **MANCHESTER** (Greater Manchester)

Cafe Istanbul 79–81 Bridge Street, (0161) 833 9942. For more than fifteen years, this has been one of Manchester's best loved ethnic cafés. Turkish cuisine is the order of the day and the value for money (especially the set lunch) remains remarkable. Two dozen hot and cold meze precede grills, kebabs and casseroles, and there some decent wines to quaff.

Café Primavera 48 Beech Road, (0161) 862 9934. Boldly decorated converted shop with contemporary brasserie décor and a menu to match. Tagliatelle alla putanesca, pan-fried loin of lamb with couscous and a sun-dried tomato and basil salsa, and rich chocolate marquise show the style. The wine list has plenty of good, 'very cheap' drinking.

Sanam 145–153 Wilmslow Rd, (0161) 224 1008/8824. 'Probably as good value as you will find in Manchester' for no-nonsense curry-house food of the old school. Reliability is the key. King prawn karahi, aloo channa, and pilau rice have been listed among recent successes. Unlicensed, but drink lassi or a milkshake.

Siam Orchid 54 Portland Street, (0161) 236 1388. Worth knowing about as an alternative to the Cantonese places in Chinatown. The menu is straighforward Thai (fish-cakes, curries, stir-fries, and so on). A second branch, Royal Orchid, is at 36 Charlotte Street, Manchester, tel: (0161) 236 5183.

Victoria & Albert Hotel Water Street, (0161) 832 1188. Jokes and gimmicks galore, but serious cooking in the hotel's Sherlock Holmes Restaurant. John Benson-Smith delivers flamboyant dishes such as black pudding with leeks and mustard seed gravy, best end of lamb baked in hay and lavender, and a showy assortment of sweets. The wine list spreads itself well.

● **MANNINGTREE** (Essex)

Stour Bay Cafe 39–43 High Street, (01206) 396687. Vibrant worldwide cooking that spans the globe, taking in Italy, the Pacific Rim and the Far East along the way. Expect dishes such as crispy chicken salad with papaya and black-bean vinaigrette, cassoulet, and chargrilled yellowfin tuna with chilli oil, lime and caponata. Some cracking modern wines complete the picture.

● **MARTINHOE** (Devon)

Old Rectory Martinhoe, (01598) 763368. Reminiscent of one of those delightful family-run hotels that are highly prized in France, but are considered rare treasures in England. Suzanne Bradley's four-course dinners might include leg of lamb baked in hay, or steamed John Dory with lime and ginger hollandaise.

● **MARY TAVY** (Devon)

Stannary Mary Tavy, (01822) 810897. Forward-looking vegetarian food in a grand Victorian-Gothic setting on the edge of Dartmoor. Organic produce is used with commitment, and self-sufficiency underpins the set-up. Typical dishes might include tagliatelle with truffles and nuts, and spiced beetroot sponge with scrambled egg sauce. Open Friday to Sunday, evenings only.

● **MERLEY** (Dorset)

Les Bouviers Oakley Hill, (01202) 889555. Smartly updated cottage restaurant with a keen and exuberant chef/proprietor. The décor is all pastel shades, the cooking is overtly French. Choose from a catalogue of dishes that might include warm crab and celeriac cake, New Forest wild boar with gin and juniper berries, or brochette of seasonal fruits.

● **MILNROW** (Greater Manchester)
Meme's 22 Dale Street, (01706) 353651. In her bright, relaxed bistro, the industrious Lisa King produces monthly blackboard menus featuring some winning dishes, including black pudding with apple sauce, poussin stuffed with chorizo, and warm fruit compote. She also finds time to make jars of marmalade and superb breads.

● **MINCHINHAMPTON** (Gloucestershire)
Markey's The Old Ram, Market Square, (01453) 882287. Once a pub, now a relaxed country restaurant run by Ian and Ann Markey. The menu is short, much of the produce is local, and ideas are culled from far and wide. Tian provençale, melon and duck salad with spring onions and ginger, sea bass on wilted spinach, and chicken breast with cranberries are typical.

● **MORETONHAMPSTEAD** (Devon)

As the Guide *went to press, the restaurant at this location closed.*

● **MORPETH** (Northumberland)
Brasserie 59 Bridge Street, (01670) 516200. Great value and highly consistent cooking in a well-liked Northumbrian bistro. At lunch-time there are bar meals as well as a set menu, offering perhaps fish soup, steak and kidney pie, seafood crêpes and a 'minestrone of summer fruits'. Evening menus are more ambitious.

● **NANCENOY** (Cornwall)
Trengilly Wartha Inn Nancenoy, (01326) 340332. 'A pub that believes in inventive food', which could mean twice-

baked leek and cheese soufflé, rare roast pigeon breast on a salad of bitter greens, and 'appetising' steamed ginger pudding. The remote setting is irresistible, as are the intelligent wine list and the great selection of single malts.

● **NEWCASTLE UPON TYNE** (Tyne & Wear)
Café Procope 35 The Side, (0191) 232 3848. Laid-back, arty café with utilitarian décor and a lively menu of multi-ethnic 'fusion' food. 'Hearty, healthy and wholesome' sums up the cooking, service is polite and the bill is likely to be low. Thai fish-cakes with chilli dip, Lithuanian potatoes, rye-bread pizza, and kissel cranachan have been endorsed.
Magpie Room St James's Park Stadium, (0191) 232 3408. 'Big city glitz' on the sixth-floor of St James' Park football stadium. Staff sport the black and white of the Magpies (aka Newcastle United) and John Blackmore (ex-Blackmore's) cooks. The kitchen has scored with spicy chicken sausage with calvados sauce, and seared scallops with butter-beans and lentils.

● **NEWENT** (Gloucestershire)
Three Choirs Restaurant Newent, (01531) 890223. By day this is a cafeteria, serving visitors to the Vineyard, but on Friday and Saturday evenings it is transformed into a candlelit restaurant. A lively menu offers the likes of grilled Welsh goats'-cheese salad, seafood casserole, tagliatelle with a creamy bacon and tomato sauce, and lemon tart. Don't miss out on the Three Choirs wines.

● **NEWMARKET** (Suffolk)
Number Nine 9 Park Lane, (01638) 667999. 'Just what we have been waiting for in Newmarket.' The décor is all greens, reds and yellows, with racing prints on the walls, and the kitchen moves with the times. Expect such things as home-smoked chicken timbale with orange chutney, Cajun lamb with couscous and rocket, and caramelised pear tart.

● **NORTHALLERTON** (North Yorkshire)
Bettys 188 High Street, (01609) 775154. The most northerly branch of a mini-

chain of long-established Yorkshire tea-rooms. Like its relatives, this outlet prides itself on freshly baked cakes and breads, great coffee, a full range of cosmopolitan savoury dishes and first-rate children's facilities. Well worth queuing for.

● **NORTH BOVEY** (Devon)
Blackaller Hotel North Bovey, (01647) 440322. A pretty riverside setting adds to the pleasure of eating in this three-hundred-year-old woollen mill. 'Beautifully presented' fixed-price dinners might include hot prawn soufflé, chicken with lime and coriander sauce, and caramelised lemon tart. Personal, attentive service.

● **NORTON** (Shropshire)
Hundred House Hotel Bridgnorth Road, (01952) 730353. Family-run Georgian country inn with unconventional décor, intriguing herb gardens, a *carte* offering dishes such as lemon and sage marinated pork chop with caponata and polenta, and a brasserie-style menu in the bar. Landlord David Phillips knows his ales and keeps some promising wines.

● **NORWICH** (Norfolk)
Green's 82 Upper St Giles Street, (01603) 623733. Seafood is the main business in this green-painted restaurant close to the theatres. Best bets are the blackboard specials, which might include tempura of vegetables and fish, ravioli of scallops, and exotic ways with monkfish and sea bass. Steaks please the carnivores. Desserts are well executed.

● **NOTTINGHAM** (Nottinghamshire)
Saagar 473 Mansfield Road, (0115) 962 2014/969 2860. Long-established suburban Indian close to Mapperley Park. The food is mainly straightforward Punjabi with a few regional forays. Good dishes have included vegetable samosas, king prawn pakora, tandoori lamb and 'excellent' shahjahani chicken.

● **ODIHAM** (Hampshire)
Grapevine 121 High Street, (01256) 701122. Popular French bistro enthusiastically supported by the local community. Service is cheery, prices are commendable, especially for the early-bird evening menu, and the wine list

roams the globe. Appreciation has been shown for steamed halibut with beurre blanc, and casseroled lamb with sweet potatoes.

● **OLDBURY** (West Midlands)
Jonathans' 16–20 Wolverhampton Road, (0121) 429 3757. 'The amazing world of Johnathans' comprises a hotel, three restaurants and countless other attractions with nostalgic Victorian overtones. Soup is served in a stoneware Nottingham jar, the range of desserts includes a renowned trifle, fish and meat are purchased from Birmingham's wholesale market.

● **ORFORD** (Suffolk)
Butley-Orford Oysterage Market Hill, (01394) 450277. Locally bred oysters, mussels and home-smoked fish (including exemplary salmon) are the attractions in this long-serving East Anglian venue. Expect crowds, queues and plenty of riotous noise during the Aldeburgh Festival season, but be advised to check opening times in winter.

● **OVER STRATTON** (Somerset)
New Farm Over Stratton, (01460) 240584. Converted hamstone barn close to the A303, with useful B&B and an enterprising monthly menu. Typically adventurous dishes might include spicy citrus pickled prawns on avocado salad, Mediterranean beef salad, or flamed pork tenderloin with brandy, paprika and cream in a filo basket.

● **OXFORD** (Oxfordshire)
Browns 5–11 Woodstock Road, (01865) 511995. All-day bar/restaurant catering for young and old, offering forthright food without flim-flam at realistic prices. A jazz pianist plays in the evenings. This is the original of a quartet with branches in Brighton, Bristol and Cambridge.
Munchy Munchy 6 Park End Street, (01865) 245710. Ethel Ow delivers a highly distinctive version of South-east Asian home-cooking at this buzzing café. The menu is limited, but the food shows plenty of creative touches: duck flavoured with coriander and pomegranate seeds, or spiced lamb with fennel and red pepper. Drink tea, imported beer or wine.

Museum Of Modern Art 30 Pembroke Street, (01865) 722 733. Handy refreshment for art buffs touring the museum and exhibitions. Daily specials augment a menu that divides equally between vegetarian and carnivorous. Expect bagels, ploughman's, salads, lentil curry with rice, and chicken and leek pie. Open for lunch Tuesday to Sunday, and Thursday evenings only.

● **PARRACOMBE** (Devon)
Heddon's Gate Hotel Heddon's Mouth, (01598) 763313. A wonderfully secluded location at the head of a valley in Exmoor National Park is a big plus at this small, privately run hotel. The dinner menu is short, but raw materials are carefully chosen: grilled king scallops, ragoût of Devon oxtail, and sauté duck breast with balsamic vinegar sauce are typical.

● **PENKRIDGE** (Staffordshire)
William Harding's House Mill Street, (01785) 712955. Country restaurant in a centuries-old house that was once a stable block. Roulade of smoked mackerel, game pot-au-feu, and chicken with tarragon sauce and lime mousse are typical of the kitchen's output. Pleasant surroundings, courteous service, excellent value. Handy for the motorway network.

● **PINNER** (Greater London)
La Giralda 66–68 Pinner Green, (0181) 868 3429. A taste of Spain in the suburbs, with bags of atmosphere, a cracking Spanish wine list and sound Continental cooking. Starters such as fabada (beans with chorizo and bacon) are the real thing, fish tastes of the sea and puddings count 'rich and delicious' chocolate torte among their number. Service is friendly and value outstanding.

● **POLPERRO** (Cornwall)
Kitchen The Coombes, (01503) 272780. Tiny cottage restaurant at the heart of 'a shrine to the tourist trade'. The Batesons feed the visitors efficiently from a longish menu that globetrots for culinary inspiration. Gravlax is recommended, fish specials are worth investigating, and the wine list offers plenty of interesting, affordable drinking.

● **POOL IN WHARFEDALE** (West Yorkshire)
Monkman's Bistro Pool Bank, (0113) 284 1105. Boldly decorated modern bistro-with-rooms in the handsome Victorian residence formerly occupied by Pool Court. Chris Monkman's team offers a menu that encompasses daube of beef, wild mushroom risotto, and haddock with poached egg and Pommery mustard sauce. Good selection of wines by the glass.

● **PORTREATH** (Cornwall)
Tabb's Tregea Terrace, (01209) 842488. Relaxed local restaurant in a converted granite forge. Seasonal menus are excellent value for such dishes as sauté chicken livers on a mustard crouton, provençale fish casserole, braised wild rabbit with apricots, and chocolate marquise. The Victorian Sunday breakfast has also been enjoyable. Decent wines.

● **POWERSTOCK** (Dorset)
Three Horseshoes Powerstock, (01308) 485328. 'The kind of pub I'd like to own,' mused a visitor. The attractions of this highly ranked country inn are fresh fish from the Weymouth boats, some interesting wines, 'great' beers and a 'breathtakingly beautiful' setting deep in Thomas Hardy's Wessex.

● **REDMILE** (Leicestershire)
Peacock Inn Main Street, (01949) 842554. Immensely popular pub/restaurant in a village not far from Belvoir Castle. The setting is emphatically English, but the food is mostly French. New chef Franc Garbez cooks such dishes as goats' cheese in puff pastry with pine kernels, spicy lamb with cumin, olives and couscous, and apple pancakes with calvados.

● **REETH** (North Yorkshire)
Burgoyne Hotel On the Green, (01748) 884292. Elegant and exquisitely furnished hotel at the heart of an enchanting Dales village. The kitchen shows a preference for indigenous produce: local beef, crab from Whitley Bay and cheese from Wensleydale, for example. Service is unobtrusive. Wines are reasonably priced.

● **RICHMOND** (Surrey)
Petersham Hotel, Nightingales
Nightingale Lane, (0181) 940 7471.
Flamboyant Victorian mansion with a
spectacular riverside location overlooking
the Thames. Tim Richardson offers an
up-beat version of hearty old English
cooking with haute cuisine flourishes.
The cooking doesn't always achieve its
aims, but black pudding kebabs, and
saddle of lamb have succeeded. Not
cheap.
Rani 3 Hill Street, (0181) 332 2322.
Newish branch of the long-established
Gujarati vegetarian restaurant in Finchley
(see main entry, London). Décor and
menus are similar to the original: mixed
bhajias have been recommended, along
with masala dosa, pea and mushroom
curry, and potato-stuffed aubergine.
Cobra beer suits the food.

● **ROCHDALE** (Greater Manchester)
After Eight Hurst Hill Hotel, 2 Edenfield
Road, (01706) 46432. Tastefully
furnished Georgian house, with a
wonderfully relaxed atmosphere, friendly
service and consistent cooking. Expect
dishes such as tangy cheese soufflé, pork
in cider sauce, and home-made apricot
and Amaretto pavlova. Vegetarians have
their own menu, and the wine list is
'comprehensive'.

● **ROCHFORD** (Essex)
Renouf's Bradley Way, (01702) 541334.
Derek Renouf is a redoubtable
restaurateur who has been catering for
the inhabitants of south Essex for as long
as most people can remember. The food
here is classic French with all the
trimmings: crab soup with cognac,
poached salmon with hollandaise, and
raspberries and cream are typical.

● **ROMSEY** (Hampshire)
Bertie's 80 The Hundred, (01794)
830708. The latest offering from David
Birmingham, owner of Hunters in New
Alresford and Winchester (see main
entries). The setting is a converted pub
with '30s décor and a Bertie Wooster
theme, but the cooking is up-to-the-
minute. Lamb's kidneys with braised red
cabbage, spinach and tomato roulade,

and chilled raspberry soufflé have been
recommended. More reports, please.

● **SAFFRON WALDEN** (Essex)
Old Hoops 15 King Street, (01799)
522813. Oak-beamed restaurant in the
heart of historic Saffron Walden.
'Outstanding-value' lunches supplement
a *carte* that might list locally made wild
boar and apple sausages, lamb dijonnaise,
and veal chop with cream sauce. Fruit
pancakes are a favourite finale, and
service earns full marks. Wines are from
Lay & Wheeler.

● **ST MARTIN'S** (Isles of Scilly)
St Martin's Hotel Lower Town, (01720)
422092. A fabulous setting on Tean
Sound is one of the attractions of this
highly regarded hotel; another is the
cooking of Roux-trained chef Patrick
Tweedie. Dinner in the Tean Restaurant
might begin with warm salad of scallops
with grilled new potatoes, before confit of
pigeon with braised lettuce and
cardamom sauce.

● **SALISBURY** (Wiltshire)
Harpers 6–7 Ox Row, (01722) 333118.
A fixture of the Salisbury restaurant
scene for many years, Harpers is
renowned for its bargain-price lunches.
Shoppers pack into the upstairs room
overlooking the Market Square for good
helpings of, perhaps, pasta in a tomato,
chilli and ginger sauce. Evening meals are
slightly more elaborate: grilled sea bass
with red pepper, vermouth and basil
sauce, for example.

● **SCARBOROUGH** (North Yorkshire)
Lanterna 33 Queen Street, (01723)
363616. 'As rock solid as always' and
something of a benchmark for eating out
in Scarborough. Fads may come and go
but Gianluigi and Janet Arecco continue
to serve good trattoria food of the old
school based on sound ingredients.
'Perfectly cooked' asparagus, goujons of
sole, and 'mouthwatering' zabaglione
have been appreciated.

● **SEAVIEW** (Isle of Wight)
Seaview Hotel High Street, (01983)
612711. Enjoy a pub meal and a pint in
the bar or go for a full meal in the dining-

room of this ever-popular seaside hotel. In summer you can also sit in the garden overlooking the Solent, eat mussels and sip Muscadet. The Haywards are aimiable hosts who are firmly committed to using local produce, especially fish.

● **SHEFFIELD** (South Yorkshire)
Mediterranean 271 Sharrowvale Road, (0114) 266 1069. Tapas are served at lunch-time and early evening (5.30 to 7) in this converted shop away from the city centre. The restaurant offers a blackboard menu with fish as the strong suit: chargrilled squid with chilli, brill with king scallops, and zarzuela (Spanish fish stew) have been praised. Lemon tart is a good sweet.

Le Neptune 141 West Street, (0114) 279 6677. Handily placed on the tram route, close to university and city centre. Fish cooking – with a French acccent – is the main business, and the kitchen generally succeeds with casserole of monkfish and scallops, grey mullet in mustard sauce with samphire, and exotic mahi-mahi with beurre blanc.

● **SHERBORNE** (Dorset)
Pheasants 24 Greenhill, (01935) 815252. There are 'signs of serious cooking' in Andrew Overhill's welcoming restaurant-with-rooms. The short *carte* promises salmon fish-cake with chive butter, medallions of venison with spätzli, and poached figs with cinnamon ice-cream. A 'pleasingly eclectic' wine list is supplied by Christopher Piper.

● **SHERINGHAM** (Norfolk)
Arthur Browne's 23–29 Wyndham Street, (01263) 822242. A useful venue for holidaymakers and families on the North Norfolk coast. The menu is dominated by pizzas with up-to-the-minute toppings, but the repertoire also extends to salad of grilled king prawns, steaks, and crème brûlée. Service is friendly, wines are pleasantly quaffable.

● **SHIPTON-UNDER-WYCHWOOD** (Oxfordshire)
Lamb Inn High Street, (01993) 830465. A Cotswold classic, with centuries of

history under its belt, and an atmosphere that is tweed-suited English to a T. Choose from the no-nonsense bar menu, lunchtime buffet or the fixed-price dinner menu, which is built around local produce. Real ales and some better-than-average pub wines.

● **SPEEN** (Buckinghamshire)
Old Plow Inn Flowers Bottom Lane, (01494) 488300. Quintessential Chiltern watering-hole that is now devoted entirely to food. The bistro gets more votes than the restaurant, but the food is thoroughly up to date in both. Salmon marinated in Chinese spices, linguine with wild mushrooms, duck with black-bean sauce, and 'Rick Stein's' tandoori monkfish have been praised. Difficult to find, so phone for directions.

● **STOCKLAND** (Devon)
Kings Arms Inn Stockland, (01404) 881361. Massive eighteenth-century thatched pub with a serious attitude to food, drink and hospitality. The blackboard menu advertises gravlax, crispy roast duck, Cotley rack of lamb, and iced Grand Marnier soufflé. Snacks are also served at lunch-time. Good beers, excellent wines.

● **STOKE BRUERNE** (Northamptonshire)
Bruerne's Lock The Canalside, (01604) 863654. The setting, by a lock on the Grand Union Canal next to the waterways museum, is a great draw. Links with the Loire are responsible for grilled goats' cheese, while the Italian connection produces pasta and good olive oils. Pear tarte Tatin is a recommended sweet. Service is unhurried.

● **STOKE-ON-TRENT** (Staffordshire)
Ria 61–67 Piccadilly, (01782) 264411. Family-run Thai restaurant that brings light to an ethnic wilderness. The longish menu covers all the staples from satays and fish-cakes to curries and noodles; specialities include 'Volcano chicken', sizzling beef with peppercorns and Chinese wine, and pan-fried pomfret with palm sugar and chilli sauce. Open evenings only.

● **STRATFORD-UPON-AVON**
(Warwickshire)
Opposition 13 Sheep Street, (01789)
269980. A godsend for Stratford theatre-
goers, offering generous portions of bistro
food at affordable prices. Service is
prompt and menus cover everything from
eggs Benedict on a muffin to chicken in
tarragon sauce, and pork fillet with
tagliatelle.
Russons 8 Church Street, (01789)
268822. 'The best sort of unpretentious
eating-house' and a godsend for
Stratford. Pre-theatre menus are
naturally a great attraction and the
kitchen works well with fish and pasta.
Grilled sardines, and stir-fried monkfish
with vegetables appear beside tortellini
verdi, and guinea-fowl in red wine sauce.

● **STRETTON** (Leicestershire)
Ram Jam Inn Great North Road,
(01780) 410776. 'Does any other
motorway service stop in the country
offer such quality?' asks a traveller. This
invigorating roadside inn by the A1
provides excellent value from an all-day
menu and a specials board. Soups,
farmhouse cheeses, and restaurant dishes
such as mackerel with horseradish and
oregano sauce have been highlighted.

● **SURBITON** (Surrey)
Chez Max 85 Maple Road, (0181) 399
2365. Pretty pink neighbourhood
restaurant that makes one nostalgic for
French bistros of 20 years ago. Saffron-
coloured fish soup, snails, skate terrine,
duck with green peppercorn sauce, and a
trio of chocolate mousses typify the
bourgeois style. Good French bread,
cheeses and coffee. Service is ultra-
charming.

● **SUTTON GAULT** (Cambridgeshire)
Anchor Inn Sutton Gault, (01353)
778537. Seemingly miles from anywhere,
on the New Bedford River, this ancient
ferry inn has much to commend it.
Atmospheric heavily timbered rooms,
high-quality wines, and straightforward
country cooking based on sound local
ingredients are some of its virtues.
Bedrooms and breakfasts are added
temptations.

● **SWANAGE** (Dorset)
Cauldron Bistro 5 High Street, (01929)
422671. Enthusiastically run bistro with a
lively attitude towards supplies and
ingredients: local seafood shares the
limelight with bison, ostrich and 'wild
blue' pork. Moules marinière, loin of
Dorset lamb with orange and redcurrant
sauce, and banana and toffee ice-cream
are typical. Thai dishes also appear.

● **TEWKESBURY** (Gloucestershire)
Le Bistrot André 78 Church Street,
(01684) 290357. One-room
neighbourhood bistro near the abbey,
with a jovial owner, cheerful décor and a
frog motif to emphasise its chummy
Frenchness. The blackboard menu deals
in such things as French onion soup,
snails, oxtail provençale, and apple tart.
Open evenings only, Monday to
Saturday.

● **TIDEFORD** (Cornwall)
Heskyn Mill Tideford, (01752) 851481.
Atmospheric eighteenth-century corn
mill complete with water wheels and
orginal machinery. The kitchen makes
use of local fish and game for a menu that
embraces fillet of wild salmon with wild
mushrooms and prawns, pheasant breast
stuffed with cream cheese and garlic, and
pear and ginger pudding.

● **TOPSHAM** (Devon)
Drake's Fore Street, (01392) 875172.
'Wine and Ale House' says the billing, but
there is also promising food to be had at
this lively place not far from Exeter.
Recent recommendations illustrate the
style: Roquefort mousse with spinach
salad, venison sausages with beetroot and
garlic, grilled salmon with tomato
vinaigrette, and white chocolate
cheesecake.

● **TORQUAY** (Devon)
Burley's 43 Babbacombe Downs Road,
(01803) 316661. In a Victorian hotel with
'a lovely view' over Babbacombe Downs,
Danny Burley cooks with flair and
ambition. Successes include seafood in
saffron jelly, red mullet with oyster sauce
and parsnip chips, and rack of lamb with
a basil and mustard crust. An almond

tulip filled with marmalade ice-cream is a recommended finale.

Mulberry Room 1 Scarborough Road, (01803) 213639. Lesley Cooper's superior home cooking is much appreciated by holidaymakers and locals alike: ingredients are fresh, prices modest and wines well-chosen. Caponata, grilled chicken breast with a parsley crust, cassoulet, and pavlova are typically delightful offerings. Now open for dinner Wednesday to Saturday.

● **TRESCO** (Isles of Scilly)
Island Hotel Tresco, (01720) 422883. Wonderful sea views and a heavenly setting on the Island of Flowers. Amuse-gueules and 'brillant' bread spiked with pink peppercorns and walnuts have been praised, along with crab and tomato soup, and tuna steak with deep-fried ravioli. Service is unashamedly friendly, and hot towels appear at the end of the meal.

● **WANTAGE** (Oxfordshire)
Foxes 8 Newbury Street, (01235) 760568. Converted shop in the centre of town filled with paintings and vulpine ornaments. The menu is short, but the kitchen conjures up some promising ideas: smoked salmon and goats' cheese tart with ratatouille, pot-roast partridge, and caramel oranges with cinnamon parfait, for example.

● **WARWICK** (Warwickshire)
Findons 7 Old Square, (01926) 411755. Home-smoked produce is a feature of this friendly restaurant in a listed Georgian house. Salmon is served as a starter with cucumber and yoghurt, while main courses include haddock with Savoy cabbage and mustard sauce, and duck breast with strawberry and red wine sauce. Chocolate mille-feuille makes a fine finale. Ten house wines.

● **WENDOVER** (Buckinghamshire)
Prince of India 10–12 Aylesbury Road. Very creditable curry-house cooking in a dimly lit brick building that looks like a converted pub. No surprises on the menu, but chef's specials are worth exploring and vegetables are particularly good. Fresh ingredients, distinctive spicing, reasonable prices.

● **WEYBRIDGE** (Surrey)
Colony 3 Balfour Road, (01932) 842766. Long-established provincial Chinese restaurant offering a safe-and-sound menu of Pekinese and Szechuan favourites. Successes from recent meals have included 'squab' (minced pork and prawns wrapped in lettuce), deep-fried shredded beef with chilli, sizzling lamb, and steamed sea bass. Peking duck is a good version.

● **WEYMOUTH** (Dorset)
Perry's 4 Trinity Road, (01305) 785799. Seafood is the big draw at this tidy restaurant overlooking Weymouth harbour. Moules marinière, and salmon, sole and prawn en croûte have pleased piscophiles; others might be tempted by rack of Dorset lamb, or duck breast with stir-fried vegetables. Service is 'extremely pleasant', and house wine has been endorsed.

● **WHITLEY BAY** (Tyne & Wear)
Le Provençale 183 Park View, (0191) 251 3567. On the market as we went to press, but still providing a great service to the local community. Generous French cooking, old and new, is the order of the day. Visitors can expect anything from coq au vin to lemon sole filled with scallop mousse. Early-evening brasserie meals are served on Wednesday and Thursday.

● **WINCHESTER** (Hampshire)
Nine The Square 9 Great Minster Street, (01962) 864004. Wine bar-cum-restaurant in the shadow of the cathedral, providing 'excellent' food in a classy but relaxed setting. The menu has an Italian bias, pasta is made on the premises, but the kitchen also looks to the East for dishes such as Thai-style bream. Wines are of a high standard, as is the service.

● **WINDERMERE** (Cumbria)
Holbeck Ghyll Holbeck Lane, (01539) 432375. Improvements continue apace at David and Patricia Nicholson's converted Victorian hunting lodge. An all-day menu in the restaurant extension is just one new feature; otherwise there is the prospect of more formal dining from a

repertoire based on local ingredients. Service is ever helpful.

● **WOODSEAVES** (Staffordshire)
Old Parsonage High Offley, (01785) 284446. Sunday lunch is a popular occasion at this restaurant-with-rooms set in open country away from Staffordshire's conurbations. Warm black-pudding salad, thickly sliced roast loin of pork, gateau of Mediterranean vegetables, and apple and treacle tart are typical of the repertoire.

● **WOOLTON HILL** (Hampshire)
Hollington House Woolton Hill, (01635) 255100. Magnificent Edwardian house on the outskirts of Newbury that has enjoyed a high culinary reputation in recent years. A new chef with a heavyweight CV was about to be appointed as we went to press, although the prestigious wine cellar will presumably remain intact. Reports on the new regime, please.

● **YORK** (North Yorkshire)
Bettys 6–8 St Helen's Square, (01904) 659142. The most tourist-oriented of a gang of four near-legendary tea-rooms with branches throughout Yorkshire. Like its relatives, this outlet is a cross between European pâtisserie and traditional North Country tea-shop with

some good-value brasserie dishes thrown in for good measure. Ideal for families.
Grange Hotel Clifton, (01904) 644744. Stylish Regency hotel, five minutes' walk from the Minster. The new Seafood Bar (complete with a horse-racing mural) serves everything from plates of oysters to crab salad with tarragon mayonnaise, while the lively basement brasserie is renowned for its locally made wild boar sausages, and salmon fish-cakes.
Kites 13 Grape Lane, (01904) 641378. In an area famed for its tourist 'ghost walks', this upstairs venue serves food that is straight out of the global village. Moroccan vegetable soup with couscous, salmon fillet with fettuccine and sun-dried tomatoes, and a brûlée of mixed berries with goat's cheese have passed muster. Numerous young ladies serve while 'classic Muzak' plays.

● **YOXFORD** (Suffolk)
Jacey's Charcoal Pit Blythburgh House, (01728) 77298. Chargrills and kebabs are the mainstays of this popular converted draper's shop. The long skewers are hung on stands at the table and the supporting cast includes garlic and herb butters, coleslaw and chips. Other choices range from excellent pasta and pancakes to chicken and apricot curry. Great value.

Scotland

● **ALLOA** (Clackmannanshire)
Gean House Gean Park, Tullibody Road, (01259) 219275. Magnificent country mansion built in 1912 as a family wedding present, but now a luxurious hotel. New chef Martin Russell offers such dishes as marinated fillet of halibut, honey-roast quail, baked salmon with braised chicory and coriander, and spiced pear mousse cake. Light meals are served throughout the day.

● **ARCHIESTOWN** (Moray)
Archiestown Hotel Archiestown, (01340) 810218. You will find reliable, well-cooked food, friendly service and 'a warm non-flappable atmosphere' in this country hotel. Eat excellent langoustines,

turbot and oxtail from the fixed-price menus in the restaurant, or enjoy the same dishes for less in the slightly more informal bar/bistro. More reports, please.

● **ARDUAINE** (Argyll & Bute)
Loch Melfort Hotel Arduaine, (01852) 200233. A useful base camp for travellers and holidaymakers, with brilliant views across the bay to the Sound of Jura. Seafood is the main theme, and the Sunday buffet is not to be missed. Service is commended by almost everyone. Don't leave without visiting nearby Arduaine gardens.

● **BIGGAR** (South Lanarkshire)
Culter Mill Coulter Village, (01899) 20950. Once a grain mill, now an

effectively decorated bistro and
restaurant complete with agricultural
memorabilia. Meals are eaten upstairs.
Fried wun-tuns, casserole of rabbit,
mixed seafood bake, and fresh fruit with
ice-cream have been favourably received.
Service is courteous and attentive.

● **BOWMORE** (Argyll & Bute)
Harbour Inn The Square, (01496)
810330. Delightful little quayside inn
with a crowded bar, comfortable
bedrooms and an up-and-coming
restaurant. Local fish, meat and game are
used for dishes such as pan-fried scallops
with broccoli, rack of Islay lamb, and fillet
steak with brandy and green
peppercorns. Orange marmalade mousse
is a typical sweet.

● **CROMARTY** (Highland)
Thistles 20 Church Street, (01381)
7471. Highly useful, family-run
restaurant on the ground floor of an
eighteenth-century listed building.
Snacks and light meals are available at
lunch-time, while regularly changing
dinner menus promise wholesome
sustenance in the shape of gnocchi with
pesto, scallop and monkfish kebabs, and
pork fillet with prunes.

● **EDINBURGH** (Edinburgh)
Ann Purna 45 St Patrick's Square,
(0131) 662 1807. Excellent-value South
Indian and Gujarati cooking in
immaculate smoke-free surroundings.
Kachoris (lentil pastries) with tamarind
dip are are a favourite starter; other
recommended dishes include mixed
pakoras, sag paneer and mixed vegetable
korma. Expansion is planned, along with
a new range of vegan dishes.
Howie's 75 St Leonard's Street, (0131)
668 2917. One of a trio of cheap-and-
cheerful eating places dotted around
Edinburgh. The setting is an imposing
converted bank in a 'great location' and
the place gets packed. Set lunches are
brilliant value for sweet-cured Orkney
herring, leg of lamb with apple and
rosemary, and chocolate and praline
terrine.
Le Marché Noir 2–4 Eyre Place, (0131)
558 1608. The décor has been brightened

up and the set-lunch menu continues to
provide what looks like excellent value.
Dishes read well, but the results have
been patchy of late. The Gallic theme
shows itself in well-composed salads,
cheeses, and desserts such as bread-and-
butter pudding with apricot crème
anglaise.
Pepito's 24A Stafford Street, (0131) 225
9575. Eat tacos and drink tequila sunrise
in this relaxed, inexpensive West End
basement restaurant. The menu covers all
the Mexican staples, from guacamole and
tostadas to nachos, chilaquiles and
burritos filled with picadillo (spicy
minced beef). Pecan meringue is a
suitably seductive sweet.
Pierre Victoire 10 Victoria St, (0131)
225 1721. This is the original of Pierre
Levicky's chain of bargain-basement
French eating-houses. Branches are
springing up like mushrooms in towns
and cities across the land; almost all are
franchised and quality is variable. The
set-price offer has become a legend in its
own lunch-time. Find one near you.
Rainbow Arch Morrison Street, (0131)
221 1288. Part of a Chinese complex also
including a 'noodle shack' and a dim-sum
cellar. The setting is bright and spacious,
the décor soothing, and the food
generally hits the mark. Successes have
included pan-fried vegetable dumplings,
outstanding steamed sea bass, and
aubergine slices in spicy garlic sauce.
Suruchi 14A Nicolson Street, (0131)
556 6583. Culturally inclined Indian
restaurant where music and artistic
events are part of the show. Simla chaat
(a cold dish of chick peas and potatoes),
dhaba gosht (lamb with ginger), tarka
dhal, and fragrant basmati rice have been
enjoyed. Keralan banana fritters filled
with coconut makes an unusual dessert.
Waterfront Wine Bar 1C Dock Place,
(0131) 554 7427. An atmospheric
waterside setting and a fizzingly good, but
affordable, wine list bring the crowds to
this bar by the docks. Fish is well handled:
deep-fried sprats, and collop of salmon
and scallops with chervil mayonnaise

have been recommended. Tables in the conservatory are at a premium.

● **FAIRLIE** (North Ayrshire)
Fins Fencefoot Farm, (01475) 568989. Fresh local seafood is the star turn in this comfortable restaurant in converted farm stables. Rainbow trout and lobsters from the farm feature alongside home-smoked haddock, but the menu might also offer pan-fried king scallops with warm fennel salad, or brill with basil, chive and red pepper coulis. The location appeals and the atmosphere is welcoming.

● **GLASGOW** (Glasgow)
Café Antipasti 337 Byres Road, (0141) 337 2737. Newish Glasgow café offering antipasti and much more besides. Breakfast is served from 9am, and the full menu includes lots of pasta, pizzas, risottos, and main dishes such as grilled lamb chops with charred summer vegetables. Also look for the odd-sounding meatball baguette with tomatoes and peppers.

● **KELSO** (Borders)
Sunlaws House Heiton, (01573) 450331. Baronial architecture, great swathes of park and woodland, not to mention centuries of colourful history, are just some of the attractions at Sunlaws. Daily-changing dinner menus might offer such dishes as potted hare, smoked haddock and fennel mousse, steaks, and bread-and-butter pudding.

● **KILCHRENAN** (Argyll & Bute)
Ardanaiseig Hotel Kilchrenan, (01866) 833333. Imposing and architecturally significant Victorian country house noted for its spectacular wild woodland gardens planted with thousands of exotic trees and shrubs. A new chef produces such things as parsnip and apple soup, baked trout with Grand Marnier and red pepper sauce, and hazelnut meringue with Kahlua sauce.

● **KINBUCK** (Stirling)
Cromlix House Kinbuck, (01786) 822125. Spectacularly situated in a 3,000-acre estate, this awesome period mansion continues to improve under the stewardship of David and Ailsa Assenti. The kitchen can handle everything from high-flown extravaganzas to traditional Sunday lunch of tomato consommé, roast sirloin, and crème brulée.

● **PEEBLES** (Borders)
Prince of India, (01721) 724455. Pleasingly decorated Indian offering some 'really good' provincial curry-house food. Spicy kebabs, herbed lamb, dhal, and vegetables have been greatly enjoyed. Breads are 'superb' and wines are very drinkable. More reports, please.

● **SCARISTA** (Western Isles)
Scarista House Scarista, (01859) 550277. Enchanting and miraculously peaceful white-walled Georgian manse enviably sited right by the beach looking out towards the Atlantic. Jane Callaghan's fixed-price dinners are based resolutely around organic and natural produce; farmed fish is out. Breads, cakes and preserves are made on the premises.

● **SPEAN BRIDGE** (Highland)
Old Pines Gairlochy Road, (01397) 712324. Enthusiastically run restaurant-with-rooms, with a cosy atmosphere and cooking based on local ingredients. Four-course dinners take in warm broccoli mousse with home-smoked salmon, courgette soup, stuffed roast leg of lamb with rowan jelly, and brown sugar meringues with elderflower ice-cream. Scottish cheeses complete the picture.

● **STONEHAVEN** (Aberdeenshire)
Tolbooth Old Pier, (01569) 762287. Enterprising seafood restaurant in a 'super' setting overlooking Stonehaven harbour. The menu promises everything from home-smoked salmon to caviare sushi, and chargrilling is a feature, as in sea bass with citrus sauce, or halibut with Mediterranean vegetables. Steaks come from high-quality Aberdeen Angus. More reports, please.

Wales

● **ABERAERON** (Cardiganshire)
Hive on the Quay Cadwgan Place, (01545) 570445. Seasonal café-cum-restaurant in a converted wharf by Aberaeron's two harbours. The Holgate family specialise in bees and honey, also providing coffee and cakes, light lunches and fish from their own boat. Dinners (served July and August only) have not always been as impressive as daytime refreshment. A 'short, but perfectly adequate' list includes a few organic wines, and Welsh mead.

● **CARDIFF** (Cardiff)
Chikako's 10–11 Mill Lane, (01222) 665279. Genuinely Japanese and run with dedication by Chikako Cameron. Her three-course menu is split between dishes prepared in the kitchen (teriyaki, tonkatsu and noodles) and those created at the table (sukiyaki, shabu-shabu, yosenabe). She will also make sushi if given advance warning. Open evenings only.

Quayles 6–8 Romilly Crescent, (01222) 341264. Recommended as a useful spot for lunch in Cardiff, with particularly good soups and puddings. The evening menus offer fair cooking in the shape of goats' cheese with tomatoes and artichokes, paté with green peppercorns, and sole with fried potatoes. The wine list is short and to the point.

Riverside Cantonese 44 Tudor Street, (01222) 227333. A useful choice for reliable, cooked-to-order dim-sum in a street filled with ethnic food shops and delis. Steamed spare-ribs with chilli and black-bean sauce, grilled Pekinese dumplings and king prawn cheung-fun have hit the mark. The full menu takes few risks. Open all day.

● **GLANWYDDEN** (Aberconwy & Colwyn)
Queen's Head Glanwydden, (01492) 5146570. Wheelwright's cottage that has been converted into a civilised, neat and tidy dining pub with a sound reputation locally. Conwy seafood is a strong suit (crab salad has been first rate) and the

menu extends to decent soups, braised Welsh lamb, and a host of puddings, including chocolate brandy trifle.

● **LLANABER** (Caernarfonshire & Merionethshire)
Llwyndu Farmhouse Llwyndu, (01341) 280144. 'Homey, incredibly comfortable and authentic' farmhouse B&B providing dinner for non-residents. The kitchen produces eclectic dishes along the lines of salmon and Gruyère paté, stir-fried chicken livers with grapes, spare-ribs with treacle and pineapple, and lamb with basil sauce. 'Terrific value'.

● **LLANDEILO** (Carmarthenshire)
Cawdor Arms Hotel Rhosmaen Street, (01558) 823500. Long-serving coaching-inn-cum-hotel with a menu that has noticeable Welsh overtones: leek and potato soup, black pudding salad, and faggot of Usk venison with onion sauce, for example. There are also global ideas such as cod in herb batter on a bed of bean sprouts, and chicken with sun-dried tomato risotto.

Fanny's 3 King Street, (01558) 822908. Modest Victorian-style restaurant and tea-room opposite the church, with an appealing family atmosphere. Cakes and pastries are a speciality, and two-course lunches have a wholesome vegetarian bias. Totally non-smoking. Open Tuesday to Saturday, 10 to 5, and bank holidays.

● **LLANFYLLIN** (Powys)
Seeds 5 Penybryn Cottages, (01691) 648604. Seeds flourishes in the 'stony ground' away from the main action in Powys. Mark and Felicity Seager's fixed-price menus win approval for cream of spinach soup, hoki with herb and garlic sauce, excellent lamb, 'perfectly cooked vegetables' and Welsh cheeses. The wine list reads promisingly.

● **LLANGOLLEN** (Denbighshire)
Gales 18 Bridge Street, (01978) 860089. Happy-go-lucky wine bar (with accommodation) a short walk from Llangollen Railway and Canal Wharf. The blackboard menu offers everything from salads, and jacket potatoes, to roast

chicken with mornay sauce, and home-made ice-creams. The wine list is a cracker loaded with real discoveries at fair prices. Great for families.

● **LLYSWEN** (Powys)
Griffin Inn Llyswen, (01874) 754241. Fifteenth-century sporting-inn close to the River Wye with a bustling convivial atmosphere and well-kept ales. Fish and game dominate the menu, and robust casseroles are reckoned to be a strong point. Soups are fresh-tasting, cheeses are Welsh, and wines are better than the pub average.

● **MOLD** (Flintshire)
Chez Colette 56 High Street, (01352) 759225. A little corner of France anchored in North Wales, with French prices to boot. The tablecloths are paper, there are no frills, but the kitchen delivers sound renditions of moules farcies, boeuf bourguignon, poulet basquaise and navarin d'agneau. Finish with ice-cream, a sorbet, or some Camembert. Wines are just right.

● **PORTHKERRY** (Vale of Glamorgan)
Egerton Grey Porthkerry, (01446) 711666. Wonderfully secluded Victorian rectory with glorious views over Porthkerry Park. Chef Craig Brookes produces complex dishes including crab and salmon terrine wrapped in leeks and vine leaves, and honey-roast duck with whisky sauce and an apple and tarragon mousse. Convenient for Cardiff Airport.

● **ST GEORGE** (Aberconwy & Colwyn)
Kinmel Arms St George, nr Abergele, (01745) 832207 Converted coaching-inn with sea views, offering a daily bar menu, real ales, reasonably priced wines and serious restaurant food. Local fish and game figure strongly: in baked salmon with red pepper butter and watercress cream, or roast venison with green peppercorns. More reports, please.

● **SWANSEA** (Swansea)
Annie's 56 St Helen's Road, (01792) 655603. Vigorously supported converted schoolhouse where Anne Gwilym continues to nourish the local community. Monthly fixed-price menus are backed by modestly priced wines. Smoked haddock soup, sewin with marsh samphire, pheasant with gingered pear and stir-fried greens, and summer fruit terrine are typical offerings.
Barrows 42 Newton Road, (01792) 361443. Wine bar/restaurant in a side street overlooking Oystermouth Castle. Monkfish with vegetables, and pheasant with pepper sauce have been singled out, along with 'super' sauté potatoes. Real ale is an alternative to the decent selection of reasonably priced wines. Very pleasant service, good value.

Channel Islands

● **GOREY** (Jersey)
Jersey Pottery Restaurant Gorey, (01534) 851119. A well-liked island institution and a great place for seafood. Lunch in the Garden Restaurant might feature anything from mussels in saffron and local cider, Jersey oysters, and spider crabs, to grilled fish with roasted peppers. Duck, steaks and chicken are offered for meat eaters.

● **ST BRELADE** (Jersey)
Sea Crest Hotel Petit Port, (01534) 46353. Perfectly sited overlooking La Pulente Headland and a short walk from the golden sands of St Ouen's Bay. Gerard Le Miere has been cooking here since 1971 and his style is Anglo-French. Look for fresh fish (anything from grilled sole to salmon with lobster and chive sauce) and expect much flambéeing.

● **ST PETER PORT** (Guernsey)
La Frégate St Peter Port, (01481) 724624. Enchanting views of the harbour and castle are a bonus at this long-serving stalwart of the Guernsey scene. Regulars speak well of the seafood (anything from prawn pancakes to scallops with bacon) and lunch is always a good bet. Service is as polished as can be.

Le Nautique Quay Steps, (01481) 721714. Much liked for its quayside setting, friendly service and extensive menu. The restaurant is in a converted wine cellar. Seafood, not surprisingly, is the thing to eat here, and it comes with a French accent. The wine list has been described as 'restricted'.

● SARK (Sark)

Founiais Restaurant Harbour Hill, (01481) 832626. A 'sun-baked terrace' is one of the attractions of this friendly restaurant. Sunday lunch is exceptional value, and might include warm salad of chicken livers and bacon, grilled turbot with crisp fresh vegetables, and 'light' bread-and-butter pudding.

Northern Ireland

● BELLANALECK (Co Fermanagh)

Sheelin Bellanaleck, (01365) 348232. Afro-European cooking in a pretty thatched house is the unlikely but intriguing combination here. Starters are straightfoward, main dishes range from Moroccan couscous, yassa (marinated chicken breast with lemon, mustard and onions), and vegetable curry, to sole normande, and steak with garlic butter.

General lists

New entries

These restaurants are new to the Guide this year, although some may have appeared in previous years, or in the Round-ups last year.

London

Abingdon, W8
Alastair Little Lancaster Road, W11
Andrew Edmunds, W1
Anglesea Arms, W6
Avenue, SW1
Blenheim, NW8
Bradleys, NW3
B Square, SW11
Café Japan, NW11
Café Nico, W1
Coast, W1
The Collection, SW3
Cookhouse, SW15
Criterion Brasserie, W1
Cucina, NW3
Drones, SW1
Euphorium, N1
Exxo, W1
Fables, SW6
Golden Dragon, W1
Gourmet Garden, NW4
Green Olive, W9
Gresslin's, NW3
Livebait, SE1
Maison Novelli, EC1
Matsuri, SW1
Mezzo, W1
Mirch Masala, SW16
Montana, SW6
L'Odeon, W1
L'Oranger, SW1
Red Pepper, W9
Royal Garden Hotel, The Tenth, W8
Saint, WC2
Searcy's Brasserie, EC2
Stafford Hotel, SW1
Sugar Club, W11
Thai Bistro, W4
33, SW1
Village Bistro, N6
Vong, SW1
Zafferano, SW1

England

Abberley, Elms
Altrincham, Juniper
Ambleside, Glass House
Ambleside, Sheila's Cottage
Bath, No. 5 Bistro
Bigbury-on-Sea, Burgh Island
Birmingham, Leftbank
Bowness-on-Windermere, Linthwaite House
Bray, Fat Duck
Bristol, Glass Boat
Cartmel, Aynsome Manor
Cheltenham, Epicurean
Deddington, Dexter's
Derby, Darleys on the River
Durham, Bistro 21
Elland, La Cachette
Great Yeldham, White Hart
Huddersfield, Café Pacific
Hythe, Boathouse Brasserie
Kelsale, Hedgehogs
King's Cliffe, King's Cliffe House
Knutsford, Belle Epoque Brasserie
Leamington Spa, Lansdowne
Leeds, Rascasse
Liskeard, Bacchus Bistro
Liverpool, Far East
Liverpool, Lyceum Library
Lydgate, White Hart
Madingley, Three Horseshoes
Malmesbury, Old Bell Hotel
Manchester, Tai Pan

Middlesbrough, Purple Onion
Moreton-in-Marsh, Annie's
Nayland, White Hart
New Polzeath, Cornish Cottage Hotel
Northampton, Le Sous-Sol
Nottingham, Café de Paris
Oswestry, Walls
Oxford, Le Petit Blanc
Richmond, Burnt Chair
Richmond, Chez Lindsay
St Mary Bourne, George Inn
Sale, Hanni's
Sandgate, Sandgate Hotel, La Terrasse
Sawbridgeworth, Shoes
Sheffield, Rafters
Sheffield, Smith's of Sheffield
Shere, Kinghams
Stoke Holy Cross, Wildebeest Arms
Stratford-upon-Avon, Liaison
Tadcaster, Singers
Taplow, Cliveden, Terrace
Virginstow, Percy's at Coombeshead
Worleston, Rookery Hall
Yarmouth, George Hotel

Scotland

Ayr, Fouter's Bistro
Balquhidder, Monachyle Mhor
Dalry, Braidwoods
Edinburgh, Café Saint-Honoré
Edinburgh, Silvio's
Edinburgh, Valvona & Crolla Caffè Bar

Glasgow, Mitchells
Inverness,
    Restaurant No 1
Newton Stewart,
    Kirroughtree Hotel
Perth, Let's Eat

Wales

Capel Garmon, Tan-y-
    Foel

Crickhowell, Bear Hotel
Llandegla, Bodidris
    Hall

Northern Ireland

Bangor, Shanks
Helen's Bay, Deanes on
    the Square

Republic of Ireland

Dingle, Beginish
Dingle, Waterside
Donegal, Harvey's Point
Dublin, Thornton's
Rathmullan, Rathmullan
    House
Schull, Restaurant in
    Blue

Closures

Whatever happened to that restaurant? Those listed below have closed since the last edition of the Guide, though one or two may have re-opened under a different name.

London
Jones Restaurant and Bar
Mijanou
Nosh Brothers
Surinder's

England
Alnwick, John
  Blackmore's
Bilbrough, Bilbrough
  Manor
Boston Spa, Café
  Provence
Cranleigh, La Barbe
  Encore
Chichester, Droveway
Halford, Sykes House
Helford, Riverside
Ipswich, Kwok's
  Rendezvous
Manchester, Woodlands
Tunbridge Wells,
  Cheevers

Scotland
Cullen, Bayview Hotel

Edinburgh, Crannog
Glasgow, Crannog

Wales
Chirk, Starlings Castle

Isle of Man
Ballasalla, Rosa's Place

Republic of Ireland
Gorey, Eugenes

London restaurants by cuisine

Boundaries between some national cuisines – British, French and Italian particularly – are not as marked as they used to be. Thus, the restaurants listed below are classified by the predominant influence, although there may be some crossover.

American
Avenue, SW1
Bradleys, NW3
Christopher's, WC2
Montana, SW6

Belgian
Belgo Noord, NW1

British
Alfred, WC2
Butlers Wharf Chop House, SE1
Connaught, W1
Dorchester, Grill Room, W1
English Garden, SW3
French House Dining Room, W1
Greenhouse, W1
Quality Chop House, EC1
Rules, WC2
The Savoy, Grill Room, WC2
Waltons, SW3
Wilsons, W14
Wiltons, SW1

Chinese
Cheng-Du, NW1
Dorchester, Oriental, W1
Fung Shing, WC2
Golden Dragon, W1
Mandarin Kitchen, W2
Mr Kong, WC2
Poons, WC2
Royal China, W2
Vegetarian Cottage, NW3
Zen Central, W1

Fish
Brady's, SW18
Café Fish, SW1
Livebait, SE1
Lobster Pot, SE11
Lou Pescadou, SW5
Le Suquet, SW3
Two Brothers, N3
Upper Street Fish Shop, N1

French
Alexandra, SW20
Les Associés, N8
Aubergine, SW10
Au Jardin des Gourmets, W1
Brasserie St Quentin, SW3
Le Cadre, N8
Chez Max, SW10
Chez Nico at Ninety Park Lane, W1
Criterion Brasserie, W1
La Dordogne, W4
L'Estaminet, WC2
Four Seasons, W1
Le Gavroche, W1
Green Olive, W9
Grill St Quentin, SW3
Hyde Park Hotel, The Restaurant, SW1
Inter-Continental Hotel, Le Soufflé, W1
Interlude de Chavot, W1
Magno's Brasserie, WC2
Le Meridien Hotel, Oak Room, W1
Le Mesurier, EC1
Mon Plaisir, WC2
L'Odéon, W1
Le Palais du Jardin, WC2
Le P'tit Normand, SW18
Pied-à-Terre, W1
Les Saveurs, W1
The Savoy, River Restaurant, WC2
La Tante Claire, SW3
La Truffe Noire, SE1
Village Bistro, N6

Greek
Daphne, NW1
Kalamaras, W2

Hungarian
Gay Hussar, W1

Indian/Pakistani
Bombay Brasserie, SW7
Great Nepalese, NW1

Lahore Kebab House, E1
Mirch Masala, SW16
Ragam, W1
Salloos, SW1
Tamarind, W1

Indian vegetarian
Kastoori, SW17
Rani, N3
Rasa, N16
Sabras, NW10
Sree Krishna, SW17

Indonesian/ Straits
Gourmet Garden, NW4
Melati, W1
Singapore Garden Restaurant, NW6

Italian
Alba, EC1
Al San Vincenzo, W2
L'Altro, W11
Bertorelli's, WC1
Billboard Café, NW6
Cantina del Ponte, SE1
Como Lario, SW1
Daphne's, SW3
Del Buongustaio, SW15
Granita, N1
The Halkin, SW1
L'Incontro, SW1
Neal Street Restaurant, WC2
Olivo, SW1
Orsino, W11
Orso, WC2
Osteria Antica Bologna, SW11
Osteria Basilico, W11
Pizzeria Castello, SE1
Red Pepper, W9
Riva, SW13
River Café, W6
Zafferano, SW1

Japanese
Ajimura, WC2
Arisugawa, W1

Café Japan, NW11
Inaho, W2
Matsuri, SW1
Mitsukoshi, SW1
Miyama, W1
Moshi Moshi Sushi,
    EC2 & EC4
Saga, W1
Suntory, SW1
Tatsuso, EC2
Tokyo Diner, WC2
Wagamama, WC1

Korean
Bu San, N7

Mauritian
Chez Liline, N4

North African/
Middle
Eastern
Adams Café, W12
Al Bustan, SW1
Al Hamra, W1
Iznik, N5

Laurent, NW2

Swedish
Anna's Place, N1

Thai
Bahn Thai, W1
Blue Elephant, SW6
Mantanah, SE25
Sri Siam, W1
Sri Siam City, EC2
Thai Bistro, W4
Thai Garden, E2
Thailand, SE14

London budget eating

At these restaurants it should be possible to have a three-course meal, including coffee, a half-bottle of house wine and service, at any time the restaurant is open, for £20 or less per person. Meals may often cost much more than this, but, by choosing carefully, it should be possible to keep to a £20 budget. These restaurants are marked in the Guide with the £ symbol.

Adams Café, W12
Andrew Edmunds, W1
Anglesea Arms, W6
Billboard Café, NW6
Brady's, SW18
Café Japan, NW11
Daphne, NW1
Eagle, EC1
Fire Station, SE1
Fung Shing, WC2
Gourmet Garden, NW4
Great Nepalese, NW1

Iznik, N5
Kalamaras, W2
Kastoori, SW17
Lahore Kebab House, E1
Lansdowne, NW1
Laurent, NW2
Mirch Masala, SW16
Mr Kong, WC2
Moshi Moshi Sushi, EC2
Moshi Moshi Sushi, EC4
Osteria Basilico, W11
Pizzeria Castello, SE1

Poons, WC2
Ragam, W1
Rasa, N16
Sabras, NW10
Sree Krishna, SW17
Thai Garden, E2
Tokyo Diner, WC2
Two Brothers, N3
Upper Street Fish Shop, N1
Vegetarian Cottage, NW3
Wagamama, WC1

Party bookings for 25 or more in private rooms

Alba, EC1
Alexandra, SW20
Atlantic Bar and Grill, W1
Bahn Thai, W1
Blenheim, NW8
Brasserie St Quentin, SW3
B Square, SW11
Cafe Royal, Brasserie, W1
Chiaroscuro, WC1
Chinon, W14
Claridge's, W1
La Dordogne, W4
L'Escargot, W1
L'Estaminet, WC2
Fables, SW6
Fire Station, SE1
First Floor, W11
Fung Shing, WC2

Golden Dragon, W1
The Halkin, SW1
Hilaire, SW7
L'Incontro, SW1
Kalamaras, W2
Lanesborough, The Conservatory, SW1
Lansdowne, NW1
Leith's, W11
Lou Pescadou, SW5
Maison Novelli, EC1
Mr Kong, WC2
Mon Plaisir, WC2
Montana, SW6
Neal Street Restaurant, WC2
Noughts 'n' Crosses, W5
192, W11
L'Oranger, SW1

Orsino, W11
Pizzeria Castello, SE1
Quaglino's, SW1
Ransome's Dock, SW11
Rules, WC2
St George's Hotel, The Heights, W1
The Savoy, River Restaurant, WC2
Snows on the Green, W6
Soho Soho, W1
Sree Krishna, SW17
Sri Siam, W1
Stafford Hotel, SW1
Tabac, W10
La Truffe Noire, SE1
Village Bistro, N6

The Good Food Club 1996

Many thanks to all the following people who contributed to this year's
Guide ...

Ms Jean Aberdour
Mrs Jill Abraham
Dr A.H. Abrahams
Dr Sidney
  Abrahams
A.D. Abrams
J. Abramsky
Sir John J. Acland
Miss Sally Acomb
Kate Adams
Robert Adams
Peter Adcock
William Adolph
Ms Jacqueline
  Ah-Fong
M. van Agnew
John Aird
Lesley Aird
S.T. Akers
Nigel Alabaster
R.C. Albert
Edward Album
Mr and Mrs David
  Alcock
Ian and Alison
  Aldridge
R.C. Aldridge
Minda and Stanley
  Alexander
Dr and Mrs A.A.
  Alibhai
C. Allen
Martin Allen
Ms Judith Allen-
  Buyers
Mrs E. Alston
Jamie Ambrose
K.E. Amsden
Derek Andrews
Gwen and Peter
  Andrews
M.M. Angeloglou
Mr and Mrs Kurt
  Angelrath
Mrs A.E. Anstead
Trevor Appleby
Mrs Cynthia Archer
Mrs Heather Archer
Miss M. Archer
P.F. Arden
Mrs Y. Aris
M.E. Arnold

Dr Philip Arnold
Mrs H.G. Ashburn
Brian Ashby
M.P. Ashley
Peter Ashley
Mrs Hazel Astley
George Atkinson
M.W. Atkinson
Andrew Averill
Ms Lorraine Awdry
Michael Awty
George Ayres
D.S. Baber
K.B. Bacon
Mr and Mrs R.
  Baggallay
Jane and Martin
  Bailey
Richard Bailey
Rod Bailey
Mrs S. Bailey
Martin Bainbridge
Mr and Mrs J. Baird
Mr and Mrs I.
  Balaam
Charlie Ballantyne
Ian Balmer
Ms Diana Bannister
Mr and Mrs Bill
  Barber
Dr M.C. Barchard
Andrew and Mary
  Barclay
H.F.H. Barclay
S. Barder
Micheael Bardsley
Chris Barker
John Barker
Lt Col K.A.S.
  Barker
Ms Stella Barnass
K.J. Barnes
Ms Erica Barnett
Mr and Mrs K.A.
  Barnett
P.A. Barnett
Michael Barrington
Tony Barrow
B.J. Barry
Richard Barry
Dr G.D.
  Bartholomew

Matthew Bartlett
Mr and Mrs G.D.
  Barwell
Alan Bates
Dr Jonathan Bates
Mrs M.G. Bateson
Eleanor and
  Desmond Bath
Jeremy Bath
Mrs Romney
  Bathurst
Mrs Marion Batt
Dr John Batty
Ms Susan Baulch
Michael and Helen
  Baws
Conrad Bayliss
Philip Bean
Mr and Mrs R.
  Beard
Lord Beaumont
Peter Beaumont
Mr and Mrs Thomas
  Beaumont
Ms E. Becker
Ms Diana Beckett
F.R. Beckett
Quentin and Irene
  Bedoyere
Mr and Mrs Simon
  Bedwell
P. Behenna
Chris Beighton
John Beining-
  Riches
Mrs A. Bellerby
Prof John Bennett
Norman Bennett
Mr and Mrs R.G.
  Bennett
J.P. Bennett-Powell
Mrs Marjorie
  Bentham
William Bentsen
Mrs Joan Berad
Bill Beresford
Norman Berlis
Mrs Gabriele
  Berneck
Miss C. Berry
Mr and Mrs E.
  Berry

P.E. Berry
Mr and Mrs
  Michael Besomi
Miss J.F. Beusch
Jeff Bidwell
Mrs J. Binnie
David and Elsie
  Binstead
Chris Birch
G.H. Birch
Michael Bird
R.G. Birt
I. Birtwell
Ms Anne Blackburn
C.T. Blackburn
Mr and Mrs Tim
  Blackwell
Mrs M.L. Blacow
John Blagden
Diana Blake
Howard Blake
Mr and Mrs J.L.
  Blakey
Nick Blakey
Mrs J.A. Blanks
Mr and Mrs E.A.
  Blenkarne
Mrs M.G.
  Blenkinsop
Edward Blincoe
Mr and Mrs S. Bliss
J. Blunden
Dr S.M. Blunden
K.W. Blyth
Julian Boles
Mrs Julia Bolwell
N.J. Bonham-Carter
Mr and Mrs E.W.
  Booth
Jane Booty
Martin and Elaine
  Borish
Mrs Linda Bosher
John Bosomworth
Peter Bottomley
Philippe Boucheron
Canon M.A.
  Bourdeaux
Mrs Gillian
  Bouskill
Mike Boustred
J.J. Bowden

A.J. Bowen
Dr F. Bowie
J.L. Bowker
Kevin Bowyer
P.J. Bowyer
Mrs J.A. Boyd
Peter Boyes
Brian Braby
Mr and Mrs K.G. Bracey
Sarah Bradbury
Julian Bradley
Drs David and Elsa Bradshaw
Barry Brahams
A.R.O. Bramley
David and Barbara Brann
Nial Brannigan
Dr A.M. Braverman
Karyn and Richard Bray
Mr and Mrs Nick Breeze
M.J. Brett
Mr and Mrs Edwin Brew
Mrs Brewer
Mrs Jonica Bridge
Commodore Richard Bridges
Mr and Mrs John Brierley
Dr R.H. Britnell
J.F. Britten
B.J. Britton
K.M. Broddy
V. Brogden
Roy Bromell
H. Bromley
Ms Louise Brook
C.L. Brookes
Douglas Brooks
Alun Brooks-Moore
David Brown
Dr and Mrs D.G. Brown
Duncan Brown
Michael Brown
Wallace Brown
Nick Browne
Mr and Mrs D.W.K. Bruce
George Bruce
Dr and Mrs J. Brunskill
Robin Brunton
Mr and Mrs Edgar Bryant
Mrs K. Bryden
Mrs Daphne Bullock

Mr Michael Burch
Dr A. Burden
Mr C. Burdon
Paul Burn
Peter Burnham
E.B. Burns
John and Barbara Burns
Ms Lisa Burns
Mr M.H. Burr
His Honour Judge Michael Burr
Mrs Mary Burston
Ian Burton
Ms S. Burton
M. Busby
Mrs K.B. Bushen
Jane Butler
Mr and Mrs Paul Butler
J.G. Butlin
M.J. Byrne
Ms Carole Byron
Ms Sally Byron-Johnson
Peter Byworth
D. Cahill
Prof Robert Cahn
Dr Anne Calder
Ms C. Caldwell
Mrs S.M. Calvert
Michael Calwell
Mrs Diane Cameron
Ben Campbell
Mrs Phyllis Campbell
J. Candell
G.A. Cannon
Mark and Catherine Cannon
D.G. Carr
Ms M. Carr
Peter Carr
Dr John Carroll
Christopher Carrow
John Carter
Ms Miranda Carter
N. Carter
P.E. Carter
Mrs S. Cartlidge
J.A.H. Cartwright
Dr and Mrs J.S. Cartwright
Robert Carty
Richard Cashmore
Mr and Mrs L.A. Catford
Dr R.E. Catlow
J.A. Cave
Alan Chadwick
R.G. Chadwick
Mrs Susan Chait

J.E. Chalk
Mrs Mary Chamberlin
Richard and Milana Chamberlain
Nitesh Chapanery
A.W.T. Chapman
Ronald Chapman
Susan Chappell
Mr and Mrs Barry Charles
S. Charles
Mrs E. Chatten
Mrs E.A. Cherrington
W.J. Chesneau
Mrs Gillian Childs
T. Chippendale
Ms Ann Chiswick
J.L. Christie
Mrs S.B. Clamp
Mrs G. Clark
M.M.A. Clark
Mrs Patricia Clark
W.M. Clarke
Mrs B. Clatworthy
R.E. Claude
Philip Clay
Ms Sue Claybyn
Mrs Margaret Clayson
R.S. Clayton
Alan Clegg
Mrs Jennifer Clegg
Dr E.J. Clery
Kenneth Cleveland
Mrs V. Clewley
Mrs M.D. Cliff
P. Clifford
E. Clifford White
Mr and Mrs Geoffrey Clift
Simon Clifton
Doug and Avrille Close
P. Clough
Iain Cochrane
S. Cochrane
Mr and Mrs L. Coggel
W.F. Coghill
Prof J. Cohen
Prof Percy Cohen
Ms Wendy Cohen
Dr John Coker
A. Cole
Mr and Mrs G.G. Coleman
Paul and Pauline Collinge
Stephen Collinson
Ms P. Collyns

Mrs Hannah Colton
M. Colton
Ms Elizabeth Colville
R.T. Combe
V. Comber and J. Bellini
Miss S.G. Comins
M. Comninos
Robert Constant
Ms Sally Conway
Miss B.J.B. Cook
W.T. Cook
A. Cooper
Peter Cooper
Philip Cooper
Dr and Mrs J.C.W. Cope
Mrs Katharine Copeland
A. Copley
J. Corbluth
E.A. Corkish
Garry Corkish
Mrs A. Cornall
L.J. Cornell
Mrs Katy Corrales
David Costain
Mrs J. Coton
Simon Cottrell
Mr and Mrs C. Coultass
I.D. Courtnage
N.A. Coussmaker
Teresa Cowherd
Margaret and Stuart Cox
Michael Cox
Roger Cox
Richard Coxon
Mrs D. Coyne
J.H. Craig
R.D. Cramond
Mark Cran
Mr and Mrs Peter Crane
Jock Craven
K. Craven
J.D. Crawley
Mrs Pamela Crichton
T.E. Crompton
Ms Helen Crookston
R.J. Crosby
J.D. Crosland
Rodney Cross
Simon Crutchley
Richard Cullen
Noel Cunningham-Reid
C.J. Cussens

Jill Cutting
Dr and Mrs S.R.D. da Prato
Ms Dorothy Daniels
Mr and Mrs L. Darby
Wing Cdr R. Dauncey
David Davey
Mr and Mrs P. Davey
Major A.M. David
W.H. Davidson
Anthony Davies
Brian Davies
Dr Dorian Davies
Duncan Davies
Mr and Mrs Evan Davies
Graham Davies
Ian Davies
J. Davies
Dr Jill Davies
J.M.P. Davies
P. Davies
P.W.H. Davies
R.G. Davies
Tim Davies
Andrew Davis
Alan and Jacqueline Dawes
Ms Angelina Dawson
Mr and Mrs Keith Dawson
Sheelagh Dawson
M.J. Day
Mr and Mrs Charles Daybell
Mr and Mrs D. Deacon
Air Commodore John De'Ath
N.C. Dee
Keith Deane
M. Deeks
Mr and Mrs A.E. Demby
Mrs Ann Dempsey
Jonathan and Louise Denby
Geoffrey Dence
Mr and Mrs George Denton
I.C. Dewey
Mrs V. Dews
Jack Digby
J. Dillon
Simon Dixon
A. Docherty

Mr and Mrs Ken Dodsworth
Mr and Mrs Ian Donaldson
Mrs S. Donkin
Graham Dooley
James and Mary Douglas
Ms Rona Douglas
Bruce Douglas-Mann
R.J. Dover
Justin Downes
R.T. Downey
Colin Dowse
J.T. Drazin
David Dry
Mrs Anne du Croz
John Ducker
Mrs A. Duffin
Ian Duke
Rev James Duncan
Mrs Linda Dunlop
Denis Durno
Mr and Mrs Durston
Clive Dutson
Claude Duval
Ms Amanda Dwek
Paul Dwyer
Dr M. Dyer-Smith
John Earthy
Colin Eastaugh
Dr and Mrs Lindsay Easton
Mr and Mrs K. Eckett
Ms Linda Edward
Mrs Aileen Edwards
Dr and Mrs E.M.H. Edwards
Mrs Frances Edwards
Guy Edwards
J.W. Edwards
Roger Edwards
Mr and Mrs Philip Egerton
Mrs Elizabeth Eggington
John Elder
Philip Eley
G. Elflett
Steven Elief
Mrs C.M. Elkington
R.A. Elliott
D.R. Ellis
Mrs F.E. Ellis
J.G. Ellis
R.C. Ellis

Mr and Mrs D.D. Embury
Prof and Mrs C.E. Engel
Robert Entwistle
Mrs Pam Ernest
Dr Edgar Ernstbrunner
Mr and Mrs John Ette
Mrs S.A Eustice
David Evans
Peter Evans
Ramon Evans
Mr and Mrs Barry Everett
Mrs A. Ewens
Claire and David Fader
John Fahy
Mohammed Faisal
Jed Falby
N. Fallowfield
Mrs K. Farmer
Ms Ann Farrow
Ruth Fasht
R. Fausset
Peter and Josie Fawcett
Clive Feingold
G.A. Fenn
Ruth Fenney
A.B.X. Fenwick
Ms Alison Ferguson
Mrs G.E. Fickling
R.L. Field
Prof F. Fielden
R.J. Filby
G.B. Findlay
Dr N. Finer
T.R. Finlow
Dr N.B. Finter
M. Firth
Mrs Alison Fisher
M.H. Fishman
Julian Fitz-Earle
Mrs Elizabeth Fitzpatrick
T.C. Flanagan
Mrs Ann Fletcher
A.T.R. Fletcher
Clare Fletcher
Mrs D.R. Flint
Keith Flinter
M.R.D. Foot
Adrian Foreman
Michael Forrest
Mrs P.L. Forrest
Mrs Margaret Forrester
Mrs Christina Forster

William Forsyth
Mr and Mrs Roger Forward
Mrs C. Foster
J.M. Foster
Peter Foster
Stephen Foster
Miss T.E. Foster
R.J.N. Fowler
Mrs Joan Fox
R.D. Fox
Tony Fox
Mrs P. Frankel
R. Frankenburg
A.P.P. Frankl
R. Frankland
Dr M.L. Franks
Mrs Sarah Fransen
D.O. Fraser
Mr and Mrs S. Fraser
John Freebairn
Dr and Mrs Anthony Freeman
John Freeman
M.R. Freeman
Mrs V. de Freitas-Sacchilary
C.W. Freyer
Ms Patricia Frost
Ms Claire Fuller
Mrs D. Furby
K.F. Gabbertas
John Gagg
Mrs W.M. Gallagher
Mr and Mrs I.J.B. Galloway
C.A. Ganderton
Bernard Garston
Miss B. Gaskell
Mr and Mrs D.M. Gavin
Dr Ian Gavin
A.J.C. Geddes
Sqn Ldr M.S. Geddes
F.E. Geldeard
Hunter Gholson
Mrs A. Gibbons
Mr and Mrs Austin Gibbons
Stephen Gibbs
Richard Gibson
Ken Gilbert
Mrs Mary Ann Gilchrist
Mrs G. Giles
Ian Gilkison
Mr and Mrs P.G. Gill

Caroline Gillies
J.M. Gillies
Mrs J. Gilligan
D.A. Gilmour
S.H. Gilpin
Ms Sarah Girling
Ms Christine
  Gleadell
J. Gloster-Smith
Mrs P.M. Glover
Roger Glover
Christopher Godber
Mrs Gillian
  Goddard
Brian Godden
Ms Sue Godden
Mr and Mrs J.C.
  Godfrey
M.A. Godwin
Ms Maria Goldberg
Joy and Raymond
  Goldman
Mrs Rebecca
  Goldsmith
Richard Goldstein
G. Goldston
Mark Golinsky
Peter Gomola
Tom Gondris
Steve Goodacre
Mr and Mrs David
  Goodall
D. Goodger
Colin Goodman
David Gordon
Mrs V.K. Gordon
M. Gordon-Russell
Mrs A. Gore
Dr John Gosden
Mrs J.B. Gould
Mrs C. Govier
Dr P.E. Gower
M.B. Gowers
Mrs A. Graham
D. Graham
Ms Jill Grain
S. Grainger
Simon Grant
Dr Travers Grant
Michael Gray
Bill Green
Mrs D.P. Green
Jeffrey Green
L.H. Green
T.G. Green
Alan Greene
Ms Francis Greene
C. Greenhow
Jim Greenwood
Prof K.J. Gregory
Dr Karen Gregory
M. Gregory

A.K. Grice
Edward Griffen
Moira Griffiths
Peter Griffiths
N.M. Grimwood
Lt K.R. Groves
B.G. Gunary
A. Gunnis
Claire and Jim
  Gunyon
Pamela and
  Raymond Guy
Ms Alison
  Habershaw
Rita Hale
Mr and Mrs Hall
Dr Bryan Hall
C.J. Hall
Gail Hall
Mrs P.A. Hall
Mr and Mrs Peter
  Hall
J.H. Hallam
W.J. Hallett
Tom Halsall
Mr and Mrs R.E.
  Halstead
Nicholas Hamblin
Mr and Mrs W.M.J.
  Hames
James Hamilton
John Hamilton
J. Hamilton Nairn
G.B.T. Hammond
Mrs M. Hampson-
  Moores
G.S. Hand
F.G. Hankins
Mrs E. Hannah
Rod Hannam
Michael Hannett
Dr A.E. Hanwell
Bob Harding
R. Harding
Ms Cathy Hardman
Mrs Anne Hardy
Jonathan Harfield
David Harkness
Mrs June Harney
Robert Harper
R.B. Harries
A.G. Harris
D. Harris
G.G. Harris
James Harris
Katy Harris
Raymond Harris
Barry Harrison
Duncan Harrison
Mr and Mrs D.J.
  Harrold
D.J. Harrow

P.D. Hart
J.D. Hartley
Alan Harvey
Dr Peter Harvey
Oliver Hatch
D. Hatton
Ms Joy Hatwood
Eric Hauxwell
Frank Hawkins
G.H. Hawkins
Mr and Mrs d'Arcy
  Hay
R.G. Haydon
Dr A.M. Hayes
Chris Hayhurst
Ms Siobhan Haynes
Cdr A.C.
  Haythornthwaite
Mrs J. Healy
Canon Neil
  Heavisides
Mr and Mrs P.
  Hellawell
Ms Veronica
  Hemmings
Hugh Henry
Peter Hensher
Craig Herron
Lord Herschell
Dr and Mrs J.
  Herzberg
Gad Heuman
Chris Hickling
D.A. Hickling
Michael Hicks
F.R. Hilborne
A.A. Hill
A.C. Hill
Alan Hill
K.E. Hill
Mr and Mrs M. Hill
Dr Oscar Hill
Robert Hill
Wendy Hillary
Mrs H.C. Hillman
Mr and Mrs D.W.
  Hills
Mrs L.C. Hinchley
E. Hinds
Mr and Mrs R.
  Hinds
Mr and Mrs G.A.
  Hinton
Mrs Elizabeth Hjort
Ms Penelope Hoare
Michael Hocking
Mrs Marilyn
  Hodsdon
Desmond Hogan
Sir Michael Hogg
Mrs Anne Hoggan
Simon Hoggart

Christopher
  Holborow
David Holbrook
Roger Hole
Ian Holland
Andrew Hollett
Ms Deborah
  Holliday
Mrs K. Hollis
Nick Hollis
Mr and Mrs David
  Holmes
Mr and Mrs R.
  Holmes
Mrs R.A. Homan
John Hondros
Mr and Mrs Honour
Dr and Mrs David
  Hooker
J. Hooper
Mrs Nicola Hopkins
Mr and Mrs S.W.
  Hopkins
Ralph Hopton
Mr and Mrs R.H.
  Horncastle
Mrs M. Horne
Mr and Mrs W.R.
  Horne
Mrs F. Horsley
Mrs S.P. Horsley
Linda Horton-
  Fawkes
Keith Hotten
Basil Hoult
David House
Ms E. Howard
Michael Howarth
Zelda and Ian
  Howarth
Mrs Kate Howe
D.P. Howell
Geoffrey Howell
Major-General
  Lloyd Howell
John Howells
T.H. Howells
Mrs Dianne
  Howlett
Mr and Mrs Huck
Mr and Mrs David
  Hudd
Mr and Mrs Peter
  Hudson
Mrs S. Hudson
Bob Hughes
Connie Hughes
John and Jennifer
  Hughes
Jon Hughes
Mrs Pamela Hull
Ms Alison Hulland

Sir Alan Hume
Mme Francoise
  Humphrey
Dr Tim Hunt
D.R. Hunter
William Hunter
Rev J.W. Hunwicke
C.J. Hurd
J.D.W. Hurd
Marvin Hurst
R.A. Husain
M. Hutchings
D.J. Hutchinson
Benny Hutchison
Mrs J. Hutchison
Robin and Inge
  Hyman
T.J. Hypher
Peter and Christine
  Iles
S.J. Illingworth
Mrs Rosemary Inge
Michael Irvine
Dr S. Irving
Mrs P.M. Islip
Leslie Iversen
Mrs B.W. Jack
Mr and Mrs
  Jackman
James McG.
  Jackson
Mrs M.B. Jackson
P.H. Jacobsen
Eric and Lois Jaffe
Mrs G. James
K.W. James
John Jamieson
Edward Jamilly
M. Janson
Martin Janson
David Jebb
Mr and Mrs P.
  Jeffery
Elizabeth Jenkins
David Jervois
Dr Michael Jewess
Ms Jane Jewkes
B.M. Joce
Gareth Johns
Mrs S. Johns
Kate Johnson
Miss R.I. Johnson
Dr I.H.D. Johnston
Alasdair Johnstone
Mrs M. Johnstone
R.M. Jolly
Miss Angharad
  Jones
Mrs Audrey Jones
C.F.C. Jones
C.R. Jones
Mr and Mrs D.W.
  Jones

David Jones
Derek Jones
Douglas Jones
Ms Elizabeth Jones
Ian Jones
Mrs J. Jones
K. Jones
Mark Jones
Medwyn Jones
Paul Jones
Dr and Mrs R.W.
  Jones
Sarah Jones
Peter Jordan
N.A. Joseph
Nathan and Sarah
  Joseph
B. Jowitt
Peter Jowitt
Mr and Mrs M.
  Joyce
M.R. Judd
G. Kahan
A.K. Kameen
Dr Leon Kaufman
J.G. Kavanagh
Ms Georgiana
  Keane
W.B. Keates
John Keating
Mr and Mrs J.
  Keeble
Dr and Mrs B.E.
  Keen
Ms Sheila Keene
A. Kellett-Long
Dominic Kelly
Mr and Mrs W.T.
  Kelly
Roger Kenber
P.M.H. Kendall
Jim Kenyon
Joseph Keppie
Ms Marion Kerr
Rev Peter Kettle
Ms Elizabeth Key
Mrs M.A. Keywood
David and Sally
  Kibble
J.H. Kilby
Mr and Mrs Peter
  Kimble
P.J. King
Roy King
Mr and Mrs R.
  Kingslake
Mrs J. Kingsley
Dr B.W. Kington
James Kinley
Mrs P. Kinney
G.L. Kipling

Mr and Mrs
  Michael Kirk
Ms Janet Kite
Dr Michael and
  Mary Klaber
Mrs Sylvia Knapp
Mrs J. Knight
A.J. Knights
Mrs N. Knoop
C. Kone
Dr Lionel
  Kopelowitz
Mr and Mrs Niels
  Krag
Prof I.R.H. Kramer
P. Krause
Dr and Mrs Lionel
  Kreeger
Dr P.A. Laite
Mr and Mrs B.A.
  Lambert
A.J. Lamberty
Mrs J.M. Lambeth
Gordon Lammie
Ian Lancaster
Ms Lydia Lancaster
P. Lane
Tim Lang
Ms N. Lank
Mr and Mrs A.
  Lanzl
Mr and Mrs W.
  Lapthorne
Mr and Mrs P.
  Laszlo
Joel Latner
Jessica Latta
A. Laurence
Mr and Mrs Kevan
  Lavender
Andy Lawman
Dr and Mrs J.R.
  Lawrence
Mrs M.E. Lawrence
Stephen Lawrence
Susanne Lawrence
A.J. Lawrie
Norman Lazenby
Mr and Mrs David
  le Fevre
J.L.R. Leach
S. Leach
Christopher Lee
Geoffrey Lee
Cdr J.M. Lefeaux
Ms Paula Leigh
C.L. Leighton
P.L. Leonard
D.J. Lethem
Lionel Leventhal
A.S. Levitt
Dr Alun Lewis

Clive Lewis
Mr and Mrs Jerry
  Lewis
Mrs Anne Lewis-
  Smith
Ms Jane Light
Mr and Mrs R.G.
  Lightwood
Ms L. Lim
John Lindsay
Ian Lindsey
Ms Jenny Linford
D.R. Linnell
H.C. Lipscomb
Mrs M. Littleboy
Richard Littlejohns
Mr and Mrs B.T.E.
  Livesey
A.F. Llewellin
Mr and Mrs N.
  Llewellyn
James Lloyd
Rob Lloyd
Ms Samantha Lloyd
Ms Tracey Lloyd
J.R.C. Loader
Andrew
  Lobbenberg
Herbert Lobl
Mrs Brigitta Lock
Paul Lock
Ms Janet Lockett
Mrs S.M. Lockyear
Ms Victoria Logue
Field Marshal Lord
  Bramall
Ian Louden
Kristian Louth
Mr and Mrs F.E.H.
  Lovelace
John Lovelock
Andrew Low
Mrs V. Low
Mr and Mrs P.A.
  Lowater
Sean Lowde
Ms Catherine Lowe
C.P. Lowell
Janet and Tom
  Lowndes
Paul Lucas
P.S. Luckin
J.N. Lunn
Ms Katharine Lyall
Ms Toni Lyng
Graham Lyons
Miles Maceacharn
R.B. MacGeachy
Mr and Mrs J.A.
  MacInnes
A.J. Macintosh
C.F. Mack

Dr A.I. Macleod
Elizabeth
  Macpherson
Charles Maddocks
Mr and Mrs Chris
  Madigan
Dr B.A. Maguire
Peter Mahaffey
Mr and Mrs D.L.
  Maidment
Mr and Mrs Terry
  Malaure
G. Malcolm
Ms Chris
  Mallaband
M.J. Mallett
Ros Mallinson
Ms Betty Malmo
Mr and Mrs David
  Malyon
Mrs Joan Manchip
George Mandow
Trevor Manhire
M. March
Andrew Marks
Laurence Marks
Mr and Mrs
  Maurice Markson
Dr C. Markus
Mrs M.T. Marley
E.A.L. Marliniw
Leonard Marlow
Mr and Mrs Noel
  Marriott
Mrs June Marsden
Ms Chris Marsh
Mrs J. Marsh
Dr and Mrs
  Rosemary Marsh
W. Marsh
Prof John Marshall
R.A. Marshall
R.F.D. Marshall
R.O. Marshall
Mr and Mrs T.F.
  Marshall
Mr and Mrs St John
  Marston
Dr D.J.R. Martin
Ian Martin
Ms Jeanett Martin
Roger and Joan
  Martin
Tony and Heather
  Martin
Christopher Mason-
  Watts
Robert Masters
W.G. Mather
Miss G. Mathew-
  Joyce
M.R. Matthews

Mr and Mrs M.R.A.
  Matthews
Mrs Margaret
  Matthews
S. Matthews
Mrs T. Matthews
Ian May
Mr and Mrs Nick
  McAndrew
Ms Janet McCallum
Mr and Mrs G.A.
  McConnell
Jean McConnell
John McCracken
Mr and Mrs
  McCraith
Ms Ruth McCulloch
Ms B. McDowall
Mrs B. McDowell
Alastair McEwan
Mr and Mrs I.S.
  McEwan
Prof and Dr I.D.
  McFarlane
Charles McFeeters
Colin and Lilian
  McGhee
Dr Ian McGill
Mrs Jenny
  McGlyne
Mrs May McIver
Mr and Mrs
  Maurice McKee
Mr and Mrs John
  McKenna
Colin McKerrow
Ms Anna McKinney
Ian McLaren
G.M.H.
  McLoughlin
J.P. McMahon
Mr and Mrs B.S.
  McNicholas
Dr Irene McNicol
Richard Meacock
H.C. Medcalf
W.G. Medd
Dr Ted Megaw
Ms Angela Megson
William Meikle
Lucas Mellinger
P.O.J. Melville
Ms Diane Mercer
M.E. Mercer
Ms Hilary Meth
Earl of Mexborough
John and Karen
  Middleweek
Ms Caroline
  Midmore
Lady Milburn
Paul Milican

Ms Ruth Millan
Mr and Mrs Alan
  Miller
Raphael Miller
Don Mills
G.E. Mills
Michael Mills
O.S. Mills
Ms Marion Milmo
Mrs S.B. Milne
Ms Amy Minden
Adrian Mitchell
Mrs Jane Mitchell
J.S. Mitchell
Mrs Shirley
  Mitchell
Miss R.C. Moles
Dr P.L. Mollison
John Molyneux
C. Moncreiffe
Dr Barry Monk
William Monk
Dr L.R. Montague
Ms Julie
  Montgomery-
  Smith
Colin Moore
E.A. Moore
Jon Moore
L.F. Moore
T.J. Moorey
Ms Annie Moreton
Mrs L.K. Morffew
Cliff Morgan
Hugh Morgan
Aubrey Morris
Miss Deborah
  Morris
Mrs K. Morris
Prof Norman Morris
V.G.F. Morris
Mrs Renée Morris-
  Young
Mr and Mrs Aryeh
  Moss
Brian Moss
Keith Moss
Richard Moy
David Mudd
Dr Catherine
  Mufford
Mr and Mrs Matt
  Mulcahy
A. Mumford
Paul Munday
K. Mundy
David Munro
G.R. Murray
Mr and Mrs M.D.
  Murray
Mrs S. Murray

Mr and Mrs P.
  Murray-Smith
Jane Myddelton
R.E. Nagle
Julia Napier
Kerry Napuk
Mr and Mrs B.
  Natton
Dr and Mrs A.
  Naylor
C.H. Naylor
David Naylor
Thomas Neate
Mrs Anne Needham
Mrs Sandra Neher
R.H. Nelson
Mr and Mrs
  Malcolm
  Nettleton
Dr Richard Neville
Mrs Francesca
  Newbery
P.A. Newell
Stephen Newell
Philip Newfield
Brian Newman
H.P. Newman
Alec Newsham
John Nicholas
Tim Nichols
Ms Mavis
  Nicholson
Dr J.R. Norman
Michael Norman
Peter Normanton
J.G. Norris
Mr and Mrs Philip
  Norris
Graham Norwood
David Nutt
Charles Oatwig-
  Thain
Mr and Mrs M.
  O'Brien
John Oddey
Dr C. Offord
W.L. Ogden
R.A.L. Ogston
Prof Anthony Ogus
Mrs M. O'Higgins
L.S. Oliver
Ms Susan O'Neil
  Roe
J.J. Ooms
Greg O'Reilly
Mr and Mrs Frank
  Orford
David Osborn
Tom Osborne
Ms Jill Otley
Mrs B.J. Otway

Mr and Mrs J. Overton
Mrs M.A. Owens
P.C. Owens
William Pack
R. Packham
Mrs M.C. Packman
Aidan Paddick
J.B. Page
Dr S.D. Page
Nadia Pallatt
Mr and Mrs R. Palmer
Mr and Mrs Panton
E.A. Parczuk
Derek Parker
Jim Parker
J.J. Parker
Dr R.B. Parker
Mrs Sue Parker
J.A Parkinson
Dr M.J. Parks
David Parnell
David Parry
G. Parry
Mrs H. Parsons
Mr and Mrs John Parsons
T.G. Parsons
Charlotte Pasetti
D.A. Passey
Archibold Paterson
Robin Paterson
James Patrick
Mark Patrick
N. Patterson
Michael Pattison
Stephen Pawley
J.R.G. Pay
David Pearson
John Pearson
Ms Susan K. Peat
Mr and Mrs Oliver Peck
David Peel
Geoff Peel
Ms Pam Peers
Mrs Jane Penson
Mr and Mrs C.S. Perkins
G. Perkins
Ms Deborah Perlin
Helen Peston
Mrs C.S. Petherick-Brian
Malcolm Pettit
Peter Petts
E. Pheby
Michael Phelan
C. Philips
Stephen Phillips
R.A.R. Phillips

Dr and Mrs D. Pickering
Michael and Elaine Pickersgill
Dr A.D. Picton
Richard Pierce
R.G. Pilkington
Mr and Mrs S. Pilling
David Pinder
C. Piper
C.A. Pissarides
Michael Pitel
Miss Angela Pitt
Hugh Pitt
Mrs J. Plante Cleall
Mr and Mrs Clive Platman
Prof Peter Plesch
Mrs A.M. Pochon
Simon Pollentime
Mr and Mrs B. Pomphrey
David Poole
Ms Lucy Portch
K. Porteous Wood
Judith Pottesman
John Poulter
Malcolm Povey
Joan Powell
Ms Debra Power
Prof and Mrs G. Pratt
Mr and Mrs S.G. Pratt
Mr and Mrs Steven Preece
D.B. Prell
Mrs A. Preston
H.H.H. Preston
A.J. Price
Mrs Susan Price
Colin and Sally Price-Smith
Mrs S.M. Priest
D.J. Priestley
Peter Prior
Mrs Sue Pritt
Prof R.P.M. Procter
Simon Pugh
Robert Pullar
Howard Pursey
Mrs Joan Putz
Mr and Mrs Louis Pyke
Axel Queval
Ms Ingrid Radford
Ms Jean Radford
David Raines
Mrs Joan Rainey
Luke and Anne Rainey

John Rainsford
Anna Ralph
Mrs J.F. Ralph
Miss L. Ramsay
Mrs Sarah Ramsden
Miss J.M. Ramsey
Mr and Mrs T. Randall
Dr A.M. Rankin
Mr and Mrs G. Ransom
Mrs Caroline Raphael
Mr and Mrs Arnold Rattenbury
Peter Ratzer
Gerald Ratzin
Marc Rawcliffe
Mrs D. Rawlings
K. Rawson
Martin Raybould
Mrs Mary Rayner
Prof Stephen Reckert
Mrs Rosemary Recordon
Mr and Mrs M. Redfern
Dr A.R. Reece
Alec Reed
Ms Camilla Rees
Mr and Mrs Reeves
Mr and Mrs Andrew Reeves
Simon and Lorraine Reeves
Mike Reid
Dr and Mrs W. Reith
Mrs Avril Rennie
J.P. Rettie
John Reuter
Mr and Mrs John Reuter
Ms Carolyn Reynier
Janet Rich
Mr and Mrs David Richards
Heather Richards
David Richardson
Miss K.L. Richardson
Paul Richardson
S.J. Richardson
Carol Riddick
Robin Riddihough
Mr and Mrs Peter Riggs
P.F.B. Riley
Gordon Ringrose
F. Ripley
Ms Charlotte Rix

Ms Celia Robbins
Alan Roberts
Mr and Mrs J. Roberts
Mrs L.M. Roberts
David Robertson
Mrs Maureen Robertson
Mr and Mrs Nigel Robertson
Mrs A. Robinson
D.R. Robinson
J.A. Robinson
M.A. Robinson
Mrs Philippa Robinson
R.S. Robinson
Mrs Sheila Robinson
Mrs Sue Robinson
John Robotham
J. Rochelle
A. Rodgers
Anne Rogers
Sir Frank Rogers
Dr Eric Rose
Mrs Evelyn Rose
G.A. Rose
Mr and Mrs Jeffery Rose
Mrs Cicely Ross
Mark Rostovsky
Anthony Rota
Ms Anita Rouse
Michael Rowland
W.R. Rowland
Mrs Jill Rowley
I.J. Roxburgh
Mrs Angela Royle
Jan Royle
Peter Rudd
Stephen Rudge
A.J. Rugg
Dr I. Runcie
Mrs Pat Rushall
Elizabeth Russell Taylor
Mr and Mrs B. Rustchynskyj
Max Rutherston
J.S. Rutter
W. Ruxton
Mrs A.L. Ruysenaars
Charles Ryall
Ms Ilse Ryder
R.S. Ryder
Mrs C. Ryland
Mrs P.A. Rymond
Miss N. Sacchetti
Ms Joy Sadlier
Kashif Salim

Mrs S. Sality
J.G. Samson
Ms Julia Samuel
Barry Samuels
Mrs Sheila Sanders
Ms Kate Santon
Louise Sargent
Dr C.J.P. Saunders
D.M.S. Saunders
Ms Rosemarie
  Saunders
Ms Anne Savage
Mrs J.A. Sawkins
Mrs C. Sawyer
Paul Saxon
R.J. Sayer
Derek Scantlebury
Dr C.J. Schilling
Michael Schofield
R. Schwarz
P.D. Scott
S. Scott
Stella Scott
Tony Scull
Mrs Ann Scurfield
J.M. Seddon
J.R.E. Sedgwick
Mrs Alison Sennett
M. Serventi
Keith Seston
Ms Christine
  Seward-Byld
R. Shaile
S. Share
Mrs Sheila Sharp
Dr J.T.R. Sharrock
Frank Shaw
Mrs M. Shaw
Sir Giles Shaw
Michael and
  Elizabeth Shaw
Mr and Mrs P.J.
  Shaw
Peter Shaw-Sadler
Ms Lucy Sheather
Barry and Glennis
  Sheldon
David Shephard
Mrs Elspeth
  Shepherd
Mrs Louise
  Sheppard
R.J. Shersby
A. Sherwood
Ms Lorraine Short
Sandi Short
T.W. Short
Mrs C. Shroeder
Brian Silverstone
George Sim
B. Simmons

Mr and Mrs L.J.
  Simmons
Andrew Simpson
C.H. Sims
Brendan Sinnolt
P.E. Skerrett
Philip Skottowe
D.A. Slade
Fred Slegg
Mr and Mrs K.
  Smales
Simon Small
N.S.L. Smart
R. Smedley
B.M. Smith
D.C. Smith
Ms E. Smith
Godfrey Smith
Ms Jane Smith
Mrs Jennifer Smith
Jonathan Smith
J.R.M. Smith
Matthew Smith
Neil Smith
Mr and Mrs N.L.V.
  Smith
R.C.F. Smith
Robin Smith
Miss S.A. Smith
Mrs J.C. Smye
N.M. Smyth
Jonathan Sofer
D.A. Soley
D.J. Solomon
Mrs Jane Solomons
E.V. Somers
Nicholas Somers
J.E. Sommer
R.M. Sorbie
Mrs M. South
Wing Cdr R.M.
  Sparkes
J. Sparks
Alan Spedding
Dr M.E. Speechly-
  Dick
Mrs A.F. Spencer
L. Spencer
Drs R.and J.
  Spencer-Jones
Jeremy Spenser
Mr and Mrs W.R.
  Spink
J.F. Spinlove
Prof M. Spiro
Ms L. Squire
Mr and Mrs A.J.W.
  Stancomb
George Standing
T.J. Stanford
David Stanley
T.J.G. Stannus

M. Stansherd
Stuart Stanton
R.W. Stanyon
Mike and Gillian
  Staples
Mr and Mrs P.J.K.
  Staples
Mrs G.A. Starling
Wing Cdr Anthony
  Staveley
R. Steadman
Mrs G.M. Stein
F.M. Steiner
Rev and Mrs Peter
  Stell
Mrs Denise
  Stephens
Anthony Stern
Mrs Denise Stevens
Dr and Mrs J.
  Stewart
Capt and Mrs J.S.
  Stewart
A.W. Still
R. Stirling
M. Stockford
Chris Stocking
Richard Stokes
Diana Stone
Dr and Mrs J. Stone
Mr and Mrs John
  Stone
Mr and Mrs Richard
  Stone
J.C. Stott
Colin Street
Mr and Mrs John
  Street
Mr and Mrs Jason
  Streets
P.J. Strick
Mrs E. Stringer
Hilary and Malcolm
  Strong
Mrs M. Stuart
Tessa Stuart
Michael Sugden
Barry Sullivan
Dr and Mrs M.
  Sullivan
Miss D. Summerlin
Brian Sutcliffe
Mrs E. Sutherland
Peter Sutton
Mrs A.J.G.
  Swainson
Mr and Mrs I. Swan
Mrs Sabrina Sykes
Ms Brenda Symes
Keith Symons
J. Talbot

Mr and Mrs Ian
  Tanner
J.A. Tarrant
Dennis Tate
Dr and Mrs P.H.
  Tattersall
A. Taylor
Mrs A.C. Taylor
Chris Taylor
F. Taylor
George Taylor
Graham Taylor
Mrs J. Taylor
Mr and Mrs K.W.
  Taylor
Mr and Mrs P.
  Taylor
Mr S. Taylor
Mr and Mrs Steven
  Taylor
Mrs Amabel Taylor-
  Billett
Stephanie Teed
Mrs Valerie
  Tempest
Ms Bernis Terhune
Alan Thomas
Mrs C.S. Thomas
Mrs E.M. Thomas
Ms Maureen
  Thomas
Tom Thomas
Paul Thomason
Clive Thompsett
Mr and Mrs Colin
  Thompson
J.R. Thompson
Ms Pauline
  Thompson
Mr and Mrs Peter
  Thompson
W.G. Thompson
Mrs Sheila
  Thomson
Dr Geoff Thorley
Dr A.G. Thornton
D. Thornton
Mrs J.F. Thorpe
Michael Thursfield
Kay Thwaites
Mrs Ruth Tilsley
Captain David Tilt
H. Tint
Miss C.M. Tite
Andy Todd
C. Todd
Mrs Jan Todd
Michael Tomlinson
S.D. Toner
Wendy Tong
Ms Clare Torry
Michael Townson

Ms Jane Traies
Ms Sylvia Trench
James Trotman
Mrs Patricia Trub
N. True
Nick Tsatsas
Jonathan Turley
A. Turner
B.W.B. Turner
Ed Turner
Mr and Mrs G. Turner
J.G. Turner
John Turner
Sheena Turner
Stuart Turner
Mrs Barbara Tyler
D.R. Tyler
Ms Debbie Tyler
Iain Tyson
P.G. Uloth
Nicholas Underhill
I.M.W. Ure
J. Vanderbilt-Sloane
Casper van Dongen
J.E. van Trigt
Mr and Mrs Dick Vardy
Ms Gloria Varley
J. Varley
Capt A.M. Verdon
J. Vernon
Andrew Vertes
Mr and Mrs U.I. de Villiers
Mrs B. Vinson
Stephen Vokes
Dr A. Voller
Michael Wace
Dr M.H.G. Waddington
Mark Waghorn
Mick Waghorn
P.H. Wainman
Mrs Loraine Waites
J.A. Wakerley
R. Walden
Mr and Mrs A. Walford
Tom and Angela Walford
C. Walker
Martin Walker
M.F. Walker
Mrs Sharon Walker
Mrs V. Walker-Dendle
D.M. Wallace
Mrs Griselda Wallace
Rosalind Waller

Mrs D. Wallin
D.J. Wallington
Barry Wallwork
Dr Nigel Walsh
Alison Ward
K.R.A. Ward
Mrs Kathy Ward
Mr and Mrs T.E. Ward-Hall
A.J. Wardrop
Ms Rachel Ware
Ms Rachel Warner
Andrew Warren
Mrs P.M. Warrington
John Warwicker
Bruce Wass
Graham Wassell
Dr Helen Watanabe
J.S. and F. Waters
Paul Watkins
Mrs B. Watson
David Watters
E.K. Watts
Mrs J.S. Webb
Dr M. Webb
Richard Webb
Rory Webster
Mr and Mrs R.J. Webzell
Watson Weeks
Sanford Weiner
Mr and Mrs Andrew Weir
Michael Wellby
Adrian Wells
Dr Frank Wells
Dr and Mrs P. Wells
Christopher West
J.F.M. West
Mr and Mrs M.J. West
Peter West
Mrs Madeleine Westlake
Charles Weston
Brian and Sue Wharton
Julie Wheat
Ms Michele Wheaton
Rev J.G. Wheeldon
Ben Whitaker
Dr G.T. Whitaker
Mr and Mrs Colin White
David White
Graham White
J.R. White
Mr and Mrs Charles Whitehead
R.J. Whitelam

Jennifer Whitelaw
I.C. Whitfield
Mrs Sandra Whitham
Mr and Mrs M.C. Whiting
R.D. Whitley
Charles Whitman
Henry Whitrow
Mr and Mrs Stephen Whittle
Ms S.R. Wiggins
Mrs Fiona Wilcock
T.B. Wilcox
Mr and Mrs D.C. Wild
R.C. Wiles
J. Wilkes
David Wilkins
Mrs E.J. Wilkinson
Mr and Mrs H. Wilkinson
R.A. Wilkinson
P. Willer
K. William-Powlett
Mrs Alma Williams
Dr B.D.M. Williams
Ms Charlotte Williams
David Williams
Donald Williams
Dr E. Williams
Dr and Mrs G.J. Williams
J.R. Williams
Ms Melanie Williams
Mr and Mrs P.G. Williams
P.H. Williams
R.A. Williams
Mr and Mrs R.W. Williams
Rhodri Williams
Richard Williams
Mrs Vanessa Williams
N.M. Williamson
Stephen Williamson
Mr and Mrs M.J. Williets
Jerome Willis
Ms Celia Wills
Mrs Jean Willson
Mrs Jan Wilman
Dr Bryan Wilson
Mr and Mrs C. Wilson
Wing Cdr G.J. Wilson
Mrs Margot Wilson

Peter Wilson
Mr and Mrs Peter Wilson
Prof P.N. Wilson
Ralph Wilson
R.W. Wilson
Alan Winchester
Anthony Wingate
H. Winson
Mr and Mrs Mike Winsor
E.C. Winter
Miss P.F. Winter
G.M. Wisenfeld
Mr and Mrs Paul Withers
Mr and Mrs T. Withers
Alan Wood
Hugh Wood
K.R. Wood
Robert Wood
Mr Arthur Woode
J.D.A. Wooders
Bernard Woodford
M.B. Woodgate
Mrs A.D. Woodhouse
Mrs M. Woods
Barbara Wooldridge
R.C. Woolgrove
Alan Worsdale
Alan Wright
Mrs C. Wright
Chris Wright
Duncan Wright
Ms Geraldine Wright
Mr and Mrs G.L. Wright
Mrs H. Wright
Dr J.D. Wright
P.L. Wright
Sarah Wright
Mr and Mrs Stephen Wright
Mrs Jill Wyatt
Mr and Mrs John Wyatt
R.A. Wyld
Mrs Thelma Wynn
Helen and John Wynne
O.R.W. Wynne
Geoffrey Yates
Graham Yeats
Ms Liz Yeomans
A.B. Yool
Mr and Mrs Douglas Young
Dr P.L. Zacharias

Index of main entries

LHT LHT LHT III

Notes

Notes

Report Form

To the Editor *The Good Food Guide*
FREEPOST, 2 Marylebone Road, London NW1 1YN

Or send your report by electronic mail to: *guidereports@which.co.uk*

From my personal experience the following establishment should/should not be included in the *Guide* (please print in BLOCK CAPITALS):

_____

_____

Telephone_____

I had lunch/dinner/stayed there on (date) _____ 19____

I would rate this establishment _____ out of five.

please continue overleaf

My meal for ____ people cost £ _____ *attach bill where possible*

☐ Please tick if you would like more report forms

Reports received up to **June 1997** will be used in the research of the 1998 edition.

I am not connected in any way with management or proprietors.
Name and address (BLOCK CAPITALS, please)

_____

_____

Signed _____

To the Editor *The Good Food Guide*
FREEPOST, 2 Marylebone Road, London NW1 1YN

Or send your report by electronic mail to: *guidereports@which.co.uk*

From my personal experience the following establishment should/should not be included in the *Guide* (please print in BLOCK CAPITALS):

_____

_____

Telephone_____

I had lunch/dinner/stayed there on (date) _____ 19____

I would rate this establishment _____ out of five.

please continue overleaf

My meal for ____ people cost £ _____ *attach bill where possible*

☐ Please tick if you would like more report forms

Reports received up to **June 1997** will be used in the research of the 1998 edition.

I am not connected in any way with management or proprietors.
Name and address (BLOCK CAPITALS, please)

_____

_____

Signed _____

To the Editor *The Good Food Guide*
FREEPOST, 2 Marylebone Road, London NW1 1YN

Or send your report by electronic mail to: *guidereports@which.co.uk*

From my personal experience the following establishment
should/should not be included in the *Guide* (please print in BLOCK
CAPITALS):

_____

_____

Telephone_____

I had lunch/dinner/stayed there on (date) _____ 19____

I would rate this establishment _____ out of five.

please continue overleaf

My meal for ____ people cost £ _____ *attach bill where possible*

☐ Please tick if you would like more report forms

Reports received up to **June 1997** will be used in the research of the 1998 edition.

I am not connected in any way with management or proprietors.
Name and address (BLOCK CAPITALS, please)

_____

_____

Signed _____

To the Editor *The Good Food Guide*
FREEPOST, 2 Marylebone Road, London NW1 1YN

Or send your report by electronic mail to: *guidereports@which.co.uk*

From my personal experience the following establishment should/should not be included in the *Guide* (please print in BLOCK CAPITALS):

_____

_____

Telephone_____

I had lunch/dinner/stayed there on (date) _____ 19___

I would rate this establishment _____ out of five.

please continue overleaf

My meal for ____ people cost £ _____ *attach bill where possible*

☐ Please tick if you would like more report forms

Reports received up to **June 1997** will be used in the research of the 1998 edition.

I am not connected in any way with management or proprietors.
Name and address (BLOCK CAPITALS, please)

Signed _____

To the Editor *The Good Food Guide*
FREEPOST, 2 Marylebone Road, London NW1 1YN

Or send your report by electronic mail to: *guidereports@which.co.uk*

From my personal experience the following establishment should/should not be included in the *Guide* (please print in BLOCK CAPITALS):

_____

_____

Telephone_____

I had lunch/dinner/stayed there on (date) _____ 19___

I would rate this establishment _____ out of five.

please continue overleaf

My meal for ____ people cost £ _____ *attach bill where possible*

☐ Please tick if you would like more report forms

Reports received up to **June 1997** will be used in the research of the 1998 edition.

I am not connected in any way with management or proprietors.
Name and address (BLOCK CAPITALS, please)

_____

_____

Signed _____

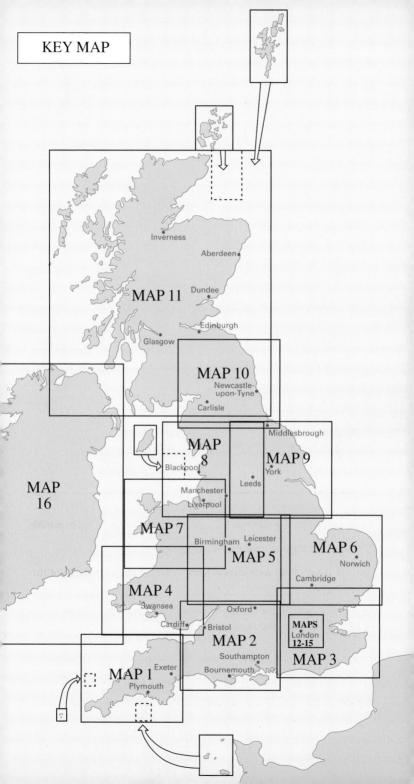

KEY MAP

MAP 11

Inverness

Aberdeen

Dundee

Edinburgh

Glasgow

MAP 10

Newcastle-upon-Tyne

Carlisle

Middlesbrough

MAP 8

Blackpool

MAP 9

York

Leeds

Manchester

Liverpool

MAP 16

MAP 7

Birmingham

Leicester

MAP 5

MAP 6

Norwich

Cambridge

MAP 4

Swansea

Cardiff

Oxford

Bristol

MAP 2

MAPS
London 12-15

MAP 3

Southampton

Bournemouth

MAP 1

Exeter

Plymouth

MAP 1

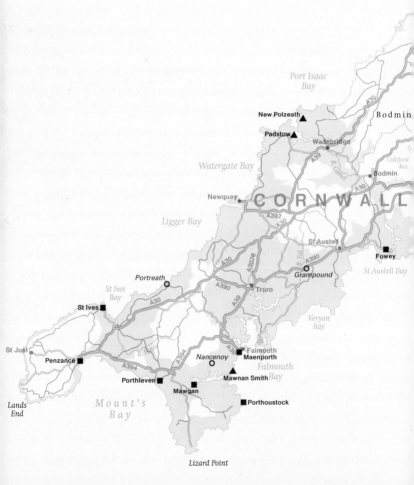

Restaurant
Restaurant with accommodation
Round-up entry
Combined restaurant and round-up entries

0   5   10 miles
0   15 kms
© Copyright

Isles of Scilly
28 miles WSW of Land's End

New Grimsby
St Martin's
Tresco
Hugh Town

Lundy Island

B u d e
B a y

Port Isaac Bay

New Polzeath
Padstow
Wadebridge
B o d m i n

Colliford Res.

R. Camel

Watergate Bay

A39

Newquay

C O R N W A L L

A39

A30

Bodmin

A392

A30

Ligger Bay

A390

St Austell

Fowey

St Austell Bay

A3078

Portreath

R. Fal

A390

Grampound

St Ives Bay

St Ives

A30

A390

Truro

Veryan Bay

St Just

A30

A39

A394

Penzance

R. Hel

A394

Nancenoy

A39

Falmouth
Maenporth

Falmouth Bay

Porthleven

A394

Mawnan Smith

Mawgan

Porthoustock

Lands End

M o u n t ' s
B a y

Lizard Point

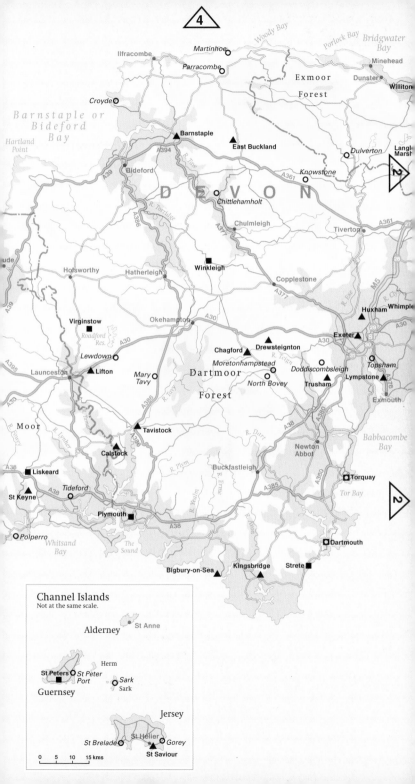

MAP 2

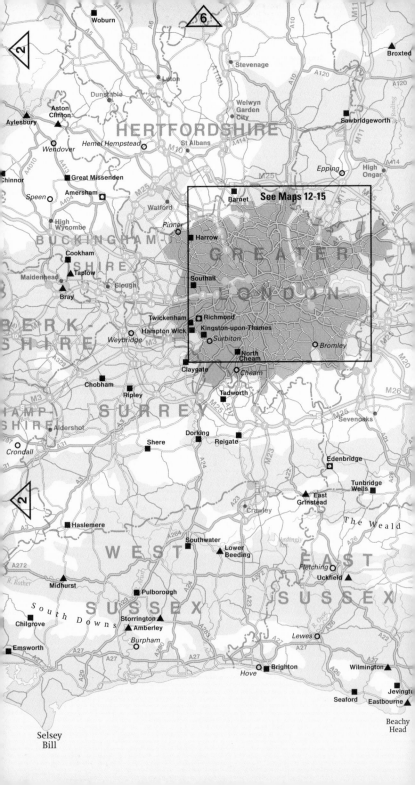

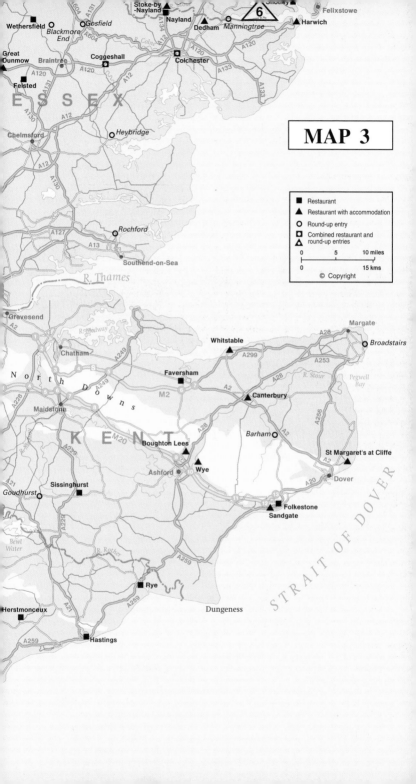

MAP 3

Restaurant
Restaurant with accommodation
Round-up entry
Combined restaurant and round-up entries

0   5   10 miles
0   15 kms
© Copyright

ESSEX

Wethersfield
Blackmore End
Gosfield
Stoke-by-Nayland
Nayland
Dedham
Manningtree
Shotley
6
Felixstowe
Harwich

Great Dunmow
Braintree
Coggeshall
Colchester

Felsted

Chelmsford

Heybridge

Rochford

Southend-on-Sea

R. Thames

Gravesend

Chatham

R. Medway

Margate
Broadstairs

Whitstable

Faversham

R. Stour
Pegwell Bay

North Downs

Canterbury

Maidstone

Barham

St Margaret's at Cliffe

KENT

Boughton Lees
Ashford
Wye

Dover

Goudhurst
Sissinghurst

Folkestone
Sandgate

Bewl Water

R. Rother

Herstmonceux

Rye

Dungeness

Hastings

STRAIT OF DOVER

MAP 4

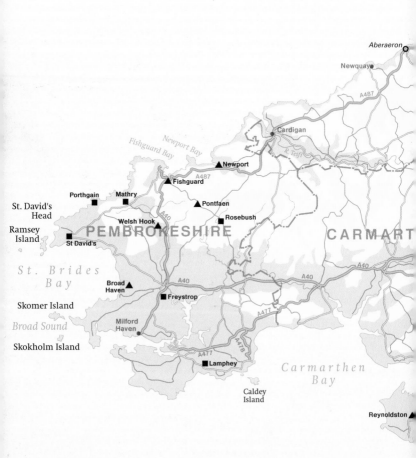

C A R D I G A N

B A Y

Aberaeron ○

Newquay ●

A487

Cardigan ●

R. Teifi

Fishguard Bay   *Newport Bay*

▲ Newport

A487

▲ Fishguard

Porthgain ■   Mathry ■

▲ Pontfaen

St. David's
Head

Welsh Hook ▲   ■ Rosebush

Ramsey
Island

PEMBROKESHIRE   **CARMART**

■ St David's

A40   A40   A40

*St. Brides
Bay*

Broad
Haven ▲   ■ Freystrop

Skomer Island   A477

Broad Sound   Milford
Haven ●   A477   A478

Skokholm Island

*Carmarthen
Bay*

■ Lamphey

Caldey
Island

Reynoldston ▲

B R I S T O L

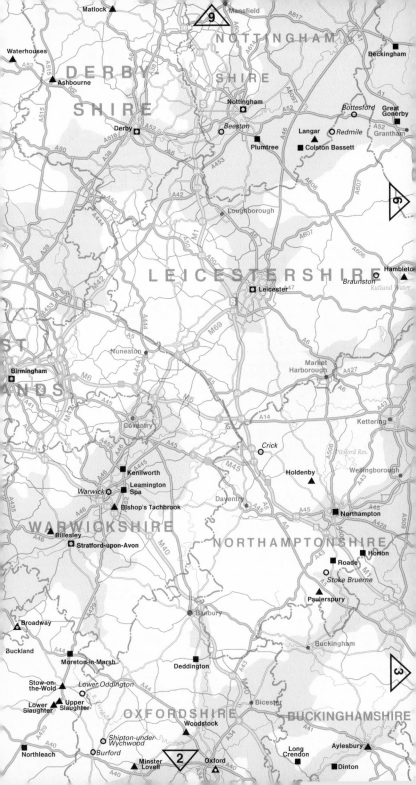

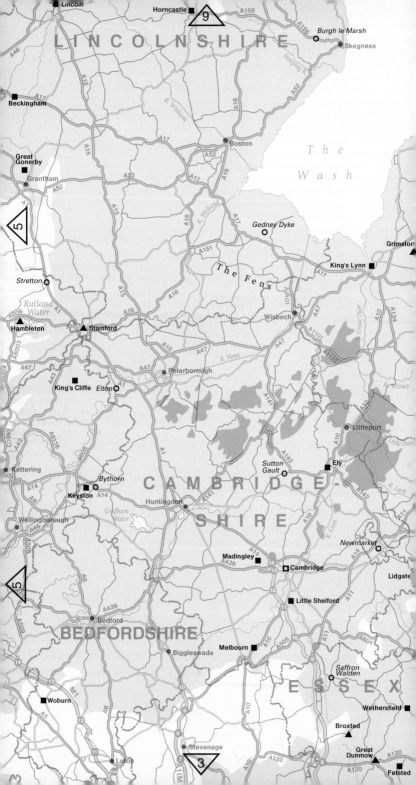

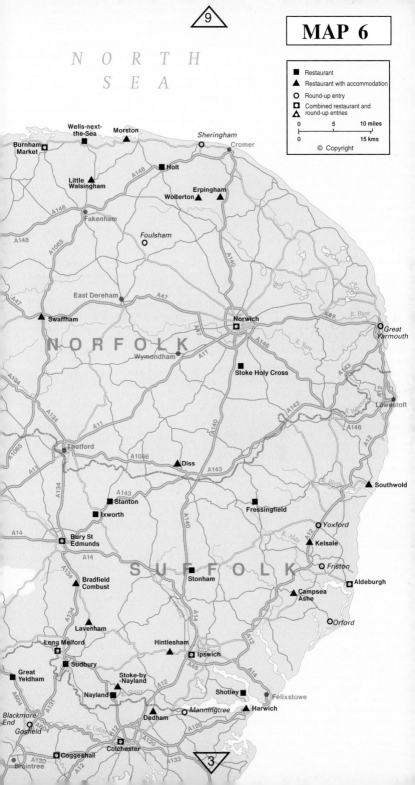

MAP 6

△ 9

NORTH SEA

Restaurant ■
Restaurant with accommodation ▲
Round-up entry ○
Combined restaurant and round-up entries ▣
Combined restaurant and round-up entries △

0   5   10 miles
0   15 kms
© Copyright

Wells-next-the-Sea ■
Morston ▲
Sheringham ○
Cromer
Burnham Market ▣
Holt ■
Little Walsingham ▲
A148
Wolterton ▲ Erpingham ▲
A1065
Fakenham ●
A148
Foulsham ○
A47
East Dereham ●
A47
Swaffham ▲
NORFOLK
Norwich ▣
A47
A11
Wymondham ●
Great Yarmouth ○
R. Bure
A47
A146
R. Yare
A140
A134
A11
A146
Stoke Holy Cross ■
A143
Lowestoft ○
A146
A12
A134
A1065
A1066
Thetford ▣
A1066
Diss ▲
A143
Southwold ▲
A11
Stanton ■
A143
Fressingfield ■
Blyth
Ixworth ■
A140
Yoxford ○
A14
Bury St Edmunds ▣
Kelsale ▲
R. Alde
A14
SUFFOLK
Friston ○
A134
Bradfield Combust ▲
Stonham ■
Aldeburgh ▣
A134
Campsea Ashe ▲
Lavenham ▲
A14
Long Melford ▣
Hintlesham ▲
Orford ○
A12
Sudbury ■
Ipswich ▣
Great Yeldham ■
Stoke-by-Nayland ▲
A45
Nayland ▣
A14
Shotley ■
Felixstowe
Blackmore End ○
Gosfield ○
A604
Dedham ▲
Manningtree ○
Harwich ▲
A131
R. Stour
A120
Braintree ●
Coggeshall ○
Colchester ▣
A120
A12
A133
△ 3
R. Colne

MAP 7

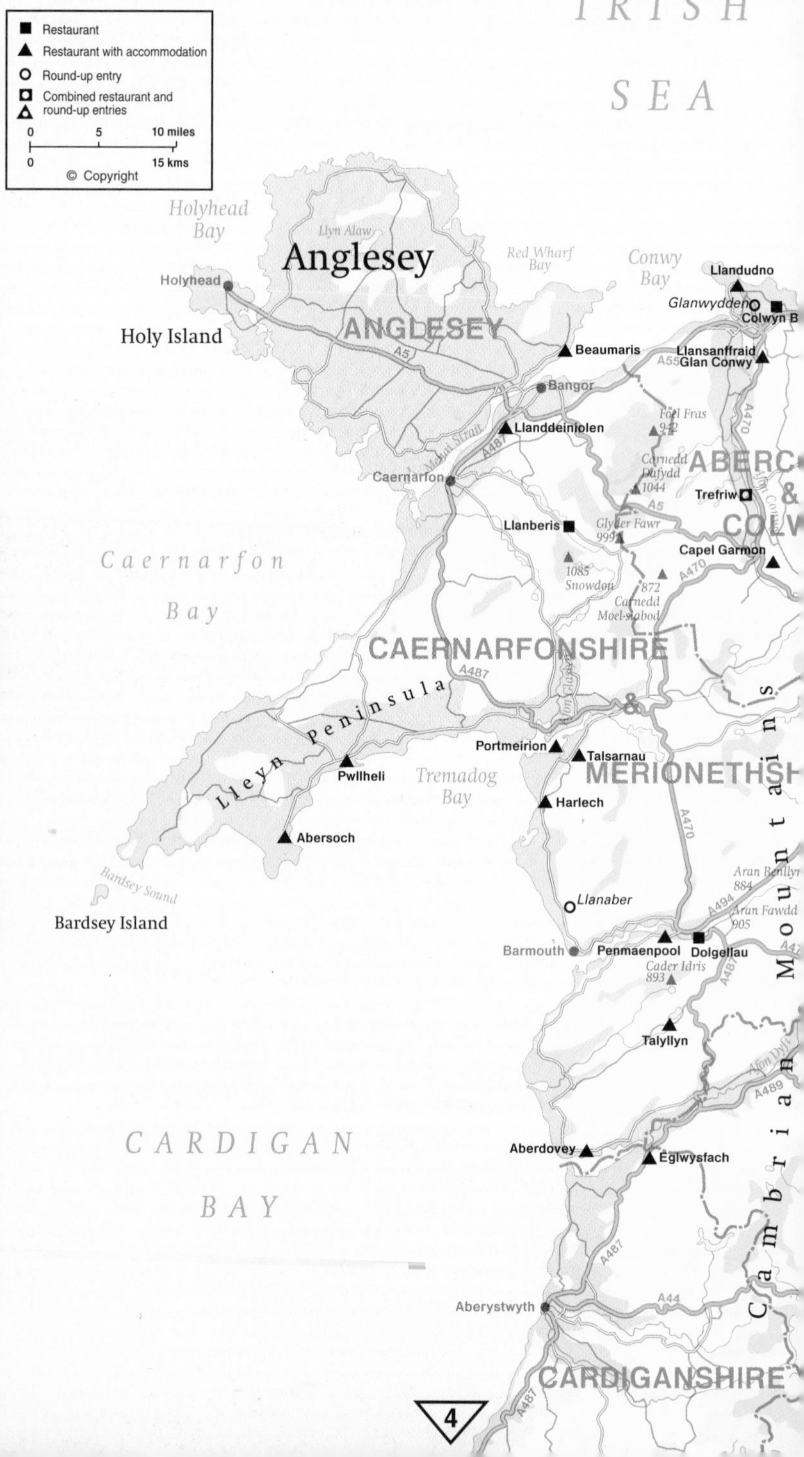

Restaurant
Restaurant with accommodation
Round-up entry
Combined restaurant and round-up entries

0   5   10 miles
0   15 kms
© Copyright

IRISH

SEA

Holyhead Bay

Llyn Alaw

Red Wharf Bay

Conwy Bay

Anglesey

Holyhead

ANGLESEY

Holy Island

▲ Beaumaris

Llandudno

Glanwydden ○

Colwyn B ■

● Bangor

▲ Llansanffraid Glan Conwy ▲

▲ Llanddeiniolen

Foel Fras 942

● Caernarfon

Carnedd Dafydd ▲1044

Trefriw ○

ABERC & COLV

■ Llanberis

Glyder Fawr 999▲

▲ Capel Garmon ▲

Caernarfon

Bay

▲ 1085 *Snowdon*

Carnedd Moel-siabod 872

CAERNARFONSHIRE

Portmeirion ▲ ▲ Talsarnau

MERIONETHSH

Lleyn Peninsula

● Pwllheli

Tremadog Bay

▲ Harlech

▲ Abersoch

Bardsey Sound

○ Llanaber

Aran Benllyn 884

Aran Fawdd 905

Bardsey Island

Barmouth ● Penmaenpool ■ Dolgellau

Cader Idris 893▲

▲ Talyllyn

CARDIGAN

BAY

Aberdovey ▲ ▲ Eglwysfach

Aberystwyth ●

CARDIGANSHIRE

△ 4

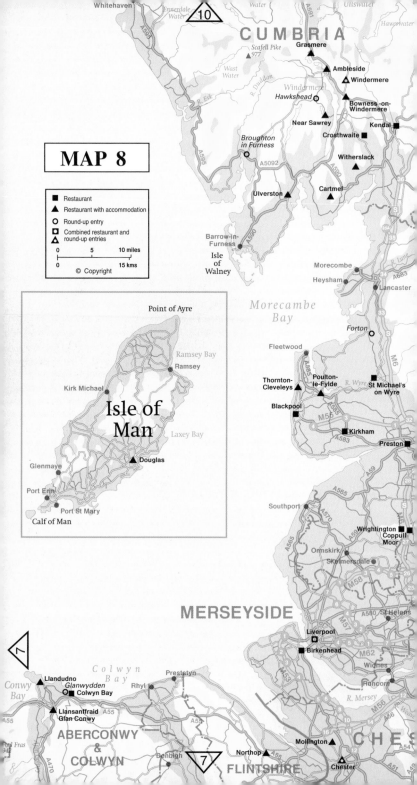

MAP 8

- ■ Restaurant
- ▲ Restaurant with accommodation
- ○ Round-up entry
- ▣ Combined restaurant and
- △ round-up entries

```
0        5        10 miles
0            15 kms
© Copyright
```

Whitehaven
Ennerdale Water
Wast Water
10
Scafell Pike 977
R. Duddon
Grasmere
Ambleside
Windermere
Hawkshead
Bowness -on-Windermere
Near Sawrey
Kendal
Crosthwaite
Broughton in Furness
A5092
Witherslack
Cartmel
Ulverston
Barrow-in-Furness
A590
Isle of Walney

CUMBRIA
Ullswater
Haweswater
A591
A595
A590

Point of Ayre
Ramsey Bay
Ramsey
Kirk Michael
Isle of Man
Laxey Bay
Glenmaye
Douglas
Port Erin
Port St Mary
Calf of Man

Morecombe
Heysham
Lancaster
Morecambe Bay
Forton
Fleetwood
Thornton-Cleveleys
Poulton-le-Fylde
R. Wyre
St Michael's on Wyre
Blackpool
M55
Kirkham
A583
Preston
A59
A565
Southport
A570
Wrightington
Coppull Moor
Ormskirk
Skelmersdale
M58

MERSEYSIDE
A580 St Helens
Liverpool
Birkenhead
M62
Widnes
M53
Runcorn
R. Mersey
M56

7
Conwy Bay
Colwyn Bay
Llandudno
Glanwydden
Colwyn Bay
Rhyl
Prestatyn
Llansantffraid Glan Conwy
A55
A55
Mollington
CHES
ABERCONWY & COLWYN
Denbigh
Northop
7
FLINTSHIRE
Chester
A470
A51

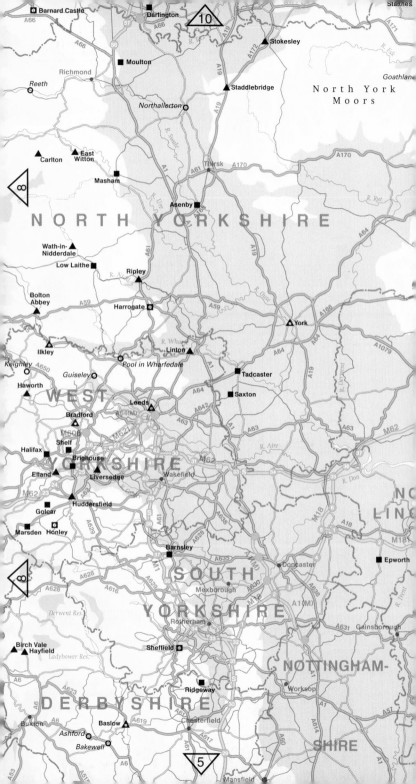

MAP 9

- ■ Restaurant
- ▲ Restaurant with accommodation
- ○ Round-up entry
- ▢ Combined restaurant and round-up entries
- △

0   5   10 miles
0   15 kms
© Copyright

■ Whitby

A171

A170

Scarborough ○

A64

A66

Flamborough Head

Langtoft ○

A166

Bridlington ●

Yorkshire Wolds

A168

Bridlington
Bay

A63

EAST RIDING
OF YORKSHIRE

■ Lockington

A1035

A1079

Beverley ○

A1079

A165

Walkington ▲

KINGSTON
UPON HULL

A63

Kingston
upon Hull

R. Humber

Winteringham ▲

■ Barton-upon-Humber

A15

NORTH
LINCOLNSHIRE

A160

◆ Scunthorpe

A18

A46

Grimsby ○

Spurn Head

M180

A173

Cleethorpes

N.E.
LINCOLNSHIRE

A159

A15

A631

A1103

A46

A16

Louth ▲

The Wolds

A158

A57

A158

A16

LINCOLNSHIRE

● Lincoln

Burgh
le Marsh ○

A158

■ Horncastle

A46

Skegness ●

A46

Biggar
A702
A721
A703
A72 Peebles
Culter Fell
755
A702
M74
Hart Fell
808
Moffat
Daer
Res.
Queensberry
697
A74
DUMFRIES &
GALLOWAY
A701
A74(M)
R. Esk
Nith
Dumfries
A74(M)
A75
Canonbie
R. Eden
A74
Carlisle
A689 Brampton
A689
M6
Melmerby
Cross Fell
893
A596
Cockermouth
Skiddaw
931
Penrith
Cow
Green
Res.
A596
A66
A66 Applethwaite
Workington
Bassenthwaite
Lake
Braithwaite Keswick
Watermillock
Ullswater
Ullswater
Appleby
A66
Whitehaven
Derwent
Water
Grange in
Borrowdale
Hawesweater
Ennerdale
Water
Crummock
Water
A595
CUMBRIA
Wast
Water
Scafell Pike
977
Grasmere
A591
A595
Ambleside
A685

A697
A68
A72
A7 Galashiels
Melrose
Kelso
R. Tweed
Selkirk
A68
B O R D E R S
Hawick
A7
Caldcleugh
608
The Chev
Kielder Water
A69
A69

MAP 10

MAP 11

Shetland Islands
Not to same scale

0 10 20 30 kms
0   10   20   30 miles

Unst
Fetlar
Outer Skerries
Whalsay
Bressay
Lerwick
Mainland
Walls
Esha Ness
Muckle Roe
Papa Stour
Fitful Head

Orkney Islands
Not to same scale

0 10 20 30 kms
0   10   20   30 miles

N. Ronaldsay
Sanday
Westray
Stronsay
Eday
Rousay
Shapinsay
Mull Head
Brough Head
Mainland
Rora Head
Hoy
Dunnet Head
Stroma
John o'Groats
St Margaret's Hope
S. Ronaldsay
Deerness

Cape Wrath
Stroma
Duncansby Head
Thurso
Wick
Helmsdale
Handa I.
Ben Hope
Ben Loyal
Ben Klibreck
Tarbat Ness
Dornoch
Kylesku
Achiltibuie
Ullapool
Quinag
Suilven
Ben More Assynt
Cromarty
Nairn
Inverness
Black Isle
Dingwall
Muir of Ord
Ben Wyvis
Elgin
Drybridge
Banff
Fraserburgh
Rattray Head
Peterhead
Buchan Ness

ABERDEENSHIRE
MORAY
Archiestown
Aviemore
Cairngorm
Huntly
Inverurie
ABERDEEN
Aberdeen
Stonehaven
Montrose

Cairngorm Mountains
Grampian Mountains
Kingussie
Spean Bridge
Fort William
Ben Nevis
Kinloch Rannoch
Kentallen
Killiecrankie
Pitlochry
Ballater

Butt of Lewis
Eye Peninsula
Stornoway
Shiant Is.
ISLE OF LEWIS
Great Bernera
Uig
HARRIS
Scalpay
Taransay
Scaristà
WESTERN ISLES
OUTER HEBRIDES
Flannan Isles
Scarp
North Uist
Benbecula
Wiay
South Uist
Eriskay
Berneray
Ronay

The Minch
Rubha Reidh
Rubha Hunish
Rona
Raasay
Scalpay
Island of Skye
Stein
Colbost
Dunvegan
Portree
The Storr
Soay
Rhum
Canna
Eigg
Muck
Coll

Arisaig
Kinlochmoidart
Strontian
Sound of Sleat
Loch Hourn
Mallaig

INNER HEBRIDES
The Little Minch

H I G H L A N D

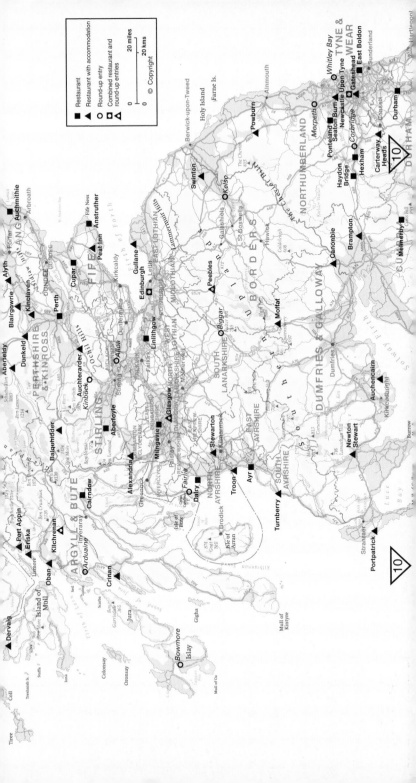

Greater London

BARNET

Stanmore

HARROW

Finchley
Rani
Two Brothers

HARIN

Wood Green

Le Cadre

Toffs

Les Associés

Chez Liline

Hendon
Gourmet Garden

Akasaka

Village Bistro

Café Japan

WEMBLEY

Willesden

Hampstead

See Map 13

CAMDEN

Sabras

BRENT

ISLIN

A40(M)

See Map 15

HAMMERSMITH AND FULHAM

Acton

Noughts 'n' Crosses

Balzac Bistro

Alastair
Little Lancaster Road

Orsino
Chez Moi
Rotisserie

CITY OF WEST-MINSTER

Ealing

Anglesea Arms
Brackenbury

Chinon

KENSINGTON AND CHELSEA

See Map 14

Adams Café
Thai Bistro
Chiswick

Wilsons
Snows on the Green

Brentford

La Dordogne

HAMMERSMITH

Montana

Blue Elephant

Ransome's Dock
B Square

Rebato's

Riva

River Café

Fables

Buchan's

Sonny's

Fulham

Canteen

Stepping Stone

Crowthers

Phoenix

Cookhouse

Conrad London

Enoteca

Lavender

Brixton

Vincent's

Del Buongustaio

Brady's

Richmond

Twickenham

WANDSWORTH

Wandsworth

Le P'tit Normand

Osteria Antica Bologná

Le Gothique

Chez Bruce

WANDSWORTH

Kastoori

Wimbledon

Sree Krishna

Streatham

Alexandra

Merton

Kingston upon Thames

Morden

Mitcham

Mirch Masala

KINGSTON UPON THAMES

Malden

MERTON

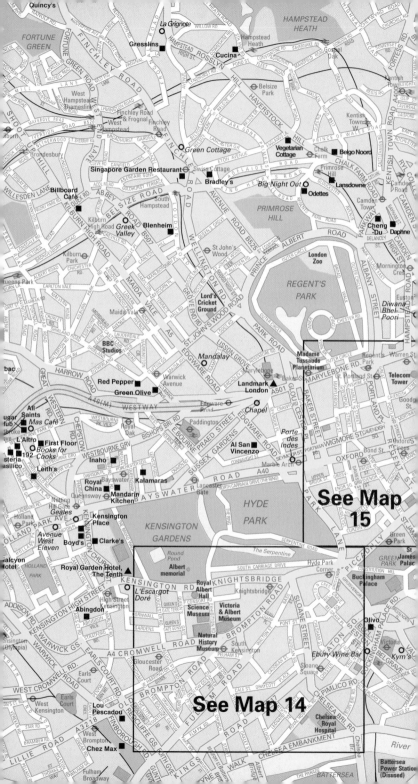

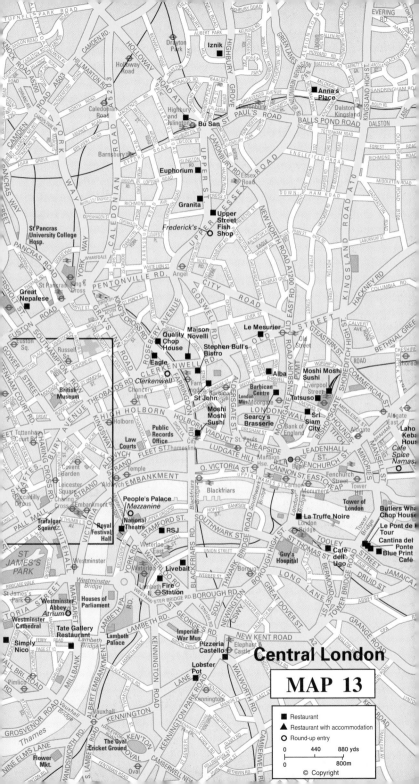

Iznik

Anna's Place

Highbury
and
Islington

Bu San

Drayton
Park

Holloway
Road

BALLS POND ROAD

Dalston
Kingsland

St Pancras
University College Hosp.

Euphorium

Granita

Frederick's

Upper
Street
Fish
Shop

Great
Nepalese

St Pancras

King's
Cross

Angel

Le Mesurier

Quality
Chop
House

Maison
Novelli

Stephen Bull's
Bistro

Eagle

Clerkenwell

Alba

Moshi Moshi
Sushi

St John

Barbican
Centre

Tatsuso

British
Museum

Moshi
Moshi
Sushi

Searcy's
Brasserie

Sri
Siam
City

Laho
Keba
Hous

Public
Records
Office

Law
Courts

Covent
Garden

Leicester
Square

Cheapside

Mansion
Hse.

Cafe
Spice
Namas

Piccadilly
Circus

Charing
Cross

Trafalgar
Square

Blackfriars

Tower of
London

Butlers Wha
Chop House

People's Palace
Mezzanine

La Truffe Noire

National
Theatre

RSJ

Le Pont de
Tour

Cantina del
Ponte

Blue Print
Café

Cafe
dell
Ugo

Royal
Festival
Hall

ST
JAMES'S
PARK

Guy's
Hospital

Livebait

Westminster
Abbey
Atrium

Houses of
Parliament

Fire
Station

Tate Gallery
Restaurant

Westminster
Cathedral

Lambeth
Palace

Imperial
War Mus.

Simply
Nico

Pizzeria
Castello

Lobster
Pot

Central London

MAP 13

The Oval
Cricket Ground

Flower
Mkt.

Thames

■ Restaurant
▲ Restaurant with accommodation
○ Round-up entry

0   440   880 yds
0   800m

© Copyright

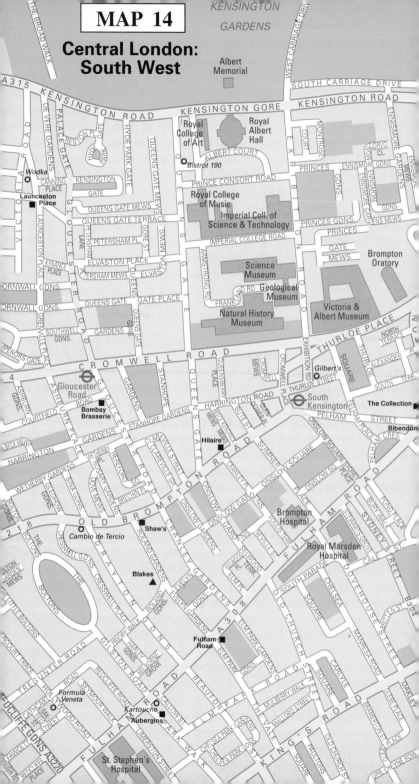

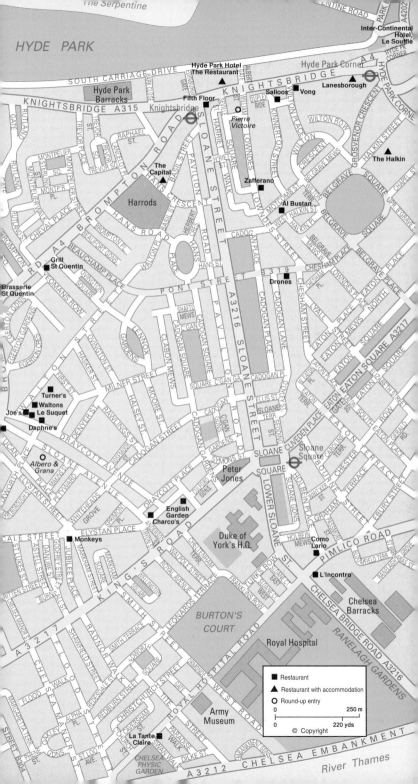

HYDE PARK

The Serpentine

Inter-Continental Hotel, Le Souffle

Hyde Park Corner

HYDE PARK

SOUTH CARRIAGE DRIVE

Hyde Park Barracks

Hyde Park Hotel
The Restaurant

Fifth Floor

KNIGHTSBRIDGE A315   Knightsbridge   KNIGHTSBRIDGE

Salloos   Vong   Lanesborough

Pierre Victoire

The Halkin

The Capital

Zafferano

Al Bustan

Harrods

Grill St Quentin

Brasserie St Quentin

Drones

SLOANE STREET

EATON SQUARE A3217

EATON SQUARE

Turner's
Waltons
Joe's   Le Suquet
Daphne's

Albero & Grana

SLOANE SQUARE

Peter Jones

Sloane Square

English Garden
Charco's

Duke of York's H.Q.

Monkeys

Como Lario

PIMLICO ROAD

L'Incontro

Chelsea Barracks

KING'S ROAD

BURTON'S COURT

Royal Hospital

Chelsea Barracks

Duke of York's H.Q.

RANELAGH GARDENS

CHELSEA BRIDGE ROAD A3216

■ Restaurant
▲ Restaurant with accommodation
○ Round-up entry

0   250 m
0   220 yds
© Copyright

Army Museum

La Tante Claire

CHELSEA PHYSIC GARDEN

CHELSEA EMBANKMENT   River Thames

A3212

Central London: West End

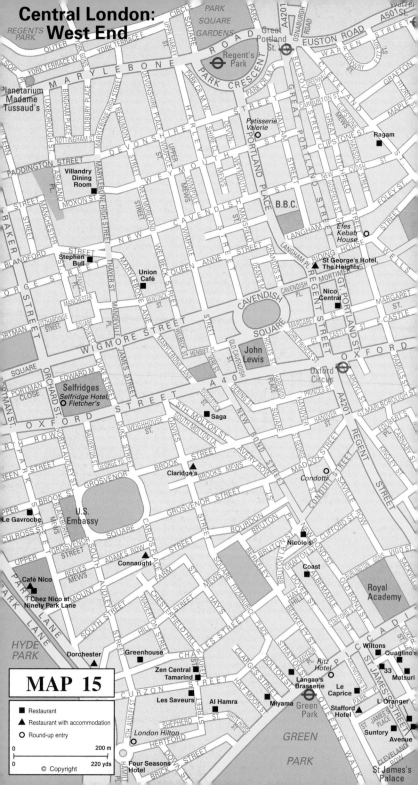

REGENTS PARK

PARK SQUARE GARDENS

Planetarium
Madame Tussaud's

Villandry
Dining
Room

Patisserie
Valerie

Ragam

B.B.C.

Efes
Kebab
House

Stephen Bull

Union
Café

St George's Hotel,
The Heights

Nico
Central

CAVENDISH
SQUARE

John
Lewis

Oxford
Circus

Selfridges
Selfridge Hotel,
Fletcher's

Saga

U.S.
Embassy

Claridge's

Condotti

Le Gavroche

Nicole's

Café Nico

Connaught

Coast

Chez Nico at
Ninety Park Lane

Royal
Academy

HYDE
PARK

Dorchester

Greenhouse

Wiltons

Quaglino's

Zen Central
Tamarind

Ritz
Hotel

33

Matsuri

Les Saveurs

Al Hamra

Langan's
Brasserie

Le
Caprice

L'Oranger

Miyama

Stafford
Hotel

MAP 15

■ Restaurant
▲ Restaurant with accommodation
○ Round-up entry

Suntory

Avenue

London Hilton

GREEN
PARK

St James's
Palace

0   200 m
0   220 yds
© Copyright

Four Seasons
Hotel

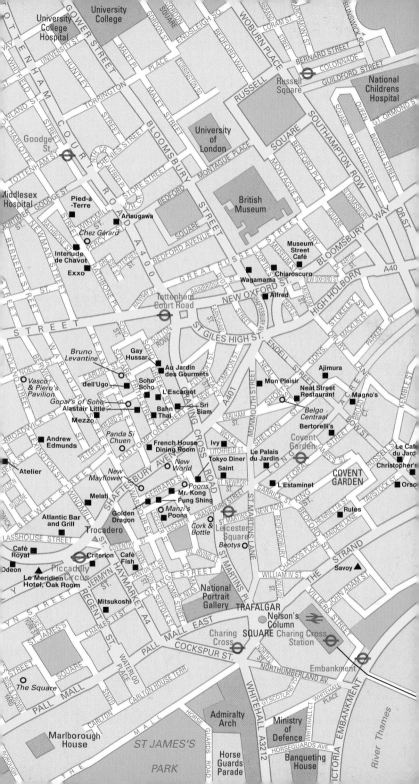

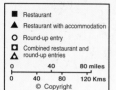

MAP 16

■ Restaurant
▲ Restaurant with accommodation
○ Round-up entry
◻ Combined restaurant and
△ round-up entries

0   40   80 miles
0   40   80   120 Kms
© Copyright

Inishtrahull Sound

Rathlin I.

ATLANTIC

OCEAN

Rosapenna

Portrush

Rathmullan

Coleraine

Limavady

Londonderry

LONDONDERRY

Strabane

DONEGAL

Ballyclare

Carrickfergus

Helen's Bay

Bangor

Antrim

Belfast

Donegal

TYRONE

A N T R I M

Lurgan

Portadown

DOWN

Downpatrick

St. John's Point

Donegal Bay

FERMANAGH

Enniskillen

Armagh

Sligo

Bellanaleck

Monaghan

MONAGHAN

IRISH

SEA

Ballina

Crossmolina

S L I G O

Castlebaldwin

Carrick-
on-Shannon

LEITRIM

Fenagh

Cavan

CAVAN

LOUTH

Newport

M A Y O

ROSCOMMON

LONGFORD

Drogheda

M E A T H

Letterfrack

I R E L A N D

Dunshaughlin

Oughterard

G A L W A Y

Athlone

WESTMEATH

Moycullen

Galway

Howth

Dublin

DUBLIN

OFFALY

KILDARE

Bray

Ballyvaughan

Kildare

Birr

Portlaoise

LAOIS

Wicklow

WICKLOW

C L A R E

TIPPERARY

KILKENNY

CARLOW

Arklow

Gorey

Shannon

LIMERICK

Adare

Kilkenny

M7

Listowel

LIMERICK

Tipperary

Cashel

Kilmaganny

WEXFORD

Kilmallock

Clonmel

Dingle

Tralee

Kanturk

C O R K

WATERFORD

Waterford

ST. GEORGE'S CHANNEL

Killorglin

Mallow

KERRY

Midleton

Youghal

Kenmare

Cork

Shanagarry

Ballylickey

Douglas

Cobh

Durrus

Bantry

Clonakilty

Kinsale

Ahakista

Schull

Ballydehob

ATLANTIC OCEAN